Foundations of the Theory of Prediction

THE DORSEY SERIES IN PSYCHOLOGY

FLEISHMAN *Studies in Personnel and Industrial Psychology*

FISKE & MADDI *Functions of Varied Experience*

BARNETTE *Readings In Psychological Tests and Measurements*

BENNIS, SCHEIN, BERLEW, & STEELE *Interpersonal Dynamics: Essays and Readings on Human Interaction*

RATNER & DENNY *Comparative Psychology: Research in Animal Behavior*

COURTS *Psychological Statistics: An Introduction*

DEUTSCH & DEUTSCH *Physiological Psychology*

ROZEBOOM *Foundations of the Theory of Prediction*

FOUNDATIONS OF THE THEORY OF PREDICTION

by

WILLIAM W. ROZEBOOM
Department of Psychology and Center for Advanced Study in Theoretical Psychology
University of Alberta

1966

THE DORSEY PRESS ■ HOMEWOOD, ILLINOIS

First Printing, October, 1966

Library of Congress Catalog Card No. 65–12423

Printed in the United States of America

For William, Steven, and Cynthia

Table of Contents

PART I. THE STATISTICS OF PREDICTION

CHAPTER PAGE

1. INTRODUCTION ... 3
Organization of the Material. A Note of Caution.

2. BASIC CONCEPTS ... 7
Populations. Variables. Distributions. Multivariate Distributions. Transformations.

3. STATISTICAL PROPERTIES OF DISTRIBUTIONS ... 22
Measures of Central Tendency—the "Average." Measures of Dispersion, or Spread. The Significance of Averages and Measures of Variation. Standard Scores. The Coefficient of Variation. Distribution Shapes. Moments.

4. STATISTICAL REGRESSION AND THE THEORY OF PREDICTION ... 58
The Decision Problem. Decision Theory Disengaged. The Goodness of Information (Part I). Prediction and Probability: A Glimpse of Vistas Beyond. Statistical Regression: The Basic Theory. Curve Fitting: The Least-Squares Solution. Linear Regression. Comments and Cautions. Multivariate Prediction.

PART II. TEST THEORY: THE ASSESSMENT OF PREDICTORS

5. VALIDITY ... 187
Empirical Validity. Predictive Validity and Concurrent Validity. Face Validity. Interpretive Validity. The Definition of the Criterion: A Darkening Mystery. Content Validity. Construct Validity.

6. FACTOR ANALYSIS ... 210
Linear Dependencies and Factor Bases. Styles of Factor Solutions: I. Extraction Policies. Inferred Components and the Problem of Communalities. A Numerical Example. Styles of Factor Solutions: II. Terminal Patterns. Higher-Order Factors. Hierarchical Factor Solutions.

7. CENTROIDS AND VARIANCE STRUCTURE ... 292
The Fundamental Partitioning Theorem. Saturation Components and Dispersion Components. Penetrance, Saturation, and Homogeneity. Saturation and Reflection. Variance Structure and Linear Transformations.

8. RELIABILITY 375
Hypothetical Test Results and the Concept of "True Score." Alternative Approaches. The Accuracy of Test Observations: The Reliability Index and the Reliability Coefficient. Empirical Approximations to Reliability. The Standard Error of Measurement and the Estimation of True Scores. Reliability and Validity. Coda: The Concept of "Test Potential."

9. THE VARIANCE STRUCTURE OF COMPOSITE TESTS 427
The General Composition Theorem. Validity and Test Length. Internal-Consistency Theory and the Alpha Coefficient. Empirical Estimation of Error Homogeneity. Item Weighting. Item Weighting and Composite Reliability.

10. EPILOG 497
Sampling: The Problem of Probabilities. Nonlinearity and Other Problems of Presuppositions. The Varieties of Relational Analysis.

APPENDIX A. THE NORMAL DISTRIBUTION 571

APPENDIX B. MATRIX DERIVATIONS 574
Notation. Multiple Regression. The Inverse of a Covariance Matrix. Orthogonal Rotations. Principal Components. Eigenvalues and Eigenvectors. Saturation and Principal Components. Penetrance Ratios. Principal Components of Projection Configurations. Canonical Correlation.

REFERENCES 603

GLOSSARY 607

NAME INDEX 617

SUBJECT INDEX 619

Part I. **THE STATISTICS OF PREDICTION**

Chapter 1. **Introduction**

PROBABLY NO type of intellectual problem is quite so pervasive, whether in abstract pursuits of knowledge, affairs of state and commerce, or simple everyday living, as that of making inferences from what we already know to something else which we would also like to know. In scientific research, such inferences usually take the form of trying to reason from accumulated data to general principles which govern these data; and efforts to understand the methodological principles involved in this sort of reasoning and to improve upon extant techniques compose a major part of the professional labors of philosophers and statisticians today. The inferential needs which arise out of more immediately practical concerns, however, are usually of a simpler sort. Here, one is typically faced with the necessity for anticipating some detail of a specific situation on the basis of knowledge about the details of other similar situations – e.g., How successful will I be if I decide to make a career in electrical engineering? What is wrong with the patient with the odd symptoms in Ward B? How long can I maintain this shortage in my accounts before the bank examiners find out? We shall here refer to inferences such as these, in which an attempt is made to estimate some feature of a particular person, object, situation, etc., prior to actual knowledge about that feature, as *predictions,* even though in many instances such as medical diagnoses and personality assessments, what is being "predicted" is a state of affairs already in existence. (Frequently, "prediction" is thought to be limited to forecasting the future. However, while to "pre-dict" is literally to *say in advance*, what it is that the prediction antedates need only be more conclusive evidence about the event in question rather than the event's own occurrence in time.)

For problems where we are fortunate enough to be dealing with phenomena governed by precise, known laws, prediction involves little more than an application of deductive logic. If I make a bank deposit of $100 at 4% interest compounded quarterly, I can deduce that barring atomic holocaust, bank failure, or similar unpleasantries, my deposit will be worth $148.87 ten years from now. Similarly, an astronomer feels no uncertainty in predicting what the declination of the noonday sun will be on any given day of the forthcoming year. Unfortunately, however, most of the predictions with which we are faced in practical affairs are not so clear-cut. If I don't dash back to the parking meter with another nickel, how much longer can I remain overparked without getting a ticket? Should I sell my stocks now, or hope for a higher market next week? And what should Jones conclude about the advisability of radiation therapy for his umbilicitis if 30% of patients so treated have been known to recover completely, 25% to show partial recovery, 35% to show no change, 7% to get worse, 2% to die of radiation burns, and 1% to have disappeared before the effects of therapy could be evaluated?

Just because we are faced with a situation in which prediction cannot be made with certainty, however, it by no means follows that we cannot use what information we do have to make a better prediction than could be made by sheer guessing. What does follow is that we must resort to a more sophisticated line of reasoning in order to decide *what* to predict, and also to devise measures which show *how good* (i.e., how trustworthy, or successful) such predictions are likely to be. Now, it so happens that while many important problems in the general theory of inference still await solution, the more restricted *theory of prediction*, in the broad sense described above, has become fairly well understood. Moreover, the amount of mathematical skill required to master the bulk of this material is quite nominal—all that is needed is a little elementary (high school level) algebra and some receptivity to mathematical thinking. But while excellent presentations of the major technical concepts of prediction theory—notably, correlation and regression—can be found in many statistical textbooks, these are usually imbedded in a context of sampling problems and are accessible to a statistically unsophisticated reader only after he has struggled through hours of preliminaries which, however important these may be for a more thorough grasp of statistical theory, are not required for a working understanding of prediction technique. It is the present intent to provide a handbook of first principles, developed to somewhat greater depth than is available in other introductory sources. While the included materials span a wider range of difficulty than is usual for a single text and contain innovations throughout which should be of interest even—or especially—to students who are already acquainted with the area, this book is addressed primarily to the reader who desires a technical understanding of prediction theory, but whose prior statistical background is negligible or superficial.

Organization of the Material

Chapters 2 and 3 survey basic concepts in descriptive statistics. The coverage is somewhat broader than strictly necessary for subsequent applications, for not only may the reader find it handy to have a summary of this sort, discussion within a wider systematic context of those statistics which *are* needed later should also assist a sturdier command of these devices. However, for various reasons such as prior familiarity or temporal exigency, the reader may not care to study all of Chapters 2 and 3 in detail. Sections which may be skimmed or omitted without appreciable handicap have consequently been starred, and a short list of exercises will be found at the end of Chapter 3 on which the reader may test his mastery of statistical fundamentals. Whenever he is able to solve these problems without undue strain, he may pass confidently to Chapter 4, in which the theory of prediction is finally developed. Chapters 5–9 subsequently address a body of more specialized ideas, collectively known as "test theory," which appraise in various ways the sources of data from which predictions can be made. Chapters 5 (Validity) and 8 (Reliability) present the basics of this material, and continue at about the same level of difficulty as Chapter 4. The starred chapters (6, 7, and 9) on variance structure, on the other hand, are somewhat more advanced, and while they presuppose no background knowledge which is not explicitly developed in previous chapters, it is unlikely that the reader will find them effortlessly accessible unless he has lived with the statistical concepts in Chapters 2–4 long enough for these to have become familiar and cherished intellectual companions. In particular, the doubly starred sections on item weighting in Chapters 7 and 9 will undoubtedly prove formidable to persons for whom this book is truly a first experience with test theory. Finally, Chapter 10 (Epilog) attempts after a fashion to redress the most acute deficiencies in the previous chapters' coverage by summarizing without proof or detailed discussion certain theorems from statistical sampling theory which are especially important for practical applications of prediction theory, and by alerting the reader to additional relevant problems and procedures whose detailed consideration lies beyond the scope of this book.

In this, as in other works where the main flow of ideas is substantially carried by mathematical notation, the reader will find that one of the greatest obstacles to swift comprehension will be his difficulty in recalling just what the various special symbols mean. The new terms which are introduced throughout the following chapters compactly express precisely defined concepts in such fashion that statements, which if written in ordinary English would sprawl over perhaps the better part of a page in an impenetrable tangle of grammar, can be crisply set forth in formulas which occupy less than a line of print. The concepts themselves are easy enough to grasp if an honest effort is made to do so, but the symbols which express them cannot be learned instantaneously, any more than any other new language can be mastered by a single reading of its dictionary. Consequently, the reader will at first find it repeatedly necessary to freshen his understanding of these terms by returning to their definitions for review. There is no way to make this learning painless, but in effort to ease the burden somewhat, a glossary of symbols is appended on pp. 607ff.

A Note of Caution

Since the purpose of this book is to convey understanding of the nature of statistical prediction with maximal clarity and a minimum of distraction by tangential issues, we shall as much as possible avoid discussion of technical complications which would add greatly to the logical and mathematical sophistication required of the reader while contributing little to his comprehension of the materials under study. As a result, several of the technical concepts to be introduced here are somewhat simplified in their presentation, either in a slurring over of fine details or in adoption of definitions which have less generality than is adequate to the use of these notions in their broader applications. For example, all statistical concepts are here introduced in terms of populations comprising a finite number of members, even though modern mathematical statistics has long since assimilated populations of the higher orders of infinity, and indeed, has in effect virtually abandoned the concept of "population" altogether. Again, we shall systematically ignore the distinction between *numbers* and the *numerals* by which we refer to them; for a careful heeding of the difference between symbol and the thing symbolized, critical as this distinction often is for more advanced problems, is likely to contribute only a confusing complexity of expression at the introductory level. There is nothing at all unusual about such simplification—it is doubtful whether any elementary text has ever been written which has not made specialists in the field wince at some of its treatments. There is always some danger, however, that unless forewarned, an especially capable student, who in his own thinking is already pressing on to deeper levels of insight, may mistake textual inadequacies for confusion on his own part. Consequently, the reader is duly cautioned that while the ensuing discussion attempts to convey an accurate account of the theory of prediction so far as can reasonably be managed on an introductory level, there are many details which, for more advanced purposes, need to be scrutinized with greater care than has seemed desirable here. Many of the footnotes which grace the ensuing pages attempt to direct attention to some of these additional complexities, but the reader should not surrender to them all responsibility for critical judgment.

Chapter 2. **Basic Concepts**

THE TYPE of prediction problems with which we are here concerned are those in which, on the basis of information about what sorts of attributes the members of a certain group tend to have, we wish to estimate the attributes of a specific individual who is known to belong to that group. Consequently, we need to devise concepts which permit discussion of groups and the attributes found within them in a fashion which is both simple and precise. We begin with the notions of "population" and "variable." Together, these generate the all-important statistical concept of a "distribution" and its properties, which will finally put us in the business of predicting.

Populations

By a "population," we mean *a group, or class, of entities.* A "member" of a population is any one of the entities of which the group is composed. In the simplest case, where the "entities" involved are ordinary objects, the notion of "population" is easy to grasp. Thus the class of all fifth-grade American school children, the class of all living albino rats, the class of all stars larger than our sun, and the class of marbles now in Jimmy Jones's pants' pockets are various populations of objects. It will be observed that a given object may be a member of many populations at once. Thus the reader is simultaneously a member of the class of literate humans, the class of mammals living in the twentieth century, and the class of persons having an interest in techniques of prediction. In fact, any characteristic or combination of characteristics (e.g., having a cavity in one's lower left wisdom tooth; being either bald or redheaded; having a broken shoelace and only 36 cents to one's name) which is true of a person defines a population to which that person belongs, namely, the class of persons sharing this characteristic. It should also be noted that it is possible for all the members of one population P_1 also to be members of another population P_2. In this case, P_1 is said to be a *sub-*

population or *subclass* of P_2. For example, the class of all college Freshmen is a subpopulation of the class of all college students.

The "entities" which collectively make up a population need not always be simple objects. If we say that 37% of Henry Smith's dreams are about money, or that the average noonday temperature in Grouch Center, Iowa, last year was 58° Fahrenheit, we are making statistical statements about populations whose members, respectively, are dreams and moments in time—both highly immaterial forms of entities. Neither do the members of a population need to be *single* entities. Thus when we investigate the physical similarity of identical twins or the incidence of divorce in contemporary urban America, the populations under consideration are composed of *pairs* of persons, namely, identical twins in the first instance and married couples in the second. Similarly, a question about the average size of a litter of kittens concerns a population whose members are groups of kittens born at (approximately) the same time from the same mother. In many common statistical problems in which the population being studied seems to be composed simply of people, the individual population member is not a person in his historical entirety, but a temporal cross section or "time slice" of him—i.e., the person at a particular moment in time. For example, if we ask whether there is a relationship between a person's physical health and his ability to think creatively, we must recognize that health and creativity vary not only from person to person, but also from time to time in the same person, so that the population over which data are to be gathered consists of specific persons at specific times. In fact, the successive time slices in a given person's life themselves form a population, the statistical properties of which enter into a number of everyday psychological concepts. Thus when we say that Jones is a happier man than Smith, what seems to be meant is that Jones's momentary degree of happiness, though variable, is still on the average—the average, that is, within the population of his moments in time—greater than Smith's. Fortunately, there is little present need for explicit recognition of the somewhat exotic nature of many of the populations encountered in statistical analysis, and there will be little loss if the reader conceives a "population" to be primarily a collection of persons or objects.

Variables

The term "variable," despite its prevalence in the modern literature of science, logic, and mathematics, is a highly ambiguous word which in various contexts is used to mean quite different things.[1] The usage which will be employed here is the one which predominates in scientific and

[1] For what is probably the best extant discussion of the various meanings of the term "variable" in science and mathematics, see Menger (61). A technically detailed analysis of the scientific sense of "variable" is attempted in Rozeboom (67).

statistical[2] discourse. Basically, a "variable" (in the scientific sense) over a population P is *a set of properties or attributes which are mutually exclusive and exhaustive within P.* A set of properties is mutually exclusive and exhaustive for a population P when each member of P must possess at least one, but no more than one, property in this set. For example, consider the set of possible heights which a person might have: being 2 inches tall, being 35 inches tall, being 173 inches tall, and so forth—the various attributes, in other words, that would be described by alternatively substituting all positive numbers in place of "x" in the predicate schema, "being x inches tall." For any given person at a specific time, say Henry Jones at 2:14 P.M., January 6, 1965, there is at least one of these heights which is true of him at this time. Further, if Henry Jones is 67.5 inches tall at 2:14 P.M., January 6, 1965, he cannot at that time *also* be 68.2 or 16.4 or 182.0 or any other number of inches tall. The various possibilities for how tall a person is form a mutually exclusive and exhaustive set of attributes within the population of persons at specific times, and this set therefore constitutes a "variable," known as *Height,* over this population. Similarly, the sets of attributes described by substituting various numbers for "x" in the predicate schemata, "weighing x pounds," "having an IQ of x," and "having x brothers or sisters," are likewise mutually exclusive and exhaustive over the persons-at-specific-times population and thus also describe variables over this population, namely, the *Weight* variable, the *Intellectual-capacity* variable, and the *Number-of-siblings* variable.

In this book, variables (in the sense just defined) will be symbolized by boldface letters, usually uppercase. For example, it might be stipulated that "**H**" is to refer to the Height variable. Frequently, we shall wish to make statements which are true about all variables. In this case, we shall speak ambiguously about "variable **X**," "variable **Y**," etc., with the understanding that the reader may interpret **X**, **Y**, etc., to be any variable he wishes consistent with whatever contextual restrictions may be in force. (Boldface numbers and lowercase letters will also occasionally occur in derivative senses to be explained as the occasion arises.)

It should be noted that not all variables are quantitative, as are Height, Weight, and Number-of-siblings. The predicate schemata, "having x hair" and "belonging to species x," each generate mutually exclusive and exhaustive sets of properties within a population of animals when "x" is replaced with either color descriptions or "no" in the first case, and the names of various species in the second. These property sets constitute the "qualitative" or "categorical" variables, *Hair-color* and *Species.*

By a "value" of a given variable, we mean any one of the attributes which make up the set. Thus *being 27 inches tall, being 58 inches tall,* etc., are various values of the Height variable. Roughly speaking, whether

[2] Statisticians also frequently use the term "variate" to refer to variables in this sense.

two different properties are values of the same or different variables is determined by whether or not it is possible for a single entity to possess both. Since a person cannot weigh both 64 pounds and 183 pounds at the same time, these must be two different values of the same variable, whereas since a person can simultaneously weigh 183 pounds and have red hair, *weighing 183 pounds* and *having red hair* must be values of different variables.

The reason that we group properties into mutually exclusive and exhaustive sets which then become labeled "variables" is the great simplification this technique affords in describing the incidence of and relations among the attributes possessed by the various members of a population. However, a general discussion of the role of "variables" in scientific methodology is far beyond our present concern.

For most purposes in science and statistics, it is highly convenient to represent the values of a variable by numbers.[3] Thus instead of saying that the various values of the Number-of-siblings variable are *having no brothers or sisters, having one brother or sister, having two brothers or sisters,* etc., it is much easier to say that the values are simply 0, 1, 2, etc. Such a representation of properties by numbers is called a *scaling* of the variable.[4] Since there are many alternative ways to scale a variable, it is always necessary, when using scaled variables, to attach to the name of the variable an indication of the scale being employed. Thus if we wish to indicate the value, *being 58 inches tall,* of the Height variable simply by the number 58, we do not know which height is being referred to unless it is specified that the "58" indicates height in *inches,* rather than feet, yards, centimeters, or some other unit of measurement. Consequently, it will be convenient to speak of the *Height-in-inches* variable, the *Height-in-feet* variable, etc., as if these were different variables, while realizing, of course, that any value n of the Height-in-inches variable corresponds to the value $n/12$ of the Height-in-feet variable. We shall have more to say about matters of scaling later.

By the expression, "the value of variable **X** for entity i," we shall mean the one value of **X** which is true of i. Thus if Henry Jones weighs 174 pounds at 2:14 P.M., January 6, 1965, the value of the Weight-in-pounds variable for Henry Jones at this time is 174. When we wish to refer to the value of a variable **X** for an entity i without actually specifying *what* that value is, we shall use an italicized letter with appropriate subscript, namely, "X_i." That is, the symbol "X_i" (and similarly for others like it) is to be translated as "the value of variable **X** for entity i."

---

[3] Actually, it is not *numbers*—i.e., certain abstract aspects of objective reality—which are used to represent the values of a variable, but *numerals*—i.e., the symbols which are normally used to designate numbers.

[4] The methodology of scaling is complex and still imperfectly understood. For a useful introduction to the literature on scaling, see Lorge (56), Stevens (74), or Torgerson (79, Chapter 2). More advanced references are Suppes and Zinnes (75), and Rozeboom (70).

Since the variables encountered in actual predictive practice, especially in applied psychology, are frequently "tests" of one sort or another, we shall also speak of *i*'s *score* on **X** as a more flexible synonym for "the value of variable **X** for entity *i*." That is, a "score" on some variable is simply a value of that variable. It should be emphasized, however, that this is merely a stylistic convenience which in no way should be construed to suggest that the concepts and methods under discussion are restricted to psychological testing.

Distributions

This is the fundamental concept of statistics. While a logically precise definition of "distribution" would call for more technical detail than is useful here, it will suffice for present purposes to define "the distribution of variable **X** in population *P*" as *the set of values of* **X** *holding for the members of P*, or, alternatively, *the set of scores made by the members of P on variable* **X**, with the understanding that a given value of the variable is to be counted in the distribution as many times as there are members in *P* which have this score. Thus if the Rollers is a gang composed of five juvenile delinquents, two of whom have never been arrested, one of whom has been arrested twice, and two of whom have been arrested three times, the distribution of Number-of-arrests within The Rollers is the set of scores 0, 0, 2, 3, 3. A distribution is specified by naming a population and a variable over that population—two different variables over the same population define two different distributions, as does the same variable over two different populations. Thus the distribution of Weight-in-pounds in college Freshmen, the distribution of Weight-in-pounds in college Seniors, and the distribution of Number-of-arrests in college Seniors are all different distributions. It should also be noted that one distribution will be part of another if the population involved in the first is a subpopulation of the one involved in the second. Thus the distribu-

23	58	5	43	32	105	40	47	0	36
50	34	78	37	73	3	5	35	50	25
1	70	26	42	46	66	27	18	45	41
0	44	100	57	20	59	70	76	56	79
60	36	42	8	45	80	102	51	30	61
41	65	24	40	47	35	33	0	64	39
6	48	13	38	63	22	66	38	42	31
30	45	67	26	78	44	31	53	26	54
68	17	38	58	28	44	68	40	63	45
56	24	36	33	48	70	9	36	59	18

Table 2.1. Number of lecture hours cut by each of the 100 members of the ΑΒΓ Fraternity, Brainsweat University, during the Fall Semester, 1964.

tion of Weight-in-pounds in college Freshmen is a subdistribution of the distribution of Weight-in-pounds in college students.

A number of alternative techniques have been devised for describing distributions. Several of these see extensive application in actual practice and will be discussed briefly here. The details of these methods are not really necessary for understanding the subsequent chapters, however, and the reader may pass quickly over any points which do not grip his interest.

Frequency Tables. The most obvious way to describe a distribution is simply to make a list of the scores which occur in the population, as illustrated in Table 2.1. But not only is this technique especially uncommunicative about the distinguishing features of the distribution, it also becomes prohibitively tedious when the size of the population is large. A simpler and more insightful method is to partition the various possible values of the variable into regions, called "class intervals," and then to state for each class interval the number of members in the population whose scores fall in that interval. A tabular organization of these data, as shown in Table 2.2, is known as a *frequency table*. Such a presentation makes it possible to see by simple inspection those regions of possible values in which the actual scores tend to concentrate. One prima facie disadvantage of the frequency table is that the *exact* distribution becomes a little blurred—e.g., to learn from Table 2.2 that six members of the Alpha Beta Gamma Fraternity each cut between 15.5 and 23.5 lecture hours during the semester does not suffice to know precisely what these six values were. However, when the width of an interval is small compared to the total span of the distribution, the information so lost is insignificant.[5]

Hours Cut	Number of Students	Hours Cut	Number of Students
Under 7.5	8	63.5 to 71.5......	10
7.5 to 15.5	3	71.5 to 79.5......	5
15.5 to 23.5	6	79.5 to 87.5......	1
23.5 to 31.5	12	87.5 to 95.5......	0
31.5 to 39.5	15	95.5 to 103.5......	2
39.5 to 47.5	19	103.5 to 111.5......	1
47.5 to 55.5	7	Over 111.5..........	0
55.5 to 63.5	11	Σ	100

Table 2.2. Frequency table for the data in Table 2.1.

[5] In most applied problems, the distributional data which have been obtained are treated as approximations to more inclusive distributions from which the data on hand are samples. In this case, the blurring of the precise sampling distribution which results from its summary in a frequency table is actually an advantage, for this tends to smooth off irregularities due to sampling error. Discussion of such matters, however, belongs to *inferential statistics*, a difficult subject which will be scrupulously avoided in this book until Chapter 10.

Histograms and Frequency Polygons. The data conveyed by a frequency table may be made even more intuitively accessible by expressing it in graphical form as follows: Draw a horizontal line and let the various points along it represent the various scale values that the variable can assume. (Thus if points A and B on the line represent scale values of 8 and 12, respectively, the point halfway between A and B represents scale value 10.) Now divide this line into segments corresponding to the class intervals in the frequency table, and upon each of these construct a rectangle whose base is the line segment and whose height is proportional to the number of scores in the distribution falling in the corresponding class interval. The resulting structure, as shown in Figure 2.1, is known as a *histogram.* Instead of showing the number of cases in the interval by a bar, we can alternatively place a dot over the midpoint of the interval at a distance above the baseline proportional to the number of cases in the interval. Connecting these dots by straight lines, as in Figure 2.2, then produces an irregularly shaped figure known as a *frequency polygon.* Although histograms tend to be used in practice somewhat more often than do frequency polygons, neither technique has any appreciable superiority over the other. In either case, whatever general trends of score-clustering may be present in the data are made visually conspicuous.

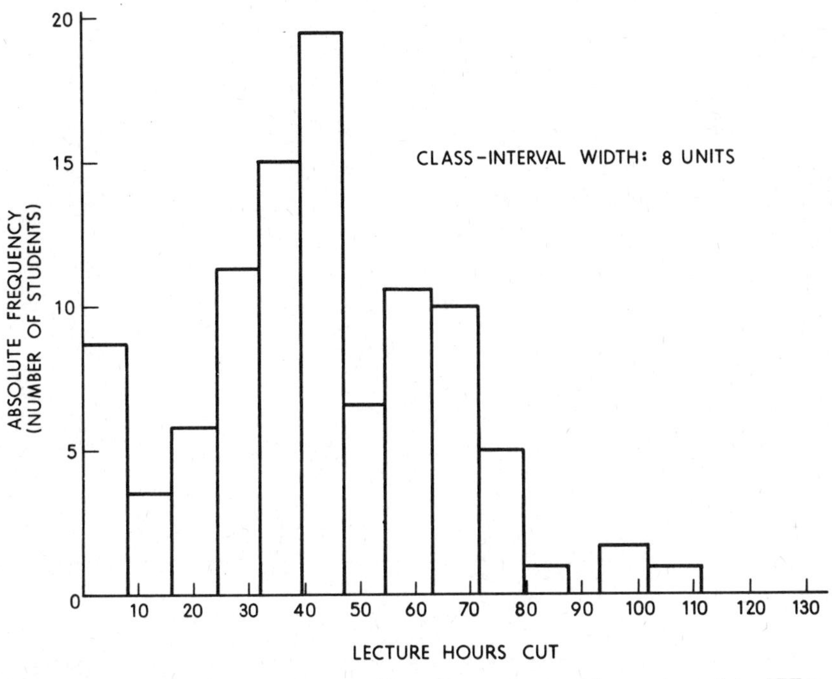

Figure 2.1. Histogram showing the distribution of lecture hours cut by members of the ΑΒΓ Fraternity, Brainsweat University, during the Fall Semester, 1964. The height of a rectangle indicates the number of scores falling in the interval spanned by that rectangle.

Since the height of a bar in a histogram, or point in a frequency polygon, indicates the number of entities in the population having scores in the indicated range, a vertical line is erected at one end (usually the left) of the graph and scaled to show what height corresponds to what frequency of occurrence. There are two ways, however, in which these frequencies can be expressed. One is to show the actual number of scores in the distribution falling in the interval. This is known as the *absolute frequency.* The other is to show what *proportion* of the total scores fall in that interval, i.e., the *relative frequency.* That is, the relative frequency of scores in an interval is the absolute frequency in that interval, divided by the total number of scores in the distribution. (Relative frequency may also be written as a percent, namely, absolute frequency divided by total number of scores, times 100.) Since relative frequency is strictly proportional to absolute frequency, both may be shown on the same graph—the only difference is in how the vertical dimension of the graph is calibrated. It seldom occurs in descriptive statistics, however, that the number of scores in a class interval is of interest apart from its relation to the total. Accordingly, unless stated otherwise, we shall henceforth understand "frequency" to mean "relative frequency."

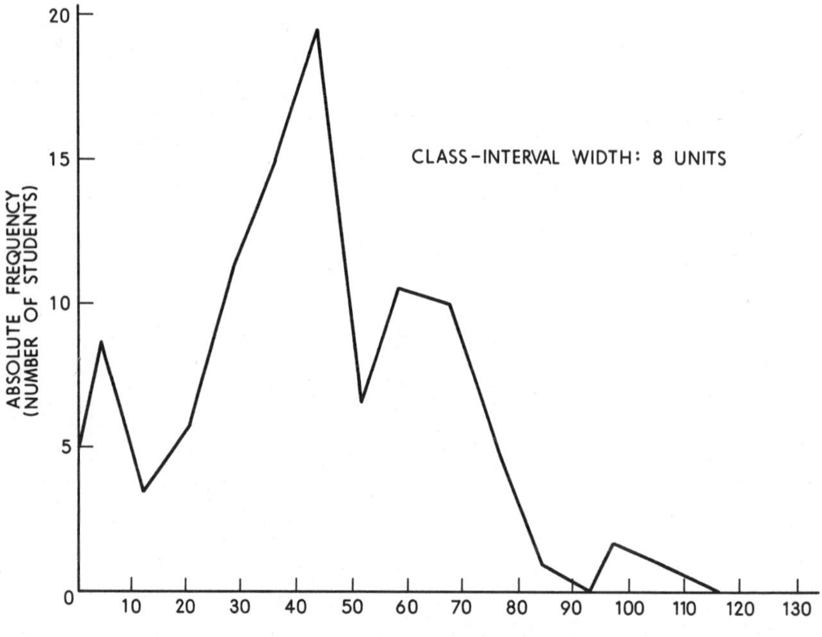

Fig. 2.2. Frequency polygon for the data in Table 2.1. The height of the curve over the midpoint of an interval shows the number of scores falling in that interval. Figures 2.1 and 2.2 are alternative graphical representations of Table 2.2.

Frequency-Density Curves. It will be observed that in a histogram or frequency polygon, the frequency of scores within a given class interval is very much dependent upon the interval width which has been more or less arbitrarily selected. Thus if we double the interval width, we also, on the average, double the proportion of cases falling in each interval. Graphically, this means that as interval width decreases, the height of the histogram or frequency polygon also decreases (see Figure 2.3). For various reasons which need not be discussed here, this is inconvenient. To avoid the difficulty, however, we need only to scale the vertical axis of our graph to show not actual frequency but *frequency per unit interval,* otherwise known as *frequency density.* The density of scores within a class interval is the proportion of scores within that interval divided by the interval's width. For example, if 12% of the ΑΒΓ Fraternity cut between 23.5 and 31.5 lecture hours a semester, the frequency density of this distribution between 23.5 and 31.5 is .12/8, or .015. It is easy to see that if the frequency axis of a histogram or frequency polygon is rescaled to show frequency density, the size of the class interval has very little effect upon the overall height of the curve (see Figure 2.4). In fact, when the distribution is such that all fractional scale values of the variable are possible (e.g., Height-in-inches or Weight-in-pounds, but not Number-of-siblings), and the population contains an indefinitely large number of

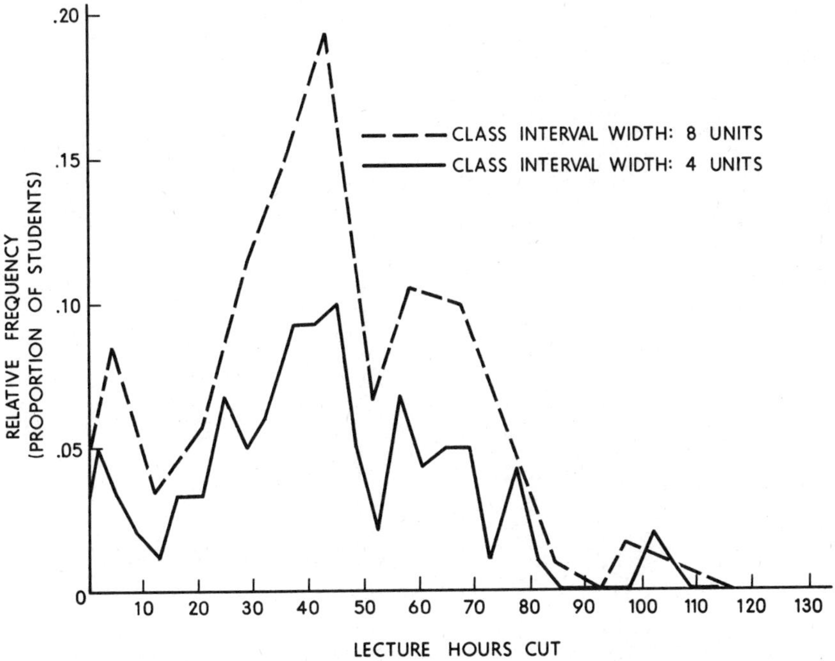

Figure 2.3. Relative-frequency polygons for the data in Table 2.1, illustrating how a change in the width of the class interval changes the overall height of the curve.

members, we can expect that as we choose smaller and smaller class-interval widths, the graph will more and more resemble a smooth curve whose shape is approximately what would be obtained by rounding off the sharp corners of the earlier figures in the series. The limiting case of this, when the class interval is arbitrarily small in width, is known as a *frequency-density curve* (more technically, *frequency-density function*). What the height of the frequency-density curve above a particular value of the variable indicates is the frequency density of the distribution within an arbitrarily small class interval including that value of the variable. From this it follows (the proof belongs to calculus) that the area under the frequency-density curve between any two values of the variable is proportional to the number of scores in the distribution which fall in this interval. Any histogram or frequency polygon which has been rescaled to show frequency density and from which the traces of partitioning into class intervals have been effaced (mainly, by erasing the vertical sides of

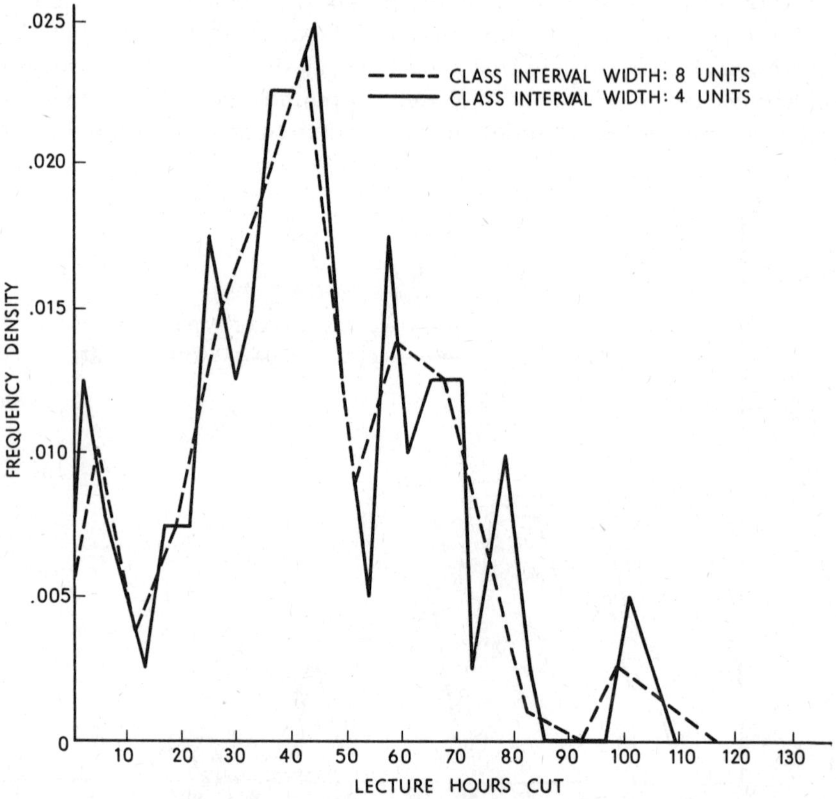

Figure 2.4. Frequency-density polygons for the Table 2.1 data, using the same class intervals as Figure 2.3. When the vertical axis of a histogram or frequency polygon is rescaled to show frequency per unit interval width (i.e., frequency density), rather than bare frequency, in a class interval, the overall height of the curve is unaffected by changes in the width of the class interval.

the bars in the histogram) may be regarded as an approximation to the frequency-density curve of the distribution.[6]

Cumulative-Frequency Functions and Percentiles. Still another way to describe a distribution is by a graph which shows, for each possible value of the variable, the proportion of scores in the distribution which are *lower* than this one (see Figure 2.5). Such a graph (more accurately, the mathematical function which such a graph pictures) is known as a *cumulative-frequency function.* Cumulative-frequency functions are not as intuitively revealing of the properties of their distributions as are frequency-density curves, and with one important exception their chief use is in more advanced statistical theory, where for technical reasons the cumulative-frequency function is by far the most satisfactory way to describe a distribution. The exception is that the cumulative-frequency function of a distribution also conveys the *percentile*[7] equivalents of scores in that distribution. By the latter, we mean the percent of the population

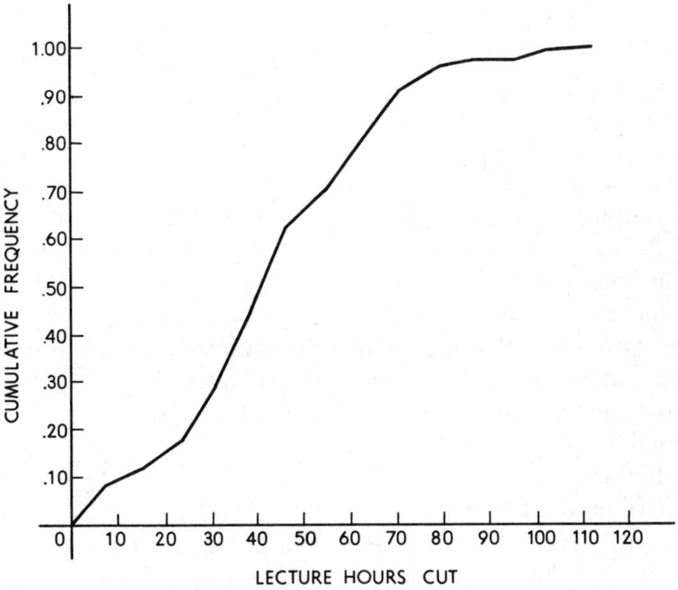

Figure 2.5. Cumulative-frequency function for the data in Table 2.1. The height of the curve over a value of the variable indicates the proportion of scores in the distribution which are lower than this value.

[6] A limiting frequency-density curve does not literally exist for a *finite* set of scores, however, unless the exact value of each score is deliberately blurred a little, because if a nonzero proportion of the population has *exactly* the same score X, the frequency density at X becomes infinitely large as the class interval including X becomes infinitely small. The loss in exactitude which results from a class-interval tabulation of the data accomplishes this blurring nicely.

[7] For technical reasons, the term "percentile" is becoming superceded by "centile."

whose scores are lower than the score in question, and this is simply the cumulative frequency at this score times 100. For example, if 95% of all college students are under six feet tall, then the percentile equivalent of the score 6.0 on the Height-in-feet variable—and likewise the percentile equivalent of score 72 on the Height-in-inches variable—is 95, while a person who is exactly six feet tall is said to be at the 95th percentile for college students. Percentile equivalents are of particular importance in the interpretation of test scores, for as a rule, a person's test performance is informative only to the extent that it can be compared to those of other persons; and a person's percentile rank on the test—i.e., the percentile equivalent of his test score—provides a direct indication of this.

Multivariate Distributions

The distributions discussed so far have involved only one variable per distribution. However, there is also frequently occasion to study the "simultaneous," or "joint," distribution of several variables in a given population. Such a distribution is known as a *multivariate* (i.e., "many variables") distribution. A brief description of the bivariate case—i.e., the joint distribution of two variables—will serve to convey the general idea.

The joint distribution of variables **X** and **Y** in population P is the set of pairs of scores on **X** and **Y**, respectively, made by the members of P. That is, a bivariate distribution records what values of the two variables occur together—specifically, are made by the same entity—in population P. For describing a bivariate distribution more conveniently than by a simple listing of co-occurrant scores (see Table 2.3), we can make use of the same techniques used to describe a univariate distribution by adding an additional dimension to the table or graph. To construct a *bivariate-frequency table,* the range of possible values for each variable is partitioned into class intervals and the two lists of intervals placed at right angles to each other, giving rise to a two-dimensional array of categories in which each combination of a class interval of values of **X** with a class interval of **Y**-values is represented by a cell in the table (see Table 2.4). Then the joint distribution of **X** and **Y** is described by writing in each cell the number (or proportion) of members of the population whose scores on **X** fall in the indicated **X**-interval *and* whose scores on **Y** also fall in the indicated **Y**-interval.

Scattergrams. While it is possible to construct bivariate histograms, frequency polygons, and frequency-density curves, these require three-dimensional models (two dimensions for the variables and a third for frequency) and are hence obviously inconvenient for most purposes. A more satisfactory method is to construct a two-dimensional graph on which the horizontal and vertical coordinates represent values of **X** and **Y**, respectively, but where the frequency of each particular combination of these variables is indicated not by the height of a coordinate in the

23, 2.2	58, 2.0	5, 3.2	43, 2.2	32, 2.0	105, .3	40, 1.9	47, 2.2	0, 2.1	36, 2.4
50, 1.8	34, 1.6	78, 1.2	37, 2.1	73, 1.0	3, 2.0	5, 1.6	35, 2.3	50, 1.9	25, 2.1
1, 2.4	70, 1.6	26, 2.0	42, 1.9	46, 1.5	66, 1.7	27, 2.8	18, 3.4	45, 2.1	41, 1.6
0, 2.8	44, 1.3	100, .6	57, 1.6	20, 1.3	59, 1.4	70, 1.1	76, 1.9	56, 1.3	79, 1.3
60, 1.6	36, 2.1	42, 2.4	8, 2.3	45, 2.3	80, .9	102, .4	51, 2.2	30, 1.8	61, 1.8
41, 1.4	65, 1.5	24, 3.2	40, 2.6	47, .8	35, 2.0	33, 2.7	0, 1.5	64, 1.9	39, 1.8
6, 1.8	48, 1.7	13, 2.7	38, 1.7	63, 1.6	22, 2.1	66, 1.3	38, 2.5	42, 2.0	31, 2.9
30, 2.3	45, 2.0	67, .9	26, 1.2	78, .8	44, 1.6	31, 1.5	53, 1.5	26, 2.6	54, 1.3
68, 1.5	17, 1.8	38, 2.2	58, 1.5	28, 2.3	44, 1.9	68, 1.2	40, 1.7	63, 1.1	45, 1.8
56, 1.9	24, 2.5	36, 2.5	33, 1.3	48, 2.5	70, 1.3	9, 1.7	36, 1.8	59, 1.7	18, 2.4

Table 2.3. Number of lecture hours cut and semester's grade-point average ($A = 4$, $B = 3$, etc.) for each of the 100 members of the ΑΒΓ Fraternity, Brainsweat University, during the Fall Semester, 1964.

third dimension but by the density of marking material deposited on the graph. The most prevalent way of doing this is to place a dot for each member of the population at the position on the graph corresponding to that individual's joint scores on **X** and **Y**. Such a graph (see Figure 2.6) is known as a *scattergram*, and shows at a glance what tendency there may be for certain combinations of values on **X** and **Y** to occur more frequently than others in this population. For example, it will be seen in Figure 2.6 that excessive class-absenting tends to be accompanied by especially low grade-point averages. We shall have a great deal more to say about relationships of this sort in Chapter 4.

Transformations

It was pointed out earlier that when we elect to designate the values of a variable by a set of numbers, there are many different ways to do this. Thus when scaling the Number-of-arrests variable, while it is most natural to represent *having never been arrested* by *0*, *having been arrested once* by *1*, *having been arrested twice* by *2*, etc., we could just as well, e.g., designate *having never been arrested* by *−5* and more generally let *having been arrested n times* be represented by that number which is five less than *n*. (Such scaling might even have some value if, for example, there were a law that a person who has been arrested more than five times is deprived of certain civil rights. Then a negative scale value tells how many arrests a person still has coming with impunity under this law.) We shall adopt the definition that one scaled variable **X**′ is a *rescaling* of another

Grade-Point Average \ Lecture Hours Cut	Under 7.5	7.5–15.5	15.5–23.5	23.5–31.5	31.5–39.5	39.5–47.5	47.5–55.5	55.5–63.5	63.5–71.5	71.5–79.5	79.5–87.5	87.5–95.5	95.5–103.5	103.5–111.5	Over 111.5
Over 3.65															
3.35–3.65			1												
3.05–3.35	1			1											
2.65–2.95	1	1		2	1										
2.35–2.65	1		1	2	3	2	1								
2.05–2.35	1	1	2	3	4	4	1	1							
1.75–2.05	2		1	2	4	6	2	3	1						
1.45–1.75	2	1		1	2	4	2	4	4	1					
1.15–1.45			1	1	1	2	1	2	3	2					
.85–1.15								1	2	1	1				
.55– .85						1				1			1		
.25– .55													1	1	
Under .25															

Lecture Hours Cut

Table 2.4. Bivariate-frequency table for the data in Table 2.3.

variable **X** if the scale values of **X**′ collectively represent the same set of attributes as do the scale values of **X**. Thus Height-in-feet is a rescaling of Height-in-inches and conversely, since a scale value of n on Height-in-feet represents the same degree of tallness as does a scale value of $12n$ on Height-in-inches.

The rule, operation, or procedure by which we pass from a scale value of some variable to the corresponding value on a rescaling of that variable is called a *transformation.* Thus, the transformation by which values of Height-in-inches are obtained from values of Height-in-feet is multiplying times twelve; and the *inverse transformation*—i.e., the procedure by which we pass back again to the original scale, in this instance from Height-in-inches back to Height-in-feet—is to divide by twelve. In all cases which shall be of concern to us here, the way in which one scale is transformed into another can be expressed by an algebraic equation. Thus if ϕ is some algebraic manipulation (e.g., multiplying by 12, or adding 2, or subtracting 5 and cubing the difference), we can express the fact that variable **X**′ is derived from variable **X** by the transformation ϕ by stating that for any entity i, $X_i' = \phi(X_i)$ [e.g., $X_i' = 12X_i$, $X_i' = X_i + 2$, $X_i' = (X_i - 5)^3$]—that is, that the scale value on **X**′ for an entity i is equal to the number obtained by applying the manipulation ϕ to i's scale value on **X**.

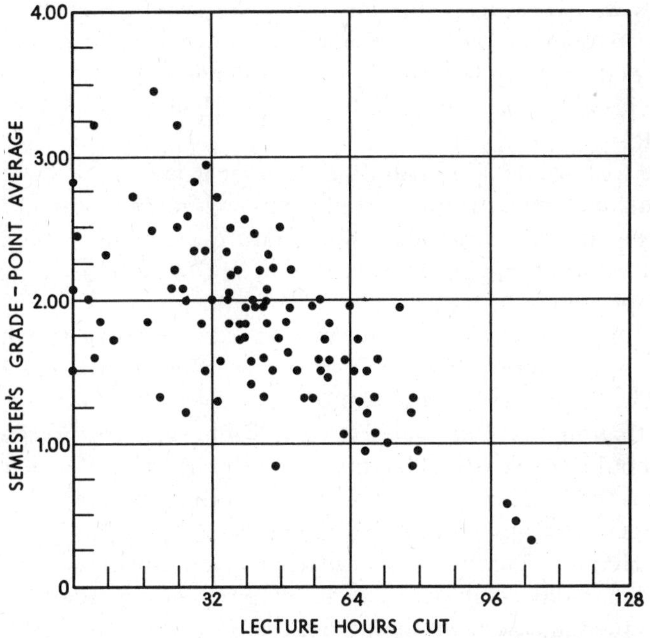

Figure 2.6. Scattergram, showing the joint distribution of lecture hours cut and semester's grade-point average for the members of the ABΓ Fraternity (data from Table 2.3).

Chapter 3. **Statistical Properties of Distributions**

In the previous chapter, we discussed techniques for describing a distribution in its entirety. In most statistical problems, however, it is necessary to abstract certain features of the distributions involved. Accordingly, we shall now examine some of the various *ways* in which one distribution can differ from another.

Suppose we know that we shall have a week's vacation sometime next July and are trying to decide where to go. We have narrowed our choice down to two cities, New Bushwak and Adastra Heights, each of which appears equally charming apart from possible differences in the temperatures we expect to encounter there. Suppose further that we have been able to obtain the distribution of noonday temperatures in each of these cities during the month of July for the past fifty years, as shown in Figure 3.1. On the basis of this information, which city should we choose to visit if—

A. We wish to get away from the summer heat?
B. We don't care how hot or cold it gets so long as we can judge accurately in advance what the temperature will be, since we are very limited in what luggage we can bring and want to be equipped appropriately?

Inspecting Figure 3.1, we observe that while Adastra Heights has a higher proportion of *very* hot days than does New Bushwak, the *general trend,* or what is *typical* of temperature, is nonetheless lower in Adastra Heights than in New Bushwak. Hence it would seem that in case A, our choice should be Adastra Heights, since this is the city which, on the whole, has the cooler temperatures. On the other hand, we also observe that temperature appears to be less *variable* in New Bushwak than in Adastra Heights. That is, temperatures in New Bushwak tend to have greater day-to-day similarity than do temperatures in Adastra Heights. Consequently, in case B we should opt for New Bushwak, for if we pack our luggage in anticipation of the temperature which is most typical of the city which we choose to visit, we shall expect to be less in error if our choice is New Bushwak than if it is Adastra Heights.

The preceding illustration calls attention to two important features of distributions which repeatedly demand explicit recognition in statistical work, namely, the *central tendency* or what is *typical* of the scores in a distribution on the one hand, and their *spread*, or *variability*, on the other. These properties are entirely independent of each other—knowing the central tendency of a distribution in general reveals nothing about its variability, and conversely. (This can readily be appreciated with the help of Figure 3.1 by reflecting that either curve could be freely shifted to the right or left without changing its width.) It also becomes clear that if these properties are at all important, it will be necessary to give them a more precise definition than has been done so far, for while, e.g., there can be no doubt that inspection of Figure 3.1 leaves a strong *feeling* that temperatures in Adastra Heights are on the whole lower but more variable than in New Bushwak, such intuitive reactions are not very reliable and frequently are of no help at all—witness Figure 3.2. What we need, therefore, are some quantitatively exact measures of central tendency and variability.

Measures of Central Tendency—the "Average"

Since the notion of a "general trend," or "most typical score," is inherently vague, it should come as no surprise to learn that when we attempt to arrive at a precise definition of central tendency, we find not one but many possible definitions which by no means always yield the same result. By far and away the most useful of these are the *arithmetic mean* and, to a lesser extent, the *median*, but others also find occasional application to specialized purposes.

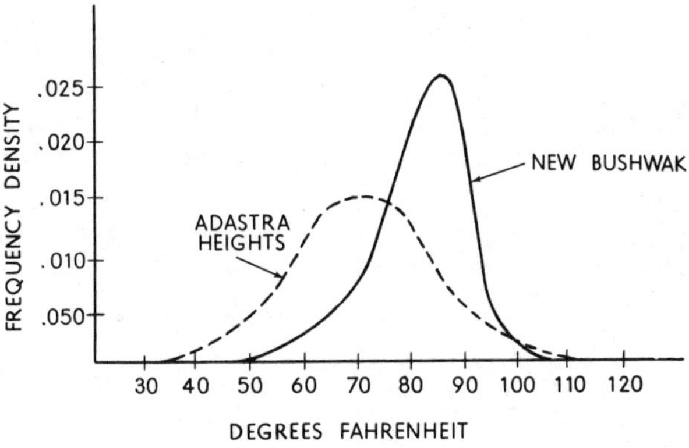

Figure 3.1. Frequency-density curves for the distribution of July noonday temperature for the past fifty years in two imaginary cities, Adastra Heights and New Bushwak.

The Mode. Of the various types of "average" which have seen actual use, the mode is the easiest to determine by simple inspection. The mode of a distribution is that value of the variable which occurs most frequently in the distribution. For example, if the ages of the nine children in a certain Sunday School class are 10, 9, 10, 10, 8, 9, 9, 11, and 10, the age which occurs most frequently is 10, so 10 is the modal age in this class. On a frequency-density graph, the mode is quickly spotted as the point of maximum density—i.e., that value of the variable over which the curve reaches its greatest height.

However there are serious objections against using the mode as a working measure of typicality, of which we shall here mention only three. (1) The mode may agree very poorly with intuitive impressions of central tendency. For example, in Figure 3.2 the mode of distribution B is at the extreme left of the distribution, and certainly does not feel very representative of the distribution as a whole. (2) The mode is not uniquely determined, since there may not be one single value of the variable which occurs more frequently than any other. For example, in a rectangular distribution (i.e., one whose frequency-density curve is shaped like a rectangle), *all* values of the variable which occur at all are modes.[1] (3) While a mode is easy to determine visually, it is extremely

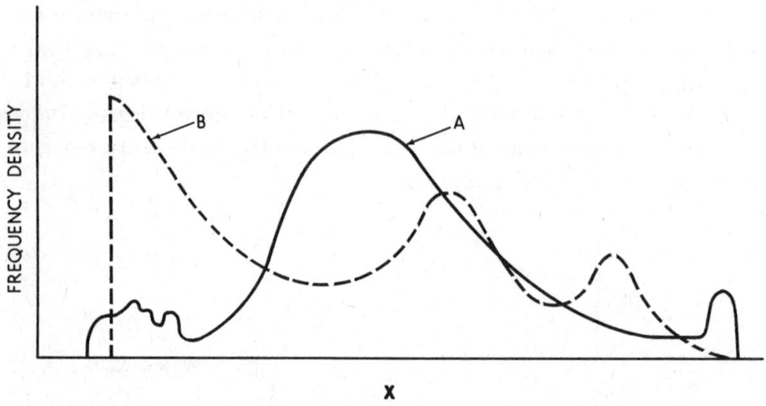

Figure 3.2. Two oddly shaped hypothetical distributions. Which has the higher central tendency? Which shows the greater variability?*

*Distributions A and B have approximately the same mean and standard deviation.

[1] A distribution which has more than one mode is said to be "bimodal," "trimodal," etc. (or, less definitely, "multimodal"), according to the number of modes present. It has also become customary to speak of "secondary" modes of a distribution in reference to values of the variable which, though not occurring as frequently as the "primary" mode, still have greater incidence than the adjacent values and which hence constitute humps on the frequency-density curve. In Figure 3.2, distribution B has two secondary modes in addition to the primary mode at the extreme left.

difficult to work with *mathematically,* for there is no algebraic computation—i.e., a finite series of operations involving only addition, subtraction, multiplication, and division—which will derive the mode of a distribution from its constituent scores. As will be seen, this same objection seriously contaminates many otherwise respectable statistical concepts.

The Median. As usually defined, the *median* of a distribution is its 50th percentile. That is, the median is that value of the variable which is greater than exactly 50% of the scores in the distribution. Graphically, a vertical line erected at the median on a frequency-density curve (see Figure 3.4, p. 40) cuts the area under the curve into two equal halves.

For some reason, the median appears to have the greatest intuitive appeal as the most "typical" score in a distribution. While we are most likely to choose the arithmetic mean (see below) for computational purposes, the psychological supremacy of the median is revealed by the fact that when the mean and median of a distribution differ markedly—e.g., as in the distribution of Weight-in-milligrams in the population comprising a dog and his fleas—there is an almost irresistible desire to take the median for our measure of central tendency. This favoritism is probably to be explained at least in part on the grounds that "central tendency" slides easily into "middle score," and no value of the variable is more middling in the sense of being equally surrounded on both sides than is the 50th percentile of the distribution. That is, an arbitrarily selected score is as likely to fall above as below the median of the distribution from which it is drawn. This and certain other virtues[2] of the median are more than counterbalanced, however, by two disadvantages: (1) The first difficulty, which is actually not too serious in itself, is that the definition of the median as the 50th percentile cannot be literally applied to a distribution composed of a finite number of scores, since strictly speaking, no percentile of such a distribution is uniquely determined—either the percentile doesn't exist at all or it corresponds to a whole interval of scale values.[3] Consequently, we adopt a slightly different definition of the median for distributions over finite populations; namely, that if the scores in the distribution are ranked in numerical order, the median is the middle score in this series if there is an odd number of scores, or the number halfway between the two middle scores if there is an even num-

---

[2] Of particular importance is the median's "order invariance." That is, any rescaling of a variable which leaves the order of scores unchanged (i.e., a rescaling such that if X_i is smaller than X_j, then *i*'s score on the transformed scale is smaller than *j*'s score on the transformed scale) transforms the median of the original distribution into the median of the transformed distribution.

[3] When a distribution contains only a finite number of scores and these are taken literally—i.e., are not considered to be spread out through some interval—then the distribution's cumulative-frequency function is composed of horizontal lines like an ascending staircase.

ber of scores. (2) The second and really nasty objection to the median is that like the mode, the median is not an algebraic function of the scores in the distribution. That is, it is not possible to define the median by an equation constructed wholly out of algebraic operations. This leaves the median intractable to mathematical manipulation, and hence largely useless for assisting mathematical insight into complex statistical problems.

The Arithmetic Mean, or "Expected" Value. Of all measures of central tendency, the arithmetic mean has proved to be the most useful. It has, in fact, become so familiar that a person who speaks of an "average" may usually be presumed to make reference to the arithmetic mean unless he explicitly states otherwise.[4] The arithmetic mean of a distribution is the sum of the scores in the distribution, divided by how many there are, and the joy and beauty of this is that not only does the arithmetic mean have a strong intuitive claim to centrality (see below), it is also exceedingly simple to express and manipulate algebraically.

Let the members of population P be ordered in some arbitrary fashion, so that we can indicate its various members by the expressions, "the first member of P," "the second member of P," and more generally, "the ith member of P," where i is any positive integer equal to or smaller than the number of members of P. Also, let "$M_{\mathbf{X}}$" designate the arithmetic mean of variable $\mathbf{X}$ in population P.[5] (To be completely explicit, we should attach a second subscript to "$M_{\mathbf{X}}$" to indicate the population concerned, since the mean of a variable is not a property of the variable in itself, but only of its distribution in some particular population, and the symbol "$M_{\mathbf{X}}$" is hence strictly speaking ambiguous. However, it is customary to label statistical symbols only with subscripts indicating the variables involved, and to depend upon the context of usage to identify the population.) Then for a population P containing, say, four members, the arithmetic mean of $\mathbf{X}$ in P is defined as the number obtained by taking the value of $\mathbf{X}$ for the first member of P plus the value of $\mathbf{X}$ for the second member of P plus the value of $\mathbf{X}$ for the third member of P plus the value of $\mathbf{X}$ for the fourth member of P, and dividing this sum by four. That is, in symbols,

$$M_{\mathbf{X}} = \frac{X_1 + X_2 + X_3 + X_4}{4} .$$

For example, if the IQs of Mrs. Jukes's four children are 57, 102, 78, and 89, respectively, the arithmetic mean IQ for Mrs. Jukes's children is

$$M_{\mathbf{IQ}} = \frac{57 + 102 + 78 + 89}{4} = \frac{326}{4} = 81.5 .$$

[4] One exception to this rule are the "average" incomes, etc., reported in newspapers and magazines. Because the distributions are frequently so skewed, the central tendencies of economic data are usually reported in the form of medians, the technical precision of which is then lost in the newspaper reports by calling them "averages."

[5] The notation "$\bar{X}$" is also frequently used to designate the mean of $\mathbf{X}$.

More generally, for a population containing n members,

$$[3.1] \qquad M_X =_{\text{def}} \frac{X_1 + X_2 + \ldots + X_{n-1} + X_n}{n} .$$

("$=_{\text{def}}$" is translated "equals by definition.")

A special notation, using the Greek capital letter "Σ" (sigma), has been developed to render the summation in [3.1] and similar formulas more compact. Let E_i be some simple or compound mathematical expression containing one or more symbols with a subscript i—for example, X_i, $(Z_i - 6)^2$, X_iY_i (i.e., the product of X_i and Y_i), etc. Then $\sum_{i=1}^{n} E_i$ abbreviates the expression which results from adding together the expressions obtained by successively substituting 1, 2, . . . , n for i in E_i. Thus for the examples just given,

$$\sum_{i=1}^{4} X_i =_{\text{def}} X_1 + X_2 + X_3 + X_4 ,$$

$$\sum_{i=1}^{3} (Z_i - 6)^2 =_{\text{def}} (Z_1 - 6)^2 + (Z_2 - 6)^2 + (Z_3 - 6)^2 ,$$

and

$$\sum_{i=1}^{n} X_iY_i =_{\text{def}} X_1Y_1 + X_2Y_2 + \ldots + X_nY_n .$$

Frequently, explicit reference to the number of terms, n, in the summation is omitted from the notation, and sometimes even the subscript i is dropped—i.e.,

$$[3.2] \qquad \sum E =_{\text{def}} \sum_i E_i =_{\text{def}} \sum_{i=1}^{n} E_i =_{\text{def}} E_1 + \ldots + E_n .$$

The Σ-notation just introduced is so basic to statistical thinking that the reader must thoroughly familiarize himself with it if he is to achieve honest understanding of the statistical concepts which follow. As an exercise to insure that this familiarity has been attained, the following elementary but exceedingly important relationships should be examined, both in abstract and in application to specific examples, until it becomes obvious why they hold. In these equations, F_i and G_i are any mathematical expressions containing one or more symbols bearing a subscript i (of course, "i" may be replaced by any other subscript letter throughout the equations), and c is any numerical constant.

$$[3.3] \qquad \sum_{i=1}^{n} cF_i = c \sum_{i=1}^{n} F_i$$

$$\text{Example:} \quad \sum_{i=1}^{3}(2X_i) = 2\left(\sum_{i=1}^{3} X_i\right) .$$

[3.4] $$\sum_{i=1}^{n} (F_i + c) = \sum_{i=1}^{n} F_i + nc$$

$$\text{Example:} \quad \sum_{i=1}^{5} (X_iX_i + 8) = \left(\sum_{i=1}^{5} X_iY_i\right) + 5 \cdot 8$$

$$= \left(\sum_{i=1}^{5} X_iY_i\right) + 40 .$$

[3.5] $$\sum_{i=1}^{n} (F_i + G_i) = \sum_{i=1}^{n} F_i + \sum_{i=1}^{n} G_i$$

$$\text{Example:} \quad \sum_{i=1}^{4} (X_i^2 + Y_i) = \left(\sum_{i=1}^{4} X_i^2\right) + \left(\sum_{i=1}^{4} Y_i\right) .$$

These equations follow by substitution of cF_i, $(F_i + c)$, and $(F_i + G_i)$, respectively, for E_i in the definition of $\sum_{i=1}^{n} E_i$ in [3.2], regrouping the terms in the resulting expression to the right of the equality sign, and then rewriting the latter in Σ-notation. Some unnecessary parentheses have been added in the examples to help clarify any doubts that may arise about the extension of algebraic grouping conventions to Σ-expressions. The reader should also make sure it is obvious to him that if F_i and F_i' are mathematically equivalent expressions (as are, e.g., X_iY_i and Y_iX_i, or $c(X_i + 2)$ and $(cX_i + 2c)$, then they are freely interchangeable in a Σ-formula. In particular,

[3.6][6] $$\sum_{i=1}^{n} F_i = \sum_{i=1}^{n} F_i' \qquad \text{(if } F_i = F_i' \text{ for every } i\text{)}$$

$$\text{Example:} \quad \sum_{i=1}^{n} X_i(X_i + 6) = \sum_{i=1}^{n} (X_i^2 + 6X_i) .$$

With [3.3]–[3.6] in mind, the reader should have no trouble manipu-

[6] In this and subsequent formulas, the parenthetical addition to the right of the equation states a condition presupposed by the formula.

lating equations involving Σ-expressions as easily as he would any other algebraic formula. For example,

$$\sum_{i=1}^{n}(X_i+Y_i)^2 = \sum_{i=1}^{n}(X_i^2+2X_iY_i+Y_i^2) = \sum_{i=1}^{n}X_i^2+2\sum_{i=1}^{n}X_iY_i+\sum_{i=1}^{n}Y_i^2 .$$

Using the Σ-convention just explained, we can now define the arithmetic mean of a variable **X** in a population P with n members to be

$$\text{[3.7]} \qquad \mathrm{M}_{\mathbf{X}} =_{\text{def}} \frac{\sum_{i=1}^{n} X_i}{n},$$

or more tersely,

$$\mathrm{M}_{\mathbf{X}} = \frac{\sum_{i} X_i}{n}.$$

*It is also possible to define the mean of a distribution without having a sequential listing of its individual scores if we know for each alternative value of the variable how many (or what proportion) of the population members have that score. (This is what is given, in effect, by a histogram, frequency polygon, or frequency table if we assume, for simplicity, that all the scores in a class interval fall on the midpoint of the interval.) It is difficult to discuss this method comprehensively without getting into more mathematical complications than seem desirable here, but the principle should be mentioned if only to clarify for readers who have already encountered this definition how it differs from formula [3.7]. Suppose that n_X is the number of entities in population P having X for their value of **X**. Then we can find the sum of the scores in the distribution of **X** in P by multiplying each value X of **X** by its absolute frequency n_X and adding these products together. Writing this sum as $\sum_X X \bullet n_X$, the formula for the mean of **X** in P by this method is then

$$\text{[3.8][7]} \qquad \mathrm{M}_{\mathbf{X}} = \frac{\sum_X X \bullet n_X}{n} = \frac{\sum_X X \bullet n_X}{\sum_X n_X} = \sum_X X \bullet p_X ,$$

[7] Strictly speaking, this formula applies only to variables with a finite number of values. To go beyond this would get into the complications we here wish to avoid. For the reader who is familiar with calculus, the generalization of formula [3.8] to the distribution of a continuous variable in an infinite population is

$$\mathrm{M}_{\mathbf{X}} = \int_{-\infty}^{\infty} X \bullet f_X \, dX ,$$

where f_X is the frequency density of the distribution at value X of **X**.

where $p_X =_{\text{def}} n_X/n$ is the relative frequency of X in this distribution. Notice that summation in [3.8] is over X, rather than over i as in formula [3.7]. That is, when computing the sum in [3.8], all possible values are substituted for X throughout the formula to the right of the summation sign. To illustrate, suppose that the distribution of **X** in P consists of five scores: 24, 24, 30, 30, 30. Then $p_{24} = 2/5 = .4$, $p_{30} = 3/5 = .6$, $p_X = 0$ for all X not equal to 24 or 30, and hence from [3.8],

$$\mathrm{M}_{\mathbf{X}} = 24(.4) + 30(.6) + \text{(a series of zero terms)} = 27.6\ ,$$

which, of course, is the same result as would be obtained by applying formula [3.7].

The intuitive appeal of the arithmetic mean lies in its "middleness" in the sense of "halfway between." It is easy to see that the arithmetic mean of two scores is the number halfway between them, and further, that if the scores in a distribution are separated into two groups with the same number of scores in each, the mean of the distribution is halfway between the means of the two halves. More generally, the arithmetic mean is that value of the variable such that the sum of the distances that above-$\mathrm{M}_{\mathbf{X}}$ scores in the distribution are above $\mathrm{M}_{\mathbf{X}}$ equals the sum of the distances that below-$\mathrm{M}_{\mathbf{X}}$ scores are below it. Physically, if a uniformly thick sheet of cardboard or metal is cut into the shape of the frequency-density curve of a distribution, its arithmetic mean is the point along the base at which the cutout will balance on a fulcrum.

In mathematical statistics, the arithmetic mean of a distribution is also known as the *expected* value of the variable in the population under concern. The origins of this usage allegedly go back to a quite literal meaning of "expectation" in pre-statistical days, when speculations in risky commercial operations used to be sold on the basis of the "expected" worth of the venture. Early formulations of the theory of prediction identified this "expectation" with the arithmetic mean of the probability distribution over the venture's possible financial returns, and even today, the equating of arithmetic means with psychological expectations forms an important intuitive shoring for application of modern regression theory to problems of prediction (Chapter 4).

Nonarithmetic Means. The arithmetic mean, though conceptually basic, is only one of a family of means which can be defined on a distribution by considering transformations of the variable. Any number which is derived from the scores in a distribution by (*a*) rescaling the variable, (*b*) computing the arithmetic mean of the transformed scores, and (*c*) reconverting this mean back to the original scale, may be regarded as a type of mean corresponding to the rescaling transformation employed. Specifically, let ϕ be some rule of transformation, let $\phi(X)$ be the number which results from performing the transformation ϕ on scale value X of variable **X**, and let ϕ^{-1} be the inverse of ϕ—i.e., ϕ^{-1} is the transformation such that for any X, $\phi^{-1}(\phi(X)) = X$. Then, if "T" is some phrase describing transformation ϕ, we define the "T-mean," $\text{TM}_{\mathbf{X}}$, of the distribution of **X** in population P to be

[3.9] $$\text{TM}_{\mathbf{X}} = \phi^{-1}\left(\frac{\sum_{i=1}^{n} \phi(X_i)}{n}\right).$$

About the only members of this family additional to the arithmetic mean (which is obtained when ϕ is any linear transformation, such as multiplying by one) which have seen practical application are the *harmonic mean* ($\text{HM}_{\mathbf{X}}$) in which $\phi(X) = 1/X$, the *geometric mean* ($\text{GM}_{\mathbf{X}}$) in which $\phi(X) = \log(X)$, and the *quadratic mean* ($\text{QM}_{\mathbf{X}}$) in which $\phi(X) = X^2$. Specifically, these means are defined under the restrictions noted as

[3.10] $$\text{HM}_{\mathbf{X}} =_{\text{def}} \frac{1}{\dfrac{\sum_i 1/X_i}{n}} = \frac{n}{\sum_i 1/X_i},$$

[3.11] $$\text{GM}_{\mathbf{X}} =_{\text{def}} \text{antilog}\left(\frac{\sum_i \log(X_i)}{n}\right)$$

$(X_i \geqslant 0 \text{ for all } i \text{ in } P)$

$$= \sqrt[n]{X_1 X_2 \ldots X_{n-1} X_n},$$

and

[3.12] $$\text{QM}_{\mathbf{X}} =_{\text{def}} \sqrt{\frac{\sum_i X_i^2}{n}} \qquad (X_i \geqslant 0 \text{ for all } i \text{ in } P).$$

The reason why geometric and quadratic means are restricted to variables which take only positive values is that in the case of $\text{GM}_{\mathbf{X}}$, logarithms of negative numbers do not exist, while for $\text{QM}_{\mathbf{X}}$, since the square of a number m is the same as the square of $-m$, the squaring operation does not preserve uniqueness—i.e., does not have an inverse—when **X** takes both positive and negative values and hence in this case does not meet the condition for being a rescaling transformation. That is, if $X'_i =_{\text{def}} X_i^2$, knowing a person's score on the transformed scale $\mathbf{X}'$ does not sufice to reveal his score on the original scale **X** unless it is also known that the **X**-scores are all restricted either to positive or to negative values. (The quadratic mean can thus also be defined for distributions which contain only negative values; however, we shall have no need for this possibility.)

Harmonic and geometric means will be of no concern in this book, but the quadratic mean will see important application in what follows. Consequently, it is worth stressing that when applicable, the quadratic mean of a variable **X** *is* an "average" value of **X**. It is that value of **X** which corresponds to the arithmetic mean in population P of a quadratic rescaling of **X**.

****Weighted Averages.*** If $X_1, \ldots, X_n$ are a set of quantities while $w_1, \ldots, w_n$ are "weights" such that each w_i is between 0 and 1 while $\sum_{i=1}^{n} w_i = 1$, the sum

$$\text{[3.13]} \qquad \mathrm{WM}_{\mathbf{X}} =_{\text{def}} \sum_{i=1}^{n} w_i X_i \qquad \left(\sum_{i=1}^{n} w_i = 1\right)$$

is known as a *weighted average* (more precisely, a weighted arithmetic mean) of $X_1, \ldots, X_n$. It may be seen from [3.7] that the arithmetic mean of $X_1, \ldots, X_n$ is the special case of [3.13] in which $w_i = 1/n$ for each i. If the X_i in [3.13] are thought of as the set of alternatively possible values of **X** rather than as the **X**-scores for individuals $1, \ldots, n$, then $\mathrm{WM}_{\mathbf{X}}$ may be interpreted as the arithmetic mean that variable **X** would have in a population in which each value X_i occurs with relative frequency w_i (cf. formula [3.8]). In similar fashion, we may define weighted nonarithmetic means, weighted medians, and other weighted "averages" of all sorts. What is of primary interest about such weighted averages is not that we are likely to introduce them into a problem deliberately, but that they may emerge spontaneously. When carrying through some mathematical analysis, being able to interpret a certain complex expression which has turned up in an equation as an "average" of certain quantities involved in the problem may contribute greatly to an understanding of what that equation means.

Henceforth, we shall adopt the convention that the terms "average" and "mean," when unqualified, denote the arithmetic mean.

Measures of Dispersion, or Spread

It was seen at the beginning of this chapter that not only is there a need for exact expressions of how large, on the whole, the scores in a distribution tend to be, but we must also develop measures of how much variation, inconsistency, or irregularity the scores show if we are to be able to give any precision, e.g., to our feeling that July noonday temperatures seem to show less uniformity in Adastra Heights than in New Bushwak (Figure 3.1). A number of concepts have been devised for this purpose, falling roughly into two types: (1) measures of *span*, based on the scale distance between two fixed positions in the distribution; and (2) concepts expressing the *typical deviation* from the distribution's central tendency.

****Measures Based on Span.*** The most familiar measure of spread belonging to this category is the *range,* which is simply the difference between the highest and the lowest scores in the distribution. Thus in the example presented in Table 3.1, the brightest and the dullest Jones boys have IQs of 120 and 80, respectively, so the range of IQ in this family is 120 minus 80, or 40. For precise work, however, the range is a rather

X: IQ $\qquad$ P: Jones boys

i	X_i	$D_{\mathbf{X}i}$	$D^2_{\mathbf{X}i}$
Pete	96	4	16
Zeke	99	1	1
Elmer	120	20	400
Hank	80	20	400
Morty	105	5	25
Σ	500	50	842
Σ/n	100.0	10.0	168.4

$$D_{\mathbf{X}i} = |X_i - \mathrm{M}_{\mathbf{X}}| = \begin{cases} \mathrm{M}_{\mathbf{X}} - X_i \text{ if } X_i \leqslant \mathrm{M}_{\mathbf{X}} \\ X_i - \mathrm{M}_{\mathbf{X}} \text{ if } X_i > \mathrm{M}_{\mathbf{X}} \end{cases}$$

$$\text{Mean} = \mathrm{M}_{\mathbf{X}} = \overline{X} = \frac{\sum_i X_i}{n} = 100.0$$

$$\text{Range} = \text{Max}\,(\mathbf{X}) - \text{Min}\,(\mathbf{X}) = 120 - 80 = 40$$

$$\text{Average Deviation} = \mathrm{AD}_{\mathbf{X}} = \mathrm{M}_{D_{\mathbf{X}}} = \frac{\sum_i D_{\mathbf{X}i}}{n} = 10.0$$

$$\text{Standard Deviation} = \mathrm{SD}_{\mathbf{X}} = \sigma_{\mathbf{X}} = \mathrm{QM}_{D_{\mathbf{X}}}$$

$$= \sqrt{\frac{\sum_i D^2_{\mathbf{X}i}}{n}} = \sqrt{168.4} = 12.97$$

$$\text{Probable Error} = \mathrm{PE}_{\mathbf{X}} = \mathrm{Mdn}_{D_{\mathbf{X}}} = 5.0$$

Table 3.1. Distribution of IQ in the population of Jones boys, illustrating various measures of dispersion.

unsatisfactory statistic. One by now familiar objection is its failure to be an algebraic function of the individual scores in the distribution. Another is that the range does not take into consideration *enough* of the differences among the scores, and hence may easily fail to reflect our intuitive assessment of the amount of variation in the data. For example, suppose the distribution of IQ in the Jones-boys population, namely, 80, 96, 99, 105, 120 (from Table 3.1), is compared to the distribution of IQ in the Smith brothers, where the IQs of the latter are, say, 80, 81, 112, 117, 120. In both cases the range is the same, namely, 40. Yet it is clear that IQ in the Smith brothers shows considerably more variation among the nonextreme cases than in the Jones boys, and hence we should like to say that there is greater dispersion of IQ in the Smith brothers than in the Jones boys, even though this difference is not revealed by the range.[8]

Instead of describing the spread of a distribution by the distance spanned between its extremes, we can just as well pick out two other positions in the distribution (e.g., its 10th and 50th percentiles, its 40th and 60th percentiles, etc.) and state the scale difference between these. Obviously there is no limit to the different width measures which can be defined in this way. In addition to the range, one other span-based statistic which is encountered in practice often enough to warrant passing mention here is the *semi-interquartile range.* This is defined as half the distance between the 25th and 75th percentile of the distribution—i.e., one half the interval covered by the middle 50% of the scores.

Measures of Typical Deviation. The question of how variable are the scores in a distribution may be rephrased quite naturally as a question of how far away from the center of the distribution the scores tend to be, or how similar on the whole they are to their "typical" value. These reformulations clearly indicate a procedure for measuring variation which, moreover, gives each score in the distribution due consideration; namely, determine how far each score is from the distribution's "average," and then, in turn, take an "average" of these deviations. Since there are many varieties of "average," however, there are an even greater number of different ways to define such a "typical" deviation. Of these possibilities, three have seen practical application: the *average deviation,* the *probable error,* and above all, the *standard deviation.* Each of these is a measure of typical deviation from the distribution's arithmetic mean, though there are reasons why it would be more appropriate to take the average deviation around the median, rather than around the mean.[9]

---

[8] Perhaps the strongest objection to the range as a measure of spread comes from inferential statistics. When attempting to estimate the statistical properties of a distribution from the corresponding statistical properties of a sample of scores drawn from it, the range of the sample provides a very poor estimate of the range or any other measure of variability in the population sampled. Also, in most theoretical distributions, the range is infinite.

[9] See fn. 5, p. 65.

Suppose we are given the distribution of a variable **X** within a certain population *P*. We may then define a new variable, the "Deviation-on-**X**" variable, or $\mathbf{D_X}$ for short, over population *P* which tells for each member *i* of *P* how far away *i*'s **X**-score is from the arithmetic mean of **X** in *P*. More precisely, an entity's Deviation-on-**X** score is defined as

$$[3.14] \qquad D_{\mathbf{X}i} =_{\text{def}} |X_i - \mathrm{M}_{\mathbf{X}}| \ ,$$

where the two vertical bars are the conventional symbol for the "absolute value," or *magnitude*, of the expression between them—i.e., "| |" designates the function which drops the minus sign from negative numbers but leaves positive numbers unchanged. The second column of Table 3.1 shows the distribution of Deviation-on-IQ scores in the Jones-boys population. Since the arithmetic mean of IQ in the Jones boys is 100.0, and Elmer Jones has an IQ of 120, his Deviation-on-IQ score is 120 minus 100, or 20. Likewise, Hank Jones, whose IQ is 80, is equally far away from the mean as Elmer, and hence has the same Deviation-on-IQ score, even though Hank lies below the mean while Elmer is above it. (When representing the amount of variation among scores by their "typical" deviation, it is important to appreciate that is the *magnitude* of a score's divergence from the distribution's central tendency which shows how atypical that score is. The *algebraic* difference $X_i - \mathrm{M}_{\mathbf{X}}$ between a score X_i and $\mathrm{M}_{\mathbf{X}}$ will not suffice for this purpose, for these differences are negative about as often as positive, show the direction as well as the size of the difference, and have a mean of zero.) We may now define the "average deviation ($\mathrm{AD}_{\mathbf{X}}$) of variable **X** in population *P*" to be the *arithmetic mean of Deviation-on-***X** *scores* in *P*; the "standard deviation ($\sigma_{\mathbf{X}}$,[10] or $\mathrm{SD}_{\mathbf{X}}$) of **X** in *P*" to be the *quadratic mean of Deviation-on-***X** *scores* in *P*; and the "probable error ($\mathrm{PE}_{\mathbf{X}}$) of **X** in *P*" to be the *median Deviation-on-***X** *score* in *P*. The computation of these measures is illustrated in Table 3.1.

The *probable error* of a distribution has the interesting property that since it is the median distance that scores in the distribution lie away from their mean, half[11] of the scores are at a distance of one PE or less from the mean.[12] That is, a score is as likely as not to be within one PE of the mean. This and whatever other features of medians grant them intuitive appeal

[10] The symbol "σ", which has become conventional notation for the standard deviation, is the Greek lowercase sigma. There is no relation between this usage and that of uppercase sigma (Σ) to indicate summation.

[11] Strictly speaking, this must be qualified to the extent that the median of an odd finite number of scores is not greater than *exactly* half of the scores.

[12] The PE and semi-interquartile range of a distribution are very similar in that each is half of a span which includes a central 50% of the distribution. When the 25th and 75th percentiles of a distribution are equidistant from its mean, as is true of any symmetric distribution, its probable error and semi-interquartile range are numerically identical.

as measures of typicality have until recently made the probable error a popular form for reporting the dispersions found in empirical data. However, the PE is a "terminal" statistic—i.e., it cannot be algebraically defined, and is hence mathematically recalcitrant—so with the contemporary emergence of high-powered mathematical models for data analysis, the PE has virtually disappeared from use.

The *average deviation* (sometimes called the "mean deviation") of a distribution has many virtues. It is pedagogically delightful in the ease with which its significance can be grasped. The AD is just what its name implies: the average (arithmetic mean) amount by which the scores in the distribution deviate from their mean value. It is an arithmetic joy in the ease by which its numerical value can be computed—one has only to determine the mean of the scores, take the difference between each score and this mean without regard for which is the larger, and then average these differences. Finally, the AD is an intuitively useful measure of variation in that it is the amount by which an arbitrarily selected score in the distribution is "expected" to diverge from the distribution's mean. But alas, the average deviation, too, belongs to that multitude of statistics which fail to be an algebraic function of the scores in the distribution. Writing the definition of the AD in mathematical notation, we have

$$\text{[3.15]}\qquad \begin{aligned} \mathrm{AD}_{\mathbf{X}} &=_{\text{def}} \frac{\sum_i D_{\mathbf{X}i}}{n} \\ &= \frac{\sum_i |X_i - \mathrm{M}_{\mathbf{X}}|}{n}. \end{aligned}$$

But the absolute-value function in the second line is not algebraic, and so with a tear of farewell and a sigh for what might have been, we dismiss the average deviation from further serious consideration.

As the reader is probably aware, the measure of spread which has by now triumphed over all others is the *standard* (i.e., quadratic mean) *deviation,* symbolized in statistical notation by "σ." The SD has no particular intuitive superiority as a measure of variation, nor is it true, as the statistical novice is frequently told, that with a wisdom transcending comprehension by ordinary minds, the statistician has introduced the standard deviation in order to give extra weight to the more extreme scores in the distribution.[13] Actually, the statistician's affection for the SD is

[13] It is found in inferential statistics that when the statistical properties of a population are inferred from those of an observed sample of that population, the standard deviation of the sample is usually more informative about the parent population's standing on all measures of variation than is the sample's average deviation. But this has nothing to do with the question of which measure of variation is best *as a measure of variation.*

much more crassly opportunistic: not merely is the SD an "average" deviation; it is, with one small qualification, a mathematically compliant *algebraic function of the individual scores in the distribution.* (The qualification is that strictly speaking it is σ^2, rather than σ, which is algebraically definable, since square root involves additional complications.) It will be recalled from [3.12] that to take the quadratic mean of a set of scores, we square each score, take the arithmetic mean of these squares, and then un-square the result. But the square of a negative number is the same as the square of its absolute value. Hence writing the definition of the standard deviation of a variable **X** in a population P in mathematical notation, we have

[3.16]
$$\sigma_{\mathbf{X}} =_{\text{def}} \text{QM}_{\mathbf{D_X}} = \sqrt{\frac{\sum_i D^2_{\mathbf{X}i}}{n}} = \sqrt{\frac{\sum_i |X_i - \text{M}_{\mathbf{X}}|^2}{n}} = \sqrt{\frac{\sum_i (X_i - \text{M}_{\mathbf{X}})^2}{n}},$$

and the final formula on the right is, apart from the qualification noted, the algebraic function sought.

Another formula for the standard deviation which, though equivalent to [3.16], is much more mathematically and computationally convenient, is

[3.17]
$$\sigma_{\mathbf{X}} = \sqrt{\frac{\sum_i X_i^2}{n} - \text{M}^2_{\mathbf{X}}}.$$

This is easily seen to follow from [3.16] by observing that $\sum_i (X_i - \text{M}_{\mathbf{X}})^2 = \sum_i (X_i^2 - 2X_i\text{M}_{\mathbf{X}} + \text{M}^2_{\mathbf{X}}) = \sum_i X_i^2 - 2\text{M}_{\mathbf{X}} \sum_i X_i + n\text{M}^2_{\mathbf{X}} = \sum_i X_i^2 - 2n\text{M}^2_{\mathbf{X}} + n\text{M}^2_{\mathbf{X}} = \sum_i X_i^2 - n\text{M}^2_{\mathbf{X}}$.

*Equation [3.17] has an interesting consequence which cannot be expected to mean a great deal to the reader at present, but will prove illuminating in later chapters. It sometimes occurs that while a variable **X**

comes with both positive and negative values in population P, we are also interested in the distribution of the *magnitude* of those values. In particular, we may wish to know how large, on the whole, the scores on **X** tend to be irrespective of their sign—a question which, for mathematical reasons just discussed, is most conveniently answered by consideration of the variable's quadratic mean magnitude. (This, it will be recalled, was the problem which confronted us a few paragraphs back when we wished to measure how far an individual score in a distribution typically diverges from the distribution's mean.) Now, squaring both sides of [3.17] and reorganizing gives

[3.18] $$\frac{\sum_i X_i^2}{n} = M_{\mathbf{X}}^2 + \sigma_{\mathbf{X}}^2 .$$

But since $X_i^2 = |X_i|^2$, the expression on the left in [3.18] is also the squared quadratic mean magnitude of **X**. Hence

[3.19] $$QM_{|\mathbf{X}|}^2 = M_{\mathbf{X}}^2 + \sigma_{\mathbf{X}}^2 .$$

In view of the well-known properties of a right triangle, [3.19] may be expressed graphically as shown in Figure 3.3. Specifically, the quadratic mean magnitude of a variable equals the hypotenuse of a right triangle whose legs are respectively the variable's arithmetic mean and standard deviation. Applied to a variable for which the quadratic mean as well as the arithmetic mean is defined—namely, a variable which takes only positive values, so that $|X_i| = X_i$ and $QM_{|\mathbf{X}|} = QM_{\mathbf{X}}$—equation [3.19] and Figure 3.3 show that its quadratic mean can never be smaller than its arithmetic mean. We may draw upon this fact to note a corresponding relation between a variable's standard and average deviations. As de-

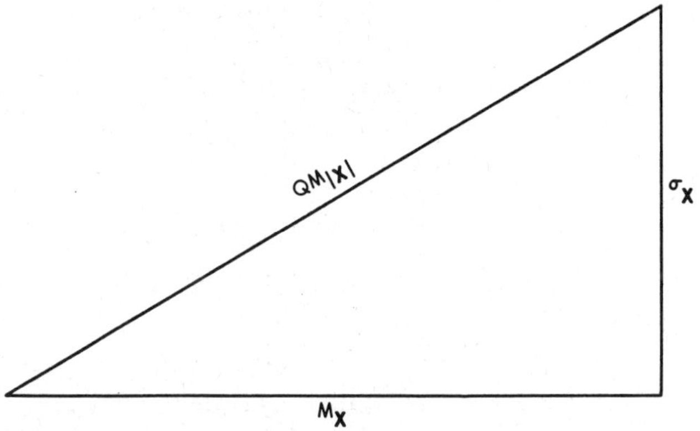

Figure 3.3. A geometric interpretation of equation [3.19].

fined above, $AD_X = M_{D_X}$ and $\sigma_X = QM_{D_X}$. Hence if the arbitrary symbol "**X**" in [3.19] is replaced by "D_X", we find that

[3.20] $$\sigma_X^2 = AD_X^2 + \sigma_{D_X}^2,$$

which proves that a variable's standard deviation is always equal to or larger than its average deviation. We find in practice, for reasons which will appear shortly, that the AD tends to be about four fifths as large as the SD. Similarly, a distribution's probable error tends to be about 2/3 σ.

The Variance. No summary of measures of spread would be complete without mention of the *variance* (Var). The variance of a variable in some population P is simply the square of the distribution's standard deviation—i.e., from [3.17],

$$\text{Var} \underset{\text{def}}{=} \sigma_X^2$$

[3.21] $$= \frac{\sum_i X_i^2}{n} - M_X^2$$

$$= M_{(X^2)} - M_X^2 .$$

The variance has no intuitive value at all for describing variability, but its mathematical convenience (it is, without qualification, an algebraic function of the individual scores in the distribution, and a very simple one at that) and its simple relation to the standard deviation have made it an indispensible concept for the mathematical statistician, in whose formulas, like it or not, the variance is bound to show up.

The Significance of Averages and Measures of Variation

Before putting the statistical concepts developed above to use, it is perhaps worthwhile to pause for a final clarification of what *sort* of meaning these numbers have, and how they may be represented on a graph of the distribution. In our first group—measures of central tendency—we are dealing with *typical scores*. Hence, an "average" is *a particular value of the variable*. That is, if the mean Height-in-inches in a certain group of people is 63.7, this "63.7" is one of the values of the Height-in-inches variable and will likely (though not necessarily) be the height in inches of one or more persons in the population. It is in this sense that we frequently describe a variable's average in some population as the score of an "average" member of the population (e.g., the weight of the "average" man, the IQ of the "average" child, etc.), even though strictly speaking it is only scores, not individuals, which can be average.[14] In short,

[14] If we tried to average n people, rather than their scores on some variable, we would have to stack them in a pile and slice the pile into n equal parts.

when describing the distribution of a variable **X** in a population P, there is a certain value of **X** which has the special property of being the distribution's mean, another value of **X** (possibly the same as the former) which is the distribution's median, etc. Consequently, a measure of central tendency is shown graphically by calling attention to one particular value of the variable. An effective, though not the only, way to do this on a graph of the distribution is to erect an arbitrarily tall vertical line whose position along the horizontal axis marks the appropriate score (see Figure 3.4). In this connection, it should be observed that a "typical" score may conveniently be used as a point of reference in scaling the variable. Thus, instead of stating the actual score of an individual i on a variable **X**, we can just as well say how many points i's score is above or below the mean. Of this, more later.

On the other hand, a number which describes the amount of variation in a distribution is, for all measures of spread mentioned here with the exception of the variance, *a difference between two particular values of the variable.* This is obvious in the case of measures based on span, and not much less so for measures of typical deviation, since each of the latter is an "average" of differences between two values of the variable. Consequently, a measure of variation may be represented graphically by a line segment, preferably horizontal (since this is the dimension on the graph which reflects score differences) but otherwise arbitrary in position, whose *length* shows the graphical separation between two scores which are one unit of variation apart (see Figure 3.4). The similarity here to the scale markers drawn in the corner of a map to show what map distances correspond to what amounts of geographical separation is more

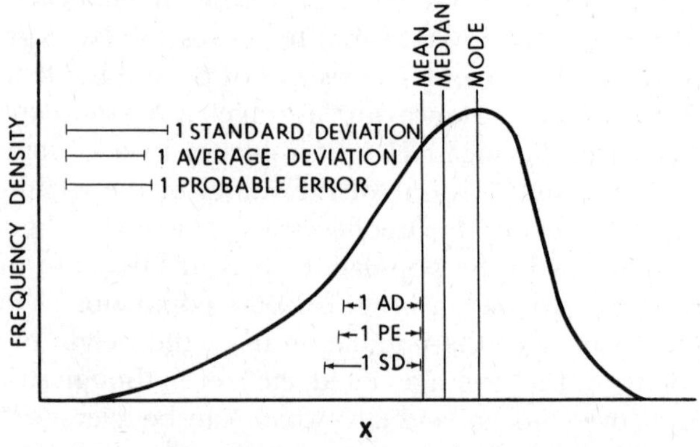

Figure 3.4. Hypothetical frequency-density curve, illustrating graphical representations of various measures of central tendency and variability. The fashion in which the different measures of average and spread differ among themselves depends upon the distribution's shape.

than coincidental. Different measures of variation—σ, AD, PE, etc.—which, of course, are represented by line segments of different lengths, may be conceived as different units for measuring the separation between scale values just as geographical distances can variously be described in terms of miles, kilometers, yards, etc. Thus if Pat's IQ is 97 while Mike's IQ is 117, and the SD and PE of IQ in the population are 15 and 10, respectively, Mike is 1.33 standard deviations, and 2.00 probable errors, superior to Pat in IQ.

Standard Scores

It was pointed out in Chapter 2 that the set of attributes which constitute a scientific variable may be scaled in many alternative ways, thereby generating a whole family of scaled variables corresponding to the same underlying attribute set. Given such a wealth of alternatives, what considerations can be advanced to make the choice of a particular scaling less than entirely arbitrary?

Usually, the language in which data are initially recorded mentions numbers—i.e., the number of arrests, number of inches tall, number of questions answered correctly on a test, etc.—which may be regarded as the "raw-score" scale of the variable. That is, a *raw score* on some variable may be defined as a score on whatever scaling of the variable arises most naturally. Given a raw-score scale, however, it is usually advantageous, for statistical purposes at least, to transform the raw scores into another scale whose numerical values have an immediate interpretation in terms of how an individual with a given score compares with the members of a certain "normative" population P. Such a rescaling of raw scores is called a *standardized* scale. For example, *Percentile-rank-on-***X** in population P is a standardized rescaling of variable **X** because the percentile equivalent of a value X of **X** in P tells the percent of members of P with scores lower than X.

A standardization technique which is especially important for the theory of prediction in general, and for applied testing in particular, is the one which yields what are known as *standard scales.*[15] A raw-score variable **X** is converted into a standard scale **X**$'$ by transforming **X** in such a way that relative scale distances remain unchanged—i.e., that if the numerical scale difference between individuals h and i on **X** is m times the difference between individuals j and k, then the corresponding differences on **X**$'$ remain in this same proportion—but where the distribution of **X**$'$-scores in the normative population P has more convenient statistical properties than does the distribution of **X** in P. Technically, a standard scale is derived from the raw-score scale by a "linear" transformation, so-called because if the transformed scores are plotted graph-

[15] *Standard* scales must not be confused with standard*ized* scales. The former are a special case of the latter.

ically against the raw scores to which they correspond, the resulting figure is a straight line. A variable **X**′ is a linear transformation of variable **X** if and only if the relationship between the values of **X**′ and **X** for any individual i is of the form

$$X_i' = aX_i + b \qquad [3.22]$$

$$\text{Examples: } X_i' = 2X_i + 3;$$

$$X_i' = -.3X_i + 6.7\ ,$$

where a and b are any two fixed positive or negative numbers. That is, the transformation by which **X**′ is obtained from **X** is "linear" if values of **X**′ are obtained by multiplying (or dividing, since dividing by m is the same as multiplying by $1/m$) the corresponding values of **X** by some fixed number, and then adding (or subtracting, since subtracting m is the same as adding $-m$) some fixed number to this product. (We can also add first and then multiply, since adding m and then multiplying by c is the same as multiplying by c and then adding cm.) For example, if a certain royal potentate, who happens to be 5 feet 3 inches tall, has decreed that within his kingdom a person's height is to be reported on a scale, **H**′, which tells how many inches taller or shorter than His Egotistical Majesty a person is, and **H** is a person's height in feet, then **H**′ is a linear transformation of **H** as expressed by the equation

$$H_i' = 12H_i - 63\ .$$

The value X_i of a variable **X** for an individual i can ordinarily be conceived as i's "distance," in terms of some unit of measurement, from a certain reference-point value of the variable. Specifically, the "unit of measurement" for this scale of the variable is the distance between two individuals whose scores have a numerical difference of one, while the "reference point" is that value of the variable which is represented on the scale by the number zero. Since a linear transformation leaves the relative distances between individuals unchanged, a rescaling of the form described by [3.22] may be regarded as merely a shift in reference point and unit of measurement. (Thus when the **H**′-scale of height is derived from Height-in-feet as above, the reference point is shifted from the minimum possible height to the height of His Egotistical Majesty, and the unit of measurement from one foot to one inch.) Therefore, a "standard" scale—which, it will be recalled, is derived from raw scores by a linear transformation—may be described as a scale on which the reference point and unit of measurement have been selected for their statistical convenience. Now, the most natural reference point and unit of measurement from the statistical viewpoint are, respectively, the mean and the standard deviation of whatever distribution one is working with. Consequently, the statistically "natural" scale for a variable **X** within some population P is the scale whose values tell how many SDs an individual is away from the mean in this population. Scores on such a scale are called "Z-scores," and are frequently used in statistical analysis because, as will be seen, they greatly simplify the formulas which express statistical relationships.[16] Since the number of SDs separating a person's score from the mean is the number of times a sigma-stick can be laid off between this score and the mean (cf. the graphical representations of M and σ in Figure 3.4), the Z-score equivalent of a raw-score X with respect to a normative population P is given by the formula

$$[3.23] \qquad Z_{\mathbf{X}_i} =_{\text{def}} \frac{X_i - \mathrm{M}_{\mathbf{X}}}{\sigma_{\mathbf{X}}},$$

in which $\mathrm{M}_{\mathbf{X}}$ and $\sigma_{\mathbf{X}}$ are, of course, the mean and SD in population P. For example, if Jones has an annual income of $10,000 when the mean and SD of annual income in the United States is $5,000 and $2,000, respectively, Jones's annual income in dollars is (10,000–5,000)/2,000 = 2.5 sigmas above the mean; hence with respect to U.S. norms, Jones's Z-score on Annual-income-in-dollars is 2.50. Similarly, if Smith makes only $3,500 a year, his Z-score on Annual-income-in-dollars is –.75.

It is important to note that Z-scores and other standardized scales *are relative to a particular population,* namely, the one providing the statistics used to define the scale. Consequently, there is not one Z-score equivalent to a given raw score, but as many as there are normative populations. No confusion is likely to arise from this when only a single population is under scrutiny, but when several populations are being compared, care must be taken not to be misled by standardized scores. For example, if **Q** is a multispecies intelligence test on which humans have a mean of 1,000 and SD of 80, while mammals as a whole have a mean and SD of 420 and 140, respectively, poor old feebleminded Jukes, whose score on **Q** is 840 and who with respect to humans has a miserably low Z-score of –2.0, still has a Z-score of +3.0 by the norms for all mammals. Similarly, Jukes is at (say) only the 2d percentile of intelligence in humans, but at the 99th percentile for all mammals.

It should also be noticed that Z-scores make possible comparisons between the values of different variables when a basis for comparison would not otherwise exist. For example, suppose that Jimmy correctly answers 85% of the questions on a spelling test, but only 50% of the questions on an arithmetic test. In which subject, Spelling or Arithmetic, is he better? One's first impulse is to answer that since Jimmy was right only half the time in Arithmetic but considerably more than this in Spelling he is obviously superior in the latter. But this impulse must ruthlessly be

---

[16] The Z-score was the original "standard" score, and these two concepts are still defined as equivalent in some texts. However, the notion of "standard" score has generally become liberalized today to refer to *any* statistically convenient linear transformation of raw scores.

squelched, for what constitutes a good performance on tests such as these depends on how difficult they are—e.g., if the spelling test was composed of second-grade words while the "arithmetic" questions were taken from a workbook in advanced college physics, it might be suspected that Jimmy is not really so inferior in Arithmetic after all. For want of a meaningful direct comparison between raw spelling and raw arithmetic scores, we may let the distribution of scores on these tests in Jimmy's class furnish statistical norms for the comparison. Specifically, if the means in Jimmy's class on the Spelling and Arithmetic tests were 60% and 40%, respectively, with corresponding SDs of 25% and 5%, we see that Jimmy is one sigma above the mean on Spelling, but two sigmas above the mean in Arithmetic. This leads naturally to the conclusion that by the standards of his class, at least, Jimmy is better in Arithmetic than in Spelling.[17]

What does a linear transformation such as [3.23] or, more generally, [3.22], do to the mean and SD of a distribution? That is, how are the mean and SD of $\mathbf{X}'$ in a population P related to the mean and SD of $\mathbf{X}$ in P if $X_i' = aX_i + b$? Even before deriving a mathematical solution to this question, the answer should be intuitively clear—and it will be well worth the reader's effort to make sure that it *is* intuitively clear. Since a linear transformation is no more than a shift in reference point and unit of measurement, a member i of P who is average on $\mathbf{X}$ (i.e., X_i equals the mean of $\mathbf{X}$ in P) should also be average on $\mathbf{X}'$; hence the mean of $\mathbf{X}'$ in P should be related to the mean of $\mathbf{X}$ in P in the same way that X_i' is related to X_i. That is,

[3.24] $$\mathrm{M}_{\mathbf{X}'} = a\mathrm{M}_{\mathbf{X}} + b \quad (X_i' = aX_i + b) \ .$$

Moreover, if two individuals i and j are one SD apart on $\mathbf{X}$, they should remain so on $\mathbf{X}'$. Hence if $\sigma_{\mathbf{X}}$ equals $X_j - X_i$, then $\sigma_{\mathbf{X}'}$ equals either $X_j' - X_i'$ or $X_i' - X_j'$, depending on whether a is greater or less than zero (since if a is negative, the transformation inverts the order of the scores and makes X_j' smaller than X_i' if X_j is larger than X_i). But if $\sigma_{\mathbf{X}} = X_j - X_i$ and $\sigma_{\mathbf{X}'} = X_j' - X_i'$, then, since $X_j' - X_i' = (aX_j + b) - (aX_i + b) = a(X_j - X_i)$, it follows that $\sigma_{\mathbf{X}'} = a\sigma_{\mathbf{X}}$. Similarly, if $\sigma_{\mathbf{X}'} = X_i' - X_j'$ because a, through being negative, reverses the order of the scores, $\sigma_{\mathbf{X}'} = X_i' - X_j' = a(X_i - X_j) = -a(X_j - X_i) = -a\sigma_{\mathbf{X}} = |a|\sigma_{\mathbf{X}}$. Whether a is positive or negative, then, it follows that

[3.25][18] $$\sigma_{\mathbf{X}'} = |a|\sigma_{\mathbf{X}} \quad (X_i' = aX_i + b) \ .$$

[17] Actually, when interpreting Z-scores in this way, consideration must also be given to the "shape" of the distribution—see below.

[18] Notice that if formula [3.25] multiplied $\sigma_{\mathbf{X}}$ by the sign of the constant of multiplication as well as by its magnitude, we would find ourselves confronted with a negative value for $\sigma_{\mathbf{X}}$ when $a < 0$—which, by definition of a standard deviation, is impossible.

In other words, a linear transformation changes the mean of the distribution in the very same way it changes an individual score. Merely adding (or subtracting) a constant to (from) each score does not change their SD, however, for the latter is a measure of the *differences* among the scores, and these differences are left unchanged by increasing or decreasing all the scores by the same amount. On the other hand, multiplying (or dividing) each score by the same number also enlarges (shrinks) their differences by this same amount, so their SD is also multiplied (divided) by the magnitude of this constant.

Mathematically, the proofs of [3.24] and [3.25] verge on the trivial. Applying [3.3]–[3.6], we see that

$$\mathrm{M}_{\mathbf{X}'} = \frac{\sum_i X'_i}{n} = \frac{\sum_i (aX_i + b)}{n} = \frac{a\sum_i X_i + nb}{n} = a\mathrm{M}_{\mathbf{X}} + b \; .$$

Similarly,

$$\sigma^2_{\mathbf{X}'} = \frac{\sum_i (X'_i - \mathrm{M}_{\mathbf{X}'})^2}{n} = \frac{\sum_i ([aX_i + b] - [a\mathrm{M}_{\mathbf{X}} + b])^2}{n}$$

$$= \frac{\sum_i (a[X_i - \mathrm{M}_{\mathbf{X}}])^2}{n} = \frac{a^2 \sum_i (X_i - \mathrm{M}_{\mathbf{X}})^2}{n} = a^2\sigma^2_{\mathbf{X}} ,$$

from which [3.25] follows by taking the square root of each side.[19]

Example. On a certain professional basketball team, the average Height-in-inches is 80.0, with an SD of 4.0. The manager has learned of a growth hormone which will increase a person's height by 5% and has also developed a technique by which two inches of callus can be added to the bottom of a player's feet. If these treatments are applied to each team member, what will be the team's new mean and SD on Height-in-inches? The *hard* way to answer this would be to compute each player's new height separately, and then determine the mean and SD of these scores. However, in view of the relations just noted, a much simpler solution is available. If **H** and **H**′ are a person's Height-in-inches before and after treatment, respectively, then $H'_i = 1.05H_i + 2.0$. Hence, from [3.24] and [3.25],

$$\mathrm{M}_{\mathbf{H}'} = 1.05\mathrm{M}_{\mathbf{H}} + 2.0 = 1.05(80.0) + 2.0 = 84.0 + 2.0 = 86.0 \; ,$$

$$\sigma_{\mathbf{H}'} = 1.05\sigma_{\mathbf{H}} = 1.05(4.0) = 4.2 \; .$$

[19] Recall that the square root of a^2 is by convention positive irrespective of whether a itself is positive or negative. Hence the absolute-value symbol in [3.25].

Applying formulas [3.24] and [3.25] to the definition of Z-scores (formula [3.23]), it is now easy to see, taking $1/\sigma_{\mathbf{X}}$ for a in [3.24] and $M_{\mathbf{X}}/\sigma_{\mathbf{X}}$ for b, that the distribution of Z-score equivalents for any variable **X** in the normative population P has a mean of zero and an SD of one—i.e.,

$$M_{\mathbf{Z_X}} = 0\,, \quad \sigma_{\mathbf{Z_X}} = 1\,. \qquad [3.26]$$

If we would now like to convert raw scores into some standard scale $\mathbf{X}'$ with a preselected mean of m and SD of c, we need only convert raw scores into Z-score equivalents, then multiply the latter by c and add m. (It is obvious from [3.24]–[3.26] that if $X'_i = cZ_{\mathbf{X}i} + m$, then $M_{\mathbf{X}'} = m$ and $\sigma_{\mathbf{X}'} = c$ as desired.) For example, the standard "T" scale, which is frequently used to report psychological test results, is defined to have a mean of 50 and an SD of 10 in the normative population. Hence the formula for computing a person's T-score on some variable **X**, given his raw score, is

$$\begin{aligned} T_{\mathbf{X}i} &= 10Z_{\mathbf{X}i} + 50 \\ &= 10\left(\frac{X_i - M_{\mathbf{X}}}{\sigma_{\mathbf{X}}}\right) + 50 \\ &= \frac{10}{\sigma_{\mathbf{X}}}X_i + \left(50 - \frac{10}{\sigma_{\mathbf{X}}}M_{\mathbf{X}}\right). \end{aligned} \qquad [3.27]$$

Incidentally, the difference between the first and third lines of [3.27] illustrates why Z-score scales are so convenient in statistical analysis.

*The Coefficient of Variation

Since the standard deviation of a distribution states the amount by which the latter's mean typically errs as an approximation to the individual scores in the distribution, the SD may be expected to show *how well* the distribution as a whole is represented by its mean. By itself, however, the SD is intuitively inadequate for this interpretation, since the numerical value of σ can be made as large or as small as we please simply by adjusting the unit of measurement for the variable in question. Thus while the SD of Height-in-inches among adult humans is twelve times the SD of Height-in-feet in this population, it would clearly never do to propose that the average Height-in-inches is more representative of this variable's distribution among adult humans than is the average Height-in-feet. Also, the larger the overall size of the scores in a distribution, the less impressive does a given absolute quantity of variation seem—e.g., if the distributions of raw scores (questions answered correctly) on the Spelling and Arithmetic tests in Jimmy's class both had an SD of 5 points but the mean Spelling performance was 60 questions answered correctly while the mean Arithmetic performance was only 10, we would be tempted to say that the class showed more consistency in Spelling than in Arithmetic. For interpreting a distribution's dispersion on such occasions, the most helpful statistic is the *coefficient of variation*, $\nu_{\mathbf{X}}$,[20] which is defined as the ratio of the distribution's standard deviation to its mean. That is,

$$\nu_{\mathbf{X}} =_{\text{def}} \frac{\sigma_{\mathbf{X}}}{\mathrm{M}_{\mathbf{X}}}. \qquad [3.28]$$

Since $\nu_{\mathbf{X}'} = \nu_{\mathbf{X}}$ if $X'_i = aX_i$ for any multiplying constant $a > 0$, the coefficient of variation is essentially unaffected by changes in the variable's unit of measurement, and may be regarded as a standardized SD, namely, the SD which results when **X** is rescaled, with the same reference point as before, to have a unit of measurement equal to its mean.

While [3.28] defines $\nu_{\mathbf{X}}$ for any distribution such that $\mathrm{M}_{\mathbf{X}} \neq 0$, the coefficient of variation is most meaningful for variables which take only nonnegative values (referred to hereafter as "magnitude" variables); for then $\nu_{\mathbf{X}}$ tells how large the differences among scores on **X** tend to be in population *P* in comparison to their average magnitude. It is easy to see that the coefficient of variation can never exceed unity for a magnitude variable **X** if the distribution is symmetric (see below), while the limit $\nu_{\mathbf{X}} = 1$ is reached in this case only if half the scores in the distribution are zero and the other half are all equal to $2\mathrm{M}_{\mathbf{X}}$. More generally, without restriction to symmetric distributions, $\nu_{\mathbf{X}}$ exceeds unity for a magnitude variable only when most of the scores in the distribution are bunched on or near zero while a small proportion of them are comparatively large. Thus the variability of a magnitude variable for which $\nu_{\mathbf{X}} > 1$ may reasonably be said to be *extreme*. (Of course, a variable which takes negative values as well as positive ones can combine any ordinary shape of distribution with a coefficient of variation as large as it pleases by getting its mean sufficiently close to zero.)

Distribution Shapes

While the mean and standard deviation are important properties of a distribution, they by no means exhaustively describe what the distribution is like. This can clearly be seen in Figure 3.5, wherein distributions A and B have the same mean and SD, but nonetheless appear quite different. On the other hand, two distributions may be very different in their means and SDs and still appear to be similar in other important respects. In Figure 3.5, for example, distribution C, unlike distribution A, seems to be *shaped* like distribution B. This suggests that the "shape" of a distribution may informally be described as *what is left out when only the mean and standard deviation of the distribution are specified.*

---

[20] There is no conventional symbol for the coefficient of variation. We here adopt "ν" for this purpose because while "ν" is actually the lowercase Greek letter nu, it at least *looks* like "*v*" for "variation."

It will be recalled that the frequency-density curve of a distribution, which is essentially a more refined version of a histogram or frequency polygon and for which the area under the curve between any two values of the variable equals the proportion of scores in the distribution lying within this interval, is perhaps the most intuitively satisfactory way to describe a distribution. Consequently, we shall here define a distribution's "shape" to be a certain related frequency-density curve, though strictly speaking this has technical disadvantages (to be ignored here) which are avoided by use of the cumulative-frequency curve. If the "shape" of a distribution is what is left over and above its mean and SD, then whether two distributions are alike or different in shape should be determined by whether or not they become identical upon being equated for mean and SD. Moreover, the simplest way to equalize the means and SDs of a number of distributions is to transform each variable into a Z-score scale over the population involved—i.e., to adjust the reference point and unit of scale distance in such a way that the distribution now has a mean of zero and SD of unity. Hence we may define "the shape of the distribution of variable **X** in population *P*" to be *the frequency-density curve for the distribution of* $\mathbf{Z_X}$ *in P*.[21] That is, the shape of a distribution is the curve which shows the distribution's frequency density at each sigma-distance

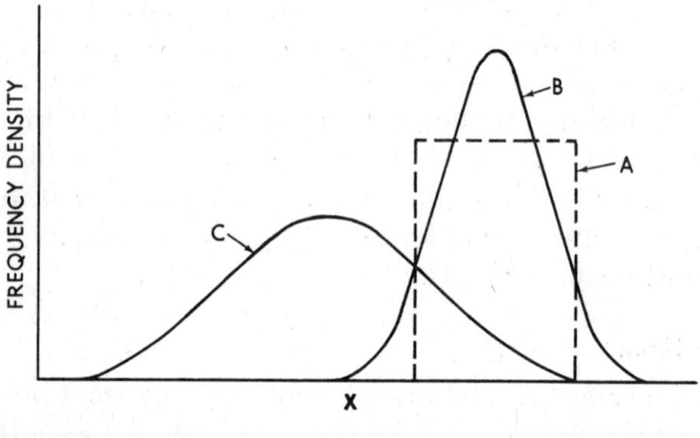

Figure 3.5. Three hypothetical distributions, illustrating the concept of distribution "shape." While distributions A and B have the same mean and standard deviation, they still appear distinctly different. On the other hand, while distributions B and C differ both in mean and in standard deviation, they nonetheless have something important in common.

[21] Actually, this is only one of a family of shape concepts. In the present case, "shape" has been defined as what remains the same about a distribution under all possible linear transformations, and should hence more precisely be called its "linear shape." In similar fashion, if T is some other type of transformation (e.g., logarithmic, exponential, etc.), we could define a concept of T-shape as what remains invariant about the distribution under all T-transformations.

from the mean. Consequently, a distribution's shape is shown by a graph, such as Figure 3.6, obtained from the distribution's frequency-density curve by a linear recalibration of the latter's horizontal axis so that the mean is now at zero and a score one SD above the mean now has a scale value of 1.0. (Technically, the scaling of the vertical axis must also be adjusted in order to keep the total area under the curve equal to unity, namely, by multiplying the old frequency-density scale values by $\sigma_{\mathbf{X}}$.)

Conversely, it should be noted that since the shape of a distribution is identical with its frequency-density curve in all respects except the scaling of the axes, the original distribution can be reclaimed from the shape-curve merely by converting the Z-scores of the latter back into the original raw scores—a task easily accomplished, if the mean and SD of the raw scores are given, by plugging particular values of $\mathbf{Z_X}$ into the formula

$$[3.29] \qquad X_i = \mathrm{M}_{\mathbf{X}} + \sigma_{\mathbf{X}} Z_{\mathbf{X}_i}$$

(from [3.23]), and computing the corresponding values of **X**. For example, in any distribution shaped as in Figure 3.6, 16% of the scores are one SD or more below the mean. Hence, if we are told that the distribution of Number-of-good-deeds-done in the population of left-handed Boy Scouts last year has a mean of 68, a SD of 23, and the shape shown in Figure 3.6, we can conclude immediately that only 16% of left-handed Boy Scouts did fewer than 45 (i.e., 68 + 23(−1)) good deeds last year. In short, *a distribution is completely described by its mean, standard deviation, and shape.*

****Properties of Distribution Shapes.*** It is frequently convenient to be able to say something about what *sort* of shape a distribution has. One important shape property a distribution may or may not display is *symmetry*. A distribution is symmetric if and only if there is some value of

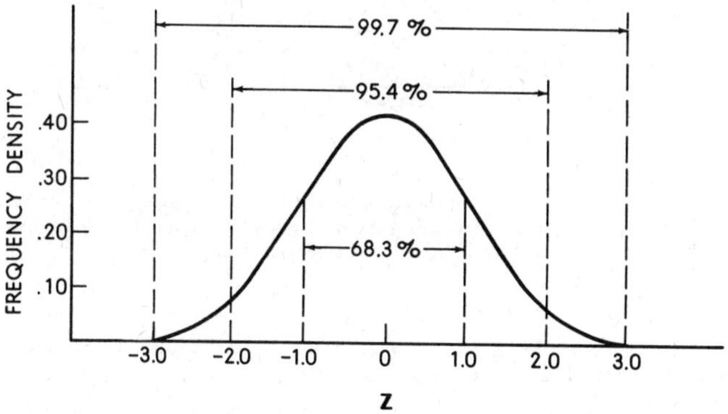

Figure 3.6. The Normal distribution shape, marked to show the proportion of the population falling within various sigma-distances of the mean.

the variable, called the "point of symmetry," such that the portion of the distribution's frequency-density curve to the left of this point is the mirror image of the portion to the right. For example, each distribution in Figure 3.5 is symmetric around its mean. It is easy to show (though not so easy that the reader will not find the demonstration a useful exercise[22]) that if a distribution is symmetric, the point of symmetry is both its median and its mean. Hence we may define a symmetric distribution as one for which the height of the frequency-density curve at a point d units above the mean equals the height at d units below the mean.

Another shape property, contrasting with symmetry, is *skew*. In Figure 3.7 it will be observed that the extremely high scores in distribution A are farther away from the mean than are the distribution's extremely low scores. Such a distribution is said to be *positively skewed*. Similarly, a *negatively skewed* distribution such as B in Figure 3.7 is one in which the most deviant scores of the distribution tend to concentrate below the mean. Technically, the amount, $Sk_{\mathbf{X}}$, by which a distribution of a variable $\mathbf{X}$ is skewed is defined as

[3.30][23] $$Sk_{\mathbf{X}} =_{\text{def}} \frac{\sum_i z^3_{\mathbf{X}i}}{n}.$$

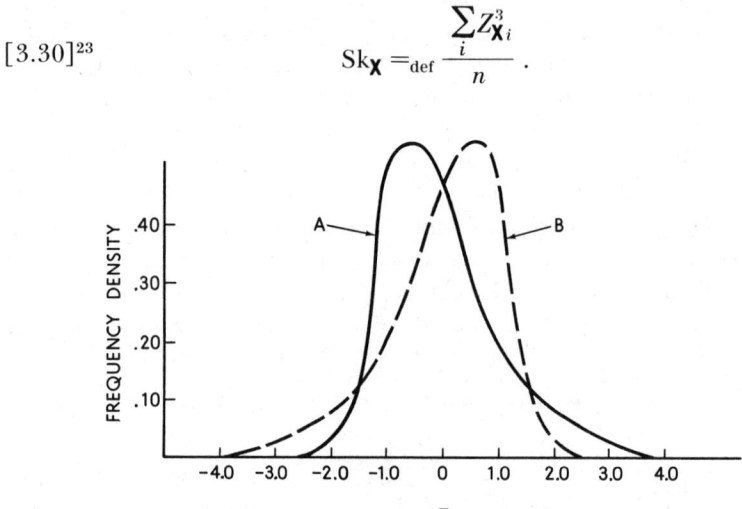

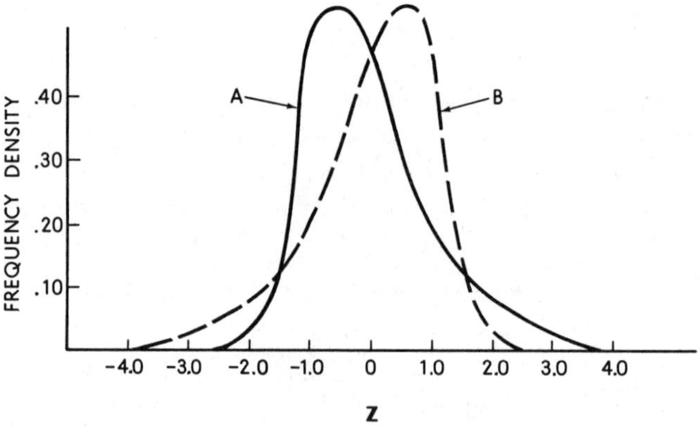

Figure 3.7. Positively (A) and negatively (B) skewed distribution shapes. The direction (positive versus negative) of skew is determined by whether the long tail of the distribution is above or below the mean.

---

[22] *Hints:* What is the combined sum of scores at $+d$ and $-d$ units away from the point of symmetry? What is the sum of these scores, in turn, for all distances d?

[23] A cruder definition sometimes given for skew is that a distribution is skewed to the extent and in the direction that its mean is above or below its median. However, this does not always yield even the same direction of skew as does the more sophisticated definition. Of course, there is no one "true" measure of asymmetry, any more than there is one "true" measure of central tendency or spread.

It should be mentioned that although all symmetric distributions have zero skew, this is also true of some asymmetric distributions.

Still another shape property which, though of limited importance, should at least be mentioned here is that of *kurtosis*. As illustrated in Figure 3.8, a distribution is *leptokurtic* or *platykurtic*, respectively, according to whether its shape is skinnier or squattier than a "normal" (see below) distribution. (Technically, though, it is the length of the distribution's tails—long in leptokurtosis, short in platykurtosis—which is most directly responsible for its kurtosis.) A distribution's kurtosis, $Kt_{\mathbf{X}}$, is defined by the formula

[3.31] $$Kt_{\mathbf{X}} =_{\text{def}} \frac{\sum_i Z_{\mathbf{X}i}^4}{n} - 3 ,$$

in which positive values indicate leptokurtosis, negative values indicate platykurtosis, and the "−3" in the formula makes comparison to a "normal" distribution as explained in fn. 30, p. 55.[24]

The Normal Distribution. Distributions obtained from empirical data, if based on enough cases to smooth out chance irregularities, are usually humped in the middle and taper off smoothly toward either extreme. Also, empirical distributions are frequently, though by no means

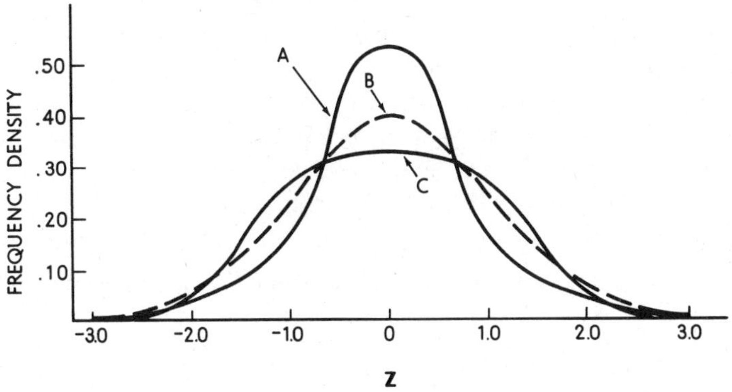

Figure 3.8. Kurtosis: Compared to a normal distribution shape (B), a leptokurtic distribution shape (A) is tall and slender while a platykurtic distribution shape (C) is short and thick.

[24] Kurtosis is also sometimes defined simply as

$$\frac{\sum_i Z_{\mathbf{X}i}^4}{n}$$

without making the explicit comparison to normality.

always, approximately symmetric. Now by a happy coincidence, the simplest mathematical function which describes such a shape—i.e., symmetric, high at the center and decreasing to zero in either direction without any abrupt changes—also happens to be the function which describes the shape that a distribution should theoretically have if the value of the variable for a given individual is the additive resultant of a large number of relatively independent causal influences. A distribution of this shape, which is shown in Figure 3.6 and whose cumulative frequencies are tabulated in Appendix B, is called a *Normal* distribution.[25] The name is altogether appropriate, for Normal distributions are both *normative* as a theoretical ideal, and *normal* in the empirical sense that a large proportion of the distributions actually encountered in practice closely resemble the Normal shape.

In view of the central importance of the Normal distribution,[26] the reader should make sure that he has at least a nodding familiarity with its special features, especially the percentile significance of various landmark Z-scores. In particular, it should be committed to memory that 68% of the scores in a Normal distribution are within one SD of the mean, that 95% are within two SDs of the mean, and that over 99% are within three SDs of the mean. With these figures conveniently in mind, the reader is equipped to appreciate the statistical meaning of a given Z-score, or of a raw score from a distribution whose mean and SD he also knows, so long as it is reasonable to assume that the distribution is roughly normal. For example, if Jimmy's Z-score (based on his class norms) in Spelling is +1.0, and the class distribution is approximately normal, it follows by a quick mental calculation that Jimmy is superior to about 84% of his classmates in Spelling. (Since 64% have Z-scores between +1.0 and −1.0, and half the remainder—i.e., (100−68)/2, or 16%—are below −1.0, Jimmy must be better than 68 + 16, or 84% of his classmates.) Similarly, if Jimmy's percentage score[27] in Arithmetic was 60% when the class mean and SD were 50% and 5%, respectively, we can deduce immediately,

[25] The formula for this curve, when h is the height of the frequency-density shape at Z_X SDs from the mean, is

$$h = \frac{1}{\sqrt{2\pi}} e^{-(Z^2)/2}$$

The statistical argument which proves that a distribution of this shape should arise under a remarkably wide variety of conditions is known today as the *Central Limit Theorem*. For a history of the Normal curve, which has had a protracted development originating with DeMoivre in 1733, see Walker (81).

[26] The first letter in "Normal" is presently capitalized to emphasize that the word here occurs in an important technical sense. However, this capitalization is not standard usage and will later be dropped. It seems easier, and has become conventional, to use the phrase "the Normal distribution" instead of the more accurate expressions, "Normal distributions" or "the Normal shape." Strictly speaking, of course, there is no *the* Normal distribution, but infinitely many of them.

[27] Steady, now: Don't become confused between percent*age* scores, which are essentially a form of raw score, and percent*iles*, which tell how a score compares with other scores in the distribution.

under an assumption of Normality, that Jimmy was in about the upper 3% of his class in Arithmetic.

Some further points of interest about a Normal distribution, in addition to the obvious but important one that its mean, median, and mode coincide, are as follows: (*a*) The points of inflection on a Normal frequency-density curve—i.e., the places at which the curve changes from concave curvature to convex—occur at one SD above and below the mean. (*b*) $AD = \sigma\sqrt{2/\pi} \simeq .8\sigma$—i.e., the average deviation of a Normal distribution is four-fifths as large as its standard deviation. (*c*) $PE \simeq .67\sigma$—i.e., the middle 50% of a Normal distribution lies within two-thirds SD of the mean. Hence these are the relations among σ, AD, and PE which may be roughly expected of an empirical distribution unless evidence to the contrary is forthcoming.

Multivariate Normal Distributions. It was pointed out in Chapter 2 that the one-variable distributions with which we have so far been preoccupied are in actuality only the simplest kind, the more general case being the joint distribution of several variables. It turns out, as will be seen next chapter, that multivariate distributions have exciting and important properties, called "correlations," not possessed by univariate distributions. Like the one-variable case, however, we can completely describe an **n**-variate distribution by giving the means, SDs and intercorrelations of the **n** variables, together with the distribution's shape. Unfortunately, just as it takes a two-dimensional figure to illustrate the shape of a univariate distribution, $\mathbf{n} + 1$ dimensions are needed to show the shape of an **n**-variate distribution, a task which proves awkward for all but the bivariate case, and even here practical difficulties arise for the resources of the printed page. Consequently, the reader will have to get his concept of the shapes of bivariate distributions by imagining various solids of the kind which could be constructed by standing a large number of pencils or other slender rods of various lengths endwise upon a flat surface,[28] and fall back on a purely mathematical conception when **n** is three or more.

When multivariate distributions are investigated, it turns out that the univariate normal distribution just discussed is only the limiting case of **n** variables jointly distributed normally. Now, although multivariate normal distributions play an important role in the theory of prediction (though, contrary to frequent misimpression, by no means an essential one), our objectives in this book do not require their detailed scrutiny; those features which become relevant will be articulated as the occasion demands. Nonetheless, the reader should be alerted to the fact that the concept of a normal distribution extends to the **n**-variate case, that multivariate distributions encountered empirically do, in fact, tend toward

[28] If the model is to be realistic, the pencils should be massed together with the tallest toward the center.

the normal shape, and that distributions of this shape conveniently possess those statistical properties required for the most powerful development of prediction theory. In view of this, plus the extensive concern of later chapters with joint distributions of two and eventually more variables, there would seem to be some virtue in a brief description of the bivariate normal distribution.

First of all, it will be recalled that a frequency-density curve for the joint distribution of two variables **X** and **Y** is a surface whose height at a given pair of values *X* and *Y* indicates the proportion (more accurately, the frequency density) of population members having this combination of **X** and **Y** values. The "shape" of this distribution may then be defined, as in the univariate case, as the distribution which results when **X** and **Y** are linearly transformed to have standardized means, SDs, and correlation. The shape of a bivariate normal distribution can be visualized rather easily as the sombrero-shaped surface which would result if the curve in Figure 3.6 were rotated around a vertical line erected at the mean. However, precisely because this figure is the *shape* of the distribution, abstracted from the specific mean, SDs, and correlation of **X** and **Y**, it conceals one other important feature, namely, that the actual distribution in general resembles a sombrero whose sides have been pushed together somewhat, making it longer in one direction than in the other. Moreover, the angle of the sombrero's long axis[29] in relation to the **X** and

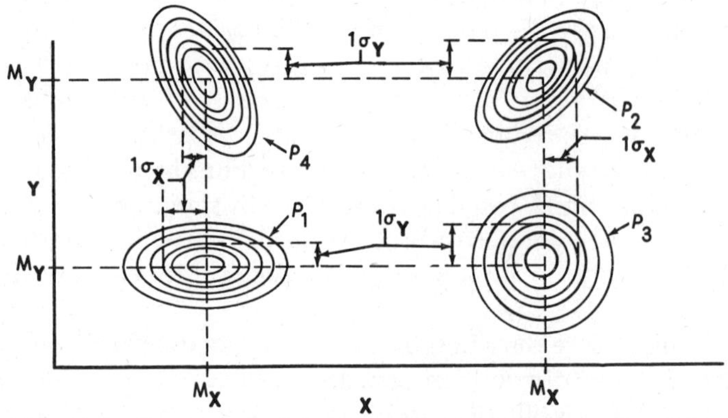

Figure 3.9. Contour maps of the bivariate normal distributions of variables **X** and **Y** in four hypothetical populations. The mean of **X** in population P_2 equals that of **X** in P_3 and is greater than M_X in both P_1 and P_4. $\sigma_X = \sigma_Y$ in both P_2 and P_3; however, there is an appreciable positive correlation between **X** and **Y** in population P_2, whereas **X** and **Y** are uncorrelated in P_3. Neither does any correlation exist between **X** and **Y** in population P_1, but here $\sigma_X = 2\sigma_Y$. In population P_4, $\sigma_X < \sigma_Y$ and there is a negative correlation between **X** and **Y**.

[29] *Note for the reader who is familiar with the concept of "regression" discussed in Chapter 4:* The major axis of the system of ellipses in a contour map of a bivariate normal distribution of variables **X** and **Y** is *not*, contrary to intuition, the same as the regression of **Y** upon **X**.

Y dimensions of the figure is of great importance in the theory of prediction. To illustrate this aspect, several bivariate normal distributions are shown in Figure 3.9 by contour maps, in which the concentric ellipses show cross sections of the sombrero at various heights. It will be noticed that the joint distribution of **X** and **Y** in population P_1 is like that in population P_2 in all respects except for the means of **X** and **Y** and the angle of the distribution to the **X** and **Y** axes. This angle, however, determines the extent to which the degree of the distribution's ellipticality is a result of a correlation between **X** and **Y**, rather than of a mere difference between their SDs. But this is getting ahead of our story, which will be told in proper sequence in Chapter 4.

*Moments

Finally, we shall mention the *moments* of a distribution, a group of statistics which, though seldom generically of value in practical applications, assume considerable importance in many advanced problems of statistical analysis. The *r*th (first, second, third, etc.) moment, $\mathbf{M}_{\mathbf{X}^r}$, of the distribution of variable **X** in population *P* is defined

$$[3.32] \qquad \mathbf{M}_{\mathbf{X}^r} =_{\text{def}} \frac{\sum_i X_i^r}{n}.$$

That is, the *r*th moment of a given distribution is simply the arithmetic mean of the *r*th power of the variable in the relevant population. The quantity defined by [3.32] is also sometimes called the "*r*th moment around the origin" to distinguish it from the variable's *r*th *central moment,* which is the *r*th moment of the difference-variable $\mathbf{X} - \mathbf{M}_{\mathbf{X}}$. That is, the "*r*th central moment" of variable **X** in population *P* is the quantity

$$\frac{\sum_i (X_i - \mathbf{M}_{\mathbf{X}})^r}{n}.$$

Most basic analytic statistics are either themselves moments or are simple functions of moments. Thus, a distribution's mean is its first moment around the origin, while its variance is its second central moment. Further, from [3.30] and [3.31], the skew and kurtosis of a distribution are the third and fourth-moment-less-three,[30] respectively, of the corresponding distribution of Z-scores.

When applied to multivariate distributions, the concept of "moment" also subsumes mean cross-products of the jointly distributed variables. Generically, an *r*th *order moment* is the mean value of a product of powers

[30] The fourth moment of a Normal distribution of Z-scores has the numerical value 3. Hence subtracting 3 from the fourth moment of a Z-score distribution shows whether this moment is greater or less than that of a Normal distribution shape.

of one or more variables, the order of the moment being the sum of the powers involved. For example,

$$M_{\mathbf{XY}} =_{\text{def}} \frac{\sum_i X_i Y_i}{n}$$

is a second-order moment of the joint distribution of **X** and **Y** (or of any multivariate distribution including **X** and **Y**) in population P, while

$$M_{\mathbf{W^3XY^2}} =_{\text{def}} \frac{\sum_i W_i^3 X_i Y_i^2}{n}$$

is a sixth-order moment. Moments involving only the first powers of two or more variables—e.g., $M_{\mathbf{XY}}$ and $M_{\mathbf{WXY}}$ but not $M_{\mathbf{X^2Y}}$—are sometimes called "mixed" moments. Mixed second-order central moments will command a great deal of our attention in subsequent chapters.

EXERCISES

To test his appreciation of the significance of means, standard deviations, and the other elementary statistical concepts developed so far, and to make sure he can deftly manipulate them to serve his whim, the reader should work the following problems, using Appendix B as necessary. If any of these cause trouble, the present chapter should be reviewed until the difficulty is overcome; for we are at last about to tackle the theory of prediction and the reader might as well try to gum his way through a 50¢ steak as to nibble at this topic without full command of the statistical milkteeth these problems exercise.

1. John's IQ is 90. If IQ is normally distributed in the population of all U.S. residents, with a mean of 100 and an SD of 15, what proportion of U.S. residents have IQs higher than John's? (*Answer:* Approximately 75%.)

2. According to the statistics in the previous question, how high an IQ must a person have in order to be in the upper 1% of U.S. residents? (*Answer:* 135 or higher—i.e., at least 2.33σ above the mean.)

3. On a test designed to measure artistic aptitude, Mary answered only six questions correctly. In the population on which this test was standardized, the distribution of raw scores (i.e., number of questions answered correctly) was approximately normal, with a mean of 70 and an SD of 12. If this test is, in fact, a valid one, what can we conclude about Mary's artistic aptitude? (*Answer:* Nothing. A score this deviant—over 5 SDs below the mean—is so statistically unlikely that an error must have been made in the scoring or some other normative condition presupposed in the interpretation [e.g., standard conditions of administration] has surely been violated.)

4. Fred is a college senior whose Z-score (norms based on all college students) for Height-in-inches is 1.5. If the mean and SD of Height-in-inches for all college students are 67.1 and 2.8, respectively, and this distribution is normal, how tall is Fred? (*Answer:* 71.3 inches.)

5. In the preceding question, how would your answer be changed if the distribution were leptokurtic and positively skewed, rather than normal? (*Answer:* Not at all—and be sure you see why.)

6. With respect to all U.S. smokers, Tom is at about the 98th percentile on Number-of-cigarettes-smoked-per-day, while his wife is only at the 16th percentile. If the distribution of this variable within U.S. smokers is normal, with an SD of 8.4, how many more cigarettes does Tom smoke a day than does his wife? (*Answer:* About 25. Be sure to see why information about the mean is unnecessary for your answer.)

7. If 1964 Personal-income-in-dollars is normally distributed in U.S. residents, with a mean of 7,000 and SD of 2,000, and if, in this population, the percentile rank of Jones's 1964 personal income is 5 points higher than Smith's, how much more money than Smith did Jones make in 1964? (*Answer:* It depends.)

8. If Smith earned $2,000 in 1964, what is the answer to Question 7? If Smith earned $7,000? (*Answer:* About $1,820 in the first case; $250 in the second.)

9. If the distribution of IQ among all U.S. residents is as given in Question 1, while among college graduates the distribution of IQ is normal with a mean of 124 and SD of 12, what is Susan's Z-score for IQ if her IQ is 118? (*Answer:* 1.2 or −.5, depending upon whether Susan is being compared to all U.S. residents, or just to college graduates. It is not actually necessary to know whether Susan is a college graduate in order to use the latter population as normative. However, for reasons which will emerge in the next chapter, it is predictively misleading to convert a person's raw score on some variable into a Z-score based on the norms of a population to which this person does not, in fact, belong.)

10. It is the policy at a certain college always to assign letter grades according to the following proportions: A, 10%; B, 20%; C, 50%; D, 15%; F, 5%. The numerical scores made by one class on their final exams were normally distributed with a mean of 56 and SD of 12. Make a table showing the letter grade which each raw score receives. (*Answer:* A, 71 and over; B, 62–70; C, 46–61; D, 36–45; F, 35 and below.)

Chapter 4. Statistical Regression and the Theory of Prediction

THE GROUND to be covered in this chapter divides naturally into two major watersheds. First we need to develop policies for predicting the (unknown) value of a variable **X** for an individual *i*, given knowledge of the distribution of **X** in a population to which *i* is known to belong. This is a problem in Decision Theory, a discipline which has proliferated so luxuriously within recent years that we are here fortunate in needing only its barest essentials.[1] Subsequently, we shall develop formulas for the systematic application of these policies under variations in the predictor data available (Regression Theory) and measures of their predictive worth (Correlation Theory).

The Decision Problem

Tired, dirty, and hungry, graduate student Cedric Jones has returned from a three-day speleological field trip with just enough time to shave and shower before joining his very best girl for a leisurely dinner and whatever subsequent companionable pleasures the evening may see fit to bestow. His roommate greets him with the news that about ten minutes earlier, Cedric had received a telephone call from an unidentified aunt to the effect that since she has a six-hour layover while changing trains, she would be delighted if her dear nephew Cedric would join her at the depot and keep her company until train time. Now, among the various less-than-rhapsodic emotions with which Cedric receives this news is perplexity about the identity of his caller; for as a matter of fact, he has four aunts, each of whom is sufficiently footloose that she might well be the old girl waiting for him at the depot. There is Aunt Gertrude,

[1] For a more comprehensive introduction to Decision Theory, see Chernoff and Moses (12).

who has an insatiable appetite for the most intimate details of Cedric's personal affairs. Then there is Aunt Agatha, who was recently expelled from WCTU for her excessively stern, inflexible moral attitudes. Also, there is Aunt Hortense, who still thinks that Cedric is a little boy and who sent him a sack of jellybeans and a Tinkertoy set last Christmas. And finally, there is Aunt Matilda, who in preatomic days simplemindedly invested her entire inheritance in some worthless mining stocks which eventually proved to be the controlling interest in one of the richest uranium deposits ever discovered. Cedric is now faced with a problem in estimation, or "prediction." The information available tells him that one of his aunts is expecting him at the depot, but leaves it a toss-up which of the four she is. He is, to put it mildly, unenthusiastic about complying with the request, and sees no reason at all why he should indulge Gertrude, Agatha, or Hortense in this way—if expedient, he could always pretend later that he never received the message. On the other hand, if it is Aunt Matilda and he doesn't go, a cherished relative worth several million dollars will become provoked at him—and Matilda is noted both for her lavish generosity when gratified and the vindictiveness of her displeasure. Which aunt should Cedric assume has called him? Well, dear reader, what would *you* do: place your bet on Matilda and sacrifice your evening, or choose an alternative and take a chance on alienating a fortune?

The moral of this homey little story is not that rich aunts should be humored, but that no conclusions about which out of a set of alternatively possible predictions is the *best* is possible without some consideration of the *consequences* which are likely to follow from the prediction. To see this in a simpler situation, suppose that one of tomorrow's Major League baseball contests is the San Francisco Giants versus the Chicago Cubs. If in past games between these two teams this season the Giants have won 58% against the Cubs' 42%, which team shall we predict will win tomorrow? It is tempting to jump immediately to the conclusion that since, on the basis of past performance, the Giants have the greater likelihood of winning, we should predict them also to be tomorrow's winners—and indeed, this conclusion is correct if our purpose in making the prediction is merely to be right. But making a prediction is not merely a case of judging which of the possibilities being weighed has the greatest probability of occurrence. Rather, to make a prediction is to make a *decision*, to commit oneself to a course of action dictated by the event predicted, *on the basis of* these probabilities. And the merit of a given prediction is hence governed not only by its likelihood of coming true, but also by the consequences which will accrue, under the various possible outcomes, from the action entailed by the prediction. For example, if predicting the winner of tomorrow's Cubs-Giants game involves the placing of a monetary bet, and Jones has found some simple soul so enamored of the

Giants that he is eager to back them with odds of ten to one, Jones would be well advised to predict—i.e., to act as though he believed—that the Cubs will win, despite their inferior record. More generally, we find that problems of prediction always take place within a context of potential consequences which weigh—or *should* weigh—in the decision, whether the prediction is an estimate of the benefit to be obtained from use of a dangerous new cancer therapy, a guess based on Smith's undergraduate scholastic performance and Graduate Record Examination score about how well he would be able to do graduate work in chemistry, or a gossipy remark that the young couple down the street is about to get a divorce. Conversely, selecting a course of action from a number of available alternatives, when the consequences of that action are determined by which of a certain set of possible events ultimately proves to be the case, is in effect a prediction about these events in that the action chosen is more appropriate to some of these possible events than to others.[2]

The basic problem of the Theory of Prediction, then, is to find a procedure whereby the likelihoods of various alternatively possible events can be weighed beside the implications the event would have, if it befell, for the benefit to be received from each of the alternative actions available, in order to decide which of these potential happenings should be bet on. Now, the various possible ways that a presently uncertain event can turn out may always be conceived as the various values of a certain variable, and the likelihoods of these alternative possibilities as a distribution of that variable. Consequently, we may develop the theory of prediction by exploring the question of what score we should predict would be obtained by an arbitrary selection from a known distribution of scores.

Suppose, then, that you are confronted with a situation in which you know the distribution of a variable $\mathbf{X}$ in a population P and are asked to estimate what the value of $\mathbf{X}$ would be for an individual chosen at random from P. To work with a specific example, suppose that you are the purchasing agent and budget comptroller for a TV program, "This Is Your Wife," on which a guest star, affectionately known to the production crew as the "Goat," and his wife bicker over their marital difficulties. A special one-shot program is in the planning on which some not-yet-selected veteran of several wrecked marriages is to be confronted

[2] More precisely, the general circumstances under which decision making can be treated as a case of simple prediction are as follows: Let $R_1, \ldots, R_n$ be the set of alternative actions under consideration, the ultimate merits of which will be determined by events still forthcoming or, though having already occurred, are still unknown. If it is possible to analyze these uncertainties as a set of alternatively possible events $E_1, \ldots, E_n$ such that R_i would be the best (i.e., preferred) course of action if E_i were to occur, then selection of R_i as the course of action to be followed is equivalent to predicting that E_i will occur. While not all decision problems can be cast into this simple form, it presumably encompasses most if not all decisions which we are likely to conceive as "predictions." (It should be added, though, that this schema gives insufficient recognition to the cognitive overtones which are present in the intuitive concept of "predicting.")

en masse with all his ex-wives, and one of your tasks is to procure the Cadmobile convertibles which are to be given to each ex-wife as a reward for her appearance. Now it so happens that while this model automobile costs $10,000 through the local Cadmobile dealer, you have arranged a special deal with the home factory whereby if you order immediately, you can have as many Cadmobiles as you wish for $8,000 apiece. The trouble is, since the Goat for this particular program has not yet been selected, you don't know how many ex-wives will appear, and hence how many Cadmobiles to order. If you order too few, you will subsequently have to obtain the additional number needed from the local dealer at $10,000 apiece, an extra expense and hence in effect a loss of $2,000 per car. On the other hand, if you order too many, you will have to dispose of the excess at a loss estimated also at about $2,000 per car.

Now, if you have no idea at all about how many ex-wives will be appearing, your order can be no more than a blind guess. However, suppose that the list of prospective Goats has already been narrowed down to a field of ten, each of which, so far as you know, has equal likelihood of receiving the final selection. Then your problem is to predict the Number-of-ex-wives (**X**) of the person who will eventually be selected from these ten finalists (*P*); while the financial consequences of your prediction is a loss of $2,000 for each ex-wife by which the estimate is wrong. Suppose that the distribution of ex-wives in this population *P* of potential Goats is as shown in Table 4.1. Then to each prediction that you might make about the number of ex-wives the Goat will have, there corresponds a set of potential losses; namely, for each member *i* of *P*, the loss which will result from this prediction if *i* is chosen to be the Goat. Consequently, the *best* estimate of the Goat's Number-of-ex-wives is the prediction which gives rise to that set of loss-possibilities which, on the whole, seems most desirable. That is, since you cannot judge in advance what the loss resulting from your prediction will *in fact* turn out to be, you can only decide what prediction is best by considering the distribution of *potential* losses which may result from a particular prediction. Now, the whole purpose of all this fuss about how many ex-wives the Goat will have is to minimize Cadmobile expenses—i.e., to keep as low as possible the loss by which your actual Cadmobile costs are greater than what would be necessary if prediction were perfect. Hence, since you have no way to guarantee zero loss—i.e., to be *certain* of spending no more than would be necessary—you should choose your prediction by considering how large a loss you may *expect* to result from this prediction. That is, it seems reasonable to conclude that the most favorable distribution of potential losses is the one in which the *average* potential loss is smallest. As shown in Table 4.1, the average potential loss in this particular problem is $3,600 when the Goat is predicted to have five ex-wives, and this is smaller than the average potential loss under any other alternative prediction. Hence, your best estimate of the value of the Number-of-ex-wives variable in this case would seem to be five.

More generally, the pattern of reasoning followed here in predicting the value of a variable **X** for an individual i to be drawn at random from a population P is as follows: Let $L(X_i, g)$ stand for the loss which results when g (for "guess") is the value of **X** predicted for i and the actual value of **X** for i turns out to be X_i. Then for a particular g, the distribution of **X** in P determines a corresponding distribution of potential losses which would be in force were g the prediction made, namely, $L(X_1, g), L(X_2, g), \ldots, L(X_n, g)$—i.e., the numbers which are generated by the formula "$L(X_i, g)$" as "i" runs over the various members of population P. Thus in the Number-of-ex-wives problem, $L(X_i, g) = 2{,}000 \times |X_i - g|$, the loss being measured in dollars, and each column in Table 4.1 shows the distribution of potential losses under a particular g. The question of which prediction is best is then a matter of choosing which of these distributions of potential losses is most tolerable.

Let us adopt the symbol "$\hat{X}$" to designate that number which, relative to a particular policy of prediction and available information, is the "best" estimate of the value of a variable **X** in some prediction problem. That is,

[4.1] $\hat{X} =_{\text{def}}$ *the best estimate of the value of* **X** *in these circumstances,*

where the "circumstances" have to be spelled out contextually. (We shall adopt several different mathematical specifications of $\hat{X}$ in this chapter as we examine various conditions of prediction.) To arrive at a precise value for $\hat{X}$ in our present problem, namely, predicting the value of **X** for an individual i drawn randomly from a population P when the loss resulting from a prediction g is $L(X_i, g)$, let us define the "expected loss," $\text{EL}_{\mathbf{X}}(g)$, associated with a particular prediction g to be the average potential loss when g is the prediction made. That is,

[4.2] $$\text{EL}_{\mathbf{X}}(g) =_{\text{def}} \frac{\sum_i L(X_i, g)}{n}.$$

Then, since it is reasonable (at least as a first approximation) to argue that the lower the expected loss in a distribution of potential losses, the more acceptable that distribution of possibilities is,[3] we may for our

[3] To make this argument stick, it is necessary to show that minimal expected loss corresponds to maximal expected benefit. This, however, is easy to do. Let $U(X_i,g)$ be the gain, or "utility," of estimating the value of **X** for i to be g when it really is X_i. Then since loss is the amount by which the value of the prediction's consequences falls short of what would result from perfect accuracy, $L(X_i,g) = U(X_i,X_i) - U(X_i,g)$, and hence the "expected utility of predicting g as the value of **X** for i is

$$\text{EU}_{\mathbf{X}}(g) = \frac{\sum_i U(X_i,g)}{n} = \frac{\sum_i U(X_i,X_i)}{n} - \frac{\sum_i L(X_i,g)}{n} = \frac{\sum_i U(X_i,X_i)}{n} - \text{EL}_{\mathbf{X}}(g).$$

Since the first term in the formula to the right is independent of g, expected benefit and expected loss stand in a strictly inverse relationship, one being maximal when the other is minimal.

X: Number-of-ex-wives

Financial loss due to prediction error = \$2,000 × |actual value of **X** for i − predicted value of **X** for i|

and i turns out to be:	whose value of **X** is:	If the value of **X** predicted for i is: 2	3	4	5	6	7	8	9	etc.
		then the loss resulting from the error in prediction will be:								
Smith, A. A.	5	\$ 6,000	\$ 4,000	\$ 2,000	\$ 0	\$ 2,000	\$4,000	\$ 6,000	\$ 8,000	
Smith, B. B.	4	4,000	2,000	0	2,000	4,000	6,000	8,000	10,000	
Smith, C. C.	5	6,000	4,000	2,000	0	2,000	4,000	6,000	8,000	
Smith, D. D.	4	4,000	2,000	0	2,000	4,000	6,000	8,000	10,000	
Smith, E. E.	6	8,000	6,000	4,000	2,000	4,000	2,000	4,000	6,000	
Smith, F. F.	8	12,000	10,000	8,000	6,000	4,000	2,000	0	2,000	
Smith, G. G.	3	2,000	0	2,000	4,000	6,000	8,000	10,000	12,000	
Smith, H. H.	11	18,000	16,000	14,000	12,000	10,000	8,000	6,000	4,000	
Doaks, Joe	8	12,000	10,000	8,000	6,000	4,000	2,000	0	2,000	
Smith, Z. Z.	4	4,000	2,000	0	2,000	4,000	6,000	8,000	10,000	
		The *expected* (i.e., average) loss under this prediction is:								
	$M_X = 5.8$ $Mdn_X = 5.0$	\$ 7,600	\$ 5,600	\$ 4,000	\$ 3,600	\$ 4,000	\$4,800	\$ 5,600	\$ 7,200	

Table 4.1. Predicting the value of a variable **X** for an individual i to be drawn at random from a given population P. When P is the set of gentlemen listed in the first column, the distribution of **X** in P is given in the second column, while subsequent columns show the distributions of potential losses due to predictive inaccuracy associated with various possible choices of prediction. It will be noticed that the *expected* loss is minimal when the predicted value of **X** is 5, which is also the median value of **X** in this population. As shown later, this is no coincidence.

present problem define the "best" estimate of X_i to be that value of **X** which yields an expected loss which is as small as or smaller than the loss expected from any alternative prediction. That is, under the predictive circumstances now under discussion, the best estimate $\hat{X}$ of the value of **X** is such that for any alternative prediction g,

$$[4.3]^4 \qquad EL_{\mathbf{X}}(\hat{X}) \leq EL_{\mathbf{X}}(g) \; .$$

Thus in the example already discussed, the bottom line in Table 4.1 shows the expected loss under the various possible predictions about how many ex-wives the Goat will have, and since $EL_{\mathbf{X}}(g)$ is minimal when $g = 5$, the solution to our problem in this case is $\hat{X} = 5$.

From the preceding discussion, it should be clear that the "best" estimate of the value of a variable **X** for an individual i, given only the information that i is a member of a population P within which the distribution of **X** is known, is determined not only by the distribution of **X** in P, but also by the consequences which are apt to follow from the prediction. For a fixed loss-function $L(X_i, g)$, however, the "best" estimate of a score drawn at random from a distribution of scores can usually be interpreted as some form of weighted average of the scores in the distribution, the particular method of weighting and averaging being determined by the loss-function involved. In particular, there is an interesting and important correspondence between the best estimates under certain simple forms of loss and the most common measures of central tendency. Suppose that—

1. *The loss resulting from an incorrect prediction is the same no matter how inaccurate the prediction*—i.e.,

$$L(X_i, g) = \begin{cases} 0 \text{ if } g = X_i \\ k \text{ if } g \neq X_i \; , \end{cases}$$

where k is some fixed loss greater than 0. This is the sort of situation in which a prediction is either all right or all wrong—i.e., a miss is as good as a mile. Such a loss-function is in force, for example, when a person places a bet on a roulette wheel, tries to remember his wife's shoe size when buying her a birthday present (if he doesn't recall correctly, the shoes will have to be exchanged), or selects an out-of-the-way corner of the office in which to take an unauthorized break without being seen by

[4] It is possible that there will be more than one value of g for which $EL_{\mathbf{X}}(g)$ is minimal, in which case $\hat{X}$ will not be uniquely determined. Little harm will be done, however, if we continue to speak of *the* best estimate of X_i.

the boss. It is easy to see from [4.2] that the expected loss under a prediction g in this case is $EL_{\mathbf{X}}(g) = kq$, where q is the proportion of scores in the distribution *not* equal to g, so that $EL_{\mathbf{X}}(g)$ is minimal when g equals the score which occurs most frequently in the distribution. Therefore, when all inaccuracies in prediction are equally costly, the best estimate, $\hat{X}$, of a score drawn randomly from a distribution of **X** is the *mode* of the distribution.

2. *The loss is proportional to the magnitude of the difference between predicted value and actual value*—i.e.,

$$L(X_i, g) = k|X_i - g| \quad (k > 0) .$$

A loss-function of this sort has already been illustrated in the ex-wives problem, above. The magnitude of the constant k does not affect the value of g for which $EL_{\mathbf{X}}(g)$ is minimal, and may be set equal to 1 by appropriate choice of unit of measurement for the amount of loss; consequently, the best estimate of **X** in this case will be that value of g for which

$$\frac{\sum_i |X_i - g|}{n}$$

is minimal. But the latter quantity is the average deviation around g in this distribution of **X**, and is minimal when $g = \mathrm{Mdn}_{\mathbf{X}}$.[5] Therefore, when the cost of an error in prediction is proportional to the magnitude of the error, the best estimate, $\hat{X}$, of a score drawn randomly from a distribution of **X** is the *median* of that distribution.

---

[5] *Proof:* Let

$$AD_{\mathbf{X}}(g) =_{\text{def}} \frac{\sum_i |X_i - g|}{n} ,$$

while $P_{\mathbf{X}}(g)$ is the proportion of scores in the distribution which are lower than g (i.e., $100 \times P_{\mathbf{X}}(g)$ is the percentile equivalent of score g on variable **X**). Then by routine algebra it can be shown that for any two values g_1 and g_2 of **X** such that $g_1 \leqslant g_2$,

$$AD_{\mathbf{X}}(g_2) - AD_{\mathbf{X}}(g_1) = [P_{\mathbf{X}}(g_1) + P_{\mathbf{X}}(g_2) - 1](g_2 - g_1) + [P_{\mathbf{X}}(g_2) - P_{\mathbf{X}}(g_1)](g_1 + g_2 - \alpha_{12}) ,$$

where α_{12} is the average value of just those scores in the distribution which are greater than g_1 but are equal to or less than g_2, so that $g_1 \leqslant \alpha_{12} \leqslant g_2$. From this, in turn, it readily follows that for any value g of **X**, since $P_{\mathbf{X}}(\mathrm{Mdn}_{\mathbf{X}}) = .5$,

$$AD_{\mathbf{X}}(g) - AD_{\mathbf{X}}(\mathrm{Mdn}_{\mathbf{X}}) = |P_{\mathbf{X}}(g) - .5| \times (|g - \mathrm{Mdn}_{\mathbf{X}}| + g + \mathrm{Mdn}_{\mathbf{X}} - \alpha) ,$$

where α lies between g and $\mathrm{Mdn}_{\mathbf{X}}$ and is hence no greater than the larger of these. Since the right-hand side of this latter equation cannot be negative, it follows that the average deviation around the median is at least as small as the average deviation around any other value of the variable. In fact, $AD_{\mathbf{X}}(g) > AD_{\mathbf{X}}(\mathrm{Mdn}_{\mathbf{X}})$ unless $P_{\mathbf{X}}(g) = P_{\mathbf{X}}(\mathrm{Mdn}_{\mathbf{X}})$. (The reader should fill in the details of the proof as an exercise.)

3. *The loss is proportional to the square of the difference between predicted value and actual value*—i.e.,

$$L(X_i, g) = k(X_i - g)^2 \quad (k > 0) .$$

It is difficult to think of examples where a loss-function of this form would arise naturally. (One instance might be prediction of the position of a missing airplane believed to be wrecked somewhere along its scheduled line of flight if the search expands outward from the estimated position and the cost of search is so much per square mile covered.) Nevertheless, this case is of special interest, for $\mathrm{EL}_{\mathbf{X}}(g)$ is here minimal for that g which minimizes

$$\frac{\sum_i (X_i - g)^2}{n} ,$$

and this, in turn, is easily seen to occur when g is the arithmetic mean of the X_i.[6] Hence when the cost of an error of prediction is proportional to the square of the error, the best estimate, $\hat{X}$, of a score drawn randomly from a distribution of **X** is the *mean* of that distribution.

Decision Theory Disengaged

Having thus admitted to intimacies with Decision Theory by this unflinching acknowledgement that predictions can properly be made only through consideration of the various potential consequences of each predictive option, we shall now do our best to extricate ourselves from this affair. The tempestuous demands of a serious involvement with Decision Theory call for a more robustly mature theory of prediction than it is our aim to develop here. For example, if the reader had no misgivings when the "best" estimate of Number-of-ex-wives was found in the earlier example by minimizing the *mean potential loss in dollars* over the set of possible outcomes, it is time he developed some. Why should it be the *arithmetic mean* of the potential losses which is minimized? Granted that we need some way to decide which distribution of potential losses is most desirable, and that how large the loss *on the whole* is likely

---

[6] Let $d_i =_{\text{def}} X_i - g$. From [3.18], we have

$$\frac{\sum_i d_i^2}{n} = \sigma_{\mathbf{d}}^2 + \mathrm{M}_{\mathbf{d}}^2$$

and hence, by [3.24] and [3.25],

$$\frac{\sum_i (X_i - g)^2}{n} = \sigma_{\mathbf{X}}^2 + (\mathrm{M}_{\mathbf{X}} - g)^2 ,$$

which is obviously minimal when $g = \mathrm{M}_{\mathbf{X}}$.

to be is a reasonable criterion of this, the question still remains why we should take the mean, rather than the median or some other measure of central tendency, to be our index of anticipated loss.[7] Again, why should the undesirability of the various possible outcomes be scaled in terms of the number of *dollars* lost? The ultimate objective, after all, is to minimize not the loss of dollars as such but the dissatisfaction to which a certain dollar loss gives rise, and it is by no means always the case that loss in dollars is directly proprotional to the amount of distress this loss occasions. It is not possible to be clear on this point without a more substantial discussion of value theory than is appropriate here, but observations such as that most persons are willing to guard against an improbable disaster by paying an insurance premium higher than the mathematically expected dollar loss show that a dollar does *not* have the same subjective value at all levels of wealth. In other words, it is the *psychological worth*, known technically in Decision Theory as "utility," of the ultimate outcome which a prediction tries to optimize; and it is naive to assume that the prediction for which the expected utility is greatest is also necessarily the one which minimizes the expected loss when loss is scaled in terms of some unit of objective possessions. Finally, it must be appreciated that for most persons, a gamble is itself to a certain degree appealing or distasteful, so that the pattern of riskiness involved in a set of potential prediction outcomes may have its own intrinsic value which must also be considered when comparing the relative merits of alternative predictions. In light of these and other objections, it might seem that the policy of prediction expressed by formulas [4.1]–[4.3] is actually rather gratuitous.

Now as a matter of fact, Decision Theory has a tour de force by which the difficulties just raised can largely be disposed of in a single bold stroke. It can be shown that if a person's preferences satisfy certain rules of "consistency" (such as, e.g., preferring A to C whenever A is preferred to B and B is preferred to C), then it is possible to rate the various possible outcomes of a chancy situation on a scale of "utility" for that person in such a way that given several alternative sets of potential outcomes, he prefers that set of possibilities in which the mathematical expectation of utility loss is the lowest.[8] That is, the values that a person

---

[7] It can be shown that if a person makes a very long series of predictions, he is almost certain to have a smaller total loss if he chooses his prediction so as to minimize the mean potential loss in each case than if he follows some other prediction policy. While this is an important argument in favor of minimizing expected loss, it is not conclusive; for making a prediction which is one of a string long enough to average out losses is a quite different situation from one in which only a few predictions are involved, and optimal strategy need not be entirely the same in the two cases. The difference, here, is illustrated by that between an insurance company, whose total losses in proportion to income are highly predictable, and the individual insuree, whose loss is not.

[8] See Luce and Raiffa (58), Chapter 2. If the lure or dislike of gambling as such is an important determinant of value, however, these "consistency rules" may well be violated.

places on things are manifested by the preferences he shows among them; and if these preferences are suitably consistent, then there is a scale, $L(X_i, g)$, of utility loss on which the "best estimate" $\hat{X}$ determined by formulas [4.2 and 4.3] is in fact the best estimate of X_i in the sense that the distribution of potential prediction outcomes resulting from this prediction is the one on which this person most prefers to take a chance. But the fact that these utilities are bound to vary greatly from person to person, or even from moment to moment for the same person, only emphasizes the fundamental reason why, in this book, we shall allow ourselves no more than a casual dalliance with Decision Theory; namely, that to make explicit allowance for all possible loss-functions would only be to lose the elegant simplicity of the classic theory of prediction in a welter of modern complexities. Moreover, a theory of prediction in which the loss-function enters explicitly as an independent variable really has little application, for practical problems of prediction seldom allow more than the crudest estimate of the loss-function involved. Consequently, we shall so modify our definition of "best estimate" that it becomes unaffected by differences in the utilities attached to various errors of prediction, and then trace out the implications of this definition for predictions making use of varied evidence.

Accordingly, let us stipulate that *the best (utility-free) estimate, $\hat{X}$, of an unknown score drawn randomly from a distribution of scores is the arithmetic mean of that distribution.* A number of justifications can be given for this choice. First of all, it agrees with the rather vague notion that the best estimate of which alternative in a set of possibilities will be realized should be something which is "typical" of the set as a whole. In particular, it reflects the classical usage that the "expected" score in a distribution is its arithmetic mean. Secondly, as already noted, the mean of a distribution of possibilities is the best estimate in the decision-theoretical sense spelled out in formulas [4.1]–[4.3] when the utility loss is proportional to the square of the prediction error. Moreover, if the distribution is *symmetric*, so that the mean and the median coincide, the mean is also the best decision-theoretical estimate when loss is simply proportional to the magnitude of prediction error. In fact, it can be shown that the best decision-theoretical estimate of a score drawn at random from a symmetric distribution is the mean of that distribution whenever loss is a function only of the prediction error's magnitude and the loss-function is such that a small increment in the error of the estimate never becomes less costly as the magnitude of error to which this increment is added increases.[9] Even

[9] More precisely, this condition is that $L(X_i,g)$ is of the form $L'(D_i)$, where $D_i =_{\text{def}} |X_i - g|$, and for any $\epsilon \geqslant 0$, $L'(D_i + \epsilon) - L'(D_i) \leqslant L'(D_j + \epsilon) - L'(D_j)$ whenever $D_i \leqslant D_j$. Loss-functions of this sort are known technically as "convex" functions because graphically they have a bowl-shaped appearance. The simplest example is $L(X_i, g) = k \cdot |X_i - g|$, which shows a V-shaped graph when loss is plotted as a function of the algebraic prediction error, $X_i - g$. The reader will find it instructive to prove for himself the claim about best decision-theo-

better, for a symmetric distribution whose density is greatest at the center and tapers off in either direction, as is true of a normal distribution, the mean is the best decision-theoretical estimate whenever the loss which results from an error in prediction is a function only of the magnitude of this error and never gets smaller as the prediction error increases.[10] Hence even if we cannot precisely determine the loss-function for a particular applied problem in prediction, the prediction which minimizes the expected loss will in the overwhelming majority of cases be the mean of the distribution of potential outcomes so long as this distribution is symmetric and the loss resulting from a given magnitude of prediction error is the same whether the error is an underestimation or an overestimation.[11] Finally, even if the mean of the distribution of potential outcomes is not actually the best decision-theoretical estimate in a certain problem, it will usually be the case that the true best estimate can be obtained from the mean by a suitable correction based on other statistical information available; so even in this case it would be mathematically profitable to develop the theory of prediction in terms of the mean as a first-approximation "best" estimate and subsequently make whatever corrections seem desirable. We conclude, then, that our decision to omit further considerations of the loss-function, and to stipulate that the best utility-free estimate of the value of a variable is the mean of the distribution of its potential values, involves little more than token sacrifice of generality.

The Goodness of Information (Part I)

In the type of prediction problem discussed so far, the value of a variable **X** for a randomly chosen member i of a population P is estimated by considering the known distribution of **X** in P. It thus becomes natural to ask how *useful* this information is—i.e., how good a prediction does it permit. Notice that this is a question about the *worth of the information,* not about how successful the prediction in fact turns out to be in any one particular instance. If Jones, betting on a horse race, places his money on Blisterfoot because there is something about Blisterfoot's gait which reminds Jones of his wife, even though the track records show that out of

---

retical estimates just made. (*Hint:* For two possible outcomes X_a and X_b, $L(X_a, g) + L(X_b, g)$ is smallest, for a convex loss-function of the sort described, when g is halfway between X_a and X_b.

[10] That is, when $L(X_i, g)$ is of the form $L'(D_i)$, where $D_i = |X_i - g|$ and $L'(D_i) \leq L'(D_j)$ whenever $D_i < D_j$. The proof is awkward to give in a sentence or two and will be omitted here, but it turns upon the mathematical fact that $a_1b_1 + a_2b_2 \geq a_1b_2 + a_2b_1$ if $a_1 \leq a_2$ and $b_1 \leq b_2$.

[11] However, in many applied problems involving the estimation of a person's ability at some task (e.g., deciding whether or not Dr. Hackett should be allowed to practice brain surgery), the loss resulting from overestimation is likely to be more serious than the loss due to underestimation. In this case, utility loss is not a function merely of the magnitude of prediction error but also of its direction. For such problems, equating mathematical expectation with the "best estimate" may be quite inappropriate.

30 starts, Blisterfoot has never come in better than sixth, then the fact that Blisterfoot happens to win the race on which Jones bet because the seven horses which were ahead of him were disqualified does not mean that the information about Blisterfoot's gait was worth more than the track records. What statistical data of the sort we have been discussing are good for is not to guarantee a correct prediction but to give their user an idea of what possible payoffs to anticipate as a result of his prediction and thus permit a choice of prediction which leads to to the most favorable set of these potential consequences. Hence the goodness of information available for making a prediction is determined by the overall favorableness of the best set of potential payoffs which can be selected through use of that information. Now, we have already argued that the best estimate of the value of a to-be-predicted variable is the one which minimizes the amount by which the utility resulting from the eventual outcome of the prediction is expected to fall short of the utility which would have resulted under a perfect prediction. By the same line of reasoning, we may conclude that the smaller the loss expected to result from a prediction, the more valuable is the information on which the prediction is based. It would seem, then, that ideally, our measure of the goodness of the information available in making a prediction should be some function of the loss expected under optimal use of that information—i.e., that the worth of information should be defined in terms of the quantity $EL_{\mathbf{X}}(\hat{X})$.

But while analysis of the value of information must in principle bring considerations from Decision Theory to bear, the complications to which this gives rise have already been intimated. In particular, since the precise loss-function is seldom available in an applied prediction problem, it becomes desirable to find some way to describe the relative predictive merits of various sorts of data which do not depend on the utilities of the possible outcomes. And what could be more natural for this purpose than to ask how *accurate* the prediction is likely to be—i.e., *how large a prediction error is anticipated*? In other words, it is suggested that we ignore how costly the various errors of prediction would be and concentrate instead simply on the distribution of potential amounts by which our prediction is likely to be off. For example, in our earlier problem of ex-wives estimation, the various equiprobable values that the Number-of-ex-wives variable may have are 3, 4, 4, 4, 5, 5, 6, 8, 8, 11. Hence if it is predicted that the Goat will have five ex-wives, the distribution of potential prediction errors is −2, −1, −1, −1, 0, 0, 1, 3, 3, 6. The average magnitude (i.e., absolute value) of these potential prediction errors is 1.8, so a prediction of five can be "expected" to be slightly less than two ex-wives wrong.

More generally, if we know that the value of a variable **X** for an individual i is one of the numbers $X_1, \ldots, X_n$, each of which is equally likely, and we follow the utility-free policy that the best estimate of X_i in this case is the mean of these numbers, then the resulting error of prediction will be one of the equiprobable numbers $X_1 - M_{\mathbf{X}}, \ldots, X_n - M_{\mathbf{X}}$. The magnitude which is typical of this distribution of potential prediction errors may then be taken as a measure of how much our best estimate is likely to be wrong. Now, as discussed in Chapter 3, there are various ways to define what is "typical" of a set of scores, and there are correspondingly many ways to indicate what magnitude of prediction error is "likely." The two most useful measures are the *expected error of estimate,* namely, the arithmetic mean magnitude of potential prediction error, and the *standard error of estimate,* which is the quadratic mean magnitude of potential prediction error. That is, if $\hat{X}$ is the best estimate of the value of **X** under some particular policy of prediction when $X_1, \ldots, X_n$ are the equiprobable values that **X** may have, then the *expected error (of estimate),* $EE_{\mathbf{X}}$, following this policy is

$$\text{[4.4]} \qquad EE_{\mathbf{X}} =_{\text{def}} M_{|\mathbf{X}-\hat{X}|} = \frac{\sum_i |X_i - \hat{X}|}{n},$$

while the *standard error (of estimate),* $SE_{\mathbf{X}}$, under this policy is

$$\text{[4.5]} \qquad SE_{\mathbf{X}} =_{\text{def}} QM_{|\mathbf{X}-\hat{X}|} = \sqrt{\frac{\sum_i |X_i - \hat{X}|^2}{n}} = \sqrt{\frac{\sum_i (X_i - \hat{X})^2}{n}}.$$

Then in our present instance, where we are predicting the value of **X** for i, given only that X_i belongs to a certain known distribution of **X**, and where we have decided that our best estimate of X_i is the mean of this distribution, it follows immediately from formulas [4.4] and [4.5] by substitution of $M_{\mathbf{X}}$ for $\hat{X}$ that $EE_{\mathbf{X}} = AD_{\mathbf{X}}$ and $SE_{\mathbf{X}} = \sigma_{\mathbf{X}}$. We thus see that the average deviation and the standard deviation of a distribution have an additional interpretation as measures of the accuracy with which a score drawn from that distribution can be predicted.[12]

For precisely the same reason that the standard deviation is a more technically convenient measure of variability than is the average devi-

[12] The same is true, of course, for the probable error of a distribution—in fact, the very name, "probable error," presupposes this interpretation.

ation, even though the latter is somewhat easier to grasp intuitively, so is the standard error of estimate a much more mathematically useful measure of predictive accuracy than is the expected error. Hence it is worth emphasizing, as was similarly done in Chapter 3 for σ, that the standard error *is* an "average" of the potential prediction error magnitudes. It is simply the quadratic mean, rather than the conceptually simpler arithmetic mean, of these. Consequently, if the reader can appreciate how the anticipated accuracy of prediction (and hence the usefulness of the information on which the prediction is based) is measured by the expected error of estimate, he should have little difficulty in also understanding the similarly interpreted standard error. In particular, since utility-free definitions of $\hat{X}$ used in practice are almost always such that the mean potential prediction error is zero[13] (this is obvious in the case we have discussed, since here $\hat{X} = \mathrm{M}_{\mathbf{X}}$), if we know the *shape* of the distribution of potential errors (which may usually be assumed to be roughly normal), then the standard error of estimate tells us all we need to know further in order to reproduce the precise distribution of potential prediction errors, and from which we can then extract any other property of this distribution (e.g., expected error) in which we may be interested.

It is worth noting that if we give the concept of "best estimate" a utility-free definition stipulates that the "best estimate," $\hat{X}$, of the value of **X** in a certain predictive situation is the prediction under which the anticipated magnitude of error is smallest, and the standard error of estimate is taken as our measure of the latter, then what constitutes the best estimate of **X** in this situation may be computed by solving formula [4.5] for that value of $\hat{X}$ which minimizes $\mathrm{SE}_{\mathbf{X}}$. It is easily shown that for the predictive situation discussed so far, namely, predicting X_i only on the basis of information that i is to be selected randomly from a population in which the distribution of **X** is known, the value of $\hat{X}$ which minimizes $\mathrm{SE}_{\mathbf{X}}$ is $\hat{X} = \mathrm{M}_{\mathbf{X}}$,[14] which gives further support to our utility-free policy of choosing the mean of a distribution as our best estimate of a score arbitrarily drawn from it.[15] A little later, we shall apply this same method of finding $\hat{X}$ by minimizing $\mathrm{SE}_{\mathbf{X}}$ in more complicated predictive situations in which $\hat{X}$ varies according to differences in additional information to be made available.

---

[13] This is the mean of the *algebraic* errors, not of their magnitudes—i.e.,

$$\frac{\sum_i (X_i - \hat{X})}{n}, \quad \text{not} \quad \frac{\sum_i |X_i - \hat{X}|}{n}.$$

[14] Since if $d_i = X_i - \hat{X}$, we have from [4.5] in light of [3.19] and [3.25], $\mathrm{SE}_{\mathbf{X}} = \mathrm{QM}_{|\mathbf{d}|} = \sqrt{\sigma^2_{\mathbf{d}} + \mathrm{M}^2_{\mathbf{d}}} = \sqrt{\sigma^2_{\mathbf{X}} + \mathrm{M}^2_{\mathbf{d}}}$, which is minimal when $\mathrm{M}_{\mathbf{d}} = 0$ or, equivalently, when $\hat{X} = \mathrm{M}_{\mathbf{X}}$.

[15] On the other hand, had we solved for $\hat{X}$ by minimizing the expected error in [4.4], our best estimate would have turned out to be $\mathrm{Mdn}_{\mathbf{X}}$ (see fn. 5, p. 65). This is why the median of a distribution is the most natural measure of central tendency whenever the average deviation around the central tendency is used to measure variability.

Example. While taking a history examination, you feel sure that the date asked for by a certain question lies between the years 1432 and 1488, but can't for the life of you work up any preference for one date in this interval over any of the others. If your memory is correct so far as it goes, it gives you a distribution of possible answers, namely, the integers 1433 through 1487, all of which are equally likely to be the correct one. The "best estimate" to put down as your answer is therefore 1460 while the number of years you may "expect" this estimate to be in error is 13.7, since these are the mean and average deviation, respectively, of the integers 1433 through 1487. (The standard error of your estimate is 15.7, since the standard deviation of n consecutive integers is $\sqrt{(n^2-1)/12}$.)

Prediction and Probability: A Glimpse of Vistas Beyond

It may well have occurred to the more thoughtful reader that the type of prediction problem analyzed here so far is really not very typical of those which arise in actual practice. A college admissions board wishing to predict what an applicant's final grade-point average will be if he is accepted, a life insurance company judging what percentage of its gross income next year will be needed to cover claims, a physician speculating about the side effects a certain drug might have on his patient, or for that matter, your selecting a date with which to answer a history test question, these do not at all seem to fit the pattern of an entity being selected at random from a group of entities whose scores on a certain variable are already known. Actually, any comprehensive discussion of predictive techniques has to make extensive use of the notion of *probability,* a difficult and controversial concept whose treatment is beyond our present scope. (In fact, probabilities have already crept into our discussion of the predictive situation analyzed above through the stipulation that any member of the population from which selection is to occur has as much chance of being chosen as any other member.) However, for any situation in which the value of a variable **X** is being predicted for an individual i (e.g., predicting what John's final grade-point average will be when he finishes college three years from now), the available information (e.g., the distribution of final grade-point averages for past students who were like John in important respects at his present stage of development) assigns a *probability distribution* to the various values that **X** might have for i. This "probability distribution," moreover, may be thought of as a distribution of potential values of **X** in which the relative frequency of a particular score equals the probability assigned to it by the available information, and from which the presently unknown true value of **X** for i is selected randomly. In this way, the theory of prediction which has been developed here for a restricted type of problem can be extended to the general case. In particular, the "best estimate" of **X** for i is the mean of this probability distribution (as necessarily computed by formula [3.8], since this formula does not presuppose an enumeration of the individual scores in the distribution as does formula [3.7]), while the SD of the distribution is the standard error of estimate. The most serious problem in the theory of prediction at this level of sophistication, theoretically as well as practically, is to figure out from the available information the probability distribution of **X** for i. In practice, however, we almost always assume (subject to some qualifications discussed later) that if our information about an individual i puts him in population P, then the statistical information we have compiled about variable **X** for other members of P gives us an approximation to the probability distribution of **X** for i.

Example. Mary, who is five foot two, eyes of blue, but a not-so-svelte 190 pounds, has been trying to find some way to reduce. Her doctor has

	Distribution of weight lost after six months' treatment with Lardoff in 152 known cases of women who were similar to Mary in height and pretreatment weight.		Approximate probability distribution for the amount of weight that Mary would lose after six months of Lardoff treatment.
Weight loss (in lbs.)	Number of cases	Relative frequency	Probability
10 or less	0	.000	.00
11–15	1	.007	.01
16–20	3	.021	.02
21–25	4	.026	.03
26–30	7	.046	.05
31–35	12	.079	.08
36–40	19	.125	.12
41–45	24	.158	.16
46–50	25	.164	.16
51–55	22	.144	.14
56–60	15	.099	.10
61–65	12	.079	.08
66–70	6	.039	.04
71–75	2	.013	.01
76 or more	0	.000	.00
Σ	152	1.000	1.00

Table 4.2. Data from a hypothetical study of reducing drugs, showing how the distribution of a variable within an observed sample of a population is used to infer the probability that the still-unknown value of this variable for another member (or potential member) of this population is (or would be) in a given interval. (No significance attaches to the rounding off of the decimals in the last column, except perhaps the general admonition that numerical data should not be allowed to suggest more precision than they in fact have.)

suggested that she try Lardoff, a new reducing drug, but since it also tends to make its user nauseated, Mary wants to know how much weight she can expect to lose by this treatment in order to decide whether it will be worth the discomfort. Suppose that as part of a recent study of reducing techniques, 152 females similar to Mary in height and weight were placed on Lardoff treatment for six months, with a resulting distribution of weight losses as shown in Table 4.2. Then from these observed weight losses, we infer the probability that Mary would lose a given poundage were she to undergo six months of Lardoff treatment. For example, 24, or 16%, of the 152 patients to whom Mary is comparable were observed to lose between 40.5 and 45.5 pounds, so on the basis of the information available we estimate that Mary has a 16% chance (i.e., a probability of .16, or odds of 16 to 84) of losing between 40.5 and 45.5 pounds if she takes Lardoff for six months.[16] Moreover, the mean and SD of this estimated probability distribution for Mary's prospective weight loss are 46.4 and 12.3, respectively, so our best estimate is that Mary would lose about 46.4 pounds after six months on Lardoff, with about 12.3 pounds as the standard error of our estimate.

Confidence Intervals. In the event that a prediction does not demand a single-value estimate of the variable being predicted, but will tolerate a certain amount of ambiguity (and there are really very few problems where we must commit ourselves to an *exact* estimate), knowledge of the probability distribution of the variable's potential values enables us to select any interval of these values that we choose and state the likelihood that the true value will fall in this range. Thus in the previous example, there is a 32% chance that Mary's weight loss after six months of Lardoff treatment would be between 40.5 and 50.5 pounds, and a 98% chance that it would be between 15.5 and 70.5 pounds. Conversely, we can select any probability of being correct that we wish and find an interval of possible values of the variable being predicted which contains the true value with this probability. Thus, if we set ourselves the problem of predicting, with 50% likelihood of success, a range in which Mary's weight loss would fall after six months of Lardoff treatment, we find by interpolation from Table 4.2 that Mary is as likely as not to lose between (approximately) 33 and 55 pounds. Such an interval is known as a *confidence interval,* and the probability with which that interval contains the true value of the variable is its *confidence level.* That is, a "confidence interval at the *p*% confidence level," when predicting the value of a vari-

[16] In practice, estimation of a probability distribution from the observed data proceeds in a somewhat more wholistic fashion. Thus if the observed distribution seems to be approximately normal, the probability distribution will usually be assumed to be normal, and the mean and the SD of the former used to estimate the mean and SD of the latter. This smooths out the chance irregularities of an empirical distribution comprising a small number of observations.

able **X** for an entity *i*, is *a range of possible values of* **X** *which contains the true value of* **X** *for i with p% likelihood.*[17]

It will be noticed that a given confidence level does not determine a corresponding confidence interval uniquely. For example, while there is a 90% chance that Mary would lose between (approximately) 25 and 66 pounds after six months on Lardoff, there is also a 90% chance that she would lose (approximately) either less than 47 pounds or more than 50 pounds. Obviously, some of these confidence intervals are more predictively useful than others—while knowing with a 90% certainty that Mary's weight loss would be between 25 and 66 pounds gives us a range of 41 pounds in which her weight loss is comfortably sure to fall, knowing with the same assurance that the weight loss will be either less than 47 or more than 50 pounds excludes very few possibilities. Since we want our prediction to be as accurate as possible, we are usually interested in confidence intervals which, for the given level of confidence, span as small a range as possible. We shall refer to such an interval as a *minimal* interval estimate at the *p%* confidence level. It is easy to prove (and it will be a useful exercise for the reader to do so) that whenever the probability distribution is symmetric and slopes off in either direction from a central peak, as does a normal distribution, any minimal confidence interval at the *p%* level is an interval whose midpoint is the mean of the distribution and which spans the middle *p%* of the distribution. The inverse relationship between the width and confidence level of an interval estimate is particularly easy to appreciate in this case, namely, that the more certain one wishes to be that his interval estimate does, in fact, include the true value of the variable being predicted, the less precise (i.e., the wider the interval) his estimate must be.

Interval estimates are of value in many sorts of prediction problems, especially those in which the primary aim is to guard against an individual's obtaining a score on the predicted variable within a certain unacceptable range. (This, after all, is basically the problem faced by a college admissions board, an employer screening job applicants, a parole board passing judgment on the prospective moral rectitude of a prisoner, etc.) In any case, a suitably constructed interval estimate has the remarkable virtue of being simultaneously able to convey most of the important things which should be indicated when a prediction is made. Thus when the probability distribution is essentially unimodal and symmetric, a minimal interval estimate at a conventionally high level of con-

[17] The terms "interval" and "range," here, should be thought of as extending to the case where the confidence "interval" is broken into several segments—e.g., when we say that there is a 50% chance that Mary would lose either less than 33 pounds or more than 55 pounds from a six months' treatment with Lardoff. For this reason, confidence intervals are known more technically as confidence *sets*. The reader should also be warned that in inferential statistics, the concept of "confidence interval (set)" involves more sophisticated subtlety than has been suggested here.

fidence (95% is a currently popular figure) not only gives a range in which the value of the variable being predicted is almost certain to fall, but at the same time indicates the best estimate of the variable (namely, the interval's midpoint) and the amount by which this estimate is likely to be wrong (namely, a certain proportion of the interval's width, the precise fraction depending on the probability distribution's shape, the level of confidence, and the measure of "likely" error employed). For example, psychometricians are now beginning to report the results of psychological tests in the form of confidence intervals rather than single scores, thereby calling attention to the fact that even the best test is subject to error, and that a person's observed test performance furnishes only an estimate of his "true" score (see Chapter 8). This development is still too new for conventions about the confidence level to become established, so interpretation of such a report must appeal to the test manual; however, let us suppose that the 95% confidence level used so frequently in research also becomes standard for test reports. Then if your results on a certain test were given to you on a form which shows a scale of T-scores on which your performance is described by a region marked between, say, the scores 58 and 70, you could be fairly sure (*a*) that there is a 95% chance that your "true" T-score on this test lies between 58 and 70 (i.e., that your true test ability is between .8 and 2.0 SDs above the mean of the population to which you are being compared), (*b*) that the best estimate of your "true" T-score on this test is about 64 (i.e., 1.4 SDs above the mean), and (*c*) that the expected discrepancy between your "true" T-score and this estimate of 64 is about 2.4 points.[18]

What Information to Use.[19] Suppose that one day at the zoo, you notice an enclosure containing elephants and mice. Sometimes a mouse steps on an elephant (i.e., scampers across his foot) and sometimes an elephant steps on a mouse. If you knew the body weights of all the animals in this enclosure, what would be your best estimate of the body weight of the next animal therein to be squashed by being stepped on? According to the prediction policy developed earlier, the best estimate

[18] In the absence of information to the contrary, you may assume that the reported interval is minimal and that the probability distribution for your "true" score, given your test performance, is approximately normal. Under these conditions, the reported interval is from two standard errors below to two standard errors above the best estimate of your "true" score, while the expected error of estimate is four fifths of the standard error; hence the best estimate is halfway between the interval's extremes, and the expected error is one fifth of the interval's width.

[19] In this section, the reader is asked to take more or less on faith certain points which appear intuitively obvious in the context of concrete examples, but which turn out under more penetrating scrutiny to involve crucially a number of advanced problems, some of which as yet have hardly been explored, let alone solved. In particular, this section is deliberately vague about the difference between the *probability* of a property within a class and its *frequency* therein, a distinction which is of the utmost importance in probability theory, even though in practice we take the latter (with secondary adjustments, perhaps) as our working approximation to the former.

is the average body weight in a certain population, but which population? If you started to answer, "the animals in this enclosure," shame on you. To be sure, the next to-be-squashed animal is to be drawn from this population, but you also know, more restrictively, that the victim is not going to be one of the elephants. And clearly the average weight among just the mice in this enclosure should be a better estimate of the next squashee's weight than would be the average weight within a more inclusive population containing both eligible and ineligible candidates for this honor.

What this example illustrates is the not-always-so-obvious point that *in principle, when predicting the value of a variable* **X** *for an individual i, the best estimate makes use of* ALL *the information available about i.* In particular, when the probability distribution of **X** for i is inferred from the frequency distribution of **X** in a population to which i belongs, this population should be the most restricted one to which the available information assigns i. Thus if a used-car dealer has offered you a special buy on a 1962 Gasgulper, and you are wondering what sort of mileage it would give you, it would be misleading to take the average miles per gallon for all 1962 Gasgulpers as your estimate when you can see plainly that this is a V-12 station wagon, a special model which constituted only a small part of Gasgulper production that year. Only the distribution of gas consumption in the population of 1962 V-12 Gasgulper station wagons should be considered—as becomes intuitively evident if, for example, you have heard that the V-12 engine was an experimental design which was quickly abandoned because of its prohibitively poor performance.

In practice, however, this demand that all the information about i be used when predicting the value of **X** for i quickly runs into difficulties, for we are more than likely to find ourselves blessed with more information than we know what to do with. If we list all the things we know about i, say that i has properties $P_1, \ldots, P_n$, then our estimate of X_i should be based on the distribution of **X** in the class of entities who are P_1 and ... and P_n. No more inclusive distribution, such as the distribution of **X** in the class of entities which are P_1 and ... and P_{n-1}, will in principle do, for entities which also have the property P_n may well be an atypical subclass of the former (compare, e.g., the distribution of Weight-in-pounds in mammals to its distribution in the subclass of whales). But in practice, by and large, we can only infer the distribution of a variable in a given class from its distribution in an observed sample of that class,[20] and the properties $P_1, \ldots, P_n$ may in conjunction be so restrictive that few if any entities having all these properties have previously been observed, thus leaving us essentially ignorant of the distribution of **X** in

[20] One important exception to this, as discussed later in this chapter, is the case where sampling from a multivariate distribution may permit inference to a subdistribution of which few or no actual instances have been observed.

this class. In the last example, for instance, in addition to knowing that the car you are contemplating is a 1962 Gasgulper V-12 station wagon, you also know, say, that it is pink and chartreuse in color, has a cracked rearview mirror, has been sitting for three months in Frantic Fred's used car lot for sale at half the price this model usually commands secondhand, and so on for a vast number of other details. It is not likely that you or anyone else will have previously observed the gas consumption of many automobiles meeting all these specifications, even though it is the expected gas consumption within this class, if you could learn it, which would constitute your best estimate of the mileage that this particular car would give you. In practically any prediction problem, it is possible to pile up enough supplemental data about the entity in question that any statistical norms which are available no longer seem applicable. In order to let our theory of prediction be usable, therefore, we must make it permissible to disregard at least *some* of the information which may be at our command.

Now, the difficulty confronting us at the moment is actually one whose discussion is far beyond the scope of this book. What we are officially concerned with is what value of **X** to predict, given a distribution of possibilities. We have *not* undertaken to explore the much more difficult question of how to derive this distribution from the knowledge available at the time the prediction is made. Even so, in order that the reader may have some appreciation of how the predictive policies here developed are actually put to use, it has been necessary to point out that in practice, we usually estimate the probability distribution of **X** for i from the values of **X** previously observed among other individuals suitably similar to i. This leads naturally to the question of what is to count as "suitably" similar, and what to do if no individuals suitably similar to i *have* been observed. Pending a more searching analysis on another occasion, the reader will have to content himself with the expedient usually adopted in practice, namely, estimating the value of **X** for i on the basis of the most restricted class known to contain i for which usable statistical norms have been obtained. In effect, this sorts the information about i into two kinds: *usable* information which assigns i to a category within which the distribution of **X** has already been sampled, and *unusable* information which would place i in a category for which no statistical norms are available. Then, subject to correction by more advanced techniques for estimating probabilities, our best estimate of the value of **X** for i is the average value of **X** among previously observed individuals in the most restricted category to which the usable information assigns i. Thus in the earlier example about Mary and her weight problem, the data in Table 4.2 were culled (let us say) from a massive study of reducing techniques which reported the height, pretreatment weight, and sex of the subjects as well as the method of treatment and amount of weight lost.

Then, since we have some statistics about the effects of Lardoff on women of Mary's height and weight, this information about her is usable, and Lardoff data on males or women of other heights and weights are no longer directly relevant. On the other hand, even if we have reason to suspect that the effect of reducing drugs may also be influenced by the subject's age, Mary's age must be ignored if the study on which the estimate is being based did not include a further breakdown of its subjects according to age.[21]

Statistical Regression: The Basic Theory

(It is recommended that this section, which tends to be abstract, be read without excessive loitering over those places which cause difficulty. Then, after the following section on linear regression has been mastered, the present section should be returned to for additional contemplation.)

In the preceding pages, we developed a policy for predicting the value of a variable from knowledge of the distribution of its potential values, and also examined some measures of the degree of uncertainty associated with this prediction. These fundamentals may in turn be elaborated into still more powerful methods for using and judging the worth of certain *kinds* of information about individuals in making predictions about them. More precisely, we are now in position to devise formulas for converting an individual's score, whatever it may be, on a variable **X** into a prediction about his still-unknown score on another variable **Y**, and for describing how generically useful information about **X** is for predicting **Y**. Still later, we shall see even more broadly how to derive estimates from knowledge about several predictor variables.

Suppose that you are chief shipping clerk for a mail-order men's store, the Caveat Emptorium, which specializes in certain commodities used by males of all ages and which come in different sizes, the appropriate size being determined by the user's height. Occasionally a rush order is received which gives no information about the customer except his age, and since it is up to you to select the size of the product to send in these cases, you decide to develop a method for converting a customer's age into an estimate of his height. Also, to see how to see how strongly you can rely on these estimates, you would like a measure of their prospective accuracy.

Let us say that by surveying your firm's records for past orders which listed both the customer's age and height, you are able to compile the scattergram shown in Figure 4.1. Since these data come from a pre-

[21] The alert reader should easily be able to spot situations which this rough-and-ready approach finds awkward to handle. For example, what is our best estimate of **X** for i if i is known to belong both to population P_1 and to population P_2, and sampling data are available for the distribution of **X** in P_1 and also, separately, for the distribution of **X** in P_2, but not for the distribution of **X** in the population of individuals who belong both to P_1 and to P_2?

sumable representative sample of Caveat Emptorium customers, they may be regarded as an approximation to the joint distribution of Height-in-inches and Age-in-years within this population. But once this is (approximately) known, the best estimate of a customer's height, given only his age, follows immediately by the predictive policies already developed. It was argued earlier that the best utility-free estimate of an individual's score on a given variable is the average value of that variable in the most restricted population to which the usable information assigns him. But if the joint distribution of Height-in-inches and Age-in-years for your firm's customers is known, the distribution of Height-in-inches for those customers who are also a particular age X must also be known—we just ignore the data from customers who are *not* X years old. (On the scattergram in Figure 4.1, the distribution of Height-in-inches for customers who are a given age, say 10 years, is shown by the dots falling along the vertical line erected at 10 on the Age-in-years axis.[22]) Hence age is usable information in this case, and the best (utility-free)

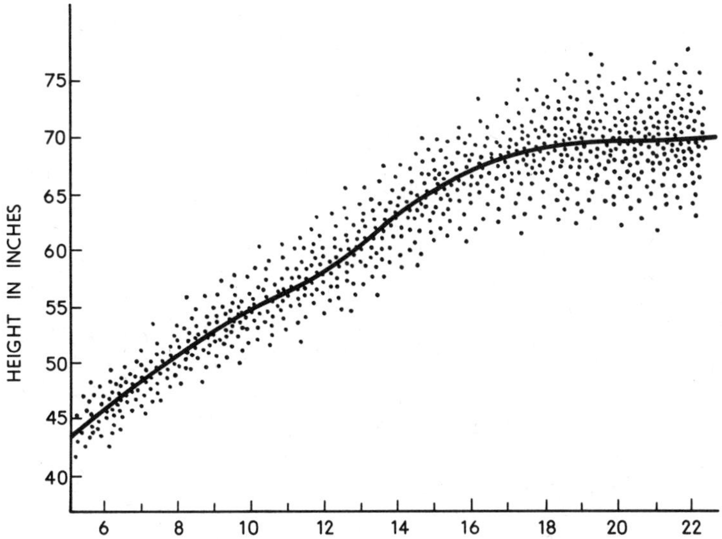

Figure 4.1. Scattergram of Height-in-inches and Age-in-years within a sample of Caveat Emptorium customers. The heavy curved line shows the average height at each age and is called the *curvilinear regression* of Height-in-inches upon Age-in-years in this population. (While these data are of course hypothetical, they have been chosen to approximate the relation between height and age actually found among U.S. males. The nature of the trend may be seen more clearly by sighting along the regression line at an angle.)

[22] Conversely, the distribution of Age-in-years among customers who are a given Height-in-inches, say 60, is shown by the points of the scattergram falling along the horizontal line erected at 60 on the Height-in-inches axis.

estimate of height for a Caveat Emptorium customer about whom the only additional thing known is his age is the average height of Caveat Emptorium customers his age. To expedite prediction according to this method, you can draw a line on the Height-in-inches × Age-in-years scattergram which shows the average Height-in-inches at each age. This line is known as the *regression*—or more precisely, to make clear that the line is free to take any shape it wishes, the *curvilinear regression*—of Height-in-inches on Age-in-years in this population. To find the best estimate of a customer's height in inches when only his age has been given, you then need only to find his age in years on the horizontal axis, trace vertically upward until you encounter the regression line, and then trace horizontally over to the vertical axis to see what height in inches is indicated.

Moreover, to see how accurate the predictions made in this way tend to be, you can compute for each customer whose data went into your scattergram the magnitude of the difference between his actual height and the height you would have predicted for him on the basis of his age, and then take an "average" of these errors (the quadratic mean being the most convenient) to represent the typical estimate error. Even better, since the average height among Caveat Emptorium customers would permit an estimate of a customer's height even if you didn't know his age, you can judge the additonal usefulness of Age-in-years for making such predictions by comparing your measure of typical error when information about age is used for the prediction to the corresponding measure of predictive accuracy when information about age is not used. Thus if there is only a difference of six inches, on the average, between a customer's true height and the height you estimate for him on the basis of his age, whereas your average error is 12 inches when you simply take the average height of Caveat Emptorium customers as your estimate, information about a customer's age enables you to cut your average prediction error in half.

Obviously this line of reasoning is completely general for prediction of any variable **Y** from any other variable **X**. Suppose that the joint distribution of **X** and **Y** in population P is known, and that the problem is to devise a policy for predicting the value of **Y** for a member i of P when the only usable information about i, in addition to his membership in P, is his score on **X**. (Variables *to* which prediction is made are called "dependent" or *criterion* variables, while those *from* which prediction is made are known as "independent" or *predictor* variables. In the present case, therefore, **X** is the independent or predictor variable and **Y** is the dependent or criterion variable.) While different members of P generally have different scores on **X**, P may be partitioned into subpopulations, each of which consists of all members of P sharing a given value of **X**.

Let "P_X" designate that subpopulation of P comprising exactly those members of P whose scores on **X** are X[23]—i.e.,

[4.6] $P_X =_{\text{def}}$ The population of which an entity i is a member if and only if i is a member of P and $X_i = X$.

Each of these subpopulations P_X has its own particular distribution of scores on **Y**, as determined from the appropriate slice from the joint distribution of **X** and **Y** in P, and as a rule, though not always, the distribution of **Y** in one subpopulation P_{X_1} is somewhat different both from its distribution in another subpopulation P_{X_2} and in the base population P. (By definition, the distribution of **Y** is the "same" in two populations if and only if the *relative* frequency of each value of **Y** is the same in both.) That is, the distribution of **Y** among members of P whose scores on **X** are equal to a given value X in general changes as X changes. For this reason, the distribution of **Y** within subpopulation P_X is called a *contingent* or *conditional* distribution. More explicitly, the "contingent (conditional) distribution of **Y**, given X, in P" is the distribution of **Y** in subpopulation P_X of P. In the highly important special case that the contingent distributions of **Y**, given X, in P are the same for all values of **X**, variable **Y** is said to be *statistically independent* of variable **X** in P.

Now if the only usable information about an individual i is that he belongs to population P and that his score on **X** is X_i, then the most restrictive population to which the usable information assigns i is P_X, the distribution of **Y** in P_X is the distribution of potential values of **Y** to be anticipated when predicting i's score on **Y**. (Thus the distribution of potential heights for an otherwise unidentified ten-year-old Caveat Emptorium customer is the distribution of height within ten-year-old Caveat Emptorium customers.) But it was for precisely this sort of situation, namely, making predictions when the distribution of potential values is known, that the predictive policies discussed earlier were developed. Hence if $\mathrm{M}_{\mathbf{Y}|X}$ (read "the contingent mean of **Y**, given that the value of **X** is X," or simply "the mean of **Y**, given X") is the arithmetic

---

[23] The subscript "X" in "P_X" is meant to be an ambiguous symbol for a particular value of **X** in the same way, e.g., that "P" and "**X**" are to be interpreted as referring to a particular but unspecified population and variable. (The precise meaning of such "ambiguous" terms is difficult to explain without recourse to concepts in formal logic, but if the reader has any background at all in elementary mathematics, he should be used to such symbols.) When it becomes necessary to distinguish between two or more values of **X** in this notation, we shall do so by adding subscripts to "X"—e.g., "P_{X_1}," "P_{X_2}," etc. "X" plays a similar role in the expressions "$\mathrm{M}_{\mathbf{Y}|X}$" and "$\sigma_{\mathbf{Y}|X}$" to be introduced shortly. This notation, though probably as convenient as any, has a drawback in that if a *specified* value of **X**, say 30, is substituted for the ambiguous value X, the expressions "P_{30}," "$\mathrm{M}_{\mathbf{Y}|30}$," etc., do not indicate the variable of which 30 is the value.

mean of **Y** among members of P whose value of **X** is X—i.e.,

[4.7] $$\mathrm{M}_{\mathbf{Y}|X} =_{\mathrm{def}} \mathrm{M}_{\mathbf{Y}} \text{ in population } P_X$$

$$= \frac{\sum_i Y_i}{n_X} \qquad \left(\begin{array}{c} i \text{ ranges over} \\ \text{members of } P_X \end{array}\right).$$

where n_X is the number of individuals in P_X—it follows from our earlier stipulations that the best (utility-free) estimate, $\hat{Y}_i$, of the **Y**-score of an individual i, about whom the only usable information is his membership in P and score on **X**, is

[4.8] $$\hat{Y}_i = \mathrm{M}_{\mathbf{Y}|X_i}.$$

(The subscript here added to the "best-estimate" symbol, which made its original appearance in [4.1] unadorned with such appendages, has here become necessary because we are now considering best estimates within several different populations, and the best estimate of the value of **Y** for an individual i will in general be different from that for another individual j if $X_i \neq X_j$.)

The line which shows for every value X of **X** the corresponding contingent mean of **Y** (i.e., $\mathrm{M}_{\mathbf{Y}|X}$, or the value of **Y** which is "expected" for a member of P whose score on **X** is X) in population P is known as the "curvilinear regression" of **Y** upon **X** in P.[24] This line is readily computed from the joint distribution of **X** and **Y** in P, and, as illustrated in Figure 4.1, can conveniently be drawn on the same graph that exhibits a scattergram of the distribution. What formula [4.8] then says is that the regression of **Y** on **X** in P shows what predictions about **Y** to make for known members of P about whom nothing else is known except their scores on **X**. That is, *the curvilinear regression of* **Y** *upon* **X** *in P is also the line which shows the best (utility-free) estimate of an individual's score on* **Y** *based solely on his score on* **X** *and his membership in P.*

The Goodness of Information (Part II). Let $\sigma_{\mathbf{Y}|X}$ (read "the contingent standard deviation of **Y**, given X") be the standard deviation of **Y** among members of P whose score on **X** is X—i.e.,

[4.9] $$\sigma_{\mathbf{Y}|X} =_{\mathrm{def}} \sigma_{\mathbf{Y}} \text{ in } P_X$$

$$= \sqrt{\frac{\sum_i (Y_i - \mathrm{M}_{\mathbf{Y}|X})^2}{n_X}} \qquad \left(\begin{array}{c} i \text{ ranges over} \\ \text{members of } P_X \end{array}\right).$$

Now, the distribution of potential values of **Y** for an individual about

[24] Similarly, the curvilinear regression of **X** on **Y** in P shows the contingent means $\mathrm{M}_{\mathbf{X}|Y}$ for the various values of **Y**. Only under exceptional circumstances does the regression of **X** on **Y** coincide with the regression of **Y** on **X**.

whom all that is known is that he is a member of P and that his score on **X** is X is simply the distribution of **Y** within population P_X. Hence the contingent standard error, $SE_{\mathbf{Y}|X}$, for estimating the value of **Y** for such an individual is the quadratic mean magnitude of estimate error in P_X. That is, if $e_{\mathbf{Y}i}$ is the algebraic error made when predicting that $\hat{Y}_i$ is the **Y**-score of individual i, i.e.,

$$[4.10]^{25} \qquad e_{\mathbf{Y}i} =_{\text{def}} Y_i - \hat{Y}_i \,,$$

it follows from the definition of "standard error" as a measure of the degree to which the prediction may be anticipated to be wrong that

$$[4.11] \qquad SE_{\mathbf{Y}|X} =_{\text{def}} QM_{|e_{\mathbf{Y}}|} \text{ in } P_X$$

$$= \sqrt{\frac{\sum_i e^2_{\mathbf{Y}i}}{n_X}} \qquad \left(\begin{array}{c} i \text{ ranges over} \\ \text{members of } P_X \end{array}\right).$$

$$= \sqrt{\frac{\sum_i (Y_i - \hat{Y}_i)^2}{n_X}}$$

and hence from [4.8] and [4.9],

$$[4.12] \qquad SE_{\mathbf{Y}|X} = \sigma_{\mathbf{Y}|X} \qquad (Y_i = M_{\mathbf{Y}|X_i}) \,.$$

Thus the quadratic mean magnitude of potential error when using prediction policy [4.8] to estimate an individual's **Y**-score based only on his membership in P and knowledge that his score on **X** is X is the contingent standard deviation of **Y**, given X, in P. (Similarly, it can be seen that the contingent expected magnitude of error, $EE_{\mathbf{Y}|X}$, when estimating a score on **Y** in this way, is the contingent average deviation, $AD_{\mathbf{Y}|X}$, of **Y**, given X, in P—i.e., the average deviation of **Y** in P_X.) Further, though we shall not introduce any special symbol to accommodate this notion, we may also speak of the "contingent shape" of the distribution of **Y**, given X, in P, since the shape of the distribution of **Y** in a subpopulation P_{X_1} needs not be the same as its shape in another subpopulation P_{X_2}. Given the contingent mean, standard deviation and shape of the distribution of **Y**, given X_i, the complete distribution of potential errors when predicting Y_i on the basis of i's score on **X** and membership in P can be reclaimed,

[25] It will be noticed that we have here defined the error of estimate to be the actual score minus the estimate, rather than by the more familiar direction, estimate minus actual score. This has the result that the estimate error $e_{\mathbf{Y}i}$ must be interpreted as the amount by which the prediction is *deficient*, rather than as the amount by which it is in excess. The reason for this reversal is that later it will be exceedingly convenient to be able to think of an actual score Y_i as comprising two components, the estimate $\hat{Y}_i$ plus a residual, and it would senselessly complicate matters to define the estimate error as the negation of this residual.

confidence intervals determined, and other questions pertaining to the goodness of the prediction answered.

The quadratic mean magnitude of potential prediction error $SE_{Y|X}$ is here called the *contingent* standard error of **Y**, given X, in P to emphasize that it depends upon the particular value of **X** on which the prediction is based. In view of certain simplifying assumptions which are frequently made, it is important to be clear that neither the contingent standard error of estimate nor the contingent distribution shape need remain the same for all predictions from **X** to **Y** in P. For example, the contingent standard deviation of Height-in-inches is appreciably smaller among five-year-olds than among 20-year-olds and consequently, when estimating a person's height from his age, we should expect our estimate to be more accurate if the person is five years old than if he is 20. In fact, if our actions in a certain problem of prediction are swayed not only by the best utility-free estimate of the criterion variable but also by our degree of confidence in that prediction, it is possible for the chief benefit in having **X** as a predictor variable to come not through its effect on the estimate, but in the way it modifies our expectation of the prediction's accuracy. For example, if the joint distribution of surgical skill and age among certified brain surgeons is as shown in Figure 4.2 (due, let us say, to opposed age trends of increasing experience and physiological aging), the importance of insuring that ability does not fall below a certain minimal level and the variation in the contingent standard error of ability as a function of age would make the latter an important predictor variable even though it makes no difference for the best utility-free estimate of the criterion. The present example is flagrantly hypothetical, however. In practice, the contingent standard error of the criterion variable is almost certain to be less sensitive to change in the value of the predictor variable than is the criterion's contingent mean. In fact, the contingent standard error not infrequently shows no appreciable change at all as the predictor variable varies, a statistical phenomenon which goes by the fearsome title of "homoscedasticity." That is, the contingent distributions of **Y**, given **X**, are *homoscedastic* in population P if the contingent standard deviation of **Y**, given X, in P is the same for all values of **X**. Because of its convenience (see below), homoscedasticity has frequently been assumed more or less automatically in applied fields such as psychological testing, and only within recent years have commercial diagnostic instruments begun to give explicit recognition to the fact that the contingent standard error of the criterion variable may *not* always be the same for all values of the predictor variable.

While the contingent standard error of estimate $SE_{Y|X}$ (or alternatively, though with less statistical convenience, the contingent average error or perhaps some other measure of spread in the contingent distributions of the criterion) tells us how much error to anticipate when predicting the value of **Y** for a particular member of P when his score on **X** has also been given, this is not the only question which may arise about the usefulness of one variable for predicting another. In particular, when predicting the value of **Y** for members of P from their **X**-scores, we may ask (1) how large an error we may expect *before* the subject's score on **X** has actually been determined—i.e., how generically accurate are estimates on **Y** based on knowledge of **X** for members of P—and (2) to what extent does knowledge about **X** *improve* predictions on **Y** for members of P beyond the predictive accuracy obtained simply through knowledge that these individuals are members of P?

The Absolute Standard Error of Estimate. The measure introduced in [4.11] for telling how accurately the **Y**-score of a member i of population P can be estimated from his score on **X** presupposes that we already know i's **X**-score. However, it is also convenient to be able to compute how far the estimate of Y_i based on i's **X**-score is likely to be wrong even when X_i is not yet known. This would assess the usefulness of this *kind* of information (i.e., knowledge about **X** for members of P) and would be of value, e.g., for deciding whether the predictive accuracy

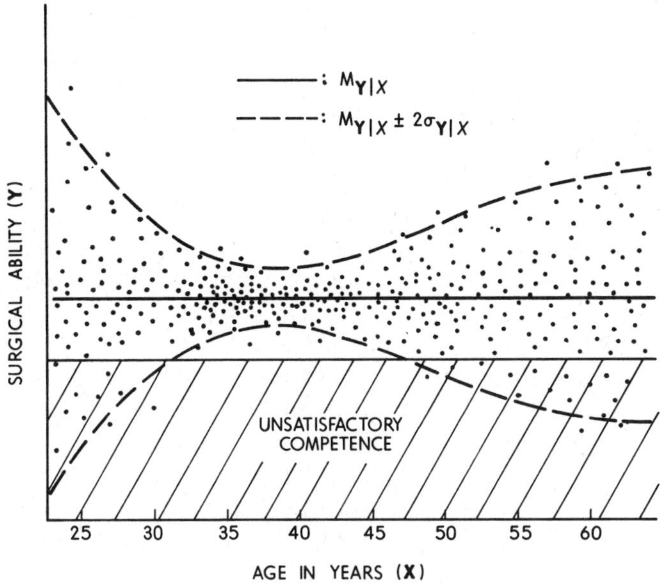

Figure 4.2. Scattergram of Age-in-years and some measure of surgical ability within a hypothetical population of brain surgeons. While average surgical ability does not change from one age level to another, as shown by the horizontal regression line, the dispersion around this average is markedly dependent upon age. Consequently, even though there is no tendency for surgical ability to vary with age in this population, information about age is nonetheless helpful for insuring that a chosen surgeon's ability exceeds the minimally acceptable level of competence.

afforded by such information is worth the outlay to obtain it. Such a measure is not difficult to devise: What we are asking is simply how large, on the whole, are the errors in the **Y**-estimates obtained for members of P from their scores on **X**, and this is most conveniently defined as the quadratic mean magnitude of the total distribution of estimate errors in P. In other words, the distribution of potential prediction errors when estimating the value of **Y** for a member of P from his **X**-score, before actual knowledge of **X** has narrowed down the possibilities, is given by the distribution of error scores $e_{\mathbf{Y}_i}$ within population P. The quadratic mean magnitude of these potential prediction errors may then be called "the *absolute* standard error of **Y**, given **X**, in P," and symbolized "$\mathrm{SE}_{\mathbf{Y},\mathbf{X}}$."[26] That is,

$$[4.13]\qquad \mathrm{SE}_{\mathbf{Y},\mathbf{X}} =_{\mathrm{def}} \mathrm{QM}_{|\mathbf{e_Y}|} \text{ in } P$$

$$= \sqrt{\frac{\sum_i e^2_{\mathbf{Y}_i}}{n}} \qquad \left(\begin{array}{c} i \text{ ranges over} \\ \text{all members of } P \end{array}\right)$$

$$= \sqrt{\frac{\sum_i (Y_i - \hat{Y}_i)^2}{n}}\ .$$

Similarly, we may define the "residual standard deviation of **X**, given **Y**, in P," symbolized "$\sigma_{\mathbf{Y},\mathbf{X}}$", to be

$$[4.14]\qquad \sigma_{\mathbf{Y},\mathbf{X}} =_{\mathrm{def}} \sqrt{\frac{\sum_i (Y_i - \mathrm{M}_{\mathbf{Y}|X_i})^2}{n}} \qquad \left(\begin{array}{c} i \text{ ranges over} \\ \text{all members of } P \end{array}\right).$$

(If the reader is not clear on the distinction between $\sigma_{\mathbf{Y},\mathbf{X}}$ and $\sigma_{\mathbf{Y}|X}$, he should compare formulas [4.9] and [4.14] with special attention to their parenthesized conditions of definition. Note that since the difference $Y_i - \mathrm{M}_{\mathbf{Y}|X_i}$ around the curvilinear regression line obviously averages to zero in P,[27] $\sigma_{\mathbf{Y},\mathbf{X}}$ is the standard deviation of these differences in P, just as $\sigma_{\mathbf{Y}|X}$ is their SD in P_X.) Under the prediction policy defined by the curvilinear regression of **Y** upon **X**, it then follows that

$$[4.15]\qquad \mathrm{SE}_{\mathbf{Y},\mathbf{X}} = \sigma_{\mathbf{X},\mathbf{Y}} \qquad (Y_i = \mathrm{M}_{\mathbf{Y}|X_i})\ .$$

[26] $\mathrm{SE}_{\mathbf{Y},\mathbf{X}}$ might also be called the "unconditional" standard error of **Y**, given **X**, in P, except that in discussions of multivariate relationships, the term "unconditional" usually denotes properties of the relevant variable's "marginal" (i.e., unconditional) distribution in P to contrast these with the corresponding properties of the variable's contingent distributions.

[27] *Study question: Why* is the average obviously zero?

The observant reader may wonder why, in the preceding formulas, we were so careful to define $SE_{\mathbf{Y}|X}$ and $SE_{\mathbf{Y},\mathbf{X}}$ separately from $\sigma_{\mathbf{Y}|X}$ and $\sigma_{\mathbf{Y},\mathbf{X}}$, even though these were subsequently equated in [4.12] and [4.15]. The reason is that $SE_{\mathbf{Y}|X}$ and $SE_{\mathbf{Y},\mathbf{X}}$, unlike $\sigma_{\mathbf{Y}|X}$ and $\sigma_{\mathbf{Y},\mathbf{X}}$, are defined in terms of a "best estimate" $\hat{Y}$ without specifying precisely how that estimate is made *and are hence relative to a particular policy for making predictions about* **Y** *from information on* **X**. The only predictive policy considered so far has been the optimal utility-free policy specified by [4.8], and as already pointed out, $SE_{\mathbf{Y}|X} = \sigma_{\mathbf{Y}|X}$ and $SE_{\mathbf{Y},\mathbf{X}} = \sigma_{\mathbf{Y},\mathbf{X}}$ in this case. However, there will soon be occasion to examine other possible policies for converting a score on **X** into an estimate on **Y** as expressed by an equation $\hat{Y}_i = \phi(X_i)$, where $\phi(X_i)$ does not necessarily equal $M_{\mathbf{Y}|X_i}$, and we shall wish to be able to speak about absolute and contingent errors of estimate in these cases as well.[28] As a rule, the context of discussion will make clear what predictive policy is presupposed by $SE_{\mathbf{Y}|X}$ and $SE_{\mathbf{Y},\mathbf{X}}$; however, when it is desirable to make this policy explicit in the notation, it may be done by a bracketed insertion of the equation which defines the policy—i.e., "$SE_{\mathbf{Y},\mathbf{X}}[\hat{Y}_i = \phi(X_i)]$" refers to the absolute standard error of **Y**, given **X**, in P when the policy is to take $\phi(X_i)$ as the estimated **Y**-score for a member of P whose score on **X** is X_i. More explicitly, then, equations [4.12] and [4.15] may be rewritten as

$$SE_{\mathbf{Y}|X}[\hat{Y}_i = M_{\mathbf{Y}|X_i}] = \sigma_{\mathbf{Y}|X}, \quad SE_{\mathbf{Y},\mathbf{X}}[\hat{Y}_i = M_{\mathbf{Y}|X}] = \sigma_{\mathbf{Y},\mathbf{X}},$$

to emphasize that they presuppose the optimal curvilinear regression policy.

The residual standard deviation of **Y**, given **X**, and hence the absolute standard error of estimate under optimal policy [4.8], has several important properties. To begin with,

$$[4.16] \qquad \sigma_{\mathbf{Y},\mathbf{X}} \leqslant \sigma_{\mathbf{Y}}.$$

That is, since $\sigma_{\mathbf{Y}}$ is the standard error for the best estimate of Y_i when it is given only that i belongs to P, optimal use of the additional information

[28] The alert reader (and even the not-so-alert reader, now that it is pointed out to him) will observe that we have now begun to use the symbol "$\hat{Y}_i$" to refer to the estimate of Y_i yielded by *any* given prediction policy, whether this policy is optimal or not. This might at first appear to be in violation of definition [4.1], which stipulated that $\hat{Y}$ is a *best* estimate. However, [4.1] also went on to add that $\hat{Y}$ is the best estimate *under the given circumstances*, where the latter may impose conditions, such as explicit consideration of utilities, or the use of prediction equations of a stipulated mathematical form, which result in a standard error of estimate greater than the unrestricted minimum given by [4.18]. We shall shortly consider optimal prediction under various restrictions which can be imposed on the shape of the prediction equation, and to avoid terminological confusion, it seems best to let $\hat{Y}_i$ be the estimate of Y_i computed from X_i by whatever prediction policy is under discussion—after all, *some* set of circumstances can always be imagined such that a given policy $\hat{Y}_i = f(X_i)$, no matter how inferior otherwise, is optimal under these circumstances.

about **X** never *decreases* our initially anticipated predictive accuracy.[29] Secondly,

[4.17] $\sigma_{\mathbf{Y},\mathbf{X}} = \sigma_{\mathbf{Y}}$ if and only if $M_{\mathbf{Y}|X} = M_{\mathbf{Y}}$ for all values of **X**.

Thus unless the best (utility-free) estimate of **Y** for a known member of P is never modified by additional knowledge about his score on **X**, overall predictive accuracy is increased by knowledge of **X**. Finally,

$$[4.18] \qquad \sigma_{\mathbf{Y},\mathbf{X}} \leqslant SE_{\mathbf{Y},\mathbf{X}}[\hat{Y}_i = \phi(X_i)]\,,$$

where ϕ is any function which converts values of **X** into estimates of **Y**. That is, the prediction policy expressed by [4.8], namely, taking the curvilinear regression of **Y** upon **X** as the line of best estimates, really is the best utility-free policy for estimating **Y** from **X** in that it yields the smallest quadratic mean magnitude of potential prediction error. The proofs of [4.16]–[4.18] follow quickly from the fact that the sum $\sum_i (Y_i - g)^2$ over the members of a subpopulation P_X of P is smaller when $g = M_{\mathbf{Y}|X}$ than when g is any other constant and may be left as exercises for the reader.[30]

Many writers use the expression, "standard error of estimate," without indicating whether it is the absolute or contingent standard error which is meant. This ambiguity is more serious in principle than in practice, for it follows from [4.11] that the summation in [4.13] of $(Y_i - \hat{Y}_i)^2$ over all *i*s with a common value X of **X** is equal to n_X times the squared contingent standard error of **Y**, given X, and hence that

$$[4.19] \qquad SE_{\mathbf{Y},\mathbf{X}} = \sqrt{\frac{\sum_i SE^2_{\mathbf{Y}|X_i}}{n}} \qquad \left(\begin{array}{c} i \text{ ranges over} \\ \text{all members of } P \end{array}\right)$$

Thus the absolute standard error of **Y**, given **X**, in P is the quadratic mean of the contingent standard error of **Y**, given X_i, over all members i of P. For the case where the estimates on **Y** are given by the curvilinear regression of **Y** on **X**, equation [4.19] implies that the residual standard

[29] The same is not always true of the *contingent* standard error, $\sigma_{\mathbf{Y}|X}$, however, since if the contingent distributions are not homoscedastic, knowledge of X_i may put i in a subpopulation P_{X_i} in which **Y** is particularly unpredictable. Of course, this does *not* mean that for such an i, prediction would be better if we disregarded X_i.

[30] The occasional assignment of proofs to the reader is not just a sneaky stunt to save the writer some work. These derivations really are elementary *so long as the concepts involved are clearly understood.* Consequently, if the reader cannot figure them out for himself, a strong suspicion arises that he is no longer entirely with it.

deviation of **Y**, given **X**, in P is a quadratic mean of the contingent standard deviations of **Y**, given scores on **X** in P, namely,

$$[4.20] \qquad \sigma_{\mathbf{Y},\mathbf{X}} = \sqrt{\frac{\sum_i \sigma^2_{\mathbf{Y}|X_i}}{n}} \qquad \left(\begin{array}{c} i \text{ ranges over} \\ \text{all members of } P \end{array}\right).$$

In particular, if the contingent distributions of **Y**, given **X**, all have the same standard deviation—i.e., are homoscedastic—it follows from [4.20] that $\sigma_{\mathbf{Y},\mathbf{X}} = \sigma_{\mathbf{Y}|X}$ for all values X of **X**; so the contingent standard error for the best curvilinear estimate of **Y** at any particular value of **X** is identical with the absolute standard error of **Y**, given **X**, so long as the contingent distributions of **Y** are homoscedastic. In any event, [4.19] shows that the absolute standard error may be taken as a reasonable approximation to the contingent standard errors if it is inconvenient to keep track of the latter. Nonetheless, it must not be forgotten that $SE_{\mathbf{Y},\mathbf{X}}$ measures anticipated error when predicting **Y** from **X** *before* the individual's score on **X** has actually been ascertained, whereas $SE_{\mathbf{Y}|X}$ reflects an adjustment in the anticipated estimate error in light of the obtained value of **X**.

The Coefficient of Alienation and the Correlation Ratio. The absolute standard error of **Y**, given **X**, in P describes the generic efficiency with which scores on variable **Y** can be predicted, in view of the known joint distribution of **X** and **Y** in P, for known members of P when knowledge of their scores on variable **X** is also available. But even without information on **X**, the bare knowledge that an individual i is a member of P would also permit an estimate of Y_i in view of the known distribution of **Y** in P.[31] A question which obviously arises, then, is the extent to which knowledge of scores on **X** *increases* our efficiency in predicting the values of **Y** for the known members of P above and beyond the predictive success achieved merely from the information about membership in P. That is, what, if anything, does knowledge of an individual's score on **X** tell us about his value of **Y** that we don't already know on the basis of the other information available?

Now as analyzed earlier, the best utility-free estimate of a score on **Y** based only on the predictee's membership in P is defined to be the ex-

---

[31] Clearly, if we know the joint distribution of **X** and **Y** in P we also know the distribution of **Y** (and also of **X**) in P. To find, e.g., the frequency of a particular value of **Y** in P we merely sum the bivariate frequencies across all values of **X** for that particular Y. The univariate distributions of **X** and **Y** in P are called "marginal" with respect to the joint distribution of **X** and **Y** in P because they can be described by marginal sums in a bivariate frequency table. Thus summing each column in Table 2.4 (p. 20) would give a frequency table for the Class-hours-cut variable, while summing the rows would give a frequency table for the Grade-point-average variable.

pected value, M_Y, of **Y** in *P* (a policy which, it will be recalled, minimizes the standard error of estimate), while the standard error, SE_Y, of this policy is the standard deviation, σ_Y, of **Y** in *P*. Therefore, since the additional knowledge forthcoming about **X** permits the absolute standard error of estimate to be reduced to $\sigma_{Y,X}$ by use of curvilinear prediction policy [4.8], it seems reasonable to measure the degree to which knowledge of **X** increases the accuracy with which **Y** can be predicted for individuals already known to belong to *P* by assessing the extent to which $\sigma_{Y,X}$ is smaller than σ_Y. There are several ways in which this comparison might be made. The most obvious method, merely subtracting $\sigma_{Y,X}$ from σ_Y, proves to be unsatisfactory because the degree of increased predictive efficiency signified by this difference depends upon the magnitude of σ_Y. (This may be appreciated by reflecting that the numerical difference between σ_Y and $\sigma_{Y,X}$ depends critically upon the unit of measurement used to scale **Y**, and that comparison of the difference $\sigma_Y - \sigma_{Y,X}$ to the corresponding difference $\sigma_W - \sigma_{W,X}$ for a third variable **W** would not reveal which of the two variables, **Y** or **W**, is more effectively predicted by **X**.) A more useful comparison of $\sigma_{Y,X}$ and σ_Y may be made by taking their *ratio*. This statistic is known as the (curvilinear) *coefficient of alienation* and may be symbolized "$\kappa_{Y,X}$"—i.e.,

[4.21] $$\kappa_{Y,X} =_{\text{def}} \frac{\sigma_{Y,X}}{\sigma_Y} .$$

From [4.16] and the fact that a standard error cannot be less than zero, it follows that

[4.22] $$0 \leqslant \kappa_{Y,X} \leqslant 1 .$$

That is, $\kappa_{Y,X}$ is always between zero and unity, with $\kappa_{Y,X} = 0$ indicating perfect prediction—i.e., that all the points in the joint distribution of **X** and **Y** lie exactly on the regression line—while $\kappa_{Y,X} = 1$ indicates (cf. [4.17]) that knowledge of **X** never modifies estimates of **Y** already made simply on the basis of membership in *P* and hence contributes nothing to predictive accuracy. *What the coefficient of alienation tells is what proportion of the standard error in predicting* **Y** *for members of P from this information alone still remains after knowledge about their scores on* **X** *is also utilized.* For example, if $\kappa_{Y,X} = .25$, errors in predicting **Y** for members of *P* are only one fourth as large, on the "average,"[32] when knowledge about **X** is sued as when the prediction is based solely on membership in *P*.

A disadvantage of the coefficient of alienation for reporting the usefulness of the predictor variable, however, is that high values of this co-

[32] While this "average" is the quadratic rather than the arithmetic mean, $AD_{Y,X}/AD_Y$ will be equal to $\sigma_{Y,X}/\sigma_Y$ if the shape of the distribution of prediction errors is the same as the shape of the distribution of **Y**. Hence $\kappa_{Y,X}$ also reveals the approximate amount by which the *expected* magnitude of prediction error has been decreased.

efficient correspond to low degrees of predictive accuracy, whereas for intuitive convenience, we should like our measure of usefulness to grow larger as predictive efficiency increases. One solution would be to subtract κ from 1, and in fact this is what we are likely to do anyway when interpreting the coefficient of alienation, since $1 - \kappa$ is the proportion by which knowledge of the predictor variable reduces the anticipated error of prediction. A measure used more frequently in practice, however, is the *correlation ratio*, or *eta* ($\eta_{\mathbf{Y.X}}$), which is defined

[4.23]
$$\eta_{\mathbf{Y,X}} =_{\text{def}} \sqrt{1 - \kappa^2_{\mathbf{Y,X}}}$$
$$= \sqrt{1 - \frac{\sigma^2_{\mathbf{Y.X}}}{\sigma^2_{\mathbf{Y}}}}\,.$$

The reader should have no difficulty in verifying that $\eta_{\mathbf{Y.X}}$, like $\kappa_{\mathbf{Y,X}}$, is always between 0 and 1, but that high values of eta signify a tight relationship between **X** and **Y**, whereas low values of eta reveal that **X** contributes little to prediction of **Y**.[33]

The reason for defining eta, our primary measure of curvilinear relationship, in what will undoubtedly appear to the reader as a senselessly complicated fashion, traces directly to the habit in modern statistics of partitioning scores into components which can then be attributed to different sources. The methods for accomplishing this, known generically as "variance analysis," are such powerful tools in advanced statistical methodology that it would be a shame, now that introduction of the correlation ratio has left the reader trembling on the brink of variance analysis anyway, not to peek into the abyss. The score on **Y** of a member i of P can be broken into two parts: (1) the value of **Y** predicted for i on the basis of the available information, plus (2) the algebraic error in this prediction. That is, from [4.10],

[4.24]
$$Y_i = \hat{Y}_i + e_{\mathbf{Y}_i}\,.$$

The predicted score, $\hat{Y}_i$, is called i's *regressed* score on **Y**, while $e_{\mathbf{Y}_i}$ is i's corresponding *error* or *residual* score. Let $\sigma_{\hat{\mathbf{Y}}}$ be the standard deviation of the scores on **Y** predicted for the various members of P, while $\sigma_{\mathbf{e_Y}}$ is the standard deviation in P of the corresponding error scores. Then for the type of problem now under discussion, where values of **Y** are being estimated for known members of P on the basis of their scores on **X**, it may be seen that if the **Y**-estimates are defined by the curvilinear regression

[33] It will also be of interest to the reader who has already gained some familiarity with the linear correlation coefficient to note that, as discussed later in this chapter, $\eta_{\mathbf{Y.X}}$ is equal to the linear correlation between the actual and estimated scores on **Y** in P. That is, $\eta_{\mathbf{Y.X}} = \mathbf{r}_{\mathbf{Y}\hat{\mathbf{Y}}}$ when $\hat{Y}_i = \mathbf{M}_{\mathbf{Y}|X_i}$.

of **Y** on **X** in P, $\sigma_{\mathbf{e_Y}}$ is simply the residual standard deviation, $\sigma_{\mathbf{Y,X}}$, of **Y**, given **X**, in P (see comment following formula [4.14]), and

[4.25][34]
$$\sigma^2_{\mathbf{Y}} = \sigma^2_{\hat{\mathbf{Y}}} + \sigma^2_{\mathbf{e_Y}} \qquad (\hat{Y}_i = \mathrm{M}_{\mathbf{Y}|X_i})$$
$$= \sigma^2_{\hat{\mathbf{Y}}} + \sigma^2_{\mathbf{Y,X}} \,.$$

That is, the variance of **Y** (i.e., $\sigma^2_{\mathbf{Y}}$) in P can be written as the sum of two parts: the variance of the predicted **Y**-scores ($\sigma^2_{\hat{\mathbf{Y}}}$), called the *controlled variance,* plus the variance of the **Y**-residual scores ($\sigma^2_{\mathbf{Y}}$), called the *error variance* or *residual variance.* (The variance, $\sigma^2_{\hat{\mathbf{Y}}}$, of the predicted scores is also frequently said to be the amount of criterion variance *accounted for* by the predictor variable.) Dividing both sides of [4.25] by $\sigma^2_{\mathbf{Y}}$ and solving for $\sigma_{\hat{\mathbf{Y}}}/\sigma_{\mathbf{Y}}$ gives

$$\frac{\sigma_{\hat{\mathbf{Y}}}}{\sigma_{\mathbf{Y}}} = \sqrt{1 - \frac{\sigma^2_{\mathbf{Y,X}}}{\sigma^2_{\mathbf{Y}}}}$$

and hence from [4.23],

[4.26]
$$\eta_{\mathbf{Y,X}} = \frac{\sigma_{\hat{\mathbf{Y}}}}{\sigma_{\mathbf{Y}}} \,.$$

In other words, the correlation ratio, $\eta_{\mathbf{Y,X}}$, tells how large the standard deviation of the predicted, or "regressed," scores on **Y** is in proportion to the standard deviation of the actual scores on **Y**, just as $\kappa_{\mathbf{Y,X}}$ tells how large the standard deviation of the **Y**-residual scores is in proportion to the actual **Y**-scores. Similarly, the equation

[4.27]
$$\eta^2_{\mathbf{Y,X}} + \kappa^2_{\mathbf{Y,X}} = 1 \,,$$

which follows from [4.23], is equivalent to

$$\frac{\sigma^2_{\hat{\mathbf{Y}}}}{\sigma^2_{\mathbf{Y}}} + \frac{\sigma^2_{\mathbf{Y,X}}}{\sigma^2_{\mathbf{Y}}} = 1 \,,$$

and hence asserts that $\eta^2_{\mathbf{Y,X}}$ is the proportion of the total variance of **Y** in P which is "controlled" through knowledge of **X**, while $\kappa^2_{\mathbf{Y,X}}$ is the proportion of the total variance of **Y** in P which is "error" variance. It is this

---

[34] *Proof:* The reader can easily demonstrate by applications of [3.3]–[3.6] to [4.24] that $\sigma^2_{\mathbf{Y}} = \sigma^2_{\hat{\mathbf{Y}}} + \sigma^2_{\mathbf{e_Y}} + 2\left[\sum_i (\hat{Y}_i - \mathrm{M}_{\mathbf{Y}})(e_{\mathbf{Y}i} - \mathrm{M}_{\mathbf{e_Y}})\right]\Big/ n$. Consider, now, the part-sum of the products $(\hat{Y}_i - \mathrm{M}_{\mathbf{Y}})(e_{\mathbf{Y}i} - \mathrm{M}_{\mathbf{e_Y}})$ among just those members of P whose values of **X** equal X. Since $\hat{Y}_i$ is the same for all members of P_X, it follows from [3.3] that the sum of $(\hat{Y}_i - \mathrm{M}_{\mathbf{X}})(e_{\mathbf{Y}i} - \mathrm{M}_{\mathbf{e_Y}})$ in P_X equals a constant times the sum of $(e_{\mathbf{Y}i} - \mathrm{M}_{\mathbf{e_Y}})$ in P_X. But when $\hat{Y}_i = \mathrm{M}_{\mathbf{Y}|X_i}$, it is obvious that the sum of $e_{\mathbf{Y}i}$ in each subpopulation P_X equals zero. Then by successive steps we see that $\mathrm{M}_{\mathbf{e_Y}}$ in P, the sum of $(e_{\mathbf{Y}i} - \mathrm{M}_{\mathbf{e_Y}})$ in P_X, the sum of $(\hat{Y}_i - \mathrm{M}_{\mathbf{Y}})(e_{\mathbf{Y}i} - \mathrm{M}_{\mathbf{Y}})$ in P_X, and finally $2\left[\sum_i (\hat{Y}_i - \mathrm{M}_{\mathbf{Y}})(e_{\mathbf{Y}i} - \mathrm{M}_{\mathbf{e_Y}})\right]/n$ all equal zero.

symmetry between η and κ which leads to the use of the correlation ratio as our official measure of the tightness of curvilinear relationship, even though the coefficient of alienation is the more directly meaningful of the two as an index of predictive accuracy.

Curve Fitting: The Least-Squares Solution

Although the best estimates of **Y** for known members of population *P*, based on their scores on **X**, are shown in principle by the curvilinear regression of **Y** on **X** in *P*, practical complications are likely to arise when we are faced with the problem of discovering just what the curvilinear regression of **Y** on **X** in *P* actually *is*. What needs to be done is to determine for each number *X* the average value of **Y** among members of *P* with this score on **X**. But apart for special cases in which **X** has only a few alternatively possible values, it will be next to impossible to sample enough members of *P* to furnish an accurate and independent approximation to $M_{\mathbf{Y}|X}$ for every single value of **X**. For example, suppose that the Adastra Heights school board wishes to know if the psychosomatic maladies frequently reported by kindergarten teachers in their district might have some connection with the number of pupils for which they

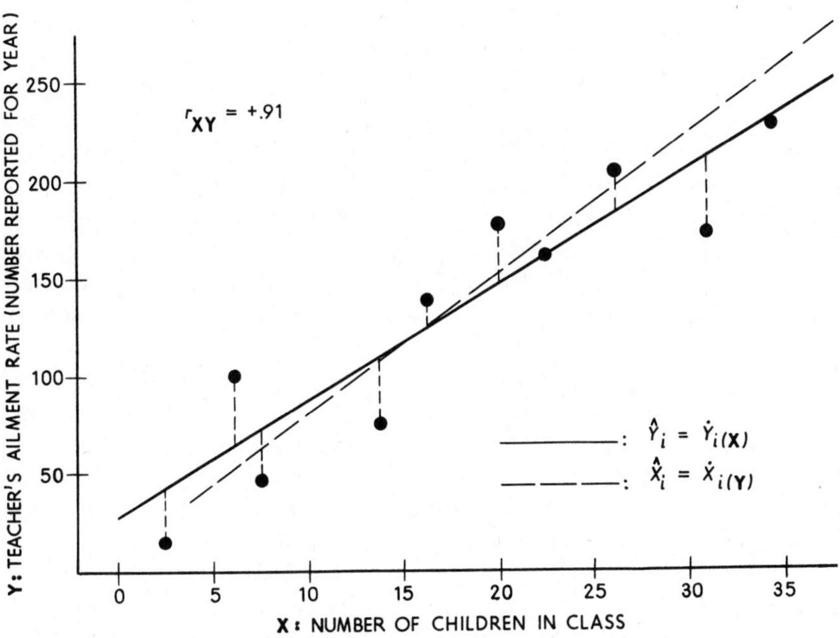

Figure 4.3. Scattergram of Number-of-children-in-class and reported Teacher's-ailment-rate for sample of ten Adastra Heights kindergarten teachers. The solid line shows the best linear estimates of ailment rate, given class size, in this population, while the lengths of the vertical dotted lines show the amounts by which these estimates are in error. (The diagonal dashed line shows the linear prediction policy that would be used to estimate class size from ailment rate. In this case, the estimate errors would be the horizontal discrepancy between the dots and the prediction line.)

are responsible. By asking a number of their kindergarten teachers to estimate how many attacks of minor ailments (headache, upset stomach, etc.) they suffered last year, the school board comes up with the scattergram shown in Figure 4.3, which then affords an approximation to the joint probability distribution of Number-of-children-in-class and Teacher's-ailment-rate within the population of Adastra Heights kindergarten teachers. Now clearly there is a tendency for teachers of the larger classes to report the higher incidences of psychosomatic disturbance. Yet this trend cannot adequately be estimated simply by computing for each value of the Number-of-children-in-class variable the average ailment rate reported by Adastra Heights kindergarten teachers with this number of pupils, for the number of cases sampled at any given class size is far too small for this—in fact, at most class sizes, no observations have been made at all.

In practice, therefore, it is usually necessary to assess the manner in which one variable **Y** is related to another, **X**, by inferring the contingent distribution of **Y** at each given value of **X** through consideration of data additional to that available merely at the particular **X**-value in question. But this we can do by asking what *shape* of underlying distribution is suggested by the obtained sample, and then computing the distribution of that shape which best fits these data. Similarly, to determine the regression of **Y** upon **X** when only a few observations are available, we would make a more or less intuitive judgment about what sort of trend these data display and then compute precisely which line of this sort would minimize prediction errors for the data at hand.[35] For example, Figure 4.3 suggests an approximately linear relationship between Number-of-children-in-class and Teacher's-ailment-rate, so the best estimate of the annual number of ailments to be reported by an Adastra Heights kindergarten teacher with a given number of pupils is shown by a straight line which, in a sense to be analyzed below, most closely approximates these observations.

Moreover, even if the precise curvilinear regression of **Y** on **X** in P can be determined in detail, it may still turn out, if this line is somewhat irregular in its shape, that the practical convenience of making estimates on the basis of a simpler curve more than outweighs the loss in predictive accuracy which this involves. We need not pause to illustrate this point, but the extraordinary mathematical ease with which predictions can be made when a straight-line relationship is presupposed (see formula [4.58], below) makes this a compellingly attractive simplifying assumption until departures from the linear become pronounced.

The upshot of our present considerations, then, is that while the uninhibited curvilinear regression of **Y** on **X** defines our theoretically op-

[35] Actually, inference from a sample of observations to the statistical properties of the distribution sampled is by no means this casual, though the ultimate result is essentially the same. (See Chapter 10, pp. 498 ff.)

timal (utility-free) policy for predicting values of **Y** from values of **X**, it may be impractical or, through insufficient sampling, impossible to follow this policy literally. The problem which then arises is how to find the best estimate of **Y**, given **X**, in P when the best-estimate function, $\hat{Y}_i = f(X_i)$, is restricted to some particular mathematical form (e.g., form $\hat{Y}_i = aX_i + b$, or $\hat{Y}_i = aX_i^2 + b\hat{X}_i + c$, or $\hat{Y}_i = aX_i^b + c$, or $\hat{Y}_i = a \cdot \sin(X_i + b)$, etc., where a, b, etc., are parameters, the alternative numerical choices for which generate the various curves of that form.) The solution to this problem, of course, is relative to whatever method we choose for deciding which of various alternative prediction curves gives the best predictions; and while clearly that prediction curve is best (at least in the utility-free sense) which, on the whole, yields the smallest potential prediction errors, this still leaves ambiguous which of the various measures of on-the-wholeness at our disposal we should choose to minimize. Now in the absence of appeal to ultimate utilities, such a choice can only amount to personal preference (which, of course, is itself an appeal to utilities of a sort). However, few properties of a statistical measure are more endearing than mathematical docility. Moreover, it would be embarrassing if our best-fitting curve of restricted form were not to coincide with the unrestricted curvilinear regression if the latter happens to be of this form. Hence there is really no practical alternative but to continue with the standard error of estimate—i.e., the quadratic mean magnitude of potential error—as our measure of predictive accuracy. Consequently, we may define the "F-form regression of **Y** upon **X** in population P" to be that function (i.e., line) of form F which, when used to estimate values of **Y** from the **X**-scores of members of P, yields a smaller absolute standard error of **Y**, given **X**, than does any alternative function of form F. That is, function f is the F-form regression of **Y** upon **X** in P if and only if f is of form F and satisfies the condition

[4.28] $$\mathrm{SE}_{\mathbf{Y},\mathbf{X}}[\hat{Y}_i = f(X_i)] \leq \mathrm{SE}_{\mathbf{Y},\mathbf{X}}[\hat{Y}_i = \phi_F(X_i)] \ ,$$

where ϕ_F is any function of form F. From [4.13], this will be seen to be true if and only if

[4.29] $$\sum_i [Y_i - f(X_i)]^2 \leq \sum_i [Y_i - \phi_F(X_i)]^2 \qquad \begin{pmatrix} i \text{ ranges over} \\ \text{all members of } P \end{pmatrix},$$

where, as before, ϕ_F is any function of form F. A more compact way to write [4.29] is

[4.29*a*] $$\sum_i [Y_i - f(X_i)]^2 = \mathit{minimum} \qquad (f \in F) \ ,$$

where "$f \in F$" means that f is of form F. Translated back into ordinary English, [4.29] or [4.29*a*] says that the F-form regression of **Y** on **X** in P is that line of form F such that the discrepancies between this line and the **Y**-scores in P, when squared and summed, are at a minimum. For this reason the curve found in this way is known as a "least-squares" solution. Since the F-form regression of **Y** on **X** in P by definition yields the smallest absolute standard error of **Y**, given **X**, in P which is possible under this form restriction, it describes the optimal (utility-free) F-form policy for converting scores on **X** into estimates of **Y** for members of P, and is frequently called the "best-fitting" line of this form.[36]

Although in principal there is an unlimited number of different curve forms which might be fitted to the points in a scattergram,[37] only a few of the mathematically simplest forms are of practical interest. And of these, one form in particular is outstanding in its algebraic convenience—namely, the straight line. In fact, the theory of prediction which emerges when linear relationships are assumed is so superior in most respects (except possibly in predictive accuracy) to policies defined by regression lines of any other form that the vast majority of practical applications to which the statistical theory of prediction has been put, such as the design, evaluation, and use of psychological tests, have presupposed linearity with scarcely a thought for whether or not this assumption was really justified. For better or worse, one is likely to encounter serious consideration of nonlinear regression only in advanced research. Since linear regression (*a*) permits the most powerful algebraic development of prediction theory, (*b*) is basic to most practical applications, and (*c*) is the simplest to explain, it is to this case that we direct the remainder of our attention in this chapter.

Linear Regression

As implied by the foregoing, the *linear regression* of one variable **Y** upon another, **X**, in population P is that straight line around which the sum of the squared discrepancies for members of P in the **Y**-dimension is at a minimum—i.e., the straight line which, when construed as a procedure for converting scores on **X** into estimates of **Y**, yields a smaller absolute standard error of **Y** in P than any other linear prediction policy. However, since our past coverage of the basic concepts in this area—regression, standard error, controlled and residual variance, etc.—moved at a spritely pace scarcely designed to comfort the hesitant and fearful, it will be helpful to take a deep breath and retrace our steps more circumspectly.

Let us return, then, for a more leisurely look at Figure 4.3. Having agreed that the underlying relationship between Number-of-children-in-class (**X**) and Teacher's-ailment-rate (**Y**) among Adastra Heights

---

[36] This use of the expression "best-fitting line," while prevalent, is actually ambiguous, for both the F-form regression of **Y** upon **X** and the F-form regression of **X** upon **Y**, which are almost always different lines, are equally "best fitting" in this sense.

[37] The curvilinear regression line is included in this family of F-form regressions, for by [4.18], $\hat{Y}_i = M_{Y|X_i}$ satisfies [4.29] when F is the limiting case of the least possible restrictions.

kindergarten teachers appears, in view of the ten cases (P) of recent note, to be approximately linear, we set ourselves the task of computing the straight line which, when the **Y**-coordinate of the line above a given value X is taken as our estimate of the **Y**-score of an Adastra Heights kindergarten teacher whose **X**-score is X, minimizes the errors of estimate within the sample population P. Consider, now, the prediction policy $\hat{Y}_i = aX_i + b$ defined by an arbitrary straight line drawn on a scattergram of these data. (That is, $\hat{Y}_i = aX_i + b$ is the prediction policy according to which an individual's **X**-score is converted into an estimate of his score on **Y** by multiplying X_i by the number a and then adding the number b.) As shown in Figure 4.4, the prediction on **Y** for any member i of P according to this policy is found by tracing vertically from i's **X**-coordinate to the prediction line. The height, $\hat{Y}_i$, of the line at this position is then the estimate of i's **Y**-score, while the vertical distance from i's scattergram point to the prediction line is the error, $e_{\mathbf{Y}i}$, which results from this estimate. That is,

[4.30]
$$\begin{aligned} e_{\mathbf{Y}i} &= Y_i - \hat{Y}_i \\ &= Y_i - (aX_i + b) \qquad (\hat{Y}_i = aX_i + b) \\ &= Y_i - aX_i - b \,. \end{aligned}$$

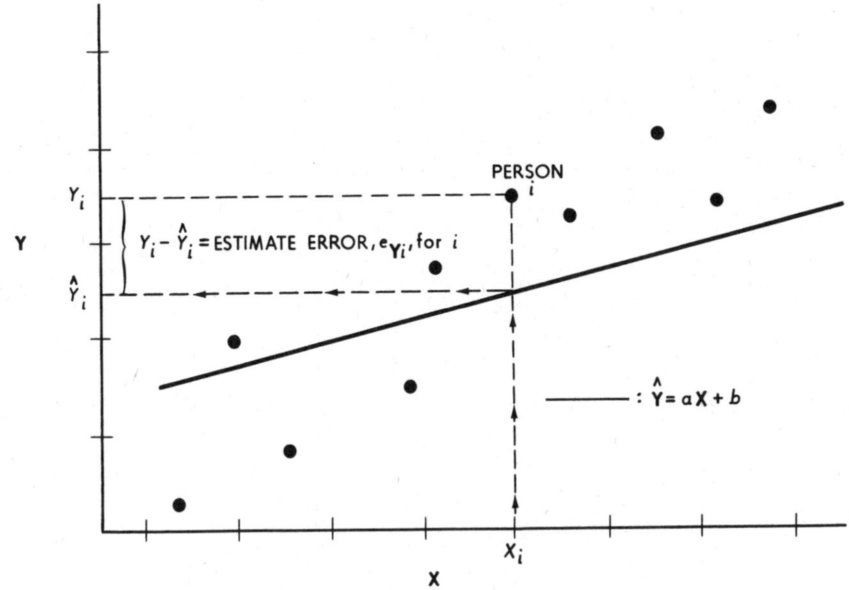

Figure 4.4. Data of Figure 4.3, showing how an arbitrary straight line $Y_i = aX_i + b_i$ can be interpreted as a policy for converting an individual's score on variable **X** into an estimate of his score on **Y**. The vertical distance between the prediction line and the scattergram point for person i is the amount by which the estimate of Y yielded by this policy is in error.

Having thus determined the individual estimate error for each member of P, our next problem is to assess how successful the prediction policy $\hat{Y}_i = aX_i + b$ is *on the whole* for members of P. That is, if a member of P were to be drawn at random and his score on **Y** estimated by this policy from his **X**-score, how far wrong would this estimate likely be? To give this a precise measure, we need to represent the distribution of estimate errors over population P by a single number which shows their typical magnitude; and we have already seen that the most satisfactory measure of central tendency in this case is the quadratic mean. In other words, our most useful measure of the efficiency with which a prediction policy estimates scores on **Y** from scores on **X** for the members of P is the absolute standard error of **Y**, given **X**, in P under this policy. In our present case, this measure is seen from [4.13] to have the value

[4.31]
$$\mathrm{SE}_{\mathbf{Y},\mathbf{X}}[\hat{Y}_i = aX_i + b] = \mathrm{QM}_{|e_{\mathbf{Y}}|}$$
$$= \sqrt{\frac{\sum_i (Y_i - \hat{Y}_i)^2}{n}}$$
$$= \sqrt{\frac{\sum_i (Y_i - aX_i - b)^2}{n}}.$$

It will be observed that this equation does not actually refer to one particular straight line. Rather, [4.31] is a general formula which may be made to yield $\mathrm{SE}_{\mathbf{Y},\mathbf{X}}$ for different policies by substituting various specific numbers for a and b. Moreover, since every possible straight line corresponds to some particular choice of numbers for a and b in $\hat{Y}_i = aX_i + b$, we can solve for the linear regression of **Y** on **X** in P—which, it will be recalled, is defined as that straight line for which the absolute standard error of **Y**, given **X**, is minimal—by computing the numbers which, when substituted for a and b in [4.31], result in the smallest numerical value of $\mathrm{SE}_{\mathbf{Y},\mathbf{X}}$.

Before deriving the solution to $\mathrm{SE}_{\mathbf{Y},\mathbf{X}}[\hat{Y}_i = aX_i + b] = minimum$, it is first desirable to introduce a highly important relational attribute found in bivariate distributions, the "linear correlation" between two variables. We begin with the *covariance* (Cov) of variables **X** and **Y** in population P, namely,

[4.32][38]
$$\mathrm{Cov}(\mathbf{X}, \mathbf{Y}) =_{\mathrm{def}} \frac{\sum_i (X_i - \mathrm{M}_{\mathbf{X}})(Y_i - \mathrm{M}_{\mathbf{X}})}{n}$$

[38] The second line is readily seen to follow from the first by observing that $\sum_i (X_i - \mathrm{M}_{\mathbf{X}})(Y_i - \mathrm{M}_{\mathbf{Y}}) = \sum_i X_iY_i - \mathrm{M}_{\mathbf{X}} \sum_i Y_i - \mathrm{M}_{\mathbf{Y}} \sum_i X_i + n\mathrm{M}_{\mathbf{X}}\mathrm{M}_{\mathbf{Y}} = \sum_i X_iY_i - n\mathrm{M}_{\mathbf{X}}\mathrm{M}_{\mathbf{Y}}$.

$$= \frac{\sum_{i-} X_i Y_i}{n} - \mathrm{M}_{\mathbf{X}} \mathrm{M}_{\mathbf{Y}}$$

$$= \mathrm{M}_{\mathbf{XY}} - \mathrm{M}_{\mathbf{X}} \mathrm{M}_{\mathbf{Y}} \, .$$

It can easily be seen that the covariance is affected by linear transformations of **X** or **Y** in the same fashion as are $\sigma_{\mathbf{X}}$ and $\sigma_{\mathbf{Y}}$, namely, by being relative to the units of measurement but not to the reference point of the scale. More precisely,

[4.33][39] $\mathrm{Cov}(\mathbf{X}', \mathbf{Y}') = ac\,\mathrm{Cov}(\mathbf{X}, \mathbf{Y}) \quad (X_i' = aX_i + b,\ Y_i' = cY_i + d)$.

Formulas such as [4.33], which reveal statistical relationships that hold when one variable is an algebraic function of others, can be written more informatively by making the function explicit in the equation. Thus instead of [4.33], we may write

[4.33*a*] $\mathrm{Cov}(a\mathbf{X} + b, c\mathbf{Y} + d) = ac\,\mathrm{Cov}(\mathbf{X}, \mathbf{Y})$,

in which "$a\mathbf{X} + b$" designates any variable $\mathbf{X}'$ such that $X_i' = aX_i + b$ for each member *i* of the population under concern, and similarly for "$c\mathbf{Y} + d$." This notation also leads to a useful condensation of equations which describe relations among values of variables which hold for all members of the population. Instead of writing, e.g., $Y_i = aX_i + b$ with the understanding that this is true for every individual *i* in *P*, we may simply state that $\mathbf{Y} = a\mathbf{X} + b$, meaning that variable **Y** is "numerically identical" with variable $a\mathbf{X} + b$ in population *P*. Formulas subsequently encountered in form $\mathbf{Y} = a_0 + a_1\mathbf{X}_1 + \ldots + a_n\mathbf{X}_n$ are therefore to be understood as saying that if the values of variables $\mathbf{Y}, \mathbf{X}_1, \ldots, \mathbf{X}_n$ for any individual *i* in the relevant population are substituted for the corresponding boldface letters in the formula, the resulting numerical equation, $Y_i = a_0 + a_1 X_{1i} + \ldots + a_n X_{ni}$, is true. This technique for designating variables by compound expressions which reveal their mathematical compositions, and equations containing symbols for variables proper, rather than for their numerical values, will see increasing use until in later chapters, subscripts for mere population members will have disappeared almost entirely. However, the change will be introduced gradually, and should occasion the reader only nominal distress.

It will be observed that the variance (i.e., σ^2) of a variable is its covariance with itself. That is, by substitution of **X** for **Y** in [4.32] and comparing [3.21], we have

[4.34] $\mathrm{Cov}(\mathbf{X}, \mathbf{X}) = \mathrm{Var}(\mathbf{X})$.

[39] Since $\sum_i (X_i' - \mathrm{M}_{\mathbf{X}'})(Y_i' - \mathrm{M}_{\mathbf{Y}'}) = \sum_i ([aX_i + b] - [a\mathrm{M}_{\mathbf{X}} + b])([cY_i + d] - [c\mathrm{M}_{\mathbf{Y}} + d]) = \sum_i a(X_i - \mathrm{M}_{\mathbf{X}})c(Y_i - \mathrm{M}_{\mathbf{Y}}) = ac \sum_i (X_i - \mathrm{M}_{\mathbf{X}})(Y_i - \mathrm{M}_{\mathbf{Y}})$.

Another obvious but important property of the covariance is its symmetry—i.e.,

[4.35] $$\text{Cov}(\mathbf{X}, \mathbf{Y}) = \text{Cov}(\mathbf{Y}, \mathbf{X}) .$$

Finally, if the value of a variable **S** for each member i of population P is equal to the sum of i's scores on variables **X** and **Y**—i.e., if $S_i = X_i + Y_i$ for each i in P, or more briefly $\mathbf{S} = \mathbf{X} + \mathbf{Y}$—the covariance of **S** with another variable **W** is simply the sum of the covariances of **W** with **X** and **Y**, respectively. That is,

[4.36][40] $$\text{Cov}(\mathbf{S}, \mathbf{W}) = \text{Cov}(\mathbf{X}, \mathbf{W}) + \text{Cov}(\mathbf{Y}, \mathbf{W}) \qquad (\mathbf{S} = \mathbf{X} + \mathbf{Y})$$

or, using composition notation,

[4.36*a*] $$\text{Cov}(\mathbf{X} + \mathbf{Y}, \mathbf{W}) = \text{Cov}(\mathbf{X}, \mathbf{W}) + \text{Cov}(\mathbf{Y}, \mathbf{W}) .$$

The descriptive significance of the covariance concept derives primarily from its intimate relation to the correlation coefficient, whose richly endowed meanings will shortly be discussed in detail. Mathematically, however, covariance is of profound importance, much more so than correlation, and while the reader cannot expect to appreciate why this is so until he has suffered and gloried with covariances through the algebraic arabesques to come, he should nonetheless make certain that he grasps clearly just what formulas [4.33]–[4.36] say. In particular, the reader who plans to study the more advanced materials in this and subsequent chapters should observe, or at least be prepared to observe when the need subsequently arises, how repeated applications of [4.33]–[4.36] will break down the variances and covariances of "composite" variables—i.e., variables which are linear combinations of other variables—into linear combinations of the variances and covariances among the variables of which they are composed. In fact, we may as well make these more complex covariance relationships explicit right now, even though for the most part they will not be required for some time, and the reader may postpone or omit the ensuing three starred paragraphs as the spirit moves him.

*Observe, then, that by repeated application of [4.36] we can show that the covariance between a variable **Y** and the sum **S** of **n** variables $\mathbf{X}_1, \mathbf{X}_2, \ldots, \mathbf{X}_n$ is

[4.37] $$\text{Cov}(\mathbf{Y}, \mathbf{S}) = \text{Cov}(\mathbf{Y}, \mathbf{X}_1) + \text{Cov}(\mathbf{Y}, \mathbf{X}_2) + \ldots + \text{Cov}(\mathbf{Y}, \mathbf{X}_n) \qquad (\mathbf{S} = \mathbf{X}_1 + \ldots + \mathbf{X}_n)$$

[4.37*a*] $$\text{Cov}(\mathbf{Y}, \mathbf{X}_1 + \ldots + \mathbf{X}_n) = \text{Cov}(\mathbf{Y}, \mathbf{X}_1) + \ldots + \text{Cov}(\mathbf{Y}, \mathbf{X}_n)$$

---

[40] Since by [3.5], $\mathrm{M}_{\mathbf{X}+\mathbf{Y}} = \mathrm{M}_{\mathbf{X}} + \mathrm{M}_{\mathbf{Y}}$, and $\sum_i ([X_i + Y_i] - [\mathrm{M}_{\mathbf{X}} + \mathrm{M}_{\mathbf{Y}}])(W_i - \mathrm{M}_{\mathbf{W}}) = \sum_i ([X_i - \mathrm{M}_{\mathbf{X}}] + [Y_i + \mathrm{M}_{\mathbf{Y}}])(W_i - \mathrm{M}_{\mathbf{W}}) = \sum_i (X_i - \mathrm{M}_{\mathbf{X}})(W_i - \mathrm{M}_{\mathbf{W}}) + \sum_i (Y_i - \mathrm{M}_{\mathbf{Y}})(W_i - \mathrm{M}_{\mathbf{W}})$.

[4.37b] $$\mathrm{Cov}\left(\mathbf{Y}, \sum_{i=1}^{n} \mathbf{X_i}\right) = \sum_{i=1}^{n} \mathrm{Cov}(\mathbf{Y}, \mathbf{X_i}) ,$$

where all three formulas say the same thing in different styles of notation. (Note that as made explicit by the boldface subscripts, summation in [4.37b] is over *variables*, not over individual values of a single variable.) More generally, by application of [4.33a] as well as [4.36] we can generalize [4.37] to any composite $\mathbf{L_X} = a_0 + a_1\mathbf{X_1} + a_2X_2 + \ldots + a_n\mathbf{X_n}$ of variables $\mathbf{X_1}, \ldots, \mathbf{X_n}$; namely,

[4.38] $$\mathrm{Cov}(\mathbf{Y}, \mathbf{L_X}) = a_1 \mathrm{Cov}(\mathbf{Y}, \mathbf{X_1}) + \ldots + a_n \mathrm{Cov}(\mathbf{Y}, \mathbf{X_n}) \qquad (\mathbf{L_X} = a_0 + a_1\mathbf{X_1} + \ldots + a_n\mathbf{X_n})$$

[4.38a] $$\mathrm{Cov}(\mathbf{Y}, a_0 + a_1\mathbf{X_1} + \ldots + a_n\mathbf{X_n}) = a_1 \mathrm{Cov}(\mathbf{Y}, \mathbf{X_1}) + \ldots + a_n \mathrm{Cov}(\mathbf{Y}, \mathbf{X_n})$$

[4.38b] $$\mathrm{Cov}\left(\mathbf{Y}, a_0 + \sum_{i=1}^{n} a_i\mathbf{X_i}\right) = \sum_{i=1}^{n} a_i \mathrm{Cov}(\mathbf{Y}, \mathbf{X_i})$$

Formula [4.38] is of especial interest, both for the frequency with which it will subsequently see use and for the ease with which it can be committed to memory. It states that the covariance of a variable **Y** with any linear combination of a set of variables $\mathbf{X_1}, \ldots, \mathbf{X_n}$ is equal to that same linear combination of the covariances of **Y** with the $\mathbf{X_i}$except for omission of the additive constant. In particular, to anticipate a special case which will later occur with delightful frequency, any variable which has zero covariances with all the variables in a given set also has zero covariance with any linear combination of the latter.

*To extend these results to more complex cases, begin by observing that the covariance of the sum of variables $\mathbf{Y_1}, \ldots, \mathbf{Y_m}$ with the sum of variables $\mathbf{X_1}, \ldots, \mathbf{X_n}$ (**m** not necessarily equal to **n**) is equal to the sum of the array of covariances defined by each pairing of a $\mathbf{Y_i}$ with an $\mathbf{X_j}$. That is,

[4.39] $$\begin{aligned}\mathrm{Cov}(\mathbf{Y_1} + \mathbf{Y_2} + \ldots + \mathbf{Y_m}, \mathbf{X_1} + \mathbf{X_2} + \ldots + \mathbf{X_n}) = \\ \mathrm{Cov}(\mathbf{Y_1}, \mathbf{X_1}) + \mathrm{Cov}(\mathbf{Y_1}, \mathbf{X_2}) + \ldots + \mathrm{Cov}(\mathbf{Y_1}, \mathbf{X_n}) \\ + \mathrm{Cov}(\mathbf{Y_2}, \mathbf{X_1}) + \mathrm{Cov}(\mathbf{Y_2}, \mathbf{X_2}) + \ldots + \mathrm{Cov}(\mathbf{Y_2}, \mathbf{X_n}) \\ \vdots \qquad\qquad \vdots \qquad\qquad \vdots \qquad \vdots \\ + \mathrm{Cov}(\mathbf{Y_m}, \mathbf{X_1}) + \mathrm{Cov}(\mathbf{Y_m}, \mathbf{X_2}) + \ldots + \mathrm{Cov}(\mathbf{Y_m}, \mathbf{X_n})\end{aligned}$$

or, more compactly,

[4.39a] $$\mathrm{Cov}\left(\sum_{i=1}^{m} \mathbf{Y_i}, \sum_{i=1}^{n} \mathbf{X_i}\right) = \sum_{i=1}^{m} \sum_{j=1}^{n} \mathrm{Cov}(\mathbf{Y_i}, \mathbf{X_j}) .$$

This follows from [4.37*b*] by substitution of $\sum_{i=1}^{m} \mathbf{Y}_i$ for **Y**. (Although there is nothing at all conceptually difficult about this, the results have begun to look formidable, and a moment's pause to reflect in gratitutde on the remarkable simplification of notation afforded by the summation sign, as put to use in [4.39*a*], is in order.) By substituting $\mathbf{X}_1, \ldots, \mathbf{X}_n$ for $\mathbf{Y}_1, \ldots, \mathbf{Y}_m$ in [4.39] and heeding [4.34 and 4.35], we get the important special case of the variance of a sum:

$$[4.40]\quad \mathrm{Var}\left(\sum_{i=1}^{n} \mathbf{X}_i\right) = \mathrm{Cov}\left(\sum_{i=1}^{n} \mathbf{X}_i, \sum_{i=1}^{n} \mathbf{X}_i\right)$$

$$= \sum_{i=1}^{n} \sum_{j=1}^{n} \mathrm{Cov}\,(\mathbf{X}_i, \mathbf{X}_j)$$

$$= \sum_{i=1}^{n} \mathrm{Var}\,(\mathbf{X}_i) + \sum_{\substack{i=1 \\ i \neq j}}^{n} \sum_{j=1}^{n} \mathrm{Cov}\,(\mathbf{X}_i, \mathbf{X}_j)$$

$$= \sum_{i=1}^{n} \mathrm{Var}(\mathbf{X}_i) + 2 \sum_{i=1}^{n} \sum_{j=1}^{i-1} \mathrm{Cov}(\mathbf{X}_i, \mathbf{X}_j)\,,$$

where the sign $\sum_{\substack{i=1 \\ i \neq j}}^{n} \sum_{j=1}^{n}$ means summation over all combinations of **i** from **1** to **n** with **j** from **1** to **m** except for those in which **i**=**j**. The reader will doubtlessly have to study equation [4.40] awhile before its meaning comes clear. What it says is that the variance of a sum of variables is equal to the sum of all the entries in the constituent variables' "covariance matrix," by which is meant the array of covariances shown in Table 6.2, p. 214, and to which the reader should now refer. The diagonal entries in this array, shown by the *V*s in Table 6.2, are the variables' self-covariances (cf. [4.34]), and since these play a special role in many situations, they may usefully be separated out from the other covariances as done in the last two lines of [4.40]. Due to the symmetry of covariance (cf. [4.35]), the entries to the upper right of the *V*-diagonal in the covariance matrix duplicate those to the lower left, which is why summing over just one of these triangular halves—as is indicated by the summation sign $\sum_{i=1}^{n} \sum_{j=1}^{i=1}$ in the last line of [4.40]—and multiplying by 2 gives the total of the off-diagonal covariances. Equation [4.40] is further clarified if we let $\overline{\mathbf{V}}_{\mathbf{X}}$ be the average variance of the **n** variables $\mathbf{X}_1, \ldots, \mathbf{X}_n$, while $\overline{C}_{XX}$ is their average covariance excluding self-covariances—i.e.,

$$\overline{V}_X =_{def} \frac{\sum_{i=1}^{n} \mathrm{Var}(X_i)}{n}, \qquad \overline{C}_{XX} =_{def} \frac{\sum_{i=1}^{n}\sum_{\substack{j=1 \\ i \neq j}}^{n} \mathrm{Cov}(X_i, X_j)}{n(n-1)}.$$

Then from [4.40],

$$\text{[4.41]} \qquad \mathrm{Var}\left(\sum_{i=1}^{n} X_i\right) = n\overline{V}_X + n(n-1)\overline{C}_{XX},$$

which shows that the variance of a sum is determined both by the average variance and the average (off-diagonal) covariance of the summed variables, with $\overline{C}_{XX}$ receiving much the heavier weight as n grows large. In the important special case when the X_i all have zero covariances with one another, [4.40] reduces to

$$\text{[4.42]} \qquad \mathrm{Var}\left(\sum_{i=1}^{n} X_i\right) = \sum_{i=1}^{n} \mathrm{Var}(X_i) \qquad \left(\begin{matrix}\mathrm{Cov}(X_i, X_j) = 0 \\ \text{when } i \neq j\end{matrix}\right).$$

*Finally, these results may be extended to the variances and covariances of any linear combinations of sets of variables by substituting a_iY_i and b_jX_j for each Y_i and X_j, respectively, in [4.39] and [4.40]. Application of [4.33*a*] then shows that

[4.43]

$$\mathrm{Cov}\left(a_0 + \sum_{i=1}^{m} a_iY_i,\ b_0 + \sum_{i=1}^{n} b_iX_i\right) = \sum_{i=1}^{m}\sum_{j=1}^{n} a_ib_j\,\mathrm{Cov}(Y_i, X_j),$$

[4.44]

$$\mathrm{Var}\left(a_0 + \sum_{i=1}^{n} a_iX_i\right) = \sum_{i=1}^{n} a_i^2\,\mathrm{Var}(X_i) + \sum_{i=1}^{n}\sum_{\substack{j=1 \\ i \neq j}}^{n} a_ia_j\,\mathrm{Cov}(X_i, X_j)$$

$$= \sum_{i=1}^{n} a_i^2\,\mathrm{Var}(X_i) + 2\sum_{i=1}^{n}\sum_{j=1}^{i=1} a_ia_j\,\mathrm{Cov}(X_i, X_j).$$

If formulas [4.39] and [4.40] have been adequately understood, [4.43] and [4.44] will raise little if any additional difficulty.

And so long as we are about the statistical behavior of composite variables anyway, this is as appropriate a time as any to make explicit an obvious but essential fact about arithmetic means which we shall soon need. If $L_X = a_0 + a_1X_1 + \ldots + a_nX_n$ is any linear combination of variables

$\mathbf{X}_1, \ldots, \mathbf{X}_n$, we see from [3.2]–[3.5] by summing over the values of $\mathbf{L}_\mathbf{X}$ for all members i of the population under consideration that

$$\sum_i L_{\mathbf{X}i} = a_0 + a_1 \sum_i X_{1i} + a_2 \sum_i X_{2i} + \ldots + a_n \sum_i X_{ni} .$$

Dividing by the number of population members then yields

[4.45]

$$\mathrm{M}_{\mathbf{L}_\mathbf{X}} = a_0 + a_1 \mathrm{M}_{\mathbf{X}_1} + a_2 \mathrm{M}_{\mathbf{X}_2} + \ldots + a_n \mathrm{M}_{\mathbf{X}_n} \quad \left(\mathbf{L}_\mathbf{X} = a_0 + \sum_{i=1}^{n} a_i \mathbf{X}_i\right)$$

or equivalently,

[4.45*a*]

$$\mathrm{M}_{(a_0 + \sum_{i=1}^{n} a_i \mathbf{X}_i)} = a_0 + \sum_{i=1}^{n} a_i \mathrm{M}_{\mathbf{X}_i} .$$

That is, the mean of a linear combination of variables is equal to that same linear combination of the means of the constituent variables.

To resume our development of measures of relationship, the *linear correlation*, $\mathrm{r}_{\mathbf{XY}}$, between variables **X** and **Y** in population P (also known as the "product-moment," or "Pearsonian" correlation) is now defined as

[4.46]

$$\mathrm{r}_{\mathbf{XY}} =_{\text{def}} \frac{\mathrm{Cov}(\mathbf{X}, \mathbf{Y})}{\sigma_\mathbf{X} \sigma_\mathbf{Y}}$$

$$= \frac{\sum_i (X_i - \mathrm{M}_\mathbf{X})\,(Y_i - \mathrm{M}_\mathbf{Y})}{n \sigma_\mathbf{X} \sigma_\mathbf{Y}} .$$

Like the covariance, $\mathrm{r}_{\mathbf{XY}}$ is symmetric in **X** and **Y**, i.e.,

[4.47]

$$\mathrm{r}_{\mathbf{XY}} = \mathrm{r}_{\mathbf{XY}} ,$$

so there is no need to be fretful over the order of subscripts in "$\mathrm{r}_{\mathbf{XY}}$". Moreover, it follows from [3.25] and [4.33] that $\mathrm{r}_{\mathbf{XY}}$ is unchanged in magnitude by any linear transformation of **X** or **Y**, though a transformation which inverts the order of scores on one variable also changes the sign of the correlation. That is,

[4.48]

$$\mathrm{r}_{\mathbf{X}'\mathbf{Y}'} = \begin{cases} \mathrm{r}_{\mathbf{XY}} \text{ if } ac > 0 \\ -\mathrm{r}_{\mathbf{XY}} \text{ if } ac < 0 . \end{cases} \quad (\mathbf{X}' = a\mathbf{X} + b,\ \mathbf{Y}' = c\mathbf{Y} + d) .$$

Hence recalling that the Z-scale of a variable is that linear rescaling (with positive multiplier) of the variable on which the mean is zero and σ equals unity (cf. [3.26]), it follows from [4.46] and [4.48] that

[4.49] $$r_{\mathbf{XY}} = \mathrm{Cov}(\mathbf{Z_X}, \mathbf{Z_Y})$$

$$= \frac{\sum_i Z_{\mathbf{X}i} Z_{\mathbf{Y}i}}{n} .$$

Formula [4.49] provides a convenient verbal definition for $r_{\mathbf{XY}}$, for what it says is that *the linear correlation between variables* **X** *and* **Y** *in population P is the average product of Z-scores on* **X** *and* **Y** *for members of P*. To optimize transfer of insight between the mathematical manipulations of covariance and the descriptive significance of correlation, it should also be vigorously appreciated that, as shown by the first line of [4.49], *correlation is a standardized covariance.* In particular, it will be important on numerous later occasions to be clear that $\mathrm{Cov}(\mathbf{X}, \mathbf{Y}) = 0$ if and only if $r_{\mathbf{XY}} = 0$.[41] (It is not, however, the case that correlations have all the clean mathematical properties of covariances. For example, the correlation between a variable **W** and the sum of two other variables **X** and **Y** is

$$r_{\mathbf{X+Y,W}} = \frac{\mathrm{Cov}(\mathbf{X}+\mathbf{Y}, \mathbf{W})}{\sigma_{\mathbf{X+Y}}\sigma_{\mathbf{W}}} = \frac{\mathrm{Cov}(\mathbf{X}, \mathbf{W}) + \mathrm{Cov}(\mathbf{Y}, \mathbf{W})}{\sigma_{\mathbf{X+Y}}\sigma_{\mathbf{W}}}$$

$$= \frac{\sigma_{\mathbf{X}}}{\sigma_{\mathbf{X+Y}}} r_{\mathbf{XW}} + \frac{\sigma_{\mathbf{Y}}}{\sigma_{\mathbf{X+Y}}} r_{\mathbf{YW}} ,$$

where by [4.40]

$$\sigma_{\mathbf{X+Y}} = \sqrt{\sigma_{\mathbf{X}}^2 + \sigma_{\mathbf{Y}}^2 + 2\sigma_{\mathbf{X}}\sigma_{\mathbf{Y}} r_{\mathbf{XY}}} ,$$

all of which is a long, long way from the simple beauty of $\mathrm{Cov}(\mathbf{X} + \mathbf{Y}, \mathbf{W}) = \mathrm{Cov}(\mathbf{X}, \mathbf{W}) + \mathrm{Cov}(\mathbf{Y}, \mathbf{W})$.) Computation of the numerical value of a correlation coefficient is illustrated in Table 4.3.

We are now equipped to continue pursuit of the linear regression of a variable **Y** upon a variable **X** in population *P*. (In view of the length of our interlude on covariance, it is recommended that the reader review pp. 98–100 before continuing.) In light of formula [3.19], the (absolute) standard error of **Y**, given **X**, under any prediction policy $\hat{Y}_i = \phi(X_i)$ may be written

[4.50] $$\mathrm{SE}_{\mathbf{Y.X}} =_{\mathrm{def}} \mathrm{QM}_{|\mathbf{e_Y}|} \qquad (\mathbf{e_Y} = \mathbf{Y} - \phi(\mathbf{X}))$$

$$= \sqrt{\mathrm{Var}(\mathbf{e_Y}) + \mathrm{M}^2_{\mathbf{e_Y}}} .$$

[41] That is, except for degenerate cases in which $\sigma_{\mathbf{Y}}$ or $\sigma_{\mathbf{X}}$ equals zero. In this event, $\mathrm{Cov}(\mathbf{X},\mathbf{Y}) = 0$ while $r_{\mathbf{XY}}$ remains undefined.

Population member	X_i	Y_i	X_i' $(=X_i - 18)$	Y_i' $(= Y_i - 130)$	$X_i'^2$	$Y_i'^2$	$X_i'Y_i'$
# 1	2	10	−16	−120	256	14,400	1,920
# 2	6	100	−12	− 30	144	900	360
# 3	8	45	−10	− 85	100	7,225	850
# 4	14	70	− 4	− 60	16	3,600	240
# 5	16	135	− 2	5	4	25	−10
# 6	20	175	2	45	4	2,025	90
# 7	23	160	5	30	25	900	150
# 8	27	200	9	70	81	4,900	630
# 9	31	170	13	40	169	1,600	520
#10	34	220	16	90	256	8,100	1,440
Σ	181	1285	1	−15	1,055	43,675	6,190
M $(= \Sigma/n)$	18.1	128.5	.1	− 1.5	105.5	4,367.5	619.0

$$\mathrm{M}_{\mathbf{X}} = 18.1 \qquad \mathrm{M}_{\mathbf{Y}} = 128.5$$

$$\mathrm{Var}\ (\mathbf{X}) = \mathrm{Var}\ (\mathbf{X}') = \mathrm{M}_{\mathbf{X}'^2} - \mathrm{M}^2_{\mathbf{X}'} = 105.5 - (.1)^2 = 105.5 - .01 = 105.49$$

$$\mathrm{Var}\ (\mathbf{Y}) = \mathrm{Var}\ (\mathbf{Y}') = \mathrm{M}_{\mathbf{Y}'^2} - \mathrm{M}^2_{\mathbf{Y}'} = 4{,}367.5 - (1.5)^2 = 4{,}367.5 - 2.25 = 4{,}365.25$$

$$\mathrm{Cov}\ (\mathbf{X},\mathbf{Y}) = \mathrm{Cov}\ (\mathbf{X}',\mathbf{Y}') = \mathrm{M}_{\mathbf{X}'\mathbf{Y}'} - \mathrm{M}_{\mathbf{X}'}\mathrm{M}_{\mathbf{Y}'} = 619.0 - (.1)(-1.5) = 619.0 + .15 = 619.15$$

$$\sigma_{\mathbf{X}} = \sqrt{\mathrm{Var}\ (\mathrm{X})} = \sqrt{105.45} = 10.27$$

$$\sigma_{\mathbf{Y}} = \sqrt{\mathrm{Var}\ (\mathrm{Y})} = \sqrt{4{,}365.25} = 66.07$$

$$\mathrm{r}_{\mathbf{XY}} = \frac{\mathrm{Cov}\ (\mathbf{X},\mathbf{Y})}{\sigma_{\mathbf{X}}\sigma_{\mathbf{Y}}} = \frac{619.15}{(10.27)(66.07)} = \frac{619.15}{678.54} = .912$$

Table 4.3. *Computing a correlation coefficient and its attendant statistics.* There are a variety of ways to compute correlations. Which method is best depends on what statistics may be wanted in additon to $\mathrm{r}_{\mathbf{XY}}$, the computing machinery at hand, and whether or not the scores have any special mathematical properties. (E.g., when one or both of the variables are dichotomous, or when the scores on both variables are ranks, special simplified formulas are applicable.) The procedure illustrated here for the data shown in Figure 4.3 is an efficient work layout which not merely yields a maximum of supplementary information, but is also especially effective at converting appreciation for the theoretical definitions of correlation and its underlying statistics into a sense of numerical manipulations. The table is self-explanatory except perhaps for the transition from the original scales $\mathbf{X}$ and $\mathbf{Y}$ to the modified scales $\mathbf{X}' = \mathbf{X} - 18$ and $\mathbf{Y}' = \mathbf{Y} - 130$. When a desk computer is available for doing the squares, cross-products, and sums, this step is superfluous, but when these operations are done by hand, transforming each variable by subtracting a convenient constant close to the variable's mean can greatly reduce the size of the numbers being operated upon without disturbing any of the variances and covariances (cf. [4.33] with $a = c = 1$).

This layout is readily extended to simultaneous computation of the intercorrelations among several variables. For $\mathbf{n}$ variables, the table requires $\mathbf{n}$ columns for raw scores, $\mathbf{n}$ columns for transformed scores (if desired), $\mathbf{n}$ columns for squares, and $\mathbf{n}(\mathbf{n} - 1)/2$ columns for cross-products. When a desk computer is used, the sums of squares and of cross-products can usually be obtained without filling in the body of the table for these columns.

It is then obvious that the best (i.e., standard-error minimizing) policy when ϕ is restricted to a given mathematical form is the one for which $\mathrm{Var}(\mathbf{e_Y}) = minimum$ and $\mathrm{M}_{\mathbf{e_Y}} = 0$, so long as the latter condition can be brought about without conflicting with the former. Now for any linear prediction policy $\hat{Y}_i = aX_i + b$, the error variable $\mathbf{e_Y}$ is a linear function of $\mathbf{X}$ and $\mathbf{Y}$, namely,

$$\mathbf{e_Y} = \mathbf{Y} - a\mathbf{X} - b\ .$$

Hence by [4.45] and [4.44], we have

$$[4.51\text{-M}] \quad \mathrm{M}_{\mathbf{e_Y}} = \mathrm{M}_{\mathbf{Y}} - a\mathrm{M}_{\mathbf{X}} - b\ ,$$

$$\begin{aligned}[4.51\text{-V}] \quad \mathrm{Var}(\mathbf{e_Y}) &= \mathrm{Var}(\mathbf{Y} - a\mathbf{X} - b) \\ &= \mathrm{Var}(\mathbf{Y}) + a^2\,\mathrm{Var}(\mathbf{X}) - 2a\,\mathrm{Cov}(\mathbf{X},\mathbf{Y}) \\ &= \mathrm{Var}(\mathbf{X})\left[a - \frac{\mathrm{Cov}(\mathbf{X},\mathbf{Y})}{\mathrm{Var}(\mathbf{X})}\right]^2 + \left[\mathrm{Var}(\mathbf{Y}) - \frac{\mathrm{Cov}(\mathbf{X},\mathbf{Y})^2}{\mathrm{Var}(\mathbf{X})}\right],\end{aligned}$$

where the reader should have no difficulty in verifying the equivalence of the last two lines of [4.51-V]. The last line of [4.51-V] has been put into the form

$$\mathrm{Var}(\mathbf{e_Y}) = C_1(a - C_2)^2 + C_3\ ,$$

where the Cs are constants determined by the joint distribution of $\mathbf{X}$ and $\mathbf{Y}$ in P. Hence $\mathrm{Var}(\mathbf{e_Y})$ is a function of the prediction-policy parameter a alone, and is minimal when $a = C_2$. It is also apparent from [4.51-M] that for any choice of a, a value of b can be found to yield $\mathrm{M}_{\mathbf{e_Y}} = 0$. The values of a and b which set $\mathrm{Var}(\mathbf{e_Y}) = $ minimum and $\mathrm{M}_{\mathbf{e_Y}} = 0$, and thereby minimize $\mathrm{SE}_{\mathbf{Y},\mathbf{X}}[\hat{\mathbf{Y}} = a\mathbf{X} + b]$, are thus found to be

$$[4.52] \quad a = \frac{\mathrm{Cov}(\mathbf{X},\mathbf{Y})}{\mathrm{Var}(\mathbf{X})}$$

$$(\mathrm{SE}_{\mathbf{Y},\mathbf{X}}[\hat{\mathbf{Y}} = a\mathbf{X} + b] = minimum)$$

$$b = \mathrm{M}_{\mathbf{Y}} - \frac{\mathrm{Cov}(\mathbf{X},\mathbf{Y})}{\mathrm{Var}(\mathbf{X})}\mathrm{M}_{\mathbf{X}}\ .$$

It will be observed that no matter how optimally the parameters a and b are chosen, there is no way to alter the second bracketed expression in the last line of [4.51-V]. Moreover,

$$\begin{aligned}\mathrm{Var}(\mathbf{Y}) - \frac{\mathrm{Cov}(\mathbf{X},\mathbf{Y})^2}{\mathrm{Var}(\mathbf{X})} &= \mathrm{Var}(\mathbf{Y}) - \frac{\sigma_{\mathbf{X}}^2\sigma_{\mathbf{Y}}^2\mathrm{r}_{\mathbf{XY}}^2}{\mathrm{Var}(\mathbf{X})} \\ &= \sigma_{\mathbf{Y}}^2 - \sigma_{\mathbf{Y}}^2\mathrm{r}_{\mathbf{XY}}^2 = \sigma_{\mathbf{Y}}^2(1 - \mathrm{r}_{\mathbf{XY}}^2)\ .\end{aligned}$$

Hence

[4.53] $$\mathrm{Var}(\mathbf{e_Y}) \geqslant \sigma^2_{\mathbf{Y}}(1 - \mathrm{r}^2_{\mathbf{XY}}) \qquad (\mathbf{e_Y} = \mathbf{Y} - a\mathbf{X} - b)\ ,$$

and

[4.54] $$\mathrm{SE}_{\mathbf{Y.X}}[\hat{\mathbf{Y}} = a\mathbf{X} + b] \geqslant \sigma_{\mathbf{Y}}\sqrt{1 - \mathrm{r}^2_{\mathbf{XY}}}\ ,$$

with equality holding when a and b are optimally chosen. We shall have much to say about this minimal residual error later.

Let us introduce the symbol "$\dot{Y}_{i(\mathbf{X})}$" to designate the value of **Y** predicted for individual i from his score on **X** by the linear regression of **Y** on **X** in P—i.e.,

[4.55] $$\dot{Y}_{i(\mathbf{X})} =_{\mathrm{def}} aX_i + b \qquad (\mathrm{SE}_{\mathbf{Y,X}}[\hat{Y}_i = aX_i + b] = \textit{minimum})\ ,$$

or in composition notation,

[4.55*a*] $$\dot{\mathbf{Y}}_{(\mathbf{X})} =_{\mathrm{def}} a\mathbf{X} + b \qquad (\mathrm{SE}_{\mathbf{Y,X}}[\hat{\mathbf{Y}} = a\mathbf{X} + b] = \textit{minimum})\ .$$

That is, $\dot{Y}_{i(\mathbf{X})}$ is the best linear estimate of Y_i, given X_i, in P. Then from [4.52], the formula for the linear regression of **Y** on **X** in P is

[4.56] $$\dot{Y}_{i(\mathbf{X})} = \frac{\mathrm{Cov}(\mathbf{X,Y})}{\mathrm{Var}(\mathbf{X})} X_i + \mathrm{M}_{\mathbf{Y}} - \frac{\mathrm{Cov}(\mathbf{X,Y})}{\mathrm{Var}(\mathbf{X})} \mathrm{M}_{\mathbf{X}}$$
$$= \mathrm{r}_{\mathbf{XY}} \frac{\sigma_{\mathbf{Y}}}{\sigma_{\mathbf{X}}} X_i + \mathrm{M}_{\mathbf{Y}} - \mathrm{r}_{\mathbf{XY}} \frac{\sigma_{\mathbf{Y}}}{\sigma_{\mathbf{X}}} \mathrm{M}_{\mathbf{X}}\ ,$$

or

[4.56*a*] $$\dot{\mathbf{Y}}_{(\mathbf{X})} = \frac{\mathrm{Cov}(\mathbf{X,Y})}{\mathrm{Var}(\mathbf{X})} \mathbf{X} + \mathrm{M}_{\mathbf{Y}} - \frac{\mathrm{Cov}(\mathbf{X,Y})}{\mathrm{Var}(\mathbf{X})} \mathrm{M}_{\mathbf{X}}$$
$$= \mathrm{r}_{\mathbf{XY}} \frac{\sigma_{\mathbf{Y}}}{\sigma_{\mathbf{X}}} \mathbf{X} + \mathrm{M}_{\mathbf{Y}} - \mathrm{r}_{\mathbf{XY}} \frac{\sigma_{\mathbf{Y}}}{\sigma_{\mathbf{X}}} \mathrm{M}_{\mathbf{X}}\ .$$

Now as it stands, equation [4.56] is an esthetic monstrosity with little intuitive meaning—probably one of the most forgetable formulas the reader has encountered in some time. Fortunately, succor is at hand. For a little algebraic reorganization of [4.56] yields

[4.57] $$\frac{\dot{Y}_{i(\mathbf{X})} - \mathrm{M}_{\mathbf{Y}}}{\sigma_{\mathbf{Y}}} = \mathrm{r}_{\mathbf{XY}}\left(\frac{X_i - \mathrm{M}_{\mathbf{X}}}{\sigma_{\mathbf{X}}}\right).$$

But $(X_i - \mathrm{M}_{\mathbf{X}})/\sigma_{\mathbf{X}}$ is simply i's Z-score on **X**, while $(\dot{Y}_{i(\mathbf{X})} - \mathrm{M}_{\mathbf{Y}})/\sigma_{\mathbf{X}}$ is that value on the Z-scale of **Y** which corresponds to i's predicted **Y**-score. Similarly, if **X** and **Y** are first transformed into Z-scores and the linear regression of $\mathbf{Z_Y}$ upon $\mathbf{Z_X}$ is computed from [4.56] by substituting $\dot{Z}_{\mathbf{Y}\,i(\mathbf{X})}$

for $\dot{Y}_{i(\mathbf{X})}$, $Z_{\mathbf{X}i}$ for X_i, and recalling that $M_{Z_\mathbf{X}} = M_{Z_\mathbf{Y}} = 0$, $\sigma_{Z_\mathbf{Y}} = \sigma_{Z_\mathbf{Y}} = 1$, and $r_{Z_\mathbf{X}Z_\mathbf{Y}} = r_{\mathbf{XY}}$, the result is

[4.58]
$$\dot{Z}_{\mathbf{Y}\,i(\mathbf{X})} = r_{\mathbf{XY}} Z_{\mathbf{X}i}$$

or

[4.58*a*]
$$\dot{\mathbf{Z}}_{\mathbf{Y}(\mathbf{X})} = r_{\mathbf{XY}} \mathbf{Z}_{\mathbf{X}} \,.$$

Thus *the best linear estimate of an individual i's Z-score on a variable* **Y**, *based on i's score on variable* **X** *and membership in population P, is simply i's Z-score on* **X** *multiplied times the linear correlation of* **X** *and* **Y** *in P.*[42] (It is to be understood, of course, that the norms for converting **X** and **Y** into Z-scales come from the distributions of **X** and **Y** in *P*.) Then instead of attempting to memorize formula [4.56], the reader need only recall that to convert a score on **X** into the best linear estimate of that individual's score on **Y**, he need merely (1) convert X_i into its Z-score equivalent, (2) multiply by $r_{\mathbf{XY}}$, and (3) convert the resulting estimate of $Z_{\mathbf{Y}i}$ into its equivalent on the original **Y**-scale—or, if preferred, into any other scale of **Y** such as a percentile equivalent.

In Figure 4.3, the linear regression of **Y** upon **X** for the ten cases illustrated is shown by the solid straight line. It is computed in Table 4.3 that $M_\mathbf{X} = 18.10$, $M_\mathbf{Y} = 128.50$, $\sigma_\mathbf{X} = 10.27$, $\sigma_\mathbf{Y} = 66.07$, and $r_{\mathbf{XY}} = .913$ for these data. Therefore, the formula for the linear regression of **Y** upon **X** in this population is

$$\frac{\dot{Y}_{i(\mathbf{X})} - 128.50}{66.07} = .913 \left(\frac{X_i - 18.10}{10.27} \right),$$

or

$$\begin{aligned} \dot{Y}_{i(\mathbf{X})} &= .913 \times \frac{66.07}{10.27} X_i - .913 \times \frac{66.07}{10.27} \times 18.10 + 128.50 \\ &= 5.87 X_i + 22.19.^{43} \end{aligned}$$

The Goodness of Information (Part III). Formula [4.56] or [4.58] shows *what* to predict under the best linear estimate policy, but how accurate are the predictions so made? Let the value, $\dot{Y}_{i(\mathbf{X})}$, of **Y** predicted from X_i for a member *i* of *P* be called *i*'s "linearly regressed" score on

[42] It is highly convenient that, as shown in part by [4.57] and [4.58], the linear regressions of **Y** on **X**, $\mathbf{Z_Y}$ on **X**, **Y** on $\mathbf{Z_X}$, and $\mathbf{Z_Y}$ on $\mathbf{Z_X}$ all yield the same estimate of Y_i, given X_i. This would not be true were not Z-scores linear transformations of the corresponding raw scores.

[43] The slight numerical difference between here and Table 4.4 is due to substitution into $r_{\mathbf{XY}}\ \sigma_\mathbf{Y}/\sigma_\mathbf{X}$ in the one case and into Cov(**X**, **Y**)/ Var(**X**) in the other. While these expressions are mathematically equivalent, rounding-off errors have less effect on the latter than on the former.

Y. Also, let "$\sigma_{\mathbf{Y} \bullet \mathbf{X}}$" designate the quadratic mean discrepancy between true scores and regressed scores on **Y** for members of P. That is,

[4.59]
$$\sigma_{\mathbf{Y} \bullet \mathbf{X}} =_{\text{def}} \sqrt{\frac{\sum_i (Y_i - \dot{Y}_{i(\mathbf{X})})^2}{n}} .$$

(In Figure 4.3, $\sigma_{\mathbf{Y} \bullet \mathbf{X}}$ is the quadratic mean length of the dotted lines from each scattergram point to the regression line.) By definition, then, $\sigma_{\mathbf{Y} \bullet \mathbf{X}}$ is the absolute standard error of **Y**, given **X**, for members of P under optimal linear estimation – i.e.,

[4.60]
$$\text{SE}_{\mathbf{Y},\mathbf{X}}[\hat{\mathbf{Y}} = \dot{\mathbf{Y}}_{(\mathbf{X})}] = \sigma_{\mathbf{Y} \bullet \mathbf{X}}$$

and for any a, b,

[4.61]
$$\sigma_{\mathbf{Y} \bullet \mathbf{X}} \leqslant \text{SE}_{\mathbf{Y},\mathbf{X}}[\hat{\mathbf{Y}} = a\mathbf{X} + b] .$$

For simplicity of expression, $\sigma_{\mathbf{Y} \bullet \mathbf{X}}$ will be called the "(absolute) linear standard error of **Y** (in P), given **X**," though strictly speaking this phrase could be applied to the quadratic mean deviation of **Y** from any given linear function of **X**.

It will be observed that $\sigma_{\mathbf{Y} \bullet \mathbf{X}}$ is essentially like $\sigma_{\mathbf{Y},\mathbf{X}}$ in its definition and interpretation except that whereas $\sigma_{\mathbf{Y},\mathbf{X}}$ is the standard error around the best-fitting line of unrestricted shape, $\sigma_{\mathbf{Y} \bullet \mathbf{X}}$ is the standard error around the best-fitting straight line. It now turns out, through a mathematical benevolence undeserved by sinful man, that the linear correlation between **X** and **Y** in P not only determines the best linear estimates of Z-scores on **Y**, given Z-scores on **X**, in P but also reveals the (absolute) standard error of these estimates. It is an immediate consequence of [4.54] and the definition of $\sigma_{\mathbf{Y} \bullet \mathbf{X}}$ that

[4.62][44]
$$\sigma_{\mathbf{Y} \bullet \mathbf{X}} = \sigma_{\mathbf{Y}} \sqrt{1 - \text{r}^2_{\mathbf{XY}}} .$$

Hence to compute how far wrong the best linear estimates on **Y** for members of P, given their **X**-scores, tend (in the quadratic-mean sense) to be, one need merely multiply the standard deviation of **Y** in P by the factor $\sqrt{1 - \text{r}^2_{\mathbf{XY}}}$.

If the value of **Y** had to be predicted for a member of P *without* knowledge of his score on **X**, the best (utility-free) estimate based only on membership in P would, as seen earlier, be the mean value of **Y** in P; and in this case the standard error of estimate would be $\sigma_{\mathbf{Y}}$. The predictions so

[44] Note that this formula is *not* symmetric in **X** and **Y**. That is, the linear standard error of **Y**, given **X**, in P will generally differ from the linear standard error of **X**, given **Y**, in P. (*Study question:* What is the necessary and sufficient condition for $\sigma_{\mathbf{Y} \bullet \mathbf{X}} = \sigma_{\mathbf{X} \bullet \mathbf{Y}}$?)

made, for comparison to those made when knowledge on **X** *is* available, may be shown on a scattergram of **X** and **Y** in P by the horizontal line $\hat{Y}_i = M_Y$ (see Figure 4.5), where the vertical distances of the scattergram points from this line are then the estimate errors whose quadratic mean equals σ_Y. It will be seen by comparison of Figures 4.3 and 4.5 that while some of the predictions $\hat{Y}_i = M_Y$ made when scores on **X** are not known are actually more accurate than the corresponding prediction $\hat{Y}_i = \dot{Y}_{i(X)}$ based on X_i, the estimate errors in the latter case are *on the whole* much smaller than when the prediction does use this information. Clearly, since $\hat{Y}_i = M_Y$ was one of the alternatives available when solving for the linear regression line, the absolute standard error of **Y**, given **X**, under optimal linear prediction must be at least as small as the standard error of **Y** when **X** is *not* given, and will be smaller than the latter unless $\dot{Y}_{i(X)} = M_Y$ for all i. The proof of

$$[4.63] \qquad \sigma_{Y \cdot X} \leq \sigma_Y$$

follows from [4.61] by taking $a = 0$ and $b = M_Y$, while the special condition under which $\dot{\mathbf{Y}}_{(X)} = M_Y$ may be seen from [4.56] to be $r_{XY} = 0$.[45]

The (absolute) linear standard error of **Y**, given **X**, when expressed

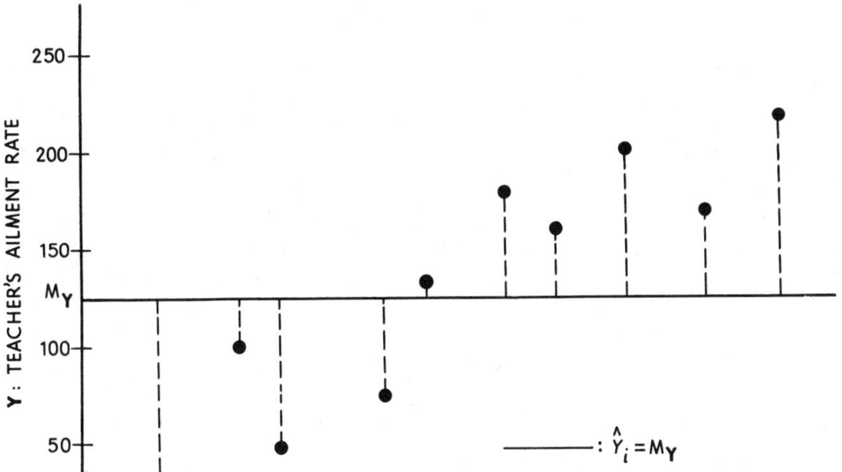

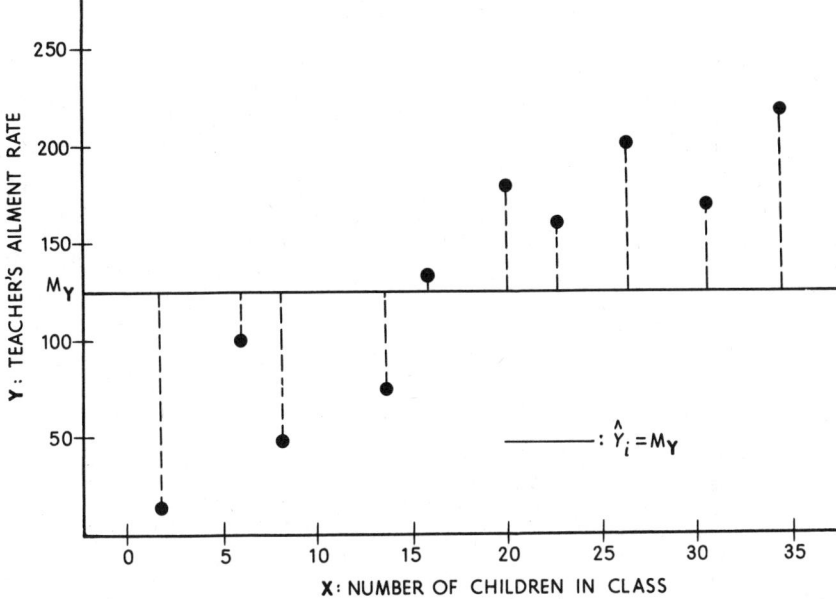

Figure 4.5. Data of Figure 4.3, showing magnitudes of estimate errors when knowledge of scores on **X** is not available. In this case, the best estimate on **Y** for a member of this population is the mean of **Y** therein, a policy which may be shown on the scattergram by a horizontal line through M_Y.

[45] It should be intuitively evident that another necessary and sufficient condition for $\dot{\mathbf{Y}}_{(X)} = M_Y$ is $\sigma_{Y \cdot X} = \sigma_Y$.

as a proportion of $\sigma_{\mathbf{Y}}$, is known as the *linear coefficient of alienation* and is symbolized "$k_{\mathbf{XY}}$." That is,

$$k_{\mathbf{XY}} =_{\text{def}} \frac{\sigma_{\mathbf{Y \cdot X}}}{\sigma_{\mathbf{Y}}}, \tag{4.64}$$

and hence, from [4.62],

$$k_{\mathbf{XY}} = \sqrt{1 - r^2_{\mathbf{XY}}} \tag{4.65}$$

or, more symmetrically,

$$r^2_{\mathbf{XY}} + k^2_{\mathbf{XY}} = 1 . \tag{4.65a}$$

The interpretation of $k_{\mathbf{XY}}$ for linear estimation is precisely the same as that of $\kappa_{\mathbf{Y,X}}$ for unrestricted curvilinear prediction: In both cases the coefficient of alienation tells what proportion of the original standard error of estimate remains after scores on the predictor variable become available as an additional source of information on which to base the prediction.[46]

Just as the linear coefficient of alienation bears a close functional similarity to the curvilinear coefficient of alienation in that they each describe how tightly the points in the joint distribution cluster around a certain regression line, so does the linear correlation coefficient $r_{\mathbf{XY}}$ correspond – almost – to the correlation ratio $\eta_{\mathbf{Y,X}}$. In fact, it should be apparent to one who has grasped the essentials of this chapter so far that if the curvilinear and linear regressions of **Y** on **X** in *P* happen to coincide, then

$$k_{\mathbf{XY}} = \kappa_{\mathbf{Y,X}} \qquad \left(\dot{\mathbf{Y}}_{(\mathbf{X})} = M_{\mathbf{Y|X}}\right) \tag{4.66}$$

and

$$|r_{\mathbf{XY}}| = \eta_{\mathbf{Y,X}} \qquad \left(\dot{\mathbf{Y}}_{(\mathbf{X})} = M_{\mathbf{Y|X}}\right) . \tag{4.67}$$

Notice that [4.67] does *not* say that $r_{\mathbf{XY}} = \eta_{\mathbf{Y,X}}$ in all cases where linear and curvilinear regressions coincide. The only direct significance of $\eta_{\mathbf{Y,X}}$ is given by its interpretation as a ratio of standard deviations (cf. [4.26]), and it is allowed to take only positive values. On the other hand, the primary meaning of $r_{\mathbf{XY}}$ is in terms of the slope of the linear regression line (cf. [4.58]), and $r_{\mathbf{XY}}$ is negative whenever the regression slants downward. That is, it is the *magnitude* of $r_{\mathbf{XY}}$ which corresponds to $\eta_{\mathbf{Y,X}}$, while in addition, the sign of $r_{\mathbf{XY}}$ shows whether values of **Y** tend to increase or to decrease with increasing values of **X**. (Of course, if $r_{\mathbf{XY}} = 0$, then there is no consistent direction in which **Y** tends to change as **X** changes.)

---

[46] The coefficient of alienation is frequently described as stating the extent to which predictions about **Y** based on **X** are better than chance guessing. However, the standard deviation of **Y** in *P*, to which $k_{\mathbf{XY}}$ compares $\sigma_{\mathbf{Y \cdot X}}$, is the standard error of **Y** under *optimal* utility-free strategy when membership in *P* is all that is given, and is smaller than the standard error would be under any procedure that could reasonably be called a blind "guess."

Still another way in which $\mathbf{r}_{\mathbf{XY}}$ and $\eta_{\mathbf{Y},\mathbf{X}}$ (and similarly $\mathbf{k}_{\mathbf{XY}}$ and $\kappa_{\mathbf{Y},\mathbf{X}}$) differ is that in contrast to the mathematical equivalence of $\mathbf{r}_{\mathbf{XY}}$ and $\mathbf{r}_{\mathbf{YX}}$, it is *not* always the case that $\eta_{\mathbf{Y},\mathbf{X}} = \eta_{\mathbf{X},\mathbf{Y}}$. An illustration of this will be given later.

Apart from the differences noted, however, the parallel between the concepts and equations for curvilinear regression and those for linear regression is profound, including the partition of total variance into controlled and residual components. Let $e_{\mathbf{Y}i\bullet\mathbf{X}}$ be the "linear residual," or error score on **Y** for an individual i under linear estimation of Y_i, given X_i, in P–i.e.,

[4.68] $$e_{\mathbf{Y}i\bullet\mathbf{X}} =_{\text{def}} Y_i - \dot{Y}_{i(\mathbf{X})}$$

or more succinctly,

[4.68*a*] $$\mathbf{e}_{\mathbf{Y}\bullet\mathbf{X}} =_{\text{def}} \mathbf{Y} - \dot{\mathbf{Y}}_{(\mathbf{X})} \ .$$

Then by definition, the **Y**-score of a member of P can be written as the sum of two components, his linearly regressed score on **Y** and his linear residual on **Y**. That is, from [4.68],

[4.69] $$Y_i = \dot{Y}_{i(\mathbf{X})} + e_{\mathbf{Y}i\bullet\mathbf{X}}$$

or equivalently,

[4.69*a*] $$\mathbf{Y} = \dot{\mathbf{Y}}_{(\mathbf{X})} + \mathbf{e}_{\mathbf{Y}\bullet\mathbf{X}} \cdot$$

Now, one step in solving for the linear regression line (cf. p. 109) was demonstration that

[4.70] $$\mathrm{M}_{\mathbf{e}_{\mathbf{Y}\cdot\mathbf{X}}} = 0 \ .$$

Hence, recalling [4.59],

[4.71] $$\sigma_{\mathbf{e}_{\mathbf{Y}\cdot\mathbf{X}}} = \sqrt{\frac{\sum_i e^2_{\mathbf{Y}i\bullet\mathbf{X}}}{n} - \mathrm{M}^2_{\mathbf{e}_{\mathbf{Y}\cdot\mathbf{X}}}}$$

$$= \sqrt{\frac{\sum_i (Y_i - \dot{Y}_{i(\mathbf{X})})^2}{n}}$$

$$= \sigma_{\mathbf{Y}\bullet\mathbf{X}} \cdot$$

Moreover, from [4.56] by recalling the effect of a linear transformation on a standard deviation,

[4.72] $$\sigma_{\dot{\mathbf{Y}}_{(\mathbf{X})}} = |\mathbf{r}_{\mathbf{XY}}| \ \sigma_{\mathbf{Y}} \ ,$$

or

[4.72*a*] $$|\mathbf{r}_{\mathbf{XY}}| = \frac{\sigma_{\dot{\mathbf{Y}}(\mathbf{X})}}{\sigma_{\mathbf{Y}}} \ .$$

Squaring [4.64] and [4.72*a*], substituting into [4.65*a*], and multiplying through by $\sigma_{\mathbf{Y}}$ yields

[4.73]
$$\sigma^2_{\mathbf{Y}} = \sigma^2_{\dot{\mathbf{Y}}_{(\mathbf{X})}} + \sigma^2_{\mathbf{Y}\bullet\mathbf{X}}$$
$$= \sigma^2_{\dot{\mathbf{Y}}_{(\mathbf{X})}} + \sigma^2_{\mathbf{e}_{\mathbf{Y}\bullet\mathbf{X}}}\,.$$

Thus we see that the total variance of **Y** in P can be broken into two additive components corresponding to the two components of the individual **Y**-scores under linear regression: (1) the *controlled* or *accounted-for variance* $\sigma^2_{\dot{\mathbf{Y}}_{(\mathbf{X})}}$ (i.e., $\mathrm{Var}(\dot{\mathbf{Y}}_{(\mathbf{X})})$, which is the variance of the linearly regressed **Y**-scores, and (2) the *error* or *residual variance* $\sigma^2_{\mathbf{e}_{\mathbf{X}\bullet\mathbf{Y}}}$ (i.e., Var $(\mathbf{e}_{\mathbf{Y}\bullet\mathbf{X}})$),which is the variance of the linear **Y**-residuals and which is also equal to $\sigma^2_{\mathbf{Y}\bullet\mathbf{X}}$, the square of the (absolute) standard error of **Y** given **X** in P under optimal linear prediction. Moreover, by [4.64] and [4.72*a*], $\mathrm{k}^2_{\mathbf{XY}}$ is the proportion of $\sigma^2_{\mathbf{Y}}$ which is error variance while $\mathrm{r}^2_{\mathbf{XY}}$ is the proportion of $\sigma^2_{\mathbf{Y}}$ which is accounted for by the predictor variable.

In order to supplement this algebraic analysis of linear regression with a numerical example, the data in Figure 4.3 are reproduced quantitatively in Table 4.4. The reader should make sure he sees clearly how each predictor score X_i is converted into an estimate $\dot{Y}_{i(\mathbf{X})}$ of the criterion, how each of these estimates is a certain extent $e_{\mathbf{Y}_i\bullet\mathbf{X}}$ in error, and how these estimate errors are smelted down into a single number $\sigma_{\mathbf{Y}\bullet\mathbf{X}}$ which then represents how large on the whole these errors tend to be. Also observe how $\sigma_{\mathbf{Y}}$ similarly represents the overall magnitude of estimate error under optimal (utility-free) prediction when Y_i is estimated solely on the basis of i's membership in P, and reflect on how $\mathrm{k}_{\mathbf{XY}}$ compares $\sigma_{\mathbf{Y}\bullet\mathbf{X}}$ with $\sigma_{\mathbf{Y}}$ to indicate the extent to which knowledge of scores on **X** increases the accuracy with which scores on **Y** can be predicted for members of P. (The ambitious student will also find it instructive to compare the numerical value of $\mathrm{k}_{\mathbf{XY}}$ with that of the ratio of the average magnitude of estimate error, given **X**, to the average deviation of **Y**—i.e., the ratio of

$$\frac{\sum_i |e_{\mathbf{Y}_i\bullet\mathbf{X}}|}{n} \quad \text{to} \quad \frac{\sum_i |Y_i - \mathrm{M}_{\mathbf{Y}}|}{n}\,.$$

How do you account for their marked similarity, and why is there any difference at all?[47]) It should also be verified that the formulas $\mathrm{M}_{\mathbf{e}_{\mathbf{Y}\bullet\mathbf{X}}} = 0$, $\sigma_{\dot{\mathbf{Y}}_{(\mathbf{X})}} = |\mathrm{r}_{\mathbf{XY}}|\sigma_{\mathbf{Y}}$, and $\sigma^2_{\mathbf{Y}} = \sigma^2_{\dot{\mathbf{Y}}_{(\mathbf{X})}} + \sigma^2_{\mathbf{Y}\bullet\mathbf{X}}$ do, in fact, hold within the limits of rounding-off errors for these data.

The Interpretation of $\mathrm{r}_{\mathbf{XY}}$***: A Summary.*** It should be apparent from the preceeding sections that $\mathrm{r}_{\mathbf{XY}}$ is a highly informative, indeed garrulous,

[47] See fn. 32, p. 92.

statistic. The linear correlation coefficient has at least four distinct major interpretations: (1) First of all, as shown in [4.56] and [4.58], r_{XY} is the major determinant of the linear regression of **Y** on **X** in P. In particular, when $\sigma_X = \sigma_Y$, r_{XY} is the slope of the regression line, though if **X** and **Y** are unequal in variability, r_{XY} must be multiplied by σ_Y/σ_X to get the regression slope. (2) Moreover, r_{XY} also reveals how accurately the regression line approximates the actual **Y**-scores, since as seen from [4.62] by letting $\sigma_Y = 1$, the standard (i.e., quadratic mean) discrepancy between actual and regressed Z-scores on **Y** in P is $\sqrt{1 - r^2_{XY}}$. It is this second interpretation of the linear correlation coefficient which, in the scant century it has been known, has made it the pampered darling of the behavioral sciences, for it provides a measure of the degree to which a welter of raw data can be reduced to a lawful linear pattern.[48] (3) Another way to assess the degree to which linearly regressed scores $\dot{Y}_{i(X)}$ approximate the actual scores Y_i is to determine the correlation between $\dot{\mathbf{Y}}_{(X)}$ and **Y**.[49] Since $\mathrm{Cov}(\mathbf{Z}_Y, \dot{\mathbf{Z}}_{Y(X)}) = r^2_{XY}$ (from [4.58*a*] by [4.38] and $\sigma_{\dot{Z}_Y(X)} = |r_{XY}|$ (from [4.58*a*]), we see that $r_{Y\dot{Y}(X)} = |r_{XY}|$—i.e., the correlation between the **Y**-scores linearly predicted from **X** and actual scores on **Y** is equal to the magnitude of r_{XY}. (4) Finally, it has been pointed out ([4.72]) that the magnitude of r_{XY} is also the standard deviation of the **Y**-scores linearly predicted from **X**, expressed as a proportion of the SD of actual **Y**-scores. This is particularly interesting in that when actual scores on **Y** are analyzed as a sum of two uncorrelated[50] components, linearly regressed score plus residual, the variance of **Y** also analyzes as a sum of the variances of these components (cf. [4.73]); hence r^2_{XY} is the proportion of the total variance of **Y** in P which is "controlled" in the sense of being contributed by that component of **Y** which is linearly predictable from scores on **X**.

Linear Regression in Bivariate Normal Distributions. Our discussion of the predictive accuracy of linear regression has so far examined only the absolute standard error of **Y**, given **X**. But it was also pointed out earlier that while the absolute standard error of estimate measures the anticipated error in predicting Y_i for a member i of P *before* i's score on the predictor variable has been ascertained, the uncertainty attached to the prediction eventually made from X_i is given by the variability of **Y** only among members of P whose score on **X** equals X_i. That is, since it is the contingent distribution of **Y**, given X_i which is the distribution of po-

---

[48] While a great many measures of the goodness of relationship have been devised, a high proportion of these derive from the linear correlation coefficient.

[49] The logical connection between describing predictive accuracy in terms of (*a*) the standard error of estimate on the one hand, and (*b*) the correlation between actual scores and predicted scores on the other, is discussed on p. 151f.

[50] In view of principle [4.40], it is clear that [4.73] can hold only if $\mathrm{Cov}(\dot{\mathbf{Y}}_{(X)}, \mathbf{e}_{Y\cdot X}) = 0$. This point is covered more thoroughly on p. 140.

X: Number-of-children-in-class **Y**: Teacher's-ailment-rate

$$\left.\begin{array}{l} M_{\mathbf{X}} = 18.10 \; ; \; \sigma_{\mathbf{X}} = 10.27 \; ; \; \text{Cov}\,(\mathbf{X},\mathbf{Y}) = 619.15 \\ M_{\mathbf{Y}} = 128.50 \; ; \; \sigma_{\mathbf{Y}} = 66.07 \; ; \quad r_{\mathbf{XY}} = +.912 \end{array}\right\} \text{From Table 4.3}$$

$$k_{\mathbf{XY}} = \sqrt{1 - r^2_{\mathbf{XY}}} = \sqrt{1 - (.912)^2} = \sqrt{.1683} = .410$$

$$\dot{Y}_{i(\mathbf{X})} = r_{\mathbf{XY}} \frac{\sigma_{\mathbf{Y}}}{\sigma_{\mathbf{X}}} X_i + M_{\mathbf{Y}} - r_{\mathbf{XY}} \frac{\sigma_{\mathbf{Y}}}{\sigma_{\mathbf{X}}} M_{\mathbf{X}} = \frac{\text{Cov}\,(\mathbf{X},\mathbf{Y})}{\text{Var}\,(\mathbf{X})} X_i + M_{\mathbf{Y}} - \frac{\text{Cov}\,(\mathbf{X},\mathbf{Y})}{\text{Var}\,(\mathbf{X})} M_{\mathbf{X}}$$

$$= \frac{619.15}{105.49} X_i + 128.50 - \frac{619.15}{105.49} \times 18.10$$

$$= 5.87 X_i + 22.25$$

Teacher	X_i	Y_i	$\dot{Y}_{i(\mathbf{X})}$	$e_{\mathbf{Y}i\bullet\mathbf{X}}$	$Y_i - M_{\mathbf{Y}}$	$(\dot{Y}_{i(\mathbf{X})} - M_{\mathbf{Y}(\mathbf{X})})^2$	$e^2_{\mathbf{Y}i\bullet\mathbf{X}}$	$(Y_i - M_{\mathbf{Y}})^2$
# 1	2	10	33.99	−23.99	−118.50	8,932.14	575.52	14,042.25
# 2	6	100	57.47	42.53	− 28.50	5,045.26	1,808.80	812.25
# 3	8	45	69.21	−24.21	− 83.50	3,515.30	586.12	6,972.25
# 4	14	70	104.43	−34.43	− 58.50	579.36	1,185.42	3,442.25
# 5	16	135	116.17	18.83	6.5	152.03	354.57	42.25

# 7	25	160	157.26	2.74	31.50	827.14	7.51	992.25
# 8	27	200	180.74	19.26	71.50	2,729.02	370.95	5,112.25
# 9	31	170	204.22	−34.22	41.50	5,733.52	1,171.01	1,722.25
#10	34	220	221.83	− 1.83	91.50	8,710.49	3.35	8,372.25
Σ	181	1,285	1,284.97	.03	0	36,348.58	7,312.87	43,652.50
Σ/n	18.1	128.5	128.50	.00	0	3,634.86 +	731.29 =	4,365.25

$$\frac{\sum_i |e_{\mathbf{Y}i\bullet\mathbf{X}}|}{n} = 23.74 \qquad \frac{\sum_i |Y_i - \mathrm{M}_{\mathbf{X}}|}{n} = 57.80$$

$$\sigma_{\mathbf{Y}\bullet\mathbf{X}} = \sqrt{\frac{\sum_i e^2_{\mathbf{Y}i\bullet\mathbf{X}}}{n}} = \sqrt{731.29} = 27.04$$

$$\sigma_{\dot{\mathbf{Y}}} = \sqrt{\frac{\sum_i (\dot{Y}_{i(\mathbf{X})} - \mathrm{M}_{\dot{\mathbf{Y}}(\mathbf{X})})^2}{n}} = \sqrt{3{,}634.86} = 60.29$$

$$\sigma_{\mathbf{Y}} = \sqrt{\frac{\sum_i (Y_i - \mathrm{M}_{\mathbf{Y}})^2}{n}} = \sqrt{4{,}363.25} = 66.07$$

Table 4.4. Data of Figure 4.3 presented numerically. Column "$\dot{Y}_{i(\mathbf{X})}$" shows the **Y**-score estimated for individual i from his score on X by the linear regression of **Y** upon **X** in this population, while $e_{\mathbf{Y}i\bullet\mathbf{X}}$, the difference between $\dot{Y}_{i(\mathbf{X})}$ and Y_i as shown graphically by the vertical dotted lines in Figure 4.3, is the amount by which this estimate is wrong. The corresponding estimate errors when the general population mean, $\mathrm{M}_{\mathbf{Y}}$, is taken as the estimate of Y_i in each case (see Figure 4.5) are shown in column "$Y_i - \mathrm{M}_{\mathbf{Y}}$." To see how much smaller on the whole the estimate errors are when information about **X** is used than when it is not, we compare the quadratic mean, $\sigma_{\mathbf{Y}\bullet\mathbf{X}}$, of the errors when **X** is given to the quadratic mean, $\sigma_{\mathbf{Y}}$, of the errors when **X** is not given by computing their ratio, $k_{\mathbf{XY}}$. To observe that partitioning the actual scores Y_i into a predicted ("regressed") component $\dot{Y}_{i(\mathbf{X})}$ plus an error term $e_{\mathbf{Y}i\bullet\mathbf{X}}$ also partitions the total variance of **Y** into corresponding "controlled" and "residual" components, note that in the bottom line of the table, the entry in the last column essentially equals the sum of the entries in the preceding two columns. That there is any difference at all is due to the inescapable loss of perfect numerical accuracy in rounding off decimals, even though the figures in the table are carried out further than would have any interpretive significance.

tential **Y**-scores for i *after* X_i has been observed, the quadratic mean magnitude potential prediction error for i is then the contingent standard error of **Y**, given X_i. Hence to describe the potential accuracy of linear prediction when the value of the predictor variable has been observed to be X, we need the *contingent* linear standard error of **Y**, given X, in P—namely, from [4.11],

$$[4.74] \qquad \sigma_{\mathbf{Y}\bullet X} =_{\text{def}} \mathrm{SE}_{\mathbf{Y}|X}[\hat{\mathbf{Y}} = \dot{\mathbf{Y}}_{(\mathbf{X})}]$$

$$= \sqrt{\frac{\sum_i (Y_i - \dot{Y}_{i(\mathbf{X})})^2}{n}} \qquad \left(\begin{matrix} i \text{ ranges over} \\ \text{members of } P_X \end{matrix}\right),$$

and while $\sigma_{\mathbf{Y}\bullet\mathbf{X}}$ will generally be a reasonable approximation to $\sigma_{\mathbf{Y}\bullet X}$ for a given value X of **X**, the two will seldom be identical unless special conditions obtain.

It turns out, however, that these special conditions and more are fulfilled if the bivariate distribution of **X** and **Y** in P is normal. While the mathematical analysis of multivariate normality is somewhat more advanced than we are here prepared to cope with, it can be shown that if the joint distribution of **X** and **Y** is normal in P, then (1) the linear and curvilinear regressions of **Y** on **X** in P coincide, so that $\dot{Y}_{i(\mathbf{X})} = \mathrm{M}_{\mathbf{Y}|X_i}$, $\sigma_{\mathbf{Y}\bullet X_i} = \sigma_{\mathbf{Y}|X_i}$, and $\sigma_{\mathbf{Y}\bullet\mathbf{X}} = \sigma_{\mathbf{Y}\cdot\mathbf{X}}$; (2) the contingent distributions of **Y**, given **X**, in P are homoscedastic, so that $\sigma_{\mathbf{Y}|X_i} = \sigma_{\mathbf{Y}.\mathbf{X}}$; and (3) the contingent distributions of **Y**, given **X**, in P are all normal in shape, as are also the marginal distributions of **X** and **Y**. Combining (1) and (2) while recalling [4.19] and [4.62], it further follows that $\sigma_{\mathbf{Y}|X_i} = \sigma_{\mathbf{Y}}\sqrt{1 - \mathrm{r}^2_{\mathbf{XY}}}$. In short, *when the joint distribution of* **X** *and* **Y** *in P is normal, the potential values of* **Y** *for an individual i, about whom the only usable information is his membership in P and his score on* **X**, *are normally distributed with a standard deviation of* $\sigma_{\mathbf{Y}}\sqrt{1 - \mathrm{r}^2_{\mathbf{XY}}}$ *around a mean which is* $\mathrm{r}_{\mathbf{XY}} Z_{\mathbf{X}i}$ $\sigma_{\mathbf{Y}}$-*units above* $\mathrm{M}_{\mathbf{Y}}$. In other words, once $\mathrm{r}_{\mathbf{XY}}$ is known in this case, along with the means and SDs of **X** and **Y**, the unrestricted best estimate of Y_i, given X_i, for a member i of P, together with the standard error of this estimate, can be computed by the simple formulas for linear regression, while confidence intervals can be derived from $\dot{Y}_{i(\mathbf{X})}$ and $\sigma_{\mathbf{Y}\bullet\mathbf{X}}$ in accord with the relationships which hold for a normal distribution.

For example, suppose that as president of the Great Northern Frostbite Insurance Company, you are understandably concerned about the excessively high claims rates on the policies written by some of your field agents. Despite your company's training program to teach agents how to distinguish good risks from bad, some of your new agents are losing the company so much money during their first year of operation that the company faces bankruptcy unless some way is found to eliminate the unsuccessful agents before their incompetence has a chance to be demonstrated in practice. A consulting psychometrist has recommended that his new test, the Frostbite Hazard Avoidance Aptitude Detector (known professionally as the FHAAD) be used for this purpose, and to judge its effectiveness, your research staff has administered it to a large sample of field-agency applicants who are then trained, commissioned, and evaluated at the end of their first year for the net profit each has earned for the company. It is discovered, let us say, that the average net profit earned for the company by an unselected applicant during his first year (a variable which we may abbreviate as "Company-profit") is −$1,000 (i.e., a loss of $1,000) with a standard deviation of $2,000, that FHAAD scores in this group have been standardized to a mean of 50 and SD of 10, and that the joint distribution of Company-profit and FHAAD scores is normal with a linear correlation between test scores and Company-profit of +.60. It will be shown later that this suffices for the FHAAD to be used as a screening device to secure your company's solvency. At the moment, however, we merely wish to examine how—and how well—a prospective field agent's first-year Company-profit can be predicted, via these statistics, from his FHAAD score.

Suppose that Henry Jones applies to your company for permission to sell your insurance. Jones then belongs to that population within which you have learned the joint distribution of Company-profit and FHAAD scores, and for want of additional usable information about Jones which would place him in a more restricted population, you hence conclude that the bivariate probability distribution of Company-profit and prospective FHAAD score for Jones is normal, with expected values on Company-profit and the FHAAD of −$1,000 and 50, respectively, with corresponding SDs of $2,000 and 10, and with a linear correlation between the two variables of +.60. Before testing Jones, your best estimate of how much net profit he would earn for the company his first year if accepted as an agent is thus −$1,000—i.e., a prediction that he would lose money for the company. On the other hand, the standard error of this pretest prediction is $2,000, so despite the unfavorable best estimate, there still remains a probability of 31% that Jones would earn a first-year profit for the company.[51] With no further information to go on, you would then either have to grant Jones an agency in wistful hope that he will turn out to be the one applicant in three who makes good his first year, or reject his application in view of the more realistic appraisal that he can be expected to lose $1,000 of company funds his first year. But suppose that Jones takes the FHAAD and comes up with a score of 70. You now have

[51] Since the joint probability distribution of Company-profit and FHAAD score for Jones is normal, the marginal probabilities of Company-profit are also distributed normally for him with a mean of −$1,000 and SD of $2,000 as given. The probability that Jones will finish his first year in the black for the company is hence that proportion of this distribution which lies above $0, a point which is .5 sigmas above the mean and has a percentile equivalent of 69.

further usable information about Jones, and the distribution of his potential first-year net earnings for the company collapses to the distribution of Company-profit among only those applicants who obtain a FHAAD score of 70. To determine what this distribution is, you observe first of all that since Jones's test score is two SDs above the mean, the best linear estimate (cf. [4.58]) of his first-year net earnings for the company places him at $+.6 \times 2.0 = 1.2$ SDs from the mean on Company-profit, or $1.2 \times \$2{,}000 + (-\$1{,}000) = \$1{,}400$. Since the joint distribution of FHAAD scores and Company-profit is normal, so that linear and curvilinear best estimates coincide, the first-year profit which Jones is statistically expected to earn for the company is then $1,400. Moreover, since the contingent standard deviation of Company-profit, given a FHAAD score of 70, is in this bivariate-normal case equal to the absolute linear standard error of Company-profit, given FHAAD score, among all applicants, it follows from [4.62] that the standard error of this estimate is $\$2{,}000 \times \sqrt{1 - .60^2}$, or $1,600. Combining this measure of predictive uncertainty with the expected Company-profit for an applicant with a FHAAD score of 70 and the normality of the contingent distributions when the joint distribution is normal, you are then able to conclude that the probability distribution for Jones's potential first-year net earnings for the company is normal with a mean of $1,400 and a SD of $1,600. From this, in turn, it follows that the probability is now 81% (i.e., the area of a normal distribution above a Z-score of $(0 - 1{,}400)/1{,}600$, or $-.875$) that Jones would make money for the company his first year—an appreciable improvement over the 31% chance your information gave him prior to obtaining his FHAAD score.

In similar fashion, the FHAAD score of any other applicant can be used to reduce your uncertainty about his first-year success.[52] Thus if Elmer Smith, who applied with Jones, and who would have seemed equally as good a prospect had not FHAAD scores been available, received a test score of 40, your best estimate of Smith's first-year benefit to the company would be a net loss of $2,200, the standard error of the estimate again being $1,600, and giving Smith, in marked contrast to Jones, only an 8% chance of finishing his first year with a net profit for the company. Moreover, even if a third applicant, Adam Doaks, received a FHAAD score of 50, so that your best estimate of his first year's net company profit is −$1,000, the same as the estimate you would have made without knowledge of his test score, the standard error of the estimate has been reduced (i.e., $1,600 in place of $2,000), so you have more confidence in the accuracy of this estimate—e.g., you now give Doaks only a 27% chance, in contrast to the pretest 31%, of benefiting the company his first year.

[52] The reader should work out the computations implied in this paragraph as an exercise to insure his grasp of the principles involved.

Comments and Cautions

The theory of regression, even in the simplest linear case with one predictor variable, provides a dazzlingly rich lode of statistical resources with which to enhance our understanding and mastery of the world about us—accompanied, unfortunately, by an industriously mined subsidiary vein of potential misinterpretations and misapplications. This section is a repository of sundry miscellaneous comments which may aid the reader to move more deftly through this bright new methodological world which, let us hope, is now opening before him.

Predictive Efficiency and the Size of the Correlation Coefficient. One of the more common misinterpretations of r_{XY} made by persons who have seen this statistic used as a measure of predictive accuracy but who have not studied its definition is to construe r_{XY} as a percentage of correct estimates. By now, of course, the reader is aware that r_{XY} is no such thing, but rather, that it reveals the extent to which knowledge of the predictor variable decreases the magnitude of estimate errors over the magnitude of errors made when this information is not used. What the reader may not as yet have paused to reflect upon, however, is the nonlinearity of the relationship between the size of r_{XY} and the amount of error reduction. Since the extremes to which r_{XY} can vary in magnitude are 0 and 1, with the latter representing perfect linear predictability, it is easy to assume, without giving the matter much thought, that a correlation of .50 should be half as good as a correlation of 1.00, and that the difference in predictive efficiency between, say, $r_{XY} = .25$ and $r_{XY} = .30$ is the same as the difference between $r_{XY} = .75$ and $r_{XY} = .80$. But this intuitive reasoning is fallacious, for it overlooks that it is not r_{XY}, but k_{XY}—the coefficient of alienation—which most directly describes the reduction in estimate error accomplished through knowledge of the predictor variable.[53] Since k_{XY} is the ratio of the (absolute) standard error of **Y** given **X** to the standard error of **Y** *not* given **X**, the quantity $1 - k_{XY}$,[54] which from [4.65] equals $1 - \sqrt{1 - r^2_{XY}}$, is the proportion by which knowledge of **X** reduces the standard error of **Y**; and as shown in Figure 4.6, r_{XY} must attain deplorably large values before this reduction becomes appreciable. Thus $r_{XY} = .50$ signifies only a 13% reduction in the standard error of estimate, while for the predictor variable to halve the standard error a correlation of .87 is necessary. Even when $r_{XY} = .990$, the estimate errors, given scores on the predictor variable, are still 14% as large, on the whole, as they are without the predictor data. High pre-

[53] Of course, if a nonlinear prediction policy is used, then it is not k_{XY} but the coefficient of alienation around that nonlinear regression line which is the measure of predictive accuracy. In this section, we shall be concerned essentially with linear prediction, and it will be a useful exercise for the reader to determine for himself the extent to which these comments also apply to the nonlinear case.

[54] The quantity $1 - k_{XY}$ is sometimes called the *index of forecasting efficiency.*

dictive accuracy is something ardently sought but seldom attained, and the reader should hold himself keenly aware of the relationship between r_{XY} and k_{XY} on such occasions as he may have practical recourse to methods of assessment and prediction whose "validity" (i.e., correlation with the criterion variable—see Chapter 5) is appreciably less than unity.

On the other hand, just as the reader must guard against simple-minded credulity over the accuracy of estimates yielded by predictor variables whose correlation with the criterion falls short of the high .90s, so must he also avoid falling into excessive scepticism about the pragmatic worth of imperfect predictors. For while the standard error of estimate has been chosen, for thoroughly respectable reasons, to be our measure of predictive *accuracy*, the *usefulness* of this accuracy is also a function of the utilities involved. Thus in the personnel problem discussed earlier, while the validity of the FHAAD test is a mere .60 and is hence able to reduce the standard error for estimating a prospective field agent's first-year net Company-profit by only 20%, this is still

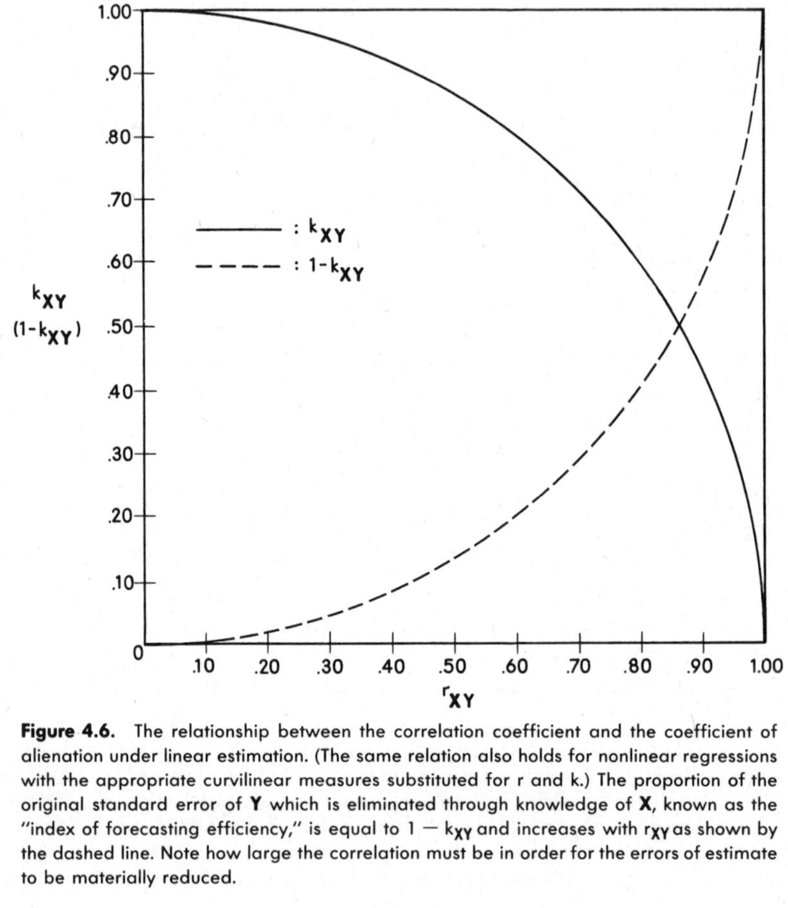

Figure 4.6. The relationship between the correlation coefficient and the coefficient of alienation under linear estimation. (The same relation also holds for nonlinear regressions with the appropriate curvilinear measures substituted for r and k.) The proportion of the original standard error of **Y** which is eliminated through knowledge of **X**, known as the "index of forecasting efficiency," is equal to $1 - k_{XY}$ and increases with r_{XY} as shown by the dashed line. Note how large the correlation must be in order for the errors of estimate to be materially reduced.

enough to save the Great Northern Frostbite Insurance Company from bankruptcy if applicants for field agencies are sufficiently numerous. For if the distribution of FHAAD scores (**X**) and first-year Company-profit (**Y**) among unselected applicants is normal with nonzero correlation, then this test can be used as a screening device to accept only applicants whose prospects are as bright as we choose to stipulate. Suppose, for example, that as president of Great Northern, you decide that for an applicant to be acceptable, you must be able to give him at least a 50% chance of earning some profit for the company his first year. This is the same as deciding that the median of the contingent distribution of potential Company-profit for an acceptable applicant, given his FHAAD score, must be greater than zero. Further, in view of the known statistics about the joint distribution of Company-profit and FHAAD scores among unselected applicants (namely, bivariate normality, $M_{\mathbf{Y}} = -1{,}000$, $\sigma_{\mathbf{Y}} = 2{,}000$, $M_{\mathbf{X}} = 50$, $\sigma_{\mathbf{X}} = 10$, and $r_{\mathbf{XY}} = .60$), you can solve for a cutoff score on the FHAAD which will pass only acceptable applicants as follows: (1) At least 50% of an applicant's *i*'s probability distribution on Company-profit, given his FHAAD score, will lie above 0 if and only if the best linear estimate, $\dot{Y}_{i(\mathbf{X})}$, of his Company-profit score is also above 0. (This follows from the normality of the contingent distributions and the coincidence of linear and curvilinear regressions of **Y** upon **X**.) (2) Since a Company-profit score over 0 is over $[0 - (-1{,}000)]/2{,}000 = .5\ \sigma_{\mathbf{Y}}$-units above the mean Company-profit, $\dot{Y}_{i(\mathbf{X})}$ will be greater than 0 if and only if $\dot{Z}_{\mathbf{Y}\,i(\mathbf{X})} > .5$ – a condition which, in turn, corresponds to $r_{\mathbf{XY}} Z_{\mathbf{X}i} > .5$. Substituting .60 for $r_{\mathbf{XY}}$ and solving for $Z_{\mathbf{X}i}$ then shows that *i*'s FHAAD score gives him a 50% or greater chance of finishing his first year in the black for the company if and only if $Z_{\mathbf{X}i} > .833$. (3) Finally, since a Z-score on **X** greater than .833 corresponds in this case to a FHAAD score greater than $50 + 10(.833) = 58.3$, this score is then a cutoff such that if applicants with FHAAD scores of 58.3 or lower are rejected, only those applicants remain whose FHAAD scores give them at least a 50% chance of earning money for the company their first year.[55]

The line of reasoning followed here is illustrated in Figure 4.7 for a somewhat more complicated demand on anticipated success. Suppose that you wish to accept only applicants who, on the basis of their FHAAD scores, are given at least a 75% chance of earning a Company-profit of $1,000 or more their first year. Since the contingent distributions of **Y** (Company-profit), given **X** (FHAAD), are normal, an applicant *i* is then acceptable if and only if the contingent distribution of **Y** among appli-

[55] Notice, moreover, that since accepted applicants whose FHAAD scores are higher than this minimal passing score will have a probability even higher than the minimal 50% of making good their first year, enforcement of the FHAAD as a screening procedure with this cutoff point would result in a distribution of net company profits from first-year agents with a mean appreciably above zero.

cants whose FHAAD score is X_i has its mean, $M_{Y|X_i}$, more than .674 $\sigma_{Y|X_i}$-units above 1,000. From the data previously stipulated for the joint distribution of **X** and **Y** in this population, it also follows that $\sigma_{Y|X_i} = \sigma_Y\sqrt{1 - r^2_{XY}} = .8\sigma_Y$, while the criterion score of 1,000 which you have set as the acceptability threshold is 1.0 σ_Y-units above M_Y. Hence X_i is an acceptable score if and only if $M_{Y|X_i}$ is more than $1.0 + .8(.674) = 1.539$ σ_Y-units above M_Y. Since also

$$\frac{M_{Y|X_i} - M_Y}{\sigma_Y} = \frac{\dot{Y}_{i\,(X)} - M_Y}{\sigma_Y} = r_{XY}\frac{X_i - M_X}{\sigma_X}$$

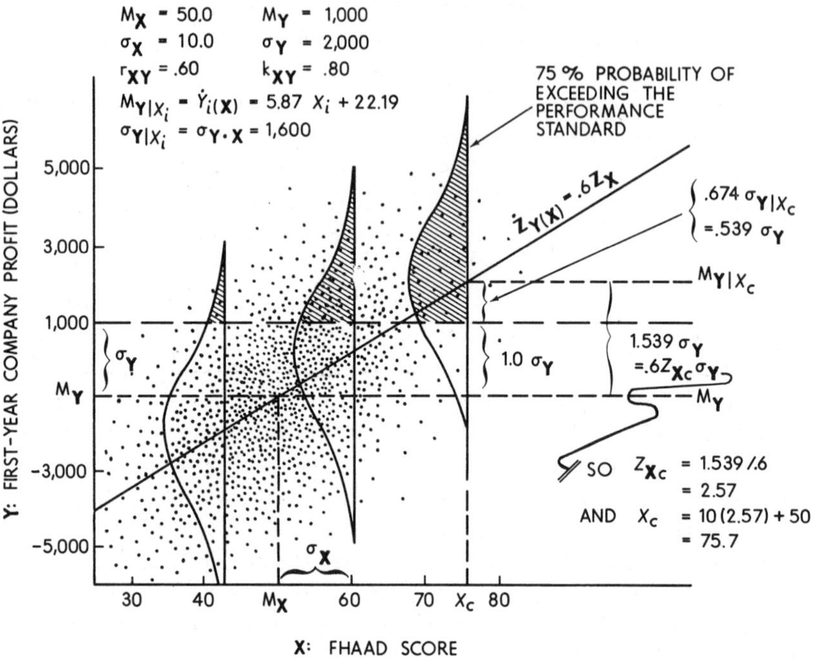

Figure 4.7. Scattergram of FHAAD scores (**X**) and net Company-profit (**Y**) earned the first year of operation for 1,000 unselected field agents of the Great Northern Frostbite Insurance Company. The scattergram points are distributed in close accord with a bivariate normal density, and the joint probability distribution if F-score and Company-profit may hence be assumed to be approximately normal with means, SDs and correlation as given. The contingent probability distributions of Company-profit, given FHAAD score, are shown at three places by the normal curves sketched on the graph. These should be imagined as rotated around their bases to stand perpendicular to the plane of the page. To find a cutoff score X_c such that an applicant with a FHAAD score of X_c or over has at least a 75% chance of exceeding \$1,000 Company-profit his first year, observe first of all that since 75% of a normal distribution falls above .674 SDs below its mean, the mean of the contingent distribution of **Y** at X_c lies at .674 $\sigma_{Y|X_c}$-units above Y = 1,000—or, since here $\sigma_{Y|X_c} = k_{XY}\sigma_Y = .8\sigma_Y$ and 1,000 is 1.0 σ_Y-units above M_Y, at a Z-score on **Y** of $.8(.674) + 1.0 = 1.539$. Since the means of the contingent distributions of **Y**, given **X**, lie on the linear regression, $\dot{Z}_{Y(X)} = r_{XY}Z_X$, of **Y** upon **X** when the joint distribution of **X** and **Y** is normal, $M_{Y|X_c}$ is 1.539 σ_Y-units above M_Y if and only if $1.539 = .6\,Z_{X_c} = .6(X_c - 50)/10$; so $X_c = 10(1.539)/.6 + 50 = 75.7$.

in the present case, solving for X in $1.539 < .6(X - 50.0)/10$ shows that the FHAAD test gives an applicant at least a 75% chance of earning a first-year net company profit of $1,000 or more if and only if he makes a test score 75.7 or higher.

While the development of screening procedures will run into somewhat more complexities than described here if the regression of the criterion variable on test scores is sufficiently nonlinear, these examples will serve to illustrate that even a predictor variable of low correlation with the criterion can in principle be used to select individuals whose likelihood of exceeding a stipulated performance standard is as high as we desire. (Notice that in the present example, solution for the cutoff score demanded only that $r_{XY} \neq 0$, and could have been carried through for test validities much lower than .60.) The usefulness of a screening instrument, therefore, is not adequately described by its standard error of estimate. On the other hand, it must be confessed that the selection procedure just described has a certain aura of unreality about it. By definition, successful screening entails the rejection of applicants for whom the test *cannot* sufficiently vouchsafe success, and the lower the test's validity, the larger the proportion of would-be-successful applicants who will be discarded (e.g., the cases in Figure 4.7 above $Y = 1{,}000$ and to the left of $X = 75.7$) and the smaller the proportion of applicants whose test performance meets the acceptance requirements. Thus in the present example, in order to guarantee that an accepted applicant has at least a 50% chance of breaking even for the company his first year, it is necessary to reject 80% of applicants (since the cutoff score of 58.3 is .83 sigmas above the mean and the distribution of test scores is normal), while to insure a 75% chance of exceeding a Company-profit score of $1,000, only about five applicants in a thousand can be accepted. In a real-life situation, personnel demands may require the acceptance of more applicants than rigorous enforcement of optimal screening would authorize. But even here the usefulness of an only modestly accurate predictor can make itself felt. Suppose that personnel requirements allow rejection of only *p*% of applicants. Then if the *p*% rejected are those with the lowest scores on the predictor variable, it can be shown that the extent to which the average performance on the criterion expected from the selected applicants is an increase over the average performance expected from the same number of randomly selected applicants is directly proportional to the correlation between predictor and performance variables. In this case, a test whose validity is .50 would yield half the personnel improvement that would be gained through a test with perfect validity.[56] The reader who would like to pursue the utility of testing procedures in personnel procurement more deeply should consult the important work by Cronbach and Gleser (20) on this subject.

[56] See Cronbach and Gleser (20), p. 308. The theorem is originally due to H. E. Brogden.

The Regression Phenomenon. The statistical theory of correlation and regression emerged during the last quarter of the nineteenth century from the genius of two Englishmen, Francis Galton and Karl Pearson. It was Galton who discovered linear regression as an empricial phenomenon and introduced in essence the concepts which describe it, while the statistician Pearson, who became Galton's junior colleague, then developed the mathematical theory that we know today. In his studies of inheritance, Galton observed a curious tendency for the children of exceptional individuals to be less outstanding on the characteristic in question than their parents. Galton's first paper on this phenomenon,[57] for example, reported a bivariate frequency table of the diameters of peas with the diameters of their offspring which exhibited an unmistakable tendency for the daughters of a pea of given diameter to deviate less from the average size than their mother's deviation. Galton subsequently obtained similar results, which he described as a "regression to mediocrity," for a variety of characteristics, the most celebrated being his study of the relationship of the heights of children to that of their parents. Today, with the incisive statistical insights of Pearson at our disposal, Galton's "regression to mediocrity" stands revealed as a mathematical consequence of two elementary biological truths. As was shown earlier (cf. [4.58]), unless two variables show perfect linear agreement, the best linear estimate of one, given a value on the other, will of mathematical necessity be less deviant, in terms of the variables own norms, than is the score from which the estimate is made. Hence since we never find a perfect correlation between the traits of parents and offspring (biological truth No. 1), the (linearly) expected size of a pea's daughters must be fewer daughter-size sigmas from the daughter mean than the parent is parent-size sigmas from the parent mean. Add to this the fact (biological truth No. 2) that the degree of variation in a given biological characteristic does not greatly change from one generation to the next, and the result is Galton's phenomenon. While "regression" in Galton's original sense depends upon stability in the standard deviations, the term has come today to indicate the purely mathematical fact which is so heavily responsible for the empirical findings, namely, that $|\dot{Z}_{\mathbf{Y}\,i(\mathbf{X})}| \leqslant |Z_{\mathbf{X}\,i}|$.

The regression phenomenon is responsible, incidently, for certain prima facie partialities in the allocation of scholastic grades which leave some students quietly grateful for undeserved benevolence and others intransigently convinced that they have been the victim of a most flagrant injustice. Suppose that John and Jim take a certain course in which the final grade is based entirely on two examinations. Jim, an able student, receives a B^+ on each of these exams and resigns himself to an expected B^+ for the semester. John, who pulled down a C^- on the first test, is re-

[57] See Pearson (64).

lieved to discover he also eked out a C⁻ on the second, for obviously—or so it might seem—this assures him of a C⁻ for the course. Imagine, then, the stirrings of surprise and, in one case, wrath when the semester's grade reports give Jim an A⁻ and John a D⁺. Is favoritism or clerical inaccuracy to blame? Not at all. So long as letter grades are assigned on a percentile basis under which B⁺ is above average and C⁻ is below, this is a simple consequence of the regression phenomenon. If scores on the two examinations do not have perfect correlation, students who received a B⁺ or higher on Test 1 will, on the average, not do so well on Test 2 as they did on Test 1. Consequently, by *maintaining* his B⁺ performance, Jim is able to climb in percentile rank on the combined tests. Similarly, students receiving C⁻ or lower on Test 1 will tend to improve on Test 2, so by bucking this trend, John's two C⁻s give him a lower percentile rank on the combined tests than he has on either one separately.

To make this point with precision, let "**X** + **Y**" designate that variable whose valuc for an individual *i* is the sum of *i*'s scores on **X** and **Y** (see p. 101). We know that

[4.75][58]
$$\sigma^2_{\mathbf{X}+\mathbf{Y}} = \sigma^2_{\mathbf{X}} + \sigma^2_{\mathbf{Y}} + 2\ \mathrm{Cov}(\mathbf{X},\mathbf{Y}) = \sigma^2_{\mathbf{X}} + \sigma^2_{\mathbf{Y}} + 2\sigma_{\mathbf{X}}\sigma_{\mathbf{Y}}\mathrm{r}_{\mathbf{XY}}\ ,$$

while from [4.45],

[4.76]
$$\mathrm{M}_{\mathbf{X}+\mathbf{Y}} = \mathrm{M}_{\mathbf{X}} + \mathrm{M}_{\mathbf{Y}}\ .$$

Let **X** and **Y** be the two tests taken by Jim and his classmates, and for simplicity assume that $\sigma_{\mathbf{X}} = \sigma_{\mathbf{Y}} = s$ and that Jim was *d* SDs above the mean on each test. Then on the combined tests **X** + **Y**, Jim's score is $(d\sigma_{\mathbf{X}} + \mathrm{M}_{\mathbf{X}}) + (d\sigma_{\mathbf{Y}} + \mathrm{M}_{\mathbf{Y}}) = 2ds + (\mathrm{M}_{\mathbf{X}} + \mathrm{M}_{\mathbf{Y}})$. But from [4.75] and [4.76], the SD of the combined tests is $\sigma_{\mathbf{X}+\mathbf{Y}} = \sqrt{s^2 + s^2 + 2ss\mathrm{r}_{\mathbf{XY}}} = s\sqrt{2(1+\mathrm{r}_{\mathbf{XY}})}$ while $\mathrm{M}_{\mathbf{X}} + \mathrm{M}_{\mathbf{Y}}$ is the combined mean; hence Jim's score on the combined tests is $2d/\sqrt{2(1+\mathrm{r}_{\mathbf{XY}})}$ sigma units from the mean. That is, by maintaining the same Z-score on both tests, Jim increases his Z-score on their sum by the factor $\sqrt{2/(1+\mathrm{r}_{\mathbf{XY}})}$. This factor equals unity only when $\mathrm{r}_{\mathbf{XY}} = 1$, and becomes larger as $\mathrm{r}_{\mathbf{XY}}$ becomes smaller. (The multiplying factor is more complicated when $\sigma_{\mathbf{X}} \neq \sigma_{\mathbf{Y}}$, but is similarly affected by $\mathrm{r}_{\mathbf{XY}}$.) Hence so long as scores on two (or more) tests show less than perfect correlation, a person who happens to be consistent in his divergence from the mean will find this divergence intensified on their sum.

---

[58] From [4.40] when $\mathbf{n} = 2$. In case the reader has not yet fully comprehended [4.40], [4.75] is also easily proved by noting that $\sum_i([X_i + Y_i] - [\mathrm{M}_{\mathbf{X}} + \mathrm{M}_{\mathbf{Y}}])^2 = \sum_i([X_i - \mathrm{M}_{\mathbf{X}}] + [Y_i - \mathrm{M}_{\mathbf{Y}}])^2 = \sum_i (X_i - \mathrm{M}_{\mathbf{X}})^2 + (Y_i - \mathrm{M}_{\mathbf{Y}})^2 + 2\sum_i (X_i - \mathrm{M}_{\mathbf{X}})(Y_i - \mathrm{M}_{\mathbf{Y}})$. It will be observed that this formula presupposes nothing about the shape of the joint distribution of **X** and **Y**. Mathematical results such as this make the linear correlation of two variables an important statistic even when their relationship is significantly nonlinear.

Departures from Linearity. It was mentioned earlier that the linear correlation coefficient does not adequately describe the degree of relationship between two variables if the trend of the relationship is nonlinear. It is worth illustrating just *how* badly r_{XY} can underestimate[59] $\eta_{Y.X}$. Suppose we were to obtain a scattergram such as the one in Figure 4.8. Since all the points fall exactly on an inverted U-curve, there is a perfect —curvilinear—relationship between **X** and **Y** in this population, and $\eta_{Y,X} = 1$. On the other hand, since there is no prevailing direction in which **Y** tends to change as **X** increases, the *linear* regression line is horizontal and $r_{XY} = 0$. In principle, then, a linear correlation of zero, which in practice is customarily construed as a complete absence of relationship, is nonetheless compatible with any degree of curvilinear relationship. The obvious moral is that no computed r_{XY} should be interpreted (*or* published without commentary for the interpretation of others) unless a scattergram or other shape-revealing record of the data has been inspected to see whether the trend really is substantially linear.

Figure 4.8 also provides a useful demonstration of another statistical fact mentioned previously—namely, that it is not necessarily true that $\eta_{Y.X} = \eta_{X.Y}$. As a preliminary, we should elevate from its previous footnote status the observation that when the joint distribution of **X** and **Y** in *P* is known, either **X** or **Y** can be taken as the predictor variable, and hence the regression (of whatever form) of **X** on **Y** can be defined as readily

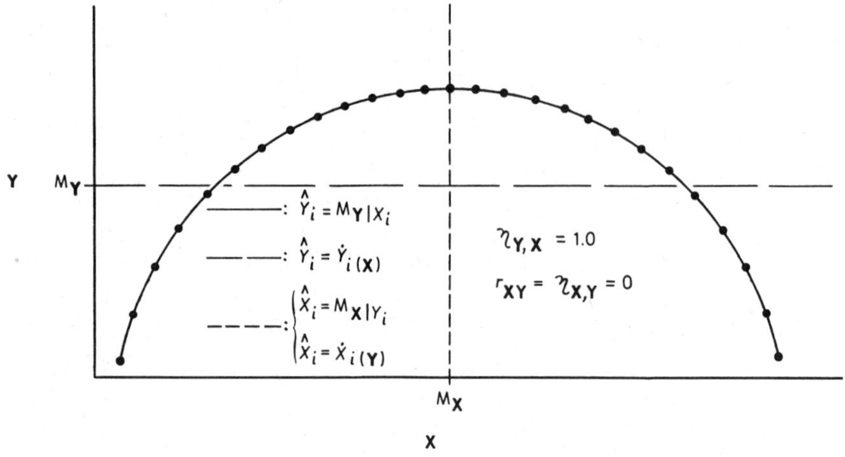

Figure 4.8. An extreme case of curvilinear regression in which there is a perfect correlation of **Y** with **X** ($\eta_{Y.X}$) while the linear correlation of **X** and **Y** (r_{XY}) and the curvilinear correlation of **X** with **Y** ($\eta_{X.Y}$) are zero. Regressions of this general shape (though of course not of this accuracy) are occasionally found empirically. For example, recent data suggest a relationship of this sort between psychological tension and task efficiency, with maximal efficiency occurring at intermediate levels of tension.

[59] It will be a simple exercise for the reader to prove that $|r_{XY}| \leq \eta_{Y,X}$. (*Hint:* Begin with formula [4.18].)

as the regression of **Y** on **X**. (Cf. dashed line in Figure 4.3.) Although the linear *correlation* between **X** and **Y** is unaffected by which of the two variables is chosen to be the predictor, the linear *regression* of **X** on **Y** does not, in general, coincide with that of **Y** upon **X**. From [4.58], the regression of **Y** on **X**, in Z-units, is $\dot{Z}_{\mathbf{Y}\,i(\mathbf{X})} = r_{\mathbf{XY}} Z_{\mathbf{X}\,i}$, whereas the regression of **X** on **Y** is $\dot{Z}_{\mathbf{X}\,i(\mathbf{Y})} = r_{\mathbf{XY}} Z_{\mathbf{Y}\,i}$. In the event that these formulas appear alike to the reader's too casual eye, the latter equation may be turned around to put its **X** and **Y** terms on the same sides of the equality sign as in the former by writing $Z_{\mathbf{Y}\,i} = (1/r_{\mathbf{XY}})\dot{Z}_{\mathbf{X}\,i(\mathbf{Y})}$, and the contrast with $\dot{Z}_{\mathbf{Y}\,i(\mathbf{X})} = r_{\mathbf{XY}} Z_{\mathbf{X}\,i}$ is then unmistakable. In particular, when $r_{\mathbf{XY}} = 0$, $\dot{X}_{i(\mathbf{Y})} = M_{\mathbf{X}}$ and $\dot{Y}_{i(\mathbf{X})} = M_{\mathbf{Y}}$; so in this case the two regression lines (which always cross at the joint means of **X** and **Y**) would intersect at right angles, with the linear regression of **Y** on **X** running horizontally (assuming that values of **X** are shown on the horizontal axis) and the linear regression of **X** on **Y** standing vertically as shown by the dotted line in Figure 4.8.

Returning now to the curvilinear regression of **X** upon **Y** in Figure 4.8, it will be observed that in contrast to the perfect curvilinear predictability of **Y** from **X**, knowledge of **Y** makes no difference for the best curvilinear estimate on **X**—both high and low values of **X** co-occur with a given value of **Y**, and all that changes as **Y** changes is the spread of the contingent distributions of **X**. Thus the best curvilinear estimate of **X**, given **Y**, is $M_{\mathbf{X}}$ at every score *Y*, and the curvilinear and linear regressions of **X** on **Y** coincide, with $\eta_{\mathbf{Y.X}} = r_{\mathbf{XY}} = 0$. This illustrates that any value of $\eta_{\mathbf{X.Y}}$ is compatible with any value of $\eta_{\mathbf{Y.X}}$. In principle, then, the efficiency with which one variable can be curvilinearly predicted from another reveals nothing about the efficiency of prediction in the opposite direction. Even so, both $\eta_{\mathbf{Y.X}}$ and $\eta_{\mathbf{X.Y}}$ have $r_{\mathbf{XY}}$ as a simultaneous lower bound (see fn. 59, p. 130).

Normative Populations and the Interpretation of $r_{\mathbf{XY}}$. Precisely because the correlation coefficient reveals so much about a relationship, a certain deliberate restraint is required to appreciate that the correlation coefficient is *not* omni-informative. It is important to be clear (1) that $r_{\mathbf{XY}}$ is only one of the statistics which determine the (linear) relationship between **X** and **Y** in a population *P*, and (2) that the relation between **X** and **Y** *is* dependent upon the particular population *P*, and may be altogether different in another population *P′*.

As made explicit in formula [4.57], the linear regression of **Y** on **X** in *P* involves not only $r_{\mathbf{XY}}$, but also the means and SDs of **X** and **Y**; whereas $r_{\mathbf{XY}}$ is unaffected (except possibly in sign) by any linear adjustment of these means or SDs and can thus reveal nothing about them. This limitation of $r_{\mathbf{XY}}$ is well to remember, for occasions do arise where the purpose at hand demands attention to these additional features of the regression. Suppose, for example, you wish to know how closely an individual's scores on **X** and **Y** are the *same* in value—e.g., you are exploring the similarity between the social attitudes of parents and their children, or are concerned about the extent to which a person's performance on a test is affected by his having taken the same test previously. The correlation coefficient by itself is then inadequate for your ends, for what it reveals is nothing about the discrepancies between the scores on **X** and **Y** as such, but only the extent to which these discrepancies fail to be linearly related to **X** (or **Y**) scores.[60] Thus the correlation between parent's score and child's score on the same scale of social attitudes will not register any population shift in attitudes between generations. Similarly, if a person *i*'s score on a test improves in the retaking by, say, a certain number of points which is the same for everyone plus an additional amount which is proportional to *i*'s initial score, this would in no way be revealed by the correlation between test and retest scores, for no matter how large these increments might be, the correlation between test and retest would be +1.00. To summarize this particular point, then, r_{XY} *will not pick up any similarities or differences between the marginal distributions of* **X** *and* **Y**.

Another place at which the correlation coefficient's failure to reflect all the properties of the regression line is apt to cause trouble is in making comparative inferences about individuals from different populations. Suppose that **X** and **Y** show a high positive correlation in both populations P_1 and P_2, and that i, who is a member of P_1, has an appreciably higher score on **X** than does j, who belongs to P_2. Does it not then follow, as it would if i and j both belonged to P_1 or to P_2, that i's score on **Y** is undoubtedly higher than j's? No, it does not follow. Even if r_{XY} in P_1 equals r_{XY} in P_2, the regression of **Y** on **X** in P_1 may be quite different from this regression in P_2 if the means or SDs of **X** and **Y** are not the same in P_1 and P_2, and there is hence no rational way to estimate the comparative standing on **Y** of the aforementioned individuals i and j from knowledge (or faith) that *within* each of these populations, **X** is a good predictor of **Y**. For example, suppose we were to determine the regression of Cube-root-of-weight-in-pounds[61] (**W**) upon Height-in-feet (**H**) within various species of animals. While the writer has no actual data available, it seems likely that r_{HW} within any given species would be

---

[60] That is, r_{XY} describes how similar Y_i is likely to be to $aX_i + b$, where a and b are freely chosen to yield optimal fit. It does *not* describe how closely the line $\hat{Y}_i = X_i$ fits the data. No tendency for M_Y to differ from M_X or for σ_Y to differ from σ_X is in any way reflected by r_{XY}. As the reader can easily verify, if $Y_i = X_i + d_i$, where by definition d_i is the discrepancy between X_i and Y_i, then the correlation between **X** and **Y** approaches 1.0 to the extent that the discrepancies lie on a straight line $d_i = aX_i + b$.

[61] Since volume is proportional to the cube of linear dimension for a given shape, taking the cube root of weight helps to secure linearity of regression. This sort of nonlinear transforming of raw scores is frequently used in scientific practice to define away problems of nonlinear regression. (P.S. If you read this footnote without being thrown at least momentarily by the three different uses of the adjective "linear," congratulations!)

in the high .90s. If you were told that animal *i* is eight feet tall while animal *j* is four feet tall, you could then judge with the utmost confidence that *i* weighs more than *j*—*if* you also know that *i* and *j* belong to the same species. On the other hand, if you were *not* told that *i* and *j* are alike in species but you still naively reason that because *i* is much taller than *j* and the correlation between height and weight is extremely high, than *i* must weigh more than *j*, there is a good chance that you have made a fool of yourself—what if, e.g., *i* is a giraffe and *j* a hippopotamus? The situation here envisioned is illustrated by the scattergram in Figure 4.9. The body proportions of giraffes are so different from those of hippopotami that while the individual cases will fall very close to the regression line *for their species*, the regressions themselves differ markedly in a way that is not at all suggested by the intraspecies r_{HW}. For predicting the weight of an animal whose height is given, clearly it makes quite a bit of difference for the prediction whether the creature is a giraffe, a hippopotamus, or some other type of organism.

If the reader feels that the vicissitudes of predicting an animal's weight, given its height, somehow fail to capture the flavor of those prediction problems which arise in his own daily life, consider the matter of intelligence testing. We have grounds on which to think that IQ scores are reasonably good indicators of intellectual capacity, yet we also find significant differences in the IQ-test performances of different ethnic groups. Does this then permit a conclusion about the intellectual su-

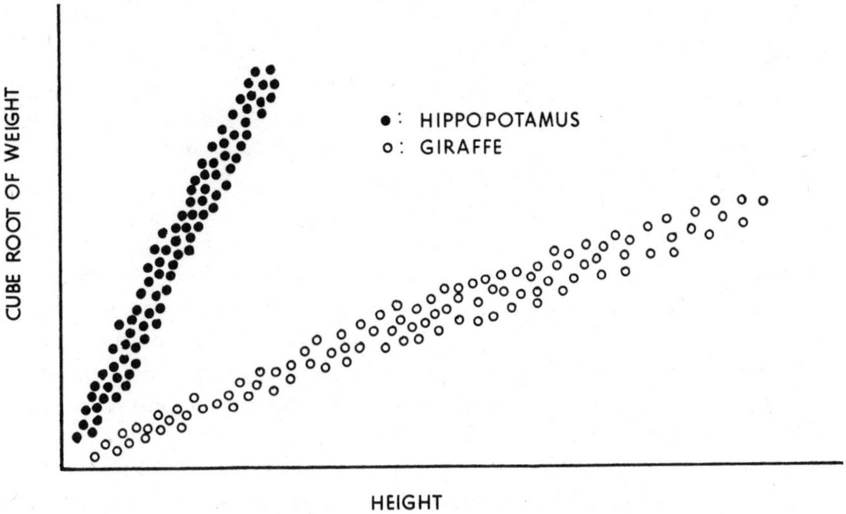

Figure 4.9. Scattergram of Height and Cube-root-of-weight for giraffes and hippopotami. While these data are strictly hypothetical, with no attempt at quantitative accuracy, they illustrate the sort of scatter that would be obtained from the real thing. Other species or genera of animals, if added to the plot, would similarly show a tight cluster around a line characteristic of that particular type of organism.

periority of one human genetic strain over another, as some racists would have it? Yes it does—to about the same extent that the superiority in height of giraffes over hippopotami justifies the conclusion that giraffes weigh more than hippopotami. While it may very well be that *within* a culturally homogeneous group there is a high correlation between IQ and intellectual capacity, we happen to know that wholly apart from the effect of capacity, IQ scores are also influenced by environmental factors which may differ significantly among ethnic groups; and so the regression of intellectual capacity upon IQ—and hence the significance of a given IQ score—can be expected to vary from one ethnic background to another. To be sure, this does not prove that there are no racial differences in intellectual capacity, but it does mean that we cannot infer them merely from group differences in IQ.

In short, *when the population under consideration changes, the interpretation of scores on the predictor variable can also be expected to change.* When speaking of correlation (or of any other statistic, for that matter), there is a tendency to stress the variables and to ignore the particular population involved. It is only too natural, for example, to ask about the relation between IQ and intellectual capacity, or between height and weight, without a thought for what specifications the domain of this relation is supposed to fulfill, or even to realize that it makes any difference. This danger is especially insidious for a prediction technique, say a psychological test, which sees extensive practical use; for opportunities quickly arise for the test to be applied to individuals who fit into a subtly—or perhaps not so subtly—different category from those on whom the test was standardized. For example, suppose that as president of Great Northern Frostbite Insurance Company, pleased with the success of the FHAAD test as a selector of superior field agents but dismayed at the small number of applicants it is passing, you have initiated an extensive advertising campaign designed to promote interest in selling your insurance. Once this campaign begins to have impact, however, the previously established significance of scores on the FHAAD becomes suspect; for by altering the conditions which draw applicants, you have also modified the nature of this population, and the extent to which the old norms still apply is no longer clear. (For example, what if there is something about your new advertising which is especially appealing to the sort of individual who is totally incapable of discriminating good frostbite risks from poor ones, but has exceptional FHAAD talent?)

Moreover, it is not necessary for the test user to *do* anything in order that a population shift be effected. The sheer passage of time will accomplish this handily, especially in a culture as dynamic as ours. Today, the lapse of even a decade is accompanied by multitudinous changes in customs, attitudes, language, educational practices, etc., which almost certainly make some difference for the relation between test performance and criterion. Just how rapidly norms pass into obsolescence is difficult to say, but any serious consumer of psychological tests or other culture-rooted instruments of assessment should remain highly sensitized to this danger.

Finally, while it would be futile to attempt a listing of all ways in which the norms available for a test can manage to be inappropriate for a population to which it is being applied, there is one other potential source of trouble which deserves special mention. It frequently occurs that the base population over which we would like to develop data relating criterion to predictor is one on which selection procedures are already being exercised and where, as things normally go, only the select pass on to opportunity for a criterion performance. If the individuals on whom the new test is standardized are confined only to those passed by the customary procedures, then the norms obtained apply to only a part of the full base population, and may very well fail to be representative for the latter. For example, suppose that Brainsweat University has become dissatisfied with its present admission procedure and plans to adopt a new entrance test which, however, has yet to be validated by its ability to predict Freshman-year grade-point average. It is seductively easy in a case like this merely to give the new test to a suitably large group of the current crop of new students and to correlate the results with grade-point average a year later. But this ignores the fact that these students have already been screened by the old methods, whereas since the new test is to be used as a replacement for these methods, what is needed is information about the regression of Freshman-year grade-point average on entrance-test scores within the population of *applicants*. If adequate interpretive norms are to be established for this test, it is in principle necessary to take a representative sample of *all* students who apply for admission, or at least of those who meet whatever requirements will still be in force when the new test is adopted, give them the test, allow them to matriculate whether they are acceptable by the old standards or not, and then see how well they do their Freshman year. In practice, fortunately, the theory of multivariate relationships permits a new test's predictive efficiency to be estimated from observations confined to the population selected by the old procedure, provided only that the standard deviation of the old test in the base population is also known (see formula [4.142], below).

Several of the immediately preceding examples raise in one form or another the question of how the regression of **Y** on **X** in a population P is related to the regression of **Y** on **X** in a population P' more restricted than P. While there are no appreciable mathematical limitations on the possible similarities and differences of regression in P and P', it is a fitting conclusion to this section and a useful introduction to the next to examine how the manner in which P' is a selection from P influences the regression of **Y** upon **X** therein. The two cases which will be scrutinized here are (1) when P' imposes a restriction on the spread of the independent variable, **X**, over what is found in P, and (2) where P' restricts the variation on some variable other than **X**.

Suppose that after having determined the regression of **Y** on **X** in the full population P, we employ **X** as a screening instrument such that only individuals in P', namely, those who surpass a certain cutoff score, are allowed to turn in scores on **Y**. How will this affect the relationship between **X** and **Y**—i.e., how will the regression of **Y** on **X** in P' differ from that in P? For example, suppose that Great Northern, after requiring a FHAAD score of 58.3 or higher of its new field agents, now wishes to check its original FHAAD norms without going to the expense of a new study on unscreened applicants. What statistical differences should appear between the old norms and the relation now found between FHAAD scores and first-year Company-profit within new agents simply because the latter have now been selected for their FHAAD superiority? The reader can readily answer this question for himself by turning to Figure 4.7 and blocking off a portion of the **X** range. If the selection of P' from P is wholly a discarding of individuals whose scores on **X** are unacceptable, then this does not affect the contingent distributions of **Y** for those values of **X** which are admissable in P'. Consequently, the (curvilinear) *regression* of **Y** on **X** will remain the same in P' as in P except, of course, for becoming indeterminate for those values of **X** which do not occur in P'. On the other hand, the restriction on admissable values of **X** decreases the standard deviation of **X** and hence, to the extent that **Y** is correlated with **X**, also that of **Y** by lessening the controlled-variance component of $\sigma^2_{\mathbf{Y}}$. (This follows from [4.25] through reflection that in general, the smaller the differences in **X**, the smaller will be the differences in the predicted values $M_{\mathbf{Y}|X_i}$ of **Y**.) Since $\sigma_{\mathbf{Y.X}}$ approximates $\sigma_{\mathbf{Y}|X}$ so long as the contingent distributions of **Y**, given **X**, are reasonably homoscedastic, the curvilinear coefficient of alienation, $\sigma_{\mathbf{Y.X}}/\sigma_{\mathbf{Y}}$, will hence increase with the shrinkage in $\sigma_{\mathbf{Y}}$ and result in a corresponding decrement in the correlation ratio $\eta_{\mathbf{Y.X}}$. What happens to $r_{\mathbf{XY}}$ under restriction of **X** is a little more complicated if the regression of **Y** on **X** in the excluded range of **X** fails to be a sufficiently linear extension of the regression in P', but to the extent that $r_{\mathbf{XY}}$ resembles $\eta_{\mathbf{Y.X}}$, a similar result is to be expected. In summary, then, *if P' is a subpopulation of P generated primarily by restricting the variability of* **X**, *the correlation (both curvilinear and linear) of* **Y** *with* **X** *should be smaller in P' than in P, but the (curvilinear) regression of* **Y** *on* **X** *should remain essentially unaltered.* It should be cautioned, however, that if the selection of P' from P also involves a shift in the distribution of other variables of which **Y** is also a function, then this conclusion is attenuated, especially in regard to the similarity of the regressions in P and P'.

On the other hand, *if P' is a selection from P through restriction on the* *variability not of* **X** *but of some other variable to which* **Y** *is also related, the result is likely to be a shift in the regression of* **Y** *on* **X**, *accompanied by a decrease in the standard error of* **Y**, *given* **X**, *and—though this is less certain—by an increase in the correlation of* **Y** *with* **X**. Some of the mathematics of this situation will be exhibited in the final section of this chapter, but it should not be difficult for the reader to get a feel for the principle involved without resorting to formulas. Imagine height-weight data for many types of animals in addition to giraffes and hippopotami added to Figure 4.9. (A given species will be represented by points falling close to a straight line radiating upwards from the lower left-hand corner of the graph, the slope of the line being much dependent on the particular species.) Clearly, if we plotted Cube-root-of-weight against Height for all animals, the points would be spread diffusely over the scattergram, with only a weak general trend for weight to increase with height. Consequently, within the inclusive population *P* of all animals, the correlation between height and weight would be low. As soon as we prune *P* down to the members of one particular species, on the other hand, the variation in weight at a given height due to species differences drops out and we are left with a tight clustering around whatever regression line—a line perhaps considerably different from the regression within the more heterogeneous population *P*—is appropriate to that type of organism.

In more abstract terms, if **Y** is a function in *P* not only of **X** but also of another variable **W** which is not perfectly predictable from **X**, then at a given value of **X**, differences among values of **W** are an additional source of variation in **Y**. Consequently, within a subpopulation P' comprising only members of *P* who have a given value W of **W**, the standard error of **Y**, given **X**, is smaller than in *P*. It can also be expected, though the reasoning is a little involved, that so long as there is not a marked reduction in the variability of **X** from *P* to P', the decrement in $\sigma_{\mathbf{Y}}$ should not be as proportionately large as the decrement in $\sigma_{\mathbf{Y},\mathbf{X}}$;[62] hence $\eta_{\mathbf{Y},\mathbf{X}}$ should be larger in P' than in *P*. The moral to be drawn, then, is that the more we can restrict the base population to which individuals are assigned for purposes of prediction, the more accurate are predictions made from the additional information available likely to be. But this was only to be expected in the first place—what it says is merely that the more you know about an individual, the better you can draw inferences about him. Moreover, assigning a member *i* of *P* to a subpopulation P' on the basis of *i*'s score on variable **W** and then estimating Y_i from X_i through the regression of **Y** on **X** in P' is logically equivalent to what may be described with much greater elegance as the prediction of Y_i from X_i and Z_i on the basis of the "multiple regression" of **Y** upon **X** and **W** in *P*. Which thus brings us to the terminal section of this chapter.

[62] It may be seen from [4.25] that the decrease in $\sigma_{\mathbf{Y}}$ will be proportionately smaller than that in $\sigma_{\mathbf{Y},\mathbf{X}}$ so long as the controlled variance, $\sigma^2_{\mathbf{Y}}$, does not decrease unduly.

Multivariate Prediction

While the prediction techniques described so far reveal how information about the value of one variable can be used to estimate the value of another, this is clearly inadequate to do justice to the multitude of situations in which information on a number of predictor variables is at our disposal. In addition to FHAAD score, for example, Great Northern Insurance Company could also readily obtain a prospective field agent's age, shoe size, length of time previously spent in saleswork, strength of handshake, number of guffaws emitted upon hearing the personnel manager's standard joke, and so on for many other items of greater or lesser predictive utility. Similarly, a college entrance board will normally have at hand a variety of data—previous scholastic record, scores on one or more entrance tests, ratings based on letters of reference, etc.—on which to base its assessment of an applicant's ability to do college work. Yet each item of information about a given individual, used by itself after the fashion of [4.8] or [4.58] to estimate the criterion variable, will in general yield a somewhat different prediction for that individual—and even if the various items did, in fact, all yield the same prediction when examined singly, we should still expect to be able to do better than this when the data are pooled. How, then, are the bits of usable information on several predictors to be combined into a single joint estimate? How good is this joint estimate? And what can be said about the relative worths of the various kinds of information participating in the estimate—e.g., to what extent is one predictor variable more useful than another, and how much predictive accuracy would be lost by ignoring some of the available information?

Multiple Regression Surfaces. Actually, the problem of *what* to predict, given information on several variables, should pose little difficulty for the reader who recalls the fundamentals developed earlier in this chapter; for multivariate prediction follows precisely the same reasoning as does the one-predictor case. Suppose that $\mathbf{Y}$, $\mathbf{X}_1$, $\mathbf{X}_2$, . . . , and $\mathbf{X}_\mathbf{m}$ are $\mathbf{m}+1$ variables whose joint distribution in population P is known, and we wish to predict the value of $\mathbf{Y}$ for a member i of P from i's scores, $X_{\mathbf{1}i}$, $X_{\mathbf{2}i}$, . . . , $X_{\mathbf{m}i}$, on the independent variables $\mathbf{X}_1$, $\mathbf{X}_2$, . . . , $\mathbf{X}_\mathbf{m}$.[63] For example, a tire manufacturer might wish to determine how the rate of wear ($\mathbf{Y}$) of a certain style of tire (P) is jointly affected by the tire's running temperature ($\mathbf{X}_1$), air pressure ($\mathbf{X}_2$), speed of rotation ($\mathbf{X}_3$), weight of load carried ($\mathbf{X}_4$), and roughness of surface being traveled ($\mathbf{X}_5$). Or a business executive interviewing prospective secretaries (P) might try to anticipate an

[63] Since it now becomes inconvenient to use different letters—$\mathbf{X}$, $\mathbf{W}$, etc.—for the different predictor variables, we shall instead distinguish them by boldface subscripts. Lowercase symbols which refer to variables distinguished by them as subscripts, or which indicate how many variables there are in a certain group, will likewise be printed in boldface—e.g., "There are $\mathbf{m}$ variables in the set $\mathbf{X}_1, \ldots, \mathbf{X}_\mathbf{m}$, while the $\mathbf{i}$th variable in the set is $\mathbf{X}_\mathbf{i}$."

applicant's secretarial suitability (**Y**) by the number of favorable adjectives in her written references ($\mathbf{X_1}$), her scores on tests of typing ($\mathbf{X_2}$) and shorthand ($\mathbf{X_3}$), and the amplitude of lateral motion in her walk ($\mathbf{X_4}$). Now, it was argued much earlier in this chapter that the best utility-free estimate of **Y** for an individual *i* is the expected value of **Y** in the most restricted class specified by the usable information about *i*. Hence the unrestricted best (utility-free) estimate of **Y** for a member *i* of *P*, given *i*'s scores on $\mathbf{X_1}, \ldots, \mathbf{X_m}$, is simply the average value of **Y** among members of *P* who have the same scores as *i* on $\mathbf{X_1}$ and . . . and $\mathbf{X_m}$, respectively. That is,

$$[4.77] \qquad \hat{Y}_i = \mathrm{M}_{\mathbf{Y}|X_{1i}\ldots X_{mi}},$$

where $\mathrm{M}_{\mathbf{Y}|X_1\ldots X_{mi}}$ is, of course, the arithmetic mean of **Y** in the subpopulation $\mathrm{P}_{X_{1i}\ldots X_{mi}}$ containing just those members of *P* whose values on $\mathbf{X_1}, \ldots, \mathbf{X_m}$ are the same as *i*'s. Thus when searching for a new secretary, if Horatio A. Smith discovers that Miss Jones has 54 favorable adjectives in her personal references, receives percentile scores of 35 and 79, respectively, on tests of typing and shorthand, and has a 4.8″ sway, formula [4.77] states that the best estimate of how suitable Smith would find Miss Jones as a secretary (as measured, say, by the maximal salary Smith would consent to pay to retain her services), based on this information alone, would be Smith's average suitability rating given to secretaries whose letters of reference contain 54 favorable adjectives, whose typing and shorthand scores on Smith's tests are at the 35th and 79th percentiles, respectively, and who walk with a 4.8″ oscillation.

The unrestricted best estimates defined by [4.77] are known as a *curvilinear multiple regression surface*. The reason for this terminology will be apparent to any reader with a modest grasp of analytic geometry, for [4.77] describes an **m**-dimensional surface in an (**m** + **1**)-dimensional space. What this means is easier to visualize than to describe in everyday language. Suppose that **m** = **2**, and that the joint distribution of **Y**, $\mathbf{X_1}$, $\mathbf{X_2}$ is shown by a three-dimensional scattergram in which the various combinations of values on $\mathbf{X_1}$ and $\mathbf{X_2}$ are represented by positions on the horizontal plane while **Y** corresponds to the vertical distance from the **X**–**Y** plane. Then the best-estimate surface $\hat{Y}_i = \mathrm{M}_{\mathbf{Y}|X_{1i},X_{2i}}$ is a more or less curved roof floating over the **X**–**Y** plane (or under it if $\hat{\mathbf{Y}}$ takes negative values), just as when **m** = **1**, $\hat{Y}_i = \mathrm{M}_{\mathbf{Y}|X_{1i}}$ is a line (i.e., a one-dimensional surface) floating over the **X**-axis as illustrated in Figure 4.1.

Moreover, just as a regression line of preassigned form can be used to predict **Y** from a single variable **X** when it is inconvenient or impossible to make use of the unrestricted best estimates of **Y**, given **X**, so can best-fitting multiple regression surfaces of specified forms be computed by the least-squares method. Specifically, if ϕ_F is a function of **m** variables defined by an equation of form F containing parameters a_0, a_1, . . . , a_p (for example, when $\mathbf{m} = \mathbf{2}$, F might be the quadratic form $\hat{Y}_i = a_0 + a_1X_{1i} + a_2X_{2i} + a_3X_{1i}^2 + a_4X_{2i}^2 + a_5X_{1i}X_{2i}$), then values can be computed for $a_0, \ldots, a_p$ which minimize the quadratic mean magnitude of error for predicting $\mathbf{Y}$ from $\mathbf{X}_1, \ldots, \mathbf{X_m}$ within the population under concern, and hence define the F-form multiple regression surface for $\mathbf{Y}$, given $\mathbf{X_1}, \ldots, \mathbf{X_m}$, in this population. That is, the F-form regression of $\mathbf{Y}$ on $\mathbf{X_1}, \ldots, \mathbf{X_m}$ in population P is that function, f_F, of form F which keeps the (absolute) standard error of $\mathbf{Y}$, given $\mathbf{X_1}, \ldots, \mathbf{X_m}$, as small as possible. It turns out that for most regression forms which are likely to be of practical interest, actual computation of the surface $\hat{Y}_i = f_F(X_{1i}, \ldots, X_{\mathbf{m}i})$ is surprisingly simple. Also, these surfaces have the interesting properties that (*a*) the arithmetic mean of the $\mathbf{Y}$-residual variable $\mathbf{e_Y}$ (i.e., $e_{\mathbf{Y}i} = Y_i - \hat{Y}_i$) in P is zero, and (*b*) the linear correlation in P between the regressed $\mathbf{Y}$-scores $\hat{\mathbf{Y}}$ and the $\mathbf{Y}$-residuals is zero. In fact, properties (*a*) and (*b*) are both so prevalent and so important that they may be taken to define a notion of "standard" form; namely, *function-form F is a standard regression form if and only if*

$$\text{[4.78]} \qquad \begin{aligned} \mathrm{M}_{\mathbf{e_Y}} &= 0 \\ \mathrm{Cov}(\mathbf{e_Y}, \hat{\mathbf{Y}}) &= 0\ , \end{aligned} \qquad (\hat{Y}_i = f_F(X_{1i}, \ldots, X_{\mathbf{m}i}))$$

where f_F is the best-fitting (i.e., standard-error minimizing) surface of form F. Let the notation "F_s" signify that form F is a standard form. Then as a consequence of [4.78] we have

$$\text{[4.79]}^{64} \qquad \mathrm{r}_{\mathbf{Y}\hat{\mathbf{Y}}} = \frac{\sigma_{\hat{\mathbf{Y}}}}{\sigma_{\mathbf{Y}}} \qquad (\hat{Y}_i = f_{F_s}(X_{1i}, \ldots, X_{\mathbf{m}i}))$$

and further, that

$$\text{[4.80]}^{65} \qquad \sigma^2_{\mathbf{Y}} = \sigma^2_{\hat{\mathbf{Y}}} + \sigma^2_{\mathbf{e_Y}} \qquad (\hat{Y}_i = f_F(X_{1i}, \ldots, X_{\mathbf{m}_s i}))\ .$$

Together, [4.78]–[4.80] yield

$$\text{[4.81]} \qquad \begin{aligned} \mathrm{SE}_{\mathbf{Y},\mathbf{X}_1\ldots\mathbf{X_m}} &=_{\text{def}} \mathrm{QM}_{|\mathbf{e_Y}|} \\ &= \sqrt{\sigma^2_{\mathbf{e_Y}} + \mathrm{M}^2_{\mathbf{e_Y}}} \qquad (\hat{Y}_i = f_{F_s}(X_{1i}, \ldots, X_{\mathbf{m}i})) \\ &= \sigma_{\mathbf{e_Y}} \\ &= \sigma_{\mathbf{Y}}\sqrt{1 - \mathrm{r}^2_{\mathbf{Y}\hat{\mathbf{Y}}}}\ . \end{aligned}$$

Hence, (1) every regression surface of standard form decomposes each actual $\mathbf{Y}$-score Y_i into a "regressed" or predicted score $\hat{Y}_i$, plus an un-

[64] Since Cov $(\mathbf{Y},\hat{\mathbf{Y}})$ = Cov $(\mathbf{e_Y} + \hat{\mathbf{Y}},\hat{\mathbf{Y}})$ = Cov $(\mathbf{e_Y},\hat{\mathbf{Y}})$ + Cov $(\hat{\mathbf{Y}},\hat{\mathbf{Y}})$ = 0 + Var $(\hat{\mathbf{Y}})$ (see [4.24] and [4.36]), and hence $\mathrm{r}_{\mathbf{Y}\hat{\mathbf{Y}}}$ = Cov $(\mathbf{Y},\hat{\mathbf{Y}})/\sigma_{\mathbf{Y}}\sigma_{\hat{\mathbf{Y}}} = \sigma_{\hat{\mathbf{Y}}}/\sigma_{\mathbf{Y}}$.

[65] By way of [4.75], since $\mathbf{Y} = \hat{\mathbf{Y}} + \mathbf{e_Y}$ and Cov $(\mathbf{e_Y},\hat{\mathbf{Y}}) = 0$.

correlated residual e_{Yi}; (2) the variance of **Y** correspondingly analyzes as a sum of two components, the controlled variance $\sigma^2_{\hat{Y}}$ and the error or residual variance $\sigma^2_{e_Y}$; (3) the square of the linear correlation, $r_{Y\hat{Y}}$, between predicted and actual scores on **Y** is that proportion of the total variance of **Y** which is controlled through knowledge of the predictor variables under this policy; and (4) the (absolute) standard error when estimating **Y** from the predictor variables under this policy is the standard error of **Y** *without* use of the predictor variables (i.e., σ_Y), reduced by the factor $\sqrt{1-r^2_{Y\hat{Y}}}$. Since in particular, both unrestricted curvilinear and linear regression surfaces are of standard form,[66] a good many of the formulas developed in previous sections of this chapter may now be seen as special cases of a very general situation.

Multiple Linear Regression. The mathematically simplest form of a regression surface in **m** predictor variables is

$$[4.82] \qquad \hat{Y}_i = a_0 + a_1 X_{1i} + a_2 X_{2i} + \ldots + a_m X_{mi} \ ,$$

where the a_js are arbitrary constants. The **Y**-score predicted by an equation of form [4.82] may be described simply as a weighted sum of the **X**-scores, plus a constant; and the coefficients $a_1, \ldots, a_m$ are, in fact, frequently referred to as the *weights* attached to the various predictors. When $\mathbf{m} = \mathbf{2}$, the surface described by [4.82] is a *plane* surface—that is, it is flat like a tabletop, though the table can be tilted at any angle. (When **m** is greater than two, surface [4.82] is known as a "hyperplane" and is not so easy to intuit geometrically.) An equation of form [4.82] is said to be *linear in* **m** *variables,* and the theory of prediction based upon best-fitting regression surfaces of this form is, of course, what is meant by "multiple linear regression." The mathematical virtues of linearity, already welcomed joyously in our previous discussion of one predictor variable, become even more appealing in the multivariate case.

Let us define the *b-coefficients of the multiple linear regression of variable* **Y** *on variables* $\mathbf{X}_1, \ldots, \mathbf{X}_m$ *in population P* to be those constants b_0, $b_1, \ldots, b_m$ such that $\hat{Y}_i = b_0 + b_1 X_{1i} + b_2 X_{2i} + \ldots + b_m X_{mi}$ is the prediction equation of form [4.82] which minimizes the (absolute) standard error of estimate when predicting **Y** for members of *P* from their scores on $\mathbf{X}_1, \ldots, \mathbf{X}_m$. That is, since minimizing the standard error is the same as minimizing $\sum_i (Y_i - \hat{Y}_i)^2$, the *b*-coefficients are the solution to

$$[4.83] \qquad \sum_i (Y_i - b_0 - b_1 X_1 \ - \ldots - b_m X_{mi})^2 = minimum \ ,$$

where of course summation is over the members of *P*. Let the value of

[66] That [4.77] satisfies [4.78] is obvious upon reflection that the average residual is zero in each contingent distribution of **Y**. That the linear regression form in **m** variables is standard will be demonstrated shortly.

$\mathbf{Y}$ predicted for a member i of P from his scores on $\mathbf{X}_1, \ldots, \mathbf{X}_m$ by the linear regression of $\mathbf{Y}$ on $\mathbf{X}_1, \ldots, \mathbf{X}_m$ be designated "$\dot{Y}_{i(\mathbf{X}_1 \ldots \mathbf{X}_m)}$" while "$\dot{\mathbf{Y}}_{(\mathbf{X}_1 \ldots \mathbf{X}_m)}$" correspondingly designates the variable whose value for a member i of P is $\dot{Y}_{i(\mathbf{X}_1 \ldots \mathbf{X}_m)}$. Similarly, let $e_{\mathbf{Y}_i \bullet \mathbf{X}_1 \ldots \mathbf{X}_m}$ be the error of the prediction for individual i, while $\mathbf{e}_{\mathbf{Y} \bullet \mathbf{X}_1 \ldots \mathbf{X}_m}$ is the corresponding error variable. That is,

$$[4.84] \qquad \dot{Y}_{i(\mathbf{X}_1 \ldots \mathbf{X}_m)} =_{\text{def}} b_0 + b_1 \mathbf{X}_{1i} + \ldots + b_m \mathbf{X}_{mi},$$

$$[4.85] \qquad e_{\mathbf{Y}_i \bullet \mathbf{X}_1 \ldots \mathbf{X}_m} =_{\text{def}} Y_i - \dot{Y}_{i(\mathbf{X}_1 \ldots \mathbf{X}_m)},$$

or using the more compact notation introduced earlier, namely, that if the value of variable $\mathbf{V}$ for each member i of P is related to his values on variables $\mathbf{W}_1, \ldots, \mathbf{W}_n$ by the function $V_i = \phi(W_{1i}, \ldots, W_{ni})$, we may omit the subscript "i" and write $\mathbf{V} = \phi(\mathbf{W}_1, \ldots, \mathbf{W}_n)$ instead,

$$[484a] \qquad \dot{\mathbf{Y}}_{(\mathbf{X}_1 \ldots \mathbf{X}_m)} =_{\text{def}} b_0 + b_1 \mathbf{X}_1 + \ldots + b_m \mathbf{X}_m,$$

$$[4.85a] \qquad \mathbf{e}_{\mathbf{Y} \bullet \mathbf{X}_1 \ldots \mathbf{X}_m} =_{\text{def}} \mathbf{Y} - \dot{\mathbf{Y}}_{(\mathbf{X}_1 \ldots \mathbf{X}_m)},$$

where the b_js are defined by [4.83]. (In corresponding extension of [4.59], "$\sigma_{\mathbf{Y} \bullet \mathbf{X}_1 \ldots \mathbf{X}_m}$" then designates the absolute standard error of prediction policy [4.84]. However, we shall not require this symbol until later.) The dot notation employed here (i.e., the dot over $\mathbf{Y}$, or separating $\mathbf{Y}$ from $\mathbf{X}_1 \ldots \mathbf{X}_m$ in the subscripts) will be recognized as a generalization of the notation introduced earlier to identify statistics associated with linear regression.

It is not practical to write the general solution to [4.83] in the form of an explicit formula for each b_j. Rather, the b_js are customarily described by a set of linear equations known as the *normal equations*, namely,

$$[4.86\text{-}0] \qquad M_{\mathbf{Y}} = b_0 + b_1 M_{\mathbf{X}_1} + b_2 M_{\mathbf{X}_2} + b_3 M_{\mathbf{X}_3} + \ldots + b_m M_{\mathbf{X}_m},$$

$$[4.86\text{-}1] \qquad \text{Cov}(\mathbf{Y}, \mathbf{X}_1) = b_1 \text{Var}(\mathbf{X}_1) + b_2 \text{Cov}(\mathbf{X}_2, \mathbf{X}_1) + b_3 \text{Cov}(\mathbf{X}_3, \mathbf{X}_1) + \ldots + b_m \text{Cov}(\mathbf{X}_m, \mathbf{X}_1),$$

$$[4.86\text{-}2] \qquad \text{Cov}(\mathbf{Y}, \mathbf{X}_2) = b_1 \text{Cov}(\mathbf{X}_1, \mathbf{X}_2) + b_2 \text{Var}(\mathbf{X}_2) + b_3 \text{Cov}(\mathbf{X}_3, \mathbf{X}_2) + \ldots + b_m \text{Cov}(\mathbf{X}_m, \mathbf{X}_2),$$

$$[4.86\text{-}3] \qquad \text{Cov}(\mathbf{Y}, \mathbf{X}_3) = b_1 \text{Cov}(\mathbf{X}_1, \mathbf{X}_3) + b_2 \text{Cov}(\mathbf{X}_2, \mathbf{X}_3) + b_3 \text{Var}(\mathbf{X}_3) + \ldots + b_m \text{Cov}(\mathbf{X}_n, \mathbf{X}_3),$$

$$\vdots \qquad \qquad \vdots$$

$$[4.86\text{-}\mathbf{m}] \qquad \text{Cov}(\mathbf{Y}, \mathbf{X}_m) = b_1 \text{Cov}(\mathbf{X}_1, \mathbf{X}_m) + b_2 \text{Cov}(\mathbf{X}_2, \mathbf{X}_m) + b_3 \text{Cov}(\mathbf{X}_3, \mathbf{X}_m) + \ldots + b_m \text{Var}(\mathbf{X}_m).$$

Since the means, variances, and covariances cited in [4.86] are all computable from the joint distribution of $\mathbf{Y}, \mathbf{X}_1, \ldots, \mathbf{X}_m$ in P and are presumed to be known, it only remains to solve for $b_1, \ldots, b_m$ in [4.86-**1**]–[4.86-**m**] by any acceptable method for coping with **m** simultaneous equations (the most convenient being a suitably programmed high-speed computer or research assistant), and finally to determine b_0 by substitution of $b_1, \ldots, b_m$ into [4.86-0]. It can be shown that normal equations [4.86] always have at least one solution for $b_0, \ldots, b_m$.[67] If one or more of the predictor variables $\mathbf{X}_1, \ldots, \mathbf{X}_m$ is an errorless linear function of the others, however, then the solution to the normal equations is not unique. We shall say more about this possibility in a moment.

Normal equations [4.86] are usually deduced from [4.83] by application of differential calculus. However, a simpler and more insightful derivation is to observe that they are mathematically equivalent to

$$[4.87\text{-}0] \qquad M_{\mathbf{e}_{\mathbf{Y}\cdot\mathbf{X}_1\ldots\mathbf{X}_m}} = 0 \,,$$

$$[4.87\text{-}\mathbf{1}] \qquad \mathrm{Cov}(\mathbf{X}_1, \mathbf{e}_{\mathbf{Y}\cdot\mathbf{X}_1\ldots\mathbf{X}_m}) = 0 \,,$$

$$[4.87\text{-}\mathbf{2}] \qquad \mathrm{Cov}(\mathbf{X}_2, \mathbf{e}_{\mathbf{Y}\cdot\mathbf{X}_1\ldots\mathbf{X}_m}) = 0 \,,$$

$$\vdots \qquad\qquad \vdots \qquad\qquad \vdots$$

$$[4.87\text{-}\mathbf{m}] \qquad \mathrm{Cov}(\mathbf{X}_m, \mathbf{e}_{\mathbf{Y}\cdot\mathbf{X}_1\ldots\mathbf{X}_m}) = 0 \,.$$

(Equation [4.87-0] follows from [4.86-0] and conversely by application of [4.45] to [4.85*a*] and [4.84*a*], while the equivalence of [4.86-**k**] and [4.87-**k**] is similarly seen by application of [4.38].) The facts stated by equations [4.87] about the residual $\mathbf{e}_{\mathbf{Y}\cdot\mathbf{X}_1\ldots\mathbf{X}_m}$ will subsequently see frequent employment, so it is important that the reader grasp clearly what they assert and why they must be true if the standard error of prediction policy [4.84] is to be minimal. With "$\mathbf{e}_{\mathbf{Y}\cdot\mathbf{X}_1\ldots\mathbf{X}_m}$" for simplicity abbreviated to "$\mathbf{e}_\mathbf{Y}$", equation [4.87-0] is an immediate consequence of the fact that b_0 can always be adjusted to minimize $M^2_{\mathbf{e}_\mathbf{Y}}$ in

$$SE_{\mathbf{Y},\mathbf{X}_1\ldots\mathbf{X}_m}[\hat{\mathbf{Y}} = \dot{\mathbf{Y}}_{(\mathbf{X}_1\ldots\mathbf{X}_m)}] = \sqrt{\mathrm{Var}(\mathbf{e}_\mathbf{Y}) + M^2_{\mathbf{e}_\mathbf{Y}}}$$

after $b_1, \ldots, b_m$ have been chosen to minimize $\mathrm{Var}(\mathbf{e}_\mathbf{Y})$. As for [4.87-**1**]–[4.87-**m**], these state that the covariance between the criterion-residual $\mathbf{e}_\mathbf{Y}$ and each predictor $\mathbf{X}_i$ is zero. If $\mathrm{Cov}(\mathbf{X}_i, \mathbf{e}_\mathbf{Y})$ were not zero, then prediction of **Y** by policy [4.84] could be further improved by adding to $\dot{\mathbf{Y}}_{(\mathbf{X}_1\ldots\mathbf{X}_m)}$ the best linear estimate of $\mathbf{e}_\mathbf{Y}$ based on $\mathbf{X}_i$; and since this improved estimate of **Y** would also be linear in $\mathbf{X}_1, \ldots, \mathbf{X}_m$, it would follow, contrary to definition, that [4.84] is not the best linear policy for predicting **Y** from $\mathbf{X}_1, \ldots, \mathbf{X}_m$. Equations [4.87-**1**]–[4.87-**m**] state, therefore, that the full potential of each $\mathbf{X}_i$ for linear prediction of **Y** is exhausted in the joint linear estimate.

[67] An explicit proof of this is beyond the present scope. However, that the normal equations always have a solution follows from (*a*) the intuitively evident fact that [4.83] always has a solution, and (*b*) the fact that, as will be shown, any solution to [4.83] must also satisfy equations [4.86].

Since $\dot{Y}_{(X_1 \ldots X_m)}$ is a linear function of $X_1, \ldots, X_m$, each of which has zero covariance with $e_{Y \cdot X_1 \ldots X_m}$, it follows by [4.38] that the covariance between $\dot{Y}_{(X_1 \ldots X_m)}$ and $e_{Y \cdot X_1 \ldots X_m}$ is also zero. This and [4.87-0] prove our previous assertion that the linear regression surface is a standard form in the sense defined by [4.78].

*It has been mentioned that the solution to normal equations [4.86] may not be unique. This raises the question whether in such a case all solutions are equally acceptable to condition [4.83] and if so, how closely do the different solutions agree in the prediction they derive from a given array of predictor scores. Actually, this is a special case of a more general problem: If we have two different sets of predictors where each variable in the one set is linearly predictable without error from the variables in the other, how does the linear regression of a given criterion variable upon the variables in the one set compare with its regression upon the variables in the other? For example, suppose that having been given predictors X_1 and X_2, we introduce three new variables X'_1, X'_2, and X'_3 defined

$$X'_1 =_{\text{def}} X_1 + X_2 \,,$$

$$X'_2 =_{\text{def}} X_1 - X_2 \,,$$

$$X'_3 =_{\text{def}} 2X_1 + 3X_2 \,.$$

What differences, if any, are there between the values of a criterion Y linearly predicted from X_1 and X_2 on the one hand, and from X'_1, X'_2, and X'_3 on the other? Let a set of variables $X'_1, \ldots, X'_n$ be said to be a *linear transformation of the set of variables* $X_1, \ldots, X_m$ when each variable X'_j $(j = 1, \ldots, n)$ is some linear function $X'_j = c_{j0} + c_{j1}X_{j_m} + \ldots + c_{jm}X_m$ of the X_i, while conversely, each variable X_i $(i = 1, \ldots, m)$ is also some linear function $X_i = c'_{i0} + c'_{i1}X'_1 + \ldots + c'_{in}X'_n$ of the X'_j. (It is important to appreciate that this definition implies that one set of variables is a linear transformation of another if and only if the second is a linear transformation of the first.) Then we can prove the following fundamental theorem: *If a criterion* Y *and two sets of predictors* $X_1, \ldots, X_m$ *and* $X'_1, \ldots, X'_n$ *are such that (a)* $Y = \dot{Y} + e_Y$, *where* $\dot{Y}$ *is a linear function of* $X_1, \ldots, X_m$ *while* $M_{e_Y} = 0$ *and* $\mathrm{Cov}(X_i, e_Y) = 0$ *for* $i = 1, \ldots, m$; *(b)* $Y = \dot{Y}' + e'_Y$, *where* $\dot{Y}'$ *is a linear function of* $X'_1, \ldots, X'_n$ while $M_{e'} = 0$ *and* $\mathrm{Cov}(X', e') = 0$ *for* $j = 1, \ldots, n$; *and (c) the set* $X'_1, \ldots, X'_n$ *is a linear transformation of the set* $X_1, \ldots, X_m$; *then* $\dot{Y} = \dot{Y}'$.[68] It will be noted that the conditions imposed on $\dot{Y}$ and e_Y by condition (*a*) and on $\dot{Y}'$ and e'_Y by condition (*b*) in this

[68] *Proof:* Using principle [4.38], it is readily deduced from stipulations (*a*)–(*c*) that Cov $(\dot{Y}, e_Y)$, Cov $(\dot{Y}', e'_Y)$, Cov $(\dot{Y}, e'_Y)$ and Cov (Y', e_Y) are all zero. Hence Var $(\dot{Y})$ = Cov $(\dot{Y}, \dot{Y} + e_Y)$ = Cov $(\dot{Y}, Y)$ = Cov $(\dot{Y}, \dot{Y}' + e'_Y)$ = Cov $(\dot{Y}, \dot{Y}')$ while similarly Var $(\dot{Y}')$ = Cov $(\dot{Y}', \dot{Y})$, so Var $(\dot{Y} - \dot{Y}')$ = Var $(\dot{Y})$ + Var $(\dot{Y}')$ − 2 Cov$(\dot{Y}, \dot{Y}')$ = 0, which in turn implies that $\dot{Y} - \dot{Y}' = c$ for some constant c. But since $M_{e_Y} = 0 = M_{e'_Y}$ while $c = (Y - \dot{Y}') - (Y - \dot{Y}) = e'_Y - e_Y$, it follows by principle [4.45] that $c = M_{e'_Y} - M_{e_Y} = 0$, and hence $\dot{Y} = \dot{Y}'$. QED

theorem are precisely the conditions stated by equations [4.87]; hence the coefficients of $\mathbf{X}_1, \ldots, \mathbf{X}_m$ and $\mathbf{X}'_1, \ldots, \mathbf{X}'_n$ in their respective linear functions $\dot{\mathbf{Y}}$ and $\dot{\mathbf{Y}}'$ satisfy the normal equations for the linear regression of $\mathbf{Y}$ upon $\mathbf{X}_1, \ldots, \mathbf{X}_m$ and upon $\mathbf{X}'_1, \ldots, \mathbf{X}'_n$, respectively. For the special case where $\mathbf{X}_1, \ldots, \mathbf{X}_m$ are identical with $\mathbf{X}'_1, \ldots, \mathbf{X}'_n$, the theorem shows that all solutions to the normal equations for the linear regression of a criterion upon a given set of predictors yield precisely the same prediction of the criterion. More generally, we see that the linear prediction of a criterion remains unaffected by replacement of the original set of predictors with any linear transformation of this set, though of course the numerical details of the prediction equation will in general be altered by such a transformation.

While b-coefficients as defined by equations [4.86] have many practical and mathematical conveniences, they are nonetheless conceptually messy in the same way that formula [4.56] is messy. The magnitudes of $b_1, \ldots, b_m$ are a function of whatever arbitrary units of measurement have been used to scale the variables, while b_0 is a caretaker constant which tidies up after the raw-score means to insure that the average prediction error is zero. A more elegant way to write [4.84] is to standardize all the variables in the form of Z-scores. The weights given to the predictor Z-scores are known as β (beta)-coefficients, and since the constant b_0 vanishes when all the means are zero, the regression equation then becomes

$$[4.88] \quad \dot{Z}_{\mathbf{Y}i(\mathbf{X}_1 \ldots \mathbf{X}_m)} = \beta_1 Z_{\mathbf{X}_1 i} + \beta_2 Z_{\mathbf{X}_2 i} + \beta_3 Z_{\mathbf{X}_3 i} + \ldots + \beta_m Z_{\mathbf{X}_m i} \,,$$

or

$$[4.88a] \quad \dot{\mathbf{Z}}_{\mathbf{Y}(\mathbf{X}_1 \ldots \mathbf{X}_m)} = \beta_1 \mathbf{Z}_{\mathbf{X}_1} + \beta_2 \mathbf{Z}_{\mathbf{X}_2} + \beta_3 \mathbf{Z}_{\mathbf{X}_3} + \ldots + \beta_m \mathbf{Z}_{\mathbf{X}_m} \,,$$

where for each predictor variable $\mathbf{X}$,

$$[4.89\text{-}\mathbf{k}] \quad (\mathbf{k} = 1, \ldots, \mathbf{m}) \qquad b_{\mathbf{k}} = \frac{\sigma_{\mathbf{Y}}}{\sigma_{\mathbf{X}_k}} \beta_{\mathbf{k}} \,.$$

From [4.86], the normal equations for the β-coefficients are

$$\begin{aligned}
&[4.90\text{-}1] & r_{\mathbf{YX}_1} &= \beta_1 + \beta_2 r_{\mathbf{X}_2\mathbf{X}_1} + \beta_3 r_{\mathbf{X}_3\mathbf{X}_1} + \ldots + \beta_m r_{\mathbf{X}_m\mathbf{X}_1} \\
&[4.90\text{-}2] & r_{\mathbf{YX}_2} &= \beta_1 r_{\mathbf{X}_1\mathbf{X}_2} + \beta_2 + \beta_3 r_{\mathbf{X}_3\mathbf{X}_2} + \ldots + \beta_m r_{\mathbf{X}_m\mathbf{X}_2} \\
&[4.90\text{-}3] & r_{\mathbf{YX}_3} &= \beta_1 r_{\mathbf{X}_1\mathbf{X}_3} + \beta_2 r_{\mathbf{X}_2\mathbf{X}_3} + \beta_3 + \ldots + \beta_m r_{\mathbf{X}_m\mathbf{X}_3} \\
&\vdots & &\vdots \\
&[4.90\text{-}\mathbf{m}] & r_{\mathbf{YX}_m} &= \beta_1 r_{\mathbf{X}_1\mathbf{X}_m} + \beta_2 r_{\mathbf{X}_2\mathbf{X}_m} + \beta_3 r_{\mathbf{X}_3\mathbf{X}_m} + \ldots + \beta_m \,.
\end{aligned}$$

In addition to providing computing formulas for the beta-weights, equations [4.90] are illuminating in their own right. It will be noticed that when $\mathbf{Z}_{\mathbf{X}_1}$ is used along with $\mathbf{Z}_{\mathbf{X}_2}, \ldots, \mathbf{Z}_{\mathbf{X}_m}$ to estimate $\mathbf{Z}_{\mathbf{Y}}$, the weight (namely, β_1) it receives for this purpose is not the same as its weight (namely, r_{YX_1}) when Z_Y is estimated from Z_{X_1} alone. Rather, the latter weight is shown by [4.90-**1**] to equal $\mathbf{X_1}$'s β-weight in the multiple regression of **Y** upon $\mathbf{X_1}, \ldots, \mathbf{X_m}$ *plus* adjustments for the multiple-regression contributions of $\mathbf{X_2}, \ldots, \mathbf{X_m}$ in prediction of **Y** to the extent that these can also be estimated from $\mathbf{X_1}$.[69] Hence prediction of **Y** from the single variable $\mathbf{X_1}$ in effect takes into account the influence on **Y** of any other variables which can also be estimated from $\mathbf{X_1}$.

In the event that predictor $\mathbf{X_k}$ has zero correlation with all the other predictors, its β-weight for criterion **Y** is seen from [4.90-**k**] to equal r_{YX_k}. Hence in the important special case where all the predictors are uncorrelated with one another, the β-coefficient of each predictor is identical with its correlation with the criterion.

Insomuch as the preceding account of multiple regression is rather condensed, it will be profitable to meditate upon the significance of formulas [4.82]–[4.90] in the context of a specific example. And while the personnel procurement problems of the Great Northern Insurance Company are perhaps beginning to pall, the present multivariate developments can probably be integrated with the reader's previously acquired understanding of one-predictor technique most effectively by returning to a setting which has already become familiar.

Suppose, then, that a second version (Form II) of the FHAAD test has become available with the same mean (50.0) and SD (10.0) as the earlier version (Form I), but having a linear correlation of +.70 with the company profit a prospective field agent would earn his first year if accepted, rather than the +.60 validity of Form I. Since FHAAD Form II is predictively superior to Form I, reducing the standard error of estimate by 28.6% (cf. Figure 4.6) instead of the 20.0% reduction accomplished by Form I, your first impulse, as president of Great Northern, is simply to discard Form I in favor of Form II. But then an avaricious thought occurs: Why not administer *both* forms and pool the results, obtaining an error reduction—or so it might seem—of 28.6% + 20.0%, or 48.6% in all. The prospect is pleasant, but how do you actually *make* this combined estimate?

Before computing the regression of Company-profit jointly on Forms I and II of the FHAAD in accordance with formulas [4.88] and [4.90], and determining whether the predictive efficiency of the joint estimate is really as great as you hope, it is useful to speculate about how such a pooling of results might be carried out intuitively.[70] Suppose that ap-

[69] That is, from [4.58] and [4.90-**1**], $\dot{Z}_{Y(X_1)} = r_{YX_1} Z_{X_1} = \beta_1 Z_{X_1} + \beta_2 \dot{Z}_{X_2(X_1)} + \beta_3 \dot{Z}_{X_3(X_1)} + \ldots + \beta_m \dot{Z}_{X_m(X_1)}$, which is precisely what results if **Y** is estimated from $\mathbf{X_1}$ by first estimating $\mathbf{X_2}, \ldots, \mathbf{X_m}$ from $\mathbf{X_1}$ and then using the latter estimates along with $\mathbf{X_1}$ in the multiple regression of **Y** upon $\mathbf{X_1}, \ldots, \mathbf{X_m}$.

[70] If the reader does not wish to belabor his intuitions, this paragraph and the one which follows may be omitted without subsequent handicap. Informal preliminaries such as these, however, help to prepare a receptive soil of appreciation in which the mathematical seeds to be strewn subsequently have a better chance of germinating.

plicant Jones, in addition to receiving a score of 70 on Form I, comes through with only a 64 on Form II. To simplify notation, let $\mathbf{Z_1}$ and $\mathbf{Z_2}$ be Forms I and II, respectively, of the FHAAD expressed in Z-score units, while $\mathbf{Z_0}$ is the Z-score equivalent of Company-profit. Also, let subscript occurrences of "$\mathbf{Z_0}$", "$\mathbf{Z_1}$", and "$\mathbf{Z_2}$" be replaced by the corresponding numerals—i.e., r_{01} for $r_{Z_0Z_1}$, $\dot{\mathbf{Z}}_{0(1)}$ for $\dot{\mathbf{Z}}_{0(Z_1)}$, etc. Then $r_{01} = .60$, $r_{02} = .70$, and for individual J(ones), $Z_{0J} = 2.0$ and $Z_{0J} = 1.4$. If Form I were used by itself to estimate Company-profit for Jones, the prediction would be $\dot{Z}_{0J(1)} = r_{01} Z_{1J} = .60 \times 2.0 = 1.20$ (cf. [4.58]), whereas the prediction from Jones's Form II score alone is $\dot{Z}_{0J(0)} = r_{02} Z_{2J} = .70 \times 1.4 = .98$. Forms I and II, then, are not wholly in agreement in their estimates of Jones's Company-profit score, and a reconciliation is called for. One's first inclination, without consideration of multiple-regression principles, is to pool these separate estimates of Z_{0J} simply by taking their average—i.e., to adopt the joint estimate $\hat{Z}_{0J} = (\dot{Z}_{0J(1)} + \dot{Z}_{0J(2)})/2 = (1.20 + .98)/2 = 1.09$. But that simple averaging is not in principle the optimal joint policy may readily be appreciated by reflecting that if r_{02} were zero, instead of .70, values of $\mathbf{Z_0}$ predicted from $\mathbf{Z_2}$ alone would always be zero, and averaging the separate predictions from $\mathbf{Z_1}$ and $\mathbf{Z_2}$ would then only be to make poorer predictions than the ones based on $\mathbf{Z_1}$ alone.[71] Predicting from combined data by averaging the estimates taken from each datum considered separately, then, tends only to contaminate the efficiency of the best single predictor.[72] More generally, no weighted average of the separate predictions can be the most efficient combined prediction, for it is easily seen (and it will be worth the reader's effort to be sure that he sees it) that unless the predictor variables receiving nonzero weight are all perfectly correlated with one another, the variance of any weighted average of the separate (linear) estimates is less than the variance of the estimates based on the best single predictor,[73] whereas the variance of the predictions under the optimal joint (linear) policy must be at least as large as, and will usually be larger than, the variance of the estimates from the best single predictor.[74] It would appear, therefore, that there must be occasions on which the optimal (linear) combination of data from Forms I and II of the FHAAD gives rise to a prediction which is *larger* in magnitude than the (linear) prediction from either form separately.

---

[71] If $r_{02} = 0$, then $\hat{\mathbf{Z}}_0 = (\dot{\mathbf{Z}}_{0(1)} + \dot{\mathbf{Z}}_{0(2)})/2 = (r_{01}/2)\mathbf{Z_1}$, which is known by the definition of $\dot{\mathbf{Z}}_{0(1)}$ to have a larger standard error than $\hat{\mathbf{Z}}_0 = r_{01}\mathbf{Z_1}$ so long as $r_{01} \neq 0$.

[72] It can be shown, however, that if r_{01} and r_{02} are sufficiently similar, an average of $\dot{\mathbf{Z}}_{0(1)}$ and $\dot{\mathbf{Z}}_{0(2)}$ is a better estimate of $\mathbf{Z_0}$ than either of these taken singly.

[73] *Hint:* Begin by showing that if $\mathbf{W} = a\mathbf{X} + b\mathbf{Y}$, $\sigma_{\mathbf{W}} \leq |a|\,\sigma_{\mathbf{X}} + |b|\,\sigma_{\mathbf{Y}}$.

[74] This follows from the fact that linear regressions satisfy [4.80]. It is, however, possible to construct nonstandard joint linear policies whose error variance is smaller than that of the best single-predictor policy, yet under which the variance of the predicted scores is also smaller than under the latter. (In such a case, there must be a positive correlation between predicted and residual **Y**-scores.)

But if averaging is not the proper way to combine predictions, and if it is legitimate for the combined estimate to be larger than either single estimate, may we not then obtain the composite estimate for Jones on $\mathbf{Z_0}$ simply by *adding* the separate predictions from his scores on $\mathbf{Z_1}$ and $\mathbf{Z_2}$? As a matter of fact, this does indeed appear to be a proper approach under suitable circumstances. As we have seen, the statistics of prediction amount to a partitioning of the criterion into a component controlled by the predictor plus an uncorrelated residual. Moreover, to the extent that alternative predictors yield different estimates of the criterion, they must be thought of as controlling somewhat different components of the latter. Consequently, so long as there is no overlap between the components of $\mathbf{Z_0}$ controlled by $\mathbf{Z_1}$ and by $\mathbf{Z_2}$, respectively, it would seem perfectly reasonable to add the separate estimates of Z_{0i} from Z_{1i} and Z_{2i} in order to arrive at a joint estimate. On the other hand, if $\mathbf{Z_1}$ and $\mathbf{Z_2}$ are themselves correlated, simple addition of the separate estimates would be double inclusion of a piece of $\mathbf{Z_0}$ controlled both by $\mathbf{Z_1}$ and $\mathbf{Z_2}$. The mathematics of this situation will be made precise later, but the point is intuitively evident on grounds that the larger the correlation between $\mathbf{Z_1}$ and $\mathbf{Z_2}$, the greater is the proportion of $\mathbf{Z_2}$ which is itself controlled by $\mathbf{Z_1}$ (and conversely), and consequently the more that the estimate of Z_{0i} from Z_{2i} includes a piece estimated, in effect, from Z_{1i} and which is hence redundant if Z_{1i} is also being used to predict Z_{0i}. Thus we should expect that the joint estimate of Z_{0i} obtained by adding the separate estimates from Z_{1i} and Z_{2i} must be attenuated to the extent that $\mathbf{Z_1}$ and $\mathbf{Z_2}$ are themselves correlated. In particular, if $\mathbf{Z_1}$ and $\mathbf{Z_2}$ show perfect correlation (as would occur, e.g., if $\mathbf{Z_2}$ were simply a duplication of $\mathbf{Z_1}$), they then both control the same component of $\mathbf{Z_0}$, and the value of Z_{0i} predicted jointly from Z_{1i} and $\mathbf{Z}_{2i}$ should be the same as the value predicted from either one separately.

Intuitive reasoning (that is, informal arguments based on knowledge of one-predictor techniques) therefore arrives at the following expectations for the linear regression of $\mathbf{Z_0}$ jointly on $\mathbf{Z_1}$ and $\mathbf{Z_2}$: (1) If $\mathrm{r}_{12} = 0$, $\dot{\mathbf{Z}}_{0(12)} = \dot{\mathbf{Z}}_{0(1)} + \dot{\mathbf{Z}}_{0(2)} = \mathrm{r}_{01}\mathbf{Z_1} + \mathrm{r}_{02}\mathbf{Z_2}$. (2) If $\mathrm{r}_{12} = 1$, $\dot{\mathbf{Z}}_{0(12)} = \mathrm{r}_{01}\mathbf{Z_1} = \mathrm{r}_{02}\mathbf{Z_2}$. Finally, since worthless predictors must not be allowed to contaminate the efficiency of better ones, we might also anticipate that (3) if $\mathrm{r}_{02} = 0$, $\dot{\mathbf{Z}}_{0(12)} = \dot{\mathbf{Z}}_{0(1)} = \mathrm{r}_{01}\mathbf{Z_1}$. Turning now to the mathematical solution, it follows from [4.78] and [4.90] by setting $\mathbf{m} = \mathbf{2}$ that

[4.91] $$\dot{\mathbf{Z}}_{0(12)} = \beta_1\mathbf{Z_1} + \beta_2\mathbf{Z_2} ,$$

where the β-weights satisfy the equations

[4.92-**1**] $$\mathrm{r}_{01} = \beta_1 + \beta_2\mathrm{r}_{21}$$

[4.92-**2**] $$\mathrm{r}_{02} = \beta_1\mathrm{r}_{12} + \beta_2 .$$

Solving for the βs in [4.92] then yields

[4.93-1] $$\beta_1 = \frac{r_{01} - r_{02}r_{12}}{1 - r_{12}^2}$$

[4.93-2] $$\beta_2 = \frac{r_{02} - r_{01}r_{12}}{1 - r_{12}^2}.$$

From [4.91] and [4.93] it will be seen that while expectations (1) and (2) are verified,[75] expectation (3) is not. For letting $r_{02} = 0$ in [4.93-2] yields

$$\beta_2 = -\frac{r_{01}r_{12}}{1 - r_{12}^2},$$

which does not vanish unless r_{01} or r_{12} equals zero. It somewhat surprisingly turns out, therefore, that a variable which is worthless for predicting the criterion by itself may nonetheless carry predictive weight when combined with other variables in a joint estimate. We shall explore this phenomenon in some depth a little later, but puzzling out now why it should be so amply merits a few moments of the reader's contemplation.[76] This finding serves both to illustrate the general methodological point that precise analysis of a problem frequently reaps unexpected dividends, and also to draw the practical moral that the predictive worth of information, unlike beauty, is more than skin deep.

Actually, discovery that a superficially useless predictor variable may carry latent significance is only one of several little nuggets of wisdom which can be extracted from [4.91]–[4.93] with nominal algebraic coaxing. For example, if $\mathbf{Z}_2$ is correlated with $\mathbf{Z}_0$ precisely to the extent accounted for by a mutual correlation with $\mathbf{Z}_1$ (i.e., if there is no correlation between the components of $\mathbf{Z}_0$ and $\mathbf{Z}_2$ not controlled by $\mathbf{Z}_1$),[77] then the joint estimate of $\mathbf{Z}_0$ from $\mathbf{Z}_1$ and $\mathbf{Z}_2$ makes use of $\mathbf{Z}_1$ alone—i.e., $\beta_2 = 0$ and $\dot{\mathbf{Z}}_{0(12)} = \dot{\mathbf{Z}}_{0(1)}$—even though $r_{02} \neq 0$. Again, if $\mathbf{Z}_1$ and $\mathbf{Z}_2$ are equally good predictors of the criterion (i.e., if $r_{01} = r_{02}$), the joint estimate $\dot{\mathbf{Z}}_{0(12)}$ is the average of the two single estimates $\dot{\mathbf{Z}}_{0(1)}$ and $\dot{\mathbf{Z}}_{0(2)}$, enhanced by the factor $2/(1 + r_{12})$. Interestingly, the same result obtains for a particular prediction $\dot{Z}_{0i(12)}$ if there is perfect consistency between i's scores on $\mathbf{Z}_1$ and $\mathbf{Z}_2$. That is, if $Z_{1i} = Z_{2i}$, the combined estimate of Z_{0i} is again the average of the single estimates, multiplied by $2/(1 + r_{12})$. Two types of effects are thus seen to be operative in multivariate prediction: (1) a tendency to average the separate predictions, thus conforming to our intuitive expectation that the pooling of data should strive for a

[75] Demonstration of (1) is trivial; demonstration of (2) is not altogether so.

[76] *Hints:* If $r_{12} \neq 0$, $\mathbf{Z}_2$ may be analyzed as a component controlled by $\mathbf{Z}_1$, plus an uncorrelated residual. What must the correlation be between this residual and the criterion variable $\mathbf{Z}_0$ in order to have $r_{02} = 0$ and $r_{01} \neq 0$?

[77] The reader should verify that this condition is equivalent to $r_{02} = r_{01}r_{12}$.

consensus, but also (2) a tendency to modify this average in the direction of a more deviant prediction, the severity of this enhancement being governed by the extent to which the separate predictors are independent of one another.[78] Finally, it is worth observing again (cf. fn. 69, p. 146) that if only i's score on $\mathbf{Z_1}$ is available but an attempt is made to exploit multivariate procedure by first estimating Z_{2i} from Z_{1i} (i.e., $\dot{Z}_{2i(1)} = r_{12} Z_{1i}$) and then applying [4.91] with $\dot{Z}_{2i(1)}$ in place of Z_{2i}, the resulting estimate of Z_{0i} is precisely what would have been obtained directly from Z_{1i} alone.

Returning now to the problem of combining scores on Forms I and II of the FHAAD into a joint prediction of a prospective Great Northern field agent's first-year Company-profit, we see that it is necessary to know not only the correlation of each form with the criterion, but also the correlation between forms. Suppose that $r_{12} = .80$ (a reasonable figure for two versions of the same test) while $r_{01} = .60$ and $r_{02} = .70$ as assumed previously. Then from [4.93], $\beta_1 = (.6 - .7 \times .8)/(1 - .8^2) = .111$, $\beta_2 = (.7 - .6 \times .8)/(1 - .8^2) = .611$, and the optimal linear policy for utilizing data from both FHAAD forms to predict Company-profit is hence

[4.94] $$\dot{Z}_{0i(12)} = .111 Z_{1i} + .611 Z_{2i} \, .$$

Accordingly, the best linear estimate of Jones's Company-profit score, given his test scores of $Z_{1J} = 2.0$ and $\dot{Z}_{2J} = 1.4$, is $\dot{Z}_{0J(12)} = .111(2.0) + .611(1.4) = 1.08$—thus suggesting that Jones's Form II score (which by itself authorized the prediction $\dot{Z}_{0J(2)} = .98$) has supplied a commendable restraint to what was probably an overexuberant estimate supplied by Form I (namely, $\dot{Z}_{0J(1)} = 1.2$). However, had Jones's Form II performance come a little closer to his level on Form I, say $Z_{2J} = 1.8$, the combined estimate of his Company-profit score would have been $\dot{Z}_{0J(12)} = .111(2.0) + .611(1.8) = 1.31$, which is higher than either of the two single estimates. This illustrates the tendency observed above, that if a person's ratings on the various predictor variables are sufficiently consistent, this consistency expresses itself not as increased confidence in the accuracy of the combined estimate (since apart from quirks of multivariate nonnormality, the contingent standard error of a joint prediction is the same no matter what the predictor scores may be) but in a more outstanding joint assessment than ventured by any one datum on its own.

To put standardized regression equation [4.94] in a form which predicts raw Company-profit from unmodified FHAAD data, we can con-

---

[78] It can be shown that $\dot{Z}_{0i(12)}$ is in general approximately equal to $2/(1 + r_{12})$ times the average of $\dot{Z}_{0i(1)}$ and $\dot{Z}_{0i(2)}$, where the error of the approximation equals $r_{12}/(1 - r_{12}^2)$ times $(r_{01} - r_{02})$ times $(Z_{1i} - Z_{2i})$ and hence approaches zero as either $\mathbf{Z_1}$ and $\mathbf{Z_2}$ approach perfect independence of each other, $\mathbf{Z_1}$ and $\mathbf{Z_2}$ approach agreement in their relation to $\mathbf{Z_0}$, or the individual i whose value of $\mathbf{Z_0}$ is being estimated shows sufficient consistency in his scores on $\mathbf{Z_1}$ and $\mathbf{Z_2}$.

vert its β-coefficients into b-coefficients by means of formula [4.89] and derive the additive constant b_0 by application of formula [4.86-0]. In practice, however, it is easier to remember simply that $\mathbf{Z}_{\mathbf{X}_i} = (\mathbf{X}_i - \mathrm{M}_{\mathbf{X}_i})/\sigma_{\mathbf{X}_i}$ and that $\dot{\mathbf{Z}}_{\mathbf{Y}(\mathbf{X}_1\ldots\mathbf{X}_m)} = (\dot{\mathbf{Y}}_{(\mathbf{X}_1\ldots\mathbf{X}_m)} - \mathrm{M}_{\mathbf{Y}})/\sigma_{\mathbf{Y}}$. Letting $\mathbf{X}_0$ be the raw Company-profit variable while $\mathbf{X}_1$ and $\mathbf{X}_2$ are the original scales of Forms I and II of the FHAAD and recalling the means and SDs assumed earlier for these variables, we have $\dot{\mathbf{Z}}_{0(12)} = [\dot{\mathbf{X}}_{0(12)} - (-1{,}000)]/2{,}000$, $\mathbf{Z}_1 = (\mathbf{X}_1 - 50)/10$, and $\mathbf{Z}_2 = (\mathbf{X}_2 - 50)/10$. Hence substituting into standardized regression equation [4.94] and rearranging terms yields

[4.95] $$\dot{\mathbf{X}}_{0(12)} = 22.2\mathbf{X}_1 + 122.2\mathbf{X}_2 - 8{,}220\ .$$

The reader should verify that feeding Jones's scores on FHAAD Forms I and II, namely, 70 and 64, respectively, into this equation does, in fact, yield a predicted Company-profit score for Jones which agrees (within the limits of rounding-off error) with his predicted Z-score computed above from regression equation [4.94].

Multiple Correlation. No method of prediction warrants serious consideration unless it also affords some intimation of its accuracy, and there is certainly no reason to exempt multiple regression from this responsibility. Specifically, we require a "multiple correlation" statistic to serve as a description of how effectively a regression surface $\hat{\mathbf{Y}} = f_{\mathrm{F}}(\mathbf{X}_1, \ldots, \mathbf{X}_m)$ estimates scores on $\mathbf{Y}$. In view of [4.79]–[4.81], however, there is little trouble in selecting a measure of predictive accuracy which not only subsumes $\eta_{\mathbf{Y},\mathbf{X}}$ and $r_{\mathbf{XY}}$ (or more precisely, the magnitude of the latter) as special cases, but applies with identical significance to all regression surfaces of standard form. This noble statistic is, of course, the linear correlation between regressed (i.e., predicted) and actual criterion scores, or, what by [4.79] is mathematically the same, the standard deviation of the regressed criterion Z-scores. No matter how many predictor variables are involved or how convulsed a nonlinear regression surface may be, its predictive accuracy lies wholly in the degree of similarity between the two variables, $\mathbf{Y}$ and $\hat{\mathbf{Y}}$. If $\hat{\mathbf{Y}}$ is defined by a regression surface of *standard* form, moreover, the best linear estimate of Y_i, given $\hat{Y}_i$, is simply $\hat{Y}_i$.[79] Hence the distribution of errors made in taking $\hat{\mathbf{Y}}$ as the estimate of $\mathbf{Y}$ is identical with the scatter of $\mathbf{Y}$ around the linear regression of $\mathbf{Y}$ on $\hat{\mathbf{Y}}$; and the linear correlation, $r_{\mathbf{Y}\hat{\mathbf{Y}}}$, between regressed and actual $\mathbf{Y}$-scores

---

[79] *Proof:* Substitute $\hat{Y}_i$ for X_i in [4.56] while noting from [4.78]–[4.80] that $\mathrm{M}_{\mathbf{Y}} = \mathrm{M}_{\hat{\mathbf{Y}}}$ and $r_{\mathbf{Y}\hat{\mathbf{Y}}}\sigma_{\mathbf{Y}}/\sigma_{\hat{\mathbf{Y}}} = 1$. Lest it seem obvious to the reader that the best linear estimate of Y_i, given $\hat{Y}_i$, is $\hat{Y}_i$ for *any* prediction policy $\hat{\mathbf{Y}} = \phi(\mathbf{X}_1, \ldots, \mathbf{X}_m)$, let him compute that this is, in fact, true only if $\mathrm{M}_{\mathbf{e_Y}} = 0$ and $\mathrm{Cov}(\hat{\mathbf{Y}}, \mathbf{e_Y}) = 0$. This observation, by the way, is doubly interesting in that it shows nonstandard regression surfaces to have a special sort of inefficiency: Given any nonstandard surface $\hat{\mathbf{Y}} = \phi(\mathbf{X}_1, \ldots, \mathbf{X}_m)$, the prediction can be improved by a correction based on the linear regression of $\mathbf{e_Y}$ upon $\hat{\mathbf{Y}}$. This fact also suffices to show that any regression form in $\mathbf{m}$ predictors is standard if and only if it can be written as $\hat{\mathbf{Y}} = a_0 + a_1 f(\mathbf{X}_1, \ldots, \mathbf{X}_m)$, in which a_0 and a_1 are free parameters while f, which can be any function of the predictor variables, may or may not contain additional parameters.

describes the magnitude of these errors (in proportion to $\sigma_{\mathbf{Y}}$) in precisely the way that any linear correlation coefficient describes the scatter around its regression line.

If the reader has an uneasy suspicion that the full significance of the remarks just concluded may have escaped him (the point is, perhaps, a bit delicate), it will suffice for him to reflect that the accuracy of any prediction policy $\hat{\mathbf{Y}} = \phi(\mathbf{X}_1, \ldots, \mathbf{X}_m)$ is given most directly by its standard error; while the (utility-free) worth of information on $\mathbf{X}_1, \ldots, \mathbf{X}_m$ lies in the extent to which such knowledge diminishes the errors of prediction that would accrue in the absence of this knowledge. As discussed earlier, the degree of this error decrement is most conveniently measured by the coefficient of alienation for the prediction policy in question—i.e., by the (absolute) standard error of $\mathbf{Y}$, given $\mathbf{X}_1, \ldots, \mathbf{X}_m$, under this policy, expressed as a proportion of the standard error of $\mathbf{Y}$ when data on the predictor variables are *not* given. This ratio is equal to $\sqrt{1 - r^2_{\mathbf{Y}\hat{\mathbf{Y}}}}$ when the prediction equation is of standard form (cf. [4.81]); and since in this case $r_{\mathbf{Y}\hat{\mathbf{Y}}}$ describes the goodness of multivariate prediction in the very same sense as its special instances $|r_{\mathbf{XY}}|$ and $\eta_{\mathbf{Y.X}}$ accomplish this for the simplest forms of regression, it is inevitable that we should adopt $r_{\mathbf{Y}\hat{\mathbf{Y}}}$ as our generic measure of multiple correlation for any regression surface of standard form.

The symbol "$R_{\mathbf{Y}(\mathbf{X}_1 \cdots \mathbf{X}_m)}$" has become conventional (with some variation in the handling of the subscripts) for the multiple correlation between $\mathbf{Y}$ and $\mathbf{X}_1, \ldots, \mathbf{X}_m$ for linear regression surfaces. Since $\hat{\mathbf{Y}} = \dot{\mathbf{Y}}_{(\mathbf{X}_1 \cdots \mathbf{X}_m)}$ is of standard form, it follows from [4.79] that

[4.96-R]
$$R_{\mathbf{Y}(\mathbf{X}_1 \cdots \mathbf{X}_m)} =_{\text{def}} r_{\mathbf{Y}\dot{\mathbf{Y}}(\mathbf{X}_1 \cdots \mathbf{X}_m)} = \frac{\sigma_{\dot{\mathbf{Y}}(\mathbf{X}_1 \cdots \mathbf{X}_m)}}{\sigma_{\mathbf{Y}}} = \sigma_{\dot{\mathbf{Z}}_{\mathbf{Y}}(\mathbf{X}_1 \cdots \mathbf{X}_m)}.$$

Similarly, the multiple coefficient of alienation, which expresses the standard error of the criterion, given the predictors, as a proportion of its original standard error, is

[4.96-K]
$$K_{\mathbf{Y}(\mathbf{X}_1 \cdots \mathbf{X}_m)} =_{\text{def}} \frac{\sigma_{e_{\mathbf{Y} \cdot \mathbf{X} \cdots \mathbf{X}_m}}}{\sigma_{\mathbf{Y}}} = \sigma_{e_{\mathbf{Z}_{\mathbf{Y}} \cdot \mathbf{X}_1 \cdots \mathbf{X}_m}} = \sqrt{1 - R^2_{\mathbf{Y}(\mathbf{X}_1 \cdots \mathbf{X}_m)}}.$$

As just reviewed in more general terms, the cash value of R as a measure of predictive accuracy lies in what it reveals about the magnitude of prediction errors under linear estimation. Specifically, $\sigma_{\mathbf{Y}} R_{\mathbf{Y}(\mathbf{X}_1 \cdots \mathbf{X}_m)}$ is the standard deviation of the regressed (i.e., predicted) $\mathbf{Y}$-scores and

$R^2_{Y(X_1 \cdots X_m)}$ is the proportion of the variance of **Y** which is jointly controlled by $\mathbf{X_1}, \ldots, \mathbf{X_m}$. Similarly, $\sigma_{e_{Y \cdot X_1 \cdots X_m}}$ $(= \sigma_Y K_{Y(X_1 \ldots X_m)})$ is the (absolute) linear standard error of **Y**, given $\mathbf{X_1}, \ldots, \mathbf{X_m}$, while $K^2_{Y(X_1 \cdots X_m)}$ is the proportion of σ^2_Y which is error variance.[80]

There is a simple formula for computing $R_{Y(X_1 \cdots X_m)}$ once the β-coefficients of the regression equation are known. From [4.88*a*] and general principle [4.38] we have

$$[4.97] \qquad \mathrm{Cov}(\mathbf{Z_Y}, \dot{\mathbf{Z}}_{Y(X_1 \cdots X_m)}) = \beta_1 \mathrm{Cov}(\mathbf{Z_Y}, \mathbf{Z_{X_1}}) + \beta_2 \mathrm{Cov}(\mathbf{Z_Y}, \mathbf{Z_{X_2}}) + \ldots + \beta_m \mathrm{Cov}(\mathbf{Z_Y}, \mathbf{Z_{X_m}}) .$$

But $\mathrm{Cov}(\mathbf{Z_Y}, \mathbf{Z_{X_k}}) = r_{YX_k}$, while in view of [4.96-R], $\mathrm{Cov}(\mathbf{Z_Y}, \dot{\mathbf{Z}}_{Y(X_1 \cdots X_m)}) = \sigma_{Z_Y} \sigma_{\dot{Z}_Y(X_1 \cdots X_m)} r_{Y\dot{Y}(X_1 \ldots X_m)} = R^2_{Y(X_1 \cdots X_m)}$. Hence [4.97] is equivalent to

$$[4.98] \qquad R^2_{Y(X_1 \cdots X_m)} = \beta_1 r_{YX_1} + \beta_2 r_{YX_2} + \ldots + \beta_m r_{YX_m} ,$$

from which R follows by taking the square root of each side.

For the special case of two predictor variables, using the simplified notation introduced for this case earlier, [4.98] and [4.93] yield

$$[4.99] \qquad R_{0(12)} = \sqrt{\frac{r^2_{01} + r^2_{02} - 2 r_{01} r_{02} r_{12}}{1 - r^2_{12}}} ,$$

a formula which, though not very intuitive, is still within the bounds of practicality.

We can now wrap up our discussion of the FHAAD test's efficiency at prognostic assessment of Great Northern field agents by computing from [4.99] that if the correlation (r_{01}) between Company-profit and Form I of the FHAAD is .60, the correlation (r_{02}) between Company-profit and Form II is .70, and the correlation (r_{12}) between the two forms is .80, the joint linear effectiveness of Forms I and II for predicting Company-profit is $R_{0(12)} = .703$. Since the correlation between Company-profit and Form II alone is .700, there is hence virtually nothing to be gained by retaining both versions of the FHAAD instead of simply replacing Form I by Form II. Specifically, the coefficient of alienation for estimating Company-profit jointly from Forms I and II is $\sqrt{1 - .703^2} = .711$, while that for Form II alone is $\sqrt{1 - .700^2} = .714$, so estimates based on both Form I and Form II data are more accurate than estimates from Form II alone by only three tenths of 1% of the original standard error. The reason for this disappointing failure to achieve significant predictive gain through joint use of both forms of the test is the high positive correlation ($r_{12} = .80$) between them—the component of Company-profit controlled by Form I is almost entirely predictable from Form II. On the other hand, were Forms I and II wholly independent of one another (i.e., $r_{12} = 0$) while retaining their present separate validities

[80] *Review question:* Why is $\sigma_{e_{Y \cdot X_1 \cdots X_m}}$ able to be *both* the standard deviation of $\mathbf{e}_{Y \cdot X \cdots X_m}$ *and* the standard error of **Y**, given $\mathbf{X_1}, \ldots, \mathbf{X_m}$?

for the prediction of Company-profit, their multiple (linear) correlation with the criterion would be $R_{0(12)} = \sqrt{r_{01}^2 + r_{02}^2} = \sqrt{.6^2 + .7^2} = .922$, which is a substantial improvement over the validity of either single estimator. This illustrates an important fact about the combination of several predictor items into a composite estimate: *With the correlations between the criterion and the separate predictor variables held constant, the algebraically smaller the correlations among the predictors, the better is their joint predictive efficiency.* This stands out with particular vividness in the special case of two predictors for which $r_{01} = r_{02}$. For in this case it follows from [4.99] that $r_{0(12)} = r_{01}\sqrt{2/(1+r_{12})}$, in which it is easily seen that the lower the correlation between the predictors, the larger is the multiplying factor $\sqrt{2/(1+r_{12})}$. That *low* correlations are desirable among the constituents of a compound prediction equation is perhaps counterintuitive at first thought, but makes sense upon reflection that to the extent the several predictors control the same component of the criterion, they are simply redundant.

Finally, it is worth noting that the correlations among three variables are not wholly independent of one another. That is, while r_{01} and r_{02} do not determine r_{12}, they place limits on the latter. For since $R_{0(12)} \leq 1$, it follows immediately from [4.99] that

$$r_{01}^2 + r_{02}^2 + r_{12}^2 - 2r_{01}r_{02}r_{12} \leq 1 . \qquad [4.100]$$

Because of its symmetry, [4.100] is the conventional formula for describing the simultaneous limitations on r_{01}, r_{02}, and r_{12}. However, some algebraic juggling of [4.100] also yields a more meaningful result, namely,

$$|r_{12} - r_{01}r_{02}| \leq \sqrt{(1-r_{01}^2)(1-r_{02}^2)} , \qquad [4.101]$$

or, since $\sqrt{1-r^2}$ equals the coefficient of alienation,

$$r_{01}r_{02} - k_{01}k_{02} \leq r_{12} \leq r_{01}r_{02} + k_{01}k_{02} . \qquad [4.101a]$$

That is, r_{12} must lie within the interval $r_{01}r_{02} \pm k_{01}k_{02}$.[81]

***Nonlinear Regression Forms.** Although the extraordinary docility of linear functions has the effect that in multivariate practice we find ourselves clinging to linear regression surfaces with the tenacity of a bulldog with lockjaw, occasions do arise, especially in scientific research, where curvilinearity is too significant to be ignored. Just how to get on with curve-fitting in such cases is a complex business. The nastiest prob-

[81] It will be instructive for the reader to demonstrate that $r_{01}r_{02}$ is the correlation between $\mathbf{Z}_1$ and $\mathbf{Z}_2$ which results from their each having a component controlled by $\mathbf{Z}_0$, while $k_{01}k_{02}$ is the maximum perturbation from this which can be effected by the components of $\mathbf{Z}_1$ and $\mathbf{Z}_2$ uncontrolled by $\mathbf{Z}_0$. (*Hint:* Show that $r_{12} = \mathrm{Cov}(\dot{\mathbf{Z}}_{1(0)}, \dot{\mathbf{Z}}_{2(0)}) + \mathrm{Cov}(\mathbf{e}_{1\cdot 0}, \mathbf{e}_{2\cdot 0}) = r_{01}r_{02} + k_{01}k_{02}r_{e_{1\cdot 0}e_{2\cdot 0}}$. The last expression is a partial correlation, as discussed below, and is more succinctly written as "$r_{12\cdot 0}$".

lem is deciding what regression form to apply, and if this is strongly dictated by rational considerations (notably, theories about the laws governing the data), it may well turn out that no effective procedure is available for computing the best-fitting parameter values other than successive approximations. There is, however, one broad class of regression forms which are computationally indistinguishable from the linear case, yet which will serve to approximate as closely as we please virtually any regression surface which arises empirically. Consider the regression form

$$[4.102] \qquad \hat{\mathbf{Y}} = b_0 + b_1\phi_1(\mathbf{X}_1, \ldots, \mathbf{X}_m) + \ldots + b_p\phi_p(\mathbf{X}_1, \ldots, \mathbf{X}_m)\ ,$$

where each $\phi_i(\mathbf{X}_1, \ldots, \mathbf{X}_m)$ is some fixed function (that is, ϕ_i does not contain any adjustable parameters) of one or more of the variables $\mathbf{X}_1$, $\ldots$, $\mathbf{X}_m$ while $b_0, b_1, \ldots, b_p$ are constants whose numerical values are selected to minimize the standard error of $\hat{\mathbf{Y}}$ as an estimate of $\mathbf{Y}$. For example, $\phi_i(\mathbf{X}_1, \ldots, \mathbf{X}_m)$ might be $\sqrt{\mathbf{X}_i}$, or $\mathbf{X}_i^2\mathbf{X}_{i+1}^3$, or $(1/\mathbf{X}_i)^{\mathbf{X}_m}$, or $\sin(\mathbf{X}_i)$, etc. Mathematically, $\phi_i(\mathbf{X}_1, \ldots, \mathbf{X}_m)$ is merely an additional variable defined as a (generally nonlinear) combination of some of the original predictors $\mathbf{X}_1, \ldots, \mathbf{X}_m$, and if we write

$$[4.103\text{-}\mathbf{i}] \quad (\mathbf{i} = 1, \ldots, \mathbf{p}) \qquad \mathbf{W}_i =_{\text{def}} \phi_i(\mathbf{X}_1, \ldots, \mathbf{X}_m)\ ,$$

[4.102] is seen to be equivalent to

$$[4.104] \qquad \hat{\mathbf{Y}} = b_0 + b_1\mathbf{W}_1 + \ldots + b_p\mathbf{W}_p\ .$$

Hence the constants $b_0, b_1, \ldots, b_p$ which minimize the standard error of prediction policy [4.102] are simply the b-weights in the linear regression of $\mathbf{Y}$ upon the modified set of predictors $\mathbf{W}_1, \ldots, \mathbf{W}_p$, and can be computed by application of normal equations [4.86] (with $\mathbf{W}$s substituted for the $\mathbf{X}$s) after the means, variances, and covariances among $\mathbf{Y}$, $\mathbf{W}_1, \ldots, \mathbf{W}_p$ have been derived from the original joint data on $\mathbf{Y}, \mathbf{X}_1, \ldots, \mathbf{X}_m$. (Thus $M_{\mathbf{W}_i} = [\sum_j \phi_i(X_{1j}, \ldots, X_{mj})]/n$, and similarly for the other statistics involving the $\mathbf{W}_i$.) Since equation [4.102] does not specify just what the functions $\phi_1, \ldots, \phi_p$ actually are, it subsumes an infinite variety of regression forms, depending on how the ϕ_i are selected. Collectively, these may be called the family of *parametrically linear* regression forms. It is exceedingly unlikely that the joint observations which have been made on variables $\mathbf{Y}, \mathbf{X}_1, \ldots, \mathbf{X}_m$ will fail to be adequately fitted by some parametrically linear regression form. In fact, a polynomial of relatively low degree will usually suffice even when $\mathbf{Y}$'s relation to the $\mathbf{X}_i$ is conspicuously nonlinear. Just what is meant by a "polynomial" form is a bit cumbersome to explain in words, but a couple of examples will convey the general concept: The linear regression form (i.e., [4.84]) is a first-degree polynomial in the predictors; $\hat{\mathbf{Y}} = b_0 + b_1\mathbf{X}_1 + b_2\mathbf{X}_2 + b_3\mathbf{X}_3 + b_{11}\mathbf{X}_1^2 + b_{22}\mathbf{X}_2^2 + b_{33}\mathbf{X}_3^2 + b_{12}\mathbf{X}_1\mathbf{X}_2 + b_{13}\mathbf{X}_1\mathbf{X}_3 + b_{23}\mathbf{X}_2\mathbf{X}_3$ is the form of a second-degree polynomial regression in three predictors; and $\hat{\mathbf{Y}} = b_0 + b_1\mathbf{X}_1 + b_2\mathbf{X}_2 + b_{11}\mathbf{X}_1^2 + b_{22}\mathbf{X}_2^2 + b_{12}\mathbf{X}_1\mathbf{X}_2 + b_{111}\mathbf{X}_1^3 + b_{222}\mathbf{X}_2^3 + b_{112}\mathbf{X}_1^2\mathbf{X}_2 + b_{122}\mathbf{X}_1\mathbf{X}_2^2$ is a third-degree polynomial in two predictors. On the whole, the most feasible way to solve for a regression surface in cases where the inadequacy of linear regression is too painful to bear is to try polynomial forms of successively higher degree until the fit attains a satisfactory level of respectability. However, the astronomical rate at which the number of regression parameters increases under enlargements in either the number of predictors or the degree of the polynomial as soon as both of these exceed unity places rather severe practical limitations on the polynomic complexity to which this method of curve-fitting can aspire, especially when the problems of sampling uncertainty (see Chapter 10, pp. 504 ff.) are heeded. (As discussed in Chapter 10, pp. 531 ff., the difficulty of fitting a nonlinear regression surface can frequently be ameliorated by first performing a nonlinear transformation upon the criterion variable.)

****Partial Correlation.*** Upon first cautious inspection, the mechanics of partial correlation are likely to present an unnervingly formidable appearance, bristling with complex formulas and confusing notations. Actually, once the generic concepts of correlation and variance have been acquired, along with some feeling for the partition of a variable into controlled and residual components, little difficulty remains beyond keeping a wary eye on the details of subscripts. The theory of partials—which includes not only partial correlations, but also partial variances and occasionally even more exotic fauna—is not only indispensable for evaluating the predictive worth of information which *supplements* other data, but is also a conceptual delight both in the simple elegance of its mathematical structure and for the transparency with which it exposes the inner workings of multivariate relationships.

Reduced to fundamentals, "partial" statistics are simply *the statistics of residuals.* More precisely, the theory of partials as it has actually been developed is mainly the theory of *linear* residuals, though its concepts have an obvious generalization (at least in principle, though not so readily in practice) to any standard regression form. In what follows, we presuppose linear functions throughout.

We have already had several occasions in this chapter to observe that when the value of a variable **Y** is linearly estimated for an individual i from his score on variable **X**, i's actual score, Y_i, equals a controlled component $\hat{Y}_{i(\mathbf{X})}$ predicted on the basis of X_i, plus a residual $e_{\mathbf{Y}_i \cdot \mathbf{X}}$, which is the algebraic amount by which this prediction is in error (to be precise, the amount by which the estimate falls short of the actual value). These error scores then constitute a **Y**-residual variable $\mathbf{e}_{\mathbf{Y} \cdot \mathbf{X}}$, which may be described as what is left of **Y** after variable **X** has been "partialled out." Similarly, if **X** is also used to estimate a second variable **W**, $\mathbf{e}_{W\cdot X}$, is a **W**-residual variable which results by removing from **W** the component, $\dot{\mathbf{W}}_{(X)}$, controlled by **X**. Then the linear correlation of the residuals $\mathbf{e}_{Y\cdot X}$ and $\mathbf{e}_{W\cdot X}$, symbolized in dot notation by "$r_{YW\cdot X}$" is an example of a *partial correlation.*[82] Similarly, the variances of $\mathbf{e}_{Y\cdot X}$ and $\mathbf{e}_{W\cdot X}$, which may be described as the variances of **Y** and **W**, respectively, with **X** partialled out and written in dot notation as $\sigma^2_{Y\cdot X}$ and $\sigma^2_{W\cdot X}$, illustrate what is meant by *partial variance.*

More precisely, $r_{YW\cdot X}$, $\sigma^2_{Y\cdot X}$, and $\sigma^2_{W\cdot X}$ are known as *first-order* partials, since only one variable has been partialled out. The residuals $\mathbf{e}_{Y\cdot X_1X_2}$ and $\mathbf{e}_{W\cdot X_1X_2}$, which remain after the components $\dot{\mathbf{Y}}_{(X_1X_2)}$ and $\dot{\mathbf{W}}_{(X_1X_2)}$ controlled by multiple regression on two predictor variables $\mathbf{X}_1$ and $\mathbf{X}_2$ have been removed from **Y** and **W**, respectively, are examples of "second order" residuals, and their correlation ($r_{YW\cdot X_1X_2}$) and variances ($\sigma^2_{Y\cdot X_1X_2}$ and $\sigma^2_{W\cdot X_1X_2}$) illustrate partial correlation and partial variance of the second order. Higher orders of partial statistics are similarly defined in terms of the number of variables partialled out. In general, if for brevity we let "μ" stand for the set of **m** variables $\mathbf{X}_1, \ldots, \mathbf{X}_m$, statistics from which $\mathbf{X}_1, \ldots, \mathbf{X}_m$ have been partialled out are defined as follows:

[4.105-E] $$\mathbf{e}_{Y\cdot\mu} =_{\text{def}} \mathbf{Y} - \dot{\mathbf{Y}}_{(\mu)} ,$$

[4.105-V] $$\begin{aligned}\sigma^2_{Y\cdot\mu} &=_{\text{def}} \mathrm{Var}(\mathbf{e}_{Y\cdot\mu}) \\ &= \sigma^2_Y(1 - R^2_{Y(\mu)}) \\ &= (\sigma_Y K_{Y(\mu)})^2 ,\end{aligned}$$

[4.105-C] $$\begin{aligned}r_{YW\cdot\mu} &=_{\text{def}} r_{\mathbf{e}_{Y\cdot\mu}\mathbf{e}_{W\cdot\mu}} \\ &= \frac{\mathrm{Cov}(\mathbf{e}_{Y\cdot\mu}, \mathbf{e}_{W\cdot\mu})}{\sigma_{Y\cdot\mu}\sigma_{W\cdot\mu}} .\end{aligned}$$

Then the variable $\mathbf{e}_{Y\cdot\mu}$ is an **m**th-order **Y**-residual, $\sigma^2_{Y\cdot\mu}$ is an **m**th-order partial variance of **Y**, and $r_{YW\cdot\mu}$ is an **m**th-order partial correlation between **Y** and **W**.[83] (Observe, however, that there is not just *one* **m**th-order **Y**-residual, **m**th-order partial variance of **Y**, etc., but as many as there are different sets of **m** variables which can be partialled out.) Other types of **m**th-order partial statistics can be defined in analogous fashion. One which will prove convenient later is the partial coefficient of alienation,

---

[82] The term "partial correlation" should not be confused with "part correlation." The latter expression is used to designate the correlation between a residual and an original variable—e.g., the correlation between **Y** and $\mathbf{e}_{W\cdot X}$.

[83] *Study questions:* The linear correlation r_{XY} between variables **X** and **Y** may be conceived as a partial correlation of what order? What would be the corresponding **X**-residual and **Y**-residual of this order?

the definition and interpretation of which should by now be obvious:

[4.105-K]
$$k_{YW\cdot\mu} =_{\text{def}} k_{e_{Y\cdot\mu}e_{W\cdot\mu}}$$
$$= \sqrt{1 - r^2_{YW\cdot\mu}}\,.$$

The dot notation for subscripts, first introduced so casually in [4.59] above, may now be seen to have a special significance and great generality in terms of partial statistics; namely, the principal statistic (i.e., σ, r, etc.) to which the dot subscript is affixed is to be interpreted as applying to the residuals of the variables cited in the subscript to the left of the dot (known as the "primary" subscripts) after their components linearly controlled by the variables cited in the subscript to the right of the dot (the "secondary subscripts") have been removed.[84]

The significance of partial variance in terms of predictive accuracy should be obvious to the reader: $\sigma^2_{Y\cdot\mu}$ is simply the error variance around the multivariate linear regression of **Y** upon the variables $\boldsymbol{\mu}$ (that is, upon $\mathbf{X}_1, \ldots, \mathbf{X}_m$), while $\sigma_{Y\cdot\mu}$ is the (absolute) standard error of the prediction policy $\hat{\mathbf{Y}} = \dot{\mathbf{Y}}_{(\mu)}$. The interpretation of partial correlation is somewhat more complex and correspondingly more interesting. Before proceeding, however, a little notational housecleaning is in order.

It can hardly have escaped the reader that the systematizing potency of dot notation notwithstanding, our subscripts are becoming discouragingly unwieldy. Consequently, it will be helpful in the ensuing discussion to parallel our general conclusions with a restricted case which permits considerable notational simplification while still communicating all the essential concepts and formulas. Specifically, let us examine four variables, $\mathbf{Z}_0$, $\mathbf{Z}_1$, $\mathbf{Z}_2$, $\mathbf{Z}_3$, all of which have been standardized as Z-scores (i.e., $M_0 = M_1 = M_2 = M_3 = 0$, $\sigma_0 = \sigma_1 = \sigma_2 = \sigma_3 = 1$). Since each variable is identified by a distinctive numeral, we may use the simplification introduced earlier in which a variable is represented in a subscript by its identifying numeral, so that, e.g., r_{12} is the (zero-order) correlation between $\mathbf{Z}_1$ and $\mathbf{Z}_2$, $\mathbf{e}_{0\cdot1}$ is the residual on $\mathbf{Z}_0$ after removal of the component by $\mathbf{Z}_1$, $\sigma^2_{3\cdot2}$ is the variance of $\mathbf{Z}_3$ after $\mathbf{Z}_2$ has been partialled out, and so forth. By examining various ways in which data on $\mathbf{Z}_1$, $\mathbf{Z}_2$, and $\mathbf{Z}_3$ can be processed to yield linear estimates of $\mathbf{Z}_0$, we can discern the roles played by the partial statistics of these variables within the total predictive machinery.

Let us begin by writing the equation for the regression of $\mathbf{Z}_0$ upon $\mathbf{Z}_1$, $\mathbf{Z}_2$, and $\mathbf{Z}_3$, and while so doing, rectify an ambiguity in the notation by which β-coefficients were introduced in [4.88]. It has already been pointed out (p. 145f.) that the β-weight given to a predictor variable $\mathbf{X}_k$ for multivariate estimation of a criterion **Y** is determined not only by

[84] The dot notation for partial statistics, along with much of the theory of partials itself, originated with G. U. Yule around the turn of this century.

the correlation between $\mathbf{X_k}$ and $\mathbf{Y}$, but also by the correlations among these and the other variables in the regression equation. (It is readily seen from [4.90], for example, that the solution for β_1 would in general be altered by omission of some of the variables $\mathbf{X_2}, \ldots, \mathbf{X_m}$ from the set of predictors.) Hence complete identification of a particular β-coefficient requires mention of (*a*) the variable being predicted, (*b*) the variable of which this is the β-coefficient, and (*c*) the other variables on which the prediction is based. It is customary to make this identification in dot notation with the variables cited in (*a*) and (*b*) as primary subscripts and the variables cited in (*c*) as secondary subscripts – i.e., $\beta_{ab \cdot c}$. Thus β_1 in [4.88] is more properly written as $\beta_{\mathbf{YX_1 \cdot X_2 X_3 \ldots X_m}}$, while in general, the β-weight of $\mathbf{X}$ in the linear regression of $\mathbf{Y}$ upon $\mathbf{X_1}, \ldots, \mathbf{X_m}$ is

$$\beta_{\mathbf{YX_k \cdot X_1 \ldots X_{k-1} X_{k+1} \ldots X_m}} .$$

(This same subscript affixed to b, rather than to β, identifies the corresponding b-coefficient. The notation suggests an intimate connection between β-coefficients and partial statistics which will be confirmed later.) Then in complete β-notation, the linear regression of $\mathbf{Z_0}$ upon $\mathbf{Z_1}, \mathbf{Z_2}, \mathbf{Z_3}$ is

$$\dot{\mathbf{Z}}_{0(123)} = \beta_{01 \cdot 23}\mathbf{Z}_1 + \beta_{02 \cdot 13}\mathbf{Z}_2 + \beta_{03 \cdot 12}\mathbf{Z}_3 . \qquad [4.106]$$

We now observe that [4.106] makes *simultaneous* use of data on $\mathbf{Z_1}, \mathbf{Z_2}, \mathbf{Z_3}$ in its estimation of $\mathbf{Z_0}$, and hence that the β-coefficient of each predictor in [4.106] reveals the importance of this datum when it is considered on a par with the other predictor data. However, there is nothing which compels us to make immediate use of all the available data so long as we do not insist upon maximal predictive accuracy at the very outset, and a perfectly legitimate alternative procedure would be to predict the criterion in *sequential* fashion by utilizing the data one by one, revising the preceding estimate in light of each newly added bit of information and observing the rate at which prediction error diminishes as the evidential base broadens. More precisely, the proposal now before us is first to make an optimal linear estimate of the criterion based on one predictor, then to add data on the second predictor in order to estimate the error of the first estimate, and so on – each new predictor variable, in turn, being added to pick up what it can of the criterion residual left by its predecessors. What this amounts to is a whittling away of prediction error by bringing successive pieces of the criterion residual under control by recruiting more and more predictors. The sum of these controlled components at any given stage of the sequence – that is, the first estimate of the criterion, plus the correction obtained by estimating the error of the first estimate, plus the second correction obtained by estimating the error of the first correction, etc. – is then an estimate of the criterion based on all the predictor data considered up to this point, and if optimally derived will equal the estimate of the criterion obtained when these same predictors are used simultaneously. Such a procedure will reveal the extent to which each predictor *supplements* the ones which precede it in the sequence, hence assessing the worth of information on this variable *after* data on its predecessors have already become available. (The reader will recall, for example, that while either form of the FHAAD test is useful by itself for prediction of Company-profit, Form I data are virtually worthless once Form II results are at hand. Conversely, while Form II is predictively superior to Form I, if Form I scores can be obtained at practically no cost while administration of Form II is much more expensive, it would merit investigation whether the predictive accuracy which Form II supplies beyond what is already available through Form I is worth the price.)

For the variables with which we are now working, then, we intend to arrive at $\dot{\mathbf{Z}}_{0(123)}$ by first computing $\dot{\mathbf{Z}}_{0(1)}$ from $\mathbf{Z}_1$, the error of which is $\mathbf{e}_{0\cdot1}$; then estimating $\mathbf{e}_{0\cdot1}$ through additional consideration of $\mathbf{Z}_2$, the error of which should be $\mathbf{e}_{0\cdot12}$; and then to estimate this error, in turn, by taking further cognizance of $\mathbf{Z}_3$. The sum of these three part-estimates is then a multivariate (linear) estimate of $\mathbf{Z}_0$ computed sequentially from $\mathbf{Z}_1, \mathbf{Z}_2, \mathbf{Z}_3$, and should be equal to the simultaneous estimate $\dot{\mathbf{Z}}_{0(123)}$.

The first step in our sequential program is to estimate $\mathbf{Z}_0$ from $\mathbf{Z}_1$ alone. By now, this should be a familiar operation—from [4.58], $\dot{\mathbf{Z}}_{0(1)} = r_{01}\mathbf{Z}_1$, with a corresponding prediction error of $\mathbf{e}_{0\cdot1} = \mathbf{Z}_0 - r_{01}\mathbf{Z}_1$. But the next move, to avail ourselves of $\mathbf{Z}_2$ in addition to $\mathbf{Z}_1$ in order to estimate $\mathbf{e}_{0\cdot1}$, demands more care. At first thought, it might seem that since $\mathbf{Z}_1$ and $\mathbf{e}_{0\cdot1}$ are unrelated (i.e., $\mathrm{Cov}(\mathbf{Z}_1, \mathbf{e}_{0\cdot1}) = 0$), the estimate of $\mathbf{e}_{0\cdot1}$ must come from $\mathbf{Z}_2$ alone and is accordingly to be found by computing the regression of $\mathbf{e}_{0\cdot1}$ upon $\mathbf{Z}_2$. But the estimate so obtained would not be optimal: $\mathbf{e}_{0\cdot1}$ *must be estimated not from* $\mathbf{Z}_2$ *but from the residual,* $\mathbf{e}_{2\cdot1}$, *left of* $\mathbf{Z}_2$ *after removal of the component controlled by* $\mathbf{Z}_1$. This can be proved most directly by computing the linear regression of $\mathbf{e}_{0\cdot1}$ upon $\mathbf{Z}_1$ and $\mathbf{Z}_2$ (e.g., substituting $\mathbf{Z}_{\mathbf{e}_{0\cdot1}}$ for $\mathbf{Z}_0$ in [4.91] and [4.93] while bearing in mind that $\mathrm{Cov}(\mathbf{e}_{0\cdot1}, \mathbf{Z}_1) = 0$) and observing that it can be written as a function of $\mathbf{e}_{2\cdot1}$ alone, but there are also other ways to grasp the point which are worth thinking through for the understanding of multivariate relationships they help to promote. (The reader may omit the remainder of this paragraph if he would just as soon not have his understanding of multivariate relationships promoted in this way.) (1) The first and most intuitive is to reflect that, as pointed out earlier (p. 146), prediction of $\mathbf{Z}_0$ from $\mathbf{Z}_1$ alone already considers the predictive significance of $\mathbf{Z}_2$ for $\mathbf{Z}_0$ insofar as $\mathbf{Z}_2$ can itself be predicted from $\mathbf{Z}_1$; hence if $\mathbf{Z}_2$ is able to supplement $\mathbf{Z}_1$ in prediction of $\mathbf{Z}_0$, it can only be the component of $\mathbf{Z}_2$ uncontrolled by $\mathbf{Z}_1$, namely, $\mathbf{e}_{2\cdot1}$, which carries this additional information. (2) It will be observed that estimating $\mathbf{Z}_0$ from $\mathbf{Z}_1$ and $\mathbf{Z}_2$ by correcting

$\dot{\mathbf{Z}}_{0(1)}$ with a linear estimate of $\mathbf{e}_{0\cdot1}$ based on $\mathbf{Z}_1$ and $\mathbf{Z}_2$ is a prediction procedure of mathematical form $\hat{\mathbf{Z}}_0 = r_{01}\mathbf{Z}_0 + \mathbf{C}_{012}$, where $\mathbf{C}_{012}$ is the correction term (i.e., $\mathbf{C}_{012} =_{\text{def}} \dot{\mathbf{e}}_{0\cdot1\,(12)}$). But this expresses $\hat{\mathbf{Z}}_0$ as a linear function of $\mathbf{Z}_1$ and $\mathbf{C}_{012}$; and if $\hat{\mathbf{Z}}_0$ is the *best* linear estimate from these, the regression coefficient of $\mathbf{Z}_1$ therein is r_{01} if and only if there is no (linear) correlation between $\mathbf{Z}_1$ and $\mathbf{C}_{012}$[85] – which, in turn, occurs if and only if $\mathbf{C}_{012}$ is determined by $\mathbf{e}_{2\cdot1}$ alone.[86] (3) Another way to see that the best estimate of $\mathbf{e}_{0\cdot1}$ from $\mathbf{Z}_1$ and $\mathbf{Z}_2$ must be uncorrelated with $\mathbf{Z}_1$ (and hence must be a function of $\mathbf{e}_{2\cdot1}$ alone) is to reflect that the correction term, if optimally determined, equals the difference between the $\mathbf{Z}_0$-residual given $\mathbf{Z}_1$ only and the $\mathbf{Z}_0$-residual given both $\mathbf{Z}_1$ and $\mathbf{Z}_2$ – i.e., $\mathbf{C}_{012} = \mathbf{e}_{0\cdot1} - \mathbf{e}_{0\cdot12}$. But then $\text{Cov}(\mathbf{Z}_1, \mathbf{C}_{012}) = \text{Cov}(\mathbf{Z}_1, \mathbf{e}_{0\cdot1}) - \text{Cov}(\mathbf{Z}_1, \mathbf{e}_{0\cdot12}) = 0$, since the correlation between a residual and any variable partialled out in forming that residual is zero. (4) Finally, it may be observed that the correlation between the $\mathbf{Z}_0$-residual left by $\mathbf{Z}_1$ and a linear estimate thereof based on $\mathbf{Z}_1$ and $\mathbf{Z}_2$ is maximal when this estimate is a linear function only of the $\mathbf{Z}_2$-residual left by $\mathbf{Z}_1$.[87]

It can thus be demonstrated *ad nauseam* that once data on $\mathbf{Z}_2$ also become available as a supplement to $\mathbf{Z}_1$-data, the best (linear) estimate of the error made in predicting $\mathbf{Z}_0$ from $\mathbf{Z}_1$ is given by the (linear) regression of $\mathbf{e}_{0\cdot1}$ on $\mathbf{e}_{2\cdot1}$. Bearing in mind that $\mathbf{e}_{0\cdot1}$ and $\mathbf{e}_{2\cdot1}$, though with zero means, are residuals of Z-scores and are hence not in general themselves Z-scores, so that regression formula [4.56] must be used rather than [4.58], we then compute that the first correction term $\mathbf{C}_{012}$ ($= \dot{\mathbf{e}}_{0\cdot1\,(12)}$) equals

$$\frac{\text{Cov}(\mathbf{e}_{0\cdot1}, \mathbf{e}_{2\cdot1})}{\text{Var}(\mathbf{e}_{2\cdot1})}\,\mathbf{e}_{2\cdot1},$$

or

$$r_{02\cdot1}\frac{\sigma_{0\cdot1}}{\sigma_{2\cdot1}}\,\mathbf{e}_{2\cdot1}.$$

In like fashion, it can be seen that to employ data on $\mathbf{Z}_3$ for estimation of the error, $\mathbf{e}_{0\cdot12}$, made when predicting $\mathbf{Z}_0$ jointly from $\mathbf{Z}_1$ and $\mathbf{Z}_2$

[85] From [4.90], setting $\mathbf{m} = \mathbf{2}$ and assuming that the β-coefficient for $\mathbf{C}_{012}$ is not zero (this assumption being violated only if $\text{Var}(\mathbf{C}_{012}) = 0$, in which case the correlation in question is ill-defined).

[86] Since $\mathbf{C}_{012}$ is a linear function of $\mathbf{Z}_1$ and $\mathbf{Z}_2$, and $\mathbf{Z}_2$ is a linear function of $\mathbf{Z}_1$ and $\mathbf{e}_{2\cdot1}$, $\mathbf{C}_{012}$ is also a linear function of $\mathbf{Z}_1$ and $\mathbf{e}_{2\cdot1}$, say $\mathbf{C}_{012} = a_1\mathbf{Z}_1 + a_2\mathbf{e}_{2\cdot1} + a_3$. Hence $\text{Cov}(\mathbf{C}_{012}, \mathbf{Z}_1) = a_1\,\text{Cov}(\mathbf{Z}_1, \mathbf{Z}_1) + a_2\,\text{Cov}(\mathbf{Z}_1, \mathbf{e}_{2\cdot1}) = a_1\,\text{Var}(\mathbf{Z}_1)$, so $\mathbf{Z}_1$ and $\mathbf{C}_{012}$ are uncorrelated if and only if $a_1 = 0$ – i.e., if and only if $\mathbf{C}_{012}$ is a function of $\mathbf{e}_{2\cdot1}$ alone.

[87] Let $\mathbf{C}_{012} = a_1\mathbf{Z}_1 + a_2\mathbf{e}_{2\cdot1} + a_3$ as explained in the previous footnote. Since the covariance of $\mathbf{Z}_1$ with both $\mathbf{e}_{0\cdot1}$ and $\mathbf{e}_{2\cdot1}$ is zero, we have $\text{Cov}(\mathbf{e}_{0\cdot1}, \mathbf{C}_{012}) = a_2\,\text{Cov}(\mathbf{e}_{0\cdot1}, \mathbf{e}_{2\cdot1})$ and $\text{Var}(\mathbf{C}_{012}) = a_1^2 + a_2^2\,\text{Var}(\mathbf{e}_{2\cdot1})$, so the correlation between $\mathbf{e}_{0\cdot1}$ and $\mathbf{C}_{012}$, namely, $\text{Cov}(\mathbf{e}_{0\cdot1}, \mathbf{C}_{012})/\sigma_{0\cdot1}\sqrt{\text{Var}(\mathbf{e}_{2\cdot1}) + (a_1/a_2)^2}$, is maximal when $a_1 = 0$ and hence when $\mathbf{C}_{012}$ is a function only of $\mathbf{e}_{2\cdot1}$.

(which is the same as estimating the error of $\mathbf{C}_{012}$ as an estimate of $\mathbf{e}_{0\cdot1}$), we take the regression of $\mathbf{e}_{0\cdot12}$ on that component of $\mathbf{Z}_3$ which is independent of $\mathbf{Z}_1$ and $\mathbf{Z}_2$, namely, $\mathbf{e}_{3\cdot12}$. The second correction term is hence

$$\dot{\mathbf{e}}_{0\cdot12(123)} = \frac{\mathrm{Cov}(\mathbf{e}_{0\cdot12}, \mathbf{e}_{3\cdot12})}{\mathrm{Var}(\mathbf{e}_{3\cdot12})}\mathbf{e}_{3\cdot12} = \mathrm{r}_{03\cdot12}\frac{\sigma_{0\cdot12}}{\sigma_{3\cdot12}}\mathbf{e}_{3\cdot12}.$$

Putting original estimate and corrections together, we have a formula for the sequential estimation of $\mathbf{Z}_0$ in which each successive term to the right adduces a new datum to correct the previous estimates:

[4.107][88] $$\dot{\mathbf{Z}}_{0(123)} = \mathrm{r}_{01}\mathbf{Z}_1 + \mathrm{r}_{02\cdot1}\frac{\sigma_{0\cdot1}}{\sigma_{2\cdot1}}\mathbf{e}_{2\cdot1} + \mathrm{r}_{03\cdot12}\frac{\sigma_{0\cdot12}}{\sigma_{3\cdot12}}\mathbf{e}_{3\cdot12}.$$

More generally, if we have an estimate, $\dot{\mathbf{Y}}_{(\mu)}$, of a criterion **Y** based on data on variables $\boldsymbol{\mu}$ (i.e., $\mathbf{X}_1, \ldots, \mathbf{X}_m$), the revised estimate of **Y** obtained by including data on an additional predictor **W** is

[4.108][89] $$\dot{\mathbf{Y}}_{(\mathbf{W}\mu)} = \dot{\mathbf{Y}}_{(\mu)} + \frac{\mathrm{Cov}(\mathbf{e}_{\mathbf{Y}\cdot\mu}, \mathbf{e}_{\mathbf{W}\cdot\mu})}{\mathrm{Var}(\mathbf{e}_{\mathbf{W}\cdot\mu})}\mathbf{e}_{\mathbf{W}\cdot\mu}$$

$$= \dot{\mathbf{Y}}_{(\mu)} + \mathrm{r}_{\mathbf{YW}\cdot\mu}\frac{\sigma_{\mathbf{Y}\cdot\mu}}{\sigma_{\mathbf{W}\cdot\mu}}\mathbf{e}_{\mathbf{W}\cdot\mu}.$$

Before concluding that we have gone through an extraordinarily tedious argument merely to transform a crisp formula (namely, [4.106]) into a turgid one ([4.107]), the reader should reflect that not only do [4.107] and, more generally, [4.108] show how to revise predictions in light of new information, they also expose what partial statistics have to do with prediction. Specifically, the degree of accuracy with which the residual error in the prediction of **Y** from $\mathbf{X}_1, \ldots, \mathbf{X}_m$ can be estimated through appeal to data on still another predictor **W** is given by the **m**th order correlation between **Y** and **W** with $\mathbf{X}_1, \ldots, \mathbf{X}_m$ partialled out.

---

[88] While our arguments have made *plausible* that the expression to the right of the equality sign in [4.107] equals the one on the left (which is defined by [4.106]), we have not actually *proved* it. The reader should see whether he can do so. *Hints:* (*a*) Observe that constants a_1, a_2, and a_3 can always be found such that $a_1\mathbf{Z}_1 + a_2\mathbf{e}_{2\cdot1} + a_3\mathbf{e}_{3\cdot12} = \dot{\mathbf{Z}}_{0(123)}$. (*b*) Argue that the constants so found are the *b*-coefficients in the linear regression of $\mathbf{Z}_0$ on $\mathbf{Z}_1$, $\mathbf{e}_{2\cdot1}$, and $\mathbf{e}_{3\cdot12}$. (*c*) Solve for these *b*-coefficients through use of the normal equations, observing that the covariances among $\mathbf{Z}_1$, $\mathbf{e}_{2\cdot1}$, and $\mathbf{e}_{3\cdot12}$ are all zero (cf. fn. 90, p. 163), that $\mathrm{Cov}(\mathbf{Z}_0, \mathbf{e}_{2\cdot1}) = \mathrm{Cov}(\dot{\mathbf{Z}}_{0(1)} + \mathbf{e}_{0\cdot1}, \mathbf{e}_{2\cdot1}) = \mathrm{Cov}(\mathbf{e}_{0\cdot1}, \mathbf{e}_{2\cdot1})$, and similarly $\mathrm{Cov}(\mathbf{Z}_0, \mathbf{e}_{3\cdot12}) = \mathrm{Cov}(\mathbf{e}_{0\cdot12}, \mathbf{e}_{3\cdot12})$.

[89] In contrast to [4.107], formula [4.108] does *not* presuppose that the variables have been standardized as Z-scores. One way to prove [4.108] is to observe that the regression of **Y** on **W** and $\boldsymbol{\mu}$ coincides with the regression of **Y** on $\dot{\mathbf{Y}}_{(\mu)}$ and $\mathbf{e}_{\mathbf{W}\cdot\mu}$, and then to determine the latter.

With [4.108] to show how much of the error in predicting $\mathbf{Y}$ is eliminated with consideration of each new datum, we can readily compute the component of criterion variance which comes under control at each step of a sequential prediction procedure. Since [4.107] expresses $\dot{\mathbf{Z}}_{0(123)}$ as a linear function of the three mutually uncorrelated variables $\mathbf{Z}_1$, $\mathbf{e}_{2\cdot 1}$, and $\mathbf{e}_{3\cdot 12}$,[90] it is a simple consequence of [4.107] by principle [4.42] that

$$[4.109] \qquad \mathrm{Var}(\dot{\mathbf{Z}}_{0(123)}) = r^2_{01} + r^2_{02\cdot 1}\sigma^2_{0\cdot 1} + r^2_{03\cdot 12}\,\sigma^2_{0\cdot 12},$$

where each term to the right shows the controlled variance added with each new predictor. More generally,

$$[4.110]^{91} \qquad \mathrm{Var}(\dot{\mathbf{Y}}_{(\mathbf{W}\mu)}) = \mathrm{Var}(\dot{\mathbf{Y}}_{(\mu)}) + r^2_{\mathbf{YW}\cdot\mu}\,\sigma^2_{\mathbf{Y}\cdot\mu}.$$

That is, the increment in controlled criterion variance achieved by supplementing predictor variables μ with an additional predictor $\mathbf{W}$ equals $r^2_{\mathbf{YW}\cdot\mu}\,\sigma^2_{\mathbf{Y}\cdot\mu}$, which is the variance of $\mathbf{e}_{\mathbf{Y}\cdot\mu}$ controlled by $\mathbf{e}_{\mathbf{W}\cdot\mu}$. It is easy to see, since $\mathrm{Cov}(\mathbf{e}_{\mathbf{Y}\cdot\mu}, \mathbf{e}_{\mathbf{W}\cdot\mu}) = \mathrm{Cov}(\mathbf{Y}, \mathbf{e}_{\mathbf{W}\cdot\mu})$, that $r^2_{\mathbf{YW}\cdot\mu}\,\sigma^2_{\mathbf{Y}\cdot\mu}$ is also the variance of $\mathbf{Y}$ controlled by $\mathbf{e}_{\mathbf{W}\cdot\mu}$ when $\mathbf{Y}$ is estimated from $\mathbf{e}_{\mathbf{W}\cdot\mu}$ alone.[92] What an additional predictor contributes to predictive accuracy is thus capture of that portion of the criterion variance which is controlled by the component of the new predictor not already predictable from the old ones. The quantitative significance of this gain will be examined in a moment.

A number of interesting formulas can be derived from [4.110]. By observing that $\mathrm{Var}(\dot{\mathbf{Y}}_{(\mu)}) = \mathrm{Var}(\mathbf{Y}) - \sigma^2_{\mathbf{Y}\cdot\mu}$ and $\mathrm{Var}(\dot{\mathbf{Y}}_{(\mathbf{W}\mu)}) = \mathrm{Var}(\mathbf{Y}) - \sigma^2_{\mathbf{Y}\cdot\mathbf{W}\mu}$, substituting into [4.110] and solving for $r_{\mathbf{YW}\cdot\mu}$, we arrive at a result which is sometimes offered in definition of partial correlation; namely,

$$[4.111] \qquad r^2_{\mathbf{YW}\cdot\mu} = 1 - \frac{\sigma^2_{\mathbf{Y}\cdot\mathbf{W}\mu}}{\sigma^2_{\mathbf{Y}\cdot\mu}}.$$

(Once it is seen that the standard error of $\mathbf{Y}$, given $\mathbf{W}$ and μ, is equal to the standard error of $\mathbf{e}_{\mathbf{Y}\cdot\mu}$, given $\mathbf{e}_{\mathbf{W}\cdot\mu}$, [4.111] also follows immediately from the relationship between correlation and standard error (cf. [4.62]) and the definition of $r_{\mathbf{YW}\cdot\mu}$ as the correlation between $\mathbf{e}_{\mathbf{Y}\cdot\mu}$ and $\mathbf{e}_{\mathbf{W}\cdot\mu}$.) Equation [4.111] shows that the degree to which predictions of $\mathbf{Y}$ from $\mathbf{W}$ and μ together is more efficient than prediction from the variables in

[90] *Study problem:* Prove that a linear residual $\mathbf{e}_{\mathbf{Y}\cdot\mu}$ has zero covariance with any linear function of the variables in the set μ, and hence in particular that $\mathbf{e}_{\mathbf{Y}\cdot\mu}$ has zero covariance with any other residual whose subscripts refer only to variables included in μ.

[91] From [4.108] by [4.44], observing that by the theorem of fn. 90, above, $\mathrm{Cov}(\dot{\mathbf{Y}}_{(\mu)}, \mathbf{e}_{\mathbf{Y}\cdot\mu}) = 0$.

[92] Since $\mathbf{Y} = \dot{\mathbf{Y}}_{(\mu)} + \mathbf{e}_{\mathbf{Y}\cdot\mu}$ while $\mathrm{Cov}(\dot{\mathbf{Y}}_{(\mu)}, \mathbf{e}_{\mathbf{W}\cdot\mu}) = 0$, we have $\mathrm{Cov}(\mathbf{Y}, \mathbf{e}_{\mathbf{W}\cdot\mu}) = \mathrm{Cov}(\dot{\mathbf{Y}}_{(\mu)}, \mathbf{e}_{\mathbf{W}\cdot\mu}) + \mathrm{Cov}(\mathbf{e}_{\mathbf{Y}\cdot\mu}, \mathbf{e}_{\mathbf{W}\cdot\mu}) = \mathrm{Cov}(\mathbf{e}_{\mathbf{Y}\cdot\mu}, \mathbf{e}_{\mathbf{W}\cdot\mu})$ or $\sigma_{\mathbf{Y}}\sigma_{\mathbf{W}\cdot\mu}r_{\mathbf{Ye}_{\mathbf{W}\cdot\mu}} = \sigma_{\mathbf{Y}\cdot\mu}\sigma_{\mathbf{W}\cdot\mu}r_{\mathbf{YW}\cdot\mu}$. Hence $\sigma^2_{\mathbf{Y}\cdot\mu}r^2_{\mathbf{YW}\cdot\mu} = \sigma^2_{\mathbf{Y}}r^2_{\mathbf{Ye}_{\mathbf{W}\cdot\mu}} = \mathrm{Var}(\dot{\mathbf{Y}}_{(\mathbf{e}_{\mathbf{W}\cdot\mu})})$.

μ alone is described by the partial correlation $r_{YW\cdot\mu}$ in the very same way that r_{YW} describes the degree to which prediction of **Y** from **W** is more efficient than prediction from no predictor variables.

Several useful variants of [4.110] may be developed by rewriting this equation in terms of partial and multiple correlations. Since $R^2_{Y(\mu)} = \mathrm{Var}(\dot{Y}_{(\mu)})/\sigma^2_Y$, $R^2_{Y(W\mu)} = \mathrm{Var}(\dot{Y}_{(W\mu)})/\sigma^2_Y$ and $\sigma^2_{Y\cdot\mu}/\sigma^2_Y = (1 - R^2_{Y(\mu)})$, substitution into [4.110] after division through by σ^2_Y yields

$$R^2_{Y(W\mu)} = R^2_{Y(\mu)} + r^2_{YW\cdot\mu}(1 - R^2_{Y(\mu)}) \,. \tag{4.112}$$

Subtraction of both sides from 1 and regrouping the terms on the right then leaves

$$(1 - R^2_{Y(W\mu)}) = (1 - R^2_{Y(\mu)})(1 - r^2_{YW\cdot\mu}) \,. \tag{4.113}$$

This is in particularly convenient form for iteration into a formula expressing the multiple correlation coefficient as a function of partial correlations of ascending order between the criterion and each successive predictor. Thus the multiple correlation between $\mathbf{Z}_0$ and $\mathbf{Z}_1$, $\mathbf{Z}_2$, $\mathbf{Z}_3$ is shown by repeated application of [4.113] to be

$$(1 - R^2_{0(123)}) = (1 - r^2_{01})(1 - r^2_{02\cdot1})(1 - r^2_{03\cdot12}) \,, \tag{4.114}$$

or solving for R,

$$R_{0(123)} = \sqrt{1 - (1 - r^2_{01})(1 - r^2_{02\cdot1})(1 - r^2_{03\cdot12})} \,. \tag{4.114a}$$

Observation that the parenthesized expressions in [4.113] are all squares of coefficients of alienation permits an especially terse formulation:

$$K_{Y(W\mu)} = K_{Y(\mu)} k_{YW\cdot\mu} \,, \tag{4.115}$$

or, expressed in terms of standard error by multiplying both sides by σ_Y,

$$\sigma_{Y\cdot W\mu} = \sigma_{Y\cdot\mu} k_{YW\cdot\mu} \,. \tag{4.116}$$

That is, each new predictor increases predictive accuracy by reducing the standard error of estimate to a certain fraction of its previous value, this fraction being the coefficient of alienation between the criterion and the new predictor after the previous predictors are partialled out. To assess the usefulness of this increment in predictive accuracy, let "supplementary savings" measure $S_{Y,W[\mu]}$ be defined

$$[4.117] \qquad S_{Y,W[\mu]} =_{\mathrm{def}} \frac{\sigma_{Y\cdot\mu} - \sigma_{Y\cdot W\mu}}{\sigma_Y}$$

$$= K_{Y(\mu)} - K_{Y(W\mu)} \,.$$

The numerical value of $S_{Y,W[\mu]}$ then tells what additional proportion of the original standard error σ_Y of **Y** is eliminated when the predictors in μ are augmented by **W**. For the special case where μ is empty, $S_{Y,W}$ is the proportion by which **W** decreases the standard error of **Y** when it is the only predictor and, as mentioned in a previous footnote, is sometimes called the "index of forecasting efficiency." From [4.115] and [4.117] it follows that

[4.118] $$S_{Y,W[\mu]} = K_{Y(\mu)}(1 - k_{YW\cdot\mu}) ,$$

which then describes the worth (relative to σ_Y) of **W** as a *supplement* to μ for predicting **Y**, as contrasted to its corresponding worth,

[4.119] $$S_{Y,W} = 1 - k_{YW} ,$$

for predicting **Y** by itself. (The reader who prefers to think in terms of coefficients of correlation, rather than of alienation, may substitute $\sqrt{1 - R^2}$ and $\sqrt{1 - r^2}$ for K and k, respectively, in [4.118] and [4.119] if he has the fortitude to live with the result.) Perhaps no more incisive comparison can be made between the initial predictive worth of a variable as determined by its zero-order correlation with the criterion and its supplementary predictive value as determined (in part) by its partial correlation with the criterion than is afforded by formulas [4.118] and [4.119]. Specifically, we see that $1 - k_{YW\cdot\mu}$ has essentially the same interpretation as a measure of **W**'s supplementary worth as a predictor as does $1 - k_{YW}$ for **W**'s initial predictive efficiency, except that to arrive at this measure in the supplementary case, $1 - k_{YW\cdot\mu}$ must also be attenuated by the extent to which the criterion can already be successfully estimated without **W**'s help.

Returning to formula [4.115], it is of interest to note that its iteration expresses multiple K as a product of partial ks of ascending order, e.g.,

[4.120] $$K_{0(123)} = k_{01}k_{02\cdot1}k_{03\cdot12} ,$$

the extension of which to any number of predictors is obvious. So interpreted, formula [4.115] or [4.116] makes especially visible the manner in which prediction error decreases as more and more predictors are brought into play. Imagine a graph, such as Figure 4.10, p. 169, based on [4.115] or [4.116] and showing for an indefinitely long series of predictor variables the magnitude of $K_{Y(\mu)}$ or $\sigma_{Y\cdot\mu}$ as a function of the number of predictors reached at a given stage in the sequence. The precise form of this curve will depend, of course, upon the statistical details of the variables involved and the particular order in which they are applied. Nonetheless, a general shape can be anticipated: Beginning at a value of 1 for $K_{Y(\mu)}$ and σ_Y for $\sigma_{Y\cdot\mu}$ when μ consists of no predictors, the curve will sink lower and lower as the number of variables in μ increases, the rate of decrease becoming smaller as the series progresses and asymptotically approaching (or perhaps eventually reaching) a lower limit which in principle may be zero but which in practice will be appreciably higher than this. Such a trend shows that if the cost of information is more or less proportional to the number of predictors employed, a point will eventually be reached where the predictive accuracy achieved by additional information will not be worth the price, especially when the curve is near its limit. It should also be appreciated that the speed with which the curve approaches its limit depends upon the order in which the predictor variables are applied. This suggests that in attempting to achieve maximal predictive accuracy with a minimum of predictors, one should seek a sequence of predictors for which the standard error of the criterion diminishes with the greatest rapidity. It would be exceedingly useful in this respect if, for any given set of predictors, there were one sequence of these for which the error curve (i.e., $K_{\mathbf{Y}(\boldsymbol{\mu})}$ or $\sigma_{\mathbf{Y}\bullet\boldsymbol{\mu}}$ as $\boldsymbol{\mu}$ increases) is always as low as or lower than the error curve for any alternative sequence of that set. Deplorably, such a uniformly most accurate sequence does not necessarily exist. If it does exist, however, it may be found with a minimum of computation by selecting for the first predictor the one which correlates most highly with the criterion, secondly the predictor with the highest first-order partial correlation with the criterion after the first predictor has been partialled out, thirdly the predictor with the highest second-order partial correlation with the criterion after the first two predictors have been partialled out, and so on. And while selection of $\mathbf{m}$ variables in this way from a set of $\mathbf{n}$ ($\mathbf{m} < \mathbf{n}$) available predictors does not *guarantee* obtaining that selection of size $\mathbf{m}$ from these $\mathbf{n}$ whose multiple correlation with the criterion is highest, it is unlikely to produce a selection which is appreciably poorer than optimal.

An obvious consequence of [4.120], since each factor on the right cannot be greater than unity, is that $K_{0(123)}$ is equal to or smaller than each partial k in this product. But this is also true for any other sequence from Z_1, Z_2, Z_3. Hence $K_{0(123)}$ is at least as small as any coefficient of alienation between $\mathbf{Z}_0$ and $\mathbf{Z}_1$, $\mathbf{Z}_2$, or $\mathbf{Z}_3$ with any of the others partialled out. More generally, if $\boldsymbol{\mu}$ is a set of variables included in a larger set $\boldsymbol{\mu}'$ which also contains an additional variable $\mathbf{X}$ (i.e., $\boldsymbol{\mu}'$ consists of $\mathbf{X}$, the variables in $\boldsymbol{\mu}$, and perhaps other variables as well),

[4.121-K] $$K_{\mathbf{Y}(\boldsymbol{\mu}')} \leqslant k_{\mathbf{YX}\bullet\boldsymbol{\mu}} \, .$$

For some reason, this conclusion appears more striking if rephrased in terms of correlation—i.e.,

[4.121-R] $$R_{\mathbf{Y}(\boldsymbol{\mu}')} \geqslant r_{\mathbf{YX}\bullet\boldsymbol{\mu}} \, .$$

Let a partial statistic be said to be "based on" a set of variables $\mathbf{X}_1, \ldots, \mathbf{X}_m$ if the variables partialled out of it are included among $\mathbf{X}_1, \ldots, \mathbf{X}_m$.

Then [4.121-R] says that the multiple correlation between **Y** and a set of predictors $\boldsymbol{\mu}'$ is at least as great as any partial correlation of any order based on $\boldsymbol{\mu}'$ between **Y** and any variable included in $\boldsymbol{\mu}'$.

Before illustrating the foregoing relationships with a numerical example, it is desirable to show how partial correlations of a given order can be computed from lower-order partials. The correlation between $\mathbf{Z_0}$ and $\mathbf{Z_2}$ with $\mathbf{Z_1}$ partialled out may be derived by analyzing $\mathbf{Z_0}$ and $\mathbf{Z_2}$ into components controlled by $\mathbf{Z_1}$, plus residuals, as follows: Since $\mathbf{Z_0} = \dot{\mathbf{Z}}_{0(1)} + \mathbf{e}_{0\cdot 1} = r_{01}\mathbf{Z_1} + \mathbf{e}_{0\cdot 1}$ and $\mathbf{Z_2} = \dot{\mathbf{Z}}_{2(1)} + \mathbf{e}_{2\cdot 1} = r_{21}\mathbf{Z_1} + \mathbf{e}_{2\cdot 1}$, $\text{Cov}(\mathbf{Z_0},\mathbf{Z_2}) = r_{01}r_{21}\,\text{Cov}(\mathbf{Z_1},\mathbf{Z_1}) + r_{01}\,\text{Cov}(\mathbf{Z_1},\mathbf{e}_{2\cdot 1}) + r_{21}\,\text{Cov}(\mathbf{Z_1},\mathbf{e}_{0\cdot 1}) + \text{Cov}(\mathbf{e}_{0\cdot 1},\mathbf{e}_{2\cdot 1})$. But $\text{Cov}(\mathbf{Z_1},\mathbf{e}_{0\cdot 1}) = \text{Cov}(\mathbf{Z_1},\mathbf{e}_{2\cdot 1}) = 0$, while $\text{Cov}(\mathbf{Z_0},\mathbf{Z_2}) = r_{02}$, $\text{Cov}(\mathbf{Z_1},\mathbf{Z_1}) = 1$, and $\text{Cov}(\mathbf{e}_{0\cdot 1},\mathbf{e}_{2\cdot 1}) = \sigma_{0\cdot 1}\sigma_{2\cdot 1}r_{02\cdot 1} = (\sigma_0 k_{01})(\sigma_2 k_{21})r_{02\cdot 1} = k_{01}k_{21}r_{02\cdot 1}$. Hence

$$[4.122] \qquad r_{02} = r_{01}r_{21} + k_{01}k_{21}r_{02\cdot 1},$$

and solving for the partial yields

$$[4.123] \qquad r_{02\cdot 1} = \frac{r_{02} - r_{01}r_{21}}{k_{01}k_{21}} = \frac{r_{02} - r_{01}r_{21}}{\sqrt{(1 - r_{01}^2)(1 - r_{21}^2)}}.$$

Moreover, while [4.123] was derived under the simplifying assumption that $\mathbf{Z_0}$, $\mathbf{Z_1}$, and $\mathbf{Z_2}$ have zero means and unit SDs, it is evident (cf. [4.105-C] and [4.48]) that a partial correlation is invariant under any linear transformations of the variables with positive multipliers. Hence formula [4.123] applies to any three variables, whether standardized as Z-scores or not.

More generally, the $(\mathbf{m}+\mathbf{1})$th-order correlation between variables **Y** and **W** after **X** and **m** other variables $\boldsymbol{\mu}$ have been partialled out may be derived from the **m**th-order correlations among **Y**, **W**, and **X** with $\boldsymbol{\mu}$ partialled out by letting $\mathbf{e}_{Y\cdot\mu}$, $\mathbf{e}_{W\cdot\mu}$, and $\mathbf{e}_{X\cdot\mu}$ replace $\mathbf{Z_0}$, $\mathbf{Z_2}$, and $\mathbf{Z_1}$, respectively, in [4 123] while observing that the correlation between $\mathbf{e}_{Y\cdot\mu}$ and $\mathbf{e}_{W\cdot\mu}$ with $\mathbf{e}_{X\cdot\mu}$ partialled out is the same as the correlation between **Y** and **W** with **X** and $\boldsymbol{\mu}$ partialled out (namely, the correlation between $\mathbf{e}_{Y\cdot X\mu}$ and $\mathbf{e}_{W\cdot X\mu}$ in both cases). That is,

$$[4.124] \qquad r_{YW\cdot\mu} = \frac{r_{YW\cdot\mu} - r_{YX\cdot\mu}r_{WX\cdot\mu}}{k_{YX\cdot\mu}k_{YW\cdot\mu}} = \frac{r_{YW\cdot\mu} - r_{YX\cdot\mu}r_{WX\cdot\mu}}{\sqrt{(1 - r_{YX\cdot\mu}^2)(1 - r_{WX\cdot\mu}^2)}}.$$

Recalling that in our previous numerical example, the correlations among Company-profit ($\mathbf{Z_0}$), and Forms I ($\mathbf{Z_1}$) and II ($\mathbf{Z_2}$) of the FHAAD test were $r_{01} = .60$, $r_{02} = .70$, and $r_{12} = .80$, we can now compute from [4.123] that $r_{01\cdot 2} = (.7 - .6 \times .8)/\sqrt{(1-.7^2)(1-.8^2)} = .458$ and $r_{01\cdot 2} = (.6 - .7 \times .8)/\sqrt{(1-.7^2)(1-.8^2)} = .093$, while the corresponding coefficients of alienation are $k_{01} = .80$, $k_{02} = .714$, $k_{12} = .60$, $k_{02\cdot 1} = .889$, and $k_{01\cdot 2} = .996$. The latter figures, applied by formula [4.118], sketch in a few vivid strokes the portrait earlier drawn more obscurely and laboriously of the respective contributions by $\mathbf{Z_1}$ and $\mathbf{Z_2}$ to prediction of $\mathbf{Z_0}$. The reductions of prediction error accomplished by $\mathbf{Z_1}$ and $\mathbf{Z_2}$ when each is taken by itself as the sole predictor of **Y** are 20% and 28.6%, respectively (i.e., $S_{01} = 1 - .80 = .20$ and $S_{02} = 1 - .714 = .286$), which in either case is useful if not impressive. However, while $\mathbf{Z_2}$ supplements $\mathbf{Z_1}$ to gain an additional error reduction of 8.9% (i.e., $S_{02[1]} = .80 \times (1 - .889) = .089$) for a total predictive efficiency of 28.9%, $\mathbf{Z_1}$ achieves almost the combined accuracy by itself, and the supplementary savings contributed by $\mathbf{Z_2}$ is a negligible .3% (i.e., $S_{01[2]} = .714 \times (1 - .996) = .003$).

To flesh out this example with more combinatorial possibilities, suppose that a rating scale $\mathbf{Z_3}$, based on certain items of personal biography, is also discovered to be a modest predictor of a Great Northern field agent's Company-profit score while being unrelated to FHAAD performances. Specifically, assume that $r_{03} = .40$ and $r_{13} = r_{23} = 0$. From this set of three predictor variables, there are then eight possible combinations which might be used to predict $\mathbf{Z_0}$ (namely, $\mathbf{Z_1}$, $\mathbf{Z_2}$, $\mathbf{Z_3}$, $\mathbf{Z_1 Z_2}$, $\mathbf{Z_1 Z_3}$, $\mathbf{Z_2 Z_3}$, $\mathbf{Z_1 Z_2 Z_3}$, or none) and six sequences (namely, $\mathbf{Z_1 Z_2 Z_3}$, $\mathbf{Z_1 Z_3 Z_2}$, $\mathbf{Z_2 Z_1 Z_3}$, $\mathbf{Z_2 Z_3 Z_1}$, $\mathbf{Z_3 Z_1 Z_2}$, $\mathbf{Z_3 Z_2 Z_1}$) by which predictor data can be applied. The partial statistics required to describe these possibilities are listed in Table 4.5, while multiple coefficients of alienation for the various data combinations are worked out in Table 4.6 and displayed graphically in Figure 4.10. While no further discussion of these statistics will be undertaken here, Figure 4.10 well merits a pause for observation and comtemplation. In particular, the reader should note the larger error reduction effected by $\mathbf{Z_3}$ when used to supplement $\mathbf{Z_1}$ or $\mathbf{Z_2}$ than when used alone (why?), and also ponder what his choice—and its success—would be were he to attempt selection of the best pair of predictors by inspecting only the zero-order correlations. The reader may also find it useful, both as an exercise and for what the end product reveals to him, to convert Figure 4.10 into a graph showing $R_{0(\mu)}$ in place of $K_{0(\mu)}$.

While a multiple correlation can change in only one direction—upward—as more and more predictors are recruited, it is not possible to be so definite about what happens to a correlation when other variables are partialled out. This depends a great deal upon the pattern of intercorrelations among the variables involved. How partialling affects a correlation will be examined in the next three paragraphs. However, the reader who already feels surfeited with the mathematics of partial cor-

Zero Order	r_{01}	$= .6000$	r_{02}	$= .7000$	r_{03}	$= .4000$
	k_{01}	$= .8000$	k_{02}	$= .7141$	k_{03}	$= .9165$
	r_{12}	$= .8000$	r_{13}	$= 0$	r_{23}	$= 0$
	k_{12}	$= .6000$	k_{13}	$= 1$	k_{23}	$= 1$
First Order	$r_{02 \cdot 1}$	$= .4583$	$r_{03 \cdot 1}$	$= .5000$	$r_{23 \cdot 1}$	$= 0$
	$k_{02 \cdot 1}$	$= .8888$	$k_{03 \cdot 1}$	$= .8660$	$k_{23 \cdot 1}$	$= 1$
	$r_{01 \cdot 2}$	$= .0933$	$r_{03 \cdot 2}$	$= .5601$	$r_{13 \cdot 2}$	$= 0$
	$k_{01 \cdot 2}$	$= .9956$	$k_{03 \cdot 2}$	$= .8284$	$k_{13 \cdot 2}$	$= 1$
	$r_{01 \cdot 3}$	$= .6547$	$r_{02 \cdot 3}$	$= .7637$	$r_{12 \cdot 3}$	$= .8000$
	$k_{01 \cdot 3}$	$= .7559$	$k_{02 \cdot 3}$	$= .6455$	$k_{12 \cdot 3}$	$= .6000$
Second Order	$r_{03 \cdot 12}$	$= .5625$	$r_{02 \cdot 13}$	$= .5292$	$r_{01 \cdot 23}$	$= .1127$
	$k_{03 \cdot 12}$	$= .8268$	$k_{02 \cdot 13}$	$= .8485$	$k_{01 \cdot 23}$	$= .9936$

Table 4.5. Partial coefficients of correlation and alienation of all orders among variables Z_0, Z_1, Z_2, and Z_3 when $r_{01} = .60$, $r_{02} = .70$, $r_{03} = .40$, $r_{12} = .80$, $r_{13} = 0$, and $r_{23} = 0$.

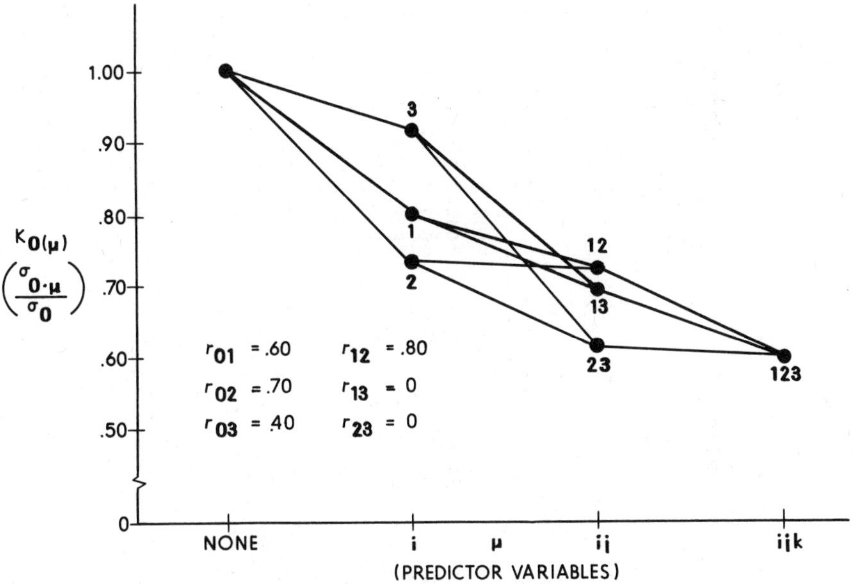

Figure 4.10. Illustrative reduction of prediction error as a function of the information μ on which the prediction is based. Each dot shows the multiple coefficient of alienation for estimation of criterion Z_0 from the indicated selection μ of predictor variables from the set Z_1, Z_2, Z_3, while the connecting lines trace the progressive decrease in standard error as information is applied sequentially. (Data from Table 4.6.)

Sequence ijk	One Predictor $K_{0(i)} = k_{0i}$	Two Predictors $K_{0(ij)} = K_{0(i)}k_{0j \cdot i}$	Three Predictors $K_{0(ijk)} = K_{0(ij)}k_{0k \cdot ij}$
123:	$K_{0(1)} = k_{01} = .8000$	$K_{0(12)} = K_{0(1)}k_{02 \cdot 1} = .8000 \times .8888 = .7110$	$K_{0(123)} = K_{0(12)}k_{03 \cdot 12} = .7110 \times .8268 = .5878$
132:	$K_{0(1)} = k_{01} = .8000$	$K_{0(13)} = K_{0(1)}k_{03 \cdot 1} = .8000 \times .8660 = .6928$	$K_{0(132)} = K_{0(13)}k_{02 \cdot 13} = .6928 \times .8485 = .5878$
213:	$K_{0(2)} = k_{02} = .7141$	$K_{0(21)} = K_{0(2)}k_{01 \cdot 2} = .7141 \times .9956 = .7110$	$K_{0(213)} = K_{0(21)}k_{03 \cdot 21} = .7110 \times .8268 = .5878$
231:	$K_{0(2)} = k_{02} = .7141$	$K_{0(23)} = K_{0(2)}k_{03 \cdot 2} = .7141 \times .8284 = .5916$	$K_{0(231)} = K_{0(23)}k_{01 \cdot 23} = .5916 \times .9936 = .5878$
312:	$K_{0(3)} = k_{03} = .9165$	$K_{0(31)} = K_{0(3)}k_{01 \cdot 3} = .9165 \times .7559 = .6928$	$K_{0(312)} = K_{0(31)}k_{02 \cdot 31} = .6928 \times .8465 = .5878$
321:	$K_{0(3)} = k_{03} = .9165$	$K_{0(32)} = K_{0(3)}k_{02 \cdot 3} = .9165 \times .6455 = .5916$	$K_{0(321)} = K_{0(32)}k_{01 \cdot 32} = .5916 \times .9936 = .5878$

Table 4.6. Multiple coefficients of alienation for estimating Z_0 from one or more of the predictor variables Z_1, Z_2, and Z_3 when $r_{01} = .60$, $r_{02} = .70$, $r_{03} = .40$, $r_{12} = .80$, $r_{13} = 0$, and $r_{23} = 0$, showing the various series of values through which K can pass as the predictors are adopted sequentially. These values are shown graphically in Figure 4.10.

relation may omit this discussion without serious jeopardy to his comprehension of multivariate relationships.

Partialling a variable **X** out of the correlation between variables **Y** and **W** can affect the relationship in two distinct ways. As shown by [4.122], r_{YW} can be analyzed as the sum of two components: (1) a quantity $r_{YX}r_{WX}$ which results from the given relations, r_{YX} and r_{WX}, of **Y** and **W** to a common third variable **X**, plus (2) a quantity $k_{YX}k_{WX}r_{YW \cdot X}$ which is the correlation between the components of **Y** and **W** independent of **X** (i.e., $r_{YW \cdot X}$), diminished by a proportion $k_{YX}k_{WX}$ which, like (1), is determined by the relations of **Y** and **W** to **X**. Component (1) may be described as the *correlation induced by* **X** *between* **Y** *and* **W**, with the understanding that this "induction" is a mathematical consequence of treating r_{YX} and r_{WX} as premises for analysis, and is *not* necessarily to be construed as a causal action of **X** upon **Y** and **W**. However, the mutual involvement of **Y** and **W** with **X** also results in the multiplier $k_{YX}k_{WX}$ which attenuates the contribution, $r_{YW \cdot X}$, from sources unrelated to **X**, and which may accordingly be called a "suppression factor." These are two quite different effects of **X** on r_{YW}—the magnitude of the induced correlation, $r_{YX}r_{WX}$, cannot exceed $1 - k_{YX}k_{WX}$ (which is the degree of influence not allocated by the suppression factor to $r_{YW \cdot X}$, and which may be conceived as a weight assigned by **X** to the relationship it induces between **Y** and **W**, comparable to the weight it gives to residual influences), but otherwise, any value of the induced correlation may co-occur with any value of the suppression factor. We thus find two separate ways in which **X**, by its relations to **Y** and **W**, serves to conceal the relationship between **Y** and **W** due to other factors: It induces a certain degree of relationship between **Y** and **W**, and it also determines a particular apportionment of influence between its own contribution to r_{YW} and the contribution from independent sources. Conversely, partialling **X** out of r_{YW} (1) deletes the correlation induced between **Y** and **W** by **X**, and (2) liberates the correlation between **Y** and **W** unaccounted for by **X** from the suppression factor by which **X** constrains it in r_{YW}. Since operation (2) is a multiplicative enhancement of a component of r_{YW}, it tends to increase the magnitude of the correlation. Hence as illustrated in Table 4.5 by the various orders of correlation between Z_0 and Z_3, if there is little induced correlation to be removed, the correlation between **Y** and **W** will grow larger in proportion to its original size as other variables are partialled out. On the other hand, if r_{YW} is composed in significant measure of correlation induced by one or more of the variables to be partialled out,[93]

[93] While the notions of "induced correlation" and "suppression factor" were introduced above only for one induction variable, they may easily be generalized by observing that when a set $\boldsymbol{\mu}$ of variables are partialled out of r_{YW}, the latter continues to analyze as an induced component plus suppressed residual, namely,

$$r_{YW} = \text{Cov}\,(\dot{Z}_{Y(\mu)}, \dot{Z}_{W(\mu)}) + K_{Y(\mu)}K_{W(\mu)}r_{YW \cdot \mu}.$$

which occurs when (but not only when) the latter include variables with which **Y** and **W** mutually have an appreciable correlation, partialling may have more spectacular results. If the correlation induced between **Y** and **W** by **X** is in the same direction as the residual correlation—i.e., if $r_{YX}r_{WX}$ and $r_{YW \cdot X}$ are both positive or both negative—then removal of the induced component will cause the correlation to decrease in magnitude, perhaps sharply so (cf. the transition from r_{01} to $r_{01 \cdot 2}$ in Table 4.2). Conversely, if the induced and residual components in r_{YW} with respect to **X** are opposed in direction, partialling out **X** will disclose a residual correlation either larger in magnitude than, or opposed in sign to, the initial correlation. When r_{YW} contains a substantial component induced by the variables to be partialled out, it is not possible to prescribe any general trend that $r_{YW \cdot \mu}$ will follow as μ is increased. In particular, the size and direction of a zero-order correlation affords no clue as to what its higher-order partials may be like. If none of the induced or residual correlations among a set of variables are negative, removal of induced correlation through partialling has the effect of diminishing the correlation. But this tendency is opposed by the simultaneous release of the suppression factor, so even in this case an overall trend cannot be forecast.

What is known in the psychometric literature as a *suppressor variable* is a particularly conspicuous instance of the effects just described. By this term is meant a variable with zero or near-zero correlation with the criterion, but with appreciable correlation with another predictor. Suppose that **S** is a "suppressor" variable for the relation between criterion **Y** and another predictor **X**. Then by definition, $r_{YS} = 0$ (or approximately so), $r_{YX} \neq 0$, and $r_{XS} \neq 0$. Since $r_{YS}\, r_{XS} = 0$ whatever r_{XS} may be, **S** induces no correlation between **Y** and **X**. However, $k_{YS}k_{XS} = k_{XS} < 1$, so $r_{YX \cdot S} = r_{YX}/k_{XS} > r_{YX}$ and partialling out the suppressor variable **S** consequently enhances the correlation between **Y** and **X**, the increment being proportional to the severity of suppression while the latter, in turn, is an increasing function of the size of correlation between **S** and **X**. Note, however, that this enhancement is a multiplicative effect, so that $r_{YX \cdot S}$ is directly proportional to r_{YX} for a given degree of suppression. Incidently, the nature of the suppression effect is particularly easy to grasp in this case. For simplicity, assume that **X**, **Y**, and **S** all have zero means and equal SDs. Then analyzing **X** and **Y** into components controlled by **S**, plus residuals, gives $\mathbf{X} = r_{SX}\mathbf{S} + e_{X \cdot S}$ while since **Y** is uncorrelated with **S**, $\mathbf{Y} = e_{Y \cdot S}$. Therefore $\text{Cov}(\mathbf{Y},\mathbf{X}) = \text{Cov}(e_{Y \cdot S}, e_{X \cdot S})$ while $\text{Var}(\mathbf{Y}) = \text{Var}(e_{Y \cdot S})$ and $\text{Var}(\mathbf{X}) = r^2_{XS}\,\text{Var}(\mathbf{S}) + \text{Var}(e_{X \cdot S})$; hence computation of r_{YX} and $r_{YX \cdot S}$ shows them to be identical except for an additional variance component, $r^2_{XS}\,\text{Var}(\mathbf{S})$, in the denominator of r_{YX}. Partialling out the suppressor variable, then, increases the correlation between **X** and **Y** by removing a component of **X** which increases **X**'s variance but contributes nothing to its covariance with **Y**. Such a component of Var(**X**), controlled by a variable whose correlation with the criterion is zero, is sometimes referred to as "invalid variance." In describing variance components as "valid" or "invalid," however, it must be appreciated that it is not variance as such which has predictive validity, but only the score components which have these variances.

While the term "suppressor variable" is drawn from the inhibiting effect of **S** upon the relation between **Y** and **X**, it is also instructive to note, conversely, the effect of **X** on the relation between **Y** and **S**. Since by hypothesis both r_{YX} and r_{SX} differ appreciably from zero, r_{YS} contains an appreciable component induced by **X** and hence if $r_{YS} = 0$, this induced component must be counterbalanced by a residual correlation of opposite sign. In particular, if the variables have been scored in such a way that r_{YX} and r_{SX} are both positive,[94] then partialling **X** out of r_{YS} discloses a negative residual correlation, $r_{YS\cdot X}$, whose magnitude, moreover, is in no way limited by the (approximately) zero value of r_{YS}. Thus as observed without analysis in the remark following equations [4.93], zero correlation needs not signify an absence of linear predictive relevance. Rather, $r_{YX} = 0$ may arise either through a flaccid lack of connectedness between **X** and the determinants of **Y**, or through a precarious counterbalancing of tensions in a system of conflicting relationships in which any disturbance of the equilibrium (i.e., by partialling out a factor) may precipitate a radical shift in the pattern of intercorrelations.

Before our discussion of multivariate relationships can properly be terminated, we have one more important connection between multiple regression and partial correlation to observe. As exhibited by formulas [4.107]–[4.110], the multiple regression of one variable upon a set of others can be written to display the involvement of various orders of partial variances and partial correlations among the variables. However, [4.107]–[4.110] are altogether asymmetric in the predictor variables: By describing how each variable supplements its predecessors, they fail to clarify what, if anything, partial correlations have to do with predictive significance when some or all of the predictors are given equal status. This deficiency may be remedied by showing that the β-coefficients in [4.88] are actually partial statistics of order $\mathbf{m} - 1$. For ease of demonstration, let us work with regression equation [4.106]. By analyzing $\mathbf{Z}_3$ into a component controlled by $\mathbf{Z}_1$ and $\mathbf{Z}_2$, plus residual, we have

$$\dot{\mathbf{Z}}_{0(123)} = \beta_{01\cdot 23}\mathbf{Z}_1 + \beta_{02\cdot 13}\mathbf{Z}_2 + \beta_{03\cdot 12}(\dot{\mathbf{Z}}_{3(12)} + \mathbf{e}_{3\cdot 12}).$$

Hence, since $\dot{\mathbf{Z}}_{3(12)} = \beta_{31\cdot 2}\mathbf{Z}_1 + \beta_{32\cdot 1}\mathbf{Z}_2$,

$$\dot{\mathbf{Z}}_{0(123)} = (\beta_{01\cdot 23} + \beta_{03\cdot 12}\beta_{31\cdot 2})\mathbf{Z}_1 + (\beta_{02\cdot 13} + \beta_{03\cdot 12}\beta_{32\cdot 1})\mathbf{Z}_2 + \beta_{03\cdot 12}\mathbf{e}_{3\cdot 12}. \quad [4.125]$$

[94] It will be recalled that transforming a variable through multiplication by −1 changes the sign of all its correlations with other variables.

It will be observed that [4.125] expresses the best estimate of $\mathbf{Z_0}$, given $\mathbf{Z_1}$, $\mathbf{Z_2}$, and $\mathbf{Z_3}$, in a form where $\mathbf{Z_3}$ is brought in to supplement a prior estimate based simultaneously on $\mathbf{Z_1}$ and $\mathbf{Z_2}$. Hence the coefficients of $\mathbf{Z_1}$ and $\mathbf{Z_2}$ in [4.125] are the same as their respective coefficients in the regression of $\mathbf{Z_0}$ upon $\mathbf{Z_1}$ and $\mathbf{Z_2}$,[95] and consequently

[4.126] $$\dot{\mathbf{Z}}_{0(123)} = \dot{\mathbf{Z}}_{0(12)} + \beta_{03\cdot12}\,\mathbf{e}_{3\cdot12}\,.$$

Then comparison of [4.126] with [4.107], while recalling that the joint contribution of $\mathbf{Z_1}$ and $\mathbf{Z_2}$ in [4.107] is also $\dot{\mathbf{Z}}_{0(12)}$ (cf. [4.108]) shows that

[4.127][96] $$\beta_{03\cdot12} = r_{03\cdot12}\,\frac{\sigma_{0\cdot12}}{\sigma_{3\cdot12}} = r_{03\cdot12}\,\frac{K_{0(12)}}{K_{3(12)}}\,.$$

More generally, we find (the reader should by now be able to carry through the proof without assistance) that for a criterion $\mathbf{Y}$, a set of predictors $\boldsymbol{\mu}$, and an additional predictor $\mathbf{W}$,

[4.128] $$\dot{\mathbf{Y}}_{(\mathbf{W}\mu)} = \dot{\mathbf{Y}}_{(\mu)} + b_{\mathbf{YW}\cdot\mu}\,\mathbf{e}_{\mathbf{W}\cdot\mu}\,,$$

and hence from [4.108],

[4.129] $$b_{\mathbf{YW}\cdot\mu} = r_{\mathbf{YW}\cdot\mu}\,\frac{\sigma_{\mathbf{Y}\cdot\mu}}{\sigma_{\mathbf{W}\cdot\mu}}$$

or

[4.130] $$\beta_{\mathbf{YW}\cdot\mu} = r_{\mathbf{YW}\cdot\mu}\,\frac{K_{\mathbf{Y}(\mu)}}{K_{\mathbf{W}(\mu)}}\,.$$

In short, the weight given to any predictor $\mathbf{W}$ in the multiple regression equation – i.e., in terms of analytic geometry, the slope of the regression surface in the $\mathbf{W}$-dimension (that is, the rate of change in $\dot{\mathbf{Y}}_{(\mathbf{W}\mu)}$ as $\mathbf{W}$ changes with $\boldsymbol{\mu}$ held constant) – is the correlation sustained between the criterion and $\mathbf{W}$ independently of the other predictors, times an adjustment for inequalities in the degree to which they also vary independently of the other predictors. This is the multivariate equivalent of the special case with one predictor, in which the regression slope of $\mathbf{Y}$ upon $\mathbf{X}$ is the correlation between $\mathbf{Y}$ and $\mathbf{X}$, adjusted for inequalities in their standard deviations (cf. [4.56]). In fact, since the best estimate of $\mathbf{e}_{\mathbf{Y}\cdot\mu}$, given

---

[95] It is obvious from [4.90] that if a variable $\mathbf{W}$ has zero correlation with each variable in a set $\boldsymbol{\mu}$, the β-coefficients of the variables in $\boldsymbol{\mu}$ for the regression of $\mathbf{Y}$ on $\boldsymbol{\mu}$ are the same as in the regression of $\mathbf{Y}$ on $\mathbf{W}$ and $\boldsymbol{\mu}$.

[96] A useful alternative proof for [4.127] is to take the covariance of $\mathbf{e}_{3\cdot12}$ with both sides of [4.125], yielding $\mathrm{Cov}(\mathbf{e}_{3\cdot12}, \dot{\mathbf{Z}}_{0(123)}) = \beta_{03\cdot12}\sigma^2_{3\cdot12}$, and then to observe that since $\dot{\mathbf{Z}}_{0(123)} + \mathbf{e}_{0\cdot123} = \mathbf{Z}_0 = \dot{\mathbf{Z}}_{0(12)} + \mathbf{e}_{0\cdot12}$, $\mathrm{Cov}(\mathbf{e}_{3\cdot12}, \dot{\mathbf{Z}}_{0(123)}) = \mathrm{Cov}(\mathbf{e}_{3\cdot12}, \mathbf{e}_{0\cdot12}) = \sigma_{3\cdot12} \times \sigma_{0\cdot12} r_{03\cdot12}$. Equating the two solutions for the covariance then yields [4.127].

$\mathbf{e}_{\mathbf{W}\cdot\boldsymbol{\mu}}$ is $r_{\mathbf{YW}\cdot\boldsymbol{\mu}}(\sigma_{\mathbf{Y}\cdot\boldsymbol{\mu}}/\sigma_{\mathbf{W}\cdot\boldsymbol{\mu}})\mathbf{e}_{\mathbf{W}\cdot\boldsymbol{\mu}} = b_{\mathbf{YW}\cdot\boldsymbol{\mu}}\mathbf{e}_{\mathbf{W}\cdot\boldsymbol{\mu}}$, the b-weight given to a predictor **W** in the multiple regression of **Y** on **W** and a set of additional predictors $\boldsymbol{\mu}$ is seen to be simply the slope of the regression of $\mathbf{e}_{\mathbf{Y}\cdot\boldsymbol{\mu}}$ upon $\mathbf{e}_{\mathbf{W}\cdot\boldsymbol{\mu}}$.

Equations [4.129] and [4.130] show that to solve for the regression coefficients in the multiple regression of a criterion upon a set of **m** predictors does not differ appreciably from deriving a set of (**m** − 1)th-order partial correlations and variances. As a matter of fact, solution of the normal equations for the regression coefficients can be organized in such a way that successive steps in the computation grind out in passing many of the partial correlations and partial variances of various orders among the criterion and predictors. What is especially useful about such a computing routine (unless the work is being done by a high-speed computer) is that most of the calculations on the way to the final solution, which have to be made in any case but which would otherwise be meaningless numbers, are now salvaged for their own statistical significance and the heightened understanding they afford of the pattern of relationships involved. (For details of this procedure and other useful material concerning multivariate relationships, see DuBois (24).) On the other hand, if it is intended that these same predictors be put to more than one use, such as predicting several criteria, then the most economical way to proceed is first to compute what is known as the "inverse" of the matrix of correlations among the predictors. Even without high-speed computer service this is not much more difficult than solving for a single set of regression coefficients, and once it has been accomplished, many different manipulations of the predictor data, each of which by itself would take a great deal of computational labor, can now be managed with only modest additional effort.[97] Discussion of such methods requires some background in matrix algebra, however, and is hence beyond the scope of the present work.

An important consequence of equations [4.112] and [4.130] is that

[4.131] $$R^2_{\mathbf{Y}(\mathbf{W}\boldsymbol{\mu})} - R^2_{\mathbf{Y}(\boldsymbol{\mu})} = r^2_{\mathbf{YW}\cdot\boldsymbol{\mu}} K^2_{\mathbf{Y}(\boldsymbol{\mu})} = K^2_{\mathbf{W}(\boldsymbol{\mu})} \beta^2_{\mathbf{YW}\cdot\boldsymbol{\mu}} .$$

The quantity $R^2_{\mathbf{Y}(\mathbf{W}\boldsymbol{\mu})} - R^2_{\mathbf{Y}(\boldsymbol{\mu})}$ $(= K^2_{\mathbf{Y}(\boldsymbol{\mu})} - K^2_{\mathbf{Y}(\mathbf{W}\boldsymbol{\mu})})$ is the proportion of controlled criterion variance that would be sacrificed if variable **W** were to be dropped from the set of predictors $\mathbf{W},\boldsymbol{\mu}$. (This is like $S_{\mathbf{Y},\mathbf{W}[\boldsymbol{\mu}]}$ except that the latter compares standard errors whereas the former compares residual variances.) It follows from [4.131] that deletion of a predictor from a multiple regression equation can diminish the proportion of controlled variance by at most the square of that predictor's β-weight, while if the omitted variable is itself highly predictable from the remaining pre-

[97] See, for example, equation [B.16], Appendix B.

dictors, the loss of accuracy in predicting the criterion will be much less than this. Equation [4.131] becomes especially significant when it is desired to eliminate superfluous predictors from a multiple regression in which one or more of the coefficients appear dubiously small in size. It shows, to begin with, that a variable's β-coefficient in a multiple regression equation does not, in general, adequately measure how important it is for that variable to be retained when the set of predictors is winnowed down to a smaller number. The β-weight of predictor **X** might be a great deal larger than that of **W**, yet if **X** is highly redundant with the remaining predictors while **W** is not, it may well be that **X** can be discarded with negligible sacrifice of predictive accuracy whereas elimination of **W** would cost the full amount of its squared regression coefficient. On the other hand, irrespective of the pattern of predictor relations, a variable's β-weight immediately gives an upper limit to the importance of its retention in the regression. Thus if the β-weight of **X** is less than .10 in magnitude, **X** may be omitted with a loss of at most 1% in controlled criterion variance. A word of caution must immediately be added, however. We cannot eliminate several puny-β predictors *simultaneously* without risking the loss of more controlled variance than is indicated by the sum of the squared β-weights for the deleted variables. This is because as soon as one variable is eliminated from the regression, the weights of the remaining predictors must be adjusted accordingly and the cost of discarding another variable now has for its upper bound the square of its coefficient in the reduced equation. Specifically, suppose that we have determined the linear regression of criterion **Y** upon the predictors **X**,**W** and a number of additional variables $\boldsymbol{\mu}$, and we now choose to eliminate **W**. By an obvious generalization of [4.125], it may be seen that the β-coefficient of **X** in the regression of **Y** upon **X**,$\boldsymbol{\mu}$ is

$$[4.132] \qquad \beta_{\mathbf{YX}\cdot\boldsymbol{\mu}} = \beta_{\mathbf{YX}\cdot\mathbf{W}\boldsymbol{\mu}} + \beta_{\mathbf{YW}\cdot\mathbf{X}\boldsymbol{\mu}}\beta_{\mathbf{WX}\cdot\boldsymbol{\mu}}.$$

That is, **X**'s β-weight for **Y** after elimination of **W** equals its β-weight for **Y** in the unreduced regression *plus* the product of **W**'s β-weight for **Y** in the unreduced regression with **X**'s β-weight in the regression of **W** upon **X**,$\boldsymbol{\mu}$. Thus the β-weight of **X** for **Y** remains unchanged when another predictor **W** is deleted from the regression if and only if either **W** has zero weight for **Y** in the unreduced regression or **X** is useless, supplementary to $\boldsymbol{\mu}$, for predicting **W**. (In particular, iteration of [4.132] proves the intuitively obvious fact that any number of variables which show up with zero coefficients in a regression equation can be deleted simultaneously without loss of predictive accuracy or change in the regression coefficients of the remaining predictors.) In practice, successive elimination of minimal-weight predictors runs into complications in that the term $\beta_{\mathbf{WX}\cdot\boldsymbol{\mu}}$ in [4.132] is not contained in the unreduced regression equation and calls in effect for computation of a supplementary regression equation for each predictor eliminated. Once the inverse of the original matrix of predictor correlations is available, however, the supplementary $\beta_{\mathbf{WX}\bullet\boldsymbol{\mu}}$-statistics can be derived with little additional effort.[98]

If the linear regression of **Y** upon **W** and variables $\boldsymbol{\mu}$ in population P is also the best-fitting regression surface of any form, it follows from [4.84] that the linear regression of **Y** upon **W** within any subpopulation P_μ, comprising members of P with a given set of scores μ on the variables in $\boldsymbol{\mu}$, is

$$\dot{Y}_{i(\mathbf{W})} = b_{\mathbf{YW}\bullet\boldsymbol{\mu}} W_i + c_\mu \quad (i \in P_\mu) ,$$

where $b_{\mathbf{YW}\bullet\boldsymbol{\mu}}$ is, as before, the b-coefficient of **W** in the multiple regression of **Y** upon **W**,$\boldsymbol{\mu}$ in population P and c_μ is a constant determined by the particular set of scores μ. The correlation, $r_{\mathbf{YW}|\mu}$, between **Y** and **W** in restricted population P_μ is then

$$r_{\mathbf{YW}|\mu} = \frac{\sigma_{\dot{\mathbf{Y}}(\mathbf{W})|\mu}}{\sigma_{\mathbf{Y}|\mu}} = b_{\mathbf{YW}\bullet\boldsymbol{\mu}} \frac{\sigma_{\mathbf{W}|\mu}}{\sigma_{\mathbf{Y}|\mu}} = r_{\mathbf{YW}\bullet\boldsymbol{\mu}} \left(\frac{\sigma_{\mathbf{W}|\mu}}{\sigma_{\mathbf{W}\bullet\boldsymbol{\mu}}}\right)\left(\frac{\sigma_{\mathbf{Y}\bullet\boldsymbol{\mu}}}{\sigma_{\mathbf{Y}|\mu}}\right) .$$

If further, the distributions of **Y** and **W** contingent upon variables $\boldsymbol{\mu}$ in P are homoscedastic, so that $\sigma_{\mathbf{Y}|\mu} = \sigma_{\mathbf{Y}\bullet\boldsymbol{\mu}}$ and $\sigma_{\mathbf{W}|\mu} = \sigma_{\mathbf{W}\bullet\boldsymbol{\mu}}$, it follows that

[4.133] $$r_{\mathbf{YW}|\mu} = r_{\mathbf{YW}\bullet\boldsymbol{\mu}} \qquad \text{(linearity and homoscedasticity)} .$$

For this reason, partial correlation is often described as the correlation which obtains between the primary variables when the variables partialled out are *held constant*. However, while the correlation, $r_{\mathbf{YW}\bullet\boldsymbol{\mu}}$, between **Y** and **W** with $\boldsymbol{\mu}$ partialled out will ordinarily be a reasonable approximation to their contingent correlation, $r_{\mathbf{YW}|\mu}$, among individuals whose scores on the variables in $\boldsymbol{\mu}$ are literally held constant at μ, the identity in general holds exactly only if the joint distribution of **Y**,**W**,$\boldsymbol{\mu}$ conforms to the conditions indicated. Nonetheless, since these conditions do, in fact, hold in multivariate normal distributions, their assumption will not often create too intolerable an estrangement from reality.

More generally, the relations which hold between partial statistics and the effect of holding variables constant when sufficient linearity and homoscedasticity obtain allow us to convert the correlations observed in a restricted population P' into an estimate of the corresponding correlations in the base population P from which P' is selected. Specifically, suppose that P' is derived from P by some restriction on the joint distribution of variables $\mathbf{X}_1, \ldots, \mathbf{X}_m$ — i.e., there is a certain selection region of joint scores on $\mathbf{X}_1, \ldots, \mathbf{X}_m$ (which in principle may consist of scattered

[98] See, e.g., Johnson and Jackson (47), pp. 386 f., or equations [B.27] and [B.29], Appendix B.

points or any other bizarre selection pattern, but in practice is almost certain to be a continuous region) such that the restricted population P' consists of just those members of base population P whose joint scores on the $\mathbf{X_i}$ fall in the selection region. (Actually, equations [4.134]–[4.143] below require only that P' be some population in which the contingent joint distribution of variables **Y** and **W**, given each combination of scores $X_1, \ldots, X_m$ on $\mathbf{X_1}, \ldots, \mathbf{X_m}$, is the same in both P and P'.) To simplify notation, let $\boldsymbol{\mu}$ abbreviate the set of selection variables $\mathbf{X_1}, \ldots, \mathbf{X_m}$ while $\boldsymbol{\mu}_i$ is the set $\boldsymbol{\mu}$ with $\mathbf{X_i}$ removed, so that the b-coefficient of $\mathbf{X_i}$ in the regression of a variable **Y** upon $\mathbf{X_1}, \ldots, \mathbf{X_m}$ in P may be written "$b_{\mathbf{YX_i}\cdot\boldsymbol{\mu}_i}$." Also, let a prime (′) added to a statistical symbol signify that this symbol designates the value of this statistic in P', while unprimed symbols refer to P. (E.g., $r_{\mathbf{YX_i}}$ is the correlation between **Y** and $\mathbf{X_i}$ in base population P whereas $r'_{\mathbf{YX_i}}$ is the corresponding correlation in the restricted population P'.) From [4.84] and [4.105-C], in view of [4.37] and [4.87], the covariance between any two variables **Y** and **W** in P may be written

[4.134]

$$\begin{aligned} \mathrm{Cov}(\mathbf{Y},\mathbf{W}) &= \mathrm{Cov}\,(\mathbf{e}_{\mathbf{Y}\cdot\boldsymbol{\mu}} + \dot{\mathbf{Y}}_{(\boldsymbol{\mu})}, \mathbf{e}_{\mathbf{W}\cdot\boldsymbol{\mu}} + \dot{\mathbf{W}}_{(\boldsymbol{\mu})}) \\ &= \mathrm{Cov}\,(\mathbf{e}_{\mathbf{Y}\cdot\boldsymbol{\mu}}, \mathbf{e}_{\mathbf{W}\cdot\boldsymbol{\mu}}) + \mathrm{Cov}\,(\dot{\mathbf{Y}}_{(\boldsymbol{\mu})}, \dot{\mathbf{W}}_{(\boldsymbol{\mu})}) \\ &= \sigma_{\mathbf{Y}\cdot\boldsymbol{\mu}}\sigma_{\mathbf{W}\cdot\boldsymbol{\mu}} r_{\mathbf{YW}\cdot\boldsymbol{\mu}} + \sum_{i=1}^{m}\sum_{j=1}^{m} b_{\mathbf{YX_i}\cdot\boldsymbol{\mu}_i} b_{\mathbf{WX_j}\cdot\boldsymbol{\mu}_j} \mathrm{Cov}\,(\mathbf{X_i},\mathbf{X_j}) \,, \end{aligned}$$

while similarly, the covariance between **Y** and **W** after restriction of the population to P' is

[4.135]

$$\mathrm{Cov}'(\mathbf{Y},\mathbf{W}) = \sigma'_{\mathbf{Y}\cdot\boldsymbol{\mu}}\sigma'_{\mathbf{W}\cdot\boldsymbol{\mu}} r'_{\mathbf{YW}\cdot\boldsymbol{\mu}} + \sum_{i=1}^{m}\sum_{j=1}^{m} b'_{\mathbf{YX_i}\cdot\boldsymbol{\mu}_i} b'_{\mathbf{WX_j}\cdot\boldsymbol{\mu}_j} \mathrm{Cov}'(\mathbf{X_i},\mathbf{X_j}) \,.$$

Now suppose that the unrestricted curvilinear regressions of both **Y** and **W** upon $\mathbf{X_1}, \ldots, \mathbf{X_m}$ in P coincide with the corresponding linear regressions. If so, then this coincidence also persists in P' and hence

[4.136-i] $b_{\mathbf{YX_i}\cdot\boldsymbol{\mu}_i} = b'_{\mathbf{YX_i}\cdot\boldsymbol{\mu}_i}$, $b_{\mathbf{WX_i}\cdot\boldsymbol{\mu}_i} = b'_{\mathbf{WX_i}\cdot\boldsymbol{\mu}_i}$

$(\mathbf{i} = \mathbf{1}, \ldots, \mathbf{m})$

(linearity assumptions) .

If this linearity also extends to the regression of **Y** upon $\mathbf{W}, \boldsymbol{\mu}$ (or to the regression of **W** upon $\mathbf{Y}, \boldsymbol{\mu}$) while the contingent distributions of **Y** and **W**, given $\boldsymbol{\mu}$, are homoscedastic, we further have that for any combination μ of values on selection variables $\boldsymbol{\mu}$, $\sigma_{\mathbf{Y}\cdot\boldsymbol{\mu}} = \sigma_{\mathbf{Y}|\mu} = \sigma'_{\mathbf{Y}\cdot\boldsymbol{\mu}}$, $\sigma_{\mathbf{W}\cdot\boldsymbol{\mu}} = \sigma_{\mathbf{W}|\mu} = \sigma'_{\mathbf{W}\cdot\boldsymbol{\mu}}$, and $r_{\mathbf{YW}\cdot\boldsymbol{\mu}} = r_{\mathbf{YW}\,\mu} = r'_{\mathbf{YW}\cdot\boldsymbol{\mu}}$, so that in particular,

$$[4.137] \quad \sigma_{\mathbf{Y}\cdot\boldsymbol{\mu}}\sigma_{\mathbf{W}\cdot\boldsymbol{\mu}}r_{\mathbf{YW}\cdot\boldsymbol{\mu}} = \sigma'_{\mathbf{Y}\cdot\boldsymbol{\mu}}\sigma'_{\mathbf{W}\cdot\boldsymbol{\mu}}r'_{\mathbf{YW}\cdot\boldsymbol{\mu}} \qquad \left(\begin{matrix}\text{linearity and}\\ \text{homoscedasticity}\end{matrix}\right).$$

(A sufficient though not a necessary condition for [4.136] and [4.137] to hold is for the joint distribution of $\mathbf{Y}, \mathbf{W}, \mathbf{X}_1, \ldots, \mathbf{X}_m$ in P to be normal.) Substituting [4.136] and [4.137] into [4.134] and eliminating $\sigma'_{\mathbf{Y}\cdot\boldsymbol{\mu}}\sigma'_{\mathbf{W}\cdot\boldsymbol{\mu}}r'_{\mathbf{YW}\cdot\boldsymbol{\mu}}$ by combining with [4.135] then yields

[4.138]

$$\begin{aligned}\mathrm{Cov}(\mathbf{Y},\mathbf{W}) &= \mathrm{Cov}'(\mathbf{Y},\mathbf{W})\\ &\quad + \sum_{i=1}^{m}\sum_{j=1}^{m} b'_{\mathbf{YX}_i\cdot\boldsymbol{\mu}_i} b'_{\mathbf{WX}_j\cdot\boldsymbol{\mu}_j}\left[\mathrm{Cov}(\mathbf{X}_i,\mathbf{X}_j) - \mathrm{Cov}'(\mathbf{X}_i,\mathbf{X}_j)\right]\end{aligned}$$

(linearity and homoscedasticity).

The assumptions behind [4.138] also imply that it continues to hold if we substitute $\mathbf{Y}$ for $\mathbf{W}$ or $\mathbf{W}$ for $\mathbf{Y}$, so we can obtain the unrestricted correlation $r_{\mathbf{YW}}$ from general formula [4.138] by the computation $r_{\mathbf{YW}} = \mathrm{Cov}(\mathbf{Y},\mathbf{W})/\sqrt{\mathrm{Cov}(\mathbf{Y},\mathbf{Y})\cdot\mathrm{Cov}(\mathbf{W},\mathbf{W})}$. More generally, if the requisite linearity and homoscedasticity hold for the joint distribution of variables $\mathbf{Y}, \mathbf{W}_1, \ldots, \mathbf{W}_n, \mathbf{X}_1, \ldots, \mathbf{X}_m$ in P, and we know how much the restriction from P to P' has reduced the variances and covariances among the selection variables, we can compute the variances and covariances among $\mathbf{Y}$ and the $\mathbf{W}$ in P, and from there derive the multiple correlation of $\mathbf{Y}$ with the $\mathbf{W}_i$ in P, by application of formula [4.138] to the joint-distributional statistics for $\mathbf{Y}, \mathbf{W}_1, \ldots, \mathbf{W}_n, \mathbf{X}_1, \ldots, \mathbf{X}_m$ in restricted population P'.

In the special case where there is only one selection variable $\mathbf{X}_1 = \mathbf{X}$, regression coefficient $b'_{\mathbf{YX}_1\cdot\boldsymbol{\mu}_1}$ (and similarly $b'_{\mathbf{WX}_1\cdot\boldsymbol{\mu}_1}$) in [4.138] simplifies to $r'_{\mathbf{YX}}(\sigma'_{\mathbf{Y}}/\sigma'_{\mathbf{X}})$ and [4.138] becomes

[4.139]

$$\mathrm{Cov}(\mathbf{Y},\mathbf{W}) = \sigma'_{\mathbf{Y}}\sigma'_{\mathbf{W}}(r'_{\mathbf{YW}} + r'_{\mathbf{YW}}r'_{\mathbf{YX}}s_{\mathbf{X}}) \qquad \left(\begin{matrix}\text{linearity and homoscedasticity;}\\ \text{one selection variable } \mathbf{X}\end{matrix}\right),$$

where $s_{\mathbf{X}}$ is a selection factor which expresses how restriction from P to P' alters the variance of the selection variable, namely,

$$[4.140] \qquad s_{\mathbf{X}} =_{\mathrm{def}} \frac{\mathrm{Var}(\mathbf{X})}{\mathrm{Var}'(\mathbf{X})} - 1\,.$$

From [4.139] we also have

$$[4.141] \quad \mathrm{Var}(\mathbf{Y}) = \sigma'^2_{\mathbf{Y}}(1 + r'^2_{\mathbf{YX}}s_{\mathbf{X}}) \qquad \left(\begin{matrix}\text{linearity and homoscedasticity;}\\ \text{one selection variable } \mathbf{X}\end{matrix}\right),$$

[4.141]

(and similarly, of course, for Var(**W**)), so

[4.142]
$$r_{YW} = \frac{r'_{YW} - r'_{YX} r'_{WX} s_X}{\sqrt{(1 + r'^2_{YX} s_X)(1 + r'^2_{WX} s_X)}} \quad \left(\begin{matrix}\text{linearity and homoscedasticity;} \\ \text{one selection variable } \mathbf{X}\end{matrix}\right).$$

If, as a further special case, we wish to know how selection on **X** affects the correlation between **Y** and **X**, we can set **W** = **X** in [4.142] to obtain

[4.143]
$$r_{YX} = \frac{r'_{YX}(\sigma_X/\sigma'_X)}{\sqrt{1 + r'^2_{YX} s_X}} \quad \left(\begin{matrix}\text{linearity and homoscedascity;} \\ \text{one selection variable } \mathbf{X}\end{matrix}\right).$$

****Multiple-Partial Correlation.*** While this chapter has attempted to convey a working understanding of the basic mathematical phenomena in multivariate relationships, there is no end to the variations which can be developed on these themes, especially in regard to relationships among residuals. While most of these intricacies may safely be left to the specialist, there is one more we shall mention here, not so much because the reader is likely to find it of frequent service as for the esthetically irresistible completion it brings to a number of the formulas developed above.

The contrast between simultaneous and sequential (i.e., correctional) procedures for multivariate prediction, as illustrated by [4.106] versus [4.107], is not limited to the two extremes discussed above. Simultaneous and sequential methods can just as readily be combined in any pattern that one might wish. Specifically, the predictor variables may be divided into g groups $\boldsymbol{\mu}_1, \boldsymbol{\mu}_2, \ldots, \boldsymbol{\mu}_g$, and the criterion **Y** estimated through a succession of multivariate stages by first estimating **Y** from its simultaneous regression on the variables in $\boldsymbol{\mu}_1$, then correcting $\dot{\mathbf{Y}}_{(\boldsymbol{\mu}_1)}$ with the regression of $\mathbf{e}_{Y \cdot \boldsymbol{\mu}_1}$ upon the components of the variables in $\boldsymbol{\mu}_2$ which are unaccounted for by the variables in $\boldsymbol{\mu}_1$, then correcting $\dot{\mathbf{Y}}_{(\boldsymbol{\mu}_1 \boldsymbol{\mu}_2)}$ with the regression of $\mathbf{e}_{Y \cdot \boldsymbol{\mu}_1 \boldsymbol{\mu}_2}$ upon the components of the variables in $\boldsymbol{\mu}_3$ unaccounted for by the variables in $\boldsymbol{\mu}_1$ and $\boldsymbol{\mu}_2$, and so on.[99] What this comes to is replacing the regression of **Y** on the variables in $\boldsymbol{\mu}_1, \boldsymbol{\mu}_2, \ldots, \boldsymbol{\mu}_g$ with its regression on the variables in $\boldsymbol{\mu}_1, \boldsymbol{\mu}_2 \cdot \boldsymbol{\mu}_1, \boldsymbol{\mu}_3 \cdot \boldsymbol{\mu}_1 \boldsymbol{\mu}_2, \ldots, \boldsymbol{\mu}_g \cdot \boldsymbol{\mu}_1 \boldsymbol{\mu}_2 \cdots \boldsymbol{\mu}_{g-1}$, where "$\boldsymbol{\mu}_i \cdot \boldsymbol{\mu}_j$" refers to the set of residuals of variables in $\boldsymbol{\mu}_i$ after removal from each of its components jointly controlled by the variables in $\boldsymbol{\mu}_j$. If $\mathbf{n}_i$ is the number of variables in group $\boldsymbol{\mu}_i$, the regression equation for

[99] The reader who has stuck it out this far will have no trouble seeing that, e.g., the best linear estimate of **Y** from $\mathbf{X}_1, \mathbf{X}_2, \mathbf{W}_1, \mathbf{W}_2$ is the best linear estimate, $\dot{\mathbf{Y}}_{(X_1 X_2)}$, based on the regression of **Y** on $\mathbf{X}_1$ and $\mathbf{X}_2$, plus the estimate of $\mathbf{e}_{Y \cdot X_1 X_2}$ given by the latter's regression on $\mathbf{e}_{W_1 \cdot X_1 X_2}$ and $\mathbf{e}_{W_2 \cdot X_1 X_2}$. Whenever the variables in a set $\boldsymbol{\mu}_i$ are adduced to correct the estimate of **Y** previously obtained from the variables in a set $\boldsymbol{\mu}_j$, no matter what simultaneous or sequential procedures have been used to apply the variables in $\boldsymbol{\mu}_j$, the estimate of $\mathbf{e}_{Y \cdot \boldsymbol{\mu}_j}$ based on all the variables in $\boldsymbol{\mu}_i$ and $\boldsymbol{\mu}_j$ takes the form of an estimate based only on residuals of variables in $\boldsymbol{\mu}_i$ after all variables in $\boldsymbol{\mu}_j$ have been partialled out.

$\dot{\mathbf{Y}}_{(\boldsymbol{\mu}_1\boldsymbol{\mu}_2\ldots\boldsymbol{\mu}_{g-1})}$, so modified, is then a linear function of $\mathbf{n}_1$ original predictors, $\mathbf{n}_2$ residuals of order $\mathbf{n}_1$, $\mathbf{n}_3$ residuals of order $\mathbf{n}_1+\mathbf{n}_2, \ldots$, and $\mathbf{n}_g$ residuals of order $\mathbf{n}_1+\mathbf{n}_2+\ldots+\mathbf{n}_{g-1}$. It is not at all difficult to determine the regression weights given to each variable in such an equation, although notation for the general case grows cumbersome: If $\mathbf{X}_{i\mathrm{j}}$ is the **j**th variable in group $\boldsymbol{\mu}_i$, and $\boldsymbol{\mu}_{i(\mathrm{j})}$ is the set of variables in $\boldsymbol{\mu}_i$ other than $\mathbf{X}_{i\mathrm{j}}$, then $\mathbf{X}_{i\mathrm{j}}$ enters the prediction at stage i in the form of a residual $\mathbf{e}_{\mathbf{X}_{i\mathrm{j}}\boldsymbol{\cdot}\boldsymbol{\mu}_1\boldsymbol{\mu}_2\ldots\boldsymbol{\mu}_{i-1}}$ whose regression coefficient is

$$b_{\mathbf{YX}_{i\mathrm{j}}\boldsymbol{\cdot}\boldsymbol{\mu}_{i(\mathrm{j})}\boldsymbol{\mu}_1\boldsymbol{\mu}_2\ldots\boldsymbol{\mu}_{i-1}}\ .$$

That is, when estimating **Y** by a correction procedure based on successive groups of variables, each predictor residual introduced at stage i receives the same weight as its original variable (i.e., the variable of which this is the residual) receives in the simultaneous regression of **Y** upon all original predictors introduced up to and including stage i. Both [4.106] and, through consideration of [4.129], [4.107] may be seen to be special cases of this general rule; [4.106] when $g=1$, $\mathbf{n}_1=3$, and [4.107] when $g=3$, $\mathbf{n}_1=\mathbf{n}_2=\mathbf{n}_3=1$.

Estimation of the criterion residual $\mathbf{e}_{\mathbf{Y}\boldsymbol{\cdot}\boldsymbol{\mu}_j}$ from the residuals $\boldsymbol{\mu}_i\boldsymbol{\cdot}\boldsymbol{\mu}_j$ left of the variables in $\boldsymbol{\mu}_i$ by the variables in $\boldsymbol{\mu}_j$ calls, as usual, for some indication of the accuracy of these estimates. The measure for this, of course, is already at hand, namely, the multiple correlation of $\mathbf{e}_{\mathbf{Y}\boldsymbol{\cdot}\boldsymbol{\mu}_j}$ with the residuals in $\boldsymbol{\mu}_i\boldsymbol{\cdot}\boldsymbol{\mu}_j$—only now, because it is a multiple correlation among residuals, it goes by the fancy title of "multiple-partial correlation." Specifically, we define the multiple-partial correlation, $R_{\mathbf{Y}(\boldsymbol{\mu}_i)\boldsymbol{\cdot}\boldsymbol{\mu}_j}$, between **Y** and a set of variables $\boldsymbol{\mu}_i$ after another set of variables $\boldsymbol{\mu}_j$ have been partialled out as

[4.144-R]

$$R_{\mathbf{Y}(\boldsymbol{\mu}_i)\boldsymbol{\cdot}\boldsymbol{\mu}_j} =_{\mathrm{def}} R_{\mathbf{e}_{\mathbf{Y}\cdot\boldsymbol{\mu}_j}(\boldsymbol{\mu}_i\boldsymbol{\cdot}\boldsymbol{\mu}_j)} = \sqrt{\frac{\mathrm{Var}\,(\dot{\mathbf{e}}_{\mathbf{Y}\boldsymbol{\cdot}\boldsymbol{\mu}_j(\boldsymbol{\mu}_i\boldsymbol{\cdot}\boldsymbol{\mu}_j)})}{\mathrm{Var}\,(\mathbf{e}_{\mathbf{Y}\boldsymbol{\cdot}\boldsymbol{\mu}_j})}} = \sqrt{1-\frac{\sigma^2_{\mathbf{Y}\boldsymbol{\cdot}\boldsymbol{\mu}_i\boldsymbol{\mu}_j}}{\sigma^2_{\mathbf{Y}\boldsymbol{\cdot}\boldsymbol{\mu}_j}}}$$

Similarly, the multiple-partial coefficient of alienation is

[4.144-K]

$$K_{\mathbf{Y}(\boldsymbol{\mu}_i)\boldsymbol{\cdot}\boldsymbol{\mu}_j} =_{\mathrm{def}} \frac{\sigma_{\mathbf{Y}\boldsymbol{\cdot}\boldsymbol{\mu}_i\boldsymbol{\mu}_j}}{\sigma_{\mathbf{Y}\boldsymbol{\cdot}\boldsymbol{\mu}_j}}\ .$$

Multiple-partial R is an exceedingly general correlational concept which includes as special cases both multiple correlation when $\boldsymbol{\mu}_j$ is empty, and partial correlation (or more precisely its absolute value) when $\boldsymbol{\mu}_i$ contains only one predictor.

The reader who refuses to be dismayed by the typographical complexities of formulas [4.144] will perceive that they have a childishly simple significance which nonetheless reveals clearly the underlying unity of multiple and partial correlational concepts. Suppose that we have at our command a totality $\boldsymbol{\mu}$ of predictor variables which can be used to estimate a criterion **Y**. The (linear) standard error of **Y**, given $\boldsymbol{\mu}$—namely, $\sigma_{\mathbf{Y}\cdot\boldsymbol{\mu}}$—then measures the efficiency by which **Y** can be (linearly) estimated from data on all the variables in $\boldsymbol{\mu}$. Now, since the numerical value of $\sigma_{\mathbf{Y}\cdot\boldsymbol{\mu}_i}$ is affected by the choice of scale for **Y**, interpreting *how good* a predictive accuracy of $\sigma_{\mathbf{Y}\cdot\boldsymbol{\mu}}$ may be requires a standard for comparison. One such standard is the standard error of **Y** in the absence of information on *any* of the variables in $\boldsymbol{\mu}$, namely $\sigma_{\mathbf{Y}}$, and the comparison ratio $\sigma_{\mathbf{Y}\cdot\boldsymbol{\mu}}/\sigma_{\mathbf{Y}}$ is then the multiple coefficient of alienation $K_{\mathbf{Y}(\boldsymbol{\mu})}$. However, the goodness of $\sigma_{\mathbf{Y}\cdot\boldsymbol{\mu}}$ may also be judged in comparison to the standard error of **Y** when data on some but not all of the variables in $\boldsymbol{\mu}$ are used for the estimate. The comparison ratio in this case is $\sigma_{\mathbf{Y}\cdot\boldsymbol{\mu}}/\sigma_{\mathbf{Y}\cdot\boldsymbol{\mu}_i}$, where $\boldsymbol{\mu}_i$ is the subset of $\boldsymbol{\mu}$ to which comparison is being made, and by [4.144-K] this ratio is seen to be the multiple-partial coefficient of alienation $K_{\mathbf{Y}(\boldsymbol{\mu}-\boldsymbol{\mu}_i)\cdot\boldsymbol{\mu}_i}$, where "$\boldsymbol{\mu}-\boldsymbol{\mu}_i$" designates the set of variables in $\boldsymbol{\mu}$ additional to those in $\boldsymbol{\mu}_i$. *All coefficients of alienation—multiple, partial, or multiple-partial—are simply a ratio of the criterion's standard error under one set of predictors to its standard error under a less inclusive set, and show the proportion of standard error under the latter which still remains after the more powerful predictive resources of the former have been exploited.* Similarly, the magnitude of any correlation coefficient—multiple, partial, or multiple-partial—may be interpreted as a measure of relative predictive accuracy in virtue of its relationship (cf. Figure 4.6) to the corresponding coefficient of alienation.

It is obvious from [4.144-K] that for any three groups of predictors $_i$, $\boldsymbol{\mu}_j$, and $\boldsymbol{\mu}_k$,

[4.145] $$K_{\mathbf{Y}(\boldsymbol{\mu}_j)\cdot\boldsymbol{\mu}_k} K_{\mathbf{Y}(\boldsymbol{\mu}_i)\cdot\boldsymbol{\mu}_j\boldsymbol{\mu}_k} = K_{\mathbf{Y}(\boldsymbol{\mu}_i\boldsymbol{\mu}_j)\cdot\boldsymbol{\mu}_k}\,.$$

This equation, which subsumes [4.115], is so extraordinarily general that its meaning is not likely to come clear without some examination of specific instances. To simplify subscripts and help clarify the $\boldsymbol{\mu}$-notation, let us inspect the relations among variables $\mathbf{Z}_0, \mathbf{Z}_1, \ldots, \mathbf{Z}_m$ using the convention about subscripts adopted previously. Then from [4.110], letting **Y** be $\mathbf{Z}_0$, $\boldsymbol{\mu}_i$ be the pair of variables $\mathbf{Z}_2$ and $\mathbf{Z}_3$, $\boldsymbol{\mu}_j$ be the single variable $\mathbf{Z}_1$, and $\boldsymbol{\mu}_k$ be empty,

$$k_{01} k_{0(23)\cdot 1} = K_{0(123)}\,.$$

A more complicated example is

$$K_{0(12)}K_{0(34)\cdot 12}k_{05\cdot 1234} \begin{array}{c} \nearrow\!\!\!\!= \; K_{0(12)}K_{0(345)\cdot 12} \;=\!\!\!\!\searrow \\ \searrow\!\!\!\!= \; K_{0(1234)}k_{05\cdot 1234} \;=\!\!\!\!\nearrow \end{array} K_{0(12345)}\,.$$

Perhaps most instructive of all is to write the multiple coefficient of alienation for prediction of $\mathbf{Z_0}$ from $\mathbf{Z_1}, \ldots, \mathbf{Z_m}$ as a product of ascending partials as in [4.120],

$$K_{0(123\cdots m)} = k_{01} k_{02\cdot 1} k_{03\cdot 12} (\cdot\cdot\cdot) k_{0m\cdot 123\cdots m-1},$$

and then to observe that any segment of this product—i.e., the product of any set of consecutive ks, no matter where chosen—is the multiple-partial coefficient of alienation for predicting $\mathbf{Z_0}$ from the variables named in the series of primary subscripts after the variables common to all the secondary subscripts in the series have been partialled out. For example, $k_{03\cdot 12}\, k_{04\cdot 123}\, k_{05\cdot 1234}$ equals $K_{0(345)\cdot 12}$.

In short, once the various orders of partial correlations among a set of variables have been computed, they may be converted into the corresponding (and more directly meaningful) coefficients of alienation and from thence any multiple or multiple-partial correlation within the set obtained via the corresponding multiple or multiple-partial coefficient of alienation. While most of these multiple-partials will be of little practical significance for the multivariate objectives which are likely to be one's primary concern, they are available at so little extra labor from the statistics which *are* likely to be required that one should be willing to succumb to the temptation of computing them upon the slightest provocation.

Part II. **Test Theory: The Assessment of Predictors**

In Chapter 4, we explored in some detail the logic by which a known (or presupposed) multivariate probability distribution can be sculptured into a precision policy for optimal conversions of data into estimates of an unknown. Our concern there focused upon the predictions and their accuracy, while the predictor variables were regarded, in effect, as an imperfectly transparent medium through which we attempted to discern the criterion variable as best we could. When the predictors are themselves made the object of scrutiny, however, a surprisingly rich array of additional patterns, prospects, and problems emerges, and it is with this shift in perspective that Part II is concerned. In particular, we shall examine the notions of "validity" and "reliability," which are the two primary concepts in terms of which fallible instruments of diagnosis and forecast have come to be appraised. Most of the technical developments of these concepts have arisen from research on psychological tests or similar instruments, and for simplicity of exposition the discussion will center largely around predictors of this sort. We shall try, however, not to leave the impression that the considerations which follow apply only to psychological variables.

While the present development of reliability theory (Chapters 8 and 9) is preceded by two starred chapters on the relational structure of sets of variables, neither of these are a prerequisite for comprehension of Chapter 8. However, the reader who wishes to pursue the more advanced materials on internal consistency and item weighting in Chapter 9 will find it necessary to study Chapter 7 and to have some acquaintance with the major concepts of factor analysis (Chapter 6).

Chapter 5. **Validity**

GENERICALLY, the notion of "validity" has to do with the adequacy with which a test (i.e., a predictor) does, in fact, test what it is supposed to be testing; and the reader who sensibly, if naively, reasons that the correlation between test and criterion should amply suffice to describe this state of affairs has reckoned without the conceptual fecundity of test theorists. Actually, the literature abounds with phrases in which some adjective has been prefixed to "validity" for reference to some particular aspect or problem in the interpretation of test scores. Those prefix-validities which are currently most prominent in the discourse of persons who talk about such things are "empirical validity," "predictive validity," "concurrent validity," "face validity," "content validity," and "construct validity." None of these expressions has ever been defined with sufficient precision to bring joy to the beleaguered heart of a logician, and their grammatical form misleadingly suggests that they refer to various *kinds* of validity. Actually, what is signalized by the various prefixes "empirical," "predictive," etc., is not a plurality of validity modalities, but certain methodological distinctions among the criteria for which our predictors are supposedly testing and our grounds for believing that they are, in fact, testing successfully.

Empirical Validity

Let us define the expression, *the objective validity of variable* **X** *as a test for variable* **Y** *in population P*, or simply "the (unqualified) validity of **X**" when **Y** and *P* are contextually understood, to mean the linear correlation between **X** and **Y** in *P*.[1] It is important to be clear that a test has as many different objective validities as there are different criteria with

[1] Strictly speaking, we should refer to "validity" so defined as *linear validity*, thereby making explicit that what is meant is the accuracy of the predictor under linear estimation, even though its predictive success might well be greater than this were curvilinear prediction policies considered.

which it can be correlated and different populations in which it and the criterion are jointly distributed. In a far from trivial sense, every variable is a "test" of every other variable—with, however, an objective validity of zero or near-zero in most cases.[2] Now, what is primarily to be understood by the *empirical validity* of **X** as a test for **Y** is simply **X**'s objective validity for **Y** in the relevant population. However, the adjective "empirical" also carries strong overtones to the effect that by means of a sufficient number of observations on joint values of **X** and **Y** we have actually been able to learn what the approximate numerical value of this correlation is, or at least that such observations *could* successfully be carried out. Concommitently, it is intimated that what **X** is claimed to be a test of is something observable which has been clearly and quantitatively defined independently of the test.

Suppose, for example, that some eminent hirsutologist proposes that a good test of baldness is the amount of light reflected by a person's head under certain standard conditions of illumination. And suppose too that this contention is hotly contested by other authorities. How is this vital issue to be settled? The scientific procedure would be to ascertain joint scores on the Head-reflection and Degree-of-baldness variables within a suitably large sample of the relevant population and compute the correlation between them. However, the intrepid researcher who actually attempted to carry this project through would quickly realize that it cannot be done—not because of practical difficulties such as professional incompetence or trouble in acquiring a research grant, but for the elemental reason that nobody knows just what a "degree of baldness" is. Although generations of men have with varied emotions studied the increasing visibility of their scalps, not one seems to have had the courage to spell out the concept of "baldness" to the point where values on a scale of this variable have any clear meaning. Consequently, a test for "baldness" in the everyday sense of this term cannot, even in principle, have any empirical validity simply because the intended criterion is too vaguely conceived. On the other hand, our researcher *can* readily determine the empirical validity of Head-reflection as a test of some observable criterion which is stipulated to be what *he* henceforth elects to mean by "degree of baldness"—e.g., the average number of hairs per square centimeter on the portion of a person's scalp above a plane passing through the eyebrows and auditory canals, or the measured resistance

[2] The fact that a test has many validities of varying degrees of accuracy lies behind a useful metaphor advanced by Cronbach (19, pp. 602 ff.) in which he speaks of a test's *bandwidth* and *fidelity*. By "bandwidth" Cronbach means the range of different criteria which can be estimated with at least moderate accuracy from the test, while "fidelity" refers to the test's validity for a particular criterion, presumably the one with which the test correlates best. He observes that high fidelity can usually be obtained (if at all) only at the expense of bandwidth, whereas a test which has only moderate correlation with any given criterion may nonetheless justify its existence by being a modestly useful predictor of a great many variables in which its user is interested.

encountered by a comb dragged over the head in a standard manner, or the average baldness rating given to the person by three selected judges on a seven-point scale, or the proportion of test lice which upon release on the person's head are still found in residence a week later, etc. Such replacements of obscure ideas from everyday language with more technically workable concepts are routine in any scientific investigation, and are known as *operational definitions.* When one speaks of the "empirical validity" of a test **X** when what **X** is supposed to be a test of is described in everyday vague terms, it is implied that an operationally defined criterion has been selected. Observe, however, that the empirical validity of **X** will depend upon which of the variously available operational definitions has been chosen. Thus it is most unlikely that the correlations of Head-reflection with Hair-density, Comb-resistance, Baldness-rating, and Lice-retention, respectively, would turn out to be numerically identical. It would be a sign of misunderstanding in this case to ask which correlation is the *correct* empirical validity of Head-reflection as a test of baldness, for none of them are. Rather, the test has a separate validity for each different proposed criterion, and it is merely a historical accident, so to speak, that these various criteria should have a common conceptual ancestor. It should also be noted that the test itself may be taken as an operational definition of what it purports to test for—e.g., we may let Head-reflection be our objective standard for "Degree-of-baldness." However, it is then no longer appropriate to speak of the test as having *empirical* validity. The correlation between Head-reflection and Head-reflection is obviously high, but the relation is logical, not empirical. This is why it was stated above that the notion of "empirical validity" carries with it the idea that the criterion has been defined independently of the test.

If the sensitive or knowledgeable reader wonders if these rather casual remarks about operational definitions and the determination of objective validity are an altogether adequate confrontation of the methodological issues involved, his suspicions are only too well justified. A satisfactory account of what our concepts mean, and how we are able to acquire knowledge about the external realities to which they supposedly refer, is perhaps the most profoundly difficult problem which has ever confronted human reason, and continues to challenge not merely test theory but the entire domain of science and philosophy. Our discussion of "validity" has so far just begun to work its shoulders under a burden which will weigh down with increasing oppressiveness as we proceed.

Predictive Validity and Concurrent Validity

As explained in Chapter 1, the term "prediction" has been used throughout this book to mean any inference about the still unknown details of some event, regardless of where that event occurs in time. However, a somewhat more common usage of the term is to construe "prediction" as an inference about the *future*. It is this temporal orientation which is reflected in the distinction between *predictive validity* and *concurrent validity*. What is implied by saying that a test has "predictive" validity is that the test scores can with some useful degree of objective validity be used to estimate a future criterion, whereas "concurrent" validity pertains to the test's correlation with a contemporaneous criterion. Thus a child's score on a scale of Authoritarian-attitudes might have concurrent validity as an index of how sternly he is disciplined at home, and predictive validity for assessing how permissive he will be toward his own children twenty years from now. Similarly, a baseball team's win/loss record at midseason has predictive validity for the team's final standing at the end of the season, and concurrent validity as a clue to the size of its manager's ulcer. Of course, it is barbarous to describe this difference as predictive versus concurrent *validity*, for what is at issue is not the test's validity as such, but its time relation to the criterion. Considering also the danger of confusion between the temporal and atemporal senses of "prediction," it would seem desirable to retire the expressions "predictive validity" and "concurrent validity" in favor of *prognostic utility* and *diagnostic utility*, respectively.

Face Validity

Suppose that you are one of the anonymous seers who construct the "personality quizzes" which have become a stock feature in Sunday supplements and popular magazines,[3] and that for your next creation you have decided to whip up a test entitled "How strong is your sex drive?" for a men's magazine. If you put together a set of items of the sort

"My favorite form of literature is (*a*) poetry, (*b*) western novels, (*c*) comic books, (*d*) pornography."

"The trouble with women's bathing suits, nowadays, is that they are too (*a*) immodest, (*b*) expensive, (*c*) itchy, (*d*) opaque."

in which answers such as (*d*) in the examples given are scored as indicative of a strong sex drive, your test has been constructed to have high *face validity*. That is, a test is said to have "face validity" if intuitively it *looks* as though it should measure what it purports to. Conversely, if your test for sex drive consisted of items pertaining to the subjects' preferences among automobile styles and brands of cigarettes, most of your readers might well fail to perceive that their answers had any relevance to their sexual motivation, in which case your test would be lacking in face validity for them. Another example: A physician's query,

[3] To the immense relief of all persons interested in psychology as a serious intellectual discipline, these seem to be waning in popularity in favor of articles on sex and space exploration.

"How do you feel?" has considerably more face validity as a test of his patient's physical health than does a white blood cell count or urinalysis.

It must be understood, however, that the "face validity" of a test has nothing to do with the objective relation between the test and what it measures. It merely reflects a psychological attitude toward the test by persons who contemplate it. (Usage of the expression, "face validity," is unclear as to whether the test's face validity should be said to vary from person to person according to how much credence that particular person places in the test, or whether it is to be understood as an average credibility within some relevant population of contemplators.) Clearly, this need have little bearing on the correlation between test and criterion. Thus it might be argued (how correctly need not concern us) from a psychoanalytic view of human motivation that persons who give conspicuously lustful responses to the questions in your sex-drive test are actually compensating for subconscious doubts about their sexual adequacy, whereas the sophisticated advertising behind competitive styles of automobiles and cigarettes have invested them with such potent symbolic values that preferences among them may richly betray a person's deepest motives, especially sexual ones. In general, human resources in honest ignorance, gullibility, self-deception, and plain stupidity are too fulsomely abundant to treat the intuitive credibility of a test as any useful sign of its objective validity. Thus with one exception, face validity has little importance for the theory of prediction.

The exception to the general irrelevance of face validity lies in the area of psychological tests on which the subject's interpretation of the test's significance may influence his performance and hence affect the test's objective validity. For example, most tests of abilities and aptitudes present the subject with a set of problems on which the quality of the subject's performance is a useful index of his ability only if he is sufficiently interested in doing well. Consequently, if the subject does not credit the test with relevance to the purpose for which he is taking it, his effort may be inadequate and his performance hence misleading. Conversely, it is frequently important that face validity be held to a minimum on personality tests (real ones, that is), since the usefulness of an item for the intended purpose of the test may be weakened if the subject's response is biased by the way he would *like* to be viewed by himself or others. Thus on a test for honesty used by an employer to screen prospective personnel, it is perhaps questionable whether all applicants with felonious intent would answer truthfully to

> "I frequently feel an urge to steal things. (True or False?)"

whereas a more subtle item such as

> "A person is likely to be taken advantage of unless he is careful. (True or False?)"

might correlate reasonably well with an operational criterion of dishonesty even while affording the subject little clue as to how his response will be interpreted.[4]

Interpretive Validity

There is still another facet to the distinction between apparent and objective validity which has been oddly neglected in the test-theory literature. In keeping with the customary phrase form for validity concepts we may call this aspect of test appearances *interpretive validity,* though a more accurate wording would be "validity of the test interpretation." The intent here is to contemplate the degree to which the conclusions a test user draws from the test scores are in fact correct. This is not at all the same thing as objective validity, for the information which is objectively contained in the test data in the form of reduced contingent criterion variance need not be properly extracted by the test user. That is, what a test interpreter *thinks* a given test score implies is not necessarily the same as what it *does* imply.

Suppose, for example, that scores on test **X** are converted into estimates of a criterion variable **Y** by a linear prediction equation $\hat{\mathbf{Y}} = a\mathbf{X} + b$ in which constants a and b are not necessarily optimal. The standard error of this policy is

[5.1]

$$\mathrm{SE}_{\mathsf{Y.X}}[\hat{\mathbf{Y}} = a\mathbf{X} + b] = \sqrt{(\mathrm{M}_{\mathsf{Y}} - a\mathrm{M}_{\mathsf{X}} - b)^2 + \sigma^2_{\mathsf{Y}} + a^2\sigma^2_{\mathsf{X}} - 2a\sigma_{\mathsf{X}}\sigma_{\mathsf{Y}}\mathrm{r}_{\mathsf{XY}}}$$

(from [4.50], [4.51-M], and [4.51-V]). We know that optimal choice of a and b can reduce this standard error to a minimum of $\sigma_{\mathsf{Y}}\sqrt{1 - \mathrm{r}^2_{\mathsf{XY}}}$. However, even when it has been possible to obtain a sampling approximation to the joint distribution of **X** and **Y** in the relevant population this still yields only an approximation to the optimal a and b; while in testing practice, objective validity data are usually (1) nonexistent, (2) taken from populations other than the one of immediate concern, or (3) ignored. Hence the interpretive validity of a linear prediction policy will always be poorer than is indicated by the test's objective linear validity, perhaps considerably so. This observation also applies, of course, to prediction policies of any form if we measure objective validity by the curvilinear correlation coefficient, and in fact one especially important way in which interpretations can go astray is through linear inferences from a test whose relation to the criterion is markedly curvilinear.

---

[4] Of course, there is nothing objectionable in a subject's being able to interpret a question and bias his answer accordingly if the manner in which he does or does not dissemble is what is diagnostically significant about the question. In fact, one widely used personality inventory includes a scale for detecting lack of candor, in which the liar hopefully gives himself away by describing himself as a model of shining virtue on items which confess to certain near-universal human frailties.

To appreciate the dangers which lurk in test usage when interpretive validity diverges sufficiently from objective validity, observe from [5.1] that in order for the standard error of prediction policy $\hat{\mathbf{Y}} = a\mathbf{X} + b$ to be no greater than the standard deviation of **Y**, it is necessary to have

$$a^2 \leqslant 2a\left(\frac{\sigma_{\mathbf{Y}}}{\sigma_{\mathbf{X}}}\,\mathrm{r}_{\mathbf{XY}}\right) - \left(\frac{\mathrm{M}_{\mathbf{Y}} - a\mathrm{M}_{\mathbf{X}} - b}{\sigma_{\mathbf{X}}}\right)^2 ,$$

which in turn requires both that a have the same sign as $\mathrm{r}_{\mathbf{XY}}$ and that

$$[5.2] \qquad |a| \leqslant 2\left|\frac{\sigma_{\mathbf{Y}}}{\sigma_{\mathbf{X}}}\,\mathrm{r}_{\mathbf{XY}}\right| \qquad (\mathrm{SE}_{\mathbf{Y},\mathbf{X}}[\hat{\mathbf{Y}} = a\mathbf{X} + b] \leqslant \sigma_{\mathbf{Y}}) .$$

Now, $(\sigma_{\mathbf{Y}}/\sigma_{\mathbf{X}})\mathrm{r}_{\mathbf{XY}}$ is the regression weight of **X** for prediction of **Y** and is the value of a when $\mathrm{SE}_{\mathbf{Y},\mathbf{X}}[\hat{\mathbf{Y}} = a\mathbf{X} + b]$ is minimal. Hence if the interpretive weight given to the test scores—i.e., the coefficient of **X** in $\hat{\mathbf{Y}} = a\mathbf{X} + b$—exceeds its optimal magnitude by more than a factor of 2 (or worse, if it has the wrong sign), the resulting criterion estimates will be less accurate, on the whole, than if scores on **X** are disregarded and the criterion's mean is taken as the estimate for all subjects. What gives this conclusion especial poignancy is that a great many test users disregard regression principles when interpreting test scores and naively take a subject's rank on the test as his estimated rank on the criterion. This amounts to estimating **Y** by the policy $\hat{\mathbf{Z}}_{\mathbf{Y}} = \mathbf{Z}_{\mathbf{X}}$, which may be read into [5.1] and [5.2] by putting $a = 1$, $b = 0$, $\sigma_{\mathbf{Y}} = \sigma_{\mathbf{X}} = 1$, and $\mathrm{M}_{\mathbf{Y}} = \mathrm{M}_{\mathbf{X}} = 0$. On the other hand, predicting that each subject is average on the criterion is to adopt the policy $\hat{\mathbf{Z}}_{\mathbf{Y}} = \mathrm{M}_{\mathbf{Z}_{\mathbf{Y}}}$, whose standard error is $\sigma_{\mathbf{Z}_{\mathbf{Y}}}$ and by [5.2] is superior to policy $\hat{\mathbf{Z}}_{\mathbf{Y}} = \mathbf{Z}_{\mathbf{X}}$ unless $\mathrm{r}_{\mathbf{XY}} \geqslant .50$. Thus *if a test's objective validity for a given criterion is less than .50, treating unregressed standardized test scores as estimates of the similarly standardized criterion scores results in greater predictive inaccuracy than simply taking the criterion's mean for all estimates.* (Of course if the use being made of the test is not a point estimate—e.g., if its application is to select subjects which surpass a certain criterion level—then this conclusion does not apply.)

We see, therefore, that while objectively a test can be no worse than irrelevant, the validity—or rather, invalidity—of an inappropriate interpretation can make the test results not merely useless but actually detrimental. When the test interpretation consists in point estimates of the criterion, as assumed in the preceding paragraph, the test's objective validity is an upper bound on its interpretive validity if the latter is defined for this case as $\sqrt{1 - (\mathrm{SE}_{\mathbf{Y},\mathbf{X}}/\sigma_{\mathbf{Y}})^2}$. (The imaginary values assumed by this measure when $\mathrm{SE}_{\mathbf{Y},\mathbf{X}} > \sigma_{\mathbf{Y}}$ seem wryly appropriate.) Point estimates are not the only way to interpret test scores, however, and there is an important sense in which interpretive validity can in principle approach perfection even though objective validity remains modest. Specifically, if we are content to forego categorical conclusions in favor of *probability* judgments in our interpretation of test scores, then it is possible for the degree of likelihood we attach to an inference about the criterion to be in essential agreement with the criterion's objective uncertainty given the test data. For example, suppose that the joint distribution of test **X** and criterion **Y** in the population under concern is normal, and that our mode of test interpretation is to make interval estimates of **Y**. If, given a subject's test score, we infer simply that his Z-score on **Y** lies in the interval $r_{XY}Z_X \pm d$ for some given half-interval width d, then if p_d is the proportion of a normal distribution which lies within d/k_{XY} sigma units of the mean, there is a probability of $1-p_d$ that our inference is wrong. But if our *conclusion* from the test score is that Z_Y has a $100 \times p_d\%$ chance of falling within the interval $r_{XY}Z_X \pm d$, then there is no way in which the test interpretation involves error and hence no imperfection of interpretive validity. In practice, of course, an interval estimate accompanied by a certain degree of subjective confidence will not necessarily have been assigned the *correct* uncertainty, so this more sophisticated sort of interpretive validity can also fall considerably short of ideal, even to the point of confidence judgments which are more unrealistic than the uncertainty which would be felt about the criterion were there no test scores at hand to misinterpret. We may conclude, then, that whatever objective validity a test may have for a given criterion, the validity (i.e., accuracy) of a particular *interpretation* to which it is subjected may range anywhere from unblemished veridicality to oaf-handed abuses in which it were better that the test not be consulted at all.

The Definition of the Criterion: A Darkening Mystery

So far, our account of prefix-validities has dealt with relatively simple issues, but now the story grows more somber. With the sole exception of a moment's hesitation over the nature of "baldness" in the discussion of empirical validity, we have spoken throughout this book as though we were dealing with well-defined variables—variables, that is, whose various values have all been conceptually identified, so that we can name a particular value and know at least what it would *mean* to assert that some individual has this score, even though there might be practical difficulties in actually determining whether the assertion is true or not. (For example, we know perfectly well what it would mean to say that the earth is 7,895 miles in diameter at the poles. It means that the smallest number of mile-long measuring sticks laid end to end and passing through intervening obstacles as necessary that would span the distance from one pole to the other is 7,895, though of course it would prove awkward to prove or disprove this claim by direct methods.) However, a little critical reflection on many of the illustrative test criteria cited previously reveals how idealistic this supposition actually is. We casually spoke, for example, of tests for disciplinary sternness, sex drive, physical health, and honesty.

But really, now, have we any idea of what it is that we would be testing for? What are the different values assumed by the Sternness-of-discipline or Degree-of-honesty variables, and how, even in principle, could we determine which particular value holds for a given individual? What would it be like to have a Sex-drive score of 26 on some scale—any scale—of this variable? And if Jimmy Jones's best friend just gave him a bloody nose, how many points does this subtract from his index of Physical-health?

When confronted with vagueness of this sort in our prior Degree-of-baldness example, it was argued that since the ordinary-language concept of "baldness" has no definite meaning, we are free to replace this notion with any more precise operational definition which serves our need, or at least with any that captures the spirit of the original. But unfortunately, despite the philosophical hopes of an earlier era (circa 1920–50), explicit operational definitions based on what is directly knowable are of but limited service (though where appropriate, they remain indispensible) in making commonsense ideas scientifically respectable. In the special case of "baldness," the ordinary intent of this notion makes apparent that if we had a complete description of the distribution of hair on a person's head, no conceivable additional data could further assist us in deciding how bald that person is;[5] hence all that is lacking for a precise concept is simply for us to make up our minds about what abstraction from hair distribution is to count as "baldness."[6] However, what set of observations would suffice as an abstraction basis for a clarified concept of, say, "honesty"? Presumably, our decisions about how honest a person is are based on the way he behaves when confronted with certain opportunities for self-benefit or self-protection at the expense of ethical ideals, such as finding a well-stocked billfold with the owner's name in it, or being in control of the ballot box after a close election, or being asked whether the rumor about his behavior at last night's party is really true. But for any list of honesty-testing situations we might compile, no matter how extensive, we could always conceive of still other situations in which a person's behavior, were we to know it, would further modify or confirm our judgment about his honesty. Even more awkwardly, what are we to say about the differential honesties of persons at times when they are not actually *in* situations which allow their honesty to be manifested. We would normally hold, say, that John Teach Smith and his wife Angelica continue to be a black-hearted scoundrel and a paragon of virtue, respectively, even while they are both sleeping peace-

[5] We ignore the possibility that the circumstances under which a person loses his hair—e.g., having his head shaved—is considered relevant to whether or not he is "bald" at a given moment.

[6] In light of this consideration, it would seem that of the various "operational definitions" for baldness suggested earlier, only Hair-density is really a legitimate *definition* of the Degree-of-baldness variable.

fully in bed. Whatever we intend to denote by "honesty," it must be something *other* than an abstraction from the observable behaviors and circumstances from which we infer it. But if we cannot explicitly *define* honesty by an operational definition over observable attributes, but can only say that honesty, whatever it may be, is something whose *symptoms* are certain aspects of a person's behavior in appropriate circumstances, how are we to justify ever taking these behaviors in these circumstances as symptoms of honesty in the first place? Obviously we cannot establish their diagnostic validity empirically, for we have no knowledge about the criterion in this case apart from that which the predictors themselves afford. And it may as well be stated frankly here and now that no satisfactory answer to this problem will be forthcoming, or even attempted, in this book. Search for clarification and explanation of how it is that we are apparently able to devise concepts which penetrate beyond what has been observed, and succeed after a fashion in acquiring knowledge about realities inaccessible to our direct experience, is one of the most active quests of advanced contemporary research in philosophy and scientific method; and while some answers are little by little beginning to take shape, any serious discussion of the issues is grossly beyond our present scope.[7] We can and shall, however, have a look at the manner in which test theorists, in their own humble[8] way, have grappled with these matters as they bear upon the interpretation of test scores.

To press onward, then, the concepts of "content validity" and "construct validity" derive from considerations of how we might justify inference from test observations to criteria about which we have no knowledge except *by means of* these tests or similar observations. That is, when confronted with a problem of content or construct validity, we cannot appeal to an empirically determined correlation between test and criterion but must provide an argument for why it is reasonable to interpret the test as a measure of something else which, in general, can be observed only indirectly. In cases to which "construct validity" applies, there is an unabashed postulation of unobserved or "theoretical" variables which are assumed to be more or less casually responsible for the observed test scores. "Content validity," on the other hand, pertains to an older, less audacious, form of construction in which the criterion does not, prima facie, differ in kind from the test itself (or at least not from the "true score" component—discussed later—of the test variable), and in some cases may even be in principle directly determinable.

[7] The reader who would like to acquire some familiarity with the more respectable literature on these matters may get off to an excellent start by browsing in such notable works as Feigl and Brodbeck (27), Braithwaite (8), Feigl, Scriven, and Maxwell (29), Nagel (62), Feigl and Maxwell (28), and Pap (63).

[8] Not really.

Content Validity

By the "composite" of a person's scores on several different variables, let us mean the merger of these scores by some fixed procedure into a single resultant score for that person. The distribution of these composite scores in a given population is then the distribution of a "composite variable" which is defined by a certain function of its constituent variables. (In physics, for example, "Density" is a composite variable whose constituent variables are Mass and Volume, since an object's density is its mass divided by its volume.) A test may then be said to have content validity when (*a*) the criterion variable is a *composite* of all the variables of a certain specified kind, which will be called the "domain" of the criterion, and (*b*) the test obtains a composite score (or, in the limiting case, a single score) on a *sample* of the criterion's domain.[9] For instance, how anemic a person is may be defined by the density of red cells in his blood. Direct determination of this by counting all the red cells in the subject's blood and dividing by its volume would be difficult to manage technically and would greatly inconvenience the subject. However, it *is* quite practical to count the red cells in a small drop of the subject's blood and to take the computed density in this sample as an estimate of the red-cell density in the aggregate of all his drops of blood. Again: On what grounds may a list of spelling words as administered, say, by an English teacher to her students, be justified as a test of *English-spelling ability*—not just as a test of ability to spell the particular words on the list, mind you, but as a test of English-spelling ability without restriction? Simply that if "English-spelling ability," unrestricted, is defined as a person's total ability to spell all the words of the English language, then performance on the test exhibits at least a *part* of a person's ability on the total. Or suppose that for the edification of entering Freshmen, the fraternities at Brainsweat University develop a checklist of ten items of offensive professorial behavior on which to rate members of the faculty for how big an s.o.b. each one is. Clearly, the ways in which a professor can be an s.o.b. are not limited to any ten items, even if these include, say, how strict he is about cutting class, how frequently he gives written assignments and surprise quizzes, how tough it is to pass his course without studying for it, and how nasty he gets about cribbing on exams and term papers, reading newspapers or matching pennies during class lectures, and other natural exuberances of misunderstood youth. Even so, these are certainly important contributors to a professor's total s.o.b. stature, and if professor *P* rates substantially higher than professor *U* on

[9] Content validity has often been characterized only as a test's more or less representative sampling from a domain of items, with no concern expressed by the discussant for what composite over that domain is to be considered the criterion, or even signs of recognition that the concept of "content validity" requires some such composite (see, e.g., Lennon, 53). What such accounts construe a content-valid test to be a predictor *of* is never made clear.

the checklist, it is unlikely that this order is reversed on the complete criterion. In each of these three examples—blood count, spelling test, and s.o.b. checklist—it will be seen that the test variable comprises a selection from the constituents which, in aggregate, make up the criterion, so that a person's score on the test logically contributes to his score on the criterion. Such a test has "content validity" because its contents, or components, are included in the criterion's domain.

There is a great deal which can be said, mathematically and methodologically, about the subject of content validity, more than has appeared in the technical literature and certainly more than can satisfactorily be discussed here, especially since we have eschewed consideration of statistical sampling. We should, however, call attention to certain difficulties which make appraisal of a test's significance from the standpoint of content validity considerably more problematic than seems generally to be appreciated.

To begin with, content validity guarantees for a test only that its items are *logically relevant* to the criterion in virtue of actually being ingredients of the latter. By itself, this implies very little about the statistical correlation between test and criterion. It is possible for a sample to be highly representative of what it samples (e.g., blood-sampling as a test for anemia), but it can also fail abjectly to do so. For example, if a test of English-spelling ability were to contain only names of commercial products heavily advertised on TV, or technical terms of some highly specialized profession, we might well expect to find poor correlation between the test and other less biased measures of English spelling. The *face* validity of a test which samples its criterion[10] can easily seduce its user into negligence about the test's more important predictive credentials. Actually, content validity is a reasonable basis on which to accredit a test only if it meets minimal standards of representative sampling from the criterion's domain.

Secondly, a fundamental but outstandingly neglected prerequisite for judging a test's content validity is specification of just what the composite criterion *is*. The composition of the test itself does little to clarify this, for there are an unlimited number of potential composite criteria whose components are simultaneously sampled by the test. Thus the spelling test given to her sixth-grade pupils by Miss Smith presumably has content validity for, among other things, (1) Sixth-grade-spelling (defined, say, by what Miss Smith's school system expects a sixth grader to know of spelling), (2) the ability to spell all words known to Miss Smith, (3) Command-of-commercial-spelling (i.e., ability over a domain of words specified, say, by the graduation requirements of the local business school), (4) English-spelling ability (without restriction), (5)

[10] Note that while face validity and content validity are not the same, a test which has the latter is very apt to have the former as well.

Sixth-grade-scholastic-achievement (i.e., a composite of all things which Miss Smith has tried to teach her sixth graders), and (6) General-competence, this last being a composite of how good a person is at *everything*. Moreover, it takes much more than a few commonplace phrases (as have been used in the present examples) to specify the domain of a composite variable with any useful precision, and definitions of composites which determine, either explicitly or by implication, exactly what variables do or do not fall within their scope virtually never occur in practice. Even in unusually simple cases such as spelling abilities, whose constituents can explicitly be enumerated by reference to extant word lists such as dictionaries, the final operational definition is seldom actually carried out. What is more likely is that the composite's domain presents near-insuperable problems of delimitation to begin with. What items, for example, are comprised by "arithmetic ability," an expression used frequently in everyday discourse to denote, presumably, a composite measure of a person's abilities at various problems in arithmetic? For even the most elementary forms of arithmetic, it is impossible to enumerate the different possible problems of that form individually—e.g., the phrase, "the ability to add n_1 and n_2," generates descriptions of an infinitude of different specific abilities as various numbers are substituted for "n_1 and n_2." A good start toward defining the domain of "arithmetic ability" would be to list the various problem forms which are to be classed as arithmetic—e.g., problems of the forms $n_1 + n_2$, $n_1 \div n_2$, $n_1 \times n_2 - n_3$, etc. But how does one list *all* the forms of arithmetic? And where does arithmetic leave off and more complex mathematics begin—is "Find to the 20th decimal the limit of $\sum_{i=1}^{n} 1/i^2$ as n approaches infinity," or "What is 69.13 raised to the 172th power?" or "Find the cube root of 4," a problem in *arithmetic* or not? What restrictions, if any, are to be set on the numbers on which the arithmetic forms operate—e.g., do or do not "What is the sum of π and e?" and "What is the sum of $3 + 2\sqrt{-1}$ and $17/4 - \sqrt{-1}$?" count as arithmetic instances of the form "What is the sum of n_1 and n_2?" And how, in defining our domain of specific items, are we to deal with different ways of presenting a problem—e.g., do "Multiply 7 by 2," "Multiply 2 by 7," "What is seven times two?" and "What is 2×7?" define four different specific abilities or only one? (After all, a person who is shaky on the fact that $n_1 \times n_2 = n_2 \times n_1$ or on the equivalence of "7" with "seven" and "×" with "times" might well be able to work the problem in one form but not in another.) In the case of mathematical problems, moreover (and if definition of "arithmetic ability" presents problems, think how much worse the more general composite, "mathematical ability" must be), we at least feel intuitively that we can recognize one when we see it, even if precise definitions elude us. But how often can we honestly feel even this minimal assurance about the meaning of composite concepts actually in use. Consider, for example, the important variable "Presidential-suitability," meaning a composite of a person's qualifications for the Presidency of the U.S. Certainly we periodically judge how various men of affairs stand on this variable, often with high conviction and strident fervor, yet have we really any notion of how to circumscribe what goes into the determination of Presidential-suitability?

To compound the woes of defining a composite criterion, even if its domain has been successfully identified, a decision must still be reached about the manner in which the composite is formed. Is, e.g., a person's English-spelling ability a simple arithmetic mean of his abilities on the individual words, or do some words receive more weight than others—or should the composite be defined by an even more complicated nonlinear function over the individual words it comprises? The question of weighting may seem to be of small consequence when dealing with a relatively homogeneous domain such as that of spelling problems, but it appears much less so when the domain includes different types of items. For example, should a problem in long division be worth no more in determining what is meant by "arithmetic ability" than a simple ability to add two digits? And how should a man's personal charm be weighed against his decisiveness when evaluating his Presidential-suitability? This issue of differential weighting also draws attention to uncertainties about the definition and scaling of the individual variables in the composite's domain. How, for example, do we scale the ability to spell "hippopotamus"? Is it a two-valued, or "dichotomous," variable—either the subject can spell it or he can't—or do we allow for gradations in this ability? And for that matter, what do we *mean* by "the ability to spell 'hippopotamus,'" anyway? We test for it by confronting a subject with the problem and observing his response; yet uttering the series of sounds, "aich-eye-pee-pee-oh-pee-oh-tee-aye-em-you-ess," is not logically equivalent to having the ability to spell "hippopotamus," but is merely an imperfectly correlated symptom thereof. We shall have a bit more to say about the nature of abilities later. Here the intent is merely to call attention to the unpalatable fact that over and above problems of domain and weighting, the definition of a composite variable also suffers from whatever vagueness and ontological uncertainty may adhere to any of its constituent variables. To think, then, that we likely have much idea of what we are talking about when we appraise the "content validity" of some particular test is simply open-mouthed naivete.

Because many test theorists have held composite criteria to be more respectably in keeping with the spirit of scientific empiricism than are inferred theoretical criteria, it is also worth observing that even if a composite were to be so clearly defined that the value of any one of its constituent variables could readily be observed for a given individual, it would still be impossible, in most cases of practical interest, to determine scores on the composite variable except by inference from scores on a test which samples only a small portion of the domain. Even so simple a composite criterion as the ability to add two integers comprises an infinity of individual items, only 0% of which can actually be tested directly insomuch as any finite number, no matter how large, is still only 0% of an infinite totality. In fact, even when the domain of the composite is finite, as in the case of English-spelling ability, an attempt actually to observe the entire domain by successive presentation of all the individual items would introduce practice effects, fatigue, etc., which should modify the character of the later items to a greater or lesser extent. (Thus a person's ability to spell "hippopotamus" now is not necessarily altogether the same as his ability to spell "hippopotamus" 30 seconds from now after having first been asked how to spell "sphygmomanometer.") It is a mistake, then, to think that composite variables defined over a domain of variables which individually raise no special problems of observation are free from the taint of nonobservability which stigmatizes the theoretical variables contemplated by "construct validity" (see below).

Finally, since despite these difficulties we can and frequently do attempt, however fuzzily, to make use of composite concepts, it is instructive to examine the conditions which must be satisfied if our most direct observational access to a composite variable – namely, by observing a sample of variables from its domain – is to provide an objectively valid measure of it. We shall not attempt to answer this question in full generality but will make certain simplifying assumptions which do not seriously specialize the conclusions.

Suppose, then, that we have identified a set of $\mathbf{n_C}$ variables $\mathbf{X_1}, \ldots,$ $\mathbf{X_{n_C}}$ whose sum is taken to define a composite criterion **C**, i.e.,

$$\mathbf{C} =_{\text{def}} \mathbf{X_1} + \ldots + \mathbf{X_{n_C}} = \sum_{i=1}^{n_C} \mathbf{X_i}. \tag{5.3}$$

Also, let **T** be a test formed by summing $\mathbf{n_T}$ items, say $\mathbf{X_1}, \ldots, \mathbf{X_{n_T}} (\mathbf{n_T} \leq \mathbf{n_C})$, from **C**'s domain, i.e.,

$$\mathbf{T} =_{\text{def}} \mathbf{X_1} + \ldots + \mathbf{X_{n_T}} = \sum_{i=1}^{n_T} \mathbf{X_i}. \tag{5.4}$$

(It might seem more psychologically satisfying to define **C** and **T** as averages, rather than sums, of the items they comprise, but this would modify the present definitions only by multiplication of each by a constant, namely, $1/\mathbf{n_C}$ and $1/\mathbf{n_T}$, respectively, and would hence change only the units of measurement for raw scores on **T** and **C**.) Clearly test **T** has content validity as a measure of criterion **C**, but what we would now like to know is the *objective* validity of **T** for **C**.

To keep the analysis as simple as possible, we assume that all variables in the domain of **C** have unit variance and that the interitem correlations are all equal—i.e.,

[5.5-ij] $(\mathbf{i},\mathbf{j} = \mathbf{1}, \ldots, \mathbf{n_C})$

$$\mathrm{Cov}(\mathbf{X_i}, \mathbf{X_j}) = \begin{cases} 1 \text{ if } \mathbf{i} = \mathbf{j} \\ r \text{ if } \mathbf{i} \neq \mathbf{j}\,. \end{cases} \qquad \text{(assumed)}$$

The notation "$\mathbf{i},\mathbf{j} = \mathbf{1}, \ldots, \mathbf{n_C}$" means that the indices **i** and **j** run over all combinations of an assignment to **i** from **1** to $\mathbf{n_C}$ with an assignment to **j** from **1** to $\mathbf{n_C}$, so formula [5.5-**ij**] actually represents $\mathbf{n_C^2}$ different equations. For $\mathbf{i} = \mathbf{j}$, assumption [5.5-**ii**] yields $\mathrm{Cov}(\mathbf{X_i}, \mathbf{X_i}) = \mathrm{Var}(\mathbf{X_i}) = \sigma^2_{\mathbf{X_i}} = 1$, while for two different items $\mathbf{X_i}$ and $\mathbf{X_j}$, $r_{\mathbf{X_i}\mathbf{X_j}} = \mathrm{Cov}(\mathbf{X_i}, \mathbf{X_j})/(\sigma_{\mathbf{X_i}}\sigma_{\mathbf{X_j}}) = r/(1 \times 1) = r$. Next, we pause while the reader returns to Chapter 4 for a review of formulas [4.39] and [4.40]. . . . . All right, ready to plunge on? It follows immediately from [4.40] and assumptions [5.5] that

[5.6]
$$\mathrm{Var}(\mathbf{T}) = \mathbf{n_T} + \mathbf{n_T}(\mathbf{n_T} - 1)r \qquad ([5.5]^{11})$$
$$= \mathbf{n_T}(\mathbf{n_T}r + 1 - r)$$

[5.7]
$$\mathrm{Var}(\mathbf{C}) = \mathbf{n_C} + \mathbf{n_C}(\mathbf{n_C} - 1)r \qquad ([5.5])$$
$$= \mathbf{n_C}(\mathbf{n_C}r + 1 - r)$$

while using [4.39],

[5.8]
$$\mathrm{Cov}(\mathbf{T}, \mathbf{C}) = \mathrm{Cov}\left[\mathbf{T}, \mathbf{T} + \sum_{\mathbf{i}=\mathbf{n_T}+1}^{\mathbf{n_C}} \mathbf{X_i}\right]$$
$$= \mathrm{Var}(\mathbf{T}) + \mathrm{Cov}\left(\sum_{\mathbf{i}=1}^{\mathbf{n_T}} \mathbf{X_i}, \sum_{\mathbf{i}=\mathbf{n_T}+1}^{\mathbf{n_C}} \mathbf{X_i}\right)$$
$$= \mathrm{Var}(\mathbf{T}) + \mathbf{n_T}(\mathbf{n_C} - \mathbf{n_T})r \qquad ([5.5])$$
$$= \mathbf{n_T}(\mathbf{n_C}r + 1 - r)\,.$$

Hence,

[5.9]
$$r_{\mathbf{TC}}{}^2 = \frac{\mathrm{Cov}(\mathbf{T},\mathbf{C})^2}{\mathrm{Var}(\mathbf{T}) \cdot \mathrm{Var}(\mathbf{C})} \qquad ([5.5])$$
$$= \frac{\mathbf{n_T}(\mathbf{n_C}r + 1 - r)}{\mathbf{n_C}(\mathbf{n_T}r + 1 - r)}$$

[11] To continue our practice of parenthetical annotation of restrictive conditions which hold on stated formulas, we shall list the index number of prior equations which assert these restrictions when such equations have been given.

where we show r^2_{TC} rather than r_{TC} to save the nuisance of a square root sign.

Formula [5.9] is not very communicative as it stands, but when properly caressed, it confides interesting secrets. One is that if $r = 0$,

$$[5.10] \qquad r^2_{TC} = \frac{n_T}{n_C} \qquad ([5.5];\ r = 0)\ ,$$

which says that if the items in the domain of a composite **C** all have zero intercorrelations, the validity of test **T** for criterion **C** is the square root of the proportion of items composing **C** which are sampled by **T**. If the variables in **C**'s domain are unrelated to one another, therefore, **T** will have negligible validity for **C** unless the test contains a sizable proportion of the criterion's domain.

For most composite concepts of practical interest, however, the domain is much, much larger than the number of items on any test of manageable length. To see what happens in this case, observe that [5.9] can be put into form

$$[5.11] \qquad r^2_{TC} = \frac{n_T r + \epsilon}{n_T r + 1 - r} \qquad ([5.5])$$

where

$$\epsilon =_{\text{def}} \frac{n_T}{n_C}(1 - r)\ ,$$

and is insignificant if the proportion of **C**'s domain included in **T** is sufficiently small. That is, assuming r to be nonnegative,[12]

$$[5.12] \qquad r^2_{TC} \geqslant \frac{n_T r}{n_T r + 1 - r} \qquad ([5.5],\ r \geqslant 0)$$

in which the inequality approaches an identity as the sampling proportion n_T/n_C approaches zero. Hence if $r > 0$, the validity of **T** for **C** rapidly approaches unity as the number, n_T, of test items increases, even when r is relatively low. This fact can be appreciated most readily by computing the number of test items required to attain a fixed level of validity. Solving [5.11] for n_T shows that

$$[5.13] \qquad n_T \leqslant \left(\frac{r^2_{TC}}{1 - r^2_{TC}}\right)\left(\frac{1 - r}{r}\right) < \left(\frac{r^2_{TC}}{1 - r^2_{TC}}\right)\left(\frac{1}{r}\right) \qquad ([5.5],\ r \geqslant 0)$$

which says that the number of test items necessary to achieve a given validity is less than proportional to the reciprocal of the interitem correlation r. (From [5.13] it may be observed, e.g., that even when the interitem correlations are as small as $r = .10$, less than 10 test items are needed for a validity as high as $\sqrt{.5}$, or .71.) Hence so long as the variables in

[12] Negative r is a pathological case which has little if any practical importance. (See inequality [7.94].)

the domain of a composite criterion do not have essentially zero correlation with one another, it is fairly easy, in this simplified case at least, for a content-valid test to yield a respectably accurate estimate of the criterion. Moreover, correlation of test **T** with any unsampled item $\mathbf{X_k}$ ($\mathbf{k} > \mathbf{n_T}$) in **C**'s domain is easily seen (the proof may be left to the reader) to be

$$[5.14] \qquad r^2_{\mathbf{TX_k}} = \frac{\mathbf{n_T} r^2}{\mathbf{n_T} r + 1 - r} \qquad ([5.5])$$

or from [5.14] and [5.11] when the sampling proportion is negligible,

$$[5.15] \qquad r_{\mathbf{TX_k}} = r_{\mathbf{TC}} \sqrt{r} \qquad ([5.5],\ \mathbf{n_T}/\mathbf{n_C} = 0)\ .$$

We may also quickly see by adapting [5.11] to the limiting case where $\mathbf{n_T} = 1$ that the correlation between the full composite **C** and any item $\mathbf{X_k}$ in its domain is

$$[5.16] \qquad r_{\mathbf{CX_k}} = \sqrt{r + \frac{1-r}{\mathbf{n_C}}} \qquad ([5.5])\ ,$$

or simply $r_{\mathbf{CX_K}} = \sqrt{r}$ when the domain is very large. Hence if test **T** samples a moderately large number of items from the criterion's domain (even if the sampling *proportion* is vanishingly small), it yields an almost perfect measure of the criterion, while its correlation with any single unsampled item in the criterion's domain is approximately $\sqrt{r}$, which is also the criterion's own correlation with this constituent.

The most critical simplifying restriction in the preceding analysis is the assumption that all intercorrelations among items in the composite's domain are the same. Even in the more general case, however, these results still hold approximately, with r replaced by the average inter-item correlation, so long as the items included on the test are a suitably representative sample of the total domain. We may conclude, then, that a necessary and prima facie sufficient condition for a composite concept defined over a large number of individual variables to be potentially useful is for the average correlation among the latter to be positive. The practical payoff in this case is that any decent estimator of the composite—in particular, a well-constructed test with content validity for this criterion—will also usefully (just how usefully depending on the correlation coherence of the composite's domain) predict various specific items included in the composite as need for such predictions arises. And is this not, in fact, what we expect from our composite concepts in everyday life? When we assess a person's "English-spelling ability" or "arithmetic ability" by observing his performances on a sample of problems, we certainly feel, justifiedly or not, that we have *also* learned something about how well he can do on still other spelling or arithmetic problems. And when we judge a candidate's "Presidential-suitability" on the basis of presently observed constituents thereof (past governmental experience, political affiliations, charisma, etc.), we are above all hopefully forecasting his probable success at dealing with the various national and international crises which will grace the next term of office. Analysis of composite concepts in everyday use makes unmistakeably clear that a near-universal implicit presupposition of these is that the individual elements of the composite's domain are at least moderately valid estimators of one another.

In summary of this rather extended critique of "content validity," then, we have the following conclusions: (1) While no attempt was made to quantify the notion, a test has "content validity" for any criterion conceived as a composite – i.e., an average or other summary measure – over a group of variables of which the items composing the test are a sample. (2) Composite criteria of the sort envisioned in discussions of content validity are practically never defined with greater precision than the commonsense intuitions of a bright ten-year-old child. (3) For virtually all composite criteria of interest, the domain is far too large to permit simultaneous observation of a person's scores on all the variables included therein; hence scores on the criterion cannot be determined except by inference from scores on a content-valid test of it. (4) In general, it is not only useless but misleading to introduce a composite criterion unless we have reason to believe that the variables participating in the composite are positively intercorrelated. This last conclusion, however, has a further important implication. If the variables in the domain are too numerous to observe individually, on what grounds *could* we reasonably believe them to be positively intercorrelated? Only, it would seem, if we surmise *that they have some feature in common which would induce this correlation.*[13] If so, then it may be suspected that a test which is alleged to assess merely a composite over observables is in actuality being surreptitiously construed to measure a *theoretical* variable hypothesized to unify the composite's domain. Hence consideration of content validity ineluctably feeds into the problems of *construct* validity.

Construct Validity

It was previously claimed that a great many concepts of science and everyday life refer to entities which cannot themselves be perceived, even in part, but which we are somehow able to learn about by inference from their effects on the things which we can observe. For example, consider

[13] If the variables included in a good-sized sample of the domain are found to be significantly correlated, then it seems reasonable to infer that this intercorrelation undoubtedly pervades the entire domain. But a good case can be made for the position that it is precisely the likelihood, given such an observation, that one or more unifying factors underlie the domain which gives the statistical inference its tenability.

once again the attribute of being able to spell "hippopotamus." As pointed out earlier, the *ability* to do this is not the same thing as the actual *doing* of it, for either can occur without the other. Thus the reader is perfectly capable, presumably, of spelling "hippopotamus"—i.e., this ability is an attribute which he has right at this very moment—even though he is not now actually vocalizing or writing this series of letters. Conversely, a person whose literary talents are less advanced than the reader's might recite the sequence "h-i-p-p-o-p-o-t-a-m-u-s" by reading the letters one by one from a prompt card his remedial spelling teacher has placed before him and still remain bereft, even during the act of vocalization, of what is normally meant by "the ability to spell 'hippopotamus'." And yet, it is only through observations of what a person *does* when confronted with the task of spelling this word that we come to know his ability to spell it. The epistemological relevance of the act to the ability is that Degree-of-ability-to-spell-"hippopotamus" is a theoretical variable postulated specifically to account for the observed fact that given equal opportunity and incentive to spell "hippopotamus," people characteristically differ from one another in the way they respond. When one person does consistently better than another on a problem where the difference cannot be ascribed to a systematic bias in the conditions under which the problem is presented, we must assume—or least we inevitably *do* assume—that this is due to some underlying difference in the persons themselves which persists (though not necessarily without hope of modification) even at times when they are not actually doing the problem. Performance scores *obtained under the standard test-circumstances* are then a measure of the ability variable postulated to account for them. Such a test is said to have *construct validity* because, while test and criterion are logically distinct from one another, if we did not assume the test to have validity for the criterion, we would have no good reason for assuming the criterion to exist at all. That is, the observed test-circumstance → test-result connection is the evidential basis (or at least part of it) for the concept of the criterion in the first place.

By definition, then, a test has "construct validity" when it is construed to be a test of some variable hypothesized to explain a given body of data of which the test behavior is itself a paradigm instance. It is only recently that this theory-dependent characteristic of tests has been made explicit,[14] for it derives from an interpretation of scientific concepts which was vehemently rejected by the positivistic views of scientific knowledge that were ascendent during the first half of this century.[15] It

[14] The term "construct validity" first made its appearance on pp. 14ff. of the American Psychological Association's 1954 manual, *Technical recommendations for psychological tests and diagnostic techniques* (2). Its most definitive exposition to date has been made by Cronbach and Meehl (21).

[15] For a somewhat gamey but stimulating taste of this older outlook as applied to test theory, see Bechtoldt (6).

is now coming generally to be agreed,[16] however, that much of scientific and commonsense belief pertains to entities—not just "convenient fictions," but genuine existents—which we learn about only indirectly through their effects on what can be observed. The detailed nature of the process by which we acquire such knowledge is as yet understood but crudely.[17] Even so, one facet which seems clear is that, however justified, an especially potent source of inference to underlying determinants is a pattern of observed interrelationships. The postulation of "abilities" to help explain the effect of problem presentations on a person's manifest behavior is one illustration of this. Actually, abilities are only one instance of a vast array of low-grade theoretical attributes technically known as "dispositions" and identified by means of (*not* identified *with*) a person's or object's reaction to particular test conditions. Thus "fragility" refers to whatever state of a chunk of matter is responsible for its tendency to shatter when subjected to sudden stress, while "combustibility" accounts for why some but not all objects burst into flame when heated.[18] A somewhat different case of inference to theoretical entities arises when an array of observation variables manifests a provocative pattern of empirical correlations. This situation has been the inspiration for much of the advanced research in psychometrics and test theory during the past several decades, though the mathematical developments thereof have reached a much higher level of sophistication than have their methodological foundations. Of these developments, the most notable has been *factor analysis*.

"Factor analysis" is a statistical technique by which to discern within the confusingly manifold interrelations of an aggregate of empirical variables the concealed presence of a smaller, more elegant, array which may (or then again, may not) explain why the observed variables have the correlational affinities they do. To return for illustration to the domain of spelling abilities, suppose that upon analysis of the scores obtained from some population of subjects on a long test of spelling words, it is found that quality of performance on each individual word of the test has a correlation of .25 with performance on every other. Our first inferential move is to treat a subject's performance on each word as a measure (though not necessarily a perfect one) of his *ability* to spell that word. More than this, however, the pervasive intercorrelations among the individual spelling abilities (i.e., the ability to spell "hippopotamus,"

[16] See numerous articles collected in the references cited in fn. 7, p. 196.

[17] For the beginnings of a theory of the formal patterns by which theoretical constructs inductively emerge from empirical observations, see Rozeboom (67).

[18] For a time, it was hoped by philosophers of science that dispositional concepts could be defined as abbreviations for "If . . . , then . . . " statements. Careful logical analysis has shown this to be generally untenable, but while it now appears inescapable that dispositional concepts presuppose theoretical states in one fashion or another, the analysis is somewhat more complicated than indicated here.

the ability to spell "hypotenuse," the ability to spell "hypothesis," etc.) urges a further inference to something that these specific abilities have in common. In pursuit of this speculation, let us see what follows from the hypothesis that in the population tested,

$$\mathbf{Z_i} = .5\mathbf{F} + \mathbf{e_{i \bullet F}}$$

for each spelling word **i** on the test, where $\mathbf{Z_i}$ is the Z-scale for the Performance-on-word-**i** variable, **F** is the "common factor" with unit variance hypothesized to underlie performances on the various words, and $\mathbf{e_{i \bullet F}}$ is the residual component of $\mathbf{Z_i}$ uncorrelated with **F** (see Chapter 4, p. 115). If we also assume that $\mathrm{Cov}(\mathbf{e_{i \bullet F}}, \mathbf{e_{j \bullet F}}) = 0$ for any two different test words **i** and **j**—i.e., that there is no linear correlation among test-word performances in this population not attributable to factor **F**—then the factorial hypothesis entails that

$$\begin{aligned} r_{\mathbf{Z_i Z_j}} &= \mathrm{Cov}(\mathbf{Z_i}, \mathbf{Z_j}) = \mathrm{Cov}(.5\mathbf{F} + \mathbf{e_{i \bullet F}}, .5\mathbf{F} + \mathbf{e_{j \bullet F}}) \\ &= .25\,\mathrm{Var}(\mathbf{F}) + \mathrm{Cov}(\mathbf{e_{i \bullet F}}, \mathbf{e_{j \bullet F}}) \\ &= .25 \, . \end{aligned}$$

We can hence explain (correctly or incorrectly as the case may be) the observed pattern of intercorrelations in this population by postulating a single theoretical variable which, like the individual spelling abilities, cannot be observed directly, but which exposes its existence by inducing a correlation among spelling performances on different words and which, moreover, is highly correlated (as shown by arguments developed later) with a subject's total score on the spelling test. What more can be learned about the nature of this construct variable depends on further correlational research. If spelling abilities do not correlate appreciably with other psychological traits, we might call **F** something like "general spelling ability" and let it go at that. On the other hand, if item performances on spelling tests, vocabulary tests, tests of grammar and literary style, etc., all show the same intercorrelations, we would begin to think more broadly of **F** as a "primary verbal factor," or, if the correlation pattern were to extend to all mental abilities, "general intelligence."[19]

Of course this example, with its assumption of precisely the same correlation for each pair of spelling items, is somewhat idealized. In practice, we would expect a more complex pattern. We might find, for instance (though this is still unrealistically simple), that spelling words separate into several groups—say nouns vs. verbs vs. adjectives, etc.—such that performances on words within each group correlate highly with one another while words selected from different groups show zero correlation, so that knowing how well a person did on a list of nouns would be

[19] For an important recent discussion of correlational patterns and factor identity, see Campbell and Fiske (9).

useful for predicting how well he can spell other nouns but would reveal nothing about his skill at verbs or adjectives. In this case we could not reasonably postulate a common "general spelling ability" factor (though we could still define "general spelling ability" as a composite of all specific spelling abilities); instead, the evidence would support the existence of several independent spelling factors, one for each intracorrelated group. Still another possibility is that the specific word abilities might all show some degree of positive intercorrelation, yet form clusters such that the correlations within each cluster are appreciably higher than the correlations between items from different clusters—e.g., performances on nouns correlate .80 with one another, performances on verbs have an intercorrelation of .90, but performance on a noun correlates only .20 with performance on a verb. This, in turn, would suggest a general factor common to all spelling abilities as well as several additional more specific group factors.

We shall turn to the mathematical details of factor analysis in a moment. The present point is that for better or worse, modern test theory has evolved powerful analytic techniques with which to prune a thicket of empirical correlations down to an inner structure of hypothetical sources, and which simultaneously establish the construct validities of the tests from which these theoretical variables are inferred by deriving an estimate of the correlation between each test and theoretical construct. Admittedly, factor analysis is by no means so sure a route to hidden truth as the present remarks might seem to imply, for as will be discussed in Chapter 6, a given correlational pattern will support a plurality of alternative factorial hypotheses and convincing procedures for adjudicating among these are still lacking. What is to be noted here is that the notion of "construct validity" is far from the appeal to magical spirits or search for metaphysical absolutes that some writers with commendably sceptical temperament have taken it to be. It merely makes explicit—and hence amenable to clarification and correction—certain primordial inductive extrusions from past experience that shape our thinking irrespective of whatever conscious assent we give to them.

*Chapter 6. **Factor Analysis**

THE CONCLUDING PARAGRAPHS of Chapter 5 somewhat misleadingly suggest that factor analysis is primarily a method for deriving theoretical hypotheses. Actually, this is only one of the uses, though an important one, to which factor analysis can be put. More basically, factor analysis searches out the algebraic regularities within an array of correlation coefficients, and studies how these can be most suggestively expressed by a linear transformation of the original set of variables.

A fully satisfactory account of factor analysis requires extensive application of matrix algebra, as well as the heuristic support of a geometric analogy in which variables are represented by "vectors" (i.e., lines of various lengths radiating outward in various directions from a common center, or "origin") within a multidimensional space in such fashion that the length of each vector equals the standard deviation of the variable it represents while the cosine[1] of the angle between two vectors equals the correlation between the corresponding variables. While this vector model will be briefly illustrated later, such advanced methods lie beyond the scope of this book. The intent of this chapter is to communicate a working understanding of the conceptual and mathematical foundations of factor analysis, and for the most part, this can be accomplished handily within the framework of multivariate analysis already developed in Chapter 4. The presentation will be limited to basics, however, and the reader who develops a craving for computational details and technical elaborations should consult the recent definitive text by Harmon (44).[2]

The term "factor analysis" subsumes a rather large variety of procedures for making explicit the mathematical regularities which may exist

[1] If the reader's trigonometry is rusty, he might like to be reminded that the "cosine" of an angle is a function whose value is 1 for an angle of 0 degrees, 0 for an angle of 90 degrees, and −1 for an angle of 180 degrees.

[2] Many texts have been written on factor analysis. In addition to Harmon (44), the major mathematical references are Thurstone (78) and Lawley and Maxwell (51). Readers seeking less mathematical depth will also find Thomson (77) and Adcock (1) useful.

within an array of correlation coefficients. Classification of these methods may conveniently be organized around two major dichotomies: (*a*) defined factors versus inferred factors, and (*b*) orthogonal factors versus oblique factors. Distinction (*a*) concerns whether the factors extracted from a set of variables are exact mathematical transformations of the original variables, or are genuine inferential leaps to variables which can be estimated only imperfectly from the empirical data. Important as this difference is for the interpretation of factors, however, it primarily concerns a choice of statistics to be fed into the factoring routine, and is hence largely peripheral to the mathematical foundation of factor analysis. Distinction (*b*) on the other hand is an essential part of the mathematical theory insomuch as it concerns the correlations allowed among the factors. Two "factors"—that is, variables—are said to be *orthogonal* to one another when their linear correlation is zero, and *oblique* otherwise. (This terminology derives from the geometric vector model mentioned in the preceding paragraph. "Orthogonal" means *right-angled,* and two variables which have zero correlation are represented in this model by vectors which form a right angle. Similarly, the vectors which represent two correlated variables are "oblique," or *slanted* toward or away from each other.) Virtually all factorial procedures begin with an orthogonal solution, however, and move on to oblique factors, if at all, only for advanced considerations. It is hence most strategic to work up a solid grasp of defined, orthogonal factors before venturing the heady complications of inferred and oblique solutions.

Linear Dependencies and Factor Bases

In the broadest sense of the term, a "factor" is any variable, observed, inferred, or defined, which is treated as an independent variable in the regression equations for one or more dependent variables, and which may hence be said to "control" or "account for" a certain portion of the variance of the latter. At the same level of generality, to "factor-analyze" a variable is simply to find a way in which the analyzed variable can be expressed as a linear combination of other variables. In particular, computing the linear regression of a variable $\mathbf{Y}$ upon variables $\mathbf{X_1}, \ldots, \mathbf{X_n}$ is one way to factor-analyze $\mathbf{Y}$, since this expresses $\mathbf{Y}$ as a linear function of $\mathbf{X_1}, \ldots, \mathbf{X_n}$ and a "unique" factor $\mathbf{e_{Y \cdot X_1 \ldots X_n}}$, this last being the residual of $\mathbf{Y}$ left by $\mathbf{X_1}, \ldots, \mathbf{X_n}$ (see Chapter 4, p. 145). Thus for the Great Northern prediction problem of Chapter 4, the regression of Company-profit ($\mathbf{X_0}$) on Forms I ($\mathbf{X_1}$) and II ($\mathbf{X_2}$) of the FHAAD test was found (p. 151) to be

$$\dot{\mathbf{X}}_{\mathbf{0}(\mathbf{X_1X_2})} = 22.2\mathbf{X_1} + 122.2\mathbf{X_2} - 8{,}220\ .$$

Hence the Company-profit variable may be written

$$\mathbf{X}_0 = \dot{\mathbf{X}}_{0(X_1X_2)} + \mathbf{e}_{X_0 \bullet X_1X_2}$$
$$= 22.2\mathbf{X}_1 + 122.2\mathbf{X}_2 + \mathbf{e}_{X_0 \bullet X_1X_2} - 8{,}220\ ,$$

which analyzes $\mathbf{X}_0$ as a linear combination of the three "factors" $\mathbf{X}_1$, $\mathbf{X}_2$, and $\mathbf{e}_{X_0 \bullet X_1X_2}$. Let a variable which has been linearly standardized to have zero mean and unit variance—i.e., converted to a Z-scale—be said to be *normalized.*[3] Then if all the variables in the present example are normalized, the decomposition of $\mathbf{X}_0$ (written "$\mathbf{Z}_0$" after normalization) into factorial components becomes

$$\mathbf{Z}_0 = .111\mathbf{Z}_1 + .611\mathbf{Z}_2 + .711\mathbf{Z}_e\ ,$$

where $\mathbf{Z}_e$ is the normalized residual of $\mathbf{X}_0$ left by $\mathbf{X}_1$ and $\mathbf{X}_2$.[4] The coefficients .111, .611, and .711 of the three normalized factors, $\mathbf{Z}_1$, $\mathbf{Z}_2$, and $\mathbf{Z}_e$ respectively, in the factorial decomposition of the normalized $\mathbf{Z}_0$ are known as the *loadings* of variable $\mathbf{X}_0$ on these factors. More generally, "the loading of variable **X** on factor **F**" may be defined as *the β-weight of* **F** *in the multiple regression of* **X** *jointly on* **F** *and the other factors into which* **X** *has been decomposed.* (Note that since the regression coefficient of one variable for another is relative to the other predictor variables which have been included in the regression, the loading of a given variable upon a given factor in general depends in part on how the remaining factors have been chosen.) In this particular example the factoring is oblique because, while $\mathbf{Z}_e$ is uncorrelated with $\mathbf{Z}_1$ and $\mathbf{Z}_2$,[5] Forms I and II of the FHAAD were stipulated to have a correlation of .80. The example could be made to illustrate an orthogonal factor solution by computing $\dot{\mathbf{X}}_{0(X_1X_2)}$ in the sequential fashion of [4.107], thus replacing factor $\mathbf{X}_2$ with its component $\mathbf{e}_{X_2 \bullet X_1}$ orthogonal to $\mathbf{X}_1$.

However, while it is clarifying to appreciate that factor analysis is mathematically no more than a particular way of thinking about multiple-regression relationships, the example just given is highly atypical. The situation ordinarily envisioned by factor analysts is one in which the variables whose statistical relationships have been determined em-

---

[3] The logical place to have introduced this usage, which by no means originates here, was with the initial discussion of Z-scores in Chapter 3. Since that discussion was immediately followed with description of the normal distribution, however, and since nonlinear transformation of a nonnormally distributed variable into one with a normal distribution is also known as "normalization" of the variable, introduction of "normalization" in the present sense would only have been unnecessarily confusing at that time. Actually, the expression "normalized variable" occurs in the literature with a variety of meanings, and our chief motive for using it in the present sense of "Z-score scale" is to gain access to the highly convenient term "orthonormal," defined later.

[4] It will be recalled (cf. [4.96-K] that the standard deviation of the residual $\mathbf{e}_{X_0 \cdot X_1X_2}$ equals the standard deviation of $\mathbf{X}_0$ times the multiple coefficient of alienation, $K_{X_0(X_1X_2)}$. Hence when $\mathbf{X}_0$ and $\mathbf{e}_{X_0 \cdot X_1X_2}$ are both normalized, the coefficient of $\mathbf{Z}_e$ in this factorial decomposition of $\mathbf{Z}_0$ is simply $K_{X_0(X_1X_2)}$.

[5] *Review question*: Why?

pirically—hereafter called the *data variables*[6]—are *all* simultaneously regarded as dependent variables, while the factors into which they are decomposed are defined as linear functions of the data variables or, in the case of inferred factors, as linear functions of certain hypothesized components of the data variables. At first thought this might seem foolish: If the data variables are to be analyzed as linear combinations of factors which are themselves, in turn, defined as composites of the data variables, aren't we just going in circles? Well, yes—in a way we are, but sometimes the view from one point on a circle is more interesting than from another. Complete analysis of a set of variables into defined factors is merely a linear transformation of the set,[7] and a person's scores on such factors jointly contain exactly as much information about him, no more and no less, as do his scores on the original variables. But some ways to say the same thing are more illuminating than other ways (consider, for example, the convenience of standard scores as compared to the equivalent raw scores), and transformation of a set of data variables into a set of factors may very well reveal important relationships which are difficult to discern among the variables in their original form. In particular, extraction of factors economically exhibits the degree of linear dependence among the data variables.

Suppose that at the behest of an undershirt manufacturer who wishes a report on the chest statistics of adult American males, we have obtained scores from a great many subjects on four chest-data variables: maximum diameter-in-inches of chest when inhaling ($\mathbf{X}_1$); minimum diameter-in-inches of chest when exhaling ($\mathbf{X}_2$); normal diameter-in-inches of chest ($\mathbf{X}_3$), operationally defined as the average of $\mathbf{X}_1$ and $\mathbf{X}_2$; and chest expansion in inches ($\mathbf{X}_4$), operationally defined as the difference between a person's maximum and minimum chest diameter. For convenient reference, these variables are listed with their definitions in Table 6.1, along with the means (which are irrelevant for our interests if not for the undershirt manufacturer's) and standard deviations which

Variable	*Description*	*Mean*	*SD*
$\mathbf{X}_1$	Diameter of chest at maximum inflation, in inches	40.0	1.13
$\mathbf{X}_2$	Diameter of chest at minimum inflation, in inches	36.0	.89
$\mathbf{X}_3$	Normal chest diameter in inches ($=_{\text{def}}$ $[\mathbf{X}_1+\mathbf{X}_2]/2$)	38.0	1.00
$\mathbf{X}_4$	Chest expansion in inches ($=_{\text{def}}$ $\mathbf{X}_1-\mathbf{X}_2$)	4.0	.40

Table 6.1. Variables observed in a hypothetical study of chest statistics in a population of adult U.S. males.

[6] We shall also occasionally use the term "data variables" in an extended sense to denote any set of variables being subjected to a factorial decomposition.

[7] *Reminder*: A *set* of variables $\mathbf{X}'_1, \ldots, \mathbf{X}'_m$ is a linear transformation of another set $\mathbf{X}_1, \ldots, \mathbf{X}_n$ if each $\mathbf{X}'_i$ is identical with some linear combination of $\mathbf{X}_1, \ldots, \mathbf{X}_n$, while conversely, each $\mathbf{X}_j$ is identical with some linear combination of $\mathbf{X}'_1, \ldots, \mathbf{X}'_m$ (cf. p. 144).

we shall suppose were found by the study. To describe all the pairwise relationships among the variables we use a checkerboard layout called a *matrix*. If there are **n** variables (**n** being **4** in our present example), then the matrix has **n** rows and **n** columns, one row and one column for each variable as shown in Table 6.2. The intersection of the **i**th row and the **j**th column provides a cell in which the covariance, or if preferred, the correlation, between variable $\mathbf{X_i}$ and variable $\mathbf{X_j}$ may be entered. There is a certain redundancy in a covariance or correlation matrix because, since $\text{Cov}(\mathbf{X_i}, \mathbf{X_j}) = \text{Cov}(\mathbf{X_j}, \mathbf{X_i})$, the entry in the **i**th row and **j**th column necessarily equals the entry in the **j**th row and **i**th column: hence the upper-right triangular half of the matrix is a mirror image of the lower-right half (see Table 6.3). Because of this repetition, one triangular half of the matrix is frequently left blank in practice. The *principal diagonal* (henceforth called simply *the* diagonal) of a covariance matrix, namely, the entries located at the intersection of a row **i** with the same column **i**, is of particular interest in that, since $\text{Cov}(\mathbf{X_i}, \mathbf{X_i}) = \text{Var}(\mathbf{X_i})$, it shows the variances of the variables. In a correlation matrix, the diagonal elements are of course all 1, since the correlation of any variable with itself is always unity. The matrices in Table 6.3 show the covariances and corresponding correlations which we shall assume were observed among the chest-data variables in our present example. The reader should study Tables 6.2 and 6.3 until he is sure that he understands clearly how a covariance matrix is defined and what its special features are—notably, the display of variances along the diagonal and its symmetry around that diagonal. Note, too, that a correlation matrix is a special case of a covariance matrix. Specifically, it is the covariance matrix for a set of normalized variables.

C_{ij}	X_1	X_2	X_3	...	X_n
X_1	V_1	C_{12}	C_{13}	...	C_{1n}
X_2	C_{21}	V_2	C_{23}	...	C_{2n}
X_3	C_{31}	C_{32}	V_3	...	C_{3n}
.	.	.	.	...	.
.	.	.	.	...	.
.	.	.	.	...	.
X_n	C_{n1}	C_{n2}	C_{n3}	...	V_n

Table 6.2. Matrix layout for exhibiting the covariances among **n** variables $\mathbf{X_1}, \ldots, \mathbf{X_n}$. $C_{ij} =_{\text{def}} \text{Cov}(\mathbf{X_i}, \mathbf{X_j})$, $V_i =_{\text{def}} C_{ii} = \text{Var}(\mathbf{X_i})$. Observe that the covariance matrix shows the variances of the variables by the diagonal entries $\mathbf{V_1}, \ldots, \mathbf{V_n}$ as well as the covariance for each pair of different variables. When the $\mathbf{X_i}$ have all been standardized to unit variance, their covariance matrix shows the correlations among the variables and is called (guess what?) a "correlation matrix."

Laying aside our (imaginary) empirical covariances among chest-data variables $\mathbf{X}_1, \ldots, \mathbf{X}_4$ for the moment, let us reflect upon the mathematical relationships which we know to obtain among these variables in virtue of their definitions. Any one of the variables is only imperfectly predictable from any one of the others, yet by definition,

$$\mathbf{X}_3 = .5\mathbf{X}_1 + .5\mathbf{X}_2\,,$$

$$\mathbf{X}_4 = \mathbf{X}_1 - \mathbf{X}_2\,.$$

Hence the multiple correlations, $R_{\mathbf{X}_3(\mathbf{X}_1\mathbf{X}_2)}$ and $R_{\mathbf{X}_4(\mathbf{X}_1\mathbf{X}_2)}$ of $\mathbf{X}_3$ and $\mathbf{X}_4$, respectively, with $\mathbf{X}_1$ and $\mathbf{X}_2$ must be both equal to 1–i.e., the residual variances of $\mathbf{X}_3$ and $\mathbf{X}_4$ after $\mathbf{X}_1$ and $\mathbf{X}_2$ have been partialled out are both zero. It is consequently unnecessary in our chest-data survey to make a separate record of observations on each of the four data variables; just $\mathbf{X}_1$ and $\mathbf{X}_2$ suffice to convey all the ways in which subjects differ on the variables in the study. Moreover, if it is felt that $\mathbf{X}_3$ and $\mathbf{X}_4$ (normal chest diameter and chest expansion, respectively) are more important for the aims of the study than are $\mathbf{X}_1$ and $\mathbf{X}_2$ (maximum and minimum chest diameter), it is simple algebra to show that

$$\mathbf{X}_1 = \mathbf{X}_3 + .5\mathbf{X}_4\,,$$

$$\mathbf{X}_2 = \mathbf{X}_3 - .5\mathbf{X}_4\,,$$

so alternatively, all the data can be summarized by $\mathbf{X}_3$ and $\mathbf{X}_4$ alone. The same is true for any other pair of variables selected from $\mathbf{X}_1, \ldots, \mathbf{X}_4$. Nor for that matter need we confine ourselves to the four data variables as given: Nothing prevents us from including in our study any further linear combinations of $\mathbf{X}_1, \ldots, \mathbf{X}_4$ which may interest us–e.g., $\mathbf{X}_a =_{\text{def}} a_0 + a_1\mathbf{X}_1 + a_2\mathbf{X}_2$, $\mathbf{X}_b =_{\text{def}} b_0 + b_1\mathbf{X}_1 + b_2\mathbf{X}_2$, etc.–though, of course, these additional variables all remain perfectly predictable from $\mathbf{X}_1$ and $\mathbf{X}_2$ or from any other pair selected from $\mathbf{X}_1, \ldots, \mathbf{X}_4$. Conversely, we can take any two variables $\mathbf{X}_a$ and $\mathbf{X}_b$ defined as arbitrary linear combinations of $\mathbf{X}_1, \ldots, \mathbf{X}_4$, and so long as $\mathbf{X}_a$ is not perfectly predictable from

C_{ij}	$\mathbf{X}_1$	$\mathbf{X}_2$	$\mathbf{X}_3$	$\mathbf{X}_4$
$\mathbf{X}_1$	1.280	.960	1.120	.320
$\mathbf{X}_2$	.960	.800	.880	.160
$\mathbf{X}_3$	1.120	.880	1.000	.240
$\mathbf{X}_4$	.320	.160	.240	.160

(*a*)

r_{ij}	$\mathbf{X}_1$	$\mathbf{X}_2$	$\mathbf{X}_3$	$\mathbf{X}_4$
$\mathbf{X}_1$	1	.949	.990	.707
$\mathbf{X}_2$	.949	1	.984	.447
$\mathbf{X}_3$	.990	.984	1	.600
$\mathbf{X}_4$	.707	.447	.600	1

(*b*)

Table 6.3. Covariance matrix $\{C_{ij}\}$ and correlation matrix $\{r_{ij}\}$ for the variables listed in Table 6.1. Observe that the diagonal element C_{ii} equals the square of the SD of variable $\mathbf{X}_i$ in Table 6.1 and that the entries in the correlation matrix can be computed from the entries in the covariance matrix by the formula $r_{ij} = C_{ij}/\sqrt{C_{ii}C_{jj}}$. The numerical correlations in this example are larger than is usual for an empirical correlation matrix.

$\mathbf{X_b}$ or conversely,[8] $\mathbf{X_a}$ and $\mathbf{X_b}$ will likewise serve to summarize $\mathbf{X_1}, \ldots, \mathbf{X_4}$ and their linear combinations. That is, $\mathbf{X_1}, \ldots, \mathbf{X_4}$ or any linear composite thereof may in turn be written as a linear function of $\mathbf{X_a}$ and $\mathbf{X_b}$.[9]

If no member of a set of variables is an exact linear function of the others, the variables in the set are said to be *linearly independent* of one another. Conversely, if $\mathbf{Y} = a_0 + a_1\mathbf{X_1} + \ldots + a_n\mathbf{X_n}$ for some choice of numerical constants $a_0, \ldots, a_n$, variable $\mathbf{Y}$ is said to be *linearly dependent* upon variables $\mathbf{X_1}, \ldots, \mathbf{X_n}$.[10] The effect of linear dependencies within a set of variables is nicely illustrated by our present chest-data example. What is striking in this instance is the *two*ness of it all. No special mathematical significance attaches to the fact that $\mathbf{X_3}$ and $\mathbf{X_4}$ were defined in terms of $\mathbf{X_1}$ and $\mathbf{X_2}$ rather than conversely—the fashion in which the relationships have come about is irrelevant so long as they *have* come about. What is significant is that to reproduce $\mathbf{X_1}, \ldots, \mathbf{X_4}$ as exact linear functions (i.e., no residual errors) of a set of linearly independent summary variables, it requires not one, or three, or four such variables to do the job, as might be true for some other distribution of four data variables, but exactly two in this case, no matter which pair out of the many, many available alternatives is chosen. This is the sort of situation which, more generally, gives rise to the concept of the *dimensionality* of a set of variables.

If it is possible to write all the $\mathbf{n}$ variables in the set $\mathbf{X_1}, \ldots, \mathbf{X_n}$ as (exact) linear functions of the $\mathbf{m}$ variables in another set $\mathbf{X'_1}, \ldots, \mathbf{X'_m}$ (where some or all of the $\mathbf{X'_i}$ may or may not coincide with some of the $\mathbf{X_j}$), while there is no smaller number of variables (i.e., less than $\mathbf{m}$) of which $\mathbf{X_1}, \ldots, \mathbf{X_n}$ are all linear functions, then the set of variables $\mathbf{X_1}, \ldots,$

---

[8] It may seem redundant to stipulate that $\mathbf{X_a}$ is not perfectly predictable from $\mathbf{X_b}$ *and conversely*, but actually it is not. In the degenerate case where $\mathbf{X_b}$ is constant—i.e., $\sigma_{X_b} = 0$—$\mathbf{X_b}$ is perfectly predictable from $\mathbf{X_a}$ but the converse is not true unless $\mathbf{X_a}$ is also constant. (A more advanced statistical treatise would also qualify the equivalence between perfect predictability and perfect linear dependence with a reservation about cases with zero probability of occurrence.)

[9] If $\mathbf{X_a}$ and $\mathbf{X_b}$ are both linear functions of $\mathbf{X_1}, \ldots, \mathbf{X_4}$, then they can also be written as linear functions of $\mathbf{X_1}$ and $\mathbf{X_2}$ alone (since $\mathbf{X_3}$ and $\mathbf{X_4}$ are likewise linear functions of $\mathbf{X_1}$ and $\mathbf{X_2}$ and can be eliminated in favor of the latter). But this pair of equations can then be solved to express $\mathbf{X_1}$ and $\mathbf{X_2}$ as linear functions of $\mathbf{X_a}$ and $\mathbf{X_b}$ except for special cases which are excluded by stipulating that $\mathbf{X_a}$ and $\mathbf{X_b}$ are not perfectly predictable from one another. (Proof of this last claim is not difficult, but requires a more extensive argument than would be of any use here.) Finally, $\mathbf{X_1}$ and $\mathbf{X_2}$ may then be eliminated in favor of $\mathbf{X_a}$ and $\mathbf{X_b}$ in any equation expressing still another variable as a function of the former.

[10] Unfortunately, "independent" and "dependent" are highly ambiguous terms which have at least four major mathematical meanings. One is the distinction between the dependent and independent variables in an equation. Secondly, there is a use of "independent" to mean "zero correlation." Thirdly, variable $\mathbf{Y}$ is said to be "statistically independent" of variable $\mathbf{X}$ when the contingent distributions of $\mathbf{Y}$, given $\mathbf{X}$, are the same for every value of $\mathbf{X}$ (see p. 83). Finally, there is the present sense in which "independent of" means "not perfectly predictable from." The more thoughtful reader will wish to note that "independence" in the third sense implies "independence" in the second sense, which in turn implies it in the fourth sense, but not conversely.

$\mathbf{X_n}$ is said to have **m** *dimensions.* Obviously the dimensionality of any **n** variables cannot be greater than **n**, but whether it is less than this depends on the nature of the variables: the more their dimensionality falls short of the total number of variables in the set, the more tightly must they be linearly interrelated. If each variable $\mathbf{X_i}$ ($\mathbf{i} = 1, \ldots, \mathbf{n}$) is a linear function, $\mathbf{X_i} = a_{i0} + a_{i1}\mathbf{X}'_1 + a_{i2}\mathbf{X}'_2 + \ldots + a_{im}\mathbf{X}'_m$ of the **m** variables $\mathbf{X}'_1, \ldots, \mathbf{X}'_m$ while **m** is also the dimensionality of the set $\mathbf{X_1}, \ldots, \mathbf{X_n}$, then the set $\mathbf{X}'_1, \ldots, \mathbf{X}'_m$ is said to be a *basis* for the set $\mathbf{X_1}, \ldots, \mathbf{X_n}$. The variables in any basis for the set $\mathbf{X_1}, \ldots, \mathbf{X_n}$ are all linear functions of the $\mathbf{X_i}$,[11] while moreover any **m** variables $\mathbf{X}'_1, \ldots, \mathbf{X}'_m$ defined as arbitrary linear functions of the $\mathbf{X_i}$ are a basis for $\mathbf{X_1}, \ldots, \mathbf{X_n}$ so long as the $\mathbf{X}'_i$ are linearly independent of one another. An *orthogonal* basis is, of course, one in which the covariances among the basis variables are all zero. An orthogonal basis can always be found for any set $\mathbf{X_1}, \ldots, \mathbf{X_n}$; in fact, any set of variables has an infinitude of different orthogonal bases.[12] Whether orthogonal or oblique, a basis for a set of variables $\mathbf{X_1}, \ldots, \mathbf{X_n}$ is a linear transformation thereof which has maximal economy in terms of the number of different scores needed to report for each subject how he stands on all variables in the set; while if the basis is also orthogonal, even the imperfect predictability which obtains among correlated data is avoided. Hence an orthogonal basis for a set of variables may be conceived as an expression of these variables from which all redundancy has been removed.

A useful way to summarize these facts about linear dependencies is the following: A set S of variables may be called a *space* of variables if S includes all variables which are linear combinations of other variables in S; while variables $\mathbf{X_1}, \ldots, \mathbf{X_n}$ are said to *span* space S when a variable **Y** is included in S if and only if **Y** is a linear function of $\mathbf{X_1}, \ldots, \mathbf{X_n}$.[13] A particular space of variables can be designated, therefore, by listing a set of variables which span it—e.g., we might stipulate that space $S_{\mathbf{X}}$ is the set of all linear combinations of variables $\mathbf{X_1}, \ldots, \mathbf{X_n}$. If variables $\mathbf{X}'_1, \ldots, \mathbf{X}'_m$ all lie in the space spanned by $\mathbf{X_1}, \ldots, \mathbf{X_n}$ (i.e., each $\mathbf{X}'_i$ is a linear

[11] This important fact is not so obvious as it might at first intuitively seem, for if the $\mathbf{X_i}$ are all linear functions of **m** linearly independent variables $\mathbf{X}'_1, \ldots, \mathbf{X}'_m$ where **m** is *larger* than the dimensionality of $\mathbf{X_1}, \ldots, \mathbf{X_n}$, then the $\mathbf{X}'_j$ are *not*, in turn, all errorless linear functions of the $\mathbf{X_i}$. That they are, however, when **m** is the dimensionality of the $\mathbf{X_i}$ follows from consideration that we can always find **m** variables among the $\mathbf{X_i}$ which are linearly independent of one another, and for which the equations expressing them as linear functions of $\mathbf{X}'_1, \ldots, \mathbf{X}'_m$ can then be solved to yield each $\mathbf{X}'_j$ as a linear function of the selected $\mathbf{X_i}$.

[12] *Proof*: Any oblique basis $\mathbf{X}'_1, \ldots, \mathbf{X}'_m$ for the $\mathbf{X_i}$ can be transformed into an orthogonal one by taking, say, first $\mathbf{X}'_1$, then the residual component of $\mathbf{X}'_2$ uncontrolled by $\mathbf{X}'_1$, then the residual component of $\mathbf{X}'_3$ uncontrolled by $\mathbf{X}'_1$ and $\mathbf{X}'_2$ etc. The nonuniqueness of an orthogonal basis for the $\mathbf{X_i}$ may readily be appreciated by noting that $\mathbf{X}'_1$ can be any linear function of the $\mathbf{X_i}$, the second orthogonal basis variable can be any linear function of components of the $\mathbf{X_i}$ orthogonal to $\mathbf{X}'_1$, and so on.

[13] The reader should be clear that each variable $\mathbf{X_i}$ ($\mathbf{i} = 1, \ldots, \mathbf{n}$) is included in the set of variables which are linear functions of $\mathbf{X_1}, \ldots, \mathbf{X_n}$.

function of $\mathbf{X}_1, \ldots, \mathbf{X}_n$), while likewise each $\mathbf{X}_i$ lies in the space of $\mathbf{X}'_1, \ldots, \mathbf{X}'_m$, then any variable equal to a linear combination of the $\mathbf{X}_i$ is also equal to some linear combination of the $\mathbf{X}'_i$, and the two sets $\mathbf{X}_1, \ldots, \mathbf{X}_n$ and $\mathbf{X}'_1, \ldots, \mathbf{X}'_n$ both span the same space. The *dimensionality* of a space of variables is the smallest number of variables necessary to span it, while a *basis* for the space is any set of linearly independent variables which span it. (An immediate consequence of these definitions is that the dimensionality of a space is equal to the number of variables in any basis for it.) Since to be given a subject's scores on a set of variables amounts in principle (though not computationally in practice) to being given his scores on all linear combinations of these variables, a set of observations on a subject may be conceived simply as an observation of his position in the space spanned by the variables on which the observations were made; and this position can be expressed in terms of any system of "coordinates"—i.e., a set of variables which span that space—which are convenient.

The relevance of all this to factor analysis is that to factor-analyze a set of data variables is simply to solve for a basis for these variables (or, in the case of inferred factors, to solve for a basis for certain hypothesized components of the data variables) by computations performed on their covariance matrix. Before turning to a general review of factor solutions, however, let us consider how an orthogonal basis might be derived for our chest-data variables (Table 6.1) from their covariance matrix in Table 6.3.

When previously reflecting upon the two-dimensionality of our set of chest-data variables, we took copious advantage of prior knowledge that a subject's scores on $\mathbf{X}_3$ and $\mathbf{X}_4$ were defined from his scores on $\mathbf{X}_1$ and $\mathbf{X}_2$. But suppose that we *didn't* know this? How could we begin merely with the observed covariations among $\mathbf{X}_1, \ldots, \mathbf{X}_4$ and discover their dimensionality? Or what if variables $\mathbf{X}_3$ and $\mathbf{X}_4$ were *almost*, but not quite, related to $\mathbf{X}_1$ and $\mathbf{X}_2$ in the manner stipulated (as would be expected, e.g., if chest-diameter maxima and minima had been measured twice for each subject, one pair of observations being reported as scores on $\mathbf{X}_1$ and $\mathbf{X}_2$, and the other pair being used to compute scores on $\mathbf{X}_3$ and $\mathbf{X}_4$)? How might we then learn that $\mathbf{X}_1, \ldots, \mathbf{X}_4$ could *almost*, but not quite, be reduced to a two-dimensional basis? The answer is fairly obvious if we are clear on what the dimensionality of a set of variables signifies. To say that $\mathbf{X}_1, \ldots, \mathbf{X}_n$ have $\mathbf{m}$ dimensions is to imply that all the $\mathbf{X}_i$ can be linearly estimated with perfect accuracy (at least in the population under consideration) from any $\mathbf{m}$ variables which (*a*) are linear functions of the $\mathbf{X}_i$, and (*b*) are linearly independent of one another. Very well then, to find out whether or not the set $\mathbf{X}_1, \ldots, \mathbf{X}_n$ is of dimensionality $\mathbf{m}$ we need but select, as arbitrarily as we please, $\mathbf{m}$ linearly independent variables $\mathbf{X}'_1, \ldots, \mathbf{X}'_m$ defined by linear functions of the $\mathbf{X}_i$, and determine the multiple regression of each $\mathbf{X_i}$ upon $\mathbf{X'_1}, \ldots, \mathbf{X'_m}$. If the residual variances of $\mathbf{X_1}, \ldots, \mathbf{X_n}$ after $\mathbf{X'_1}, \ldots, \mathbf{X'_m}$ have been partialled out are all zero, then we have proved that the dimensionality of $\mathbf{X_1}, \ldots, \mathbf{X_n}$ is $\mathbf{m}$. Moreover, even if not all the $\mathbf{X_i}$-residuals vanish, the sum of the residual variances compared to the sum of the original variances reveals how closely $\mathbf{X'_1}, \ldots, \mathbf{X'_m}$ are *approximately* a basis for the $\mathbf{X_i}$. Further, while it is seldom practical to select all the variables in a trial basis $\mathbf{X'_1}, \ldots, \mathbf{X'_m}$ simultaneously (with $\mathbf{X'_1}, \ldots, \mathbf{X'_m}$ arbitrarily defined, we would have to determine whether they were, in fact, linearly independent, while coming up with just the right value for $\mathbf{m}$ could only be a lucky guess), we can introduce basis variables, or "factors," one at a time by the sequential regression procedure discussed on pp. 159 ff. of Chapter 4 until we have arrived at the proper number. Specifically, we may start with $\mathbf{X'_1}$ defined by any linear function we wish of one or more of the $\mathbf{X_i}$ so long as $\mathrm{Var}(\mathbf{X'_1}) \neq 0$, and partial $\mathbf{X'_1}$ out of $\mathbf{X_1}, \ldots, \mathbf{X_n}$. This leaves a set of $\mathbf{n}$ residual variables, or less than $\mathbf{n}$ if some of the $\mathbf{X_i}$ are perfectly estimated by $\mathbf{X'_1}$, each of which is orthogonal to $\mathbf{X'_1}$. Next $\mathbf{X'_2}$ is defined as some linear function of one or more of the nonvanished residuals $\mathbf{e}_{X_1 \bullet X'_1}, \ldots, \mathbf{e}_{X_n \bullet X'_1}$ subject only to the condition, as before, that $\mathrm{Var}(\mathbf{X'_2}) \neq 0$. Partialling $\mathbf{X'_2}$ out of the first-order residuals $\mathbf{e}_{X_i \bullet X'_1}$ then leaves $\mathbf{n}$ or less nonvanished second-order residuals orthogonal to both $\mathbf{X'_1}$ and $\mathbf{X'_2}$, and from which $\mathbf{X'_3}$ is now defined to continue the process. At each stage we may inspect how much of the total variance of the $\mathbf{X_i}$ still remains unaccounted for by the factors extracted so far, and where among the $\mathbf{X_i}$-residuals this remaining variance is concentrated. Eventually, after $\mathbf{m}$ such steps ($\mathbf{m} \leq \mathbf{n}$), all the $\mathbf{X_i}$-residuals will have vanished and it has then been shown that the dimensionality of $\mathbf{X_1}, \ldots, \mathbf{X_n}$ is $\mathbf{m}$.

Before demonstrating this procedure in application to Table 5.3, we should review and further develop those aspects of partial statistics which have special relevance for factor analysis. It will be recalled that to partial a variable $\mathbf{F}$ (where the letter "F" will remind us that we are Factoring) out of a variable $\mathbf{X}$ is to determine the residual of $\mathbf{X}$ left after the best linear estimate of $\mathbf{X}$ based on $\mathbf{F}$ has been removed. That is, in virtue of the correlation r_{XF} between $\mathbf{X}$ and $\mathbf{F}$, $\mathbf{X}$ analyzes as the sum of two orthogonal parts: a component $\dot{\mathbf{X}}_{(F)}$ which is a linear function of $\mathbf{F}$ (see [4.56]) and may be said to be "controlled" or "accounted for" by $\mathbf{F}$, and the residual $\mathbf{e}_{X \bullet F}$, which is linearly uncorrelated with $\mathbf{F}$. In symbols,

[6.1] $$\mathbf{X} = \dot{\mathbf{X}}_{(F)} + \mathbf{e}_{X \bullet F};$$

[6.2] $$\dot{\mathbf{X}}_{(F)} = b_{XF}\mathbf{F} + c_{XF} = \frac{\mathrm{Cov}(\mathbf{X}, \mathbf{F})}{\mathrm{Var}(\mathbf{F})}\mathbf{F} + c_{XF},$$

where $b_{\mathbf{XF}}$, or $\mathrm{Cov}(\mathbf{X},\mathbf{F})/\mathrm{Var}(\mathbf{F})$, is the slope of the linear regression of **X** on **F**, and $c_{\mathbf{XF}}$ is an additive constant whose value is irrelevant for the variances and covariances with which we shall be concerned. Since $\mathrm{Cov}(\dot{\mathbf{X}}_{(\mathbf{F})}, \mathbf{e}_{\mathbf{X}\bullet\mathbf{F}})=0$, the variance of **X** correspondingly analyzes as

$$[6.3] \qquad \begin{aligned}\mathrm{Var}(\mathbf{X}) &= \mathrm{Var}(\dot{\mathbf{X}}_{(\mathbf{F})}) + \mathrm{Var}(\mathbf{e}_{\mathbf{X}\bullet\mathbf{F}})\\ &= b^2_{\mathbf{XF}}\,\mathrm{Var}(\mathbf{F}) + \mathrm{Var}(\mathbf{e}_{\mathbf{X}\bullet\mathbf{F}})\\ &= \frac{\mathrm{Cov}(\mathbf{X},\mathbf{F})^2}{\mathrm{Var}(\mathbf{F})} + \mathrm{Var}(\mathbf{e}_{\mathbf{X}\bullet\mathbf{F}})\,,\end{aligned}$$

while for the covariance between any two variables $\mathbf{X}_i$ and $\mathbf{X}_j$ in a set from which **F** is being partialled, since all components controlled by **F** are orthogonal to all residuals left by **F**,[14] we have

$$[6.4] \qquad \begin{aligned}\mathrm{Cov}(\mathbf{X}_i,\mathbf{X}_j) &= \mathrm{Cov}(\dot{\mathbf{X}}_{i(\mathbf{F})} + \mathbf{e}_{\mathbf{X}_i\bullet\mathbf{F}}, \dot{\mathbf{X}}_{j(\mathbf{F})} + \mathbf{e}_{\mathbf{X}_j\bullet\mathbf{F}})\\ &= \mathrm{Cov}(\dot{\mathbf{X}}_{i(\mathbf{F})}, \dot{\mathbf{X}}_{j(\mathbf{F})}) + \mathrm{Cov}(\mathbf{e}_{\mathbf{X}_i\bullet\mathbf{F}}, \mathbf{e}_{\mathbf{X}_j\bullet\mathbf{F}})\\ &= b_{\mathbf{X}_i\mathbf{F}}\, b_{\mathbf{X}_j\mathbf{F}}\,\mathrm{Var}(\mathbf{F}) + \mathrm{Cov}(\mathbf{e}_{\mathbf{X}_i\bullet\mathbf{F}}, \mathbf{e}_{\mathbf{X}_j\bullet\mathbf{F}})\\ &= \frac{\mathrm{Cov}(\mathbf{X}_i,\mathbf{F})\times\mathrm{Cov}(\mathbf{X}_j,\mathbf{F})}{\mathrm{Var}(\mathbf{F})} + \mathrm{Cov}(\mathbf{e}_{\mathbf{X}_i\bullet\mathbf{F}}, \mathbf{e}_{\mathbf{X}_j\bullet\mathbf{F}})\,.\end{aligned}$$

Let us simplify notation by writing $C_{\mathbf{X}_i\mathbf{X}_j}$ for the covariance between two variables $\mathbf{X}_i$ and $\mathbf{X}_j$ in place of $\mathrm{Cov}(\mathbf{X}_i,\mathbf{X}_j)$, and similarly $V_{\mathbf{X}_i}$ in place of $\mathrm{Var}(\mathbf{X}_i)$. More generally, extending this notation to partial statistics of all orders, let

$$[6.5] \qquad C_{\mathbf{X}_i\mathbf{X}_j\bullet\mathbf{F}_1\ldots\mathbf{F}_k} =_{\mathrm{def}} \mathrm{Cov}(\mathbf{e}_{\mathbf{X}_i\bullet\mathbf{F}_1\ldots\mathbf{F}_k}, \mathbf{e}_{\mathbf{X}_j\bullet\mathbf{F}_1\ldots\mathbf{F}_k})\,,$$

$$[6.6] \qquad \begin{aligned}V_{\mathbf{X}_i\bullet\mathbf{F}_1\ldots\mathbf{F}_k} &=_{\mathrm{def}} C_{\mathbf{X}_i\mathbf{X}_i\bullet\mathbf{F}_1\ldots\mathbf{F}_k}\\ &= \mathrm{Var}(\mathbf{e}_{\mathbf{X}_i\bullet\mathbf{F}_1\ldots\mathbf{F}_k})\\ &= \sigma^2_{\mathbf{X}_i\bullet\mathbf{F}_1\ldots\mathbf{F}_k}\,,\end{aligned}$$

where the $\mathbf{F}_i$ are any variables partialled out of the $\mathbf{X}_i$. The quantity $C_{\mathbf{X}_i\mathbf{X}_j\bullet\mathbf{F}_1\ldots\mathbf{F}_k}$ is a **k**th *order partial covariance*, something which we did not have occasion to mention in Chapter 4, but which is the fundamental statistic in factoring routines. It should be evident to the reader that the relation between partial correlation and partial covariance is

$$[6.7] \qquad r_{\mathbf{X}_i\mathbf{X}_j\bullet\mathbf{F}_1\ldots\mathbf{F}_k} = \frac{C_{\mathbf{X}_i\mathbf{X}_j\bullet\mathbf{F}_1\ldots\mathbf{F}_k}}{\sqrt{V_{\mathbf{X}_i\bullet\mathbf{F}_1\ldots\mathbf{F}_k}\times V_{\mathbf{X}_j\bullet\mathbf{F}_1\ldots\mathbf{F}_k}}}\,.$$

However, partial correlations (in contrast to partial covariances) are on the whole of little interest in factor analysis.

[14] *Review question*: Why?

Just as a variable's variance is partitioned into controlled and residual portions (e.g., [6.3]) by the variable's regression upon one or more predictor variables, or "factors," the simultaneous regression of a set of variables upon one or more common predictors similarly partitions their covariances as shown by equation [6.4]—in fact, [6.3] is merely the special case of [6.4] in which $\mathbf{i} = \mathbf{j}$. Let us write "$C_{X_i X_j(F)}$" instead of "$\mathrm{Cov}(\dot{X}_{i(F)}, \dot{X}_{j(F)})$" for the covariance between variables X_i and X_j which is accounted for by factor $\mathbf{F}$, and similarly "$V_{X_i(F)}$" for the variance, Var $(\dot{X}_{i(F)})$, of X_i accounted for by $\mathbf{F}$. More generally,

$$[6.8] \qquad C_{X_i X_j(F_1 \ldots F_k)} =_{\text{def}} \mathrm{Cov}(\dot{X}_{i(F_1 \ldots F_k)}, \dot{X}_{j(F_1 \ldots F_k)}) \, ,$$

$$[6.9] \qquad V_{X_i(F_1 \ldots F_k)} =_{\text{def}} C_{X_i X_i(F_1 \ldots F_k)}$$
$$= \mathrm{Var}(\dot{X}_{i(F_1 \ldots F_k)})$$
$$= V_{X_i} R^2_{X_i(F_1 \ldots F_k)} \, .$$

(Observe that we are consistently using parenthesis subscripts for statistics associated with controlled components, and dot subscripts for residual statistics.[15] The last line of [6.9] is added to remind the reader how multiple correlation participates in these relations.) Since for any variable X_i and any $\mathbf{k}$ predictors $F_1, \ldots, F_k$,

$$[6.10] \qquad X_i = \dot{X}_{i(F_1 \ldots F_k)} + e_{X_i \bullet F_1 \ldots F_k} \, ,$$

while for any pair of variables X_i and X_j simultaneously regressed on $F_1, \ldots, F_k$,

$$[6.11]^{16} \qquad \mathrm{Cov}(\dot{X}_{i(F_1 \ldots F_k)}, e_{X_j \bullet F_1 \ldots F_k}) = 0 \, ,$$

the covariance between X_i and X_j is readily seen by application of [4.39] to [6.10] and [6.11] to analyze as

[6.12]

$$C_{X_i X_j} = \mathrm{Cov}(X_{i(F_1 \ldots F_k)}, \dot{X}_{j(F_1 \ldots F_k)}) + \mathrm{Cov}(e_{X_i \bullet F_1 \ldots F_k}, e_{X_j \bullet F_1 \ldots F_k})$$
$$= C_{X_i X_j(F_1 \ldots F_k)} + C_{X_i X_j \bullet F_1 \ldots F_k} \, .$$

The residuals $e_{X_i \bullet F_1 \ldots F_k}$ may be further analyzed into controlled and residual components by their regressions upon still another set of predictors, and so on for as many groups of factors as we wish until the residuals have all vanished; while each time another group of factors is partialled out, the new residual covariances are found simply by subtracting from each old residual covariance the portion now brought

[15] Our symbol for the multiple coefficient of alienation might appear to be an exception to this, since $K_{Y(\mu)} = \sigma_{Y \cdot \mu}/\sigma_Y$. However, K is not defined *wholly* as a statistic on residuals and hence does not violate the rule for dot notation stated on p. 158.

[16] *Review question*: Why?

under control by the new predictors. In general, the covariance between $\mathbf{X_i}$ and $\mathbf{X_j}$ jointly accounted for by $\mathbf{F_1}, \ldots, \mathbf{F_k}$ is seen by application of [4.43] to the regressions of $\mathbf{X_i}$ and $\mathbf{X_j}$ upon these predictors to be

[6.13] $$C_{X_iX_j(F_1 \ldots F_k)} = \sum_{g=1}^{k} \sum_{h=1}^{k} b_{X_iF_g} b_{X_jF_h} C_{F_gF_h} ,$$

where $b_{X_iF_g}$ (more properly written $b_{X_iF_g \bullet F_1 \ldots F_{g-1}F_{g+1} \ldots F_k}$) is the b-coefficient of predictor $\mathbf{F_g}$ in the regression of $\mathbf{X_i}$ upon $\mathbf{F_1}, \ldots, \mathbf{F_k}$, so extraction of several factors simultaneously is rather complicated computationally. By remaining content to take out just one factor at a time, however, we can work with the much simpler relation already noted cumbersomely in [6.4], namely,

[6.14] $$C_{X_iX_j} = C_{X_iX_j(F)} + C_{X_iX_j \bullet F},$$

where

[6.15] $$C_{X_iX_j(F)} = b_{X_iF} b_{X_jF} V_F$$
$$= \frac{{}_{X_iF} C_{X_jF}}{V_F} .$$

This tells us that if we are given the covariance matrix $\{C_{X_iX_j}\}$[17] for a set of variables $\mathbf{X_1}, \ldots, \mathbf{X_n}$, then we can compute the covariance matrix for the components of $\mathbf{X_1}, \ldots, \mathbf{X_n}$ orthogonal to a factor $\mathbf{F_1}$ —i.e., the matrix of covariances among the $\mathbf{X_i}$ unaccounted for by factor $\mathbf{F_1}$ — so long as we know the variance of $\mathbf{F_1}$ and also its covariance, $C_{X_iF_1}$, with each variable $\mathbf{X_i}$ ($\mathbf{i} = \mathbf{1}, \ldots, \mathbf{n}$). Specifically, [6.14] and [6.15] show that the element in the **i**th row and **j**th column of the first-order residual covariance matrix $\{C_{X_iX_j \bullet F_1}\}$ is

[6.16] $$C_{X_iX_j \bullet F_1} = C_{X_iX_j} - C_{X_iX_j(F_1)}$$
$$= C_{X_iX_j} - \frac{C_{X_iF_1} C_{X_jF_1}}{V_{F_1}} ,$$

which computationally is not much of a hardship. Further, if $\mathbf{F_1}$ is defined as some linear combination of $\mathbf{X_1}, \ldots, \mathbf{X_n}$ in which the numerical coefficient of each $\mathbf{X_i}$ is known, then V_{F_1} and each $C_{X_iF_1}$ can also be computed from $\{C_{X_iX_j}\}$ by application of [4.44] and [4.38]. Moreover, once $\mathbf{F_1}$ has been extracted, a second factor $\mathbf{F_2}$ may be taken out by simply repeating this process, with the first-order residual covariance matrix $\{C_{X_iX_j \bullet F_1}\}$ in place of $\{C_{X_iX_j}\}$, to yield the matrix $\{C_{X_iX_j \bullet F_1F_2}\}$ of covariances among the components of $\mathbf{X_1}, \ldots, \mathbf{X_n}$ orthogonal to both $\mathbf{F_1}$ and $\mathbf{F_2}$. Still another repetition of the process will take out a third factor $\mathbf{F_3}$ and leave a matrix of residual covariances unaccounted for by factors

[17] We shall use the symbol "$\{Q_{ij}\}$" to designate the matrix whose element in the **i**th row and **j**th column is the quantity Q_{ij}.

$\mathbf{F_1}$, $\mathbf{F_2}$, and $\mathbf{F_3}$, etc., until as many factors have been removed as there are dimensions to the set $\mathbf{X_1}, \ldots, \mathbf{X_n}$. In general, the reduction in unaccounted-for covariance among the $\mathbf{X_i}$ accomplished by adding factor $\mathbf{F_k}$ to the $\mathbf{k-1}$ factors already extracted is shown by the relationship

$$[6.17] \qquad C_{X_iX_j \bullet F_1 \ldots F_{k-1}F_k} = C_{X_iX_j \bullet F_1 \ldots F_{K-1}} - \frac{C_{X_iF_k \bullet F_1 \ldots F_{K-1}} C_{X_jF_k \bullet F_1 \ldots F_{k-1}}}{V_{F_k \bullet F_1 \ldots F_{k-1}}}$$

proof of which is left for the reader.[18] In the important special case where $\mathbf{F_k}$ is orthogonal to $\mathbf{F_1}, \ldots, \mathbf{F_{k-1}}$, as occurs when $\mathbf{F_k}$ is a linear function of the nonvanished residuals $\mathbf{e}_{X_i \bullet F_1 \ldots F_{k-1}}$,[19] [6.17] simplifies to

[6.18]

$$\begin{aligned} C_{X_iX_j \bullet F_1 \ldots F_{k-1}F_k} &= C_{X_iX_j \bullet F_1 \ldots F_{k-1}} - \frac{C_{X_iF_k} C_{X_jF_k}}{V_{F_k}} \\ &= C_{X_iX_j \bullet F_1 \ldots F_{k-1}} - C_{X_iX_j \cdot (F_k)} \end{aligned} \qquad \begin{pmatrix} \mathbf{F_k} \text{ orthogonal to} \\ \mathbf{F_1}, \ldots, \mathbf{F_{k-1}} \end{pmatrix}$$

due to the fairly obvious but important fact that if any variable $\mathbf{F_k}$ has zero correlations with all the variables in a set $\mathbf{F_1}, \ldots, \mathbf{F_{k-1}}$, then the covariance (in contrast to the correlation) between $\mathbf{F_k}$ and any given variable is unaffected by partialling out $\mathbf{F_1}, \ldots, \mathbf{F_{k-1}}$.[20] That is,

$$[6.19] \qquad C_{X_iF_k \bullet F_k \ldots F_{k-1}} = C_{X_iF_k} \qquad (\mathbf{F_k} \text{ orthogonal to } \mathbf{F_1}, \ldots, \mathbf{F_{k-1}}) \,.$$

(If the reader will verbalize to himself just what formulas [6.17] and [6.18] say, instead of cringing from them in horror, he will discover that they are not nearly so formidable as the elaborate subscripts make them appear.) It should be noted that the diagonal elements in matrix $\{C_{X_iX_j \bullet F_1 \ldots F_k}\}$ are the variances, $V_{X_i \bullet F_1 \ldots F_k}$, of $\mathbf{X_1}, \ldots, \mathbf{X_n}$ unaccounted for by factors $\mathbf{F_1}, \ldots, \mathbf{F_k}$; hence the sum of the diagonal entries in the matrix of residual covariances after extraction of $\mathbf{F_1}, \ldots, \mathbf{F_k}$ is the total variance of the $\mathbf{X_i}$ unaccounted for by factors $\mathbf{F_1}, \ldots, \mathbf{F_k}$ and when expressed as a proportion or percentage of the original total variance, $\sum_{i=1}^{n} V_{X_i}$, of $\mathbf{X_1}, \ldots, \mathbf{X_n}$ serves as a useful measure of how closely the set of variables $\mathbf{X_1}, \ldots, \mathbf{X_n}$ can be approximated by linear functions of $\mathbf{F_1}, \ldots, \mathbf{F_k}$. If the diagonal entries in $\{C_{X_iX_j \bullet F_1 \ldots F_k}\}$ sum to zero, then all

[18] This may be derived either directly from [6.16] by replacing $\mathbf{X_i}$, $\mathbf{X_j}$, and $\mathbf{F_1}$ with $\mathbf{e}_{X_i \cdot F_1 \ldots F_{k-1}}$, $\mathbf{e}_{X_j \cdot F_1 \ldots F_{k-1}}$, and $\mathbf{e}_{F_k \cdot F_1 \ldots F_{k-1}}$, respectively, or by suitable application of [4.108].

[19] *Study question*: Why?

[20] *Study question*: Why? (*Hint*: Rewrite $\mathbf{X_i}$ and $\mathbf{F_k}$ as linear combinations of $\mathbf{F_1}, \ldots, \mathbf{F_{k-1}}$ plus residuals.)

the entries in this matrix are zero,[21] and factors $\mathbf{F}_1, \ldots, \mathbf{F}_m$ have been shown to be a *basis* for the space of variables $\mathbf{X}_1, \ldots, \mathbf{X}_n$. In particular, if each factor $\mathbf{F}_j$ was defined as some linear combination of the nonvanished $\mathbf{X}_i$-residuals left by the previous factors, then the factors are an orthogonal basis as well.

Let us see how this procedure, which is really very simple unless complications arise in obtaining the covariances between factors and data variables, works in application to the covariances in Table 6.3. Ordinarily when a set of variables are factored they are first normalized, so that the matrix initially operated upon is the data variables' correlation matrix.[22] However, to avoid suggestion that this is a necessary part of the procedure, we shall instead factor the raw-score covariance matrix in Table 6.3*a*. We may note to begin with that the total variance of the data variables in this case is $\sum_{i=1}^{4} V_{\mathbf{X}_i} = 1.28 + .80 + 1.00 + .16 = 3.24$. Since the initial objective of factoring is usually to account for as much of the total data-variable variance as possible with as few factors as possible, most factoring routines proceed with an eye to maximizing the unaccounted-for variance brought under control by each added factor, consonant with other considerations which may also influence choice of factors. Such tactics will be discussed later; at present, let us minimize computational labor by simply choosing one of the data variables, say $\mathbf{X}_1$, for our first factor $\mathbf{F}_1$. But if $\mathbf{F}_1 =_{\text{def}} \mathbf{X}_1$, then obviously $V_{\mathbf{F}_1} = V_{\mathbf{X}_1} = C_{\mathbf{X}_1\mathbf{X}_1}$ and $C_{\mathbf{X}_i\mathbf{F}_1} = C_{\mathbf{X}_i\mathbf{X}_1}$; so the variance of $\mathbf{F}_1$ and its covariances with $\mathbf{X}_1, \ldots, \mathbf{X}_4$, which by [6.18] are what we need to derive $\{C_{\mathbf{X}_i\mathbf{X}_j \cdot \mathbf{F}_1}\}$ from $\{C_{\mathbf{X}_i\mathbf{X}_j}\}$, are merely the entries in the first column (or first row) of Table 6.3*a*. That is—and this is almost always the case, although not usually in quite so simple a fashion as with the present choice of $\mathbf{F}_1$—the covariance matrix for the variables from which a factor is to be extracted contains all the information needed to compute the residual covariances. For convenient reference, the covariances between $\mathbf{F}_1$ and the $\mathbf{X}_i$ are written in the first column of Table 6.5*a*. In partialling out $\mathbf{F}_1$, it is seen that the covariance between, e.g., $\mathbf{X}_2$ and $\mathbf{X}_3$ accounted for by $\mathbf{F}_1$ is $C_{\mathbf{X}_2\mathbf{X}_3(\mathbf{F}_1)} = (C_{\mathbf{X}_2\mathbf{F}_1}C_{\mathbf{X}_3\mathbf{F}_1})/V_{\mathbf{F}_1} = (.960 \times 1.120)/1.280 = .840$, so the residual covariance between $\mathbf{X}_2$ and $\mathbf{X}_3$ after $\mathbf{F}_1$ is partialled out is $C_{\mathbf{X}_2\mathbf{X}_3 \cdot \mathbf{F}_1} = C_{\mathbf{X}_2\mathbf{X}_3} - C_{\mathbf{X}_2\mathbf{X}_3(\mathbf{F}_1)} = .880 - .840 = .040$, which value is then entered at row 2 and column 3 (and also at row 3 and column 2) of Table 6.4*a*. Similarly, the variance of $\mathbf{X}_4$ unaccounted for by $\mathbf{F}_1$ is $V_{\mathbf{X}_4 \cdot \mathbf{F}_1} = C_{\mathbf{X}_4\mathbf{X}_4 \cdot \mathbf{F}_1} = C_{\mathbf{X}_4\mathbf{X}_4} - (C_{\mathbf{X}_4\mathbf{F}_1}C_{\mathbf{X}_4\mathbf{F}_1})/V_{\mathbf{F}_1} = .160 - (.320 \times .320)/1.280 = .160 - .080 = .080$, which is entered at row 4 and column 4 of Table 6.4*a*. (The reader

[21] *Study question*: *Why* must all the residual covariances be zero if the residual variances sum to zero?

[22] *Study problem*: Prove that normalization of a set of variables does not alter the space which they span.

should derive the rest of the entries in Table 6.4*a* to make sure he understands how it is done.) The diagonal entries in Table 6.4*a* are the residual variances of $\mathbf{X_1}, \ldots, \mathbf{X_4}$ unaccounted for by $\mathbf{F_1}$, and their sum, $\sum_{i=1}^{4} V_{X_i \bullet F_1} = \sum_{i=1}^{4} C_{X_i X_i \bullet F_1} = 0 + .080 + .020 + .080 = .18$, is only 5.6% of the original 3.24; hence factor $\mathbf{F_1}$ accounts for 94.4% of the total variance of set $\mathbf{X_1}, \ldots, \mathbf{X_4}$. That $\mathbf{X_1}$ is an exact linear function of $\mathbf{F_1}$ is shown by the fact that all entries in row **1** and column **1** are zero—i.e., the residual component $\mathbf{e}_{X_1 \bullet F_1}$ left of $\mathbf{X_1}$ by $\mathbf{F_1}$ has zero variance. If we wish (though this is quite unnecessary for continuation of factoring) we can examine the *correlations* among the nonvanished residuals $\mathbf{e}_{X_i \bullet F_1}$ by computing the partial correlations $r_{X_i X_j \bullet F_1}$ from matrix $\{C_{X_i X_j \bullet F_1}\}$ (Table 6.4*a*) by application of formula [6.7]. This shows (the reader should do the computations as an exercise) that $r_{X_2 X_3 \bullet F_1} = 1$, $r_{X_2 X_4 \bullet F_1} = -1$, and $r_{X_3 X_4 \bullet F_1} = -1$, so each remaining residual is perfectly predictable from every other and we know in advance that the covariance matrix of

$C_{X_i X_j \bullet F_1}$	X_1	X_2	X_3	X_4
X_1	0	0	0	0
X_2	0	.080	.040	−.080
X_3	0	.040	.020	−.040
X_4	0	−.080	−.040	.080

a) First-Factor Residual Covariances

$C_{X_i X_j \bullet F_1 F_2}$	X_1	X_2	X_3	X_4
X_1	0	0	0	0
X_2	0	0	0	0
X_3	0	0	0	0
X_4	0	0	0	0

b) Second-Factor Residual Covariances

Table 6.4. Covariances among the residuals $\mathbf{e}_{X_i \bullet F_1}$ after factor $\mathbf{F_1}$ ($=_{def} \mathbf{X_1}$) has been partialled out of the variables whose covariance matrix is shown in Table 6.3*a*, and among the residuals $\mathbf{e}_{X_i \bullet F_1 F_2}$ after both factor $\mathbf{F_1}$ and factor $\mathbf{F_2}$ ($=_{def} \mathbf{e}_{X_2 \bullet F_1}$) have been partialled out.

$C_{X_i F_j}$	F_1	F_2
X_1	1.280	1
X_2	.960	.080
X_3	1.120	.040
X_4	.320	−.080

a) Factor Matrix

$C_{X_i F_j'}$	F_1'	F_2'	ΣC^2
X_1	1.131	0	1.279
X_2	.849	.283	.801
X_3	.990	.141	1.000
X_4	.283	−.283	.160
ΣC^2	3.060	.180	3.240
% of total	94.4	5.6	

b) Raw Factor-Structure Matrix

$r_{X_i F_j}$	F_1	F_2	Σr^2
X_1	1.000	0	1.000
X_2	.949	.316	1.000
X_3	.990	.141	1.000
X_4	.707	−.707	1.000
Σr^2	3.380	.620	4.000
% of total	84.5	15.5	

c) Normalized Factor-Structure Matrix

Table 6.5.*a*) "Factor matrix" of covariances between chest-data variables (Table 6.1) and the two factors extracted in Tables 6.4*a*,*b*. Since $\mathbf{F_1} = \mathbf{X_1}$ and $\mathbf{F_2} = \mathbf{e}_{X_2 \bullet F_1}$, the two columns of Table 6.5*a* agree with the first column of Table 6.3*a* and the second column of Table 6.4*a*, respectively.

b) "Raw factor-structure matrix" derived from Table 6.5*a* by normalizing the factors but not the data variables.

c) "Normalized factor-structure matrix," showing the correlations corresponding to the covariances in Table 6.5*a*. The data in Table 6.5*a* are not sufficient to derive Tables 6.5*b*,*c*, since the variances of $\mathbf{X_1}, \ldots, \mathbf{X_4}$, $\mathbf{F_1}$ and $\mathbf{F_2}$ are also needed.

second-order residuals after a second basis factor is partialled out will be identically zero.

To extract this second factor, we may set $\mathbf{F_2}$ equal to any linear combination of $\mathbf{e}_{X_2 \cdot F_1}$, $\mathbf{e}_{X_3 \cdot F_1}$, and $\mathbf{e}_{X_4 \cdot F_1}$;[23] for convenience, say $\mathbf{F_2} =_{\text{def}} \mathbf{e}_{X_2 \cdot F_1}$. Then the matrix $\{C_{X_iX_j \cdot F_1F_2}\}$ of second-order residual covariances is computed from Table 6.4*a* in precisely the same way that Table 6.4*a* was derived from Table 6.3*a*. Since $\mathbf{F_2} = \mathbf{e}_{X_2 \cdot F_1}$, $V_{F_2} = C_{X_2X_2 \cdot F_1}$ while the covariances between $\mathbf{F_2}$ and the residuals $\mathbf{e}_{X_i \cdot F_2}$ are equal to the entries in the second column of matrix $\{C_{X_iX_j \cdot F_1}\}$ (Table 6.4*a*). Since $\mathbf{F_2}$ is uncorrelated with $\mathbf{F_1}$ these are also the covariances of $\mathbf{F_2}$ with $\mathbf{X_1}, \ldots, \mathbf{X_4}$ (cf. [6.19]) and may be entered in the second column of Table 6.5*a* wherein we are keeping track of the relations between factors and data variables. Given V_{F_2} and the $C_{X_iF_2}$, it is readily computed by [6.18] that the matrix of residuals $\{C_{X_iX_j \cdot F_1F_2}\}$ contains only zeros as shown in Table 6.4*b*. For example, $C_{X_3X_4 \cdot F_1F_2} = C_{X_3X_4 \cdot F_1} - (C_{X_3F_2}C_{X_4F_2}) / V_{F_2} = .040 - (.040 \times -.080)/.080 = 0$. Other entries in Table 6.4*b* should be verified by the reader. The vanishing of all residuals in Table 6.4*b* as predicted shows that $\mathbf{X_1}, \ldots, \mathbf{X_4}$ are all linear functions of the two uncorrelated variables $\mathbf{F_1}$ and $\mathbf{F_2}$; hence by operations upon only the covariance matrix of the $\mathbf{X_i}$, we have (*a*) proved that $\mathbf{F_1}$ and $\mathbf{F_2}$ (i.e., $\mathbf{X_1}$ and $\mathbf{e}_{X_2 \cdot X_1}$) are an orthogonal basis for $\mathbf{X_1}, \ldots, \mathbf{X_4}$, and (*b*) demonstrated that the set $\mathbf{X_1}, \ldots, \mathbf{X_4}$ is two-dimensional.

Let us review the ground covered so far in order to clarify any perplexities which may still be troubling the reader. To "factor" a set of variables $\mathbf{X_1}, \ldots, \mathbf{X_n}$ is to identify a set of linearly independent variables $\mathbf{F_1}, \ldots, \mathbf{F_p}$ for which coefficients b_{ij} exist such that

$$[6.20\text{-}1] \qquad \mathbf{X_1} = b_{10} + b_{11}\mathbf{F_1} + b_{12}\mathbf{F_2} + \ldots + b_{1p}\mathbf{F_p}$$

$$[6.20\text{-}2] \qquad \mathbf{X_2} = b_{20} + b_{21}\mathbf{F_1} + b_{22}\mathbf{F_2} + \ldots + b_{2p}\mathbf{F_p}$$

$$\vdots \qquad \qquad \vdots$$

$$[6.20\text{-}\mathbf{n}] \qquad \mathbf{X_n} = b_{n0} + b_{n1}\mathbf{F_1} + b_{n2}\mathbf{F_2} + \ldots + b_{np}\mathbf{F_p}$$

We write "*b*"s as the factor coefficients, rather than some other choice of algebraic symbols for constants, specifically to serve reminder that these constants are, in fact, the *b*-coefficients of regression equations, in this case errorless ones. In fact, we may as well make explicit that henceforth,

$$[6.21\text{-}j] \quad (\mathbf{j} = \mathbf{1}, \ldots, \mathbf{p}) \qquad b_{ij} =_{\text{def}} b_{X_iF_j \cdot F_1 \ldots F_{j-1}F_{j+1} \ldots F_p}.$$

It is *not* presupposed by composition equations [6.20] that the number of factors, $\mathbf{p}$, is equal to or smaller than the number, $\mathbf{n}$, of variables factored, though this will, in fact, be the case for defined factors. When $\mathbf{p}$ equals the dimensionality of $\mathbf{X_1}, \ldots, \mathbf{X_n}$, then $\mathbf{F_1}, \ldots, \mathbf{F_p}$ are a basis for the

[23] Of course, $\mathbf{F_2}$ does not *have* to be a linear combination of the $\mathbf{e}_{X_i \cdot F_1}$. Any variable is acceptable for $\mathbf{F_2}$ so long as it is linearly independent of $\mathbf{F_1}$. However, if $\mathbf{F_2}$ is not in the space of $\mathbf{X_1}, \ldots, \mathbf{X_2}$ orthogonal to $\mathbf{F_1}$, then some second-order residuals will still remain after $\mathbf{F_2}$ is extracted.

space of variables spanned by the $\mathbf{X_i}$, and are themselves linear functions of the latter. In general, however, there are no restrictions on what variables, or their number, which may be treated as "factors" of the $\mathbf{X_i}$. This is shown by the important consideration that if $\mathbf{F_1}, \ldots, \mathbf{F_k}$ are any variables we please, the equation $\mathbf{X_i} = \dot{\mathbf{X}}_{\mathbf{i}(\mathbf{F_1}\ldots\mathbf{F_k})} + \mathbf{e}_{\mathbf{X_i}\bullet\mathbf{F_1}\ldots\mathbf{F_k}}$ is of form [6.20-**i**], with $\mathbf{p} = \mathbf{k} + 1$, when $\dot{\mathbf{X}}_{\mathbf{i}(\mathbf{F_1}\ldots\mathbf{F_k})}$ is replaced with the linear function in $\mathbf{F_1}, \ldots, \mathbf{F_k}$ to which it is equivalent.

To see how the composition of a covariance relates to the corresponding factorial composition of the variables involved, observe to begin with, from [4.43] applied to [6.20], that

[6.22-**ij**]
(**i**,**j** = **1**, . . . , **n**)

$$C_{\mathbf{X_i X_j}} = \sum_{\mathbf{h=1}}^{\mathbf{p}} \sum_{\mathbf{k=1}}^{\mathbf{p}} b_{\mathbf{ih}} b_{\mathbf{jk}} C_{\mathbf{F_h F_k}}$$

$$= \sum_{\mathbf{k=1}}^{\mathbf{p}} b_{\mathbf{ik}} b_{\mathbf{jk}} V_{\mathbf{F_k}} + \sum_{\mathbf{h=1}}^{\mathbf{p}} \sum_{\substack{\mathbf{k=1} \\ \mathbf{h \neq k}}}^{\mathbf{p}} b_{\mathbf{ih}} b_{\mathbf{jk}} C_{\mathbf{F_h F_k}} \cdot$$

It is revolting to contemplate computations based on [6.22] when the factors are oblique. However, if the $\mathbf{F_i}$ are *orthogonal*—i.e., $C_{\mathbf{F_i F_j}} = 0$ if $\mathbf{i} \neq \mathbf{j}$ ($\mathbf{i,j} = \mathbf{1}, \ldots, \mathbf{p}$)—then [6.22-**ij**] spectacularly simplifies to

[6.23-**ij**]
(**i**,**j** = **1**, . . . , **n**)

$$C_{\mathbf{X_i X_j}} = \sum_{\mathbf{k=1}}^{\mathbf{p}} b_{\mathbf{ik}} b_{\mathbf{jk}} V_{\mathbf{F_k}} \qquad \text{(orthogonal factors)}\ .$$

Also, since

[6.24-**ij**]
$\begin{pmatrix} \mathbf{i} = \mathbf{1}, \ldots, \mathbf{n} \\ \mathbf{j} = \mathbf{1}, \ldots, \mathbf{p} \end{pmatrix}$

$$C_{\mathbf{X_i F_j}} = \sum_{\mathbf{k=1}}^{\mathbf{p}} b_{\mathbf{ik}} C_{\mathbf{F_k F_j}}$$

$$= b_{\mathbf{ij}} V_{\mathbf{F_j}} + \sum_{\substack{\mathbf{k=1} \\ \mathbf{k \neq j}}}^{\mathbf{p}} b_{\mathbf{ij}} C_{\mathbf{F_k F_j}}$$

in the general case (see [4.38]), the covariances between data variables and *orthogonal* factors are simply

[6.25-**ij**]
$\begin{pmatrix} \mathbf{i} = \mathbf{1}, \ldots, \mathbf{n} \\ \mathbf{j} = \mathbf{1}, \ldots, \mathbf{p} \end{pmatrix}$

$$C_{\mathbf{X_i F_j}} = b_{\mathbf{ij}} V_{\mathbf{F_j}} \qquad \text{(orthogonal factors)}\ ,$$

or, solving for the factor coefficient,

[6.26-**ij**]
$\begin{pmatrix} \mathbf{i} = \mathbf{1}, \ldots, \mathbf{n} \\ \mathbf{j} = \mathbf{1}, \ldots, \mathbf{p} \end{pmatrix}$

$$b_{\mathbf{ij}} = \frac{C_{\mathbf{X_i F_j}}}{V_{\mathbf{F_j}}} \qquad \text{(orthogonal factors)}$$

$$= \frac{\sigma_{\mathbf{X_i}}}{\sigma_{\mathbf{F_j}}} r_{\mathbf{X_i F_j}} \cdot$$

Hence when the data variables are analyzed in [6.20] as linear combinations of *orthogonal* factors, their covariances likewise analyze as a sum of components, one contributed by each factor:

[6.27-**ij**] $\left(\begin{matrix}\mathbf{i,j} = \mathbf{1},\\ \ldots, \mathbf{n}\end{matrix}\right)$

$$C_{X_iX_j} = \frac{C_{X_iF_1}C_{X_jF_1}}{V_{F_1}} + \frac{C_{X_iF_2}C_{X_jF_2}}{V_{F_2}} + \ldots + \frac{C_{X_iF_p}C_{X_jF_p}}{V_{F_p}}$$

$$= \sum_{k=1}^{p} \frac{C_{X_iF_k}C_{X_jF_k}}{V_{F_k}} \qquad \text{(orthogonal factors)} \cdot$$

$$= \sum_{k=1}^{p} C_{X_iX_j(F_k)} \cdot$$

That is, when the factors are orthogonal, the total covariance between variables $\mathbf{X_i}$ and $\mathbf{X_j}$ is the sum of the components of $C_{X_iX_j}$ accounted for by each factor taken by itself. A generalization of this which strikingly brings out the elegance of orthogonal factors is that the covariance between $\mathbf{X_i}$ and $\mathbf{X_j}$ jointly accounted for by any set of mutually orthogonal predictor variables is simply the sum of the components each controls individually—i.e.,

[6.28][24]
$$C_{X_iX_j(F_1\ldots F_k)} = \sum_{h=1}^{k} C_{X_iX_j(F_h)} \qquad \text{(orthogonal } \mathbf{F_1}, \ldots, \mathbf{F_k}) \,.$$

These equations make clear what happens when orthogonal factors are extracted by the sequential procedure already illustrated. At each step the covariances accounted for by the new factor are subtracted from the corresponding residual covariances left by the preceding factors, so the covariances among the residuals $\mathbf{e}_{X_i \bullet F_1 \ldots F_k}$ after $\mathbf{k}$ factors have been partialled out are

[6.29-**ij**] (**i,j** = **1**, . . . , **n**)
$$C_{X_iX_j \bullet F_1\ldots F_k} = \sum_{h=k+1}^{p} C_{X_iX_j(F_h)} \qquad \text{(orthogonal factors)} \,.$$

Since the components of a covariance controlled by different factors need not all have the same sign, some may tend to cancel others and removal of an additional factor may cause a given covariance residual to change sign or even to grow in magnitude. (Later, though, the reader will easily be able to prove that the *sum* of the entries in the data-variable covariance matrix can only grow smaller with extraction of each factor.) Even so, equation [6.29-**ij**] makes evident that the residual covariance between $\mathbf{X_i}$ and $\mathbf{X_j}$ must eventually dwindle to zero after extraction of a number of factors equal to at most the dimensionality of $\mathbf{X_1}, \ldots, \mathbf{X_n}$.

[24] *Study problem*: Prove it. (*Hint*: See [6.13].)

There is still a further useful simplification of these relationships which can be made at virtually no loss in generality. Since the choice of a unit of measurement for a variable is usually a matter of convenience, there is no reason why the factors $\mathbf{F_1}, \ldots, \mathbf{F_p}$ in [6.20] *et seq.* should not be normalized. If so, then the variances of the $\mathbf{F_i}$ are all unity, and the terms $V_{\mathbf{F_i}}$ may be deleted from wherever they occur as multipliers. Factors which are both normalized and orthogonal to one another are said to be *orthonormal*—i.e., the set of variables $\mathbf{F_1}, \ldots, \mathbf{F_p}$ is "orthonormal" if $M_{\mathbf{X_i}} = 0$ ($\mathbf{i} = \mathbf{1}, \ldots, \mathbf{p}$) and

$$C_{\mathbf{F_i F_j}} = \begin{cases} 1 \text{ if } \mathbf{i} = \mathbf{j} \\ 0 \text{ if } \mathbf{i} \neq \mathbf{j} \end{cases}$$

for $\mathbf{i,j} = \mathbf{1}, \ldots, \mathbf{p}$. Then if the $\mathbf{F_i}$ in [6.20] are orthonormal, the relations between factor coefficients and covariance components become simply

[6.30-**ij**] $\quad b_{\mathbf{ij}} = C_{\mathbf{X_i F_j}}$ (orthonormal factors),
(**i,j** = **1**, . . . , **n**)

[6.31-**ij**] $\quad C_{\mathbf{X_i X_j}} = \sum_{\mathbf{k=1}}^{\mathbf{p}} b_{\mathbf{ik}} b_{\mathbf{jk}} = \sum_{\mathbf{k=1}}^{\mathbf{p}} C_{\mathbf{X_i F_k}} C_{\mathbf{X_j F_k}}$. (orthonormal factors)
(**i,j** = **1**, . . . , **n**)

More generally,

[6.32-**ij**] $\quad C_{\mathbf{X_i X_j}(\mathbf{F_1} \ldots \mathbf{F_k})} = \sum_{\mathbf{h=1}}^{\mathbf{k}} b_{\mathbf{ih}} b_{\mathbf{jh}} = \sum_{\mathbf{h=1}}^{\mathbf{k}} C_{\mathbf{X_i F_h}} C_{\mathbf{X_j F_h}}$, (orthonormal factors)
(**i,j** = **1**, . . . , **n**)

where, of course, this holds for any **k** factors selected from $\mathbf{F_1}, \ldots, \mathbf{F_p}$, whether they are the first **k** in the numbered sequence or not. In words, what [6.31-**ij**] says is that when variables $\mathbf{X_i}$ and $\mathbf{X_j}$ have been analyzed as linear combinations of orthonormal factors, then their covariance equals the product of their covariances with the same factor, summed across all factors. If the reader has a secret yearning for correlations rather than covariances, both sides of [6.31-**ij**] may be divided by $\sigma_{\mathbf{X_i}} \sigma_{\mathbf{X_j}}$ to yield

[6.33-**ij**] $\quad r_{\mathbf{X_i X_j}} = \sum_{\mathbf{k=1}}^{\mathbf{p}} r_{\mathbf{X_i F_k}} r_{\mathbf{X_j F_k}}$ (orthonormal factors) .
(**i** = **1**, . . . , **n**)

An important special instance of [6.31-**ij**], when $\mathbf{i} = \mathbf{j}$, is

$$V_{X_i} = \sum_{j=1}^{p} C^2_{X_i F_j} \qquad \text{(orthonormal factors)} , \tag{6.34-i}$$
$(\mathbf{i} = \mathbf{1}, \ldots, \mathbf{n})$

or, dividing both sides by $\sigma^2_{X_i}$,

$$\sum_{j=1}^{p} r^2_{X_i F_j} = 1 \qquad \text{(orthonormal factors)} . \tag{6.35-i}$$
$(\mathbf{i} = \mathbf{1}, \ldots, \mathbf{n})$

For studying the pattern of relationships between data variables and factors, there are four types of information, mathematically interconnected but importantly different in meaning, which are of interest: (*A*) the equations which express the data variables as linear functions of the factors, as in [6.20]; (*B*) the covariances or correlations between the data variables and the factors; (*C*) the covariances among the factors themselves; and (*D*) the equations expressing the factors as linear functions of the data variables or, if the factors are not basis factors, the regressions of the factors upon the data variables. Information *A*, the composition equations, can be succinctly expressed by a matrix $\{b_{ij}\}$ whose entry at row **i** and column **j** is the coefficient of factor $\mathbf{F_j}$ in the equation for variable $\mathbf{X_i}$. With one qualification to be noted shortly, we shall call this matrix of factor coefficients the *factor-pattern matrix.* (So defined, the factor-pattern matrix does not include the additive constants b_{i0} in [6.20]. However, these have so little importance for factor analysis, and can in any event be so quickly derived—when the factors are all scaled to have zero means, as is customary, $b_{i0} = M_{X_i}$—that including them in the factor-pattern matrix would only create a useless complication.) Information *B*, the covariance between each data variable $\mathbf{X_i}$ and factor $\mathbf{F_j}$, may also be conveniently stored in a matrix $\{C_{X_i F_j}\}$ whose entry at row **i** and column **j** is the covariance between $\mathbf{X_i}$ and $\mathbf{F_j}$. Such a matrix, an example of which has already turned up in Table 6.5*a*, is commonly called the "factor matrix," or better, with a qualification to be mentioned, the *factor-structure matrix.* Still another matrix $\{C_{F_i F_j}\}$ will serve to convey *C*, the covariances among the factors. When the factors are orthonormal, the matrix of factor covariances consists by definition of unities along the diagonal and zeros elsewhere, and need not be written down. Finally, the regressions *D* of the factors upon the data variables can likewise be expressed by a matrix of regression coefficients which by rights should have its own technical name to distinguish it from the matrix of factor coefficients. However, factor analysts have not seen fit to introduce any special terminology for this purpose, and we shall not attempt to remedy the deficiency here.

Of the various factor-analytic results *A* to *D*, factor matrix $\{C_{X_i F_j}\}$ stands out most prominently in the computational procedures, even though the factor coefficients b_{ij} are usually the ultimate goal of the analysis. One reason for this is that the factor matrix is an immediate consequence of the initial factoring. (Virtually all factoring routines involve sequential extraction of orthogonal factors, which as we have seen requires computation of the $\mathbf{X_i}$–$\mathbf{F_j}$ covariances.) Once $\{C_{\mathbf{X_iF_j}}\}$ is available, moreover, the regressions of both the data variables upon the factors and the regressions of factors upon the data variables may be computed as desired with the help of the $C_{\mathbf{F_iF_j}}$ or the $C_{\mathbf{X_iX_j}}$, respectively, through solution of the appropriate normal equations (see [4.86]). Best of all, if the factors are orthonormal, equation [6.30-**ij**] shows that the covariance between data variable $\mathbf{X_i}$ and factor $\mathbf{F_j}$ is also the b-coefficient of $\mathbf{F_j}$ for $\mathbf{X_i}$. Hence no computational labor is required to derive information A from information B for orthonormal factors—the factor matrix $\{C_{\mathbf{X_iF_j}}\}$ and the factor coefficient matrix $\{b_{ij}\}$ are identical. (It is clear from simultaneous equations [6.22], however, that such a simple relation emphatically does *not* obtain when the factors are oblique, or even when the factors are orthogonal but do not all have unit variance.)

While the equivalence between $\{C_{\mathbf{X_iF_j}}\}$ and $\{b_{ij}\}$ for orthonormal factors is of the highest convenience, it has also, unfortunately, been a source of confusion in that writers have frequently failed to distinguish adequately between the two. In particular, the expression "factor matrix" is often used ambiguously to refer either to the matrix of $\mathbf{X_i}$–$\mathbf{F_j}$ covariances or to the matrix of factor coefficients. To maintain the proper distance between the two concepts—and they *are* different concepts even when in the orthonormal case their numerical values coincide—Harmon (44, pp. 16f.) urges that the composition equations [6.20] and their matrix summary $\{b_{ij}\}$ be called the *factor pattern* (or simply "pattern"), while the matrix $\{r_{\mathbf{X_iF_j}}\}$ of correlations between data variables and factors are to be called the *factor structure* (or simply "structure").[25] This terminology will be adopted here with one extension: Harmon presupposes that all the factors and data variables have been normalized, but since it turns out to be most strategic *not* always to assume normalized data variables, we shall refer to $\{C_{\mathbf{X_iF_j}}\}$ and $\{b_{ij}\}$ as the *raw structure* and *raw pattern* matrices, respectively, when it is stipulated only that the *factors* are normalized; while if both the data variables and the factors have been normalized, we shall make this explicit by speaking of the "normalized" factor pattern and "normalized" factor structure. When neither factors nor data variables are declared to be normalized, we can fall back on "factor matrix" and "factor coefficient matrix," respectively. The difference between "normalized factor structure" (i.e., $\{r_{\mathbf{X_iF_j}}\}$, or $\{C_{\mathbf{X_iF_j}}\}$ with both the $\mathbf{X_i}$ and the $\mathbf{F_j}$ normalized), "raw factor structure" (i.e., $\{C_{\mathbf{X_iF_j}}\}$ with the $\mathbf{F_i}$ normalized but the $\mathbf{X_i}$ not necessarily so), and

[25] This usage was first proposed by Holzinger and Harmon (44) many years ago, but regrettably it has still not become as widely adopted as it deserves.

simply "factor matrix" (i.e., $\{C_{X_i F_j}\}$ with no normalization restrictions) are illustrated by the three matrices in Table 6.5. Recalling (see p. 212) that factor coefficients are also frequently called "factor loadings" when all $\mathbf{X_i}$ and $\mathbf{F_j}$ are normalized, we may similarly refer to the coefficients of normalized factors in the regressions of not-necessarily-normalized data variables as the "raw loadings" of those variables on those factors.

Using the terminology just introduced, equation [6.30] may be characterized as saying that for orthonormal factors, the raw factor pattern of a set of data variables is identical with the set's raw factor structure. The relation between the raw pattern coefficient b_{ij} and the corresponding normalized factor-structure element $r_{X_i F_j}$ in this case is

[6.36-**ij**] $$b_{ij} = \sigma_{X_i} r_{X_i F_j} \qquad \text{(orthonormal factors)}\ ,$$
(**i**,**j** = **1**, . . . , **n**)

We have not yet adequately meditated on the significance of equations [6.31]. The relationship there shown to obtain between the data-variable covariance matrix $\{C_{X_i X_j}\}$ and the raw structure matrix $\{C_{X_i F_j}\}$ or, equivalently, the raw pattern matrix $\{b_{ij}\}$, for orthogonal factors is sometimes called the *fundamental factor theorem.* What equations [6.31] say is that if any two rows **i** and **j** of the raw structure or raw pattern matrix are selected, and each entry in row **i** is multiplied times the entry in row **j** for that same column, then the sum of these products is the original covariance, $C_{X_i X_j}$, between data variables $\mathbf{X_i}$ and $\mathbf{X_j}$. A special case of this made explicit by [6.33] is that the sum of column-mate products for two rows **i** and **j** of the normalized structure matrix, $\{r_{X_i F_j}\}$, equals the correlation between the data variables corresponding to these rows, i.e., $r_{X_i X_j}$. Thus in Table 6.5*c*, which exhibits the normalized structure matrix for our previous chest-data example, it will be seen, e.g., that rows **1** and **2**, multiplied by columns and summed, yield $(1.000 \times .949) + (0 \times .056) = .949$, which equals the correlation entered at row **1** and column **2** in Table 6.3*b*. Similarly, the summed columnwise product of rows **2** and **4** in Table 6.5*c* is $(.949 \times .707) + (.316 \times -.707) = .671 - .223 = .448$, which misses the corresponding correlation in Table 6.3*b* only by a .001 rounding-off error. The reader should verify that this same connection holds between Table 6.5*b* (the raw structure matrix) and Table 6.3*a* (the unnormalized data-variable covariance matrix).[26] Data-variable correlations computed back from the factor-structure matrix in this way are called *reproduced* correlations. As we have just observed, original and reproduced correlations in principle should be identical. In practice, however, through rounding-off errors or, more importantly, from discontinuation of factoring while a smattering of residual covariation still remains, there may be some discrepancy between the two. The nature of a "reproduced" correlation or covariance when the factors from which the

[26] *Study question*: What is the relation of Table 6.5*a* to Tables 6.3*a*,*b*?

reproduction is made are not an exhaustive analysis of the data variables is given by equation [6.32-**ij**].

A special instance of the "fundamental factor theorem" is that the sum of the squared entries in each row **i** of the raw pattern or structure matrix for orthonormal factors equals the variance of the corresponding data variable $\mathbf{X_i}$ (cf. [6.34]). Similarly, as can readily be verified in Table 6.5*c*, the entries in $\{r_{\mathbf{X_iF_j}}\}$, when squared, sum to unity in each row. The sum of squared entries in each *column* of the raw pattern or structure matrix also has considerable importance. We observe to begin with, as a special case of [6.32-**ij**], that the squared individual entries in the raw pattern or structure matrix are accounted-for variances. That is,

[6.37-**ij**] (**i**,**j** = **1**, . . . , **n**)

$$V_{\mathbf{X_i}(\mathbf{F_j})} = b^2_{\mathbf{ij}} \qquad \text{(orthonormal factors)} .$$

The sum of the squared entries in each column of $\{b_{\mathbf{ij}}\}$, therefore, is the sum across data variables of variance accounted for by the factor corresponding to that column and is hence the total data-variable variance accounted for by that factor. Let us introduce the symbol "$V_{\mathbf{X}}$" to designate the total variance of the set of variables $\mathbf{X_1}, \ldots, \mathbf{X_n}$, and "$V_{\mathbf{X}(\mathbf{F_1}\ldots\mathbf{F_k})}$" for the total variance of the $\mathbf{X_i}$ jointly accounted for by a set of (not necessarily orthogonal) predictors $\mathbf{F_1}, \ldots, \mathbf{F_k}$. That is,

[6.38][27]

$$V_{\mathbf{X}} =_{\text{def}} \sum_{\mathbf{i=1}}^{\mathbf{n}} V_{\mathbf{X_i}} ,$$

[6.39]

$$V_{\mathbf{X}(\mathbf{F_1}\ldots\mathbf{F_k})} =_{\text{def}} \sum_{\mathbf{i=1}}^{\mathbf{n}} V_{\mathbf{X_i}(\mathbf{F_1}\ldots\mathbf{F_k})} ,$$

where [6.39] is to be understood as applying to any set of **k** predictors, and not just to the first **k** factors in [6.20]. Then the facts just noted about row sums and column sums of squared factor coefficients for orthonormal factors may be written

[6.40] (**i** = **1**, . . . , **n**)

$$\sum_{\mathbf{j=1}}^{\mathbf{p}} b^2_{\mathbf{ij}} = V_{\mathbf{X_i}} \qquad \text{(orthonormal factors)} ,$$

[27] One inadequacy of this notation is that the simple subscript "**X**" does not specify very well just what set of variables is intended. Rather than complicate the subscripts, however, this may best be left for context to clarify. The prima facie inconsistency between using "$V_{\mathbf{X}}$" for the total variance of a *set* of variables when "$V_{\mathbf{X_i}}$" denotes the variance of a single variable may be ameliorated by construing $V_{\mathbf{X_i}}$ to be the total variance of a set containing $\mathbf{X_i}$ as its only member.

[6.41-j] (j = 1, . . . , p)

$$\sum_{i=1}^{n} b_{ij}^2 = V_{X(F_j)} \qquad \text{(orthonormal factors)},$$

and

[6.42]

$$\sum_{i=1}^{n} \sum_{j=1}^{p} b_{ij}^2 = \sum_{i=1}^{n} V_{X_i}$$

$$= \sum_{j=1}^{p} V_{X(F_j)} \qquad \text{(orthonormal factors)}$$

$$= V_X \, .$$

This last result says that for orthonormal factors, the sum of all the squared coefficients in the raw pattern or raw structure matrix is equal to the total variance of the data variables.

The relative importance of the various factors in an orthogonal analysis of a set of data variables is most usefully judged by comparing the total data-variable variance each factor controls, and equations [6.41] indicate that these comparisons may conveniently be effected by entering at the bottom of each column of the raw pattern or structure matrix the sum of the squared entries in that column. It will be noticed in Table 6.5*b*, for example, that the total variance of $X_1, \ldots, X_4$ accounted for by factor F_1 is $V_{X(F_1)} = (1.131)^2 + (.849)^2 + (.990)^2 + (.283)^2 = 3.060$. The grand total of squared entries in the body of Table 6.5*b* is 3.240, which agrees, as it should, with the total variance of the X_i computed earlier (p. 224): while expressing $V_{X(F_1)}$ as a percentage of this total shows that factor F_1 accounts for 94.4% of the total variance, a figure which also agrees with the value computed earlier (p. 225) by a quite different method. More generally, the set-variance components $V_{X(F_j)}$, summed across the factors in a group of factors $F_1, \ldots, F_k$ and expressed as a proportion or percentage of the total variance V_X, measure how approximately the set $X_1, \ldots, X_n$ as a whole lies in the space of this group of factors. (More on this later.) It should be appreciated, however, that the relative importance of a factor or group of factors, as assessed by its proportionate accounted-for variance, is weighted by the particular units of measurement chosen for the various data variables. Thus if X_i has greater variance than X_j, a factor which accounts for *p*% of the variance of X_i thereby receives a greater contribution to its index of importance than it would receive from controlling *p*% of the variance of X_j. This is why the data variables are almost always normalized by factoring the correlation matrix $\{r_{X_iX_j}\}$ rather than the raw-score covariance matrix $\{C_{X_iX_j}\}$. For normalized data variables, the total variance of the set

$\mathbf{Z_1}, \ldots, \mathbf{Z_n}$ (we shall write "$\mathbf{Z_i}$" instead of "$\mathbf{X_i}$" for data variables which are stipulated to be normalized) is obviously

$$\text{[6.43]} \qquad V_{\mathbf{Z}} = \sum_{i=1}^{m} V_{\mathbf{Z}_i} = \mathbf{n} \, ,$$

while the total variance of the $\mathbf{Z_i}$ accounted for by orthogonal factor $\mathbf{F_j}$ is the sum of the squared entries in the $\mathbf{j}$th column of the normalized factor pattern or normalized factor structure matrix as illustrated in Table 6.5*c*. It will be observed in this example that when the data variables are equated for variance, the total variance controlled by factor $\mathbf{F_1}$ drops from 94.4% to 84.5%, while the variance accounted for by factor $\mathbf{F_2}$ leaps up from a puny 5.6% of the total raw-score variance to a still small but thriving 15.5%. The reason for the more respectable showing of $\mathbf{F_2}$ when normalized data replace the original raw scores is that the one data variable with an appreciable loading on $\mathbf{F_2}$, namely $\mathbf{X_4}$, also happens to have a much smaller raw-score variance than the other data variables.

Styles of Factor Solutions: I. Extraction Policies

In principle, any procedure for discovering a matrix $\{b_{ij}\}$ and a matrix $\{C_{F_i F_j}\}$ which together reproduce a given data-variable covariance matrix $\{C_{X_i X_j}\}$ by formula [6.22] may be regarded as a method of factor analysis. Those factor-analytic procedures which have evolved in actual practice, however, are almost all limited to factors defined as linear combinations of either the data variables or of certain inferred components of them. That is, the factors which are computed by most factoring routines are a *basis* for a set of variables whose covariance matrix has either been determined empirically or inferred through considerations to be discussed shortly. Even so, there is clearly no limit to the number of different ways in which a factor basis can be selected for a given set of variables. Whether this opulence of alternatives is a blessing or a curse is problematic—certainly it has been a source of much confusion, anxiety, computational labor, and interpersonal acrimony in the history of factor analysis. In any case, given the decision to factor—and anyone who has acquired a taste for multivariate relationships soon comes to look upon an unanalyzed covariance matrix as a disheveled abomination—we need to consider what we should like our factors to do in *addition* to constituting a basis for the factored variables. The purpose of whetting such desires is, hopefully, to arrive at requirements which single out a more or less unique factor solution from the infinitude of alternatives available. Of course, as soon as we become choosy it may well happen that different desires lead to different selections of factors; however, there is no need to regard one of these as the *correct* solution to the disdainful exclusion of all others. Rather, each different solution will have its own distinctive meaning and its own particular disclosure to make about the pattern of relationships among the factored variables.

The various styles of factor bases available to the consumer may conveniently be grouped into two classes: (*a*) *initial solutions* or *extraction policies* on the one hand, and (*b*) *terminal solutions* or *interpretation proposals* on the other. The first group, initial solutions, comprises different techniques for smelting down an original covariance matrix into a factor structure in order to see what sort of dimensionality emerges and to define a factor space within which search for a terminal solution may subsequently be pursued. Specifically, what differentiates one initial solution from another is how each selects the factor to be partialled out at each stage of extraction. In principle, it should make no difference which extraction policy is followed, since all complete factor bases for a given set of variables span the same space, namely, the space spanned by the factored variables. In practice, factoring ordinarily stops short of an exhaustively complete solution, or, if factoring is completed, only those factors which appear "significant" are processed further, so that different procedures for accomplishing this may eventuate in somewhat different factor spaces. Nonetheless, so long as factoring (or factor retention) is carried out to the point where the residual covariances are on the order of chance effects, the set of factors found by one style of initial solution should differ only trivially from a suitable linear transformation of the set found by another.

The factor-style problem begins to get sticky, however, when the question of *interpretation* arises. When one has gone through the labor of decomposing a set of data variables into factorial components, it is hard not to feel, consciously or otherwise, that one has thereby earned the right to construe these factors as *causal explanations* of the observed correlations—and the more strikingly the analysis exposes a pattern of redundancies among the data variables, the more compelling this urge becomes. But even if the **n** data variables have been found to have a factor basis whose dimensionality, **m**, is appreciably smaller than **n**, and this is, in fact, due to the existence of **m** causal determinants shared by these variables, it would still be an extraordinary coincidence if the **m** linear combinations of the data variables by means of which this dimensionality was discovered also happened to coincide with those linear functions of the data variables which best estimate these underlying determinants. For example, study of the data from our earlier chest-measurement illustration might suggest (if we did not know that the two-dimensionality of $\mathbf{X}_1, \ldots, \mathbf{X}_4$ arose by definition) that the chests of adult American males differ in two fundamental ways, "size" and "expansiveness," which cannot be measured directly but which have various observable manifestations such as $\mathbf{X}_1, \ldots, \mathbf{X}_4$. If so, then the two factors extracted from Table 6.3*a*, namely, $\mathbf{F}_1 = \mathbf{X}_1$ and $\mathbf{F}_2 = \mathbf{e}_{X_2 \cdot X_1}$, are not nearly so intuitively acceptable as measures of "size" and "expansiveness," respectively, as would be, say, $\mathbf{X}_3$ and $\mathbf{X}_4$ (or $\mathbf{X}_3$ and $\mathbf{e}_{X_4 \cdot X_3}$, if orthogonal factors are preferred), which are alternatively just as good a factor basis for $\mathbf{X}_1, \ldots, \mathbf{X}_4$ as are $\mathbf{X}_1$ and $\mathbf{e}_{X_2 \cdot X_1}$.[28] Once an initial basis has been obtained, therefore, the question arises whether it cannot be transformed, or "rotated," into another set of factors which span the same space of variables but lie closer to its causal grain. In practice, this leads to repeated rotations in search of the factor pattern which most closely approximates some ideal configuration deemed worthy of interpretive consideration. What defines a particular style of "terminal solution," then, is the choice of standards for what a meaningful factor pattern should be like.

For a reader who no longer believes in Santa Claus, it should come as no violent surprise to learn that while a variety of terminal factor procedures have been developed in practice, none has received any firm methodological justification beyond sometimes yielding some results which make some intuitive sense to some people. Despite the strongly moralistic sentiments which factor analysts frequently seem to develop over how factoring should or should not be done, we do not as yet have even the good beginnings of a general theory of factor patterns. Hence apart from a few remarks about oblique factors and the concept of "simple structure," we shall not attempt to say much about terminal solutions. In happy contrast to the uncertainties of terminal factoring, however, is the fact that only a limited number of extraction procedures have had much appeal, and each has a crisp mathematical meaning. Of these, the two most important are the "principal axes" solution (also known as "principal components" or "principal factors") and the "centroid" procedure.

The Principal-Factors Solution. The principal axes of a multivariate distribution are richly endowed with useful mathematical properties, most of which, however, go deeper into linear algebra than is of concern here. The supreme virtue of principal axes for derivation of an initial factor basis is that they minimize the residual data-variable variance at each stage of extraction. (Variables being factored for a basis will here be called "data variables" irrespective of the methods, empirical or otherwise, by which their covariance matrix has been obtained.) In practice, the likelihood that a given covariance matrix will factor down *exactly* to a dimensionality smaller than the number of data variables is overwhelmingly small unless the matrix has been deliberately contrived or, as occasionally happens in research, some of the data variables have

[28] As it happens, the correlations in Table 6.3*b* were derived by hypothesizing two orthogonal factors, one accounting for 90% of $\mathbf{V}_{X_3}$ and 10% of $\mathbf{V}_{X_4}$, and the other accounting for 10% of $\mathbf{V}_{X_3}$ and 90% of $\mathbf{V}_{X_4}$.

been defined as linear combinations of the others. Even so, it is of considerable interest to see how parsimonious a factor space will account for *virtually* all of the data-variable variance. That is, the smaller the number of factors required to reduce the residual variance to a negligible level, the more strongly it is suggested that the relations among the data variables originate in a relatively small number of common sources and—a further problematic assumption which is seldom made explicit—the more successfully will it be possible for a terminal factor solution to combine the data variables into useful estimators of these source variables. It is highly desirable, therefore, to have available a method for sequential extraction of factors such that the total data-variable variance accounted for by the first **k** factors ($\mathbf{k} = \mathbf{1}, \mathbf{2}, \ldots$) is at least as large as the total variance which could be accounted for by any other choice of **k** factors. A sequence of factors having this property can, in fact, always be found for any given set of data variables, and this is what is meant by the "principal-axes" factors, or simply "principal factors," of the set. Specifically, a variable $\mathbf{P_1}$ is the *first* principal factor of variables $\mathbf{X_1}, \ldots, \mathbf{X_n}$ if $\mathbf{P_1}$ is a linear combination of the $\mathbf{X_i}$ and the variance, $V_{\mathbf{X}(\mathbf{P_1})}$, of the set $\mathbf{X_1}, \ldots, \mathbf{X_n}$ accounted for by $\mathbf{P_1}$ is as large or larger than the set's variance accounted for by any other linear combination of $\mathbf{X_1}, \ldots, \mathbf{X_n}$. A variable $\mathbf{P_2}$ is the *second* principal factor of the $\mathbf{X_i}$ if $\mathbf{P_2}$ is a linear combination of the $\mathbf{X_i}$ orthogonal to $\mathbf{P_1}$ and accounts for as much or more of the set's variance than does any other linear combination of the $\mathbf{X_i}$ orthogonal to $\mathbf{P_1}$. (This is the same as defining $\mathbf{P_2}$ as the first principal factor of the residuals $\mathbf{e}_{\mathbf{X_1} \bullet \mathbf{P_1}}, \ldots, \mathbf{e}_{\mathbf{X_n} \bullet \mathbf{P_1}}$ left by $\mathbf{P_1}$.) Similarly, the third principal factor accounts for the maximal amount of residual variance left by the first two principal factors, and so on, until there are as many mutually orthogonal principal factors as there are dimensions to the space of $\mathbf{X_1}, \ldots, \mathbf{X_n}$.[29]

Although we have spoken of *the* **k**th principal factor of a set of variables, the definition of $\mathbf{P_k}$ just given actually determines it only up to a linear transformation insomuch as the variance controlled by a given factor is unchanged by any linear transformation of that factor. The literature contains three different expressions, "principal axes," "principal components," and "principal factors," all of which denote the same style of factor placement but differ slightly in how they scale these factors. The **k**th *principal axis* of data variables $\mathbf{X_1}, \ldots, \mathbf{X_n}$ is a variable which meets the conditions listed for $\mathbf{P_k}$ in the preceding paragraph but which has further been standardized to have zero mean and a variance equal to the total data variance it accounts for. (That is, the variance of the **k**th prin-

---

[29] *Study problem*: Prove that the total residual variance of $\mathbf{X_1}, \ldots, \mathbf{X_n}$ after **k** principal factors have been partialled out is as small as or smaller than the total residual variance of the $\mathbf{X_i}$ after any other **k** variables, whether in the space of the $\mathbf{X_i}$ or not, have been partialled out.

cipal axis equals the **k**th "eigenvalue"—see below—of the $\mathbf{X_i}$.) *Principal components* are identical with principal axes except that unlike the latter, principal components do not have their means standardized to zero. What determines the means of principal components will be clarified a little later; what is important here about the choice of scales for principal components is that the variance of the **k**th principal component of variables $\mathbf{X_1}, \ldots, \mathbf{X_n}$, like that of their **k**th principal axis, is equal to $V_{\mathbf{X}(\mathbf{P_k})}$. Finally, the **k**th *principal factor* of a set of variables is usually understood to be the *normalized* variable which satisfies the conditions stipulated above for $\mathbf{P_k}$. That is, the first principal factor of variables $\mathbf{X_1}, \ldots, \mathbf{X_n}$ is a variable $\mathbf{P_1}$ such that $M_{\mathbf{P_1}} = 0$, $V_{\mathbf{P_1}} = 1$, and for any variable $\mathbf{Y}$, $V_{\mathbf{X}(\mathbf{P_1})} \geqslant V_{\mathbf{X}(\mathbf{Y})}$; while the **k**th principal factor of the $\mathbf{X_i}$ is a variable $\mathbf{P_k}$ orthogonal to the first $\mathbf{k}-\mathbf{1}$ principal factors of the $\mathbf{X_i}$ such that $M_{\mathbf{P_k}} = 0$, $V_{\mathbf{P_k}} = 1$, and $V_{\mathbf{X}(\mathbf{P_k})} \geqslant V_{\mathbf{X}(\mathbf{Y})}$ for any variable $\mathbf{Y}$ also orthogonal to the first $\mathbf{k}-\mathbf{1}$ principal factors of the $\mathbf{X_i}$.

The total variance of a set of variables $\mathbf{X_1}, \ldots, \mathbf{X_n}$ accounted for by their **k**th principal factor is known as the *eigenvalue* corresponding to that factor,[30] and is conventionally symbolized "$\lambda_{\mathbf{k}}$." That is,

[6.44-**k**]
(**k** = **1**, . . . , **n**)

$$\lambda_{\mathbf{k}} = V_{\mathbf{X}(\mathbf{P_k})}$$

$$= \sum_{\mathbf{i}=1}^{\mathbf{n}} C^2_{\mathbf{X_i P_k}} \qquad (V_{\mathbf{P_k}} = 1)$$

$$= \sum_{\mathbf{i}=1}^{\mathbf{n}} V_{\mathbf{X_i \bullet P_1 \ldots P_{k-1}}} r^2_{\mathbf{X_i P_k}}.$$

A distribution of **n** variables has exactly **n** eigenvalues; however, if the dimensionality, **m**, of the set is less than **n**, then $\lambda_{\mathbf{k}} = 0$ for $\mathbf{m} < \mathbf{k} \leqslant \mathbf{n}$. An obvious consequence of [6.44] and the last two lines of [6.42] is that

[6.45]

$$\sum_{\mathbf{k}=1}^{\mathbf{n}} \lambda_{\mathbf{k}} = V_{\mathbf{X}}$$

$$= \sum_{\mathbf{i}=1}^{\mathbf{n}} V_{\mathbf{X_i}},$$

[30] More fundamentally, eigenvalues are certain mathematical properties of the data-variable covariance matrix which also turn out to satisfy equations [6.44]. Corresponding to each eigenvalue $\lambda_{\mathbf{k}}$ of $\{C_{\mathbf{X_i X_j}}\}$ is a set of **n** numbers $w_{\mathbf{k1}}, \ldots, w_{\mathbf{kn}}$, known as the **k**th *eigenvector* of this matrix, such that the linear composite $\sum_{\mathbf{i}=1}^{\mathbf{n}} w_{\mathbf{ki}}\mathbf{X_i}$ is the **k**th principal component of the set $\mathbf{X_1}, \ldots, \mathbf{X_n}$. (For further discussion of eigenvalues and eigenvectors, see Appendix B, pp. (585 ff.)

so the average eigenvalue of a principal factor is equal to the average variance of the data variables. When, as customary, the data variables are normalized, so that the average data-variable variance is unity, it follows that the average eigenvalue is also unity—which is a useful fact to remember when interpreting the importance of principal factors whose eigenvalues are given. While in general $\lambda_1 > \lambda_2 > \ldots > \lambda_n$, it is mathematically possible for two or more consecutive eigenvalues to be equal. In this case the principal factors corresponding to these equal eigenvalues are not uniquely determined, since any normalized variable lying in a space spanned by principal factors whose eigenvalues are equal will also meet the conditions to be a principal factor.[31] However, the likelihood of two different principal factors having identical eigenvalues for empirical data is virtually nil.

The chief objection—perhaps the only one—to principal factors as an extraction policy is a strictly practical one: There is no simple procedure for computing them. Methods for doing it exist, to be sure, but they involve successive approximations through matrix multiplications too laborious to carry out by hand or desk calculator except for very small **n**. Fortunately, to the immense gratification of researchers yearning to apply the methodological potency of factor analysis to massive accumulations of measurements, the recent advent of high-speed electronic computers has made computation of principal factors, together with many other matrix manipulations never before feasible on more than the most modest scale, a mere matter of minutes to solution.[32]

The principal axes of a set of variables $\mathbf{X}_1, \ldots, \mathbf{X}_n$ have a special significance in the scattergram of the joint distribution of the $\mathbf{X}_i$ which merits an attempt at presentation here, both because the property to be described is frequently used as a definition of "principal axes" and because the presentation allows for warning about a serious danger of confusion between two senses of the term "orthogonal." As discussed in Chapter 2, the joint distribution of variables $\mathbf{X}_1, \ldots, \mathbf{X}_n$ in a given population P may be envisioned as an **n**-dimensional scattergram whose coordinate system is defined by **n** straight lines or "coordinate axes," all passing through a common point called the "origin" and each placed at right angles to all the rest. Each individual i in population P is represented in this system by a point whose "projection" on the $\mathbf{X}_j$ coordinate axis is X_{ji} units—i.e., a directed distance equal to i's score on variable $\mathbf{X}_j$—away from the origin. (By the *projection* of a point p on a line L is meant the point on L closest to p, i.e., the point on L at which another line perpendicular to L and passing through p can be erected.) Once a coordinate system for the scattergram has been defined with variables $\mathbf{X}_1, \ldots, \mathbf{X}_n$

[31] *Study question*: Why?

[32] A useful handbook of computer programs for multivariate analysis is available in Cooley and Lohnes (13).

for its axes, however it is also possible to introduce a new coordinate system $\mathbf{X}_1', \ldots, \mathbf{X}_n'$ by drawing in the scattergram another set of **n** lines, no one of which lies in the space spanned by the others, through a new origin. Each of these new coordinate axes defines a variable whose value for individual i is the distance from the new origin to the projection of i's scattergram point on this line. The new origin may or may not be different from the old one; if it is, the change is called a *translation of origin*. Likewise, the new coordinate axes may or may not be parallel to the old axes; if they are not, the change is called a *rotation of axes*. In particular, if the new coordinate axes are all at right angles to one another, the change is called an *orthogonal* rotation. (Translation and orthogonal rotation of the coordinate system of a two-dimensional scattergram are illustrated in Figure 6.1, which should clarify any lingering confusion the reader may have concerning these notions.) Which brings us to WARNING, Part 1: *The "orthogonality" of coordinate axes in a scattergram must not be confused with the "orthogonality" of uncorrelated variables.* The right-angled arrangement of scattergram axes is an arbitrary though highly convenient convention which implies nothing at all about the correlations among the variables corresponding to these axes. We have, to be sure, stated that in the *vector model* of a joint distribution, the correlation between two variables is shown by the angle between the vectors representing those variables, with zero correlation modeled by orthogonally placed vectors. In a *scattergram* of that distribution, however, correlation is exhibited not by the angle between the coordinate axes for two variables, but by the degree and direction of ellipticality in the scatter of points for individuals (cf. Figure 3.9). Scattergram and vector

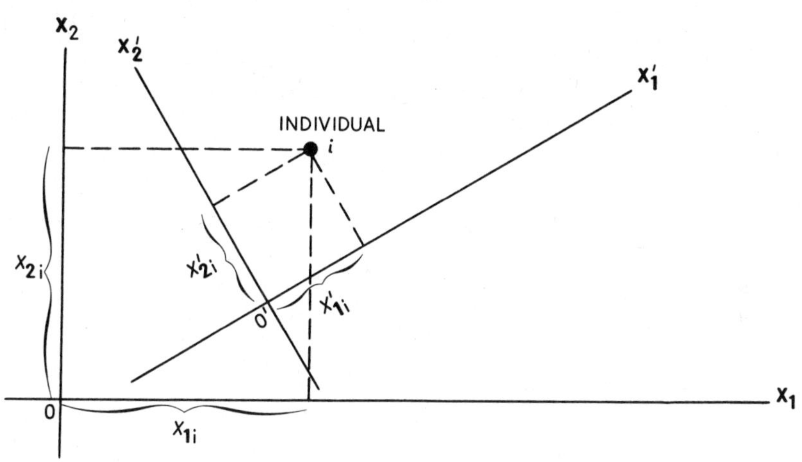

Figure 6.1. Orthogonal rotation of coordinate axes and translation of origin in the two-dimensional space of variables spanned by $\mathbf{X}_1$ and $\mathbf{X}_2$ An individual i whose scores on the original axis variables are X_{1i} and X_{2i}, respectively, has scores on the new axis variables $\mathbf{X}_1'$ and $\mathbf{X}_2'$ defined by the projection of i's scattergram point on these axes, as illustrated.

model are two quite different ways to picture the same multivariate distribution, since the former plots individuals in a coordinate system of variables while the latter plots variables either in a coordinate system of individuals or (in another version) in a coordinate system of orthogonal factors; and while the two systems are mathematically intertranslatable, there are surprisingly few intuitively meaningful correspondences between them.

It is a fundamental principle of analytic geometry that any two alternative coordinate systems for a configuration of points are so related that each of the **n** coordinate values for an arbitrary point in the one system is a linear function of its **n** coordinate values in the other system. That is, any set of variables $\mathbf{X}_1', \ldots, \mathbf{X}_n'$ defined by translation of origin and/or rotation of axes in the scattergram layout for variables $\mathbf{X}_1, \ldots, \mathbf{X}_n$ is a linear transformation of the set $\mathbf{X}_1, \ldots, \mathbf{X}_n$. Conversely, if variables $\mathbf{X}_1', \ldots, \mathbf{X}_n'$ are linearly independent of one another and each is a linear function of $\mathbf{X}_1, \ldots, \mathbf{X}_n$, then the $\mathbf{X}_i'$ coincide up to a possible shift in unit of measurement with the variables defined by some translation of origin and rotation (not necessarily orthogonal) of axes in the scattergram layout for the $\mathbf{X}_i$. (The qualification about "units of measurement" is due to the mathematical fact that if $\mathbf{X}_j'$ can be defined from $\mathbf{X}_1, \ldots, \mathbf{X}_n$ by a rotation of axes, then the coefficients in the function giving $\mathbf{X}_j'$ as a linear combination of the $\mathbf{X}_i$, when squared, must sum to unity, thus putting restrictions on the variances of variables so defined. In particular, it is shown in Appendix B that the total variance of the axis variables remains invariant under orthogonal rotation—i.e., if $\mathbf{X}_1', \ldots, \mathbf{X}_n'$ are an orthogonal rotation of $\mathbf{X}_1, \ldots, \mathbf{X}_n$, then $\sum_{i=1}^{n} V_{\mathbf{X}_i} = \sum_{i=1}^{n} V_{\mathbf{X}_i'}$.) In general, the correlations among variables $\mathbf{X}_1, \ldots, \mathbf{X}_n$ will differ from the correlations among variables $\mathbf{X}_1', \ldots, \mathbf{X}_n'$ defined by a rotation of the $\mathbf{X}_i$, and this brings us to WARNING, Part 2: *An "orthogonal" rotation of axes must not be confused with transformation into an "orthogonal" basis.* When scattergram axes $\mathbf{X}_1, \ldots, \mathbf{X}_n$ are orthogonally rotated into a new set of axes $\mathbf{X}_1', \ldots, \mathbf{X}_n'$, the correlations among the $\mathbf{X}_i'$ will *not*, in general, be all zero unless the $\mathbf{X}_i$ are orthogonal with equal variances to begin with. Likewise, while there are many ways to transform the $\mathbf{X}_i$ into an orthogonal basis, these do *not*, in general, correspond to an orthogonal rotation of axes in the scattergram layout.

It is, however, an important fact that given any distribution of variables $\mathbf{X}_1, \ldots, \mathbf{X}_n$, there is always at least one scattergram-type orthogonal rotation of the $\mathbf{X}_i$ into a new set of axis variables $\mathbf{C}_1, \ldots, \mathbf{C}_n$ such that the $\mathbf{C}_k$ are *also* orthogonal in the correlational sense. This rotation has a great many remarkable mathematical properties, one of the most fundamental being that *the* $\mathbf{C}_k$, *so derived, are the principal components of this distribution* (see Appendix B). That is, if $\mathbf{C}_1, \ldots, \mathbf{C}_n$ are arranged in descending order of variance, then each variable $\mathbf{C}_k$ produced by this very special orthogonal rotation of the $\mathbf{X}_i$ coincides with the **k**th principal factor of the $\mathbf{X}_i$ except that $\mathrm{Var}(\mathbf{C}_k) = \lambda_k$—i.e., the variance of $\mathbf{C}_k$ equals the total variance of the set $\mathbf{X}_1, \ldots, \mathbf{X}_n$ accounted for by their **k**th principal factor. If further, the rotation to principal components is accompanied by a translation of origin to put the means of the new axis variables equal to zero, we have arrived at the "principal axes" of the distribution. The situation is illustrated in Figure 6.2, in which the scattergram for the original variables, $\mathbf{X}_1$ and $\mathbf{X}_2$, shows a conspicuous upward slant indicative of a positive correlation between $\mathbf{X}_1$ and $\mathbf{X}_2$. When the coordinate axes are rotated (and translated) into the position of $\mathbf{C}_1$ and $\mathbf{C}_2$, however, it is visually apparent that the correlation has disappeared. The ellipse of scattergram points in Figure 6.2 appears to be spread out about twice as far in the $\mathbf{C}_1$ direction as in the $\mathbf{C}_2$ direction. This indicates that the standard deviation of $\mathbf{C}_1$ is about twice as large as the standard deviation of $\mathbf{C}_2$, and hence that the proportion of the total variance of $\mathbf{X}_1$ and $\mathbf{X}_2$ accounted for by their first principal factor is about $V_{\mathbf{X}(\mathbf{C}_1)}/V_{\mathbf{X}} = V_{\mathbf{X}(\mathbf{C}_1)}/[V_{\mathbf{X}(\mathbf{C}_1)} + V_{\mathbf{X}(\mathbf{C}_2)}] = V_{\mathbf{C}_1}/(V_{\mathbf{C}_1} + V_{\mathbf{C}_2}) = 4V_{\mathbf{C}_2}/(4V_{\mathbf{C}_2} + V_{\mathbf{C}_2}) = 4/(4+1) = .80$, or 80%.

The Centroid Solution. Because the principal factors of a set of data variables maximize the total data-variable variance accounted for at any given stage of factor extraction, this is the extraction procedure now recommended by most factor analysts when computer assistance is available. However, in an earlier (and still not altogether vanished) era when

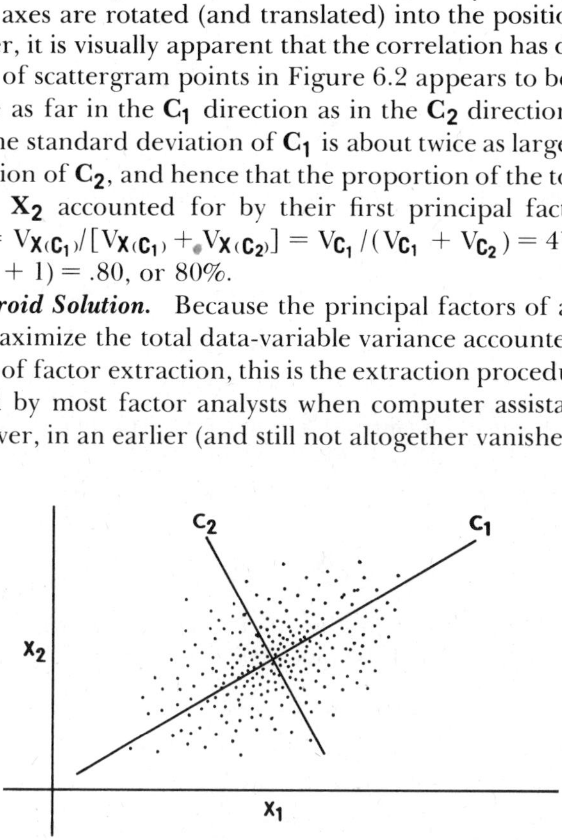

Figure 6.2. Principal axes of a multivariate distribution. With $\mathbf{X}_1$ and $\mathbf{X}_2$ as the coordinate axes of the scattergram, the joint distribution of scores shows a positive correlation which vanishes when the coordinate axes are rotated to positions $\mathbf{C}_1$ and $\mathbf{C}_2$. The origin of the principal-axes system has been translated to produce $M_{\mathbf{C}_1} = M_{\mathbf{C}_2} = 0$; however, the variables defined by these axes are clearly not normalized, since the spread along $\mathbf{C}_1$ is about twice as great as the spread along $\mathbf{C}_2$. The "principal components" of this distribution would be represented by a third pair of coordinate axes parallel to $\mathbf{C}_1$ and $\mathbf{C}_2$, respectively, but with the same origin as the $\mathbf{X}_1$–$\mathbf{X}_2$ system.

mathematical ideals had to be compromised in favor of computational practicality, the favorite factoring procedure was the *centroid* method. It is frequently claimed that the prime virtue of centroid factors is that they provide a cheap approximation to principal factors. For centroid factors after the first, this is probably a fair assessment. However, the first centroid of a set of variables (and strictly speaking, as will be seen, there *is* only one centroid to a set) is intimately linked to several important mathematical properties of the set as a whole, and well merits higher prestige than the second-class status it normally commands.

The "centroid," $\overline{\mathbf{X}}$, of a set of variables $\mathbf{X}_1, \ldots, \mathbf{X}_n$ has an absurdly simple definition: It is simply the average of the $\mathbf{X}_i$. That is,

$$[6.46] \qquad \overline{\mathbf{X}} =_{\text{def}} \frac{\sum_{i=1}^{n} \mathbf{X}_i}{\mathbf{n}} .$$

Then the "first centroid factor," $\mathbf{F}_{\overline{\mathbf{X}}}$, may be defined to be the normalized centroid, i.e.,

$$[6.47] \qquad \mathbf{F}_{\overline{\mathbf{X}}} =_{\text{def}} \mathbf{Z}_{\overline{\mathbf{X}}} = \frac{\overline{\mathbf{X}} - \mathrm{M}_{\overline{\mathbf{X}}}}{\sigma_{\overline{\mathbf{X}}}} .$$

The arithmetic mean of centroid $\overline{\mathbf{X}}$ is obviously the average mean of the $\mathbf{X}_i$—i.e., from [6.46] by way of [4.45],

$$[6.48] \qquad \mathrm{M}_{\overline{\mathbf{X}}} = \frac{\sum_{i=1}^{n} \mathrm{M}_{\mathbf{X}_i}}{\mathbf{n}} .$$

The variance of a centroid, on the other hand, is rather interesting. Application of [4.40] to [6.46] shows that

$$[6.49] \qquad \mathrm{V}_{\overline{\mathbf{X}}} =_{\text{def}} \mathrm{Var}(\overline{\mathbf{X}}) = \frac{\mathrm{Var}\left(\sum_{i=1}^{n} \mathbf{X}_i \right)}{\mathbf{n}^2} = \frac{\sum_{i=1}^{n} \sum_{j=1}^{n} \mathrm{C}_{\mathbf{X}_i \mathbf{X}_j}}{\mathbf{n}^2}$$

The numerator in [6.49] is the sum of all the entries in the covariance matrix $\{\mathrm{C}_{\mathbf{X}_i \mathbf{X}_j}\}$ for the constituent variables in $\overline{\mathbf{X}}$, while the number of entries in an $\mathbf{n}$ by $\mathbf{n}$ matrix is of course $\mathbf{n}^2$; hence $\mathrm{V}_{\overline{\mathbf{X}}}$ is simply the average entry in the covariance matrix for the $\mathbf{X}_i$. It is also obvious by application of [4.37] that the covariance between the centroid and any data variable $\mathbf{X_i}$ included in $\overline{\mathbf{X}}$ is

[6.50-**i**]
(**i** = **1**, . . . , **n**)

$$C_{X_i\overline{X}} =_{def} \mathrm{Cov}(\mathbf{X_i}, \overline{\mathbf{X}}) = \frac{\mathrm{Cov}\left(\mathbf{X_i}, \sum_{j=1}^{n} \mathbf{X_j}\right)}{\mathbf{n}} = \frac{\sum_{j=1}^{n} C_{X_iX_j}}{\mathbf{n}}.$$

That is, the covariance between the **i**th data variable and their centroid is simply the average entry in the **i**th row (or equivalently, and more in keeping with prevailing arithmetic habits, the **i**th column) of the data-variable covariance matrix. Consequently, extraction of a centroid factor is almost immorally easy: The raw factor-structure coefficient $C_{X_iF_{\overline{X}}}$ – i.e., the covariance between $\mathbf{X_i}$ and the normalized centroid – is

[6.51-**i**]
(**i** = **1**, . . . , **n**)

$$C_{X_iF_{\overline{X}}} = \frac{C_{X_i\overline{X}}}{\sigma_{\overline{X}}} = \frac{\sum_{j=1}^{n} C_{X_iX_j}}{\sqrt{\sum_{k=1}^{n}\sum_{j=1}^{n} C_{X_kX_j}}},$$

and the residual covariances among the $\mathbf{X_i}$ after $F_{\overline{X}}$ – or, equivalently, $\overline{\mathbf{X}}$ – is partialled out (see [6.16]) are

[6.52-**ij**]
(**i**,**j** = **1**, . . . , **n**)

$$C_{X_iX_j \cdot F_{\overline{X}}} = C_{X_iX_j} - \frac{C_{X_i\overline{X}}\, C_{X_j\overline{X}}}{V_{\overline{X}}} = C_{X_iX_j} - \frac{\left(\sum_{k=1}^{n} C_{X_iX_k}\right)\left(\sum_{k=1}^{n} C_{X_jX_k}\right)}{\sum_{h=1}^{n}\sum_{k=1}^{n} C_{X_hX_k}}.$$

Thus to extract $F_{\overline{X}}$, one sums each column (or row) of the covariance matrix for the $\mathbf{X_i}$ (or their correlation matrix, if normalized data variables are preferred) and also takes the grand sum of all the entries in $\{C_{X_iX_j}\}$. The entry in the **i**th row of the first column of the raw factor-structure matrix is then simply the sum of the **i**th column of the data-variable covariance matrix, divided by the square root of the grand sum; while the amount by which $\mathbf{C}_{\mathbf{X}_i \mathbf{X}_j}$ is reduced when $\mathbf{F}_{\overline{\mathbf{X}}}$ is partialled out is the product of the sums for columns **i** and **j**, divided by the grand sum. These manipulations will be illustrated with a numerical example somewhat later (pp. 269 ff.).

By all rights, the second centroid factor of $\mathbf{X}_1, \ldots, \mathbf{X}_n$ should be the normalized centroid of the data-variable residuals $\mathbf{e}_{\mathbf{X}_i \bullet \mathbf{F}_{\overline{\mathbf{X}}}}$ left after removal of $\mathbf{F}_{\overline{\mathbf{X}}}$. However, a curious complication thwarts this move. By [4.56], the regression of $\mathbf{X}_i$ upon $\overline{\mathbf{X}}$ is

$$\dot{\mathbf{X}}_{i(\overline{\mathbf{X}})} = \frac{\mathrm{C}_{\mathbf{X}_i\overline{\mathbf{X}}}}{\mathrm{V}_{\mathbf{X}}}(\overline{\mathbf{X}} - \mathrm{M}_{\overline{\mathbf{X}}}) + \mathrm{M}_{\mathbf{X}_i} \; .$$

Hence the centroid of the regressed components $\dot{\mathbf{X}}_{i(\overline{\mathbf{X}})}$ is

$$[6.53] \qquad \frac{\sum_{i=1}^{n} \dot{\mathbf{X}}_{i(\overline{\mathbf{X}})}}{\mathbf{n}} = \left[\frac{\sum_{i=1}^{n} \mathrm{C}_{\mathbf{X}_i\overline{\mathbf{X}}}}{\mathbf{n}\mathrm{V}_{\overline{\mathbf{X}}}}\right](\overline{\mathbf{X}} - \mathrm{M}_{\overline{\mathbf{X}}}) + \frac{\sum_{i=1}^{n} \mathrm{M}_{\mathbf{X}_i}}{\mathbf{n}}$$
$$= (\overline{\mathbf{X}} - \mathrm{M}_{\overline{\mathbf{X}}}) + \mathrm{M}_{\overline{\mathbf{X}}}$$
$$= \overline{\mathbf{X}} \; ,$$

since the formidable-appearing constant in brackets is seen from [6.49] and [6.50] to be merely 1. Equation [6.53] says that the average of a person's estimated scores on the individual variables $\mathbf{X}_1, \ldots, \mathbf{X}_n$, given his score on the centroid of these variables, is simply this centroid score itself. That this should be so may be made evident by observing it to be merely an instance of the general principle that the best estimate of a person's score on a linear composite $\mathbf{L}_{\mathbf{X}}$ of variables $\mathbf{X}_1, \ldots, \mathbf{X}_n$, given the person's scores on the variables in a set of predictors $\boldsymbol{\mu}$ (i.e., $\boldsymbol{\mu}$ is some set of variables $\mathbf{F}_1, \ldots, \mathbf{F}_m$), is equal to that same linear composite of the separate estimates on variables $\mathbf{X}_1, \ldots, \mathbf{X}_n$ from $\boldsymbol{\mu}$ for this person. That is,

$$[6.54]^{33} \qquad \dot{\mathbf{L}}_{\mathbf{X}(\boldsymbol{\mu})} = a_0 + \sum_{i=1}^{n} a_i \dot{\mathbf{X}}_{i(\boldsymbol{\mu})} \qquad \left(\mathbf{L}_{\mathbf{X}} = a_0 + \sum_{i=1}^{n} a_i \mathbf{X}_i\right),$$

while correspondingly

[33] *Proof*: $\mathbf{L}_{\mathbf{X}} =_{\text{def}} a_0 + \sum_{i=1}^{n} a_i \mathbf{X}_i = a_0 + \sum_{i=1}^{n} a_i(\dot{\mathbf{X}}_{i(\boldsymbol{\mu})} + \mathbf{e}_{\mathbf{X}_i \cdot \boldsymbol{\mu}}) = [a_0 + \sum_{i=1}^{n} a_i \dot{\mathbf{X}}_{i(\boldsymbol{\mu})}] + [\sum_{i=1}^{n} a_i \mathbf{e}_{\mathbf{X}_i \cdot \boldsymbol{\mu}}]$. But the expression in the second pair of brackets has a mean of zero and zero correlation with all the variables in $\boldsymbol{\mu}$ (since it is a weighted sum of variables for each of which this is true), while the expression in the first pair of brackets is a linear function of the variables in $\boldsymbol{\mu}$. Hence by the fundamental uniqueness theorem proved on p. 144, above, the first bracketed expression must be the linear regression of $\mathbf{L}_{\mathbf{X}}$ on the variabl in $\boldsymbol{\mu}$ while the second bracketed expression is the residual of $\mathbf{L}_{\mathbf{X}}$ left by $\boldsymbol{\mu}$.

[6.55][33] $$e_{L_X \cdot \mu} = \sum_{i=1}^{n} a_i e_{X_i \cdot \mu} \qquad \left(L_X = a_0 + \sum_{i=1}^{n} a_i X_i\right).$$

Then [6.53] follows from [6.54] by taking $\bar{X}$ for both L_X and μ. But this same substitution into [6.55] also shows that

[6.56] $$\frac{\sum_{i=1}^{n} e_{X_i \cdot \bar{X}}}{n} = e_{\bar{X} \cdot \bar{X}} = 0 \,,$$

which can alternatively be derived directly from [6.53] by observing that

$$\frac{\sum_{i=1}^{n} e_{X_i \cdot \bar{X}}}{n} = \frac{\sum_{i=1}^{n} (X_i - \dot{X}_{i(\bar{X})})}{n} = \frac{\sum_{i=1}^{n} X_i}{n} - \frac{\sum_{i=1}^{n} \dot{X}_{i(\bar{X})}}{n} = \bar{X} - \bar{X} = 0 \,.$$

That is, *the centroid of the residual components of a set of variables orthogonal to their first centroid is identically zero*—i.e., the errors made in linearly estimating a person's n scores on variables $X_1, \ldots, X_n$ from the average of his scores on these variables average to zero for each person. (To say that a variable is "identically equal" to a constant c means, it will be recalled, that every person in the relevant population has the same value on that variable, namely c.) What is painful about this for centroid factoring is that

$$\text{Var}\left(\frac{\sum_{i=1}^{n} e_{X_i \cdot \bar{X}}}{n}\right) = 0 \,,$$

so to take the centroid of the first-centroid residuals for a second factor would require division by zero (see [6.18]) which of course is mathematically illegitimate.

In short, we cannot define the second centroid factor of a set of variables as the normalized centroid of the first-centroid residuals $e_{X_i \cdot \bar{X}}$ *because a true second centroid just doesn't exist*—or rather, it exists only in the degenerate sense of a variable with zero variance.[34] In order for the centroid procedure to come up with any factors beyond the first, therefore, some finagling must be done. The ploy which is customarily used is to multiply some of the residuals $e_{X_i \cdot \bar{X}}$ by -1 before taking their centroid, an act which is known as a *reflection* of the variables so treated. Serious discussion of reflection will be reserved for later (pp. 341 ff.),

[34] One way to appreciate the degeneracy of a variable with zero variance is by recalling (see fn. 8, p. 216) that a variable with zero variance is perfectly predictable from any variable, and is hence linearly independent of none.

but the basic idea is simple enough: If the variance of a sum of variables is zero (which is equivalent to their centroid's having zero variance) even though not all of the constituent variables have zero variance, then it is clear from formula [4.40] that some of the constituent covariances must be negative—in fact, the average interitem covariance when self-covariances (i.e., variances) are excluded must be negative in this case. If a variable whose covariance with the sum of the other variables is negative is now reversed in sign, its former prevailingly negative contribution to the average interitem covariance is likewise reversed into a positive contribution. Consequently, the centroid of this modified set of variables will have a variance greater than zero. In practice, reflection is not confined to a single variable but is usually carried out until each residual variable, reflected or unreflected as the case may be, correlates positively with the sum of the remainder, at which point the normalized centroid of this modified set of residuals is extracted as the second centroid factor. Similar reflection of the nonvanished second-order residuals left by the first two factors then develops a usable third "centroid" which, when normalized, is the third centroid factor, and so on until the residuals have all vanished. By suitable adjustments on the residuals, therefore, as many "centroid" factors may be obtained as are needed. Just the same, it should be clearly understood that a set of variables has literally only one centroid, and only the first centroid factor coincides (up to a normalizing transformation) with it.

Other Initial Solutions. In addition to the principal axes and centroid solutions for reducing a set of variables to an initial factor basis, several other extraction procedures occur in the literature with sufficient frequency to warrant brief mention here.

The *square-root* method of factoring is essentially the one which was used in our previous chest-data example, namely, choosing one data variable, say $\mathbf{X}_1$, to define the first factor, one first-order residual, say $e_{X_2 \cdot X_1}$, to define the second factor, one third-order residual, say $e_{X_3 \cdot X_1 X_2}$, for the third factor, and so on, except that in contrast to our chest-data computations, the factors are normalized. That is, square-root factors are defined by the sequence $\mathbf{F}_1 = z_{X_1}$, $\mathbf{F}_2 = e_{X_2 \cdot X_1}/\sigma_{X_2 \cdot X_1}$, $\mathbf{F}_3 = e_{X_3 \cdot X_1 X_2}/\sigma_{X_3 \cdot X_1 X_2}$, etc., so the covariance of each variable $\mathbf{X}_i$ with square-root factor $\mathbf{F}_j$ is

$$C_{X_i F_j} = \frac{C_{X_i X_j \cdot X_1 \ldots X_{j-1}}}{\sqrt{C_{X_j X_j \cdot X_1 \ldots X_{j-1}}}}$$

Computationally, the square-root method is the least laborious of all factoring routines. However, two crippling limitations which discourage its application to empirical data are (*a*) its normally poor approximation to maximizing the total variance accounted for at each stage of factoring, and (*b*) the fact that if factoring is discontinued before all residuals have been *completely* reduced to zero, the discarded residuals must of necessity be concentrated entirely among the data variables which have not been used to define a factor. Square-root factoring is not advisable, therefore, unless the intent is to extract and use as many factors as there are data variables.

The *multiple-group* or *group-centroid* method of factoring is something of a hybrid between the centroid and the square-root procedures, at least when the multiple-group factors are orthogonal. In its original conception, however, multiple-group factoring generates oblique factors by simultaneous extraction, and we shall first describe the method in this form. To solve for **m** group factors simultaneously, one begins by grouping the data variables into **m** possibly overlapping subsets $G_1, \ldots, G_m$. A given data variable may be included in several of the groups (though this is not customary), or need not be included in any of them. For example, to extract three group factors from six data variables $\mathbf{X}_1, \ldots, \mathbf{X}_6$, we might choose G_1 as $\mathbf{X}_1$, $\mathbf{X}_2$, and $\mathbf{X}_3$; G_2 as $\mathbf{X}_2$ and $\mathbf{X}_4$; and G_3 as $\mathbf{X}_1$, $\mathbf{X}_3$, $\mathbf{X}_4$, and $\mathbf{X}_6$. Then the **k**th group factor, $\mathbf{F}_{G_k}$, is defined to be the normalized centroid—or, what is the same and omits the superfluous division by the number of items in the group, the normalized sum—of the variables in group G_k. The structure matrix for all **m** group factors is easily computed from the data-variable covariance matrix by application of formulas [4.37] and [4.40]. For example, if G_1 consists of $\mathbf{X}_1, \mathbf{X}_2$, and $\mathbf{X}_3$, the covariance of each data variable $\mathbf{X}_i$ with group factor $\mathbf{F}_{G_1}$ is

$$C_{\mathbf{X}_i\mathbf{F}_{G_1}} = \frac{\sum_{j=1}^{3} C_{\mathbf{X}_i\mathbf{X}_j}}{\sqrt{\sum_{k=1}^{3}\sum_{j=1}^{3} C_{\mathbf{X}_k\mathbf{X}_j}}}.$$

More generally, the reader should readily be able to see that each entry in the factor structure matrix $\{C_{\mathbf{X}_i\mathbf{F}_{G_j}}\}$ is computed as a sum of certain entries in the data-variable covariance matrix, divided by the square root of the sum of certain other entries in that matrix. Since the group factors will in general be correlated, we also need to compute the factor covariance matrix, but this too is easily accomplished by application of [4.39] to the appropriate entries in $\{C_{\mathbf{X}_i\mathbf{X}_j}\}$. It must be pointed out at once, however, that there is a catch to this computational ease, and the moment of truth arrives when we set out to determine the residual covariances unaccounted for by the extracted group factors in order to see how closely these factors approximate a basis for the data variables. With orthogonal factors this is elementary, but with oblique factors a complex routine of matrix operations is required which amount, in effect, to determining the multiple regression of each data variable upon the group factors, taking the covariances between pairs of regressed data variables, and then subtracting these from the original covariances. (One could, of course, simply ignore the residual covariances altogether, but unless as many group factors have been extracted as there are data variables, this would be unprofessional.) Since a set of orthogonal factors is likely to be desired for one purpose or another anyway, it is simpler in the long run to take out orthogonal group factors to begin with by first partialling out the centroid of the first group, then taking the centroid of the residuals in the second group to define the second (orthogonalized) group factor, and so on. In the limiting case where each group consists of just one data variable, this orthogonal version of multiple-group factoring becomes equivalent to the square-root procedure.

While multiple-group factors may in principle be defined by any arbitrary grouping of the variables, the only real justification for use of this method in preference to principal factors or complete centroids is belief that the variables placed in the same group do, in fact, share some important underlying determinant so that, in contrast to other initial solutions, the factors come tagged with a substantive interpretation. One way in which grouping might be so justified would be that a common causal origin for these variables has been implicated by previous research. Another occurs when the covariance matrix being factored gives evidence of "clustering" in the sense of high intercorrelations within each cluster (i.e., group) of variables compared with weaker correlations between clusters.[35] On the whole, there is nothing established by efforts at initial grouping which cannot be accomplished more confidently through subsequent rotation of an initial solution which has stressed factorial parsimony. Even so, multiple-group extraction may expedite the final solution if the multiple-group factors do, in fact, lie close to the "simple structure" (see later) of the configuration.

Finally, a style of factor solution which is assuming increasing importance in multivariate analysis is afforded by the concept of *canonical correlation.* The prospect for this arises when in addition to the to-be-factored variables $\mathbf{X}_1, \ldots, \mathbf{X}_n$, we also have data on another set of variables $\mathbf{Y}_1, \ldots, \mathbf{Y}_p$ in the same population, so that all the covariances among $\mathbf{X}_1, \ldots, \mathbf{X}_n, \mathbf{Y}_1, \ldots, \mathbf{Y}_p$ are available. Then the problem assayed by the theory of canonical correlations is to select coefficients for a linear function $\mathbf{F}_1$ of $\mathbf{X}_1, \ldots, \mathbf{X}_n$, and also for a linear function $\mathbf{G}_1$ of $\mathbf{Y}_1, \ldots, \mathbf{Y}_n$, which maximize the linear correlation between $\mathbf{F}_1$ and $\mathbf{G}_1$. To reduce the number of alternative solutions we may as well also stipulate that $\mathbf{F}_1$ and $\mathbf{G}_1$ are normalized. The two normalized composites, $\mathbf{F}_1$ of the $\mathbf{X}_i$ and $\mathbf{G}_1$ of the $\mathbf{Y}_j$, which achieve this maximal correlation are the *first canonical factors* for the pair of sets $\mathbf{X}_1, \ldots, \mathbf{X}_n$ and $\mathbf{Y}_1, \ldots, \mathbf{Y}_p$, while the *first canonical correlation* between the two sets of variables is the correlation

[35] Inferential multiple-group factoring based on clusters of data variables has been aggressively championed by Tryon (see 81 and further references there cited).

between $\mathbf{F_1}$ and $\mathbf{G_1}$. Once the first canonical factors are partialled out of their respective domains, moreover, the analysis may be repeated for the residuals. Thus the second canonical factors are the normalized linear composites of the first-order residuals, $\mathbf{F_2}$ of $e_{X_1 \cdot F_1}, \ldots, e_{X_n \cdot F_1}$ and $\mathbf{G_2}$ of $e_{Y_1 \cdot G_1}, \ldots, e_{Y_p \cdot G_1}$, whose correlation is maximal and defines the second canonical correlation between the two sets. Continuing in this way, we eventually arrive at $\mathbf{m}$ canonical factors $\mathbf{F_1}, \ldots, \mathbf{F_m}$ for the $\mathbf{X_i}$, $\mathbf{m}$ canonical factors $\mathbf{G_1}, \ldots, \mathbf{G_m}$ for the $\mathbf{Y_j}$, and $\mathbf{m}$ corresponding canonical correlations $r_{F_1 G_1}, \ldots, r_{F_m G_m}$, where $\mathbf{m}$ is the dimensionality of either the $\mathbf{X_i}$ or the $\mathbf{Y_j}$, depending on which is the smaller. (Further mathematical details about canonical factors are available in Appendix B, pp. 599 ff.)

The chief limitation to the use of canonical factoring (over and above computational difficulties, which, however, are essentially the same as those of principal factors and pose little problem for a high-speed computer) is the need for two sets of variables to be pitted against each other, along with some cogent arguments for why the total array of variables being studied should be dichotomized in this way, rather than being united in a single set whose covariance matrix is factored by more conventional methods. One always-available opportunity for canonical factoring derives from the custom (discussed immediately below) of inferentially abstracting a set of "communal components" from the data variables, whose covariances with each other and with the original data variables are taken from the data-variable covariances. In factoring these inferred components, it is then possible to ask what orthogonal linear combinations of them can successively be most closely estimated from the data variables, thereby generating canonical factors for both the data variables and their communal components. However, the uses of canonical factors defined in this particular way would seem to be largely restricted to advanced problems in the mathematical theory of multivariate relations.

The spirit of canonical correlation may be drawn upon to define factors whenever it is possible to evaluate alternative linear functions of a set of variables for their relative effectiveness at one or more ulterior tasks. For example, the theory of "discriminant functions" (see Chapter 10) develops linear functions on a given set of quantitative variables by which to convert a subject's scores on these variables into an optimal judgment about where he belongs in a categorical classification schema. Such functions, so long as they are linearly independent of one another, may then be regarded as "factors" of their constituent variables. A set of $\mathbf{m}$ orthogonal discriminant functions over variables $\mathbf{X_1}, \ldots, \mathbf{X_n}$, devised to select among $\mathbf{m+1}$ categories in such fashion that the first $\mathbf{k}$ ($\mathbf{k} = \mathbf{1}, \ldots, \mathbf{m}$) discriminant functions are the optimal set of $\mathbf{k}$ linear functions over the $\mathbf{X_i}$ for discerning a subject's category, are also sometimes called "canonical variables" and can, in fact, be derived by canonical factoring (see p. 563, Chapter 10).

Inferred Components and the Problem of Communalities

The methods of factoring described so far all agree in identifying the factors they extract as nothing more than certain linear transformations of the variables upon whose covariance matrix the analysis is performed Yet "factor analysis" was first cited in Chapter 5 as a source of theoretical explanations for observed correlations, while allusions have also been made earlier to the interpretation of factors as causal determinants of the data variables. It is now time to garnish the computational algorithms described above with a dash of inductive inference. Specifically, where creative speculation gets its chance to spice up the mathematical purity of basis factoring is in (*a*) tinkering with the diagonal elements in the original data-variable covariance matrix, and (*b*) opting for a particular choice of basis for the factor space eventually extracted from the adjusted data.

In order that factor analysis may be construed as a lens through which to peer at the causal structure of reality, two basic premises and a technical elaboration are required. The first is that when a data variable assumes its various observed values, it does so under the influence of other variables of which it is a function, linear or otherwise, according to certain principles of natural regularity. Secondly, it is also presupposed that statistical correlations (linear or otherwise) larger than what can reasonably be written off to observation error or chance effects are a result of the correlated variables' having one or more lawful determinants in common—i.e., that if there exists a significant correlation between variables $\mathbf{X}_i$ and $\mathbf{X}_j$, then there probably exist one or more variables $\boldsymbol{\tau}_1, \ldots, \boldsymbol{\tau}_m$ which belong both to the set of lawful determinants of $\mathbf{X}_i$ and to the set of lawful determinants of $\mathbf{X}_j$. The "lawfulness" of this determination may be either nomic (i.e., a "law of nature"), logical (e.g., $\mathbf{X}_i$ may be explicitly defined as a composite over a domain including $\boldsymbol{\tau}_1, \ldots, \boldsymbol{\tau}_m$), or a mixture of both. Nothing needs be assumed about the direction of causation or spatial-temporal contiguities among the correlated variables and their presumed common determinants. Thus while high correlations among a person's various specific abilities to spell "house," "louse," "mouse," and "spouse" might well be due to a common underlying psychological condition whose action is immediately prior to the overt production of each of these words, explanation of a correlation between the IQs of first cousins would presumably require appeal to common sources rather remote in space and time from the immediate determinants of these persons' intellectual functioning. Neither is the possibility precluded that one variable of a correlated pair may itself be a causal antecedent of the other, as in, e.g., a correlation between the effort a student puts into a course and the grade he subsequently receives in it. All in all, then, the basic assumptions for factor interpretation are little more than a faith that observed correlations have law-functional explanations.

To clothe this simple faith in the good works of factor analysis, however, we must also hope for a little technical assistance from nature in the form of causal relationships which can in at least some instances be usefully investigated through linear approximations. Specifically, we now go on to surmise that among the determinants of intercorrelated variables $\mathbf{X_1}, \ldots, \mathbf{X_n}$, there may exist a set $\tau_1, \ldots, \tau_m$ so scalable that the linear regressions of the $\mathbf{X_i}$ upon $\tau_1, \ldots, \tau_m$ account for virtually all of the linear correlations among them. That is, we conjecture that there may exist "source variables" $\tau_1, \ldots, \tau_m$ among the lawful determinants of $\mathbf{X_1}, \ldots, \mathbf{X_n}$ such that approximately

[6.57-**ij**][36] $$C_{X_i X_j \bullet \tau_1 \ldots \tau_m} = 0 \,,$$
$(\mathbf{i,j} = \mathbf{1}, \ldots, \mathbf{n};\ \mathbf{i} \neq \mathbf{j})$

and moreover that the linear regressions

[6.58-**i**] $$\dot{\mathbf{X}}_{i\,(\tau_1 \ldots \tau_m)} = b^*_{i0} + b^*_{i1}\tau_1 + \ldots + b^*_{im}\tau_m$$
$(\mathbf{i} = \mathbf{1}, \ldots, \mathbf{n})$

of the $\mathbf{X_i}$ upon $\tau_1, \ldots, \tau_m$ would be scientifically instructive could we but learn them. (The asterisks on the b^*s in [6.58] are to distinguish them from the bs in factor pattern [6.20].) It is important to be clear about what this assumption does *not* include. It does not insist that the $\mathbf{X_i}$ are in fact linearly related to the τ_j; it merely hopes that linear regressions may be useful approximations. It does not even imply that these linear approximations would necessarily remain useful if the source variables were scaled in the manner that might seem most natural were we to have direct knowledge of these variables—all that is requested is that there exist *some* scales for them under which equations [6.57] are approximately correct and regressions [6.58] are informative. (For example, correlations such as those envisioned by our earlier chest-data example might be accounted for by appeal primarily to an underlying determinant called "size." Moreover, the cube root of a person's weight might nicely satisfy the conditions ascribed to "size" in the linear model, even though in the customary scaling of weight, say Weight-in-pounds, the relationship between weight and chest measurements would depart appreciably from linearity.) Neither should [6.57-**ij**] be construed to say that data variables $\mathbf{X}_{X_i}$ and $\mathbf{X}_{X_j}$ have no common determinants other than $\tau_1, \ldots, \tau_m$, or that there is complete statistical independence among the residuals $\mathbf{e}_{X_i \bullet \tau_1 \cdots \tau_m}$—all that equations [6.57] posit is that $\tau_1, \ldots, \tau_m$ account for approximately all of the *linear* correlations among $\mathbf{X_1}, \ldots, \mathbf{X_n}$. Further, there is nothing in [6.57] to presuppose uniqueness either for the identities of the τ_j (e.g., the theoretical variable "size" in our chest-

[36] We show residual covariances rather than residual correlations here in order to avoid the complication that some of the residual variances $V_{X_i \cdot \tau_1 \cdots \tau_m}$ might be equal to zero, in which case the residual correlations would be undefined.

data example could presumably be interpreted as Height-in-inches just as effectively as Cube-root-of-weight-in-pounds), or for the pattern of their regression coefficients. That is, equations [6.57] are perfectly compatible with the possibility that there might also exist another set of source variables $\tau'_1, \ldots, \tau'_p$ different from (though presumably lawfully related to) $\tau_1, \ldots, \tau_m$ and with a different pattern of regression weights for the $\mathbf{X}_i$, but for which $\mathbf{C}_{X_i X_j \cdot \tau'_1 \ldots \tau'_p} = 0$ $(\mathbf{i,j} = \mathbf{1}, \ldots, \mathbf{n}; \mathbf{i} \neq \mathbf{j})$ is also approximately true. Finally, it is not demanded that *all* data variables have lawful determinants satisfying [6.57]. If factor analysis of the data-variable covariance matrix fails to yield any provocatively simplifying pattern the conclusion to be reached is simply that in this particular case, no satisfactory evidence for sources of the observed relations has been found. In summary, then, the methodological requirements for interpretative application of factor analysis are really quite humble. All that is needed is for situation [6.57] to occur with sufficient likelihood that when a pattern of relationships entailed by such a hypothesis *is* found in the data, it is, conversely, not altogether unreasonable to interpret the data as evidence favoring the hypothesis.[37]

But what implications do assumptions [6.57] have for the observed relations among the $\mathbf{X}_i$, anyway? Actually, until a specific value is selected for $\mathbf{m}$, the number of source variables, they have none. (Note that equations [6.57] are trivially satisfied by taking the $\mathbf{X}_i$ themselves for the τ_j.) Rather, equations [6.57] encourage us to search within the data-variable covariance matrix for whatever choice of $\mathbf{m}$ is in keeping with the data at hand. Before elaborating this point, however, we first need to examine more closely just what it is that hypothesis [6.57] says, and to be clear how regression equations [6.58] differ from factor-pattern equations [6.20].

Observe, then, that each regression equation [6.58-**i**] expresses a linear *estimate* of data variable $\mathbf{X}_i$ based on hypothesized source variables $\tau_1, \ldots, \tau_m$. Since this estimate is *not* presumed to be exact (in contradistinction to factor-pattern equation [6.20-**i**]) we must also give cognizance to the residuals, $\mathbf{e}_{X_i \cdot \tau_1 \ldots \tau_m}$, left in the data variables by $\tau_1, \ldots, \tau_m$. Thus a complete analysis of $\mathbf{X}_i$ in terms of these source variables is

[6.59-**i**] $\quad \mathbf{X}_i = b^*_{i0} + b^*_{i1}\tau_1 + \ldots + b^*_{im}\tau_m + \mathbf{e}_{X_i \cdot \tau_1 \ldots \tau_m}$
$(\mathbf{i} = \mathbf{1}, \ldots, \mathbf{n})$

To be succinct, let the regression of $\mathbf{X}_i$ upon $\tau_1, \ldots, \tau_m$ be written "$\mathbf{H}_i$" and called *the communal component of* $\mathbf{X}_i$ *with respect to source variables* $\tau_1, \ldots, \tau_m$. That is,

[6.60-**i**]
$(\mathbf{i} = \mathbf{1}, \ldots, \mathbf{n})$

$$\mathbf{H}_i =_{\text{def}} \dot{\mathbf{X}}_{i(\tau_1 \ldots \tau_m)} = b^*_{i0} + \sum_{j=1}^{m} b^*_{ij}\tau_j \, .$$

[37] If a premise P implies a conclusion Q, verification of Q does not, of course, demonstrate the truth of P. Just the same, inductive science rests upon the principle that under suitable circumstances, affirmation of the consequent (i.e., Q) at least increases the likelihood that the antecedent (i.e., P) is true.

Similarly, let the linear residual of $\mathbf{X}_i$ left by the τ_j be notationally simplified to "$\mathbf{U}_i$" and called *the unique component of* $\mathbf{X}_i$ *with respect to source variables* $\tau_1, \ldots, \tau_m$ —i.e.,

[6.61-**i**] (**i** = **1**, . . . , **n**)

$$\mathbf{U}_i =_{\text{def}} \mathbf{e}_{\mathbf{X}_i \cdot \tau_1 \ldots \tau_m} .$$

Then [6.59-**i**] simplifies to

[6.62-**i**] (**i** = **1**, . . . , **n**)

$$\mathbf{X}_i = \mathbf{H}_i + \mathbf{U}_i ,$$

which expresses each data variable $\mathbf{X}_i$ in the set $\mathbf{X}_1, \ldots, \mathbf{X}_n$ as the sum of two hypothesized components, a "communal component" $\mathbf{H}_i$ lying in the space spanned by the source variables postulated to account for the observed covariances among these **n** data variables, and a "unique component" $\mathbf{U}_i$ orthogonal to $\mathbf{H}_i$. The orthogonality between unique and communal components, moreover, is not confined to the pair for each data variable. We know from [4.87] that

[6.63-**ij**] $\begin{pmatrix} \mathbf{i} = \mathbf{1}, \ldots, \mathbf{n} \\ \mathbf{j} = \mathbf{1}, \ldots, \mathbf{m} \end{pmatrix}$

$$C_{\mathbf{U}_i \tau_j} = 0 ;$$

Hence, since each $\mathbf{H}_i$ is a linear function of the τ_j,

[6.64-**ij**] (**i**,**j** = **1**, . . . , **n**)

$$C_{\mathbf{U}_i \mathbf{H}_j} = 0 .$$

Finally, the crucial assumption [6.57] that source variables $\tau_1, \ldots, \tau_m$ account for (virtually) all the covariance among $\mathbf{X}_1, \ldots, \mathbf{X}_n$, may be rewritten as

[6.65-**ij**] (**i**,**j** = **1**, . . . , **n**)

$$C_{\mathbf{U}_i \mathbf{U}_j} = \begin{cases} V_{\mathbf{X}_i \cdot \tau_1 \ldots \tau_m} & \text{if } \mathbf{i} = \mathbf{j} \\ 0 & \text{if } \mathbf{i} \neq \mathbf{j} , \end{cases} .$$

where the value for $C_{\mathbf{U}_i \mathbf{U}_i}$, or $V_{\mathbf{U}_i}$, is an immediate consequence of $\mathbf{U}_i$'s definition as the component of $\mathbf{X}_i$ linearly uncontrolled by the τ_j.

The payoff of this assumption is that since the unique components of the $\mathbf{X}_i$ account for none of the covariance among the data variables, their communal components must be responsible for all of it. That is, since source variables $\tau_1, \ldots, \tau_m$ mathematically partition each data-variable covariance into a controlled and an uncontrolled portion, namely,

[6.66-**ij**] (**i**,**j** = **1**, . . . , **n**)

$$\begin{aligned} C_{\mathbf{X}_i \mathbf{X}_j} &= C_{\mathbf{X}_i \mathbf{X}_j (\tau_1 \ldots \tau_m)} + C_{\mathbf{X}_i \mathbf{X}_j \cdot \tau_1 \ldots \tau_m} \\ &= C_{\mathbf{H}_i \mathbf{H}_j} + C_{\mathbf{U}_i \mathbf{U}_i} , \end{aligned}$$

it follows immediately from [6.65] that

[6.67-ij]
(i,j = 1, . . . , n)

$$C_{H_iH_j} = \begin{cases} V_{X_i(\tau_1\ldots\tau_m)} & \text{if } i = j \\ C_{X_iX_j} & \text{if } i \neq j\,. \end{cases}$$

Hence except for the elements on the principal diagonal, the covariance matrix for data variables $\mathbf{X}_1, \ldots, \mathbf{X}_n$ is identical with the covariance matrix for their communal components with respect to source variables $\tau_1, \ldots, \tau_m$. To appreciate the nature of these diagonal elements more clearly, recall (cf. p. 152) that the proportion of a variable's variance accounted for by a set of predictors is the squared multiple correlation of that variable with those predictors. Therefore,

[6.68-i]
(i = 1, . . . , n)

$$V_{H_i} = V_{X_i(\tau_1\ldots\tau_m)} = V_{X_i} R^2_{X_i(\tau_1\ldots\tau_m)}\,,$$

and [6.67] may be rewritten

[6.69-ij]
(i,j = 1, . . . , n)

$$C_{H_iH_j} = \begin{cases} V_{X_i} R^2_{X_i(\tau_1\ldots\tau_m)} & \text{if } i = j \\ C_{X_iX_j} & \text{if } i \neq j\,. \end{cases}$$

This makes explicit that the only difference between the covariance matrices for the original data variables and for their communal components is that the diagonal entries in $\{C_{H_iH_j}\}$ are somewhat smaller than the corresponding diagonal values in $\{C_{X_iX_j}\}$. It is also helpful to see that this reduction of the diagonals is equivalent to partialling the set of unique components out of the data variables. For the covariance between data variable $\mathbf{X}_i$ and unique component $\mathbf{U}_j$ is obviously

[6.70-ij]
(i,j = 1, . . . , n)

$$C_{X_iU_j} = \begin{cases} V_{U_i} & \text{if } i = j \\ 0 & \text{if } i \neq j\,, \end{cases}$$

where the "unique variance," V_{U_i}, of $\mathbf{X}_i$ can variously be written

[6.71-i]
(i = 1, . . . , n)

$$\begin{aligned} V_{U_i} &= V_{X_i(U_i)} &&= V_{X_i} r^2_{X_iU_i} \\ &= V_{X_i(U_1\ldots U_n)} &&= V_{X_i} R^2_{X_i(U_1\ldots U_n)} \\ &= V_{X_i\bullet\tau_1\ldots\tau_m} &&= V_{X_i} K^2_{X_i(\tau_1\ldots\tau_m)}\,. \end{aligned}$$

Hence the data-variable covariance accounted for by the set of unique components is

[6.72-ij][38]
(i,j = 1, . . . , n)

$$C_{X_iX_j(U_1\ldots U_n)} = \left\{ \begin{matrix} V_{U_i} & \text{if } i = j \\ 0 & \text{if } i \neq j \end{matrix} \right\} = C_{X_iX_j\bullet\tau_1\ldots\tau_m}\,,$$

[38] *Study problem*: Prove it.

and the residual covariances which result from partialling $\mathbf{U_1}, \ldots, \mathbf{U_n}$ out of the $\mathbf{X_i}$ are

$$[6.73\text{-}\mathbf{ij}] \quad (\mathbf{i,j} = 1, \ldots, \mathbf{n}) \qquad C_{X_iX_j \cdot U_1 \ldots U_m} = \begin{cases} V_{X_i(\tau_1 \ldots \tau_m)} & \text{if } \mathbf{i} = \mathbf{j} \\ C_{X_iX_j} & \text{if } \mathbf{i} \neq \mathbf{j} \end{cases} = C_{H_iH_j}\,.$$

And what relevance do communal and unique components have for factor analysis? Simply this: The mathematical core of most factor analyses, basis factoring, is a linear transformation of the set of factored variables which brings out more clearly the pattern of their relationships, notably, their dimensionality. Yet it is just not in the nature of complex natural phenomena to disgorge sets of empirical variables whose dimensionality is smaller than the number of variables in the set. For this to occur, it is required that one or more variables in the set be perfectly predictable (or *almost* perfectly predictable, if we are in a tolerant mood) from the remainder; and however we may rationalize the discrepancies between the theoretical precision of an ideal scientific law and the more erratic reality of its empirical manifestation in terms of "errors of measurement," "chance disturbances," and the like, the raw data of recorded observations never approach the exceptionless regularity of a perfect relationship except possibly in a few well-controlled physical phenomena. The most we can hope for is some trend suggestive of an underlying lawful order contaminated by a variety of uncontrolled secondary effects. It is inevitable, therefore, that any exhaustive, or virtually exhaustive, simultaneous regression of data variables $\mathbf{X_1}, \ldots, \mathbf{X_n}$ upon a set of source variables will require at least as many sources as there are data variables. On the other hand, it by no means follows that *all* the source variables on which the data variables depend contribute to the relations among them; in fact, only sources shared by two or more of the data variables need do so. Thus as hypothesized by [6.57], it is not unreasonable to hope that a limited number of common sources will account for the covariances observed *between* variables even if they do not suffice to explain all the variance, or *self*-covariance, in the data. Now by definition, the communal components of $\mathbf{X_1}, \ldots, \mathbf{X_n}$ with respect to source variables $\tau_1, \ldots, \tau_m$ lie in the space of (i.e., are linear functions of) these τ_i, so the dimensionality of the set $\mathbf{H_1}, \ldots, \mathbf{H_n}$ must be at most equal to $\mathbf{m}$. In particular, if it is possible to account for all the between-variable, or "proper," covariances among the $\mathbf{X_i}$ by fewer common sources than there are data variables, then the dimensionality of the $\mathbf{H_i}$ must also be smaller than the number of data variables, as can be discerned by factoring the communal-components covariance matrix $\{C_{H_iH_j}\}$ into the structure matrix of a basis for the $\mathbf{H_i}$. Moreover, we have also seen that the communal-component covariances are identical with the corresponding data-variable covariances except for some shrinkage of the variances along the diagonal. Hence, *if the proper covariances among data variables*

$\mathbf{X}_1, \ldots, \mathbf{X}_n$ *can be accounted for by their linear regressions on* **m** *common source variables, where* $\mathbf{m} < \mathbf{n}$, *then it must be possible to reduce the covariance matrix of the* $\mathbf{X}_i$ *to the covariance matrix of a set of variables* $\mathbf{H}_1, \ldots, \mathbf{H}_n$ *whose dimensionality is* **m** *merely by replacing the variances along the diagonal of* $\{C_{X_i X_j}\}$ *with suitably chosen fractions thereof.* In the jargon of matrix algebra, this is put by saying that the *rank* of the data-variable covariance matrix can be reduced to **m** by reduction of its diagonal elements; and while what technically is meant by the "rank" of a matrix cannot profitably be explained here, the expression is too convenient for us to forego its use entirely. Conversely, then, if the rank of the data-variable covariance matrix *can* be lowered, by reduction of the diagonals, to a number **m** smaller than what can plausibly be attributed to mathematical necessity, chance, or other possible artefacts, then the relations among the data variables have been observed to conform to an empirical pattern which invites the conjecture that they are, in fact, due to **m** common sources.

It is important to be clear that the sort of mathematical orderliness within an array of empirical covariances which supports inference to a limited number of *common sources* is by no means as simple or computationally conspicuous as the kind of order found among the covariances of variables which manifest *linear dependencies.* In the latter case, the variables can be reduced to a smaller number of basis factors by any of a number of mechanical computing routines which extract linear composites of the factored variables. These same routines unimaginatively applied to data in which there may be evidence for common sources, on the other hand, will only show what was certain from the outset, namely, that the factor space in which the data variables lie has a dimensionality as large as the number of original variables. Our real hope is that once the attenuating haze of irrelevant variation which obscures the relations induced among the data variables by their common determinants has been partialled out, *then* linear dependencies may appear among the purified residuals. What we would like to know, in short, is not what the rank of the data-variable covariance matrix *is*, but with what ranks are its off-diagonal entries *compatible.* In searching for the dimensionality of common sources, then, we must first come up with an estimate of the data-variable variances these hypothesized sources control in order to delete the unique components. Which brings us to what is affectionately known in the literature as "the problem of communalities."

The *communality*, h_i^2, of variable $\mathbf{X}_i$ in the set of variables $\mathbf{X}_1, \ldots, \mathbf{X}_n$ is the proportion of the variance of $\mathbf{X}_i$ jointly accounted for by a set of source variables $\tau_1, \ldots, \tau_m$ which also account for all of the proper covariances among $\mathbf{X}_1, \ldots, \mathbf{X}_n$. That is,

[6.74-**i**] $(\mathbf{i} = 1, \ldots, \mathbf{n})$

$$h_i^2 =_{\text{def}} \frac{V_{X_i(\tau_1 \ldots \tau_m)}}{V_{X_i}}$$

$$= R^2_{X_i(\tau_1 \ldots \tau_m)} \qquad ([6.57])$$

$$= \frac{V_{H_i}}{V_{X_i}} \, .$$

Then as made explicit in [6.73], we partial out the assumed unique components $U_1, \ldots, U_n$ of the data variables and get down to the covariances among their components $H_1, \ldots, H_n$ lying wholly in the space—customarily called "common-factor space"—of source variables $\tau_1, \ldots, \tau_m$ by multiplying each variance V_{X_i} in $\{C_{X_i X_j}\}$ times its associated communality h_i^2. (If the data variables have been normalized, so that what is being factored is their correlation matrix, this consists simply in replacing the diagonal unities in $\{r_{X_i X_j}\}$ with the corresponding communalities.)

It is important to appreciate that "the" communalities of a given set of variables $X_1, \ldots, X_n$ are far from unique; rather, the X_i have as many different sets of communalities as there are different ways to account for their proper covariances. One especially trivial case is the set of communalities $h_i^2 = 1$ ($i = 1, \ldots, n$), which arises when $X_1, \ldots, X_n$ are themselves treated as the common sources. Another instance, slightly less trivial but not much so, is to take all but one of the data variables, say X_i, as common sources,[39] in which case the communalities of $X_1, \ldots, X_n$ (with respect to source variables $X_1, \ldots, X_{i-1}, X_{i+1}, \ldots, X_n$) become

$$h_j^2 = \begin{cases} R^2_{X_i(X_1 \cdots X_{i-1} X_{i+1} \cdots X_n)} & \text{if } j = i \\ 1 & \text{if } j \neq i \, . \end{cases} \qquad (j = 1, \ldots, n)$$

Since there are only $n - 1$ dimensions to communal-component space when the H_i are defined by the regressions of $X_1, \ldots, X_n$ on $X_1, \ldots, X_{i-1}, X_{i+1}, \ldots, X_n$, this proves that the covariance matrix for n variables can always be reduced to rank $n - 1$ by at least n different choices of communalities.[40] Still another way to construct (or rather, to hypothesize) uninteresting communalities is by augmenting one or more of the communal components $H_1, \ldots, H_n$ with respect to one set of common sources with a piece of its corresponding unique component—i.e., by replacing h_i^2 with a larger value $h_i'^2$, which conceptually amounts to factoring U_j into two orthogonal components U_j' and U_j'', and adding the assumed determinants of U_i' to the set of common sources so that $H_i' = H_i + U_i'$. Clearly, then, unless we specify a particular set of common sources in advance, rather than attempting to infer them from the data as given, it would be meaningless to ask what choice of communalities is

[39] *Study questions*: Why does any choice of $n - 1$ variables from the set $X_1, \ldots, X_n$ satisfy the conditions on $\tau_1, \ldots, \tau_m$ in [6.57]? Why would a selection of *less* than $n - 1$ of the X_i generally fail to do so?

[40] Actually, there are infinitely many different choices of communalities which will reduce the rank of a given covariance matrix by one.

correct. There is an infinitude of alternatives, any one of which, so far as we know, is as correct as any other.

On the other hand, it is by no means the case that any arbitrary set of **n** numbers between 0 and 1 will qualify as possible communalities for a given distribution of $\mathbf{X}_1, \ldots, \mathbf{X}_n$, for the off-diagonal covariances in $\{C_{\mathbf{X}_i\mathbf{X}_j}\}$ impose a lower bound on each h_i^2. For example, the fact that $V_{\mathbf{X}_i} h_i^2$ and $V_{\mathbf{X}_j} h_j^2$ are the variances of components whose covariance is $C_{\mathbf{X}_i\mathbf{X}_j}$ implies that both h_i^2 and h_j^2 must be at least as large as $r^2_{\mathbf{X}_i\mathbf{X}_j}$.[41] Neither, for that matter, are we interested in communalities which leave the rank of the communal-components covariance matrix equal to that of the data variables. It is thus a challenge to find communalities which are not only mathematically permissible but are also inferentially *provocative,* especially in regard to the implied number of common sources. The "problem of communalities," then, is to discover a set of **n** positive fractions which, when respectively multiplied times the **n** diagonal variances in the data-variable covariance matrix, reduce the latter to the lowest possible rank.[42] And while, as already observed, communalities can always be found which reduce rank to $\mathbf{n} - 1$, any reduction lower than this requires the assistance of some sort of empirical patterning in the data, the greater the reduction the more impressive the pattern so disclosed.[43]

In principle, determination of rank-minimizing communalities should be a fairly straightforward procedure. If source variables $\tau_1, \ldots, \tau_m$ accounting for all the proper data-variable covariances, *or any other set of variables which span the same space as the* τ_i, were to be partialled out of the $\mathbf{X}_i$, the residual covariance matrix would be all zero except for the unique variances on the diagonal, while the proportion of $V_{\mathbf{X}_i}$ jointly accounted for by these factors is then h_i^2 for that particular common-factor space. Moreover, the basic partialling procedure (e.g., [6.17]) in no way requires that extracted factors be data-variable composites—all that is

[41] *Proof*: Since $C_{\mathbf{H}_i\mathbf{H}_j} = C_{\mathbf{X}_i\mathbf{X}_j}$, squaring both sides and dividing by $V_{\mathbf{X}_i} V_{\mathbf{X}_j}$ shows that $h_i^2 h_j^2 r^2_{\mathbf{H}_i\mathbf{H}_j} = r^2_{\mathbf{X}_i\mathbf{X}_j}$. But a product of positive numbers no larger than unity can be no larger than the smallest multiplier, so each of the terms h_i^2, h_j^2, and $r^2_{\mathbf{H}_i\mathbf{H}_j}$ must be at least as large as $r^2_{\mathbf{X}_i\mathbf{X}_j}$.

[42] Actually, there are as many different "problems" of communalities as there are different objectives we can set for a communality solution. Except for communalities in hierarchical factor solutions (see pp. 187 ff.), however, the objective which factor analysts virtually always choose is for the communalities to yield a communal-components covariance matrix of minimal rank.

[43] Although it is sometimes held that proper choice of communalities can always reduce the rank of the covariance matrix for **n** variables to at least $\mathbf{n} - (\sqrt{8\mathbf{n}+1} - 1)/2$, it has been shown by Guttman (42) that the lowest reduction which is always possible for an arbitrary covariance matrix is only to rank $\mathbf{n} - 1$. Even so, there are mathematical reasons why an arbitrary covariance matrix for **n** variables should *tend* to have a least-common-factor dimensionality of about $\mathbf{n} - (\sqrt{8\mathbf{n}+1} - 1)/2$, so if the number of common factors found in an actual case is substantially larger than this, the interpretive significance of the solution is somewhat suspect.

needed to take out an arbitrary factor is to know its variance and covariances with the data variables. Ideally, then, we might hope to find rank-minimizing communalities by a sequential routine which at each step **k** derives values for the **k**th column of the factor-structure matrix which minimize some appropriate measure of the overall magnitude of the off-diagonal values in the resulting matrix of residual data-variable covariances. However, no such measure with the requisite mathematical properties appears to exist. Instead, common practice is to make an initial approximation to the communalities, to extract enough basis factors from the resulting estimated communal-components covariance matrix to reduce its residuals to about the order of chance effects, and then to use the proportion of each data variable's variance jointly accounted for by these factors as an improved estimate of that variable's communality. Iteration of this procedure until the estimates at the start of a cycle are in essential agreement with the communalities reproduced at the cycle's end appears usually to arrive at a consistent solution of reasonably minimal rank. (By "reasonably minimal," we recognize that the common-factor dimensionality ultimately attained depends in part on what magnitude of discrepancy from zero residuals one is prepared to shrug aside as "insignificant.") A number of procedures are available for making the initial communality estimates, but with one exception, these are technical details having little interest here, especially since it appears that when the number of data variables is reasonably large, inaccuracy in the initial estimates is not of momentous consequence. The exception is a particularly important lower bound: *The communality of any variable in a set of data variables with respect to any group of source variables satisfying* [6.57] *must be at least as large as the proportion of that variable's variance accounted for by the other variables in the set.* That is,

[6.75-**i**][44] $$h_{\mathbf{i}}^2 \geq R^2_{\mathbf{X}_i(\mathbf{X}_1 \cdots \mathbf{X}_{i-1}\mathbf{X}_{i+1} \cdots \mathbf{X}_n)} \, .$$
(**i** = **1**, . . . , **n**)

It can also be shown that in ordinary circumstances, inequality [6.76-**i**] is likely to be reasonably close to an equality for minimum-rank communalities except perhaps when **n** is rather small. Hence when computation of several multiple correlations prior to factoring poses no strain (i.e., when a high-speed computer is available), the recommended first approximation to $h_{\mathbf{i}}^2$ is $R^2_{\mathbf{X}_i(\mathbf{X}_1 \cdots \mathbf{X}_{i-1}\mathbf{X}_{i+1} \cdots \mathbf{X}_n)}$.

[44] *Proof*: To simplify subscripts, let $\mathbf{X}_i$ be $\mathbf{X}_1$. We know from [6.60] and [6.62] that the linear regression of $\mathbf{X}_1$ upon $\mathbf{X}_2, \ldots, \mathbf{X}_n$ is equivalent to some linear function $\mathbf{L}_\tau$ of $\tau_1, \ldots, \tau_m$, plus another linear function, $\mathbf{L}_U$, of the unique components $\mathbf{U}_2, \ldots, \mathbf{U}_n$. Since $\mathrm{Cov}(\mathbf{X}_1, \mathbf{L}_U)$ and $\mathrm{Cov}(\mathbf{L}_\tau, \mathbf{L}_U)$ are both zero, the correlation between $\mathbf{X}_1$ and $\mathbf{L}_\tau$ must be at least as large in magnitude as the correlation between $\mathbf{X}_1$ and $\mathbf{L}_\tau + \mathbf{L}_U$ (and will be larger than this unless $\mathbf{L}_U$ is identically equal to zero). But the squared multiple correlation of a variable with a set of other variables is an upper bound to the squared correlation of the former with any linear combination of the latter. Hence $R^2_{\mathbf{X}_1(\mathbf{X}_2 \cdots \mathbf{X}_n)} = r^2_{\mathbf{X}_1 \dot{\mathbf{X}}_1(\mathbf{X}_2 \cdots \mathbf{X}_n)} \leq r^2_{\mathbf{X}_1 \mathbf{L}_\tau} \leq R^2_{\mathbf{X}_1(\tau_1 \cdots \tau_m)} = h_1^2$.

Since solution for rank-minimizing communalities depends upon a more or less arbitrary initial choice of trial communalities, a question which naturally arises is the extent to which this choice affects the final convergent outcome. While we have already seen that innumerably many different sets of communalities are compatible with the off-diagonal data covariances, it might be hoped that at least the rank-minimizing communality solution is unique. That this is not generally so, however, is shown by the following consideration: If an orthonormal factor pattern exists for the data variables in which one of the common factors $\mathbf{F_k}$ has a nonzero coefficient for only two data variables $\mathbf{X_i}$ and $\mathbf{X_j}$, then without changing the reproduced off-diagonal covariances $\mathbf{F_k}$ may be replaced with an alternative factor $\mathbf{F'_k}$ whose coefficients for $\mathbf{X_i}$ and $\mathbf{X_j}$ are different from those of $\mathbf{F_k}$ so long as $b_{ik}b_{jk} = b'_{ik}b'_{jk}$. In such a case h_i^2 may be arbitrarily set at any value between a certain minimum and unity without changing the dimensionality of common-factor space so long as h_j^2 is adjusted appropriately, even though the different possibilities for h_i^2 and h_j^2 correspond to somewhat different spaces spanned by the common factors. Consequently, even when alternative initial communality estimates converge under iterated factoring to the same *number* of common factors, they will not necessarily converge to the same final communalities or to the same common-factor *space*. Just how severe this common-factor indeterminateness tends to be and what implications it may have in the search for interpetively meaningful factors are issues still pending resolution.

While the *motivation* for replacing the observed variances on the diagonal of $\{C_{X_iX_j}\}$ with rank-reducing proportions thereof has been seen to arise from desire to learn something about the origins of the observed relationships, we have not as yet considered the methodological status of the communal-components covariance matrix and its basis factors which are the objective *accomplishment* of this move. First and foremost, it should be vigorously appreciated that to discover communalities h_1^2, . . . , h_n^2 which reduce the rank of an empirical covariance matrix from **n** to **m** is to do no more than identify in the observed covariances a particular mathematical pattern which neither presupposes nor entails any hypothesis about hidden sources. We can make this pattern more intuitively understandable by saying it is *as though* each data variable $\mathbf{X_i}$ were the sum of two uncorrelated components, $\mathbf{H_i}$ and $\mathbf{U_i}$, such that only the $\mathbf{H_j}$ contribute to the covariances among the $\mathbf{X_i}$ even though their dimensionality is merely **m**, and still not transgress the strict logical limits of the observed data. We may even impeccably go on to add that if there *were* such components $\mathbf{H_1}, \ldots, \mathbf{H_n}$ and $\mathbf{U_1}, \ldots, \mathbf{U_n}$, then their covariances with the data variables *would* be

[6.76-**ij**]
(**i**,**j** = 1, . . . , **n**)

$$C_{X_iH_j} = C_{H_iH_j} = \begin{cases} V_{X_i} h_i^2 & \text{if } \mathbf{i} = \mathbf{j} \\ C_{X_iX_j} & \text{if } \mathbf{i} \neq \mathbf{j} \end{cases}$$

[6.77-**ij**] (**i**,**j** = **1**, . . . , **n**)
$$C_{X_iU_j} = C_{U_iU_j} = \begin{cases} V_{X_i}(1-h_i^2) & \text{if } \mathbf{i}=\mathbf{j} \\ 0 & \text{if } \mathbf{i}\neq\mathbf{j} \end{cases}$$

while the computed matrix $\{C_{H_iH_j}\}$ *would* be the matrix of residual covariances $C_{X_iX_j \cdot U_1 \ldots U_n}$ were the unique components $\mathbf{U_1}, \ldots, \mathbf{U_n}$ to be factored out of the $\mathbf{X_j}$. But if we ever so slightly waver from the subjunctive into the indicative mood of speech and say that there *are* components of the $\mathbf{X_i}$ which have these properties, or that the matrix derived from $\{C_{X_iX_j}\}$ by communality shrinkage of the diagonals *is* the matrix of residual data-variable covariances after extraction of the unique components, or that the factors subsequently defined by basis factoring of the communality-reduced empirical covariance matrix *are* the "common factors" of the $\mathbf{X_1}$, then something has been added which is challengingly different from a mere analytic processing of the data as given. When the data variables are factored into a *basis*, these factors are merely linear transformations of the original variables and their reality is unproblematic: Not only do they have existence in the sense in which any variable explicitly defined as a composite of known variables may be said to "exist," but a person's score on such a factor may be computed—not just estimated, but determined exactly—as soon as his scores on the relevant data variables are known. But for unique and communal components, the story is altogether different. Except for trivial cases, *neither the* $\mathbf{H_i}$ *nor the* $\mathbf{U_i}$ *lie in the space of* $\mathbf{X_1}, \ldots, \mathbf{X_n}$. Specifically, $R_{H_i(X_1 \ldots X_n)}$ and $R_{U_i(X_1 \ldots X_n)}$ are both less than unity unless either $h_j^2 = 1$ or $R_{H_i(X_1 \ldots X_{i-1} X_{i+1} \ldots X_n)} = 1$. That is, $\mathbf{U_i}$—and hence $\mathbf{H_i}$, since $\mathbf{H_i} = \mathbf{X_1} - \mathbf{U_i}$—is perfectly predictable from $\mathbf{X_1}, \ldots, \mathbf{X_n}$ if and only if $\mathbf{H_i}$ is either identical with $\mathbf{X_i}$ itself or with the regression of $\mathbf{X_i}$ upon the other data variables. This follows from the fact that if $h_i^2 < 1$, the multiple correlation of $\mathbf{U_j}$ with $\mathbf{X_1}, \ldots, \mathbf{X_n}$ may be analyzed as

[6.78-**i**][45] (**i** = **1**, . . . , **n**)
$$R^2_{U_i(X_1 \ldots X_n)} = \frac{1-h_i^2}{1-R^2_{X_i(\mu_i)}} = \frac{1-h_i^2}{1-h_i^2 R^2_{H_i(\mu_i)}} \qquad (V_{U_i} > 0)\ ,$$

[45] *Proof*: Since $\mathbf{U_i}$ has zero correlation with each variable in $\boldsymbol{\mu}_i$, its regression on $\boldsymbol{\mu}_i$ is identically zero. This entails that the regression of $\mathbf{U_i}$ upon $\mathbf{X_i}$ and $\boldsymbol{\mu}_i$ is identical to its regression upon the residual of $\mathbf{X_i}$ left by $\boldsymbol{\mu}_i$—i.e., from [4.108],

$$\dot{U}_{i(X_i\mu_i)} = \dot{U}_{i(\mu_i)} + \frac{\mathrm{Cov}(e_{U_i \cdot \mu_i}, e_{X_i \cdot \mu_i})}{\mathrm{Var}(e_{X_i \cdot \mu_i})} e_{X_i \cdot \mu_i} = \frac{\mathrm{Cov}(U_i, e_{X_i \cdot \mu_i})}{\mathrm{Var}(e_{X_i \cdot \mu_i})} e_{X_i \cdot \mu_i}.$$

Hence $R_{U_i(X_i\mu_i)}$ equals the correlation between $\mathbf{U_i}$ and $e_{X_i \cdot \mu_i}$, or

[A]
$$R^2_{U_i(X_i\mu_i)} = \frac{\mathrm{Cov}(U_i, e_{X_i \cdot \mu_i})^2}{\mathrm{Var}(U_i)\ \mathrm{Var}(e_{X_i \cdot \mu_i})}\ .$$

Now in view of principle [6.55], we have $e_{X_i \cdot \mu_i} = e_{H_i \cdot \mu_i} + e_{U_i \cdot \mu_i} = e_{H_i \cdot \mu_i} + U_i$, where $e_{H_i \cdot \mu_i}$ is a linear function of $\mathbf{H_j}, \boldsymbol{\mu}_i$ and is thus uncorrelated with $\mathbf{U_i}$. Hence $\mathrm{Cov}(U_i, e_{X_i \cdot \mu_i}) = \mathrm{Var}(U_i) = V_{X_i}(1-h_i^2)$, while $\mathrm{Var}(e_{X_i \cdot \mu_i}) = V_{X_i}(1-R^2_{X_i(\mu_i)})$. Substitution into [A] thus yields the first part of [6.78-**i**], while the second part follows by consideration that from [6.54], $\dot{X}_{i(\mu_i)} = \dot{H}_{i(\mu_i)} + \dot{U}_{i(\mu_i)} = \dot{H}_{i(\mu_i)}$. Original credit for this theorem belongs to Guttman (e.g., 41, Formula #40).

where $\boldsymbol{\mu}_i$ is the set of variables $\mathbf{X}_1, \ldots, \mathbf{X}_{i-1}, \mathbf{X}_{i+1}, \ldots, \mathbf{X}_n$. It is clear that the expression in the second line of [6.78-**i**] attains unity only if $\mathbf{H}_i$ is perfectly predictable from $\mathbf{X}_i, \ldots, \mathbf{X}_{i-1}, \mathbf{X}_{i+1}, \ldots, \mathbf{X}_n$. (From [6.78-**i**] and the fact, by [6.55], that $\mathbf{e}_{\mathbf{H}_i \bullet \mathbf{X}_1 \ldots \mathbf{X}_n} = -\mathbf{e}_{\mathbf{U}_i \bullet \mathbf{X}_1 \ldots \mathbf{X}_n}$, we can also derive a corresponding formula for $R^2_{\mathbf{H}_i(\mathbf{X}_1 \ldots \mathbf{X}_n)}$. However, the result is not as tidy as [6.78] and we shall not bother with it here.) At best, then, except for the two trivial cases noted, we can only imperfectly estimate the $\mathbf{H}_i$ and the $\mathbf{U}_i$ from the data variables by applying the normal equations for the regressions of the former upon the latter to the covariances in [6.76] and [6.77]. While there is no simple formula for the accuracy of these estimates in terms of known quantities alone, it is worth passing mention that since h_i^2 and $1 - h_i^2$ are the proportions of $V_{\mathbf{X}_i}$ controlled by $\mathbf{H}_i$ and by $\mathbf{U}_i$, respectively,

[6.79-**i**] (**i** = **1**, . . . , **n**)
$$R^2_{\mathbf{H}_i(\mathbf{X}_1 \ldots \mathbf{X}_n)} \geqslant r^2_{\mathbf{H}_i \mathbf{X}_i} = h_i^2 ,$$

[6.80-**i**] (**i** = **1**, . . . , **n**)
$$R^2_{\mathbf{U}_i(\mathbf{X}_1 \ldots \mathbf{X}_n)} \geqslant r^2_{\mathbf{U}_i \mathbf{X}_i} = 1 - h_i^2 .$$

It has also been shown by Guttman (40; see especially Formula #28) that the average squared multiple correlation of $\mathbf{U}_i$ with $\mathbf{X}_1, \ldots, \mathbf{X}_n$ is at least as large as

[6.81]
$$\frac{\sum_{i=1}^{n} R^2_{\mathbf{U}_i(\mathbf{X}_1 \ldots \mathbf{X}_n)}}{\mathbf{n}} \geqslant 1 - \frac{\mathbf{m}}{\mathbf{n}} ,$$

where **m** is the dimensionality of the space spanned by the communal components $\mathbf{H}_1, \ldots, \mathbf{H}_n$. Hence in cases where the dimensionality of the communal components is quite small in proportion to the number of data variables (which is possible, if not necessarily likely, when the number of variables is large), it will be possible to estimate most of the $\mathbf{U}_i$, and correspondingly most of the $\mathbf{H}_i$, with high accuracy.

The reason why the lack of perfect predictability from $\mathbf{X}_1, \ldots, \mathbf{X}_n$ to $\mathbf{H}_i$ and $\mathbf{U}_i$ is so methodologically significant even when $R_{\mathbf{H}_i(\mathbf{X}_1 \ldots \mathbf{X}_n)}$ and $R_{\mathbf{U}_i(\mathbf{X}_1 \ldots \mathbf{X}_n)}$ are close to unity is that if communal and unique components cannot be precisely computed from the data variables, they cannot be explicitly *defined* in terms of the data variables either. Hence to assume that there are in fact such components, even though their existence has not been demonstrated either by logical construction or by any other argument stronger than an appeal to explanatory convenience, is to make an inferential leap of the most unequivocal sort. In particular, to say that the proportions to which the diagonal variances in $\{C_{\mathbf{X}_i \mathbf{X}_j}\}$ are reduced prior to basis factoring *are* communalities, or approximations thereto, is to postulate the existence of a set of communal components logically distinct from any variables definable from the $\mathbf{X}_i$, yet for which the pattern of data-variable relationships is the sole evidence. Or better, we should say that to derive a communal-components covariance matrix amounts to postulating a *space* of inferred variables. For to assume the existence of $\mathbf{H}_1, \ldots, \mathbf{H}_n$ is also to assume the existence in at least a mathematical sense of all their linear combinations; while if there is a meaningful distinction between the "reality" of a composite variable and that of the variables from which it is defined, the assumed reality of the $\mathbf{H}_i$ in this stronger sense (whatever it might be) can be waived in favor of some other set of inferred variables which span the same space as do $\mathbf{H}_1, \ldots, \mathbf{H}_n$. Once the ontological chasm has been hurdled by inferring communalities, in other words, there is no further existential jeopardy in factoring the $\{C_{H_iH_j}\}$ matrix for whatever basis may strike our fancy.

In fact, now that the reader has been sternly admonished that factoring with communalities is to undertake serious philosophical responsibilities quite unlike the carefree abandon with which one is free to extract basis factors, we shall henceforth allow ourselves to speak of analyzing data variables into common and unique factors in the same existential tone that is appropriate for discussion of basis factoring. An effort to maintain precisely the right shade of subjunctive coloration would soon become linguistically preposterous, and besides, it is possible to sidestep problems about the reality of inferred factors by means of a technical artifice which capitalizes upon the fact that the equations relating a set of data variables to their hypothesized unique and communal components do not determine the latter uniquely, even for a given choice of communalities. By drawing upon ancillary variables of known existence, it is generally possible to contrive linear combinations of the data-*cum*-ancillary variables which satisfy the purely mathematical requirements on whatever inferred components we have teased out of the data variables. Specifically, if we have discovered that the covariances among $\mathbf{X}_1, \ldots, \mathbf{X}_n$ can be reproduced by writing the $\mathbf{X}_i$ as stated linear functions of orthonormal factors $\mathbf{F}_1, \ldots, \mathbf{F}_p$ whose dimensionality is greater than $\mathbf{n}$, we can augment the $\mathbf{X}_i$ by enough additional variables to bring the dimensionality of the augmented data variables equal to $\mathbf{p}$ and then find an orthonormal basis for the augmented set in which each original data variable has the desired factor coefficients. To be sure, these are highly artificial constructions altogether devoid of scientific interest. But knowledge that they can be appointed to play the role of inferred components whenever we are unable or unwilling to propose a more meaningful substantive interpretation for the latter allows us to proceed with the mathematical processing of inferred factors without undue apprehension that we have thereby fallen from methodological grace.

Factor Patterns with Inferred Components. The immediate outcome of basis-factoring the communal-components covariance matrix is a structure matrix $\{C_{H_iF_j}\}$ showing the covariances between each $\mathbf{H}_i$ and $\mathbf{m}$ normalized linear combinations $\mathbf{F}_1, \ldots, \mathbf{F}_m$ of $\mathbf{H}_1, \ldots, \mathbf{H}_n$, where $\mathbf{m}$ is the rank of $\{C_{H_iH_j}\}$. Corresponding to this structure matrix, and in fact identical with it if the $\mathbf{F}_j$ are orthonormal, is a matrix $\{b_{ij}\}$ of factor coefficients such that

$$\mathbf{H}_i = b_{i0} + b_{i1}\mathbf{F}_1 + \ldots + b_{im}\mathbf{F}_m \,. \qquad [6.82\text{-}\mathbf{i}]\ (\mathbf{i} = \mathbf{1}, \ldots, \mathbf{n})$$

(The constants b_{i0} are not included in the factor-pattern matrix, but since $M_{\mathbf{H}_i} = M_{\mathbf{X}_i}$ and the factors are stipulated to have zero means, we know that $b_{i0} = M_{\mathbf{X}_i}$.) Like all variables in the space of the $\mathbf{H}_i$, scores on the communal-components basis $\mathbf{F}_1, \ldots, \mathbf{F}_m$ can in general be estimated only imperfectly from scores on the data variables. To solve the normal equations for the regression of $\mathbf{F}_j$ on $\mathbf{X}_1, \ldots, \mathbf{X}_n$, we need, in addition to the data-variable covariances, also the covariances of $\mathbf{F}_j$ with $\mathbf{X}_1, \ldots, \mathbf{X}_n$. These are seen to be conveniently

$$[6.83\text{-}\mathbf{ij}]\ \begin{pmatrix}\mathbf{i}=\mathbf{1}, \ldots, \mathbf{n}\\ \mathbf{j}=\mathbf{1}, \ldots, \mathbf{m}\end{pmatrix} \qquad \begin{aligned} C_{\mathbf{X}_i\mathbf{F}_j} &= C_{\mathbf{H}_i\mathbf{F}_j} + C_{\mathbf{U}_i\mathbf{F}_j} \\ &= C_{\mathbf{H}_i\mathbf{F}_j} \,. \end{aligned} \qquad ([6.82])$$

While we are at it, let unique component $\mathbf{U}_i$ be normalized to $\mathbf{F}_{\mathbf{U}_i}$ —i.e.,

$$[6.84\text{-}\mathbf{i}]\ (\mathbf{i} = \mathbf{1}, \ldots, \mathbf{n}) \qquad \begin{aligned} \mathbf{F}_{\mathbf{U}_i} &=_{\text{def}} \frac{\mathbf{U}_i - M_{\mathbf{U}_i}}{\sigma_{\mathbf{U}_i}} \\ &= \frac{\mathbf{U}_i}{u_i}, \end{aligned} \qquad (h_i^2 < 1)^{46}$$

where

$$[6.85\text{-}\mathbf{i}]\ (\mathbf{i} = \mathbf{1}, \ldots, \mathbf{n}) \qquad \begin{aligned} u_i &=_{\text{def}} \sigma_{\mathbf{U}_i} \\ &= \sqrt{V_{\mathbf{X}_i} - V_{\mathbf{H}_i}} \\ &= \sigma_{\mathbf{X}_i}\sqrt{1 - h_i^2} \,. \end{aligned}$$

Combining [6.82] with [6.62], we then have

$$[6.86\text{-}\mathbf{1}]\quad \mathbf{X}_1 = b_{10} + b_{11}\mathbf{F}_1 + b_{12}\mathbf{F}_2 + \ldots + b_{1m}\mathbf{F}_m + u_1\mathbf{F}_{\mathbf{U}_1} \,.$$

$$[6.86\text{-}\mathbf{2}]\quad \mathbf{X}_2 = b_{20} + b_{21}\mathbf{F}_1 + b_{22}\mathbf{F}_2 + \ldots + b_{2m}\mathbf{F}_m \qquad + u_2\mathbf{F}_{\mathbf{U}_2}$$

$$\vdots$$

$$[6.86\text{-}\mathbf{n}]\quad \mathbf{X}_n = b_{n0} + b_{n1}\mathbf{F}_1 + b_{n2}\mathbf{F}_2 + \ldots + b_{nm}\mathbf{F}_m \qquad + u_n\mathbf{F}_{\mathbf{U}_n} \,.$$

---

[46] If $h_i^2 = 1$, $\mathbf{F}_{\mathbf{U}_i}$ may be taken to be any normalized variable which happens to be orthogonal to all the other factors.

Equations [6.86] are the factor-pattern equations for data variables which have been decomposed into common and unqiue factors. Since pattern [6.86] is merely an instance of the generic form [6.20], all formulas developed previously continue to hold for the present case, including the equivalence of factor pattern and factor structure when the factors are orthonormal, and the other useful properties of orthonormal factors discussed on pp. 229 ff. In addition, there are special aspects of [6.86] which merit attention.

First of all, factors $\mathbf{F_1}, \ldots, \mathbf{F_m}, \mathbf{F_{U_1}}, \ldots, \mathbf{F_{U_n}}$ are *not* a basis for $\mathbf{X_1}, \ldots, \mathbf{X_n}$. The $\mathbf{X_i}$ span a space of $\mathbf{n}$ dimensions (or possibly less), whereas the factors in [6.86] altogether span a space of dimensionality $\mathbf{m} + \mathbf{n}$ which includes the space of the $\mathbf{X_i}$ as a subspace. Factors $\mathbf{F_1}, \ldots, \mathbf{F_m}$ are called *common factors* because if the communalities have been chosen to minimize the rank of the $\{C_{\mathbf{H_i H_j}}\}$ matrix, each of these factors will have a nonzero coefficient for at least two of the data variables.[47] Also behind the term "common factor" is the thought of common determinants, though it is important to observe that while the entire common-factor *space* is an inductive hypothesis which has been hazarded by factoring with fractional communalities, there is nothing (or at least there need be nothing) in the way $\{C_{\mathbf{H_i H_j}}\}$ was factored into a basis which requires that $\mathbf{F_1}, \ldots, \mathbf{F_m}$ be construed as scientifically meaningful *source* variables. (More on this later.) Factors $\mathbf{F_{U_1}}, \ldots, \mathbf{F_{U_n}}$, are known as the *unique factors* of the $\mathbf{X_i}$. In contrast to the common factors, which may or may not be orthogonal among themselves, each unique factor is orthogonal to all other common and unique factors. Also, $\mathbf{F_{U_i}}$ has a nonzero coefficient *only* for variable $\mathbf{X_i}$, which is why it is customary, when the factor-pattern equations are written together as a group, to show the unique factors staggered as in [6.86]. (Properly, each equation [6.86-**i**] should show all the factors $\mathbf{F_{U_1}}, \ldots, \mathbf{F_{U_n}}$, but with zero coefficients for all except $\mathbf{F_{U_i}}$.) When reporting the factor structure or pattern of inferred factors, explicit mention of the unique factors is frequently omitted by writing only the structure or pattern matrix for the common factors, these being identical with the corresponding complete structure or pattern matrices for the communal components. No information is lost thereby, since it can be seen from [6.85-**i**] that the unique-factor loading, u_i, for $\mathbf{X_i}$ may readily be computed from the common-factor structure when $V_{\mathbf{X_i}}$ is

[47] *Proof*: Suppose that the coefficient of factor $\mathbf{F_1}$ is zero for all the data variables except $\mathbf{X_i}$. Then the regression of $\mathbf{F_1}$ upon $\mathbf{F_2}, \ldots, \mathbf{F_m}$ analyzes the contribution $b_{i1}\mathbf{F_1}$ of factor $\mathbf{F_1}$ to $\mathbf{X_i}$ into a linear combination of $\mathbf{F_2}, \ldots, \mathbf{F_m}$ plus some multiple of the residual $\mathbf{e}_{\mathbf{F_1} \cdot \mathbf{F_2} \ldots \mathbf{F_m}}$. But the latter is uncorrelated with any of the other common or unique factors in the system, and may be absorbed into the unique component of $\mathbf{X_1}$ by an appropriate diminution of h_i^2. This also adjusts the communal component of $\mathbf{X_i}$ to lie in the space of $\mathbf{F_2}, \ldots, \mathbf{F_m}$ and hence reduces the rank of $\{C_{\mathbf{H_i H_j}}\}$ by 1.

also known. When the common factors are orthonormal, it follows from [6.31], and [6.84] that

[6.87-ij]
(i,j = 1, . . . , n)

$$\sum_{k=1}^{m} C_{X_iF_k} C_{X_jF_k} = \sum_{k=1}^{m} b_{ik} b_{jk} = \begin{cases} V_{X_i} h_i^2 \text{ if } i = j \\ C_{X_iX_j} \text{ if } i \neq j, \end{cases} \quad \begin{pmatrix}\text{orthonormal} \\ \text{factors}\end{pmatrix}$$

or dividing by $\sigma_{X_i}\sigma_{X_j}$,

[6.88-ij]
(i,j = 1, . . . , n)

$$\sum_{k=1}^{m} r_{X_jF_k} r_{X_iF_k} = \begin{cases} h_i^2 \quad \text{if } i = j \\ r_{X_iX_j} \text{ if } i \neq j. \end{cases} \quad \begin{pmatrix}\text{orthonormal} \\ \text{factors}\end{pmatrix}$$

Equations [6.88] say that when rows **i** and **j** of the normalized factor-structure matrix for just the (orthonormal) common factors are columnwise multiplied and summed, the result is reproduction of either an original data-variable correlation or, if $i = j$, the proportion of V_{X_j} which lies in common-factor space. The sum of squared entries in a *column* of the common-factor structure or pattern matrix for orthonormal factors is, of course, still the total data-variable variance accounted for by the factor corresponding to that column (see [6.41]), while these squared entries summed over the entire common-factor matrix yield

[6.89]

$$\sum_{i=1}^{n} \sum_{j=1}^{m} b_{ij}^2 = \sum_{i=1}^{n} \sum_{j=1}^{m} C_{X_iF_j}^2 = \sum_{i=1}^{n} \sum_{j=1}^{m} V_{X_i(F_j)}$$
$$= V_{X(F_1 \ldots F_m)}$$
$$= \sum_{i=1}^{n} V_{H_i} \quad \begin{pmatrix}\text{orthonormal} \\ \text{factors}\end{pmatrix}$$
$$= \sum_{i=1}^{n} V_{X_i} h_i^2$$

(see [6.42]). Hence the proportion of the total variance of $X_1, \ldots, X_n$ which lies in common-factor space is a weighted average of the communalities. Specifically,

[6.90]

$$\frac{V_{X(F_1 \ldots F_m)}}{V_X} = \frac{\sum_{i=1}^{n} V_{X_i} h_i^2}{\sum_{i=1}^{n} V_{X_i}}.$$

If the data variables are normalized, this becomes simply

$$[6.91] \qquad \frac{V_{Z(F_1 \ldots F_m)}}{V_Z} = \frac{\sum_{i=1}^{n} h_i^2}{n} .$$

A Numerical Example

If the reader has not already gagged too exorbitantly on the preceding dry wad of algebraic generalities, an example juicy with human interest and seasoned with honest numbers should help to make these equations more digestable. We shall begin with a hypothetical pattern of causal relations which underlie the covariances within a set of data variables, and then factor the latter to see what the computations reveal.

Let us suppose that what determines how much a person enjoys a given movie in comparison to other viewers as measured, say, by a rating-scale technique is in part linearly determined by how strongly he happens to like the stars of the film, where the appeal of a given performer for a given viewer is independent of the particular film being viewed. Thus if $\mathbf{Z}_i$ is the normalized Degree-of-enjoyment variable for film **i**, in which the leading roles are played by actor A_1 and actress A_2, we suppose that source variables τ_1 and τ_2 exist such that

$$\mathbf{Z}_i = \beta_{i1}\tau_1 + \beta_{i2}\tau_2 + \mathbf{e}_{Z_i \bullet \tau_1 \tau_2},$$

where β_{i1} and β_{i2} are the β-coefficients in the regression of $\mathbf{Z}_i$ upon the normalized Appeal-of-A_1 (τ_1) and Appeal-of-A_2 (τ_1) variables. Let us also assume that whatever linear correlation may exist between a person's enjoyment of two different films is due wholly to his liking for their stars—i.e., that if $\mathbf{Z}_i$ is the normalized Degree-to-which-film-**i**-was-enjoyed variable, τ_j is the normalized Appeal-of-performer-A_j variable, and $A_1, \ldots, A_m$ is the complete list of performers which played the lead roles in films **#1**, . . . , **#n**, then

$$C_{Z_i Z_j \bullet \tau_1 \ldots \tau_m} = 0$$

for $\mathbf{i,j} = \mathbf{1}, \ldots, \mathbf{n};\ \mathbf{i} \neq \mathbf{j}$. Now suppose that empirical data are collected throughout the nation on how viewers enjoyed the five films listed in Table 6.6*a*. We then have five data variables $\mathbf{Z}_1, \ldots, \mathbf{Z}_5$ (Table 6.6*b*) causally determined by source variables $\tau_1, \ldots, \tau_5$ (Table 6.6*c*) and unique components $\mathbf{U}_1, \ldots, \mathbf{U}_5$ according to the pattern

$$\begin{aligned}
Z_1 &= \beta_{11}\tau_1 + \beta_{12}\tau_1 && + U_1\\
Z_2 &= \beta_{21}\tau_1 && + U_2\\
Z_3 &= \beta_{31}\tau_1 + \beta_{32}\tau_2 && + U_3\\
Z_4 &= \beta_{43}\tau_3 + \beta_{44}\tau_4 && + U_4\\
Z_5 &= \beta_{53}\tau_3 + \beta_{55}\tau_5 && + U_5 .
\end{aligned}$$

To simplify, let it be stipulated that there is no correlation between a person's liking for Lassie (τ_4) or for the Albrute Sisters (τ_5) and his liking for any of the other performers named in Table 6.6*a*, so that τ_4 and τ_5 can be assimilated into the unique components of $\mathbf{Z}_4$ and $\mathbf{Z}_5$, respectively. Then if we let the numerical values of the regression coefficients and residual SDs be as shown in Table 6.6*d*, our assumed pattern of causal determination for the five data variables is

$$[6.92\text{-}\mathbf{1}] \qquad \mathbf{Z}_1 = .60\tau_1 + 1.00\tau_2 + .49\tau_{U_1}$$

$$[6.92\text{-}\mathbf{2}] \qquad \mathbf{Z}_2 = .80\tau_1 + .60\tau_{U_2}$$

$$[6.92\text{-}\mathbf{3}] \qquad \mathbf{Z}_3 = 1.10\tau_1 + .60\tau_2 + .30\tau_{U_3}$$

$$[6.92\text{-}\mathbf{4}] \qquad \mathbf{Z}_4 = .90\tau_3 + .44\tau_{U_4}$$

$$[6.92\text{-}\mathbf{5}] \qquad \mathbf{Z}_5 = .40\tau_3 + .92\tau_{U_5}$$

where all the τ_j, common and unique, are normalized. Finally, if we suppose that source variables τ_1, τ_2, and τ_3 are correlated as in Table 6.6*e*, we may compute that the correlations among $\mathbf{Z}_1, \ldots, \mathbf{Z}_5$ are as shown in Table 6.7.

Let us assume, then, that by processing viewer-enjoyment data on the five movies in question, we have arrived at the "empirical" correlations in Table 6.7. It is immediately evident from these figures that a viewer's relative enjoyment of one of these films is predictively linked with his relative enjoyment of another. Since all the correlations are positive, this *could* mean merely that some persons like movies—all movies—better than do other persons. That is, we might immediately suspect a "general susceptibility" factor to underlie a person's responsiveness to films. Yet the marked variations among the correlations in Table 6.7 suggest that the situation may be more complex than this; and in any event, with the mathematical tools of factor analysis at hand, it is neither necessary nor professional to speculate intuitively on the original array of correlations. Rather, we should begin by making explicit the mathematical patterning, if any, these correlations display in order that the data may speak for themselves as loudly as possible. In particular, we should inquire whether the observed proper covariances *might* be linearly accounted for by fewer common sources than there are data variables.

If we wished, we could begin analysis by basis-factoring Table 6.7 to see whether $\mathbf{Z}_1, \ldots, \mathbf{Z}_5$ happen to span a space of less than five dimensions. However, this possibility is generally incompatible with the *much* more likely event that the data variables contain some unique variance,[48] so we may as well attempt to extract the presumed unique com-

[48] Equations [6.62] and [6.77] clearly preclude the possibility that any data variable containing nonzero unique variance can be a linear function of any of the other data variables. In order for variables $\mathbf{X}_1, \ldots, \mathbf{X}_n$ to have a dimensionality less than $\mathbf{n}$ even while some of them contain unique variance, the $\mathbf{X}_i$ would have to contain a subset of $\mathbf{k} < \mathbf{n}$ variables $\mathbf{X}_1, \ldots, \mathbf{X}_k$ having a dimensionality less than $\mathbf{k}$.

Film #1. *To have and to haven't*; starring Flicka Tittle and Grotch Armbuster.

Film #2. *The loneliest man on earth*; starring Grotch Armbuster (no other cast).

Film #3. *Flaming embers*; starring Flicka Tittle and Grotch Armbuster.

Film #4. *Lassie, go home*; starring Lassie and Danny Diddleswitch.

Film #5. *I was a teen-age sexagenarian*; starring Danny Diddleswitch and the Albrute sisters.

a) Films

Z_1: Normalized degree-of-enjoyment rating given by viewers to Film #1.

Z_2: Normalized degree-of-enjoyment rating given by viewers to Film #2.

Z_3: Normalized degree-of-enjoyment rating given by viewers to Film #3.

Z_4: Normalized degree-of-enjoyment rating given by viewers to Film #4.

Z_5: Normalized degree-of-enjoyment rating given by viewers to Film #5.

b) Data Variables

τ_1 : Normalized appeal-to-viewer of Grotch Armbuster.

τ_2: Normalized appeal-to-viewer of Flicka Tittle.

τ_3: Normalized appeal-to-viewer of Danny Diddleswitch.

τ_4: Normalized appeal-to-viewer of Lassie.

τ_5: Normalized appeal-to-viewer of the Albrute sisters.

c) Source Variables

β_{ij}	τ_1	τ_2	τ_3	$\sigma_{Z_i \cdot \tau_1 \tau_2 \tau_3}$
Z_1	.60	1.00	0	.49
Z_2	.80	0	0	.60
Z_3	1.10	.60	0	.30
Z_4	0	0	.90	.44
Z_5	0	0	.40	.92

d) Loadings of Data Variables on Common Source Variables

$r_{\tau_i \tau_j}$	τ_1	τ_2	τ_3	τ_4	τ_5
τ_1	1.00	−.50	.40	0	0
τ_2	−.50	1.00	.20	0	0
τ_3	.40	.20	1.00	0	0
τ_4	0	0	0	1.00	0
τ_5	0	0	0	0	1.00

e) Intercorrelations among Source Variables

Table 6.6. Origins of the empirical covariances in a hypothetical study of motion-picture preferences.

$C_{Z_iZ_j}$	Z_1	Z_2	Z_3	Z_4	Z_5
Z_1	1.00	.08	.53	.40	.18
Z_2	.08	1.00	.64	.29	.13
Z_3	.53	.64	1.00	.49	.22
Z_4	.40	.29	.49	1.00	.36
Z_5	.18	.13	.22	.36	1.00

Table 6.7. Empirical covariances observed among the variables listed in Table 6.6b in a hypothetical study of motion-picture preferences.

ponents at the outset by substituting communalities for the unities on the diagonal in Table 6.7. Or rather, we can substitute *estimates* of the communalities, since even if the rank of the data-variable covariance matrix can be lowered by appropriate reductions of its diagonal values, these can usually be found only by the convergence of successive approximations. In line with the procedure described on p. 261, wherein the variance of $\mathbf{X}_i$ controlled by the other data variables is taken for the first approximation to h_i^2, we might try as our estimates of $h_1^2, \ldots, h_5^2$, the respective values

$$R^2_{X_1(X_2X_3X_4X_5)} = .42$$

$$R^2_{X_2(X_1X_3X_4X_5)} = .50$$

$$R^2_{X_3(X_1X_2X_4X_5)} = .66$$

$$R^2_{X_4(X_1X_2X_3X_5)} = .33$$

$$R^2_{X_5(X_1X_2X_3X_4)} = .13$$

which may routinely, if tediously, be wrested from the Table 6.7 data by computing the regression of each data variable upon the others and applying formula [4.98].[49] However, let us instead suppose that an inspired guess has led us to suspect that the values

$$h_1^2 = .76$$

$$h_2^2 = .64$$

$$h_3^2 = .91$$

$$h_4^2 = .81$$

$$h_5^2 = .16$$

may be closer to what will be reclaimed from the yet-to-be-computed common-factor structure matrix. Multiplying these estimates times the diagonal variances in Table 6.7 then yields Table 6.8*a* which, as we have

[49] In practice, the most efficient way to determine the $R_{X_i(X_1 \cdots X_{i-1}X_{i+1} \cdots X_n)}$ is to compute the inverse of the data-variable covariance matrix and apply equation [10.19], Chapter 10.

seen, may equivalently be described either as the covariance matrix for the normalized data variables communal components $\mathbf{H_1}, \ldots, \mathbf{H_5}$, or as the matrix of residual covariances which remain after the inferred unique components of the data variables have been partialled out.

Having thus hopefully pruned uncorrelated distractions out of what our data variables presumably have in common, we now proceed to basis-factor Table 6.8*a* by the centroid procedure. The "centroid" of $\mathbf{H_1}, \ldots,$ $\mathbf{H_5}$, it will be recalled, is their average,

$$\overline{\mathbf{H}} =_{\text{def}} \frac{\mathbf{H_1} + \mathbf{H_2} + \mathbf{H_3} + \mathbf{H_4} + \mathbf{H_5}}{5},$$

but since the extracted factors are going to be normalized anyway, we can just as well work with the sum of the $\mathbf{H_i}$, namely,

$$\mathbf{S_H} =_{\text{def}} \mathbf{H_1} + \mathbf{H_2} + \mathbf{H_3} + \mathbf{H_4} + \mathbf{H_5},$$

in place of $\overline{\mathbf{H}}$. Now, it is an immediate consequence of [4.37] that the covariance of each variable $\mathbf{H_i}$ with the sum $\mathbf{S_H}$ is simply the sum of the covariances in the **i**th column of Table 6.8*a*, while from [4.40] the standard deviation of $\mathbf{S_H}$ is the square root of the grand sum of these covariances. Hence dividing $\sum_{j=1}^{n} C_{H_iH_j}$ by $\sqrt{\sum_{i=1}^{n}\sum_{j=1}^{n} C_{H_iH_j}}$ yields the covariance, $C_{H_iF_1}$, between the normalized first centroid factor (which we shall designate simply $\mathbf{F_1}$ without trying to indicate in the notation that $\mathbf{F_1}$ is a centroid factor) and each communal component $\mathbf{H_i}$. These calculations—summing columns and then dividing by the square root of the grand total—are carried out in the two lines below the body of Table 6.8*a*. Since $C_{H_iF_1} = C_{Z_iF_1} = r_{Z_iF_1}$ for normalized data variables and factors (see [6.83]), the computed values in the bottom line of Table 6.8*a* may also be transferred to the first column of the normalized factor-structure matrix for the $\mathbf{Z_i}$ in Table 6.9. To partial $\mathbf{F_1}$ out of the $\mathbf{H_i}$ we proceed (see [6.16], recalling that $V_{F_1} = 1$) by multiplying $C_{H_iF_1}$ times $C_{H_jF_1}$ and subtracting this product from $C_{H_iH_j}$—i.e., we subtract from the entry located at row **i** and column **j** in the body of Table 6.8*a* the product of the numbers computed for columns **i** and **j** in the bottom line of the table. For example, $C_{H_1H_2 \cdot F_1} = .08 - (.619)(.565) = .08 - .35 = -.27$, while $V_{H_3 \cdot F_1} = C_{H_3H_3 \cdot F_1} = .91 - (.886)(.886) = .91 - .78 = .13$. The residual covariances so computed are entered in Table 6.8*b*, from which it may be seen that while extraction of $\mathbf{F_1}$ has produced a nice reduction in the still-unaccounted-for covariances, there remains evidence for at least a second factor.

To extract a second centroid factor from the first-factor residuals, however, we must first squirm around the complication (cf. p. 247) that

$C_{H_iH_j}$	H_1	H_2	H_3	H_4	H_5	Σ
H_1	.76	.08	.53	.40	.18	1.95
H_2	.08	.64	.64	.29	.13	1.78
H_3	.53	.64	.91	.49	.22	2.79
H_4	.40	.29	.49	.81	.36	2.35
H_5	.18	.13	.22	.36	.16	1.05
Σ	1.95	1.78	2.79	2.35	1.05	9.92 $= 3.15^2$
$C_{H_iF_1}$	.619	.565	.886	.746	.333	

(*a*)

$C_{H_iH_j \cdot F_1}$	H_1	H_2	H_3	H_4	H_5	Σ
H_1	.38	−.27	−.02	−.06	−.03	.00
H_2	−.27	.32	.14	−.13	−.06	.00
H_3	−.02	.14	.13	−.17	−.08	.00
H_4	−.06	−.13	−.17	.25	.11	.00
H_5	−.03	−.06	−.08	.11	.05	−.01
Σ	.00	.00	.00	.00	−.01	−.01
$C_{H_iF_2}$	.340	−.539	−.317	.352	.158	

(*b*)

$C_{H_i^*H_j^* \cdot F_1}$	H_1	$-H_2$	$-H_3$	H_4	H_5	Σ
H_1	.38	.27	.02	−.06	−.03	.58
$-H_2$	.27	.32	.14	.13	.06	.92
$-H_3$	.02	.14	.13	.17	.08	.54
H_4	−.06	.13	.17	.25	.11	.60
H_5	−.03	.06	.08	.11	.05	.27
Σ	.58	.92	.54	.60	.27	2.91 $= 1.71^2$
$C_{H_i^*F_2}$	.340	.539	.317	.352	.158	
$C_{H_iF_2}$	.340	−.539	−.317	.352	.158	

(*c*)

$C_{H_iH_j \cdot F_1F_2}$	H_1	H_2	H_3	H_4	H_5	Σ
H_1	.26	−.09	.09	−.18	−.08	.00
H_2	−.09	.03	−.03	.06	.03	.00
H_3	.09	−.03	.03	−.06	−.03	.00
H_4	−.18	.06	−.06	.13	.05	.00
H_5	−.08	.03	−.03	.05	.03	.00
Σ	.00	.00	.00	.00	.00	.00
$C_{H_iF_3}$	−.511	.175	−.175	.350	.160	

(*d*)

$C_{H_i^* H_j^* \cdot F_1 F_2}$	$-H_1$	H_2	$-H_3$	H_4	H_5	Σ
$-H_1$	.26	.09	.09	.18	.08	.70
H_2	.09	.03	.03	.06	.03	.24
$-H_3$	.09	.03	.03	.06	.03	.24
H_4	.18	.06	.06	.13	.05	.48
H_5	.08	.03	.03	.05	.03	.22
Σ	.70	.24	.24	.48	.22	1.88 $= 1.37^2$
$C_{H_i^* F_3}$	.511	.175	.175	.350	.160	
$C_{H_i F_3}$	−.511	.175	−.175	.350	.160	

(*e*)

$C_{H_i H_j \cdot F_1 F_2 F_3}$	H_1	H_2	H_3	H_4	H_5	Σ
H_1	.00	.00	.00	.00	.00	.00
H_2	.00	.00	.00	.00	.00	.00
H_3	.00	.00	.00	.00	.00	.00
H_4	.00	.00	.00	.01	−.01	.00
H_5	.00	.00	.00	−.01	.00	−.01
Σ	.00	.00	.00	.00	−.01	−.01

(*f*)

Table 6.8. Factoring a matrix by the centroid method. (See text for explanation.)

a) Communal-component covariances inferred from Table 6.7, and computation of the first centroid factor for the $\mathbf{H}_i$. The bottom line follows from the line above it by division by $\sqrt{9.92}$, or 3.15.

b) First-factor residual covariances among the communal components. The $C_{H_i F_2}$ are obtained by suitable reflection of the values of $C_{H_i^* F_2}$ computed in Table 6.8c.

c) Covariances among reflected first-factor communal-component residuals, and computation of second centroid factor.

d) Second-factor communal-component residual covariances.

e) Covariances among reflected second-factor communal-component residuals, and computation of third centroid factor.

f) Third-factor residual communal component covariances.

$r_{Z_iF_j}$	F_1	F_2	F_3	F_{U_1}	F_{U_2}	F_{U_3}	F_{U_4}	F_{U_5}	$h_i^2 \left(= \sum_{j=1}^{3} r^2_{Z_iF_j}\right)$	Σr^2
Z_1	.62	.34	−.51	.49					.76	1.00
Z_2	.57	−.54	.18		.59				.65	1.00
Z_3	.89	−.32	−.18			.27			.93	1.00
Z_4	.75	.35	.35				.44		.81	1.00
Z_5	.33	.16	.16					.92	.16	1.01
$V_{Z(F_j)}$ $(= \Sigma r^2)$	2.17	.66	.47	.24	.35	.07	.19	.85	3.31	5.01
% of total	43.4%	13.2%	9.4%	4.8%	7.0%	1.4%	3.8%	17.0%	66.2%	100%

Table 6.9. Normalized factor-structure matrix for analysis of the variables in Table 6.7 into common-factor and unique-factor components as derived by the centroid computations in Table 6.8.

$\sum_{i=1}^{n} e_{H_i \cdot F_1} = 0$, as displayed all too vividly by the uniformly zero sums (except for one small rounding-off discrepancy) of all rows and columns in the body of Table 6.8*b*.[50] We solve this by reversing the direction, or "reflecting," some of the residuals $\mathbf{e}_{H_i \cdot F_1}$ before taking the second centroid. To reflect a variable, it will be recalled, is to transform it through multiplication by −1. That is, variable $\mathbf{X}'$ is the reflection of variable $\mathbf{X}$ when $\mathbf{X}' = -\mathbf{X}$. Since reflecting a variable changes the sign of its covariances with all other variables – i.e., $\text{Cov}(-\mathbf{X}, \mathbf{Y}) = -\text{Cov}(\mathbf{X}, \mathbf{Y})$ – reflecting one or more of the residuals $\mathbf{e}_{H_i \cdot F_1}$ will reverse some of the negative covariances in Table 6.8*b* and pull their sum above zero.[51] It will be shown in Chapter 7 that in general, the larger is the average covariance within a set of variables in comparison to the average variance, the larger is the proportion of the set's total variance accounted for by its centroid; hence when reflecting residuals to develop a centroid, we usually try to maximize the total still-unaccounted-for covariance. In the present instance, this is accomplished by reflecting the residuals of $\mathbf{H_2}$ and $\mathbf{H_3}$. (How to know this will be discussed in Chapter 7.) Letting

$$\mathbf{e}_{H_i^* \cdot F_1} = \begin{cases} \mathbf{e}_{H_i \cdot F_1} & \text{if } \mathbf{i} = \mathbf{1}, \mathbf{4} \text{ or } \mathbf{5} \\ -\mathbf{e}_{H_i \cdot F_1} & \text{if } \mathbf{i} = \mathbf{2} \text{ or } \mathbf{3}\ , \end{cases}$$

we arrive at the covariance matrix $\{C_{H_i^* H_j^* \cdot F_1}\}$ shown in Table 6.8*c*.[52] (To derive Table 6.8*c* from Table 6.8*b* most expeditiously, multiply each entry in rows **2** and **3** of Table 6.8*b* by −1, and then do the same for columns **2** and **3** of the matrix produced by the first operation.) Summing each column of $\{C_{H_i^* H_j^* \cdot F_1}\}$ and dividing each column sum by the square root of the grand total, just as was done previously in Table 6.8*b*, then yields the covariances (shown in the next-to-the-bottom line of Table 6.8*c*) of each modified residual $\mathbf{e}_{H_i^* \cdot F_1}$ with their normalized centroid which is to be taken as our second centroid factor $\mathbf{F_2}$. The covariances $C_{H_i^* F_2 \cdot F_1}$ are equal to the covariances between $\mathbf{F_2}$ and the unmodified residuals $\mathbf{e}_{H_i \cdot F_1}$ except for a reversal of sign for the reflected residuals, so undoing these reflections gives the covariances $C_{H_i F_2 \cdot F_1}$ in the bottom line of Table 6.8*c*. Finally, since $\mathbf{F_2}$ is orthogonal to $\mathbf{F_1}$, we have $C_{H_i F_2 \cdot F_1} = C_{H_i F_2} = C_{Z_i F_2} = r_{Z_i F_2}$, and the entries in the bottom line of Table 6.8*c* may be transferred to the second column in the normalized factor-structure matrix for the data variables in Table 6.9.

---

[50] *Study question*: Why does the fact that $\sum_{i=1}^{n} \mathbf{e}_{H_i \cdot F_1} = 0$ require that each row and column of matrix $\{C_{H_i H_j \cdot F_1}\}$ must sum to zero?

[51] *Study question*: Why is it impossible for the sum of entries in a covariance matrix to be *less* than zero?

[52] In practice, there are ways to handle reflections without actually constructing a separate table of reflected covariances such as Table 6.8*c*. (See 77, pp. 165 f.)

To partial out $\mathbf{F_2}$, we compute the second-order residuals from Table 5.8*b* in the same way that Table 6.8*b* was obtained from Table 6.8*a*. Specifically, $C_{H_iH_j \cdot F_1F_2} = C_{H_iH_j \cdot F_1} - C_{H_iF_2}C_{H_jF_2}$, since $C_{F_1F_2} = 0$ and $V_{F_2} = 1$. For example, the residual variance of $\mathbf{H_2}$ after extraction of $\mathbf{F_2}$ as well as $\mathbf{F_1}$ is seen to be $C_{H_2H_2 \cdot F_2F_1} = .32 - (.539)(.539) = .32 - .29 = .03$, while the residual covariance between $\mathbf{H_1}$ and $\mathbf{H_3}$, which had virtually vanished after extraction of $\mathbf{F_1}$, now bobs back up to $C_{H_1H_3 \cdot F_1F_2} = -.02 - (.340)(-.317) = -.02 + .11 = .09$. The results are entered in Table 6.8*d*, from which it is apparent that while the residuals are no longer of impressive size, there still remains a little off-diagonal covariance, especially between $\mathbf{H_1}$ and $\mathbf{H_4}$, unaccounted for by $\mathbf{F_1}$ and $\mathbf{F_2}$ alone. (There is also a good chunk left of $\mathbf{H_1}$'s variance, but this is of no concern since if we can factor down to a matrix of residual covariances in which the only nonnegligible entries are on the diagonal, these can be thrown into the unique variances of the data variables.) To extract a third centroid factor, then, we take precisely the same steps as before, except that this time it is reflection of the $\mathbf{H_1}$ and $\mathbf{H_3}$ residuals which maximizes the sum of residual covariances. Summing columns, dividing by the factor-normalizing square root of the grand total, and finally re-reflecting then derives the covariance of each residual $\mathbf{e}_{H_i \cdot F_1F_2}$ with the third orthonormal centroid factor $\mathbf{F_3}$ as shown in the bottom line of Table 6.8*e*. Since $C_{H_iF_3 \cdot F_1F_2} = C_{H_iF_3} = C_{Z_iF_3} = r_{Z_iF_3}$ as before, these values are also entered in column **3** of Table 6.9. After partialling out $\mathbf{F_3}$ by the computations $C_{H_iH_j \cdot F_1F_2F_3} = C_{H_iH_j \cdot F_1F_2} - C_{H_iF_3}C_{H_jF_3}$, we are delighted to observe in Table 5.8*f* that the third-order residuals have all vanished to the level of rounding-off errors and hence that communal components $\mathbf{H_1}, \ldots, \mathbf{H_5}$, if they exist, span a space of only three dimensions. It has been shown, in other words, that proper choice of communalities—specifically, the ones that were substituted for the diagonal unities in deriving Table 6.8*b* from Table 6.8*a*—will reduce the rank of the data-variable covariance matrix from five to three.

To check our original communality estimates, we sum the squared entries for the common factors in each row of Table 6.9. It will be seen that the reproduced communalities are, in fact, in excellent agreement with the values assumed in Table 6.8*a*. (That there is any difference at all is due to rounding-off error, since the initial "estimates" were actually taken from source equations [6.92].) Finally, to complete the structure matrix by including the unique factors as well, we leave the space for $r_{Z_iF_{U_j}}$ in Table 6.9 blank (i.e., a necessarily zero entry) for $\mathbf{i} \neq \mathbf{j}$, and for $r_{Z_iF_i}$ enter that number which makes the total of squared entries in that row equal to 1, thus reproducing the variance of $\mathbf{Z_i}$.

Had our initial estimate of communalities not been chosen quite so astutely, we would have computed somewhat different values for the correlations between data variables and common factors, and the third-order residual covariances would not all have vanished quite so emphatically. However, even with less satisfactory communality estimates, the off-diagonal covariances remaining after extraction of three factors will be small enough to suggest that this number may be all that is needed. The variance of $\mathbf{Z}_i$ accounted for by this first trial triplet of factors then becomes the new, improved estimate of h_i^2, and the factoring routine should be repeated to see whether the new third-order residual covariances are not now all comfortably close to zero. Repetition of this cycle, if necessary, soon converges on a set of communalities which yield a communal-components covariance matrix of rank three.[53]

In summary of this example, then, mathematical analysis of the data-variable correlations solely as they appear in Table 6.7, with no outside assistance from theories or prior empirical findings, reveals that data variables $\mathbf{Z}_1, \ldots, \mathbf{Z}_5$ can be expressed as linear functions of eight hypothetical orthonormal factors, five unique and three common, in a way that exactly reproduces the observed correlations among the $\mathbf{Z}_i$. The factors themselves have been identified not by explicit definition in terms of the $\mathbf{Z}_i$ or other known variables, but by computing a factor-structure matrix such that if a set of orthonormal variables $\mathbf{F}_1, \mathbf{F}_2, \mathbf{F}_3, \mathbf{F}_{U_1}, \ldots, \mathbf{F}_{U_5}$ *were* to have these correlations with $\mathbf{Z}_1, \ldots, \mathbf{Z}_5$, then it *would* be the case that

[6.93-1] $$\mathbf{Z}_1 = .62\mathbf{F}_1 + .34\mathbf{F}_2 - .51\mathbf{F}_3 + .49\mathbf{F}_{U_1}$$

[6.93-2] $$\mathbf{Z}_2 = .57\mathbf{F}_1 - .54\mathbf{F}_2 + .18\mathbf{F}_3 + .59\mathbf{F}_{U_2}$$

[6.93-3] $$\mathbf{Z}_3 = .89\mathbf{F}_1 - .32\mathbf{F}_2 - .18\mathbf{F}_3 + .27\mathbf{F}_{U_3}$$

[6.93-4] $$\mathbf{Z}_4 = .75\mathbf{F}_1 + .35\mathbf{F}_2 + .35\mathbf{F}_3 + .44\mathbf{F}_{U_4}$$

[6.93-5] $$\mathbf{Z}_5 = .33\mathbf{F}_1 + .16\mathbf{F}_2 + .16\mathbf{F}_3 + .92\mathbf{F}_{U_1} .$$

That the factor structure in Table 6.9 does, in fact, reproduce the correlations in Table 6.7 can—and should—be verified by computing that $r_{Z_i Z_j} = \sum_{k=1}^{3} r_{Z_i F_k} r_{Z_j F_k}$ for every $\mathbf{i} \neq \mathbf{j}$. The total data-variable variance accounted for by each factor is shown in the next-to-the-bottom line of Table 6.9, these values being computed by summing the squared entries in each column in accord with the formula $V_{Z(F_j)} = \sum_{i=1}^{n} r^2_{Z_i F_j}$, which is [6.41] specialized to normalized data. Interpretation of these variance

[53] The present example happens to be one in which, for reasons briefly discussed on p. 262, many different sets of communalities will reduce the covariance matrix to a rank of three. Consequently, the communalities upon which iterated factoring converges here depend upon the initial estimates chosen.

contributions may be further assisted by expressing each as a percentage of the total, as shown in the bottom line of Table 6.9.

But even if the observed correlations *can* be reproduced by factor pattern [6.93], what of it? Does it not seem like a particularly maladroit application of the methodological Canon of Parsimony to posit eight theoretical variables for a job which can be handled just as effectively by only five ontologically innocuous basis factors? There is enough legitimate scepticism in such a jibe that the factor analyst who desires the privilege of factoring with communalities should be prepared to give it a responsible answer. And this is to point out that while eight theoretical variables chosen without restraint to explain the relations among a mere five data variables would indeed be an act of scientific irresponsibility, five of the eight factors in [6.93] are emasculated scavengers allowed only to sop up leftover variance. What is significant about factor pattern [6.93] is that the empirical between-variable correlations can be accounted for by only three factors. This is less than what is mathematically guaranteed for the correlations among five variables and reveals an empirical patterning to the data which is certainly not intuitively evident and which, moreover, cannot be exhibited through any decomposition of the data variables into a pattern of basis factors. To think that when factoring with communalities we necessarily *are* extracting common factors is to lose one's grip on the distinction between knowledge and speculation. But so long as our factorial conclusions remain subjunctive, saying only that it is *as though* the data variables are such-and-such composites of common and unique factors, then we have unassailably brought to light important facts about the data which would otherwise have gone unperceived but which now clamor for explanation.

Styles of Factor Solutions: II. Terminal Patterns

It will be recalled from our discussion of basis factoring that a basis can be chosen for a given set of variables in innumerably many different ways. There are sound reasons to prefer a principal-factor solution or its centroid approximation for the initial extraction, since this gets down to negligible residuals with the greatest economy of dimensionality. But to select one particular set of factors, rather than some other set not a perfect linear transformation of the other, is simply to select one factor *space*, rather than another, and once this has been determined it is a matter of mathematical indifference how that space is to be spanned. That is, as observed previously, to identify a set of factors is simultaneously to identify, at least in computational potential, all their linear combinations; while conversely, the initial set can always be reclaimed by a suitable transformation of whatever alternative basis for their space we may prefer. Moreover, choice of a particular extraction procedure needs involve no assumption that the initial factors so computed are the only variables in factor space which may be of interest to us, so there is no reason to shun transformation of the initial solution into any other basis for this space which invites our whim. This option especially urges attention in the case of *inferred* factors. For while it may be reasonable—and a great many research scientists apparently feel that it is—to assume that the space of communal components inferred from a set of data variables may contain useful linear approximations to the causal sources of the observed correlations, there is nothing in the definition of an extraction procedure (with the partial exception of multiple-group factoring and the hierarchical methods to be mentioned later) to support any confidence that these coincide with the factors by means of which communal-components space has been initially spanned. Consequently, if it is hoped that the pattern of common factors derived from the covariances within a set of data variables can be coaxed into revealing more about the causal structure of these relations than just the number of common sources, it becomes necessary to experiment with various "rotations" of the initial factors to judge whether some other basis for common-factor space can be found with properties particularly suggestive of an additional substantive interpretation. By a *terminal factor solution,* then, we mean a factorial decomposition of the data variables so devised that the numerical values entered in the common-factor structure matrix may be hypothesized to approximate the covariances between the data variables and scientifically meaningful source variables.

A rotation of factors $\mathbf{F_1}, \ldots, \mathbf{F_k}$ into a new set $\mathbf{F'_1}, \ldots, \mathbf{F'_k}$ (where $\mathbf{F_1}, \ldots, \mathbf{F_k}$ need not be all the factors, not even all the common factors, into which the data variables have been decomposed) is defined by a set of equations

[6.94-i] $(\mathbf{i} = \mathbf{1}, \ldots, \mathbf{k})$

$$\mathbf{F'_i} = c_{i1}\mathbf{F_1} + \ldots + c_{ik}\mathbf{F_k}\,.$$

The matrix of coefficients $\{c_{ij}\}$ is called the "rotation matrix" or "transformation matrix" and may be arbitrarily selected subject only to the restriction that its rank be $\mathbf{k}$ and, conventionally, that it yield transformed factors with unit variances. (When the $\mathbf{F_i}$ are orthonormal, the latter condition is satisfied if and only if $\sum_{j=1}^{k} c_{ij}^2 = 1$ over each row $\mathbf{i}$ in c_{ij}. Moreover, if $\sum_{h=1}^{k} c_{ih}c_{jh} = 0$ for all pairs of rows $\mathbf{i} \neq \mathbf{j}$, the rotated factors will then also be orthonormal.) The rotation equations [6.94] may also be solved to express each $\mathbf{F_i}$ as a function of $\mathbf{F'_1}, \ldots, \mathbf{F'_k}$, say

[6.95-i] $(\mathbf{i} = \mathbf{1}, \ldots, \mathbf{k})$

$$\mathbf{F_i} = c'_{i1}\mathbf{F'_1} + \ldots + c'_{ik}\mathbf{F'_k}\,.$$

Substituting the latter into factor-pattern equations

[6.96-i] $\mathbf{X}_i = b_{io} + b_{i1}\mathbf{F}_1 + \ldots + b_{ik}\mathbf{F}_k + b_{i(k+1)}\mathbf{F}_{k+1} + \ldots + b_{ip}\mathbf{F}_p$
$(\mathbf{i} = \mathbf{1}, \ldots, \mathbf{n})$

then eventuates in the new factor pattern

[6.97-i] $\mathbf{X}_i = b_{io} + b'_{i1}\mathbf{F}'_1 + \ldots + b'_{ik}\mathbf{F}'_k + b_{i(k+1)}\mathbf{F}_{k+1} + \ldots + b_{ip}\mathbf{F}_p$,
$(\mathbf{i} = \mathbf{1}, \ldots, \mathbf{n})$

where

[6.98-ij] $$b'_{ij} = \sum_{h=1}^{k} b_{ih} c'_{hj} \ ,$$
$(\mathbf{i},\mathbf{j} = \mathbf{1}, \ldots, \mathbf{k})$

and in which the new factors $\mathbf{F}'_1, \ldots, \mathbf{F}'_k$ have replaced $\mathbf{F}_1, \ldots, \mathbf{F}_k$. Obviously equations [6.98] can be converted back into [6.97] by appeal to [6.94], so at the purely formal level the factor patterns before and after rotation describe exactly the same mathematical facts about the relations among the $\mathbf{X}_i$, and neither can be said to be any more "true" than the other. Even so, it is altogether possible that rotated factor $\mathbf{F}'_i$ correlates more highly with a scientifically *fruitful* theoretical variable $\boldsymbol{\tau}_i$ than do any of the unrotated factors $\mathbf{F}_1, \ldots, \mathbf{F}_p$.[54] The fundamental conceptual problem of terminal solutions, then, is: *What are the standards for judging which, among transformationally equivalent factor patterns, are the ones that reflect the most promising hypotheses about underlying determinants?* Once such standards have been identified, it becomes possible to devise more or less routinized computing procedures by which to scan the endless abundance of alternative factor rotations in search of patterns which most closely approximate the qualities of the stipulated ideal.

Now that the problem of terminal factors has been aired, however, there is little which can be revealed here about its solution. As is more universally characteristic of scientific procedures than is often appreciated, the practice of deriving terminal solutions has remained largely an intuitive art, while an articulated body of closely reasoned doctrine on the interpretation of factor patterns is, to put the matter gently, nonexistent. The art is not altogether lacking in verbalized method, however, and there appear to be three dominant themes which govern the psychological acceptability of a terminal solution. With commendable con-

[54] The bare fact that a variable can be defined, and may hence be said to "exist," does not vouchsafe that it holds any interest for scientific study. (For example, few scientists would expect much to be learned from study of a variable defined as the centroid of a person's birth date, carbon-dioxide content of breath, and weight of fingernail dirt, even though one or more of these constituent variables might well have interesting causal connections on its own.) Hence even though $\mathbf{F}'_1, \ldots, \mathbf{F}'_k$ will approximate source variables $\boldsymbol{\tau}_1, \ldots, \boldsymbol{\tau}_k$ only if the unrotated factors $\mathbf{F}_1, \ldots, \mathbf{F}_k$ similarly approximate corresponding linear functions of the $\boldsymbol{\tau}_i$, the original $\boldsymbol{\tau}_i$ may be scientifically interesting in a way that their composites are not.

servatism, two of these require that the factors make some sort of sense in light of extant knowledge. One way in which this can occur is through observation that a given factor correlates highly with some previously acknowledged measure of what that factor is being construed to signify. In the analysis of a battery of personality variables, for example, a common factor might turn up in a fashion suggestive of general intelligence. If the study were repeated to include an intelligence test or if the experimenter were perspicacious enough to have included an intelligence test in his battery of observations to begin with, and the correlation between the intelligence measure and the personality factor were to prove gratifyingly high, then confidence would be increased both in the interpretation given to this factor and in the surmise that a general intelligence factor is one of the source variables underlying the observed personality traits. In the better factor-analytic studies of research areas in which some of the underlying determinants have already been tentatively identified, it is standard practice to include measures of these as "marker" variables around which to begin factor interpretation. In a study so designed, a final solution in which the communal components of marker variables are closely aligned with the factors chosen to span common-factor space will usually be given preference over a solution in which the marker variables have to be written as composites of several factors. Factor patterns arrived at in this way might be described as "pre-structured" or "confirmational" patterns, since they seek to reproduce and support factorial hypotheses established previously. (Terminal factoring by this method can easily degenerate into a system of closed-circuit delusions, however, if common factors which have been placed in coincidence with the communal components of marker variables merely *because* the latter are markers are then thought to provide *evidence* for the factorial primacy of the marker variables.)

A second way in which the interpretive acceptability of a factor is guided by background knowledge is through judgment about what the data variables which load heavily (i.e., have large pattern coefficients) on this factor might have in common. If educated belief, common sense, or abstract contemplation can come up with something, post hoc though it may be, which does indeed imply a common bond for these variables while *not*, on the other hand, seriously linking them with other data variables whose loadings on this factor are meager, then faith is enhanced that this factor is, in fact, a functional ingredient of reality. Conversely, if imagination fails, then the factor is likely to be discreetly ignored or rotated away.

There remains still another important lure for taking some factor patterns more seriously than others which, like making love on a roller coaster, is not highly esteemed by all, but is likely to be pursued with especial enthusiasm by those who are responsive to its appeal. This is to look for a distribution of factor loadings whose properties as a mathematical array are more striking than can plausibly be ascribed either to chance or to human contrivance. As already stated, no convincing methodological theory of factor coefficients has yet been developed, but the factor patterns which clutch most insistently at one's consent for interpretation are those which present, in some intuitive sense, the *simplest* array. Now "simplicity," in its various manifestations, has proved as elusive to explicit definition as it has remained a guidepost for centuries of scientific endeavor. In the context of factor analysis, however, it has most frequently been interpreted to mean a maximal number of zero or near-zero factor loadings. To compute that the coefficient, b_{ij}, of factor $\mathbf{F_j}$ for data variable $\mathbf{X_i}$ is approximately zero is essentially to observe that a postulated source variable corresponding to factor $\mathbf{F_j}$ is not required to explain $\mathbf{X_i}$'s correlational behavior in this instance. The fewer the nonzero factor loadings for data variable $\mathbf{X_i}$, then, the less opulently do we need to endow $\mathbf{X_i}$ with unobserved determinants. Of course, if other variables in the study demand a source corresponding to $\mathbf{F_j}$, then there is no good reason why we should boggle at $\mathbf{F_j}$'s contributing to $\mathbf{X_i}$ also; but it also feels reasonable, somehow, to suppose that the causal structure of nature is not so interconnectedly homogeneous that every source variable participates in every observed outcome. Thus if by the "factorial complexity" of data variable $\mathbf{X_i}$ with respect to a given factor pattern we mean the number of common factors on which $\mathbf{X_i}$'s loading is "significantly" different from zero, then a factor solution in which the average factorial complexity falls substantially short of the number of common factors has greater intuitive plausibility as a model of underlying reality than does a solution in which each data variable partakes of every common factor.

A factor pattern in which factorial complexity is held to more or less a minimum is known technically as a *simple structure* solution. The expression "simple structure," along with its conceptual development as an ideal for terminal factors, originated with L. L. Thurstone.[55] And it is with search for simple structure that *oblique factors* come into their own. Important mathematical conveniences—notably, the equivalence between factor-structure and factor-pattern matrices, and the additivity of controlled covariance components (i.e., [6.28])—must be sacrificed when oblique solutions are admitted, but a convincing argument has yet to be made for the view that genuine source variables are less likely to be correlated than not. It is no rarity to find that in graphical representations of a factor pattern, certain positions in common-factor space

[55] In line with more recent terminology, the phrase "simple structure" might better be replaced with "simple pattern," since it is zero entries in the factor pattern, not in the factor structure, that we wish to minimize. In justice to Thurstone's terminology, though, it should be noted that his procedure for finding simple structure involves an auxiliary set of factors for which zero structure coefficients correspond to zero loadings on the primary factors.

are so boldly marked by the data variables that not to rotate factors to these positions, oblique though they may be, and to surmise that this is the way the world is would be something like treating the startling webwork of condensed vapor in a nuclear physicist's cloud chamber as a curious coincidence of atmospheric effects.

While serious discussion of simple structure and oblique factors is vastly beyond the present scope, a small illustration is afforded by our movie-enjoyment example. A few of the common-factor loadings in factor pattern [6.93] approach negligible values (a moderately conventional rule of thumb is that loadings of .10 or less in magnitude may be regarded as essentially zero[56]), but the factorial complexity of each data variable equals the number of common factors—certainly not a pattern which is distinguished in any interesting way from an arbitrary choice of basis for common-factor space. It so happens, however, that if we try the oblique rotation

[6.99-**1**] $$\mathbf{F}'_1 = .71\mathbf{F}_1 - .67\mathbf{F}_2 + .22\mathbf{F}_3\,,$$

[6.99-**2**] $$\mathbf{F}'_2 = .20\mathbf{F}_1 + .74\mathbf{F}_2 - .64\mathbf{F}_3\,,$$

[6.99-**3**] $$\mathbf{F}'_3 = .83\mathbf{F}_1 + .40\mathbf{F}_2 + .40\mathbf{F}_3\,,$$

we find by solving for the $\mathbf{F}'_i$, namely,

[6.100-**1**] $$\mathbf{F}_1 = .80\mathbf{F}'_1 + .52\mathbf{F}'_2 + .39\mathbf{F}'_3\,,$$

[6.100-**2**] $$\mathbf{F}_2 = -.89\mathbf{F}'_1 + .15\mathbf{F}'_2 + .73\mathbf{F}_3\,,$$

[6.100-**3**] $$\mathbf{F}_3 = -.78\mathbf{F}'_1 - 1.23\mathbf{F}'_3 + .96\mathbf{F}'_3\,,$$

substituting in [6.93], and collecting terms, that

[6.101-**1**] $$\mathbf{Z}_1 = .59\mathbf{F}'_1 + 1.00\mathbf{F}'_2 + .00\mathbf{F}'_3 + .49\mathbf{F}_{\mathbf{U}_1}$$

[6.101-**2**] $$\mathbf{Z}_2 = .80\mathbf{F}'_1 - .01\mathbf{F}'_2 + .00\mathbf{F}'_3 + .59\mathbf{F}_{\mathbf{U}_2}$$

[6.101-**3**] $$\mathbf{Z}_3 = 1.14\mathbf{F}'_1 + .64\mathbf{F}'_2 - .06\mathbf{F}'_3 + .27\mathbf{F}_{\mathbf{U}_3}$$

[6.101-**4**] $$\mathbf{Z}_4 = .02\mathbf{F}'_1 + .01\mathbf{F}'_2 + .88\mathbf{F}'_3 + .44\mathbf{F}_{\mathbf{U}_4}$$

[6.101-**5**] $$\mathbf{Z}_5 = .00\mathbf{F}'_1 + .00\mathbf{F}'_2 + .40\mathbf{F}'_3 + .92\mathbf{F}_{\mathbf{U}_5}\,.$$

To reveal the nature of this pattern with a minimum of visual distraction, let us substitute crosses for common-factor components in which the factor coefficient is .10 or greater in magnitude, *U*s for the unique

---

[56] An orthonormal factor whose coefficient for a normalized variable is less than .10 in absolute value controls less than 1% of that variable's variance.

components, and leave blank spaces elsewhere. Then [6.101] reveals the array

$$\begin{aligned}
Z_1 &= \mathrm{x} + \mathrm{x} \quad\quad + U \\
Z_2 &= \mathrm{x} \quad\quad\quad\quad\quad + U \\
Z_3 &= \mathrm{x} + \mathrm{x} \quad\quad\quad\quad\quad + U \\
Z_4 &= \quad\quad\quad \mathrm{x} \quad\quad\quad\quad\quad + U \\
Z_5 &= \quad\quad\quad \mathrm{x} \quad\quad\quad\quad\quad\quad + U\,,
\end{aligned}$$

whose factorial complexity (namely, an average complexity of only 1.4, in contrast to the average complexity of 3.0 for pattern [6.93]) is strikingly cleaner than any which can be achieved by an orthogonal rotation of the initial solution. Discovery of a simple structure such as this would goad even the most stolid investigator to search for something in the nature of his data variables which could differentiate them in this fashion. Thus in the present example, it would soon be detected that all the movies with significant loadings on simple-structure factor $\mathbf{F}_i'$ share a performer who does not, moreover, appear in the cast of films with insignificant loadings on $\mathbf{F}_i'$. However, since these data were artificially constructed in just this way to begin with, we had best not try to make too much of this.

Higher-Order Factors

By definition, oblique factors are themselves correlated to one extent or another, and an essential part of the description of an oblique factor solution is the matrix of factor covariances. Thus along with the conversion of orthonormal factors $\mathbf{F}_1$, $\mathbf{F}_2$, $\mathbf{F}_3$ into oblique factors $\mathbf{F}_1'$, $\mathbf{F}_2'$, $\mathbf{F}_3'$ in the example of the previous paragraph, it should also be computed from [6.99] that the covariances among the $\mathbf{F}_i'$ are:

$C_{F_i'F_j'}$	$\mathbf{F}_1'$	$\mathbf{F}_2'$	$\mathbf{F}_3'$
$\mathbf{F}_1'$	1.00	−.49	.41
$\mathbf{F}_2'$	−.49	1.00	.21
$\mathbf{F}_3'$	.41	.21	1.01

Now, if these oblique factors warrant serious consideration as putative approximations to scientifically meaningful source variables, then the factor covariances reflect a system of relationships among these sources which likewise invites analysis through factorial decomposition. That is, if common factors have been found in large enough supply to allow the possibility of interesting results (since the fewer variables that are factored, the less perceptibly will whatever causally induced simple structure they may have be able to stand out in contrast to alternative factor patterns), then the factor covariance matrix may itself be factored to yield "second-order" factors which, hopefully, account for the correlations among the first-order factors extracted from the data variables. Similarly, if the second-order factors are themselves oblique, their covariance matrix can be factored for third-order factors, and so on. It should hardly be necessary to add that making hardheaded methodological sense out of the connections among data variables, first-order factors, and higher-order factors is a challenge not readily to be disposed of in a few brisk sentences. So as the bemused reader envisions layer upon ever deeper layer of nature's hidden mysteries folding back under the awesome alchemy of data variables transmuted into first-order factors transmuted into second-order factors transmuted into third-order factors transmuted into . . . , we quickly move on to other matters.

Hierarchical Factor Solutions

It remains to say a word about still another group of factor styles most commonly known as "hierarchical" solutions, but which might better be characterized as *a priori,* or *rationalistic,* methods. In contrast to the *inductive,* or *a posteriori,* procedures described previously, which first extract a common-factor space of more or less minimum dimensionality and then search within it for whatever provocative factor patterns the data may disclose, factor solutions of the a priori sort presuppose a particular form of factor pattern to which the data are fitted as best they can be. A rationalistic analysis is considered successful if factor loadings can be found according to the preassigned pattern which do, in fact, reproduce the observed covariances within acceptable limits of tolerance; otherwise, it is concluded (generally with reluctance) that the data do not fit the pattern. Rationalistic factor theories have recently undergone a strong surge of development, motivated by desire to impose greater conceptual order on the manifold dimensions of human ability than has been afforded by traditional inductive factor approaches (see Guilford, 35; Humphreys, 46).

There is no limit to the number of different factor patterns which can be taken to define a priori factor solutions, and since computational procedures are largely specific to each pattern, there is little which can profitably be said here about rationalistic factor analysis beyond a few remarks about its historical development and overall methodological character. The earliest a priori pattern was actually the origin of inferential factor analysis, namely, Spearman's "two-factor" thesis that intellectual abilities are composed of a single general factor ("g") common in varying degrees to all intellectual functions, plus an array of uncorrelated specific factors, one for each different task—in short, that the common-factor space of intelligence measures is one-dimensional. During the early 1900s, Spearman and others explored methods for testing whether a matrix of correlations does, in fact, implicate a single common factor, and how to compute the factor loadings under this assumption.

The concept of "hierarchical order" was introduced in these studies to reflect the fact that when a set of variables has a single common factor on which the loadings are all positive, the variables can be so ordered that their intercorrelations consistently decrease as one scans from left to right or from top to bottom in their correlation matrix.[57] As data accumulated, however, it became increasingly evident that correlations among human abilities do not always comfortably fit the two-factor pattern. In the United States, this eventuated in the inductive multiple-factor methods described previously, in which no special effort is made to find a general factor shared by all the data variables—in fact, Thurstone's oblique simple-structure procedure minimizes the likelihood that a first-order general factor will turn up. English factor analysts, on the other hand, have for the most part clung more tightly to Spearman's tradition in preferring general or subgeneral orthogonal factors wherever possible. This has led to the development of a priori patterns postulating a single general factor which, when extracted, partitions the data-variable residuals into two or more uncorrelated groups, each of which, in turn, is unified by a general group factor which upon extraction splits the group into uncorrelated subgroups, and so on through the hierarchy of general factor, group factors, subgroup factors, sub-subgroup factors, etc., until specific (i.e., unique) factors are finally reached. A hierarchical factor pattern of this sort is illustrated in Table 6.10. It is also possible to liberalize such schemata to allow for some overlap between groups—i.e., to admit some variables which have significant loadings on more than one factor at the same hierarchical level.

Despite substantial differences in computational procedures, inductive multiple-factor solutions and Spearmanoid hierarchical methods have

Data Variable	General Factor	Group Factors		Subgroup Factors			Unique Factors							
	F_1	F_2	F_3	F_4	F_5	F_6	U_1	U_2	U_3	U_4	U_5	U_6	U_7	U_8
X_1	x	x		x			x							
X_2	x	x		x				x						
X_3	x	x		x					x					
X_4	x	x			x					x				
X_5	x	x			x						x			
X_6	x		x			x						x		
X_7	x		x			x							x	
X_8	x		x											x

Table 6.10. An illustrative hierarchical factor pattern, in which "x" indicates a nonzero factor loading. All factors are stipulated to be mutually orthogonal.

[57] This is a simple consequence of the fact that in this case the correlation between two different variables in the set is the product of their loadings on the common factor.

developed in close interactive association and disagree more in what type of factor pattern is deemed most worthy of interpretive consideration than over any basic formal principles. The affinities between the two approaches are strengthened, moreover, by recognition that the hierarchy of nth-order factors ($n = 1, 2, \ldots$), generated by a sequence of oblique simple-structure solutions in which the factor covariances of each order are the data from which the next order of factors are extracted, are equivalent to a generalized Spearman hierarchy of orthogonal first-order factors.[58] The rationalistic approach recently developed by Guttman (39), on the other hand, is a radical departure from the Spearman-Thurstone tradition. Guttman's most general pattern, which he calls the "radex," is too complex to be conveniently described here, but two special instances of it, the "simplex" and the "circumplex," are illustrated in Table 6.11. The most distinctive methodological features of radex theory are its richly a priori origin, its de-emphasis of factorial parsimony, and the unusual limitations it places on the values which factor coefficients are allowed to take.[59] Yet another product of Guttman's remarkable mathematical imagination is "facet theory" (43), a radex-type pattern which partitions a multidimensional array of specially selected data variables into components of ascending combinatorial complexity akin to a Fisherian Analysis-of-Variance partition.

There is a subtle but important difference between rationalistic and inductive factor solutions in their treatment of communalities and common-factor space. A posteriori solutions first derive communalities which attempt to minimize the rank of the reduced covariance matrix (though this criterion for the communality solution is not inherent in the inductive approach), and then search for an interesting basis for the space spanned by the communal components corresponding to these

[58] See, e.g., Wherry (85). The principle is simple: If data variables $\mathbf{X}_1, \ldots, \mathbf{X}_n$ are analyzed into first-order oblique common factors $\mathbf{F}_1, \ldots, \mathbf{F}_m$ and unique factors $\mathbf{U}_1, \ldots, \mathbf{U}_n$, and the $\mathbf{F}_j$ are in turn analyzed into second-order factors $\mathbf{F}'_1, \ldots, \mathbf{F}'_k$ and unique factors $\mathbf{U}'_1, \ldots, \mathbf{U}'_m$, then the $\mathbf{X}_i$ can be written as linear combinations of $\mathbf{F}'_1, \ldots, \mathbf{F}'_k, \mathbf{U}'_1, \ldots, \mathbf{U}'_m, \mathbf{U}_1, \ldots, \mathbf{U}_n$ by replacing each $\mathbf{F}_j$ in the composition of $\mathbf{X}_i$ with its second-order analysis. Similarly, the $\mathbf{F}'_j$ can be replaced by the third-order factorial components into which they analyze, and so on until all oblique factors have been eliminated. An interpretive drawback to hierarchical factors obtained in this way, however, is that the final solution is essentially defined by *unique*—i.e., residual—components of various orders.

[59] Guttman's most elementary pattern, the simplex, appears to have been partially inspired by correlation matrices which permit a hierarchical ordering of the data variables such that the greater the hierarchical separation between two variables, the lower is their correlation. However, detailed formulation of the simplex pattern and its eventual elaboration into the radex is almost entirely an unfolding of an appealing mathematical structure with little if any pressure toward these developments from empirical data. The number of common factors in a radex pattern generally equals the number of data variables, which for conventional factors would guarantee that the pattern could be fitted to virtually any array of observed correlations. The radex acquires mathematical stringency, however, from stipulation that the data variables load on the factors in all-or-none fashion—i.e., that for a suitable scaling of the variables, each factor coefficient is either 0 or 1.

communalities. A priori solutions, on the other hand, select communalities which maximize the fit of the preselected pattern, and apart from the simpler Spearmanoid hierarchical patterns, these in general do *not* minimize the common-factor dimensionality. Neither do the communal components of the data variables necessarily span common-factor space in an a priori pattern, though they are almost certain to do so if the pattern does not posit more common factors than there are data variables. Consequently, while inductive factoring should ideally be able to scan all possible factor-pattern alternatives, the factor space extracted by extant inductive methods will virtually never contain the factors postulated by the more complex a priori patterns even if the data do, in fact, fit one of the latter.

What judgment can be passed on the substantive interpretation of correlational data parsed by an a priori factor pattern? To an empiricist,

Data Variable	Common Factors					
	F_1	F_2	F_3	F_4	F_5	F_6
X_1	X					
X_2	X	X				
X_3	X	X	X			
X_4	X	X	X	X		
X_5	X	X	X	X	X	
X_6	X	X	X	X	X	X

a) A Simplex Pattern

Data Variable	Common Factors					
	F_1	F_2	F_3	F_4	F_5	F_6
X_1	X	X	X			
X_2		X	X	X		
X_3			X	X	X	
X_4				X	X	X
X_5	X				X	X
X_6	X	X				X

b) A Circumplex Pattern

Table 6.11. Two varieties of the Guttman radex. All factors are mutually orthogonal, and each data variable is also allowed to contain a unique component. In contrast to Spearmanoid hierarchies (e.g., Table 6.10), it is a crucial assumption of radex theory that scalings of the variables exist under which all common-factor loadings simultaneously become either zero or unity.

there is too much about rationalistic analysis that reeks of myth making, too much of coercing nature into strained compliance with our preconvictions when we should be standing aloof with keen but coldly critical vision to register what may be revealed unto us. (In particular, the factor-loading austerity postulated by the Guttman radex patterns to fend off analytic triviality corresponds to no formal property of any physical process heretofore known to man or beast.) Yet if the data do, in fact, neatly fit an a priori pattern, then this remains a brute statistical fact about the observed interrelations, untarnished by whatever implausibility may adhere to the pattern as a hypothesis about source variables, which demands due recognition in whatever substantive theory may ultimately be developed about these variables. Moreover, there are in principle many inferentially challenging factor patterns which the data might contain yet which cannot be disclosed while common-factor space is held to minimal dimensionality. Despite the dangers of overzealous commitment to a particular rationalistic approach, therefore, a priori factor styles may usefully continue to stake out pioneer settlements in wilderness country until such time as inductive approaches devise more effective techniques for adjusting communalities to achieve simple structure of all forms.

*Chapter 7. **Centroids and Variance Structure**

IN THIS CHAPTER, we shall consider some more specialized aspects of the distribution of variance within a set of variables, not merely for their importance to the theory of reliability, which is considerable, but for their own inherent mathematical interest as well. Since much of this material is new, technical details holding at best marginal interest for the novice at multivariate analysis have been included for the benefit of more advanced students. If the reader skims this chapter just deeply enough to get a purchase on the basic concepts, he may reserve more serious study of these developments until his appetite for them has been whetted by seeing them at work in Chapter 9.

The Fundamental Partitioning Theorem

In Chapter 6, we examined how the variance of a variable, or more generally the covariance between two variables, can be broken into components controlled by various factors. In particular, it was observed that if the regression coefficients of orthonormal factors $\mathbf{F}_1, \ldots, \mathbf{F}_k$ for a variable $\mathbf{X}_i$ are $b_{i1}, \ldots, b_{ik}$, respectively, then the variance of $\mathbf{X}_i$ jointly controlled by factors $\mathbf{F}_1, \ldots, \mathbf{F}_k$ is

$$V_{\mathbf{X}_i(\mathbf{F}_1 \ldots \mathbf{F}_K)} = \sum_{j=1}^{k} b_{ij} .$$

We also know, however, that the variance of $\mathbf{X}_i$ controlled by a set of predictors $\mathbf{F}_1, \ldots, \mathbf{F}_k$ is the same as the variance of $\mathbf{X}_i$ controlled by any linear transformation of this set (see Chapter 4, p. 144). Hence the quantity $V_{\mathbf{X}_i(\mathbf{F}_1 \ldots \mathbf{F}_k)}$ depends only upon the space spanned by predictors $\mathbf{F}_1, \ldots, \mathbf{F}_k$, and may be described simply as *the variance of* $\mathbf{X}_i$ *lying in the space of* $\mathbf{F}_1, \ldots, \mathbf{F}_k$, thus conveying that what is predictively relevant about a set of predictor variables is the space they span and not, in addition, the particular *way* they span it. To make this notationally explicit, let the letter "*S*" (with distinguishing subscripts as needed) be used to designate a space of variables with complete indifference to how that space is spanned. Also let "Span (S; $\mathbf{F_1}, \ldots \mathbf{F_k}$)" abbreviate the statement, "Space S is spanned by variables $\mathbf{F_1}, \ldots, \mathbf{F_k}$." Then the variance of variable $\mathbf{X_i}$ lying in or accounted for by space S is

[7.1][1]
$$V_{\mathbf{X_i}(S)} =_{\text{def}} V_{\mathbf{X_i}(\mathbf{F_1}\ldots\mathbf{F_k})} = V_{\mathbf{X_i}} R^2_{\mathbf{X_i}(S)}, \qquad (\text{Span } (S;\ \mathbf{F_1}\ldots\mathbf{F_k}))$$

where we may write

$$R_{\mathbf{X_i}(S)} =_{\text{def}} R_{\mathbf{X_i}(\mathbf{F_1}\ldots\mathbf{F_k})} = r_{\mathbf{X_i}\dot{\mathbf{X}}_{i(\mathbf{F_1}\ldots\mathbf{F_k})}} \qquad (\text{Span } (S;\ \mathbf{F_1}\ldots\mathbf{F_k}))$$

in recognition that the multiple correlation of a variable with a set of predictors is likewise a property of this variable's relation to the *space* of those predictors, irrespective of how that space is spanned. An immediate consequence of definition [7.1] is that if two sets of variables $\mathbf{F_1}, \ldots, \mathbf{F_h}$ and $\mathbf{F'_1}, \ldots, \mathbf{F'_k}$ both span the same space S, then $V_{\mathbf{X_i}(\mathbf{F_1}\ldots\mathbf{F_k})} = V_{\mathbf{X_i}(S)} = V_{\mathbf{X_i}(\mathbf{F'_1}\ldots\mathbf{F'_k})}$. While this was, to be sure, the reason for adopting [7.1] in the first place, the fact that a mere "definition" can entail it shows that definitions are not always so innocuous as they may seem.

Let "$S_1 \ldots S_k$" designate the space spanned by the combined bases of subspaces $S_1, \ldots, S_k$, respectively, and say that the spaces in a set $S_1, \ldots, S_k$ of spaces are *orthogonal* to one another when any variable lying in one space of the set is orthogonal to any variable lying in another.[2] Then

[7.3]
$$V_{\mathbf{X_i}(S_1\ldots S_k)} = \sum_{j=1}^{k} V_{\mathbf{X_i}(S_j)} \qquad (\perp(S_1, \ldots, S_k))$$

where the notation "$\perp(S_1, \ldots, S_k)$" stipulates that spaces $S_1, \ldots, S_k$ are orthogonal to one another. While [7.3] may be derived from [6.28], it

---

[1] In this chapter, we shall require notation for a variety of properties of a variable $\mathbf{X_i}$, or set of variables $\mathbf{X} = \langle \mathbf{X_1}, \ldots, \mathbf{X_n} \rangle$, relative to a space S. With one exception, notational form will be guided by the following policy: (1) When "Q" designates a relationship between variable $\mathbf{X_i}$ or set $\mathbf{X}$ and space S, the quantity of this relationship will be written as "$Q_{\mathbf{X_i}}(S)$" or "$Q_{\mathbf{X}}(S)$". (Conceptually, $Q_{\mathbf{X}}(S)$ is a function over spaces with $\mathbf{X}$ as a parameter.) (2) When Q is fundamentally a quantitative property of variable $\mathbf{X_i}$ or set $\mathbf{X}$ as a whole, we will write "$Q_{\mathbf{X_i}}$" or "$Q_{\mathbf{X}}$" for the value of Q for $\mathbf{X_i}$ or $\mathbf{X}$, and "$Q_{\mathbf{X_i}(S)}$" or "$Q_{\mathbf{X}(S)}$" for the Q-value of the projection of $\mathbf{X_i}$, or set of projections of $\mathbf{X_1}, \ldots, \mathbf{X_n}$, into space S. The exception to this rule is "$R_{\mathbf{X_i}(S)}$" (and similarly "$K_{\mathbf{X_i}(S)}$"), which should properly be written as "$R_{\mathbf{X_i}}(S)$" but which will be allowed to keep "(S)" on the subscript level with $\mathbf{X_i}$ in order to preserve the familiar form of notation for multiple correlation. Wherever notation of form "$Q_{\mathbf{X}(S)}$" is appropriate by convention (2), convention (1) also allows this measure to be written as "$Q_{\mathbf{X}}(S)$" in virtue of the fact that property Q of $\mathbf{X}$'s projection into S may also be regarded as a relation between $\mathbf{X}$ and S. Which of these options is chosen will depend on which seems to present the more visually intelligible symbol.

[2] *Study problem:* Prove that spaces S_i and S_j are orthogonal if and only if there exist orthogonal bases $\mathbf{F}_{i1}, \ldots, \mathbf{F}_{ih}$ and $\mathbf{F}_{j1}, \ldots, \mathbf{F}_{jk}$ for S_i and S_j, respectively, such that the combined set of variables $\mathbf{F}_{i1}, \ldots, \mathbf{F}_{ih}, \mathbf{F}_{j1}, \ldots, \mathbf{F}_{jk}$ is an orthogonal basis for the combined space S_iS_j.

is best perceived as a consequence of the partitioning of variable $\mathbf{X_i}$ into orthogonal components lying in the various subspaces $S_1, \ldots, S_k$. Let "$\mathbf{e}_{\mathbf{X_i}}$" designate the residual of variable $\mathbf{X_i}$ after its arithmetic mean has been partialled out—i.e.,

[7.4][3]
$$\mathbf{e}_{\mathbf{X_i}} =_{\text{def}} \mathbf{X_i} - \text{M}_{\mathbf{X_i}} \,.$$

It was seen in Chapter 4, p. 144, that if two sets of predictors $\mathbf{F_1}, \ldots, \mathbf{F_h}$ and $\mathbf{F_1'}, \ldots, \mathbf{F_k'}$ both span the same space, then for any criterion variable $\mathbf{X_i}$, $\dot{\mathbf{X}}_{\mathbf{i}(\mathbf{F_1}\ldots\mathbf{F_h})} = \dot{\mathbf{X}}_{\mathbf{i}(\mathbf{F_1'}\ldots\mathbf{F_k'})}$. Since linear estimates of $\mathbf{X_i}$ from a set of predictors spanning a space S hence depend only on the space spanned and not, in addition, on what particular set of predictors are doing the spanning, we may write "$\mathbf{e}_{\mathbf{X_i}(S)}$" for the component of $\mathbf{e}_{\mathbf{X_i}}$ controlled by any set of variables which span S. That is,

[7.5]
$$\begin{aligned}\mathbf{e}_{\mathbf{X_i}(S)} &=_{\text{def}} \dot{\mathbf{e}}_{\mathbf{X_i}(\mathbf{F_1}\ldots\mathbf{F_k})} \qquad (\text{Span}(S;\, \mathbf{F_1}\ldots\mathbf{F_k}))\\ &= \dot{\mathbf{X}}_{\mathbf{i}(\mathbf{F_1}\ldots\mathbf{F_k})} - \text{M}_{\mathbf{X_i}}\end{aligned}$$

where $\mathbf{e}_{\mathbf{X_i}(S)}$ is called the *projection* of variable $\mathbf{X_i}$ into space S. If similarly

[7.6]
$$\mathbf{e}_{\mathbf{X_i}\cdot S} =_{\text{def}} \mathbf{e}_{\mathbf{X_i}\cdot \mathbf{F_1}\ldots\mathbf{F_k}} \qquad (\text{Span}\,(S;\, \mathbf{F_1}\ldots\mathbf{F_k}))\,,$$

then the partitioning of variable $\mathbf{X_i}$ by its projection into space S is

[7.7]
$$\mathbf{e}_{\mathbf{X_i}} = \mathbf{e}_{\mathbf{X_i}(S)} + \mathbf{e}_{\mathbf{X_i}\cdot S}$$

or

[7.8]
$$\mathbf{X_i} = \text{M}_{\mathbf{X_i}} + \mathbf{e}_{\mathbf{X_i}(S)} + \mathbf{e}_{\mathbf{X_i}\cdot S}\,,$$

where of course

[7.9]
$$\text{Cov}(\mathbf{e}_{\mathbf{X_i}(S)}, \mathbf{e}_{\mathbf{X_i}\cdot S}) = 0\,.$$

Moreover, it is easily seen (e.g., by considering normal equations [4.86]) that for a set of mutually *orthogonal* spaces $S_1, \ldots, S_k$,

[7.10]
$$\mathbf{e}_{\mathbf{X_i}(S_1\ldots S_k)} = \sum_{j=1}^{k} \mathbf{e}_{\mathbf{X_i}(S_j)} \qquad (\perp(S_1, \ldots, S_k))\,,$$

while for any two variables $\mathbf{X_i}$ and $\mathbf{X_j}$ (not necessarily $\mathbf{i} \neq \mathbf{j}$) and any two orthogonal spaces S_h and S_k it follows from the definition of "orthogonal spaces" that

[7.11]
$$\text{Cov}\,(\mathbf{e}_{\mathbf{X_i}(S_h)}, \mathbf{e}_{\mathbf{X_j}(S_k)}) = 0 \qquad (\perp(S_h, S_k))\,.$$

[3] It is traditional to designate variables with arbitrary means by capital letters, and the "difference" variables defined by subtracting out their means by the corresponding lowercase letters—i.e., $\mathbf{x} =_{\text{def}} \mathbf{X} - \text{M}_{\mathbf{X}}$. The present notation, however, makes clear that $\mathbf{X} - \text{M}_{\mathbf{X}}$ is a partial statistic, namely, the zero-order partial which results when the best estimate of $\mathbf{X}$ based only on membership in the base population P is extracted, and also allows for a more elegant statement of partitioning equations.

Equations [7.10] and [7.11], which subsume [7.7] and [7.9],[4] may be called the *fundamental partitioning theorem* (not to be confused with the "fundamental factor theorem" discussed on p. 232), and from it all sorts of good things follow. Since the regressions of $\mathbf{X_i}$ and $\mathbf{e}_{\mathbf{X_i}}$, respectively, on any set of variables spanning a space S differ only by the constant $M_{\mathbf{X_i}}$, obviously

$$[7.12] \qquad V_{\mathbf{X_i}(S)} = \mathrm{Var}\,(\mathbf{e}_{\mathbf{X_i}(S)})\ ,$$

so [7.3] follows from [7.10,11] by application of [4.42]. More generally, if the covariance between variables $\mathbf{X_i}$ and $\mathbf{X_j}$ accounted for by space S is defined as

$$[7.13] \qquad C_{\mathbf{X_i X_j}(S)} =_{\mathrm{def}} C_{\mathbf{X_i X_j}(\mathbf{F_1}\ldots\mathbf{F_k})} \qquad (\mathrm{Span}(S;\ \mathbf{F_1}\ \ldots\ \mathbf{F_k}))$$
$$= \mathrm{Cov}\,(\mathbf{e}_{\mathbf{X_i}(S)}, \mathbf{e}_{\mathbf{X_j}(S)})\ ,$$

the covariance between the projections of $\mathbf{X_i}$ and $\mathbf{X_j}$ in the union $S_1 \ldots S_k$, of mutually orthogonal subspaces $S_1, \ldots, S_k$ is seen from [7.10,11] by way of [4.39] to be the sum of their covariances in these subspaces—i.e.,

$$[7.14] \qquad C_{\mathbf{X_i X_j}(S_1\ldots S_k)} = \sum_{h=1}^{k} C_{\mathbf{X_i X_j}(S_h)} \qquad (\perp(S_1, \ldots, S_k)).$$

If [7.10,11] is to be called the "fundamental partitioning theorem," then [7.14] deserves the title of the *fundamental partitioning corollary*, for an extraordinarily large number of our formulas in previous chapters are special instances of it. One is [7.3], which follows by setting $\mathbf{i}=\mathbf{j}$. Another is the important [6.28] in which each $\mathbf{F_h}$ defines a one-dimensional space.

Turning now to characterization of the variance distribution of a *set*, or "configuration," of variables, let us define the *total covariance*, $\overset{*}{C}_{\mathbf{XX}}$, of the set $\mathbf{X_1}, \ldots, \mathbf{X_n}$ to be the grand total of entries in the covariance matrix, $\{C_{\mathbf{X_i X_j}}\}$, for these variables; namely,

$$[7.15] \qquad \overset{*}{C}_{\mathbf{XX}} =_{\mathrm{def}} \sum_{\mathbf{i}=1}^{\mathbf{n}} \sum_{\mathbf{j}=1}^{\mathbf{n}} C_{\mathbf{X_i X_j}}.$$

An obvious consequence of [7.14] is that the total covariance of the $\mathbf{X_i}$ may be analyzed as a sum of part-totals lying in various orthogonal spaces. Accordingly, we define the portion of $\overset{*}{C}_{\mathbf{XX}}$ which lies in space S to be the total covariance of the components, $\mathbf{e}_{\mathbf{X_1}(S)}, \ldots, \mathbf{e}_{\mathbf{X_n}(S)}$, of the $\mathbf{X_i}$ lying in S. That is,

$$[7.16] \qquad \overset{*}{C}_{\mathbf{XX}(S)} =_{\mathrm{def}} \sum_{\mathbf{i}=1}^{\mathbf{n}} \sum_{\mathbf{j}=1}^{\mathbf{n}} C_{\mathbf{X_i X_j}(S)}.$$

---

[4] If the *complement*, S^*, of a space S is defined as the union of all spaces orthogonal to S, then $\mathbf{e}_{\mathbf{X_i}\cdot S} = \mathbf{e}_{\mathbf{X_i}(S^*)}$ and [7.7] may be written as $\mathbf{e}_{\mathbf{X_i}} = \mathbf{e}_{\mathbf{X_i}(SS^*)} = \mathbf{e}_{\mathbf{X_i}(S)} + \mathbf{e}_{\mathbf{X_i}(S^*)}$.

Now as we have seen, the entries in a covariance matrix are of two importantly distinct kinds. On the one hand there are the *proper covariances* between two different variables in the set, while on the other there are the self-covariances, or *variances*, whose interpretive significance is altogether different from that of the proper covariances. An **n** by **n** covariance matrix contains **n** diagonal entries, or self-covariances $C_{\mathbf{X}_i \mathbf{X}_i}$, and $\mathbf{n}^2 - \mathbf{n}$ or $\mathbf{n}(\mathbf{n} - 1)$ off-diagonal proper covariances $C_{\mathbf{X}_i \mathbf{X}_j}$ $(\mathbf{i} \neq \mathbf{j})$, and it is useful to make explicit that the total covariance of the $\mathbf{X}_i$ is the sum of their total variance and their total proper covariance. More generally, if we write "$V_{\mathbf{X}(S)}$" and "$C_{\mathbf{XX}(S)}$" for the *total variance* and *total proper covariance*, respectively, of set $\mathbf{X}_1, \ldots, \mathbf{X}_n$ in space S, we have

[7.17]
$$V_{\mathbf{X}(S)} =_{\text{def}} \sum_{i=1}^{n} C_{\mathbf{X}_i \mathbf{X}_i(S)}$$
$$= \sum_{i=1}^{n} V_{\mathbf{X}_i(S)} ,$$

[7.18]
$$C_{\mathbf{XX}(S)} =_{\text{def}} \sum_{i=1}^{n} \sum_{\substack{j=1 \\ i \neq j}}^{n} C_{\mathbf{X}_i \mathbf{X}_j(S)} ,$$

so obviously

[7.19]
$$C^*_{\mathbf{XX}(S)} = C_{\mathbf{XX}(S)} + V_{\mathbf{X}(S)} .$$

In particular, the total covariance $C^*_{\mathbf{XX}}$ analyzes as

[7.20]
$$C^*_{\mathbf{XX}} = C_{\mathbf{XX}} + V_{\mathbf{X}} ,$$

where of course

[7.21]
$$C_{\mathbf{XX}} =_{\text{def}} \sum_{i=1}^{n} \sum_{\substack{j=1 \\ i \neq j}}^{n} C_{\mathbf{X}_i \mathbf{X}_j}$$

and $V_{\mathbf{X}} = \sum_{i=1}^{n} V_{\mathbf{X}_i}$ as defined previously ([6.38]).

Just as the correlation between two variables is a standardized measure of agreement in which their covariance is compared to their variances (specifically, $r_{\mathbf{X}_i \mathbf{X}_j}$ is the ratio of $C_{\mathbf{X}_i \mathbf{X}_j}$ to the geometric mean of $V_{\mathbf{X}_i}$ and $V_{\mathbf{X}_j}$), so may we expect a comparison between the proper covariance and the variance of a set of variables to provide a useful index of overall agreement within the set. A detail which complicates the interpretation of set totals, however, is that not only are their numerical values very much influenced by the (generally arbitrary) number of variables in the set, but there are also $\mathbf{n} - 1$ times as many proper covariances in $\{C_{\mathbf{X}_i \mathbf{X}_j}\}$

as there are variances, so that the balance between C_{XX} and V_X is also critically affected by **n**. Hence it is more instructive to convert all set totals into averages before making comparisons. Let the *average covariance* $\overline{C}^*_{XX}$, the *average proper covariance* $\overline{C}_{XX}$, and the *average variance* $\overline{V}_X$, respectively, of a set of variables $X_1, \ldots, X_n$ be defined

[7.22] $$\overline{C}^*_{XX} =_{\text{def}} \frac{\sum_{i=1}^{n}\sum_{j=1}^{n} C_{X_iX_j}}{n^2} = \frac{C^*_{XX}}{n^2},$$

[7.23] $$\overline{C}_{XX} =_{\text{def}} \frac{\sum_{i=1}^{n}\sum_{\substack{j=1 \\ i\neq j}}^{n} C_{X_iX_j}}{n(n-1)} = \frac{C_{XX}}{n(n-1)},$$

[7.24] $$\overline{V}_X =_{\text{def}} \frac{\sum_{i=1}^{n} V_{X_i}}{n} = \frac{V_X}{n},$$

while $\overline{C}^*_{XX(S)}$, $\overline{C}_{XX(S)}$, and $\overline{V}_{X(S)}$ are the corresponding set averages which lie in a given space *S*. The relative influence of self-covariance versus proper covariance in determining $\overline{C}^*_{XX}$ is then seen from [7.20] to be

[7.25] $$\overline{C}^*_{XX} = \frac{(n-1)\overline{C}_{XX} + \overline{V}_X}{n}.$$

To clarify the meaning of $\overline{C}^*_{XX}$ and $\overline{C}_{XX}$, observe that if two variables are selected at random from the set $X_1, \ldots, X_n$ in such fashion that selection of a variable for one of the pair does not change the likelihood of drawing it for the other also, then $\overline{C}^*_{XX}$ is the expected covariance between them; while if two *different* variables are drawn at random from $X_1, \ldots, X_n$, then $\overline{C}_{XX}$ is their expected covariance.

The conscientious reader will find something hauntingly familiar about the right-hand side of equation [7.22], and a quick check of page 245 will show why. Specifically, we have already seen that *the average covariance, $\overline{C}^*_{XX}$, among a set of variables is equal to the variance of their centroid.* That is,

[7.26] $$\overline{C}^*_{XX} = V_{\overline{X}}.$$

(If the reader feels at all unclear about the definition of the centroid, $\overline{\mathbf{X}}$, of a set of variables, he is strongly urged to review p. 244.) The average proper covariance in the set is also intimately related to the centroid variance, since from [7.25] and [7.26],

[7.27] $$\overline{C}_{\mathbf{XX}} = \frac{\mathbf{n}V_{\overline{\mathbf{X}}} - \overline{V}_{\mathbf{X}}}{(\mathbf{n}-1)} .$$

Moreover, it is a simple consequence of [6.54] that the projection of $\overline{\mathbf{X}}$ into a space S is the centroid of the projections of variables $\mathbf{X}_1, \ldots, \mathbf{X}_n$ into this space—i.e.,

[7.28] $$\overline{\mathbf{e}}_{\mathbf{X}(S)} =_{\text{def}} \frac{\sum_{i=1}^{n} \mathbf{e}_{\mathbf{X}_i(S)}}{\mathbf{n}} = \mathbf{e}_{\overline{\mathbf{X}}(S)} ,$$

so any formula relating properties of $\overline{\mathbf{X}}$ and $\mathbf{X}_1, \ldots, \mathbf{X}_n$ holds equally for the projections of $\overline{\mathbf{X}}$ and $\mathbf{X}_1, \ldots, \mathbf{X}_n$ into any space S. In particular, from [7.26] and [7.27],

[7.29] $$\overline{C}^{*}_{\mathbf{XX}(S)} = V_{\overline{\mathbf{X}}(S)} ,$$

[7.30] $$\overline{C}_{\mathbf{XX}(S)} = \frac{\mathbf{n}V_{\overline{\mathbf{X}}(S)} - \overline{V}_{\mathbf{X}(S)}}{(\mathbf{n}-1)} .$$

It would appear, then, that the extent to which the variables in a set resemble one another in their behavior in a given space should be reflected in the behavior of their centroid in that space. Before developing this possibility, however, let us first explore an even more remarkable variance property of centroids.

Saturation Components and Dispersion Components

Having seen that the total variance of a set of variables can be analyzed into components lying in various orthogonal subspaces of a total space enclosing the set, we shall now observe that the set variance within a given space has a further important partition. Specifically, it will be shown that $V_{\mathbf{X}(S)}$ analyzes as the sum of two contributions, namely, the "saturation variance" of the set in that space, which is a measure of consensus among the set's projections therein, plus the set's "dispersion variance" in this space, which results from the inconsistencies among these projections.

Let the variable defined by the difference between a variable $\mathbf{X}_i$ in the set $\mathbf{X}_1, \ldots, \mathbf{X}_n$ and the centroid of this set be called the *dispersion component*, $\mathbf{D}_i$, of $\mathbf{X}_i$ with respect to this set. That is,

[7.31-i] $(\mathbf{i} = 1, \ldots, \mathbf{n})$ $$\mathbf{D}_i =_{\text{def}} \mathbf{X}_i - \overline{\mathbf{X}} .$$

If $\bar{\mathbf{X}}$ is described as the *saturation component* of $\mathbf{X}_i$ in this set, the equation

[7.32-i] $$\mathbf{X}_i = \bar{\mathbf{X}} + \mathbf{D}_i \, ,$$
$(\mathbf{i} = \mathbf{1}, \ldots, \mathbf{n})$

which is an immediate consequence of $\mathbf{D}_i$'s definition, may be read as saying that each variable $\mathbf{X}_i$ in a set can be analyzed as the sum of two components, a "saturation component" which is common to all members of the set and a "dispersion component" which is the discrepancy between $\mathbf{X}_i$ and the set-average $\bar{\mathbf{X}}$. If we think of the centroid of a set of variables as that single variable which in some sense best represents the set as a whole, just as the arithmetic mean of a distribution of scores intuitively best represents the distribution as a whole, then dispersion components $\mathbf{D}_1, \ldots, \mathbf{D}_n$ are, in effect, what there is in the set $\mathbf{X}_1, \ldots, \mathbf{X}_n$ over and above the set's prevailing trend. While $\bar{\mathbf{X}}$ abstracts the consensus of variables $\mathbf{X}_1, \ldots, \mathbf{X}_n$, the configuration of dispersion components represents in pure form the pattern of disagreement among the $\mathbf{X}_i$. Insight into how this is so will deepen as we proceed, but the fundamental nature of this purity of discord is that the sum of dispersion components $\mathbf{D}_i$ is identically equal to zero—i.e.,

[7.33] $$\sum_{i=1}^{n} \mathbf{D}_i = \sum_{i=1}^{n} (\mathbf{X}_i - \bar{\mathbf{X}}) = \sum_{i=1}^{n} \mathbf{X}_i - \mathbf{n}\bar{\mathbf{X}} = 0 \, .$$

Moreover, since this immediately implies that the variance of $\sum_{i=1}^{n} \mathbf{D}_i$ is zero, its variance lying in any arbitrary space S is also zero, and hence

[7.34] $$\sum_{i=1}^{n} \mathbf{e}_{\mathbf{D}_i(S)} = 0 \, .$$

That is, the sum of the projections of $\mathbf{D}_1, \ldots, \mathbf{D}_n$ into any arbitrary space S is identically zero. This makes clear just how inconsistent $\mathbf{D}_1, \ldots, \mathbf{D}_n$ are as a set. Added together, they completely cancel one another in every direction. Their total *variance*, on the other hand, is by no means zero in every direction. Rather, as we shall see, dispersion variance constitutes part of the total variance configuration of the $\mathbf{X}_i$ in a most interesting fashion.

It should be appreciated that while dispersion component $\mathbf{D}_i$ is what is left of $\mathbf{X}_i$ after removal of $\bar{\mathbf{X}}$, it is *not* the same as the residual $\mathbf{e}_{\mathbf{X}_i \cdot \bar{\mathbf{X}}}$ which is left when $\bar{\mathbf{X}}$ is *partialled* out of $\mathbf{X}_i$. Thus in contrast to the partition

$$\mathbf{X}_i = \dot{\mathbf{X}}_{i(\bar{\mathbf{X}})} + \mathbf{e}_{\mathbf{X}_i \cdot \bar{\mathbf{X}}} \, ,$$

$\mathbf{D_i}$ in partition [7.32] has as a rule neither zero mean nor, more importantly, zero covariance with its complementary component $\overline{\mathbf{X}}$. Consequently, the space spanned by $\mathbf{D_1}, \ldots, \mathbf{D_n}$ is not, in general, orthogonal to $\overline{\mathbf{X}}$ as is the space of residuals $\mathbf{e}_{\mathbf{X_i}\cdot\overline{\mathbf{X}}}$. Like the latter space, however, the dimensionality of the $\mathbf{D_i}$ is, apart from one special case, one less than the dimensionality of the $\mathbf{X_i}$. This is shown by the fact that $\overline{\mathbf{X}}$ and $\mathbf{D_1}, \ldots, \mathbf{D_n}$ together span the space of the $\mathbf{X_i}$, yet $\overline{\mathbf{X}}$ is linearly independent of $\mathbf{D_1}, \ldots, \mathbf{D_n}$ unless the dimensionality of $\mathbf{X_1}, \ldots, \mathbf{X_n}$ is less than $\mathbf{n}$,[5] in which case $\mathbf{D_1}, \ldots, \mathbf{D_n}$ may or may not span the same space as the $\mathbf{X_i}$.

Now let $\mathbf{F_1}, \ldots, \mathbf{F_p}$ be a set of orthonormal factors spanning a space which contains all the variables $\mathbf{X_1}, \ldots, \mathbf{X_n}$. Then the $\mathbf{X_i}$ are linear functions of the $\mathbf{F_j}$ according to some factor pattern

[7.35-i] (i = 1, . . . , n)

$$\mathbf{X_i} = b_{i0} + b_{i1}\mathbf{F_1} + \ldots + b_{ip}\mathbf{F_p}$$
$$= b_{i0} + \sum_{j=1}^{p} b_{ij}\mathbf{F_j}\,.$$

(We do not require that $\mathbf{p} \leq \mathbf{n}$ or that any of the $\mathbf{F_j}$ be unique factors, though neither are these possibilities excluded.) Since the behavior of the set $\mathbf{X_1}, \ldots, \mathbf{X_n}$ in factor space is expressed by the array of factor coefficients b_{ij}, it will be of interest to examine how the latter are distributed. To this end, let variables $\mathbf{X_1}, \ldots, \mathbf{X_n}$ be conceived as a population of $\mathbf{n}$ abstract entities whose scores on a set of $\mathbf{p}$ factor-pattern variables $\mathbf{b_1}, \ldots, \mathbf{b_p}$ are their respective loadings on the various factors $\mathbf{F_1}, \ldots, \mathbf{F_p}$. That is, each factor $\mathbf{F_j}$ in [7.35] defines a factor-pattern variable $\mathbf{b_j}$ whose value for "individual" $\mathbf{X_i}$ is the coefficient b_{ij} of $\mathbf{F_j}$ for $\mathbf{X_i}$. Then the mathematical behavior of the array of factor-pattern coefficients may be analyzed in terms of the statistical properties of the joint distribution of factor-pattern variables $\mathbf{b_1}, \ldots, \mathbf{b_p}$ in "population" $\mathbf{X_1}, \ldots, \mathbf{X_n}$. At present, we shall be concerned only with the mean and variance of loadings on each factor $\mathbf{F_j}$, though later it will be seen that the covariances among the $\mathbf{b_j}$ are also important.

Let the mean and standard deviation of the distribution of factor co-

---

[5] *Proof:* Suppose that $\overline{\mathbf{X}}$ is some linear function of the $\mathbf{D_i}$. Then we would have $\overline{\mathbf{X}} = a_0 + \sum_{i=1}^{n} a_i\mathbf{D_i} = a_0 + \sum_{i=1}^{n} a_i(\mathbf{X_i} - \overline{\mathbf{X}}) = a_0 + \sum_{i=1}^{n} a_i\mathbf{X_i} - \left(\sum_{i=1}^{n} a_i\right)\overline{\mathbf{X}}$ or, after replacing $\overline{\mathbf{X}}$ by its definition and collecting terms, $a_0 + \sum_{i=1}^{n}\left[a_i - \left(\sum_{i=1}^{n} a_i + 1\right)\Big/\mathbf{n}\right]\mathbf{X_i} = 0$. Now, if $\mathbf{X_1}, \ldots, \mathbf{X_n}$ are linearly independent, an equation of this form can be true only if the coefficient of each $\mathbf{X_i}$ is zero (since otherwise, the equation could be rewritten to express any $\mathbf{X_i}$ with nonzero coefficient as a linear function of the other variables). This, in turn, implies for each a_i that $a = \left(\sum_{i=1}^{n} a_i + 1\right)\Big/\mathbf{n}$, or $\sum_{i=1}^{n} a_i = \sum_{i=1}^{n} a_i + 1$, which is impossible.

efficients for variables $\mathbf{X}_1, \ldots, \mathbf{X}_n$ on factor $\mathbf{F}_j$ be designated "$\bar{b}_j$" and "$\sigma_{\mathbf{b}_j}$", respectively. That is,

[7.36-j] (j = 1, . . . , p)

$$\bar{b}_j =_{\text{def}} \mathrm{M}_{\mathbf{b}_j} = \frac{\sum_{i=1}^{n} b_{ij}}{\mathbf{n}},$$

[7.37-j] (j = 1, . . . , p)

$$\sigma^2_{\mathbf{b}_j} =_{\text{def}} \mathrm{Var}(\mathbf{b}_j) = \frac{\sum_{i=1}^{n} (b_{ij} - \bar{b}_j)^2}{\mathbf{n}}.$$

In light of the familiar interpretation of means and standard deviations as measures of central tendency and dispersion, respectively, $\bar{b}_j$ tells us how strong the prevailing tendency is for variables in the set $\mathbf{X}_1, \ldots, \mathbf{X}_n$ to load on factor $\mathbf{F}_j$, while $\sigma_{\mathbf{b}_j}$ assesses how inconsistent the $\mathbf{X}_i$ are in their behavior on $\mathbf{F}_j$. Our interest in these two quantities is enhanced, moreover, by recalling from [6.41] that the total variance of the $\mathbf{X}_i$ accounted for by an orthonormal factor $\mathbf{F}_j$ is the sum of the squared loadings on that factor; hence the average variance accounted for by $\mathbf{F}_j$ is

[7.38-j] (j = 1, . . . , p)

$$\bar{\mathrm{V}}_{\mathbf{X}(\mathbf{F}_j)} = \frac{\sum_{i=1}^{n} b^2_{ij}}{\mathbf{n}} = \mathrm{QM}^2_{|\mathbf{b}_j|} = \sigma^2_{\mathbf{b}_j} + \bar{b}^2_j, \qquad \text{(orthonormal factors)}$$

where the last step follows from [3.19]. Thus the average variance of $\mathbf{X}_1, \ldots, \mathbf{X}_n$ accounted for by factor $\mathbf{F}_j$ splits into two parts, one due to the degree to which the set as a whole lies on or "saturates" $\mathbf{F}_j$, while the other is contributed by the disagreement or "dispersion" among the $\mathbf{X}_i$ on $\mathbf{F}_j$; and we shall now see that these two components of $\mathrm{V}_{\mathbf{X}(\mathbf{F}_j)}$, saturation contribution $\bar{b}^2_j$ and dispersion contribution $\sigma^2_{\mathbf{b}_j}$, are precisely the variance of saturation component $\bar{\mathbf{X}}$ and the average variance of dispersion components $\mathbf{D}_1, \ldots, \mathbf{D}_n$, respectively accounted for by factor $\mathbf{F}_j$.

Since the centroid, $\mathbf{X}$, and the dispersion components, $\mathbf{D}_1, \ldots, \mathbf{D}_n$ of a set of variables $\mathbf{X}_1, \ldots, \mathbf{X}_n$ are all linear functions of the latter, they also lie in any factor space which contain the $\mathbf{X}_i$. In particular, when the $\mathbf{X}_i$ analyze according to factor pattern [7.35], the composition of $\bar{\mathbf{X}}$ in terms of these same factors is

[7.39]
$$\overline{\mathbf{X}} = \frac{\sum_{i=1}^{n} \mathbf{X}_i}{\mathbf{n}}$$
$$= \frac{\sum_{i=1}^{n} (b_{io} + \sum_{j=1}^{p} b_{ij}\mathbf{F}_j)}{\mathbf{n}}$$
$$= \frac{\sum_{i=1}^{n} b_{io}}{\mathbf{n}} + \sum_{j=1}^{p} \left(\frac{\sum_{i=1}^{n} b_{ij}}{\mathbf{n}} \right) \mathbf{F}_j$$
$$= \bar{b}_0 + \sum_{j=1}^{p} \bar{b}_j \mathbf{F}_j \,.$$

That is, the factor loading of a centroid $\overline{\mathbf{X}}$ on a given factor $\mathbf{F}_j$ is simply the average factor loading on $\mathbf{F}_j$ for those variables of which $\overline{\mathbf{X}}$ is the centroid. The factor composition of $\mathbf{D}_i$ is

[7.40-i] (i = 1, . . . , n)
$$\mathbf{D}_i = \mathbf{X}_i - \overline{\mathbf{X}}$$
$$= b_{io} + \sum_{j=1}^{p} b_{ij}\mathbf{F}_j - \left(\bar{b}_0 + \sum_{j=1}^{p} \bar{b}_j\mathbf{F}_j\right)$$
$$= (b_{io} - \bar{b}_0) + \sum_{j=1}^{p} (b_{ij} - \bar{b}_j)\mathbf{F}_j \,,$$

so the factor loading of dispersion component $\mathbf{D}_i$ on a given factor $\mathbf{F}_j$ is the deviation of the loading of variable $\mathbf{X}_i$ on $\mathbf{F}_j$ from the average loading on $\mathbf{F}_j$ in this set. Moreover, while [7.39] and [7.40] require no assumptions about the covariances among the factors, we know that for orthonormal factors, the square of a variable's loading on a given factor is the amount of its variance controlled by that factor (cf. [6.37]). Hence

[7.41-j] (j = 1, . . . , p)
$$\mathrm{V}_{\overline{\mathbf{X}}(\mathbf{F}_j)} = \bar{b}_j^2 \qquad \text{(orthonormal factors)} \,,$$

[7.42-ij] (i = 1, . . . , n; j = 1, . . . , p)
$$\mathrm{V}_{\mathbf{D}_i(\mathbf{F}_j)} = (b_{ij} - \bar{b}_j)^2 \qquad \text{(orthonormal factors)} \,,$$

and averaging over all $\mathbf{D}_i$ in [7.42],

[7.43-j] (j = 1, . . . , p)
$$\overline{\mathrm{V}}_{\mathbf{D}(\mathbf{F}_j)} =_{\mathrm{def}} \frac{\sum_{i=1}^{n} \mathrm{V}_{\mathbf{D}_i(\mathbf{F}_j)}}{\mathbf{n}}$$

$$= \frac{\sum_{i=1}^{n} (b_{ij} - \bar{b}_j)^2}{n} \qquad \text{(orthonormal factors)}$$

$$= \sigma_j^2 \ .$$

Inserting these results in [7.38] then shows that for any factor **F**,

[7.44][6] $$\bar{V}_{X(F)} = V_{\bar{X}(F)} + \bar{V}_{D(F)} \ ,$$

or in terms of total variance,

[7.45][6] $$V_{X(F)} = \mathbf{n} V_{\bar{X}(F)} + V_{D(F)} \ .$$

Variance partition [7.44] may readily be generalized to predictor spaces of more than one dimension by recalling (cf. [6.28]) that the variance of any variable in a space *S* is the sum of its variances individually controlled by the various factors constituting an orthogonal basis for *S*. Hence summing [7.44] over a set of orthogonal factors $\mathbf{F}_1, \ldots, \mathbf{F}_k$ which span an arbitrary space *S* yields

[7.46] $$\bar{V}_{X(S)} = V_{\bar{X}(S)} + \bar{V}_{D(S)} \ ,$$

or

[7.47] $$V_{X(S)} = \mathbf{n} V_{\bar{X}(S)} + V_{D(S)} \ .$$

In particular, if *S* is a space which includes all the $\mathbf{X}_i$, the total set variance analyzes as

[7.48] $$V_X = \mathbf{n} V_{\bar{X}} + V_D \ ,$$

or expressed as an average,

[7.49] $$\bar{V}_X = V_{\bar{X}} + \bar{V}_D \ .$$

That is, the total variance of variables $\mathbf{X}_1, \ldots, \mathbf{X}_n$ equals **n** times the variance of their centroid plus the total variance of their dispersion components, and similarly for the projections of the $\mathbf{X}_i$ into any space *S*. Hence the variance configuration of a set of **n** variables is identical with the variance configuration of the 2**n** variables derived by splitting each original variable $\mathbf{X}_i$ into its saturation and dispersion components, thus obtaining **n** variables $\mathbf{D}_1, \ldots, \mathbf{D}_n$ and **n** identical variables $\bar{\mathbf{X}}$.[7] We shall

[6] Stipulation of orthonormal factors and reference to a particular set of factors for $\mathbf{X}_1, \ldots, \mathbf{X}_n$ is not appended to [7.44, 45] because no assumptions about factor pattern are needed. A predictor's own variance makes no difference for the variance it controls of another variable, while any predictor **F** can always be treated as part of an orthogonal basis for some space containing the set $\mathbf{X}_1, \ldots, \mathbf{X}_n$.

[7] Lest it seem too intuitively evident that for any arbitrary variable **Y**, the total variance of $\mathbf{X}_1, \ldots, \mathbf{X}_n$ in any space *S* should equal the total variance in *S* of the set comprising **n** identical variables **Y** together with the **n** discrepancy variables $\mathbf{X}_i - \mathbf{Y}$, let the reader prove that this is, in fact, true *only* if **Y** is the centroid of the $\mathbf{X}_i$.

call the quantities $\mathbf{n}V_{\overline{X}}$ and V_D the total *saturation variance* and total *dispersion variance*, respectively, of the set $\mathbf{X}_1, \ldots, \mathbf{X}_n$, while $V_{\overline{X}}$ and $\overline{V}_D$ are then the set's average saturation and dispersion variances, respectively.

Since the nature of the distinction between saturation variance and dispersion variance can be visualized with especial clarity in the vector model of a multivariate distribution, we shall present just enough of this model, without attempting an honest mathematical explanation of it, to show what saturation and dispersion configurations look like. It was pointed out earlier that the loading, b_{ij}, of variable $\mathbf{X}_i$ on a factor $\mathbf{F}_j$ may be construed as the value of a factor-pattern variable $\mathbf{b}_j$ for "individual" $\mathbf{X}_i$. Thus by analyzing variables $\mathbf{X}_1, \ldots, \mathbf{X}_n$ as linear combinations of $\mathbf{p}$ factors $\mathbf{F}_1, \ldots, \mathbf{F}_p$, we can examine their configuration by making a $\mathbf{p}$-dimensional scattergram which shows the joint distribution of "population" $\mathbf{X}_1, \ldots, \mathbf{X}_n$ on the $\mathbf{p}$ variables $\mathbf{b}_1, \ldots, \mathbf{b}_p$, each variable $\mathbf{X}_j$ being represented by a single point whose coordinates on the various axes of the scattergram are the loadings of $\mathbf{X}_j$ on the corresponding factors. To illustrate, suppose that variables $\mathbf{X}_1, \ldots, \mathbf{X}_6$ lie in the space of two orthonormal factors $\mathbf{F}_1, \mathbf{F}_2$ according to the pattern

[7.50-1] $\mathbf{X}_1 = .3\mathbf{F}_1 + .9\mathbf{F}_2$; $V_{X_1} = .90$

[7.50-2] $\mathbf{X}_2 = .6\mathbf{F}_1 + .2\mathbf{F}_2$; $V_{X_2} = .40$

[7.50-3] $\mathbf{X}_3 = .9\mathbf{F}_1 + .1\mathbf{F}_2$; $V_{X_3} = .82$

[7.50-4] $\mathbf{X}_4 = 1.0\mathbf{F}_1 + .5\mathbf{F}_2$; $V_{X_4} = 1.25$

[7.50-5] $\mathbf{X}_5 = .8\mathbf{F}_1 + .9\mathbf{F}_2$; $V_{X_5} = 1.45$

[7.50-6] $\mathbf{X}_6 = .6\mathbf{F}_1 + 1.0\mathbf{F}_2$; $V_{X_6} = 1.36$

$$V_X = 6.18 \; ; \; \overline{V}_X = 1.03$$

(Since the model makes no use of the means of the variables, these have for simplicity been chosen equal to zero.) Then the positions of these $\mathbf{X}_i$ in their factor-pattern scattergram are shown by the six solid dots in Figure 7.1*a*. By averaging the six coefficients on each factor, the centroid of the $\mathbf{X}_i$ is seen to have the factor pattern

[7.51] $$\overline{\mathbf{X}} = .70\mathbf{F}_1 + .60\mathbf{F}_2 \; ; \; V_{\overline{X}} = .85 \; ; \; \mathbf{n}V_{\overline{X}} = 5.10 \; .$$

so $\overline{\mathbf{X}}$ may be shown in the factor-pattern scattergram by the open circle in Figure 7.1*a*. This makes visually clear that the centroid of a set of variables lies at their geometrical center in factor space.

If the point for each variable in Figure 7.1*a* is connected by a straight-line segment to the origin of the graph, as shown in Figure 7.1*b*, we arrive at the "simple" vector model for a configuration of variables.[8] Now, a basic principle of analytic geometry is that the squared distance between any two points in a multidimensional space is the squared distance

[8] The *simple* vector model of the distribution of $\mathbf{X}_1, \ldots, \mathbf{X}_n$ represents each variable by

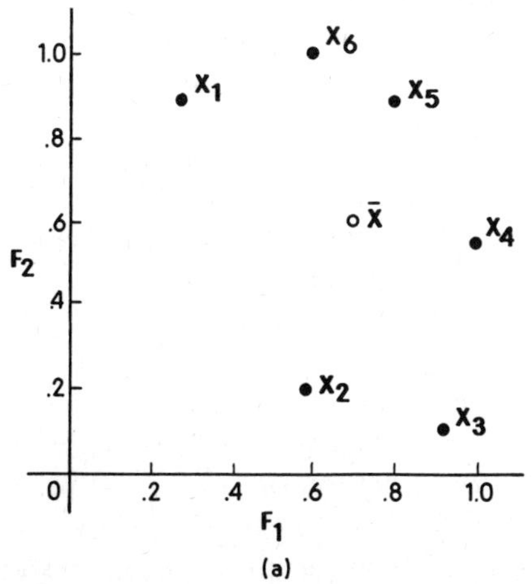

(a)

Figure 7.1.a) Scattergram of factor loadings for the set of variables (solid dots) whose factor pattern is given in [7.50]. The open circle shows the factor loadings of the set's centroid.

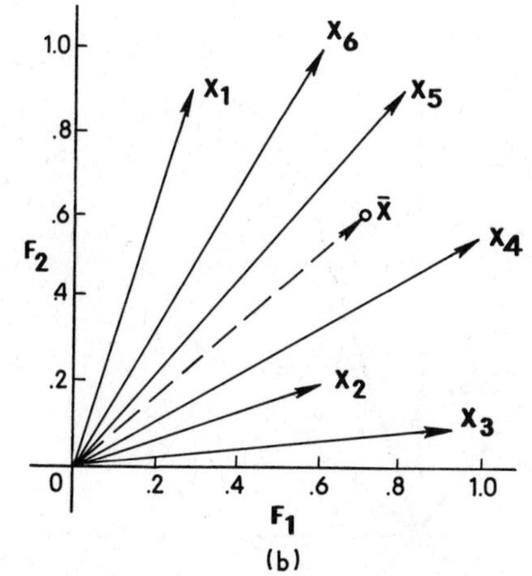

(b)

Figure 7.1.b) Simple vector model for configuration [7.50], including the set's centroid (dotted vector). The standard deviation of a variable is represented by the length of its vector, while the cosine of the angle between any two variables (vectors) equals their correlation.

---

its coordinates on a set of factors, and has no provision for the means of the variables. In the *profound* vector model of the distribution, on the other hand, each coordinate axis is one of the individuals in the population from which the scores on the $\mathbf{X}_i$ have been obtained while the score of a given individual on variable $\mathbf{X}_i$ is the coordinate of $\mathbf{X}_i$ on that axis; and one of the dimensions in this model shows means.

between the projections of those points on each coordinate axis,[9] summed over all coordinate axes, in any orthogonal coordinate system for this space. (The most famous example of this theorem is the relation between the lengths of the hypotenuse and the legs of a right triangle.) Therefore, the squared length of the vector from the origin to the point for variable $\mathbf{X}_i$ in a factor-pattern scattergram such as Figure 7.1*b* is the sum of that variable's squared loadings on the factors into which it has been decomposed. But if these factors are orthonormal, as is always stipulated for the reference axes of the model, this also equals the variance of $\mathbf{X}_i$ (cf. [6.40]). Hence the length of a variable's representative vector (measured on the scale indicated on the coordinate axes) is the standard deviation of that variable, and the square of that length is its variance. The *total* variance of a set of variables, therefore, is the sum of the squared lengths of the vectors representing that set. Moreover, the way in which the vectors spread out in different directions corresponds to the way in which the total variance of the set lies in various directions in factor space. Without attempting to explain this aspect of the vector model fully, it may be stated that any straight line passing through the origin of the coordinate system, such as the line marked "$\mathbf{F}_1'$" in Figure 7.1*c*, represents a "direction," or one-dimensional subspace of the total space spanned by the factors $\mathbf{F}_1, \ldots, \mathbf{F}_p$ composing the coordinate system. In fact, any

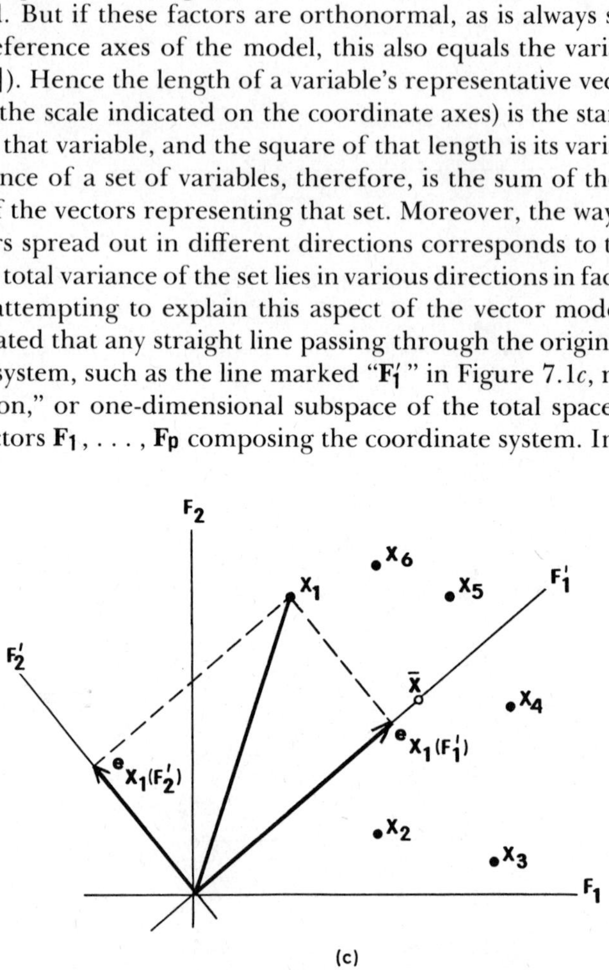

(c)

Figure 7.1.c) Decomposition of a variable into orthogonal components lying in various directions of factor space. Since $\mathbf{F}_1'$ has been chosen to pass through $\bar{\mathbf{X}}$, $\mathbf{e}_{\mathbf{X}_1(\mathbf{F}_1')}$ is the component of $\mathbf{X}_1$ accounted for by the first centroid factor of the set $\mathbf{X}_1, \ldots, \mathbf{X}_6$; while since $\mathbf{X}_1$ lies in the space spanned by $\mathbf{F}_1$ and $\mathbf{F}_2$, $\mathbf{e}_{\mathbf{X}_1(\mathbf{F}_2')}$ is the residual, $\mathbf{e}_{\mathbf{X}_1 \cdot \mathbf{F}_1'}$, left of $\mathbf{X}_1$ after the centroid factor has been partialled out.

[9] See p. 240, above, for a definition of the "projection" of a point on a line.

set of **p** mutually orthogonal lines through the origin, such as either $\mathbf{F_1}, \mathbf{F_2}$ or the other pair of lines $\mathbf{F_1'}, \mathbf{F_2'}$ in Figure 7.1*c*, defines a coordinate system corresponding to one of the alternative orthonormal factor bases for the factor space spanned by $\mathbf{F_1}, \ldots, \mathbf{F_p}$. Analysis of each variable $\mathbf{X_i}$ (more precisely, each zero-order residual $\mathbf{e}_{\mathbf{X_i}}$) as a sum of components lying in various orthogonal directions (that is, the limiting case of [7.10] in which each subspace is one-dimensional) then consists in replacing the vector for $\mathbf{X_i}$ with the set of its projections on the various coordinate axes marking these directions, as demonstrated for $\mathbf{X_5}$ in Figure 7.1*c*. The squared length of $\mathbf{X_i}$'s projection on any direction $\mathbf{F_j'}$ is the variance of $\mathbf{X_i}$ lying in the space of $\mathbf{F_j'}$, while the sum of the squared projections on $\mathbf{F_j'}$ for all the variables is the total variance of the set in that space. Decomposition of variables and their variances into sums of components lying in orthogonal subspaces of dimensionality greater than 1 may also be readily visualized in the vector model, but since printed illustrations of a space greater than two dimensions are difficult to bring off effectively, we shall not press the matter.

It should again be mentioned (cf. p. 210) that the cosine of the angle between any two vectors in a configuration such as Figure 7.1*a* is equal to the correlation between the variables represented by those vectors, which means that the smaller the angle the larger the correlation, while right angles correspond to zero correlation and angles greater than right indicate negative correlations. To prove this satisfactorily would require an excursion into trigonometry which we shall not undertake. It can, however, be seen from [7.5] and [4.56] that the projection of a variable $\mathbf{X_i}$ into the one-dimensional space defined by a normalized variable $\mathbf{F_j'}$ is

$$[7.52] \qquad \mathbf{e}_{\mathbf{X_i}(\mathbf{F_j'})} = \sigma_{\mathbf{X}} r_{\mathbf{X_i}\mathbf{F_j'}} \qquad (M_{\mathbf{F_j'}} = 0,\ V_{\mathbf{F_j'}} = 1)\ .$$

The "length" of the projection of $\mathbf{X_i}$ in the direction of $\mathbf{F_j'}$ is defined to be the factor loading, b_{ij}', that $\mathbf{X_i}$ would have on $\mathbf{F_j'}$ in an orthonormal factor system of which $\mathbf{F_j'}$ is a part, namely (cf. [6.36]),

$$[7.53] \qquad b_{ij}' = \sigma_{\mathbf{X_i}} r_{\mathbf{X_i}\mathbf{F_j'}}\ .$$

Thus the length of $\mathbf{X_i}$ in the $\mathbf{F_j'}$ direction is the standard deviation of the projection of $\mathbf{X_i}$ on the $\mathbf{F_j'}$ axis except that the "length" has a negative sign when the correlation between $\mathbf{X_i}$ and $\mathbf{F_j}$ is negative. This is the exact analog of the trigonometric principle that the projection of one line segment upon another line is $s' = s\ \mathrm{Cos}(\theta)$, where s is the length of the original line segment, s' is the length of its projection, θ is the angle between the two lines, and the length of the projection is conceived as negative when θ is greater than 90°. Hence if the vector model is to be able to get a projection of length b'_{ij} on line $\mathbf{F}'_j$ out of a vector $\mathbf{X}_i$ of length $\sigma_{\mathbf{X}_i}$, it is necessary that the angle, θ, between the vectors for $\mathbf{X}_i$ and $\mathbf{F}'_j$ be such that $\text{Cos}(\theta) = r_{\mathbf{X}_i\mathbf{F}'_i}$.

We have already observed how the centroid of a set of variables is represented in their factor-pattern scattergram and vector model. To see the configuration of dispersion components, recall from [7.40] that the coordinate of dispersion component $\mathbf{D}_i$ on each coordinate axis $\mathbf{F}_j$ is $b_{ij} - \bar{b}_j$, where b_{ij} and $\bar{b}_j$ are the coordinates of $\mathbf{X}_i$ and $\bar{\mathbf{X}}$, respectively. Hence the coordinates for $\mathbf{D}_i$ are what the coordinates for $\mathbf{X}_i$ would be if the origin of the factor-pattern scattergram were shifted to the point representing $\bar{\mathbf{X}}$, and the vectors for the dispersion components may be displayed by first drawing a vector from the point for $\bar{\mathbf{X}}$ to each point for an $\mathbf{X}_i$ as shown in Figure 7.1*d*, and then shifting (without rotation) this configuration to place its center at the origin of the coordinate system, as accomplished in Figure 7.1*e*. The manner in which the dispersion components fan out with an average projection of zero in every direction is then vividly evident. It should also be observed, however, that the *variance* of the dispersion components does not have to be distributed uniformly in all directions. The dispersion variance in any given direction is the sum of the *squared* projections of the $\mathbf{D}_i$ on the line marking that direction, where the squaring operation thwarts the efforts of one $\mathbf{D}_i$ to cancel out another, and the lengths of these projections may be greater in some directions than in others. Specifically, the extent of anisotropy in the dispersion configuration is displayed in the vector model by the severity to which, roughly speaking, their envelope (i.e., the edge of the region which encloses them) is elliptical rather than circular (or in $\mathbf{p}$-space, hyperspherical). It will emerge later that the degree of directional bias in a set's dispersion variance plays a critical role in the behavior of linear functions of the $\mathbf{X}_i$.

It was observed earlier (p. 303) that the variance distribution of a set of $\mathbf{n}$ variables is identical with that of the derived set of $2\mathbf{n}$ variables comprising (1) the $\mathbf{n}$ dispersion components of the set, and (2) $\mathbf{n}$ replications of the set's centroid. If we call the set of dispersion components the *dispersion configuration* of the set, then the complementary *saturation configuration* comprises the set's centroid taken $\mathbf{n}$ times. It is somewhat difficult to distinguish in the graph of a vector configuration between a single variable and several repetitions thereof, but this can be indicated after a fashion by drawing the replicated vector with a heavier line than the others. Alternatively, we can exhibit the set of $\mathbf{n}$ saturation components with a single "saturation-surrogate" variable defined by multiplying $\bar{\mathbf{X}}$ by $\sqrt{\mathbf{n}}$, since the variance of $\sqrt{\mathbf{n}}\,\bar{\mathbf{X}}$ lying in any space S is $\mathbf{n}\mathrm{V}_{\bar{\mathbf{X}}(S)}$. Combining the dispersion configuration and the saturation configuration or saturation surrogate for a set of variables in the same diagram, as

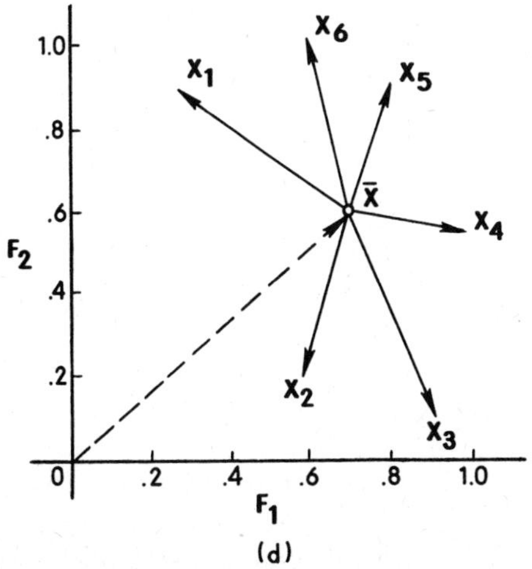

Figure 7.1.*d*) Centroid decomposition of a configuration of variables. Each variable $\mathbf{X_i}$ is expressed as the sum of two vectors, saturation component $\bar{\mathbf{X}}$ (dotted vector) and dispersion component $\mathbf{D_i}$ (solid vector from $\bar{\mathbf{X}}$ to $\mathbf{X_i}$).

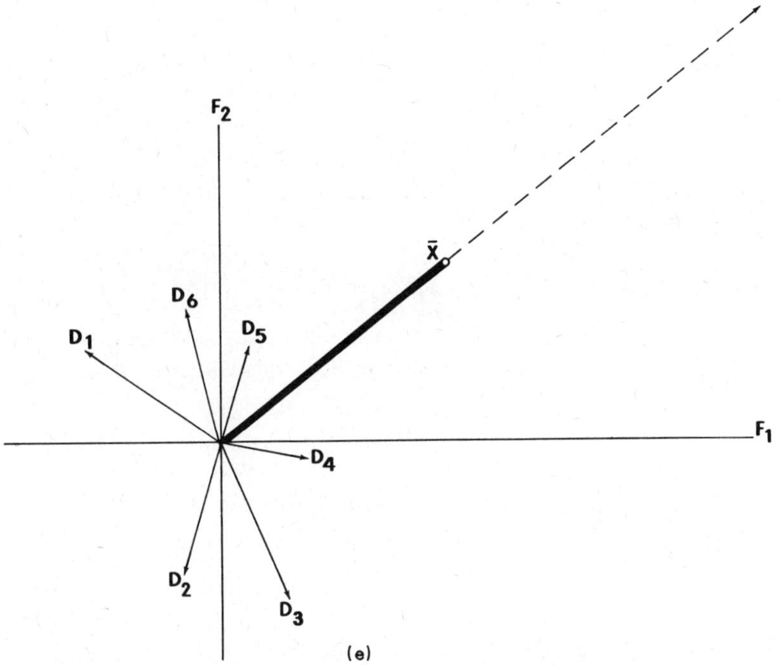

Figure 7.1.e) Vector model of configuration [7.50] analyzed into saturation and dispersion components. The saturation configuration consists of **n** (here six coincident vectors from the origin to $\bar{\mathbf{X}}$, the variance properties of which can· alternatively be shown by a single "saturation-surrogate" vector (dotted line) collinear with $\bar{\mathbf{X}}$ but $\sqrt{\mathbf{n}}$ times its length.

illustrated in Figure 7.1*e*, then completes the vector model for composition-equation [7.47].

Centroids and Principal Axes. One of the many aspects of multivariate relationships to which partition of a total configuration of variables into saturation and dispersion components brings deepened understanding is the placement of factors which maximize accounted-for variance. As discussed previously (p. 238), the "first principle factor" of a set of variables is that normalized variable which accounts for the maximum amount of the set's total variance that is possible for a single variable. Correspondingly, the first principal axis of the vector model for the set is the direction in which the largest part of the set variance lies. Now, visual inspection of the vector model of a configuration of unalyzed variables (e.g., Figure 7.1*b*) does not discern very clearly just where their first principle axis lies. Neither, for that matter, is this altogether obvious to visual inspection when the set is analyzed into dispersion and saturation configurations (Figure 7.1*e*); but the latter model does make much more perspicuous the mathematical forces which bear on the placement of that axis.

It is clear from a diagram such as Figure 7.1*e* that other things equal,[10] more of a set's total variance should lie in the direction of its centroid than in any other direction. Specifically, the first centroid factor picks up *all* of the set's saturation variance together with whatever dispersion variance also lies in that direction, whereas any other factor likewise commands only one dimension's worth of dispersion variance and loses some of the saturation variance besides. To make this intuitive argument precise, we can see from [7.47] that the total variance of set $\mathbf{X}_1, \ldots, \mathbf{X}_n$ controlled by an arbitrary factor $\mathbf{F}$ is

$$V_{\mathbf{X}(\mathbf{F})} = \mathbf{n}V_{\overline{\mathbf{X}}}\, r^2_{\mathbf{F}\overline{\mathbf{X}}} + V_{\mathbf{D}(\mathbf{F})}\,, \tag{7.54}$$

whereas the set variance controlled by the set's centroid is

$$V_{\mathbf{X}(\overline{\mathbf{X}})} = \mathbf{n}V_{\overline{\mathbf{X}}} + V_{\mathbf{D}(\overline{\mathbf{X}})}\,. \tag{7.55}$$

Hence in order for $V_{\mathbf{X}(\mathbf{F})} > V_{\mathbf{X}(\overline{\mathbf{X}})}$ to hold, it is necessary to have

$$V_{\mathbf{D}(\mathbf{F})} - V_{\mathbf{D}(\overline{\mathbf{X}})} > \mathbf{n}V_{\overline{\mathbf{X}}}(1 - r^2_{\mathbf{F}\overline{\mathbf{X}}})\,.$$

That is, if $\mathbf{F}$ is to account for more of the set variance than does $\overline{\mathbf{X}}$, then the dispersion variance lying in the direction of $\mathbf{F}$ must exceed the dis-

[10] This is a well-known qualification meaning "let's disregard any complications that might cast doubt on our conclusions."

persion variance lying in the direction of **F** must exceed the dispersion variance lying in the direction of $\overline{\mathbf{X}}$ by an amount greater than a certain proportion of the saturation variance of the set, this proportion approaching 1 as the correlation between **F** and $\overline{\mathbf{X}}$ approaches zero. For this to occur it is first and foremost necessary for the dispersion configuration, whose shape will be roughly ellipsoidal, to have its longest axis at an angle to $\overline{\mathbf{X}}$. This will always be true to at least a minimal extent if the dimensionality of $\mathbf{X}_1, \ldots, \mathbf{X}_n$ is **n**, since then the dispersion configuration lies in an (**n** − 1)-dimensional space not containing $\overline{\mathbf{X}}$ (see p. 300). Consequently a set's first principal factor tends to be pulled away from the centroid in the direction of the long axes of the dispersion configuration. But the greater the inclination of the long axes of the dispersion configuration to the centroid, the more eccentric must its ellipticality be if a factor which attempts to capture this disproportionate share of dispersion variance is to be compensated for the loss of saturation variance. We may expect, then, that so long as at least a moderate proportion of a set's total variance is invested in saturation variance, the first principal factor of the set will not diverge greatly from its centroid unless the dispersion variance shows remarkable anisotropy.

It is further instructive to run through this argument in terms of the distribution of factor-pattern coefficients. Let $\mathbf{X}_1, \ldots, \mathbf{X}_n$ be analyzed into **p** orthonormal factors $\mathbf{F}_1, \ldots, \mathbf{F}_p$ as in [7.35], while $\mathbf{b}_j$, as explained previously, is the factor-pattern variable whose value for variable $\mathbf{X}_i$ is the latter's coefficient, b_{ij}, on factor $\mathbf{F}_j$. From [7.38], we see that the average variance of the $\mathbf{X}_i$ accounted for by any factor $\mathbf{F}_j$ is the squared quadratic mean magnitude, $QM^2_{|b_j|}$, of the set's factor loadings on $\mathbf{F}_j$, and that this further decomposes into saturation contribution $\bar{b}_j^2$ and dispersion contribution $\sigma^2_{b_j}$. How the total variance in the set breaks down according to types and to orthonormal factors can be shown in a table such as:

Variance Type	Set Variance Accounted for by—				
	$\mathbf{F}_1$	$\mathbf{F}_2$	......	$\mathbf{F}_p$	All Factors
Saturation	$\mathbf{n}\bar{b}_1^2$	$\mathbf{n}\bar{b}_2^2$	......	$\mathbf{n}\bar{b}_p^2$	$\mathbf{n}V_{\overline{X}}$
Dispersion	$\mathbf{n}\sigma^2_{b_1}$	$\mathbf{n}\sigma^2_{b_2}$	......	$\mathbf{n}\sigma^2_{b_p}$	V_D
Total	$\mathbf{n}QM^2_{\lvert b_1\rvert}$	$\mathbf{n}QM^2_{\lvert b_2\rvert}$	......	$\mathbf{n}QM^2_{\lvert b_p\rvert}$	V_X

For example, the two factors in example [7.50] account for the total variance of $\mathbf{X}_1, \ldots, \mathbf{X}_6$ according to the following decomposition:

Variance Type	Set Variance Accounted for by—		
	F_1	F_2	All Factors
Saturation	2.94	2.16	5.10
Dispersion	.32	.76	1.08
Total	3.26	2.94	6.18

If we now inquire how the numerical entries in such a table can be altered by varying our choice of (orthonormal) factors for the $\mathbf{X_i}$, several conclusions stand out. (1) By including more factors in the set $\mathbf{F_1}, \ldots, \mathbf{F_p}$ than are necessary to span the space of the $\mathbf{X_i}$, we can make the entries in the columns for one or more factors as small as we please; hence little interest attaches to the question of minimizing the variance contributions of a factor unless these are restricted to basis factors. (2) The value in any cell of the table except those in the "All" column can be changed within limits by the choice of factor placement. However, since no negative entries are possible and the sum of each row is invariant under all alternative choices of orthogonal factors, no entry can exceed the value listed in its row under "All." (3) Dispersion components $\mathbf{D_1}, \ldots, \mathbf{D_n}$ in general span an $(\mathbf{n} - 1)$-dimensional space (or an $\mathbf{m}$-dimensional space if the dimensionality, $\mathbf{m}$, of the $\mathbf{X_i}$ is less than $\mathbf{n}$, as is true for the example in Figure 7.1), so if the dispersion variance is distributed evenly throughout that space, the maximum dispersion variance accounted for by any one factor is $V_{\mathbf{D}}/(\mathbf{n} - 1)$. The value of $\mathbf{n}\sigma^2_{\mathbf{b_j}}$ for a factor $\mathbf{F_j}$ can exceed this only to the extent that the dispersion configuration is elongated in the direction of $\mathbf{F_j}$, and can become as large as $V_{\mathbf{D}}$ only in the extremity that all the dispersion components lie in a single dimension. (4) The entire saturation variance can always be placed on a single factor, namely, the first centroid factor. If this is done, then the average loading, $\bar{b}_j$, on every other factor $\mathbf{F_j}$ orthogonal to $\bar{\mathbf{X}}$ must be zero. The centroid factor also generally commands some of the dispersion variance, though since $\bar{\mathbf{X}}$ rarely lies in the space of the $\mathbf{D_j}$, the tendency will be for $V_{\mathbf{D}(\bar{\mathbf{X}})}$ to be less than $V_{\mathbf{D}}/(\mathbf{n} - 1)$. Once again, then, it becomes clear that if the saturation variance of a set of variables is at least on the same order of magnitude as its dispersion variance (the proportion of saturation variance in illustrative Figure 7.1 is unrealistically high for most empirical data), and the number of variables is large enough to give the dispersion components ample space (i.e., $\mathbf{n} - 1$ dimensions) through which to scatter their variance, then the set's variance accounted for by its centroid will fail to be close to maximal only for highly unusual configurations.

While the dispersion variance accounted for by $\bar{\mathbf{X}}$ is not likely to be a major quantity, it has a configurational interpretation which should not go unheeded. Let s_i be the length of variable $\mathbf{X}_i$'s projection on the centroid axis, where a negative value for s_i indicates a negative correlation between $\mathbf{X}_i$ and $\bar{\mathbf{X}}$. If one of the factors, say $\mathbf{F}_1$, in factor pattern [7.35] is the normalized centroid, then $s_i = b_{i1}$ and our previous discussion shows immediately that

[7.56] $$V_{\bar{X}} = \bar{s}^2 ,$$

[7.57] $$\begin{aligned} V_{D(\bar{X})} &= \mathbf{n}\sigma_s^2 \\ &= \mathbf{n}V_{\bar{X}} \left(\frac{\sigma_s}{\bar{s}}\right)^2 \\ &= \mathbf{n}V_{\bar{X}}\nu_s^2 , \end{aligned}$$

where $\bar{s}$ and σ_s are the mean and SD, respectively, of the projections $s_1, \ldots, s_n$ of the $\mathbf{X}_i$ on the centroid axis, and ν_s is the coefficient of variation (see p. 47, Chapter 3) for the s_i. Equation [7.56] tells an old story, namely, that the average projection of the $\mathbf{X}_i$ on the centroid axis is equal in length to the centroid itself. The meaning of [7.57] is also easy to visualize: In the limiting condition $\sigma_s = 0$, all the $\mathbf{X}_i$ have the same projection on the centroid axis, namely, $\bar{\mathbf{X}}$. In the vector model, this occurs if the points for the $\mathbf{X}_i$ all lie in a hyperplane passing through the point for $\bar{\mathbf{X}}$ and perpendicular to the $\bar{\mathbf{X}}$-vector. (In Figure 7.1*a*, this hyperplane is the line drawn through the point for $\bar{\mathbf{X}}$ perpendicular to the line from the origin to $\bar{\mathbf{X}}$.) More generally, σ_s is the quadratic mean of how far the $\mathbf{X}_i$ points digress from this hyperplane, and ν_s ($= \sigma_s/\bar{s}$) evaluates how gross these digressions appear when assayed against the magnitude of the set's prevailing effort in the centroid's direction. If the $\mathbf{X}_i$ have all been standardized to the same variance, then σ_s is proportional to the standard deviation of the correlations between $\bar{\mathbf{X}}$ and the $\mathbf{X}_i$. In this case, $\sigma_s = 0$ implies that the $\mathbf{X}_i$ fan out in a cone (or hypercone) whose axis is $\bar{\mathbf{X}}$, while as ν_s grows larger, the conelike quality of the configuration grows more and more ragged in comparison to its length. With this image in mind, the statistic ν_s might be called the *index of radial irregularity*. In Appendix B, p. 588, it is shown that a configuration's index of radial irregularity is zero if and, essentially, only if the configuration's centroid coincides (up to a linear transformation) with one of its principal factors.

It may be noted that the value of ν_s, and hence that of $V_{D(\bar{X})}$, can be determined directly from the covariance matrix of the $\mathbf{X}_i$ without conceptualizing the computation in terms of factor loadings. We know from [7.52] that the length of $\mathbf{X}_i$'s projection on the centroid axis is

[7.58-i] $$s_i = \sigma_{X_i} r_{X_i \bar{X}} .$$
(i = 1, . . . , n)

If for notational simplicity we let the covariance between each variable $\mathbf{X}_i$ in set $\mathbf{X}_1, \ldots, \mathbf{X}_n$ and the set's centroid be abbreviated to $c_{\mathbf{X}_i}$, we have

$$[7.59\text{-}\mathbf{i}] \quad (\mathbf{i} = 1, \ldots, \mathbf{n}) \qquad c_{\mathbf{X}_i} =_{\text{def}} C_{\mathbf{X}_i\overline{\mathbf{X}}} = \sigma_{\mathbf{X}_i}\sigma_{\overline{\mathbf{X}}}r_{\mathbf{X}_i\overline{\mathbf{X}}} = \sigma_{\overline{\mathbf{X}}}s_i \,.$$

Hence the length of $\mathbf{X}_i$'s projection on $\overline{\mathbf{X}}$ differs from its covariance with $\overline{\mathbf{X}}$ only by a constant of proportionality and the relative variation in the one is the same as the relative variation in the other. That is,

$$[7.60] \qquad \nu_{c_{\mathbf{X}}} =_{\text{def}} \frac{\sigma_{c_{\mathbf{X}}}}{\bar{c}_{\mathbf{X}}} = \frac{\sigma_{s}}{\bar{s}} = \nu_{s} \,,$$

and for [7.57] and [7.55] we may then write

$$[7.61] \qquad V_{\mathbf{D}(\overline{\mathbf{X}})} = \mathbf{n}V_{\overline{\mathbf{X}}}\nu^2_{c_{\mathbf{X}}} \,,$$

$$[7.62] \qquad V_{\mathbf{X}(\overline{\mathbf{X}})} = \mathbf{n}V_{\overline{\mathbf{X}}}(1 + \nu^2_{c_{\mathbf{X}}}) \,.$$

Since $c_{\mathbf{X}_i}$ is the average entry in the **i**th column (or row) of covariance matrix $\{C_{\mathbf{X}_i\mathbf{X}_j}\}$ (see [6.50]), $\nu_{c_{\mathbf{X}}}$ is the coefficient of variation for the column averages (or totals) in the set's covariance matrix. Subsequently, we shall treat $\nu_{c_{\mathbf{X}}}$, rather than its equivalent ν_{s}, as the definition of a set's "radial irregularity."

Centroid Decomposition of a Covariance Matrix. We have seen previously ([7.14]) that when the variables in a set $\mathbf{X}_1, \ldots, \mathbf{X}_n$ are factored into components lying in various orthogonal subspaces, the set's covariance matrix correspondingly analyzes as the sum of the covariance matrices for the sets of subspace projections. Partition of the set into saturation and dispersion configurations likewise decomposes the $\{C_{\mathbf{X}_i\mathbf{X}_j}\}$ matrix in an interesting fashion.

It is readily seen from [7.32] that

$$[7.63\text{-}\mathbf{ij}] \quad (\mathbf{i,j} = 1, \ldots, \mathbf{n}) \qquad C_{\mathbf{X}_i\mathbf{X}_j} = \text{Cov}(\mathbf{D}_i + \overline{\mathbf{X}}, \mathbf{D}_j + \overline{\mathbf{X}}) = C_{\mathbf{D}_i\mathbf{D}_j} + C_{\mathbf{D}_i\overline{\mathbf{X}}} + C_{\mathbf{D}_j\overline{\mathbf{X}}} + V_{\overline{\mathbf{X}}}$$

or, since $V_{\overline{\mathbf{X}}} = \overline{C}^*_{\mathbf{XX}}$ and

$$[7.64\text{-}\mathbf{i}] \quad (\mathbf{i} = 1, \ldots, \mathbf{n}) \qquad C_{\mathbf{D}_i\overline{\mathbf{X}}} = \text{Cov}(\mathbf{X}_i - \overline{\mathbf{X}}, \overline{\mathbf{X}}) = C_{\mathbf{X}_i\overline{\mathbf{X}}} - V_{\overline{\mathbf{X}}} = c_{\mathbf{X}_i} - \overline{C}^*_{\mathbf{XX}} \,,$$

where $c_{\mathbf{X}_i}$ is the average entry in the **i**th row or column of $\{C_{\mathbf{X}_i\mathbf{X}_j}\}$ and $\overline{C}^*_{\mathbf{XX}}$ is the average of all entries in $\{C_{\mathbf{X}_i\mathbf{X}_j}\}$,

$$[7.65\text{-}\mathbf{ij}] \quad (\mathbf{i,j} = 1, \ldots, \mathbf{n}) \qquad C_{\mathbf{X}_i\mathbf{X}_j} = C_{\mathbf{D}_i\mathbf{D}_j} + (c_{\mathbf{X}_i} - \overline{C}^*_{\mathbf{XX}}) + (c_{\mathbf{X}_j} - \overline{C}^*_{\mathbf{XX}}) + \overline{C}^*_{\mathbf{XX}} .$$

The reader who is familiar with Fisherian Analysis-of-Variance designs (see pp. 543 ff., Chapter 10) will immediately recognize [7.65] as a decomposition of $C_{\mathbf{X}_i\mathbf{X}_j}$ into grand effect $\overline{C}^*_{\mathbf{XX}}$, row and column effects $C_{\mathbf{D}_i\overline{\mathbf{X}}}$ and $C_{\mathbf{D}_j\overline{\mathbf{X}}}$, respectively, and an "interaction" term $C_{\mathbf{D}_i\mathbf{D}_j}$. That is, if the grand mean of the $C_{\mathbf{X}_i\mathbf{X}_j}$ is subtracted from each, the array of column (or row averages in the reduced matrix $\{C_{\mathbf{X}_i\mathbf{X}_j} - \overline{C}^*_{\mathbf{XX}}\}$ exhibits the covariance between saturation component $\overline{\mathbf{X}}$ and each dispersion component $\mathbf{D}_i$; while if $\{C_{\mathbf{X}_i\mathbf{X}_j}\}$ is further reduced by subtracting from each entry the means of the row and column of which that entry is the intersection, the matrix which results is $\{C_{\mathbf{D}_i\mathbf{D}_j}\}$. It also follows from [7.65] by the well-known Fisherian sum-of-squares partition that

$$[7.66] \qquad QM^2_{|C^*_{\mathbf{XX}}|} = QM^2_{|C^*_{\mathbf{DD}}|} + 2\sigma^2_{\overline{C}_{\mathbf{X}}} + \overline{C}^{*2}_{\mathbf{XX}},$$

where $QM_{|C^*_{\mathbf{XX}}|}$ and $QM_{|C^*_{\mathbf{DD}}|}$ are the quadratic mean magnitudes of the entries in $\{C_{\mathbf{X}_i\mathbf{X}_j}\}$ and $\{C_{\mathbf{D}_i\mathbf{D}_j}\}$, respectively, and $\sigma_{\overline{C}_{\mathbf{X}}}$ is the standard deviation of row or column means for $\{C_{\mathbf{X}_i\mathbf{X}_j}\}$, this being equal to the standard deviation of the array of covariances $C_{\mathbf{D}_1\overline{\mathbf{X}}}, \ldots, C_{\mathbf{D}_n\overline{\mathbf{X}}}$.

Penetrance, Saturation, and Homogeneity

While it is frequently convenient mathematically to analyze the distribution of a set of variables through partitions of total or perhaps average variances, the numerical value of a variance component has little interpretive meaning in itself, since any nonzero component can be made arbitrarily large or small merely by adjusting the scale of measurement. What is important about saturation variance, for example, is not how large it is numerically, but how it compares to other variance components of the configuration. Similarly, knowing how much of a set's variance lies in a given space reveals virtually nothing about the set's distribution unless this variance can be converted into a proportion of the total. In order to expedite interpretation, therefore, it is desirable to introduce standardized measures of these components.

Let the proportion of a set's variance lying in a space S be called the *penetrance*, $P_{\mathbf{X}}(S)$, of the set into S. That is, the collective "penetrance" of variables $\mathbf{X}_1, \ldots, \mathbf{X}_n$ into space S is

$$[7.67] \qquad P_{\mathbf{X}}(S) =_{\text{def}} \frac{V_{\mathbf{X}(S)}}{V_{\mathbf{X}}} = \frac{\overline{V}_{\mathbf{X}(S)}}{\overline{V}_{\mathbf{X}}}.$$

(The letter "P" in "$P_{\mathbf{X}}(S)$" may be read either as "proportion" or as "penetrance," but despite the initial unfamiliarity of the latter, the reader will find that it lends itself to smoother sentence construction than does the former. The reason for calling attention to set-variance averages as well as totals in definition [7.67] is that averages turn out to be more convenient to work with than totals.) We may likewise refer to the proportion of an individual variable's variance in a space S as its "penetrance" into S, except that to avoid confusion between the penetrance of sets and the penetrance of individual variables, we shall use an italic "P" for the latter—i.e.,

$$[7.68] \qquad P_{\mathbf{X}_i}(S) =_{\text{def}} \frac{V_{\mathbf{X}_i(S)}}{V_{\mathbf{X}_i}} = R^2_{\mathbf{X}_i(S)},$$

where $R_{\mathbf{X}_i(S)}$, it will be recalled (cf. p. 293), is the multiple linear correlation of $\mathbf{X}_i$ with any set of predictors which span S, or, equivalently, the linear correlation between $\mathbf{X}_i$ and its projection into S. It will be observed that

$$[7.69] \qquad P_{\mathbf{X}}(S) = \frac{\sum_{i=1}^{n} V_{\mathbf{X}_i(S)}}{\sum_{i=1}^{n} V_{\mathbf{X}_i}} = \frac{\sum_{i=1}^{n} V_{\mathbf{X}_i} P_{\mathbf{X}_i}(S)}{\sum_{i=1}^{n} V_{\mathbf{X}_i}} = \frac{\sum_{i=1}^{n} V_{\mathbf{X}_i} R^2_{\mathbf{X}_i(S)}}{\sum_{i=1}^{n} V_{\mathbf{X}_i}},$$

while if the $\mathbf{X}_i$ have all been standardized to the same variance, this becomes simply

$$[7.70] \qquad P_{\mathbf{X}}(S) = \frac{\sum_{i=1}^{n} P_{\mathbf{X}_i}(S)}{\mathbf{n}} = \frac{\sum_{i=1}^{n} R^2_{\mathbf{X}_i(S)}}{\mathbf{n}} \qquad (V_{\mathbf{X}_i} = \bar{V}_{\mathbf{X}}, \mathbf{i} = \mathbf{1}, \ldots, \mathbf{n})$$

This makes clear that the penetrance of a set of variables into a space S is an average (generally a weighted one) of the penetrances into S of the individual variables in the set. It also shows that $P_{\mathbf{X}}(S)$ is in effect a squared multiple correlation coefficient[11] generalized to a set of criterion variables. Written in terms of penetrance, the partition of a set's total variance into components lying in various orthogonal spaces which collectively contain all the $\mathbf{X}_i$ is

$$[7.71] \qquad \sum_{j=1}^{m} P_{\mathbf{X}}(S_j) = 1 \qquad (\perp(S_1, \ldots, S_m);\ V_{\mathbf{X} \cdot S_1 \ldots S_m} = 0)\ .$$

Similarly, if $\mathbf{L}_{\mathbf{X}}$ is any linear combination of $\mathbf{X}_1, \ldots, \mathbf{X}_n$,

$$[7.72] \qquad \sum_{j=1}^{m} P_{\mathbf{L}_{\mathbf{X}}}(S_j) = 1 \qquad (\perp(S_1, \ldots, S_m);\ V_{\mathbf{X} \cdot S_1 \ldots S_m} = 0)\ .$$

More generally, for any set of orthogonal spaces $S_1, \ldots, S_k$,

$$[7.73] \qquad P_{\mathbf{X}}(S_1 \ldots S_k) = \sum_{j=1}^{k} P_{\mathbf{X}}(S_j) \qquad (\perp(S_1, \ldots, S_k))\ ,$$

$$[7.74] \qquad P_{\mathbf{L}_{\mathbf{X}}}(S_1 \ldots S_k) = \sum_{j=1}^{k} P_{\mathbf{L}_{\mathbf{X}}}(S_j) \qquad (\perp(S_1, \ldots, S_k))\ ,$$

both of which are simple consequences of [7.3].

To standardize the partition of set variance into saturation and dispersion components, we shall call the proportion of a set's total variance which is saturation variance the "saturation coefficient" or simply *saturation* (Sat) of the set. That is,

$$[7.75] \qquad \mathrm{Sat}_{\mathbf{X}} =_{\mathrm{def}} \frac{\mathbf{n} V_{\bar{\mathbf{X}}}}{V_{\mathbf{X}}} = \frac{V_{\bar{\mathbf{X}}}}{\bar{V}_{\mathbf{X}}}\ .$$

In view of the second line of [7.75], the saturation of a set of variables may epigrammatically be described as "the variance of the average, divided by the average of the variances." Similarly, the "dispersion coefficient" or simply *dispersion* (Disp) of the set is

$$[7.76] \qquad \mathrm{Disp}_{\mathbf{X}} =_{\mathrm{def}} \frac{V_{\mathbf{D}}}{V_{\mathbf{X}}} = \frac{\bar{V}_{\mathbf{D}}}{\bar{V}_{\mathbf{X}}}\ ,$$

and partition [7.48] becomes

$$[7.77] \qquad \mathrm{Sat}_{\mathbf{X}} + \mathrm{Disp}_{\mathbf{X}} = 1\ .$$

[11] A squared correlation coefficient is sometimes called a "coefficient of determination."

It is also occasionally helpful to have a single term for the ratio of dispersion variance to saturation variance, so we shall call this the "dispersion quotient" (DQ) for the set. That is,

[7.78]
$$DQ_{\mathbf{X}} =_{\text{def}} \frac{V_{\mathbf{D}}}{nV_{\overline{\mathbf{X}}}},$$
$$= \frac{Disp_{\mathbf{X}}}{Sat_{\mathbf{X}}}$$
$$= \frac{1 - Sat_{\mathbf{X}}}{Sat_{\mathbf{X}}}.$$

Like penetrance, saturation, and dispersion coefficients, the dispersion quotient cannot be less than zero. Whereas penetrance, saturation, and dispersion also have an upper bound of 1, however, $DQ_{\mathbf{X}}$ increases without limit as $Sat_{\mathbf{X}}$ approaches zero. Even so, $DQ_{\mathbf{X}}$ will be on the order of 1 or less unless the saturation of the set is diminutive.

It has previously been shown (pp. 299ff.) in terms of factor-pattern coefficients that the partition of a set's variance between saturation and dispersion components is in an important sense a division between pure consensus and pure inconsistency. Hence $Sat_{\mathbf{X}}$ may be construed as a standardized measure of the degree of uniformity among the variables $\mathbf{X}_1, \ldots, \mathbf{X}_n$. This interpretation of the saturation coefficient takes on additional depth when it is observed from [7.26] that

[7.79]
$$Sat_{\mathbf{X}} = \frac{\overline{C}^*_{\mathbf{XX}}}{\overline{V}_{\mathbf{X}}}.$$

That is, *the saturation of a set of variables equals the ratio of their average covariance to their average variance* when self-covariances are included in the "average covariance." $Sat_{\mathbf{X}}$ is thus rather like an average of correlation coefficients, and in fact if all the $\mathbf{X}_i$ have been standardized to the same variance, so that $V_{\mathbf{X}_i} = \overline{V}_{\mathbf{X}}$, we have

[7.80]
$$Sat_{\mathbf{X}} = \frac{\sum_{i=1}^{n} \sum_{j=1}^{n} C_{\mathbf{X}_i\mathbf{X}_j}}{n^2\overline{V}_{\mathbf{X}}}$$
$$= \frac{\sum_{i=1}^{n} \sum_{j=1}^{n} \sigma_{\mathbf{X}_i}\sigma_{\mathbf{X}_j} r_{\mathbf{X}_i\mathbf{X}_j}}{n^2\overline{V}_{\mathbf{X}}}$$
$$(V_{\mathbf{X}_i} = \overline{V}_{\mathbf{X}},\ \mathbf{i} = \mathbf{1}, \ldots, \mathbf{n})$$
$$= \frac{\sum_{i=1}^{n} \sum_{j=1}^{n} \overline{V}_{\mathbf{X}} r_{\mathbf{X}_i\mathbf{X}_j}}{n^2\overline{V}_{\mathbf{X}}}$$

$$= \frac{\sum_{i=1}^{n} \sum_{j=1}^{n} r_{X_i X_j}}{n^2}$$

$$= \bar{r}^*_{XX} ,$$

where $\bar{r}^*_{XX}$ is the arithmetic mean of all entries in the correlation matrix of the X_i. In general, however, the saturation coefficient assesses not merely the *correlational* agreement among the X_i, but the similarity of their variances as well. Thus in the vector model it is readily visualized that even if the correlations among $X_1, \ldots, X_n$ are all unity, there will still be some dispersion of the X_i around $\bar{X}$ along the centroid axis if there are any discrepancies among the lengths of the X_i-vectors. This can be brought out algebraically as follows: Let the "sigma-weighted" average correlation $\tilde{r}^*_{XX}$ (including self-correlations) among variables $X_1, \ldots, X_n$ be defined

[7.81] $$\tilde{r}^*_{XX} = \frac{\sum_{i=1}^{n} \sum_{j=1}^{n} \sigma_{X_i} \sigma_{X_j} r_{X_i X_j}}{\sum_{i=1}^{n} \sum_{j=1}^{n} \sigma_{X_i} \sigma_{X_j}} .$$

Now,

[7.82] $$\sum_{i=1}^{n} \sum_{j=1}^{n} \sigma_{X_i} \sigma_{X_j} = \left(\sum_{i=1}^{n} \sigma_{X_i} \right)^2$$

$$= (n\bar{\sigma}_X)^2$$

while

[7.83] $$\bar{V}_X = \frac{\sum_{i=1}^{n} \sigma^2_{X_i}}{n}$$

$$= QM^2_{\sigma_X},$$

where $\bar{\sigma}_X$ and QM_{σ_X} are the arithmetic and quadratic mean, respectively, of the distribution of standard deviations among the X_i. Hence

[7.84] $$Sat_X = \frac{\sum_{i=1}^{n} \sum_{j=1}^{n} \sigma_{X_i} \sigma_{X_j} r_{X_i X_j}}{n^2 \bar{V}_X}$$

$$= \frac{(\mathbf{n}\bar{\sigma}_{\mathbf{X}})^2 \sum_{i=1}^{n} \sum_{j=1}^{n} \sigma_{\mathbf{X}_i}\sigma_{\mathbf{X}_j} r_{\mathbf{X}_i\mathbf{X}_j}}{(\mathbf{n}\mathrm{QM}\,\sigma_{\mathbf{X}})^2 \sum_{i=1}^{n} \sum_{j=1}^{n} \sigma_{\mathbf{X}_i}\sigma_{\mathbf{X}_j}}$$

$$= \left(\frac{\bar{\sigma}_{\mathbf{X}}}{\mathrm{QM}_{\sigma_{\mathbf{X}}}}\right)^2 \tilde{r}^*_{\mathbf{XX}} .$$

$$= \frac{\tilde{r}^*_{\mathbf{XX}}}{1 + \nu^2_{\sigma_{\mathbf{X}}}} ,$$

in which $\nu_{\sigma_{\mathbf{X}}}$ is the coefficient of variation for the $\sigma_{\mathbf{X}_i}$, and the last line follows in view of [3.19]. Hence $\mathrm{Sat}_{\mathbf{X}}$ is the sigma-weighted average entry in $\{r_{\mathbf{X}_i\mathbf{X}_j}\}$, attenuated by the severity of the differences among the SDs of the $\mathbf{X}_i$.

When the consistency of variables is judged by their intercorrelations, however, it seems a bit strange to include self-correlations, insomuch as these must always be unity irrespective of whatever empirical agreement may be contained in the proper correlations among the variables. A question which naturally arises, then, is the manner and extent to which between-variable agreement is confounded in the saturation coefficient with self-agreement. To separate these two ingredients in $\mathrm{Sat}_{\mathbf{X}}$, let us call the ratio of the average *proper* covariance among variables $\mathbf{X}_1, \ldots, \mathbf{X}_n$ to their average variance the *homogeneity* (Hom) of the set. That is,

[7.85] $$\mathrm{Hom}_{\mathbf{X}} =_{\mathrm{def}} \frac{\bar{C}_{\mathbf{XX}}}{\bar{V}_{\mathbf{X}}} .$$

Then dividing both sides of [7.25] by $\bar{V}_{\mathbf{X}}$ yields

[7.86] $$\mathrm{Sat}_{\mathbf{X}} = \left(\frac{\mathbf{n}-1}{\mathbf{n}}\right) \mathrm{Hom}_{\mathbf{X}} + \frac{1}{\mathbf{n}}$$

$$= \mathrm{Hom}_{\mathbf{X}} + \frac{1 - \mathrm{Hom}_{\mathbf{X}}}{\mathbf{n}} ,$$

which says that saturation is a mixture of one part unity to $\mathbf{n} - 1$ parts homogeneity. Several useful alternative expressions for this relationship may be derived by solving [7.86] for $\mathrm{Hom}_{\mathbf{X}}$:

[7.87] (*a*) $$\mathrm{Hom}_{\mathbf{X}} = \frac{\mathbf{n}\,\mathrm{Sat}_{\mathbf{X}} - 1}{\mathbf{n} - 1}$$

$$= \frac{(\mathbf{n}-1)\,\mathrm{Sat}_{\mathbf{X}} - (1 - \mathrm{Sat}_{\mathbf{X}})}{\mathbf{n} - 1}$$

(*b*) $$= \mathrm{Sat}_{\mathbf{X}} - \frac{\mathrm{Disp}_{\mathbf{X}}}{\mathbf{n} - 1}$$

(*c*) $$= \left(1 - \frac{\mathrm{DQ}_{\mathbf{X}}}{\mathbf{n} - 1}\right) \mathrm{Sat}_{\mathbf{X}} .$$

From version (*b*) of [7.87], we see that

$$[7.88] \qquad \mathrm{Sat}_{\mathbf{X}} - \mathrm{Hom}_{\mathbf{X}} = \frac{\mathrm{Disp}_{\mathbf{X}}}{\mathbf{n}-1},$$

which makes clear that the saturation of a set of nonidentical variables is always a little larger than its homogeneity, but also that the discrepancy between the two can never exceed $1/(\mathbf{n}-1)$. Hence while Hom is in some ways a purer measure of consistency within a set of variables than is Sat, the additional recognition given by the latter to the self-similarity in the set has increasingly negligible issue as the number of variables in the set increases.

Like saturation, the homogeneity coefficient is basically an average correlation. If the $\mathbf{X}_i$ all have equal variances,

$$[7.89] \qquad \mathrm{Hom}_{\mathbf{X}} = \bar{r}_{\mathbf{XX}} \qquad (V_{\mathbf{X}_i} = \bar{V}_{\mathbf{X}},\ \mathbf{i} = \mathbf{1}, \ldots, \mathbf{n}),$$

where $\bar{r}_{\mathbf{XX}}$ is the arithmetic mean correlation among all pairs of different variables in the set. Also like $\mathrm{Sat}_{\mathbf{X}}$, however, high homogeneity requires high consistency of variances, as well as of correlations, among the variables being assessed. Specifically,

$$[7.90]^{12} \qquad \mathrm{Hom}_{\mathbf{X}} = \left(\frac{1 - \nu^2_{\sigma_{\mathbf{X}}}/(\mathbf{n}-1)}{1 + \nu^2_{\sigma_{\mathbf{X}}}}\right) \tilde{r}_{\mathbf{XX}},$$

where $\tilde{r}_{\mathbf{XX}}$ is the sigma-weighted average between-variable correlation defined analogously to $\tilde{r}^*_{\mathbf{XX}}$, namely,

$$[7.91]^{13} \qquad \tilde{r}_{\mathbf{XX}} =_{\mathrm{def}} \frac{\sum\limits_{\mathbf{i}=\mathbf{1}}^{\mathbf{n}} \sum\limits_{\substack{\mathbf{j}=\mathbf{1} \\ \mathbf{i}\neq\mathbf{j}}}^{\mathbf{n}} \sigma_{\mathbf{X}_i}\sigma_{\mathbf{X}_j} r_{\mathbf{X}_i\mathbf{X}_j}}{\sum\limits_{\mathbf{i}=\mathbf{1}}^{\mathbf{n}} \sum\limits_{\substack{\mathbf{j}=\mathbf{1} \\ \mathbf{i}\neq\mathbf{j}}}^{\mathbf{n}} \sigma_{\mathbf{X}_i}\sigma_{\mathbf{X}_j}}.$$

Equations [7.84] and [7.90] show that both $\mathrm{Sat}_{\mathbf{X}}$ and $\mathrm{Hom}_{\mathbf{X}}$ are the product of a measure of variance similarity with a measure of correlational agreement. It may also be seen, though, that fairly large differences among the $\sigma_{\mathbf{X}_i}$ are required to reduce the variance-similarity multiplier substantially below unity. Hence the internal consistency of a set of variables as measured by either Sat or Hom is determined primarily by the correlations among the variables, with some secondary consideration also given to the differences among their SDs.

---

[12] Since $\mathbf{n}(\mathbf{n}-1)\bar{C}_{\mathbf{XX}} = \sum\limits_{\mathbf{i}=\mathbf{1}}^{\mathbf{n}} \sum\limits_{\substack{\mathbf{j}=\mathbf{1} \\ \mathbf{i}\neq\mathbf{j}}}^{\mathbf{n}} \sigma_{\mathbf{X}_i}\sigma_{\mathbf{X}_j} r_{\mathbf{X}_i\mathbf{X}_j} = \tilde{r}_{\mathbf{XX}} \sum\limits_{\mathbf{i}=\mathbf{1}}^{\mathbf{n}} \sum\limits_{\substack{\mathbf{j}=\mathbf{1} \\ \mathbf{i}\neq\mathbf{j}}}^{\mathbf{n}} \sigma_{\mathbf{X}_i}\sigma_{\mathbf{X}_j} = \tilde{r}_{\mathbf{XX}}\left(\sum\limits_{\mathbf{i}=\mathbf{1}}^{\mathbf{n}} \sum\limits_{\mathbf{j}=\mathbf{1}}^{\mathbf{n}} \sigma_{\mathbf{X}_i}\sigma_{\mathbf{X}_j} - \sum\limits_{\mathbf{i}=\mathbf{1}}^{\mathbf{n}} \sigma^2_{\mathbf{X}_i}\right) = \tilde{r}_{\mathbf{XX}}\left[\left(\sum\limits_{\mathbf{i}=\mathbf{1}}^{\mathbf{n}} \sigma_{\mathbf{X}_i}\right)^2 - \sum\limits_{\mathbf{i}=\mathbf{1}}^{\mathbf{n}} \sigma^2_{\mathbf{X}_i}\right] = \tilde{r}_{\mathbf{XX}}[\mathbf{n}^2 \bar{\sigma}^2_{\mathbf{X}} - \mathbf{n}\bar{\sigma}^2_{\mathbf{X}}(1 + \nu^2_{\sigma_{\mathbf{X}}})] = \mathbf{n}(\mathbf{n}-1)\tilde{r}_{\mathbf{XX}}\bar{\sigma}^2_{\mathbf{X}}\,(1 - \nu^2_{\sigma_{\mathbf{X}}}/[\mathbf{n}-1])$ while $\bar{V}_{\mathbf{X}} = \bar{\sigma}^2_{\mathbf{X}}(1 + \nu^2_{\sigma_{\mathbf{X}}})$.

[13] The quantity $\tilde{r}_{\mathbf{XX}}$ is identical with the "homogeneity-ratio" measure HR recently proposed by Scott (71).

Appreciation for the meanings of Sat and Hom as measures of within-set consistency is further enhanced by considering the conditions under which these coefficients assume minimal values. When the homogeneity of a set of variables is zero, as occurs when (though not only when) the between-variable correlations are all zero, it follows immediately from [7.86] that

[7.92] $$\mathrm{Sat}_{\mathbf{X}} = \frac{1}{\mathbf{n}} \qquad (\mathrm{Hom}_{\mathbf{X}} = 0) .$$

The quantity $1/\mathbf{n}$ might be described as the "intrinsic consistency" in a set of variables, since it reflects the fact that even a set of totally unrelated variables has a prevailing direction of a sort. (Thus in the vector model of a configuration, it is readily visualized that two or more variables at right angles to one another will have a nonzero centroid which, moreover, correlates positively with each of them.) We also know, however, that saturation can get as low as zero (namely, when the set has a zero centroid, examples of which have been encountered previously); hence at maximal interitem discord, homogeneity must be not just zero, but negative. Specifically, we see from [7.87(*a*)] that

[7.93] $$\mathrm{Hom}_{\mathbf{X}} \geqslant -\frac{1}{\mathbf{n}-1} ,$$

with equality holding when $\mathrm{Sat}_{\mathbf{X}} = 0$. (Similarly, from [7.89],

[7.94] $$\bar{r}_{\mathbf{XX}} \geqslant -\frac{1}{\mathbf{n}-1} ,$$

which reveals that it is impossible for a correlation matrix to contain a large proportion of appreciably negative entries.) Conversely, the fact that $\mathrm{Hom}_{\mathbf{X}}$ is maximally negative when $\mathrm{Sat}_{\mathbf{X}} = 0$ shows that zero saturation is a situation in which the variables in the set correlate negatively with one another to the mathematical limit of their ability to do so. It is of interest to note in this connection that $\mathrm{Sat}_{\mathbf{D}} = 0$ for the dispersion configuration of a set of variables. This provides a visual image of the zero-saturation condition and also brings out that the covariances among the $\mathbf{D}_i$ are prevailingly negative.

In addition to expressing correlation similarity within a set of variables, Sat and Hom also have an important interpretation directly in terms of the set's factor structure. Let $S_{\bar{\mathbf{X}}}$ be the one-dimensional space spanned by the centroid of variables $\mathbf{X}_1, \ldots, \mathbf{X}_n$. Then from [7.55], the penetrance of the set into centroid-space is

[7.95] $$\mathrm{P}_{\mathbf{X}}(S_{\bar{\mathbf{X}}}) = \frac{\mathrm{V}_{\mathbf{X}(\bar{\mathbf{X}})}}{\mathrm{V}_{\mathbf{X}}}$$

$$= \frac{\mathbf{n}\mathrm{V}_{\bar{\mathbf{X}}} + \mathrm{V}_{\mathbf{D}(\bar{\mathbf{X}})}}{\mathrm{V}_{\mathbf{X}}}$$

$$= \mathrm{Sat}_{\mathbf{X}} + \frac{\mathrm{V}_{\mathbf{D}}}{\mathrm{V}_{\mathbf{X}}} \cdot \frac{\mathrm{V}_{\mathbf{D}(\bar{\mathbf{X}})}}{\mathrm{V}_{\mathbf{D}}}$$

$$= \mathrm{Sat}_{\mathbf{X}} + \mathrm{Disp}_{\mathbf{X}} \cdot \mathrm{P}_{\mathbf{D}}(S_{\bar{\mathbf{X}}})$$

$$= [1 + \mathrm{DQ}_{\mathbf{X}} \cdot \mathrm{P}_{\mathbf{D}}(S_{\bar{\mathbf{X}}})]\ \mathrm{Sat}_{\mathbf{X}} ,$$

where $\mathrm{P}_{\mathbf{D}}(S_{\bar{\mathbf{X}}})$ is the proportion of the dispersion variance of the $\mathbf{X}_i$ lying in centroid-space and should be on the order of $1/(\mathbf{n}-1)$ or less (see p. 312). Equation [7.95] thus says that the proportion of a set's variance accounted for by its centroid is slightly in excess of the set's saturation, the difference usually being negligible unless $\mathbf{n}$ is small or $\mathrm{Sat}_{\mathbf{X}}$ is low. If $S_{\mathbf{P}_1}$ is the one-dimensional space spanned by the first principle factor of the $\mathbf{X}_i$, we may then write

[7.96] $$\mathrm{Hom}_{\mathbf{X}} \leqslant \mathrm{Sat}_{\mathbf{X}} \leqslant \mathrm{P}_{\mathbf{X}}(S_{\bar{\mathbf{X}}}) \leqslant \mathrm{P}_{\mathbf{X}}(S_{\mathbf{P}_1}) .$$

It has already been shown that the variance of a set accounted for by its first principal factor is not likely to differ greatly from the set variance accounted for by its centroid unless the saturation of the set is low. Hence, *the saturation and homogeneity of a set of variables are lower bounds for, and frequently close approximations to, the maximal proportion of the set's variance which can be accounted for by a single factor.*

For many problems in multivariate relationships, it is instructive to examine how the consensus in a set of variables is influenced by the similarity of their components lying in certain subspaces. Let the saturation, $\mathrm{Sat}_{\mathbf{X}}(S)$, of the set $\mathbf{X}_1, \ldots, \mathbf{X}_n$ in a given space S be defined as the saturation of the set's projections into S. That is,

[7.97][14] $$\mathrm{Sat}_{\mathbf{X}}(S) =_{\mathrm{def}} \mathrm{Sat}_{\mathbf{e}_{\mathbf{X}(S)}}$$

$$= \frac{\mathrm{V}_{\bar{\mathbf{X}}(S)}}{\overline{\mathrm{V}}_{\mathbf{X}(S)}} .$$

The dispersion, dispersion quotient, and homogeneity of $\mathbf{X}_1, \ldots, \mathbf{X}_n$ in S are similarly defined as these properties of the projections of the $\mathbf{X}_i$ into S—i.e.,

[7.98][14] $$\mathrm{Disp}_{\mathbf{X}}(S) =_{\mathrm{def}} \frac{\overline{\mathrm{V}}_{\mathbf{D}(S)}}{\overline{\mathrm{V}}_{\mathbf{X}(S)}}$$

$$= 1 - \mathrm{Sat}_{\mathbf{X}}(S) ,$$

[7.99][14] $$\mathrm{DQ}_{\mathbf{X}}(S) =_{\mathrm{def}} \frac{\mathrm{Disp}_{\mathbf{X}}(S)}{\mathrm{Sat}_{\mathbf{X}}(S)}$$

$$= \frac{1 - \mathrm{Sat}_{\mathbf{X}}(S)}{\mathrm{Sat}_{\mathbf{X}}(S)} ,$$

[14] In line with the notational policy described in fn. 1, p. 293, "$\mathrm{Sat}_{\mathbf{X}}(S)$", "$\mathrm{Disp}_{\mathbf{X}}(S)$", "$\mathrm{DQ}_{\mathbf{X}}(S)$", and "$\mathrm{Hom}_{\mathbf{X}}(S)$" may also be written as "$\mathrm{Sat}_{\mathbf{X}(S)}$", "$\mathrm{Disp}_{\mathbf{X}(S)}$", "$\mathrm{DQ}_{\mathbf{X}(S)}$", and "$\mathrm{Hom}_{\mathbf{X}(S)}$", respectively.

[7.100][14]
$$\mathrm{Hom}_{\mathbf{X}}(S) =_{\mathrm{def}} \frac{\bar{C}_{\mathbf{XX}(S)}}{\bar{V}_{\mathbf{X}(S)}} = \left(1 - \frac{DQ_{\mathbf{X}}(S)}{\mathbf{n}-1}\right) \mathrm{Sat}_{\mathbf{X}}(S) .$$

If all the $\mathbf{X}_i$ are orthogonal to S, then $\mathrm{Sat}_{\mathbf{X}}(S)$, etc., remain undefined, since formulas [7.97]–[7.100] would in this case divide zero by zero. We could assign arbitrary values for these coefficients to such a space, but it is simpler just to stipulate that any formula in which reference is made to $\mathrm{Sat}_{\mathbf{X}}(S)$, etc., presupposes that $V_{\mathbf{X}(S)} > 0$ unless the quantity in question approaches a well-defined limit as $V_{\mathbf{X}(S)}$ approaches zero.

The saturation of $\mathbf{X}_1, \ldots, \mathbf{X}_n$ in any space S is readily seen from [7.97] to be

[7.101]
$$\mathrm{Sat}_{\mathbf{X}}(S) = \frac{V_{\bar{\mathbf{X}}(S)}}{V_{\bar{\mathbf{X}}}} \cdot \frac{V_{\bar{\mathbf{X}}}}{\bar{V}_{\mathbf{X}}} \cdot \frac{\bar{V}_{\mathbf{X}}}{\bar{V}_{\mathbf{X}(S)}} = \frac{P_{\bar{\mathbf{X}}}(S) \cdot \mathrm{Sat}_{\mathbf{X}}}{P_{\mathbf{X}}(S)} ,$$

or solving for $P_{\bar{\mathbf{X}}}(S)$,

[7.102]
$$P_{\bar{\mathbf{X}}}(S) = \frac{\mathrm{Sat}_{\mathbf{X}}(S)}{\mathrm{Sat}_{\mathbf{X}}} \cdot P_{\mathbf{X}}(S) .$$

We also know (cf. [7.74]) that for any set of orthogonal spaces $S_1, \ldots, S_k$,

[7.103]
$$\sum_{j=1}^{k} P_{\bar{\mathbf{X}}}(S_j) = P_{\bar{\mathbf{X}}}(S_1 \ldots S_k) \qquad (\perp(S_1, \ldots, S_k)) .$$

Hence substituting [7.101] (with appropriate substitutions for "S") into [7.103] and multiplying through by $\mathrm{Sat}_{\mathbf{X}}$ yields

[7.104]
$$P_{\mathbf{X}}(S_1 \ldots S_k) \cdot \mathrm{Sat}_{\mathbf{X}}(S_1 \ldots S_k) = \sum_{j=1}^{k} P_{\mathbf{X}}(S_j) \cdot \mathrm{Sat}_{\mathbf{X}}(S_j) \qquad (\perp(S_1, \ldots, S_k)) .$$

In particular, for a set of orthogonal spaces which collectively contain all the $\mathbf{X}_i$, [7.104] reduces to

[7.105]
$$\mathrm{Sat}_{\mathbf{X}} = \sum_{j=1}^{k} P_{\mathbf{X}}(S_j) \cdot \mathrm{Sat}_{\mathbf{X}}(S_j) \qquad \left(\begin{matrix} \perp(S_1, \ldots, S_m); \\ V_{\mathbf{X} \bullet S_1 \ldots S_m} = 0 \end{matrix}\right).$$

The saturation of a set of variables is thus seen to be a weighted average of its saturations in the various orthogonal subspaces into which the variables have been exhaustively projected. By substituting [7.86] and its equivalent for subspace saturations, namely,

[7.106]
$$\mathrm{Sat}_{\mathbf{X}}(S) = \left(\frac{\mathbf{n}-1}{\mathbf{n}}\right) \mathrm{Hom}_{\mathbf{X}}(S) + \frac{1}{\mathbf{n}} ,$$

into [7.105], it is readily found that a set's homogeneity, too, is a weighted average of its subspace homogeneities—i.e.,

$$[7.107] \quad \mathrm{Hom}_{\mathbf{X}} = \sum_{j=1}^{k} \mathrm{P}_{\mathbf{X}}(S_j) \cdot \mathrm{Hom}_{\mathbf{X}}(S_j) \qquad \begin{pmatrix} \perp (S_1, \ldots, S_m); \\ \mathrm{V}_{\mathbf{X} \bullet S_1 \ldots S_m} = 0 \end{pmatrix},$$

or more generally,

$$[7.108] \quad \mathrm{P}_{\mathbf{X}}(S_1 \ldots S_k) \cdot \mathrm{Hom}_{\mathbf{X}}(S_1 \ldots S_k) = \sum_{j=1}^{k} \mathrm{P}_{\mathbf{X}}(S_j) \cdot \mathrm{Hom}_{\mathbf{X}}(S_j) \qquad (\perp (S_1, \ldots, S_k)) .$$

Many problems in multivariate relationships turn in one fashion or another upon how the centroid variance of a set of variables is apportioned among certain orthogonal subspaces which collectively contain the set. The generic solution to this question is contained in equation [7.102], which states that the proportion of centroid variance lying in a space S exceeds the proportion of the set's total variance lying in S to the degree that the saturation of the set in S exceeds its saturation in all-space. (Finer details of this relationship will be examined in Chapter 9, pp. 439f., when the need arises.) Less generally, however, test theorists have been especially attentive to the contrast between those spaces in which a configuration of variables has *zero* homogeneity and those in which it does not, and it is instructive to explore this case at this time, both for the results themselves and as an introduction to the use in multivariate analysis of the new concepts which have been here introduced.

Let the *complement*, S^*, of a space S with respect to variables $\mathbf{X}_1, \ldots, \mathbf{X}_n$ be defined as any space orthogonal to S such that the combined space SS^* contains all the $\mathbf{X}_i$.[15] That is, by definition $\perp(S,S^*)$ and $\mathrm{V}_{\mathbf{X} \cdot S^*} = 0$; so from [7.71], [7.72], [7.105], and [7.107], respectively,

$$[7.109] \quad \mathrm{P}_{\mathbf{X}}(S) + \mathrm{P}_{\mathbf{X}}(S^*) = 1 ,$$

$$[7.110] \quad P_{\bar{\mathbf{X}}}(S) + P_{\bar{\mathbf{X}}}(S^*) = 1 ,$$

$$[7.111] \quad \mathrm{Sat}_{\mathbf{X}} = \mathrm{P}_{\mathbf{X}}(S) \cdot \mathrm{Sat}_{\mathbf{X}}(S) + \mathrm{P}_{\mathbf{X}}(S^*) \cdot \mathrm{Sat}_{\mathbf{X}}(S^*) ,$$

$$[7.112] \quad \mathrm{Hom}_{\mathbf{X}} = \mathrm{P}_{\mathbf{X}}(S) \cdot \mathrm{Hom}_{\mathbf{X}}(S) + \mathrm{P}_{\mathbf{X}}(S^*) \cdot \mathrm{Hom}_{\mathbf{X}}(S^*) .$$

Now let S_0 be a space in which the homogeneity of the $\mathbf{X}_i$ is zero. Then from [7.106] and [7.112], respectively, it follows immediately that

$$[7.113] \quad \mathrm{Sat}_{\mathbf{X}}(S_0) = \frac{1}{\mathbf{n}} \qquad (\mathrm{Hom}_{\mathbf{X}}(S_0) = 0) ,$$

[15] More precisely, we should say that any space S^* is a complement to space S with respect to variables $\mathbf{X}_1, \ldots, \mathbf{X}_n$ if $\perp(S,S^*)$ and $\mathrm{V}_{\mathbf{X} \cdot SS^*} = 0$. The reason for speaking ambiguously about "the" complement of S with respect to the $\mathbf{X}_i$ is that the context of analysis usually singles out one such space.

[7.114] $$\mathrm{Hom}_{\mathbf{X}} = \mathrm{P}_{\mathbf{X}}(S_0^*) \cdot \mathrm{Hom}_{\mathbf{X}}(S_0^*) \qquad (\mathrm{Hom}_{\mathbf{X}}(S_0) = 0)\ .$$

To see how $\overline{\mathbf{X}}$ apportions its variance between S_0 and S_0^* – which for convenient reference may be called "neuter-space" and "similarity-space," respectively – we begin by substituting [7.113] into [7.102]:

[7.115] $$P_{\overline{\mathbf{X}}}(S_0) = \frac{\mathrm{P}_{\mathbf{X}}(S_0)}{\mathbf{n}\ \mathrm{Sat}_{\mathbf{X}}} \qquad (\mathrm{Hom}_{\mathbf{X}}(S_0) = 0)$$
$$\leqslant \frac{1}{\mathbf{n}\ \mathrm{Sat}_{\mathbf{X}}}\ .$$

This shows that so long as the saturation of a set of variables is appreciable, their centroid will rapidly vanish from neuter-space as the number of variables in the set increases, even if a large proportion of the set variance lies in this space. Interpretation of [7.115] is complicated, however, by the fact that $\mathrm{Sat}_{\mathbf{X}}$ is itself influenced by the penetrance of the set into S_0, as well as being inflated by the set's intrinsic consistency (cf. p. 322) which also vanishes as $\mathbf{n}$ increases. To make more explicit what is in the denominator of [7.115], we may put [7.86] and [7.114] together to see that

[7.116] $$\mathbf{n}\ \mathrm{Sat}_{\mathbf{X}} = (\mathbf{n}-1)\mathrm{P}_{\mathbf{X}}(S_0^*) \cdot \mathrm{Hom}_{\mathbf{X}}(S_0^*) + 1 \quad (\mathrm{Hom}_{\mathbf{X}}(S_0) = 0)\ .$$

Examination of [7.116] reveals that for $\mathbf{n}\,\mathrm{Sat}_{\mathbf{X}}$ to become large as $\mathbf{n}$ increases, and hence cause $P_{\overline{\mathbf{X}}}(S_0)$ to dwindle, it is necessary for the homogeneity of the $\mathbf{X}_i$ in similarity-space to be greater than zero. To study the partition of $\overline{\mathbf{X}}$ between S_0 and S_0^* in detail, we could substitute [7.116] into [7.115]. The resulting formula is rather messy, however, and a much more elegant way to bring out the effect of $\mathbf{n}$ on a centroid's penetrance into similarity-space is to divide [7.115] into the instantiation of [7.102] by S_0^*, thus obtaining

[7.117] $$\frac{P_{\overline{\mathbf{X}}}(S_0^*)}{P_{\overline{\mathbf{X}}}(S_0)} = \mathbf{n}\ \mathrm{Sat}_{\mathbf{X}}(S_0^*)\ \frac{\mathrm{P}_{\mathbf{X}}(S_0^*)}{\mathrm{P}_{\mathbf{X}}(S_0)} \qquad (\mathrm{Hom}_{\mathbf{X}}(S_0) = 0)\ .$$

To state this result even more succinctly, let the *penetrance quotient*, $\mathrm{PQ}_{\mathbf{X}}(S)$, for set $\mathbf{X}_1, \ldots, \mathbf{X}_n$ in a space S be the ratio of the set's variance in S to its variance unaccounted for by S – i.e.,

[7.118] $$\mathrm{PQ}_{\mathbf{X}}(S) =_{\mathrm{def}} \frac{\mathrm{V}_{\mathbf{X}}(S)}{\mathrm{V}_{\mathbf{X}}(\overline{S})}$$
$$= \frac{\mathrm{P}_{\mathbf{X}}(S)}{\mathrm{P}_{\mathbf{X}}(S^*)}$$
$$= \frac{\mathrm{P}_{\mathbf{X}}(S)}{1-\mathrm{P}_{\mathbf{X}}(S)}\ .$$

That is, $\mathrm{PQ}_{\mathbf{X}}(S)$ states how many times larger the variance of the set is in S than it is in the complement of S. The penetrance quotient for the penetrance of a single variable into S is similarly defined. In particular,

$$\text{[7.119]} \qquad PQ_{\bar{\mathbf{X}}}(S) =_{\text{def}} \frac{V_{\bar{\mathbf{X}}}(S)}{V_{\bar{\mathbf{X}}}(S^*)} = \frac{P_{\bar{\mathbf{X}}}(S)}{P_{\bar{\mathbf{X}}}(S^*)} = \frac{P_{\bar{\mathbf{X}}}(S)}{1 - P_{\bar{\mathbf{X}}}(S)}$$

Then [7.117] may be rewritten

$$\text{[7.120]} \qquad PQ_{\bar{\mathbf{X}}}(S_0^*) = \mathbf{n}\ \mathrm{Sat}_{\mathbf{X}}(S_0^*) \cdot \mathrm{PQ}_{\mathbf{X}}(S_0^*) \qquad (\mathrm{Hom}_{\mathbf{X}}(S_0) = 0)\ ,$$

which says that the penetrance quotient for a set's centroid in similarity-space is a simple multiple of the set's own penetrance quotient for similarity-space, this multiplier being the number of variables in the set times the set's saturation in similarity-space.

To appreciate fully what [7.120] and other penetrance-quotient equations reveal about variance composition, it is necessary to know what the numerical magnitude of a variable's penetrance quotient for an arbitrary space S signifies quantitatively about the corresponding penetrance. The relation will here be made explicit only for $\bar{\mathbf{X}}$, but the same results hold for any other variable or set of variables. Since $P_{\bar{\mathbf{X}}}(S) + P_{\bar{\mathbf{X}}}(S^*) = P_{\bar{\mathbf{X}}}[1 + PQ_{\bar{\mathbf{X}}}(S^*)] = 1$, one mathematically immediate relationship is

$$\text{[7.121]} \qquad P_{\bar{\mathbf{X}}}(S) = \frac{1}{1 + PQ_{\bar{\mathbf{X}}}(S^*)} = \frac{1}{1 + 1/PQ_{\bar{\mathbf{X}}}(S)}$$

If the penetrance of $\bar{\mathbf{X}}$ is appreciably smaller in S than in S^*, however, a more interesting approximation holds. For any two numbers A and B, obviously

$$\text{[7.122]} \qquad \frac{A}{A+B} = \frac{A}{B}\left(1 - \frac{A}{A+B}\right).$$

The fraction $A/(A + B)$ may be expanded by iteration of [7.22] into power series

$$\text{[7.123]} \qquad \frac{A}{A+B} = \frac{A}{B} - \left(\frac{A}{B}\right)^2 + \left(\frac{A}{B}\right)^3 - \ldots - \left(-\frac{A}{B}\right)^m - \left(-\frac{A}{B}\right)^{m+1}\left(\frac{A}{A+B}\right)$$

in which if $A < B$, the last term becomes increasingly negligible as m increases. Hence the penetrance of $\bar{\mathbf{X}}$ (or of any other variable or set of variables) into a space S such that $P_{\bar{\mathbf{X}}}(S) < .5$ may be developed as a power series in the penetrance quotient of $\mathbf{X}$ for S:

$$[7.124] \quad P_{\bar{\mathbf{X}}}(S) = PQ_{\bar{\mathbf{X}}}(S) - PQ_{\bar{\mathbf{X}}}(S)^2 + PQ_{\bar{\mathbf{X}}}(S)^3 - [\text{etc.}]$$

More simply from [7.23] with $m = 2$,

$$[7.125] \quad P_{\bar{\mathbf{X}}}(S) = PQ_{\bar{\mathbf{X}}}(S) - PQ_{\bar{\mathbf{X}}}(S)^2 P_{\bar{\mathbf{X}}}(S)$$

or

$$[7\ 126] \quad P_{\bar{\mathbf{X}}}(S^*) = 1 - PQ_{\bar{\mathbf{X}}}(S) + PQ_{\bar{\mathbf{X}}}(S)^2 P_{\bar{\mathbf{X}}}(S)\ ,$$

in which the last term is smaller than $PQ_{\bar{\mathbf{X}}}(S)^3$ and may be disregarded if the penetrance quotient of $\bar{\mathbf{X}}$ in S is on the order of 10^{-1} or less. Consequently, from [7.126] by taking reciprocals of both sides of [7.117], the penetrance of $\bar{\mathbf{X}}$ into similarity-space may be written

$$[7.127] \quad P_{\bar{\mathbf{X}}}(S_0^*) = 1 - \frac{\mathrm{PQ}_{\mathbf{X}}(S_0)}{\mathbf{n}\ \mathrm{Sat}_{\mathbf{X}}(S_0^*)} + \iota \qquad (\mathrm{Hom}_{\mathbf{X}}(S_0) = 0)\ ,$$

where ι is the generally negligible positive quantity

$$[7.128] \quad \iota = \left[\frac{\mathrm{PQ}_{\mathbf{X}}(S_0)}{\mathbf{n}\ \mathrm{Sat}_{\mathbf{X}}(S_0^*)}\right]^2 P_{\bar{\mathbf{X}}}(S_0) \leqslant \left[\frac{\mathrm{PQ}_{\mathbf{X}}(S_0)}{\mathbf{n}\ \mathrm{Sat}_{\mathbf{X}}(S_0^*)}\right]^3 .$$

Besides analyzing how the partition of a set's centroid variance between neuter-space and similarity-space is brought about by the set's penetrance and homogeneity in the latter, we can also inquire how the split can be inferred from the set's behavior in observation-space. Multiplying both sides of [7.102] by $\mathrm{Hom}_{\mathbf{X}}(S)/\mathrm{Sat}_{\mathbf{X}}(S)$ shows that

$$[7.129] \quad \frac{\mathrm{Hom}_{\mathbf{X}}(S)}{\mathrm{Sat}_{\mathbf{X}}(S)}\ P_{\bar{\mathbf{X}}}(S) = \frac{\mathrm{P}_{\mathbf{X}}(S)\ \cdot\ \mathrm{Hom}_{\mathbf{X}}(S)}{\mathrm{Sat}_{\mathbf{X}}}\ .$$

Instantiating S with S_0^* in [7.129] then yields, in view of [7.114],

$$[7.130] \quad \frac{\mathrm{Hom}_{\mathbf{X}}(S_0^*)}{\mathrm{Sat}_{\mathbf{X}}(S_0^*)}\ P_{\bar{\mathbf{X}}}(S_0^*) = \frac{\mathrm{Hom}_{\mathbf{X}}}{\mathrm{Sat}_{\mathbf{X}}} \qquad (\mathrm{Hom}_{\mathbf{X}}(S_0) = 0)\ ,$$

or using [7.100],

$$[7.131] \quad \frac{\mathrm{Hom}_{\mathbf{X}}}{\mathrm{Sat}_{\mathbf{X}}} = P_{\bar{\mathbf{X}}}(S_0^*)\left(1 - \frac{\mathrm{DQ}_{\mathbf{X}}(S_0^*)}{\mathbf{n} - 1}\right) \qquad (\mathrm{Hom}_{\mathbf{X}}(S_0) = 0)\ .$$

This says that the ratio of a set's homogeneity to its saturation, a quantity easily computed from the set's covariance matrix, underestimates the centroid's penetrance into similarity-space by an approximation error no greater than one ($\mathbf{n}-1$)th of the dispersion quotient for the set in similarity-space.

Finally, for the sake of mathematical closure, we may briefly note how the dispersion variance of a configuration of variables is apportioned between neuter-space and similarity-space. Analogous to [7.102], it is readily seen that the penetrance of the set of dispersion components $\mathbf{D}_1, \ldots, \mathbf{D}_n$ of variables $\mathbf{X}_1, \ldots, \mathbf{X}_n$ into any space S is

[7.132] $$P_{\mathbf{D}}(S) = \frac{\mathrm{Disp}_{\mathbf{X}}(S)}{\mathrm{Disp}_{\mathbf{X}}} P_{\mathbf{X}}(S) .$$

Also, from [7.98] and [7.106], the relation between a set's dispersion and homogeneity in S is

[7.133] $$\mathrm{Disp}_{\mathbf{X}}(S) = \frac{\mathbf{n}-1}{\mathbf{n}} [1 - \mathrm{Hom}_{\mathbf{X}}(S)] ,$$

which also holds, of course, for the relation between $\mathrm{Disp}_{\mathbf{X}}$ and $\mathrm{Hom}_{\mathbf{X}}$. Combining [7.132] and [7.133] then yields

[7.134] $$P_{\mathbf{D}}(S) = P_{\mathbf{X}}(S) \left[\frac{1 - \mathrm{Hom}_{\mathbf{X}}(S)}{1 - \mathrm{Hom}_{\mathbf{X}}}\right] .$$

Hence the penetrance of the dispersion configuration into neuter-space is

[7.135] $$P_{\mathbf{D}}(S_0) = \frac{P_{\mathbf{X}}(S_0)}{1 - \mathrm{Hom}_{\mathbf{X}}} \qquad (\mathrm{Hom}_{\mathbf{X}}(S_0) = 0) ,$$

while the penetrance of the $\mathbf{D}_i$ into similarity-space is

[7.136] $$P_{\mathbf{D}}(S_0^*) = P_{\mathbf{X}}(S_0) \left[\frac{1 - \mathrm{Hom}_{\mathbf{X}}(S_0^*)}{1 - \mathrm{Hom}_{\mathbf{X}}}\right] \qquad (\mathrm{Hom}_{\mathbf{X}}(S_0) = 0) ,$$

with a corresponding penetrance quotient of

[7.137] $$PQ_{\mathbf{D}}(S_0^*) =_{\mathrm{def}} \frac{P_{\mathbf{D}}(S_0^*)}{P_{\mathbf{D}}(S_0)} \qquad (\mathrm{Hom}_{\mathbf{X}}(S_0) = 0)$$
$$= [1 - \mathrm{Hom}_{\mathbf{X}}(S_0^*)]\ PQ_{\mathbf{X}}(S_0^*) .$$

Thus contrary to what might have been expected in analogy to $P_{\bar{\mathbf{X}}}(S^*_0)$, there is no tendency for the dispersion variance to disappear from similarity-space as $\mathbf{n}$ grows large.

Centroid Penetrance and Common-Factor Space. Despite the almost childish simplicity of the formulas derived in the last few paragraphs, they have a surprisingly profound significance for a number of technical problems in test theory, notably those in which a distinction between common-factor space and unique-factor space is of some importance. It seems worthwhile, therefore, to restate the more salient of these results in terms most visibly applicable to such contexts.

Suppose that the variables in a set $\mathbf{X}_1, \ldots, \mathbf{X}_n$ can be analyzed into communal and unique components in the sense discussed previously (pp. 254ff.). That is,

[7.138-i] (i = 1, . . . , n)
$$\mathbf{X}_i = \mathbf{H}_i + \mathbf{U}_i \,,$$

where each $\mathbf{U}_i$ is orthogonal to all communal components and to all other unique components of the $\mathbf{X}_i$. (We do *not* assume that the space of the $\mathbf{H}_i$ is of minimal dimensionality. The results which follow apply to any partition of the $\mathbf{X}_i$ into communal and unique components such that the latter have the stipulated orthogonality properties.) Letting "$S_\mathbf{H}$" and "$S_\mathbf{U}$" designate the spaces spanned by $\mathbf{H}_1, \ldots, \mathbf{H}_n$ and by $\mathbf{U}_1, \ldots, \mathbf{U}_n$, respectively, we have $\perp(S_\mathbf{H}, S_\mathbf{U})$ and $V_{\mathbf{X}\cdot S_\mathbf{H} S_\mathbf{U}} = 0$, so we may write

[7.139]
$$S_\mathbf{H} = S_\mathbf{U}^* \,,$$

[7.140]
$$V_\mathbf{X} = V_{\mathbf{X}(S_\mathbf{H})} + V_{\mathbf{X}(S_\mathbf{U})} = V_\mathbf{H} + V_\mathbf{U} \,.$$

Since by definition $C_{\mathbf{U}_i\mathbf{U}_j} = 0$ for $\mathbf{i},\mathbf{j} = 1, \ldots, \mathbf{n}, \mathbf{i} \neq \mathbf{j}$, obviously $C_{\mathbf{UU}} = 0$ and hence

[7.141]
$$\mathrm{Hom}_\mathbf{X}(S_\mathbf{U}) = \mathrm{Hom}_\mathbf{U} = 0 \,,$$

[7.142]
$$\mathrm{Sat}_\mathbf{X}(S_\mathbf{U}) = \mathrm{Sat}_\mathbf{U} = \frac{1}{\mathbf{n}} \,,$$

while

[7.143]
$$\mathrm{Hom}_\mathbf{X}(S_\mathbf{U}^*) = \mathrm{Hom}_\mathbf{X}(S_\mathbf{H}) = \mathrm{Hom}_\mathbf{H} \,,$$

[7.144]
$$\mathrm{Sat}_\mathbf{X}(S_\mathbf{U}^*) = \mathrm{Sat}_\mathbf{X}(S_\mathbf{H}) = \mathrm{Sat}_\mathbf{H} \,.$$

The penetrance of the set $\mathbf{X}_1, \ldots, \mathbf{X}_n$ into common-factor space is

[7.145]
$$P_\mathbf{X}(S_\mathbf{H}) = \frac{V_{\mathbf{X}(S_\mathbf{H})}}{V_\mathbf{X}} = \frac{V_\mathbf{H}}{V_\mathbf{H} + V_\mathbf{U}} \,.$$

Also, in view of [7.69],

[7.146]
$$P_{\mathbf{X}}(S_{\mathbf{H}}) = \frac{\sum_{i=1}^{n} V_{\mathbf{H}_i}}{\sum_{i=1}^{n} V_{\mathbf{X}_i}}$$

$$= \frac{\sum_{i=1}^{n} V_{\mathbf{X}_i} h_i^2}{\sum_{i=1}^{n} V_{\mathbf{X}_i}},$$

where h_i^2 is the "communality" of variable $\mathbf{X}_i$—i.e., the proportion of the variance of $\mathbf{X}_i$ lying in common-factor space—as defined in [6.74]. The penetrance of the set into $S_{\mathbf{H}}$ is thus a weighted average of the individual communalities, and we may define the "variance-weighted" average communality, $\widetilde{h^2}$, for the set $\mathbf{X}_1, \ldots, \mathbf{X}_n$ to be

[7.147]
$$\widetilde{h^2} =_{\text{def}} \frac{\sum_{i=1}^{n} V_{\mathbf{X}_i} h_i^2}{\sum_{i=1}^{n} V_{\mathbf{X}_i}}$$
$$= P_{\mathbf{X}}(S_{\mathbf{H}})$$
$$= 1 - P_{\mathbf{X}}(S_{\mathbf{U}})$$
$$= \frac{V_{\mathbf{H}}}{V_{\mathbf{X}}}$$
$$= \frac{V_{\mathbf{H}}}{V_{\mathbf{H}} + V_{\mathbf{U}}}.$$

Similarly, let the penetrance of the set's centroid, $\overline{\mathbf{X}}$, into common-factor space be called the "centroid communality" of the set and written "$h_{\overline{\mathbf{X}}}^2$". That is,

[7.148]
$$h_{\overline{\mathbf{X}}}^2 =_{\text{def}} P_{\overline{\mathbf{X}}}(S_{\mathbf{H}})$$
$$= 1 - P_{\overline{\mathbf{X}}}(S_{\mathbf{U}})$$
$$= \frac{V_{\overline{\mathbf{X}}(S_H)}}{V_{\overline{\mathbf{X}}}}$$
$$= \frac{V_{\overline{\mathbf{H}}}}{V_{\overline{\mathbf{H}}} + V_{\overline{\mathbf{U}}}},$$

since obviously

$$[7.149] \qquad \overline{\mathbf{X}} = \overline{\mathbf{H}} + \overline{\mathbf{U}}$$

and

$$[7.150] \qquad V_{\overline{\mathbf{X}}} = V_{\overline{\mathbf{H}}} + V_{\overline{\mathbf{U}}} \ .$$

Since many problems in test theory turn crucially on the common-factor composition of the variables under scrutiny, it will be instructive to keep in mind that $\text{Sat}_{\mathbf{H}}$ (and hence also $\text{Hom}_{\mathbf{H}}$ unless $\mathbf{n}$ is small) is a lower-bound approximation to the proportion of the set's common-factor variance accounted for by $\overline{\mathbf{H}}$ (see [7.95], reading "**H**" for "**X**"). Thus $\text{Sat}_{\mathbf{H}}$ has an important interpretation as a measure of how strongly a single factor dominates the communal components. It is also noteworthy, in light of certain speculations which have appeared in the literature, that $\text{Sat}_{\mathbf{H}}$ (and likewise $\text{Hom}_{\mathbf{H}}$) is majestically indifferent to the common-factor configuration of the $\mathbf{X}_i$ orthogonal to their common-factor centroid. In particular, the value of $\text{Sat}_{\mathbf{H}}$ in general implies nothing about the set's common-factor dimensionality, or whether the $\mathbf{H}_i$ have any tendency to form clusters.

To begin transcription of our previous findings into common-factor terms, observe that [7.114] is a slightly more general version of the principle (cf. [6.67]) that all the proper covariances among a set of variables derive from their components in common-factor space. Specifically, it follows from [7.114] that

$$[7.151] \qquad \text{Hom}_{\mathbf{X}} = \widetilde{h^2}\ \text{Hom}_{\mathbf{H}} \ ,$$

which is essentially equivalent to $\overline{C}_{\mathbf{XX}} = \overline{C}_{\mathbf{HH}}$. If the $\mathbf{X}_i$ have been standardized to the same variance, this may be written (cf. [7.89]) as

$$[7.152] \qquad \overline{r}_{\mathbf{XX}} = \overline{h^2}\ \text{Hom}_{\mathbf{H}'} \ ,$$

where $\overline{h^2}$ is the arithmetic mean of the h_i^2 and the " ′ " in "**H**′" is in recognition that the homogeneity of a set of communal components is modified by standardization of the variances of the $\mathbf{X}_i$. More generally, we find by multiplying $\text{Hom}_{\mathbf{X}}$ and $\widetilde{h^2}$ in [7.151] by $\overline{V}_{\mathbf{H}}$ that

$$[7.153] \qquad \overline{C}_{\mathbf{XX}} = \overline{V}_{\mathbf{H}}\ \text{Hom}_{\mathbf{H}} \ .$$

This clarifies an issue which has received some attention in the recent literature, namely, the relation between the average interitem covariance for a set of variables and their average common-factor variance. $\overline{V}_{\mathbf{H}}$ is seen to exceed $\overline{C}_{\mathbf{XX}}$ in the degree to which the communal components of the $\mathbf{X}_i$ fail to be in complete agreement, while for $\overline{C}_{\mathbf{XX}}$ and $\overline{V}_{\mathbf{H}}$ to be equal it is necessary for the $\mathbf{H}_i$ to be perfectly homogeneous—i.e., for them to have equal variances and be all perfectly correlated.[16]

[16] As previously observed by Cotton, *et al.* (16), this condition requires that the $\mathbf{X}_i$ have a single common factor and—since $V_{\mathbf{H}_i} = V_{\mathbf{H}_j}$ implies $V_{\mathbf{X}_i} h_i^2 = V_{\mathbf{X}_j} h_j^2$—that the variances of the $\mathbf{X}_i$ be inversely proportional to their communalities.

Of various ways to appreciate how large a proportion of centroid variance lies in common-factor space, we may begin with [7.115], which shows that

[7.154] $$1 - h^2_{\bar{\mathbf{X}}} = \frac{1 - \widetilde{h^2}}{\mathbf{n}\,\mathrm{Sat}_{\mathbf{X}}},$$

or

[7.155] $$\begin{aligned} h^2_{\bar{\mathbf{X}}} &= \frac{\mathbf{n}\ \mathrm{Sat}_{\mathbf{X}} - 1 + \widetilde{h^2}}{\mathbf{n}\ \mathrm{Sat}_{\mathbf{X}}}, \\ &= \frac{\mathbf{n}^2 V_{\bar{\mathbf{X}}} - \mathbf{n}\bar{V}_{\mathbf{X}} + \mathbf{n}\bar{V}_{\mathbf{H}}}{\mathbf{n}^2 V_{\bar{\mathbf{X}}}} \\ &= \frac{C^*_{\mathbf{XX}} - V_{\mathbf{X}} + V_{\mathbf{H}}}{C^*_{\mathbf{XX}}} \\ &= \frac{C_{\mathbf{XX}} + V_{\mathbf{H}}}{C^*_{\mathbf{XX}}}. \end{aligned}$$

While formula [7.155] is handy for further derivations, its perspicuity leaves something to be desired. However, we can also obtain from [7.120] that

[7.156] $$\frac{h^2_{\bar{\mathbf{X}}}}{1 - h^2_{\bar{\mathbf{X}}}} = \mathbf{n}\ \mathrm{Sat}_{\mathbf{H}} \left(\frac{\widetilde{h^2}}{1 - \widetilde{h^2}}\right),$$

or

[7.157] $$\frac{V_{\bar{\mathbf{H}}}}{V_{\bar{\mathbf{U}}}} = \mathbf{n}\ \mathrm{Sat}_{\mathbf{H}} \left(\frac{V_{\mathbf{H}}}{V_{\mathbf{U}}}\right).$$

The latter is in a form particularly easy to understand, since it is an immediate consequence of the fact that $V_{\bar{\mathbf{H}}} = \bar{V}_{\mathbf{H}}\,\mathrm{Sat}_{\mathbf{H}}$ (see [7.75]) while from [7.142],

[7.158] $$\begin{aligned} V_{\bar{\mathbf{U}}} &= \bar{V}_{\mathbf{U}}\ \mathrm{Sat}_{\mathbf{U}} \\ &= \frac{\bar{V}_{\mathbf{U}}}{\mathbf{n}}. \end{aligned}$$

To clarify what [7.155] implies about a centroid's penetrance into common-factor space, we observe from [7.127] that

[7.159] $$h^2_{\bar{\mathbf{X}}} = 1 - \frac{1}{\mathbf{n}\ \mathrm{Sat}_{\mathbf{H}}}\left(\frac{1 - \widetilde{h^2}}{\widetilde{h^2}}\right) + \iota$$

where ι is the usually negligible third-order quantity

$$\iota = \left[\frac{1}{\mathbf{n}\ \mathrm{Sat}_{\mathbf{H}}}\left(\frac{1 - \widetilde{h^2}}{\widetilde{h^2}}\right)\right]^2 \left(1 - h^2_{\bar{\mathbf{X}}}\right) \leqslant \left[\frac{1}{\mathbf{n}\ \mathrm{Sat}_{\mathbf{H}}}\left(\frac{1 - \widetilde{h^2}}{\widetilde{h^2}}\right)\right]^3.$$

Formulas [7.156]–[7.159] pretty well speak for themselves, with perhaps an assist from

$$\text{[7.160]} \qquad \mathbf{n}\,\text{Sat}_{\mathbf{H}} = \mathbf{n}\,\text{Hom}_{\mathbf{H}} + (1 - \text{Hom}_{\mathbf{H}})$$

to resolve any uncertainties which may arise over the decreasing importance of intrinsic consistency in $\text{Sat}_{\mathbf{H}}$ as $\mathbf{n}$ increases. It is evident that for any fixed values of $\text{Hom}_{\mathbf{H}}$ and $\widetilde{h^2}$ above zero, the proportion of centroid variance lying in common-factor space approaches unity as the number of variables grows large, even if the $\mathbf{X}_i$ individually have very little common-factor variance. In practice, of course, there is no way to insure that the communal-component homogeneity and average communality of a set of variables will remain constant as new items are added. On the other hand, there is no mathematical reason why $\text{Hom}_{\mathbf{H}}$ or $\widetilde{h^2}$ need systematically vary with $\mathbf{n}$[17] (though such an effect could very well occur as a result of item-selection procedures), whereas there *are* mathematical reasons why, as $\mathbf{n}$ increases, $\text{Sat}_{\mathbf{H}}$ should decrease slightly and $h^2_{\bar{\mathbf{X}}}$ should rapidly approach unity.

A formula for $h^2_{\bar{\mathbf{X}}}$ which has little to offer esthetically, but which exhibits the generalized mathematical form of a historically important equation originally derived under strongly restrictive assumptions, follows by substitution of S for S in [7.103]:

$$\text{[7.161]} \qquad h^2_{\bar{\mathbf{X}}} = \frac{\widetilde{h^2}\ \text{Sat}_{\mathbf{H}}}{\text{Sat}_{\mathbf{X}}} = \frac{\mathbf{n}\,\widetilde{h^2}\ \text{Sat}_{\mathbf{H}}}{(\mathbf{n}-1)\widetilde{h^2}\ \text{Hom}_{\mathbf{H}} + 1}\,.$$

Further algebraic reshuffling of [7.161], the uninspiring details of which may be left to the reader, also shows that

[7.162]

$$h^2_{\bar{\mathbf{X}}} = \frac{\mathbf{n}\,\widetilde{h^2}}{(\mathbf{n}-1)\widetilde{h^2}+1}\left[1 - \left(\frac{1}{\mathbf{n}}\right)\left(\frac{1-\widetilde{h^2}}{\widetilde{h^2}}\right)\left(\frac{1-\text{Hom}_{\mathbf{H}}}{\text{Hom}_{\mathbf{H}}}\right)\left(1 - \frac{1}{\mathbf{n}\,\text{Sat}_{\mathbf{X}}}\right)\right],$$

which makes clear the fashion in which $\widetilde{h^2}$ is overestimated by the nonbracketed expression on the right-hand side of the equation.

Estimation of Centroid Communality. A problem which assumes considerable importance in some phases of test theory is estimation of a set's centroid communality from the set's covariance matrix. In view of [7.155], this is equivalent to estimating the set's common-factor variance, since given $\mathbf{n}\,\text{Sat}_{\mathbf{X}}$ or $C^*_{\mathbf{XX}}$ and $V_{\mathbf{X}}$ (which are directly computable from $\{C_{\mathbf{X}_i\mathbf{X}_j}\}$), $h^2_{\bar{\mathbf{X}}}$ can be determined from $\widetilde{h^2}$ or $V_{\mathbf{H}}$, and conversely. Now in principle, the most direct way to find $V_{\mathbf{H}}$ and hence $h^2_{\bar{\mathbf{X}}}$ is to analyze the

[17] Although the analysis of $\text{Hom}_{\mathbf{X}}$ in [7.90] contains a term which vanishes with increasing $\mathbf{n}$, it can properly be argued that the effect of $\mathbf{n}$ in $1 - \nu^2_{\sigma_{\mathbf{X}}}/(\mathbf{n}-1)$ merely compensates for a tendency of $\tilde{r}_{\mathbf{XX}}/(1+\nu^2_{\sigma_{\mathbf{X}}})$ to be also slightly influenced by $\mathbf{n}$.

$\{C_{X_iX_j}\}$ matrix for communalities. In practice, however, computation of communalities involves problems, not least of which is that there is no unique solution for communalities, in general not even for those which minimize the number of common factors. Thus V_H and $\widetilde{h^2}$ cannot be determined from the data variables' covariance matrix alone if only because the data do not in themselves identify what common-factor space is intended. It is, however, possible to derive *lower bounds* for V_H or $\widetilde{h^2}$, and hence for $h^2_{\bar{X}}$, which hold for any common-factor space into which the data variables can be projected, and which in many cases afford extremely close estimates of $h^2_{\bar{X}}$.[18] One such bound follows from the fact that the common-factor variance of each data variable is at least as large as its variance controlled by the other data variables (see [6.75]); hence

$$\text{[7.163]} \qquad \sum_{i=1}^{n} V_{X_i} R^2_{X_i(\mu_i)} \leqslant V_H \ ,$$

where "μ_i" designates the set of variables $X_1, \ldots, X_{i-1}, X_{i+1}, \ldots, X_n$. This is generally the best lower bound for V_H when the communal components of the data variables are factorially complex. Of much greater computational simplicity, however, and superior to [7.163] when the $\mathbf{H}_i$ are sufficiently homogeneous, is

$$\text{[7.164]} \qquad \mathrm{Hom}_X \leqslant \widetilde{h^2} \ ,$$

or

$$\text{[7.165]} \qquad \overline{C}_{XX} \leqslant \overline{V}_H \ ,$$

which follow from [7.151]. Substitution of [7.165] into [7.155] yields

$$\text{[7.166]} \qquad \frac{C_{XX} + n\overline{C}_{XX}}{C^*_{XX}} = \frac{nC_{XX}}{(n-1)C^*_{XX}} = \frac{\overline{C}_{XX}}{\overline{C}^*_{XX}} = \frac{\mathrm{Hom}_X}{\mathrm{Sat}_X} \leqslant h^2_{\bar{X}} \ .$$

This inequality may also be obtained directly from [7.130] since the latter translates into present notation as

$$\text{[7.167]} \qquad \frac{\mathrm{Hom}_H}{\mathrm{Sat}_H} h^2_{\bar{X}} = \frac{\mathrm{Hom}_X}{\mathrm{Sat}_X}$$

or

$$\text{[7.168]} \qquad \frac{\mathrm{Hom}_X}{\mathrm{Sat}_X} = h^2_{\bar{X}}\left(1 - \frac{DQ_H}{n-1}\right) \leqslant h^2_{\bar{X}} \ .$$

Let us call the approximations to $h^2_{\bar{X}}$ suggested by the use of inequalities [7.163] and [7.165] as approximations to the common-factor variance in [7.155] the "regression lower-bound estimate" and the "alpha

[18] The lower bounds for $h^2_{\bar{X}}$ presented here were first developed by Guttman (37) in a slightly more specialized context. No universal *upper* bound for $h^2_{\bar{X}}$ lower than unity is possible since common-factor space can always be construed to contain as large a proportion of the data variance as may be desired.

lower-bound estimate," respectively, of a set's centroid communality. That is,

[7.169]
$$\mathrm{Est}_R(h^2_{\tilde{\mathbf{X}}}) =_{\mathrm{def}} \frac{\mathrm{C}_{\mathbf{XX}} + \sum_{\mathrm{i}=1}^{\mathbf{n}} \mathrm{V}_{\mathbf{X}_\mathrm{i}} \mathrm{R}^2_{\mathbf{X}_\mathrm{i}(\boldsymbol{\mu}_\mathrm{i})}}{\mathrm{C}^*_{\mathbf{XX}}}$$
$$= 1 - \frac{\sum_{\mathrm{i}=1}^{\mathbf{n}} \mathrm{V}_{\mathbf{X}_\mathrm{i}\cdot\boldsymbol{\mu}_\mathrm{i}}}{\mathrm{C}^*_{\mathbf{XX}}}$$
$$\leqslant h^2_{\tilde{\mathbf{X}}} ,$$

[7.170]
$$\mathrm{Est}_\alpha(h^2_{\tilde{\mathbf{X}}}) =_{\mathrm{def}} \frac{\mathrm{Hom}_{\mathbf{X}}}{\mathrm{Sat}_{\mathbf{X}}}$$
$$= \frac{\overline{\mathrm{C}}_{\mathbf{XX}}}{\overline{\mathrm{C}}^*_{\mathbf{XX}}}$$
$$= \left(\frac{\mathbf{n}}{\mathbf{n}-1}\right) \frac{\mathrm{C}_{\mathbf{XX}}}{\mathrm{C}^*_{\mathbf{XX}}}$$
$$= \left(\frac{\mathbf{n}}{\mathbf{n}-1}\right) \left(1 - \frac{\mathrm{V}_{\mathbf{X}}}{\mathrm{C}^*_{\mathbf{XX}}}\right)$$
$$\leqslant h^2_{\tilde{\mathbf{X}}} .$$

(The reason for tagging estimate [7.170] with the letter alpha will emerge in Chapter 8.) Since the alpha estimate is assuming increasing importance in test theory, it is of interest to examine just how accurate it may be. From [7.167] we see that the proportionate error made by $\mathrm{Est}_\alpha(h^2_{\tilde{\mathbf{X}}})$ as an approximation to $h^2_{\tilde{\mathbf{X}}}$ is

[7.171]
$$\frac{\mathrm{Est}_\alpha(h^2_{\tilde{\mathbf{X}}}) - h^2_{\tilde{\mathbf{X}}}}{h^2_{\tilde{\mathbf{X}}}} = - \frac{\mathrm{DQ}_{\mathbf{H}}}{\mathbf{n}-1}$$
$$= - \frac{1 - \mathrm{Hom}_{\mathbf{H}}}{\mathbf{n}\ \mathrm{Hom}_{\mathbf{H}} + 1 - \mathrm{Hom}_{\mathbf{H}}} ,$$

which approaches insignificance over a conveniently large portion of the joint possibilities for $\mathbf{n}$ and $\mathrm{Hom}_{\mathbf{H}}$. As an index to the accuracy of $\mathrm{Est}_\alpha(h^2_{\tilde{\mathbf{X}}})$ in comparison to other estimates of $h^2_{\tilde{\mathbf{X}}}$, however, [7.171] is deceptive, for *any* arbitrary estimate of a set's common-factor variance, inserted into formula [7.155], yields a corresponding estimate of the set's centroid communality which differs from the correct value by only

[7.172]
$$\mathrm{Est}(h^2_{\tilde{\mathbf{X}}}) - h^2_{\tilde{\mathbf{X}}} = \frac{\mathrm{Est}(\widetilde{h^2}) - \widetilde{h^2}}{\mathbf{n}\ \mathrm{Sat}_{\mathbf{X}}} \quad \left(\mathrm{Est}(h^2_{\tilde{\mathbf{X}}}) = 1 - \frac{1 - \mathrm{Est}(\widetilde{h^2})}{\mathbf{n}\ \mathrm{Sat}_{\mathbf{X}}} \right) ,$$

which is not appreciable unless $\mathrm{Sat}_{\mathbf{X}}$ or $\mathbf{n}$ is small. In brief, the fact that a set's centroid usually vanishes rapidly from unique-factor space as the number of variables increases means that *any* estimate of $h^2_{\tilde{\mathbf{X}}}$ derived by [7.155] from an estimate of $\mathrm{V}_{\mathbf{H}}$ will generally show impressive accuracy.

Thus the technical precision of such an estimate is best judged by the extent to which it is an improvement over the accuracy which could be achieved even without any information about $V_{\mathbf{H}}$. Now the smallest value that $V_{\mathbf{H}}$ can have in [7.155] is zero; hence the "worst lower-bound estimate" of $h^2_{\mathbf{X}}$ is

[7.173]
$$\begin{aligned}\mathrm{Est_W}(h^2_{\mathbf{X}}) &=_{\mathrm{def}} \frac{C_{\mathbf{XX}}}{C^*_{\mathbf{XX}}}\\ &= \left(\frac{\mathbf{n}-1}{\mathbf{n}}\right) \mathrm{Est}_\alpha(h^2_{\mathbf{X}})\\ &\leq h^2_{\mathbf{X}},\end{aligned}$$

which for moderately large $\mathbf{n}$ is only negligibly smaller than the alpha lower-bound estimate.[19] The degree to which $\mathrm{Est}_\alpha(h^2_{\mathbf{X}})$ further refines the estimate through utilization of information about $V_{\mathbf{H}}$ is shown by how large the error of $\mathrm{Est}_\alpha(h^2_{\mathbf{X}})$ is in proportion to the error of $\mathrm{Est_W}(h^2_{\mathbf{X}})$. Substituting $\mathrm{Hom}_{\mathbf{X}}$ and 0, in turn, for $\mathrm{Est}(\tilde{h}^2)$ in [7.172], this is seen to be

[7.174]
$$\begin{aligned}\frac{\mathrm{Est}_\alpha(h^2_{\mathbf{X}}) - h^2_{\mathbf{X}}}{\mathrm{Est_W}(h^2_{\mathbf{X}}) - h^2_{\mathbf{X}}} &= \frac{\mathrm{Hom}_{\mathbf{X}} - \tilde{h}^2}{-\tilde{h}^2}\\ &= 1 - \frac{\mathrm{Hom}_{\mathbf{X}}}{\tilde{h}^2}\\ &= 1 - \mathrm{Hom}_{\mathbf{H}}.\end{aligned}$$

Thus the alpha estimate of $h^2_{\mathbf{X}}$ further decreases the error of the worst lower-bound estimate by a fraction equal to the set's homogeneity in common-factor space.

It is clear from [7.171] or [7.174] that in order for the alpha estimate of $h^2_{\mathbf{X}}$ to be without error, it is necessary for $\mathrm{Hom}_{\mathbf{H}} = 1$, a condition which requires not merely that the $\mathbf{X}_i$ have but a single common factor, but also that their common-factor variances be all equal. The alpha estimate may be improved upon, however, by a correction which essentially eliminates the attenuating effect of inequalities among the $V_{\mathbf{H}_i}$ through consideration of the variation among the interitem covariances. Let $\tilde{r}^2_{\mathbf{HH}}$ be the variance-weighted average squared correlation among the communal components $\mathbf{H}_1, \ldots, \mathbf{H}_n$ as defined

[7.175]
$$\tilde{r}^2_{\mathbf{HH}} =_{\mathrm{def}} \frac{\sum\limits_{\substack{i=1\\ i\neq j}}^{n} \sum\limits_{j=1}^{n} V_{\mathbf{H}_i} V_{\mathbf{H}_j} r^2_{\mathbf{H}_i\mathbf{H}_j}}{\sum\limits_{\substack{i=1\\ i\neq j}}^{n} \sum\limits_{j=1}^{n} V_{\mathbf{H}_i} V_{\mathbf{H}_j}},$$

[19] Actually, $\mathrm{Est}_\alpha(h^2_{\mathbf{X}})$ is worse than $\mathrm{Est_W}(h^2_{\mathbf{X}})$ in the exceptional case that $\mathrm{Hom}_{\mathbf{H}} < 0$, since the alpha estimate then inadvertently incorporates a negative approximation to $V_{\mathbf{H}}$.

while σ_{V_H} is the standard deviation of the communal component variances $V_{H_1}, \ldots, V_{H_n}$. Since

$$[7.175\text{-}ij] \quad (i,j = 1, \ldots, n;\ i \neq j) \qquad C_{X_iX_j} = C_{H_iH_j} = \sigma_{H_i}\sigma_{H_j} r_{H_iH_j},$$

the squared quadratic mean magnitude of the proper covariances among the data variables is

$$[7.176] \qquad QM^2_{|C_{XX}|} =_{\text{def}} \frac{\sum\limits_{i=1}^{n}\sum\limits_{\substack{j=1\\ i\neq j}}^{n} C^2_{X_iX_j}}{n(n-1)}$$

$$= \frac{\sum\limits_{i=1}^{n}\sum\limits_{\substack{j=1\\ i\neq j}}^{n} V_{H_i}V_{H_j} r^2_{H_iH_j}}{n(n-1)}$$

$$= \widetilde{r^2_{HH}}\left[\frac{\sum\limits_{i=1}^{n}\sum\limits_{j=1}^{n} V_{H_i}V_{H_j}}{n(n-1)}\right]$$

$$= \widetilde{r^2_{HH}}\left[\frac{\left(\sum\limits_{i=1}^{n} V_{H_i}\right)^2 - \sum\limits_{i=1}^{n} V^2_{H_i}}{n(n-1)}\right]$$

$$= \widetilde{r^2_{HH}}\left[\frac{n^2\overline{V}^2_H - n(\overline{V}^2_H + \sigma^2_{V_H})}{n(n-1)}\right]$$

$$= \widetilde{r^2_{HH}}\left(\overline{V}^2_H - \frac{\sigma^2_{V_H}}{n-1}\right),$$

where the move from $\sum\limits_{i=1}^{n} V^2_{H_i}$ to $n(\overline{V}^2_H + \sigma^2_{V_H})$ follows from general principle [3.18]. Hence

$$[7.177] \qquad QM_{|C_{XX}|} = \overline{V}_H \sqrt{\widetilde{r^2_{HH}}\left(1 - \frac{\nu^2_{V_H}}{n-1}\right)} \leq \overline{V}_H,$$

or

$$[7.178] \qquad n\,QM_{|C_{XX}|} \leq V_H$$

where ν_{V_H} is the coefficient of variation for the V_{H_i}. The quadratic mean magnitude of the proper covariances among the data variables is thus also a lower bound for their average common-factor variance. Substituted into [7.155], it generates a corresponding lower bound for the set's centroid communality which may be called the "quadratic lower-bound estimate" of $h^2_{\mathbf{X}}$, namely,

[7.179]
$$\mathrm{Est}_{\mathrm{Q}}(h^2_{\mathbf{X}}) =_{\mathrm{def}} \frac{\bar{C}_{\mathbf{XX}} + \mathbf{n}\,\mathrm{QM}_{|C_{\mathbf{XX}}|}}{C^*_{\mathbf{XX}}} \leqslant h^2_{\mathbf{X}}$$

The only difference between $\mathrm{Est}_\alpha(h^2_{\mathbf{X}})$ and $\mathrm{Est}_{\mathrm{Q}}(h^2_{\mathbf{X}})$ is that the latter takes the quadratic mean proper data-variable covariance for its estimate of $\bar{V}_{\mathbf{H}}$ instead of the arithmetic mean covariance used by the former. Since a quadratic mean is always at least as large as the corresponding arithmetic mean (cf. [3.19]), $\mathrm{QM}_{|C_{\mathbf{XX}}|}$ is a better lower bond on $\bar{V}_{\mathbf{H}}$ than is $\bar{C}_{\mathbf{XX}}$ and hence

[7.180]
$$\mathrm{Est}_\alpha(h^2_{\mathbf{X}}) \leqslant \mathrm{Est}_{\mathrm{Q}}(h^2_{\mathbf{X}}) \leqslant h^2_{\mathbf{X}}\,.$$

By comparing [7.177] with [7.153] expanded by [7.90] with "**H**" in place of "**X**", it is seen that $\mathrm{QM}_{|C_{\mathbf{XX}}|}$ is much less weakened as an estimate of $\bar{V}_{\mathbf{H}}$ by differences among the $V_{\mathbf{H}_i}$ than is $\bar{C}_{\mathbf{XX}}$, and also makes more effective use of the correlations among the $\mathbf{H}_i$. Expressed as a proportion of the worst lower-bound estimate of $h^2_{\mathbf{X}}$, the error of $\mathrm{Est}_{\mathrm{Q}}\,(h^2_{\mathbf{X}})$ is

[7.181]
$$\frac{\mathrm{Est}_{\mathrm{Q}}\,(h^2_{\mathbf{X}}) - h^2_{\mathbf{X}}}{\mathrm{Est}_{\mathrm{W}}\,(h^2_{\mathbf{X}}) - h^2_{\mathbf{X}}} = 1 - \sqrt{\tilde{r}^2_{\mathbf{HH}}\left(1 - \frac{\nu^2_{V_{\mathbf{H}}}}{\mathbf{n}-1}\right)} = 1 - \mathrm{Hom}_{\mathbf{H}}\sqrt{1 + \nu^2_{C_{\mathbf{XX}}}}\,,$$

where $\nu_{C_{\mathbf{XX}}}$ is the coefficient of variation for the proper data-variable covariances. Thus while neither $\mathrm{Est}_\alpha(h^2_{\mathbf{X}})$ or $\mathrm{Est}_{\mathrm{Q}}(h^2_{\mathbf{X}})$ will differ much from $h^2_{\mathbf{X}}$ if $\mathbf{n}\,\mathrm{Sat}_{\mathbf{X}}$ is large (see [7.172]), the quadratic estimate will still be an appreciable improvement in relative accuracy over the alpha estimate if there is considerable variation among the interitem covariances.

Additional lower-bound estimates of $V_{\mathbf{H}}$, and hence of $h^2_{\mathbf{X}}$, which may be useful if variables $\mathbf{X}_1, \ldots, \mathbf{X}_n$ differ widely in their covariances with one another follow from consideration of the array of covariances $C_{\mathbf{X}_i\mathbf{X}_1}, \ldots, C_{\mathbf{X}_i\mathbf{X}_n}$ for a single variable $\mathbf{X}_i$. Let "S_i" designate the sum of the squared covariances between $\mathbf{X}_i$ and the other data variables—i.e.,

[7.182-**i**]
(**i** = **1**, . . . , **n**)
$$S_i =_{\mathrm{def}} \sum_{\substack{j=1 \\ j\neq i}}^{n} C^2_{\mathbf{X}_i\mathbf{X}_j} = \sum_{j=1}^{n} C^2_{\mathbf{X}_i\mathbf{X}_j} - V^2_{\mathbf{X}_i}\,.$$

From [7.175] it follows that

[7.183-i] (i = 1, . . . , n)
$$S_i = \sum_{\substack{j=1 \\ j \neq i}}^{n} C^2_{H_iH_j} = \sum_{j=1}^{n} V_{H_i} V_{H_j} r^2_{H_iH_j} - V^2_{H_i} \leqslant V_{H_i} \sum_{j=1}^{n} V_{H_j} - V^2_{H_i} ,$$

or

[7.184-i] (i = 1, . . . , n)
$$V_{H_i} + \frac{S_i}{V_{H_i}} \leqslant \sum_{j=1}^{n} V_{H_j} = V_H .$$

Let the part of [7.184] to the left of the inequality sign be designated "f(V_{H_i})," thereby recognizing that with S_i equal to a known constant, it is a function of the unknown quantity V_{H_i}. Study of the function f(V_{H_i}) for fixed S_i shows it to be concave, reaching a minimum when $V_{H_i} = \sqrt{S_i}$ and increasing as V_{H_i} diverges from this in either direction. Thus various lower bounds for f(V_{H_i}) and hence, by [7.184], for V_H may be obtained by replacing V_{H_i} in f(V_{H_i}) with (1) $\sqrt{S_i}$, (2) an upper bound on V_{H_i} which is less than $\sqrt{S_i}$, or (3) a lower bound on V_{H_i} which is greater than $\sqrt{S_i}$. Accordingly,

[7.185-i] (i = 1, . . . , n)
$$2\sqrt{S_i} \leqslant V_H ,$$

[7.186-i] (i = 1, . . . , n)
$$V_{X_i} + \frac{S_i}{V_{X_i}} \leqslant V_H \qquad (V_{X_i} \leqslant S_i) ,$$

[7.187-i] (i = 1, . . . , n)
$$V_{X_i} R^2_{X_i(\mu_i)} + \frac{S_i}{V_{X_i} R^2_{X_i(\mu_i)}} \leqslant V_H \qquad (V_{X_i} R^2_{X_i(\mu_i)} \geqslant S_i) ,$$

which yield corresponding lower-bound estimates of h^2_X when substituted into [7.155]. Lower bound [7.186-i] or [7.187-i] is superior to [7.185] when V_{X_i} satisfies the stipulated condition, but while [7.186-i] is little if any more difficult to compute than [7.185] and is hence to be preferred over the latter whenever $V_{X_i} \leqslant S_i$, it is highly unlikely that [7.187-i], even when applicable, would ever have sufficient advantage over other lower bounds for V_H to warrant its computational labor.

Finally, it should be observed that lower bounds on h^2_X (and hence by [7.155] on V_H) can also be derived by applying any of the above techniques to group sums defined over the $\mathbf{X}_i$. Specifically, let $\mathbf{X}_1, \ldots, \mathbf{X}_n$ be sorted into $\mathbf{m}$ groups $G_1, \ldots, G_m$ such that each $\mathbf{X}_i$ is included in one and only one G_j, and let $\mathbf{X}_j'$ be defined as the sum of the $\mathbf{X}_i$ in G_j. For any analysis of the $\mathbf{X}_i$ into communal and unique components $\mathbf{H}_i$ and $\mathbf{U}_i$, $\mathbf{X}_j'$ correspondingly analyzes as $\mathbf{X}_j' = \mathbf{H}_j' + \mathbf{U}_j'$, where $\mathbf{H}_j'$ and $\mathbf{U}_j'$ are the sums of the $\mathbf{H}_i$ and $\mathbf{U}_i$, respectively, for the $\mathbf{X}_i$ in G_j; and since clearly $\text{Cov}(\mathbf{H}_j', \mathbf{U}_k') = 0$ for $\mathbf{j},\mathbf{k} = \mathbf{1}, \ldots, \mathbf{m}$ and $\text{Cov}(\mathbf{U}_j', \mathbf{U}_k') = 0$ for $\mathbf{j},\mathbf{k} = \mathbf{1}, \ldots, \mathbf{m}, \mathbf{j} \neq \mathbf{k}$, the $\mathbf{H}_j'$ and $\mathbf{U}_j'$ also satisfy the conditions for an analysis of the $\mathbf{X}_j'$ into communal and unique components. It is also apparent that $\mathbf{m}\bar{\mathbf{H}}' = \mathbf{n}\bar{\mathbf{H}}$ and $\mathbf{m}\bar{\mathbf{U}}' = \mathbf{n}\bar{\mathbf{U}}$, so $V_{\bar{H}'}/V_{\bar{U}'} = V_{\bar{H}}/V_{\bar{U}}$ or, using [7.121], $h^2_{\bar{X}'} = h^2_{\bar{X}}$. Hence any lower bound on the centroid communality of the set of group sums $\mathbf{X}_1', \ldots, \mathbf{X}_m'$ is likewise a lower bound on the centroid communality of the original set $\mathbf{X}_1, \ldots, \mathbf{X}_n$. Finding a maximal lower bound for $h^2_{\bar{X}}$ through application of the alpha estimate to such group sums will be discussed in Chapter 9 (pp. 451 ff.).

It would be pleasant to conclude this review of lower-bound estimates of centroid communality with a statement about the comparative accuracies of all these various methods. However, no tidy summary appears possible. Alpha estimate [7.170] is exceedingly easy to compute and is sufficiently accurate for most purposes unless Hom_H or $\mathbf{n}$ is quite small. If even minute increases in the accuracy of $\text{Est}(h^2_{\bar{X}})$ are important, then all lower-bound estimates should be tried and the largest value taken. Once the data-variable covariance matrix is at hand, $\text{Est}_Q(h^2_{\bar{X}})$ and the estimates based on [7.185] and [7.186] can be processed quickly, since only the largest lower bound for V_H need be passed on to [7.155]. Regression estimate [7.169] is likely to be superior to all of these when Hom_H is small and $\mathbf{n}$ is not too meager, but for even modest $\mathbf{n}$ this requires considerable labor unless computer services are available. Perhaps the most tantalizing prospects for close estimation of $h^2_{\bar{X}}$ in low-Hom_H data lie in alpha estimates computed from group sums. Depending on the nature of the data, it is possible (if not necessarily to be expected) that a grouping can be found which yields an almost perfect estimate of $h^2_{\bar{X}}$ even when other estimation procedures do poorly.

Saturation and Reflection

Our earlier observation (cf. [7.38]) that when a set of variables is analyzed into a set of orthonormal factors, the average variance accounted for by each factor is the squared quadratic mean magnitude of pattern coefficients on that factor, permits an interesting comparison between centroids and principal axes in terms of average factor loadings: *The first centroid factor of a set of variables maximizes the arithmetic mean of the set's factor loadings* (cf. pp. 311 f.), *whereas the first principal factor maximizes the quadratic mean magnitude of factor loadings.* This calls attention to the fact that since the first principal factor attends only to *magnitudes*, it is indifferent to whether its coefficient for a given variable is positive or negative. But while changing the sign of one or more pattern coefficients for a factor $\mathbf{F_j}$ leaves $QM_{|b_j|}$ undisturbed, the same is emphatically *not* true of $\bar{b}_j$, for negative terms in the latter work to cancel out positive ones. Consequently, if negative loadings on $\mathbf{F_j}$ can be reversed in direction without altering their magnitudes, $QM_{|b_j|}$ will remain constant but $\bar{b}_j$ will increase at the expense of σ_{b_j}. Now, reversing the signs of factor loadings is precisely what is accomplished by "reflecting" a variable; for if $\mathbf{X_i}$ is replaced with $\mathbf{X_i'}$, where $\mathbf{X_i'} = -\mathbf{X_i}$, the loading of the ith variable in the set on each factor $\mathbf{F_j}$ is changed from b_{ij} to $b_{i'j} = -b_{ij}$. As soon as we contemplate converting a variable's raw scores into a standardized scale, moreover, it is apparent that nothing is lost by inverting the order of the scores if we see reason to do so. For example, suppose that in a study of physical attributes leading to success in beauty contests, it is found that a contestant's body weight correlates negatively with judges' ratings and other measures to which the experimenter attaches importance. Interpretation of the findings would then be psychologically facilitated if the Body-weight variable were to be replaced by its negation on some standardized scale and called, say, the "Petiteness" variable.

When standardizing a set of variables, then, it should be routine policy to make a deliberate decision about the direction in which each variable is to be scored. Just what considerations should weigh in this judgment must ultimately rest in the purpose of the investigation. In view of the prevalent desire to make manifest whatever latent similarities may exist among the variables, however, it is certainly relevant to consider what the scoring procedures do to the set's saturation. For while the penetrance of a set into a given factor space is invariant under different choices of orientation (i.e., direction of scoring) for its variables, the selection of orientation *does* strongly influence how the set's total variance in that space is partitioned between saturation and dispersion components. For example, when variables $\mathbf{X_1}$, $\mathbf{X_2}$, $\mathbf{X_3}$, whose vector configuration is shown by the solid lines in Figure 7.2*a*, are modified by reflecting $\mathbf{X_1}$ to produce the configuration perceivable in Figure 7.2*a* by replacing the solid vector to $\mathbf{X_1}$ with the dotted vector to $\mathbf{X_1'}$, the saturation and dispersion components of the $\mathbf{X_i}$ change from the configurations shown in Figure 7.2*b* to those in Figure 7.2*c*. Figure 7.2 is somewhat atypical in that reflection of $\mathbf{X_1}$ to $\mathbf{X_1'}$ makes all the correlations among the variables positive, whereas this is not always possible for an arbitrary set of variables.[20] Nonetheless, when a set of variables has low saturation, and especially if many of the intercorrelations are negative, a question arises whether this may not be due to an arbitrary discoordination of orientations among the variables rather than an inherent lack of consistency. In the next few paragraphs we shall briefly describe some varieties of

[20] It is readily seen that for any three variables, if either just one or all three of their intercorrelations are negative, then no series of reflections can make these all positive.

directional order or disorder which might be displayed by a configuration of variables, and the extent to which these can be brought about or modified by reflection.

The strongest possible directional agreement which could occur among a number of variables is, of course, for all their intercorrelations to be +1. However, this is too degenerate a situation to sustain much interest. Another strong form of unidirectionality, this time well within the scope of empirical possibility, is for all the intercorrelations to be positive, or at least nonnegative. A configuration of variables with this property—i.e., $C_{\mathbf{X}_i\mathbf{X}_j} \geq 0$, $\mathbf{i},\mathbf{j} = 1, \ldots, \mathbf{n}$—is known as a *positive manifold* and as previously observed (see fn. 20, p. 342) cannot be reflected into existence if the data do not actively cooperate. By systematic contrast, a configuration in which no proper covariance is positive and at least one is negative might be called a "negative manifold," though this condition will virtually never occur in practice.

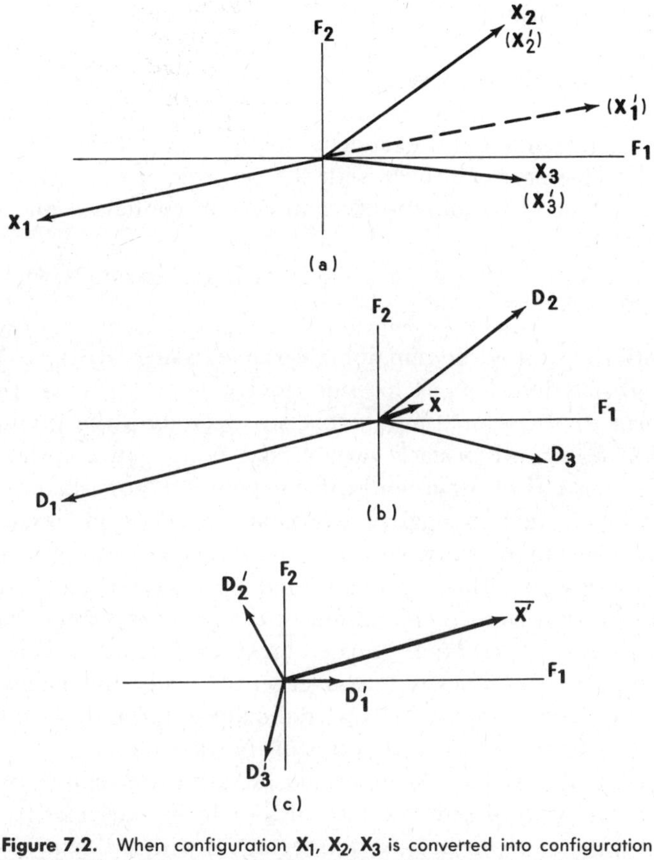

Figure 7.2. When configuration $\mathbf{X}_1$, $\mathbf{X}_2$, $\mathbf{X}_3$ is converted into configuration $\mathbf{X}_1'$, $\mathbf{X}_2'$, $\mathbf{X}_3'$ by reflection of $\mathbf{X}_1$ (Figure 7.2*a*), the saturation and dispersion configurations of the set are correspondingly converted from as shown in Figure 7.2*b* to as shown in Figure 7.2*c*.

While positive manifolds are not infrequently encountered in certain areas of research, notably the study of human abilities, the most typical configurations contain an irreducible minimum of negative covariance, and it is of interest to examine the ways in which the variables in such a set might be said to have, or not to have, a common orientation. For while the saturation or homogeneity coefficient reports the degree of overall consensus in a set, this alone conveys little about how that consensus was reached—e.g., a moderate homogeneity might be achieved by either a weakly intercorrelated positive manifold, or by a configuration comprising, say, negatively related subgroups which internally are strongly homogeneous. The most obvious sense in which a number of variables might be construed to have a common direction, even though some of their intercorrelations are negative, is for there to be some direction on which each has a positive projection. In pursuit of this idea, one standard which might be proposed for configural unidirectionality is for each variable in the set to correlate positively, or at least nonnegatively, with the set's centroid—i.e., for the sum of each column (or row) of the set's covariance matrix to be equal to or greater than zero. However, since the covariance of each $\mathbf{X_i}$ with $\bar{\mathbf{X}}$ includes a self-covariance, it is possible for the set's homogeneity to be negative, or even for the configuration to be a negative manifold, and still have every variable in the set correlate positively with the centroid. In recognition of this strange form of common-directedness, a configuration such that $\sum_{j=1}^{n} C_{X_iX_j} \geq 0$ for $\mathbf{i} = \mathbf{1}, \ldots, \mathbf{n}$ while there is at least one $\mathbf{X_i}$ whose covariance with the sum of the remaining variables is negative (i.e., $\sum_{j=1}^{n} C_{X_i X_j} < V_{X_i}$) might be described as "pseudopositive."

A form of directional agreement stronger than the pseudopositive condition occurs when each variable has nonnegative covariance with the set's centroid even without the contribution from its own variance, namely, by having nonnegative covariance with the sum (or equivalently, with the centroid) of the other variables in the set. A configuration which has this property, which is manifested by a nonnegative sum of the proper covariances in each column of the set's covariance matrix, may be said to be *convergent* (i.e., "turned together"). More specifically, let us call this property "first-order convergence," since this is just one of a family of unidirectionality concepts definable in terms of the correlations between the centroids of subgroups of the variables.

Let a set of variables be described as "**k**th-order convergent" if the centroid (or sum) of any selection of **k** or fewer variables from the set correlates positively or at least nonnegatively with the centroid (or sum) of the remaining variables. Since a configuration which is **k**th-order convergent need not be $(\mathbf{k}+\mathbf{1})$th-order convergent, this hierarchy of convergences represents an increasingly tight pattern of common-directedness. In the limit, a set is *strictly convergent* if for any partition of the variables into two groups, the centroid of the one group correlates nonnegatively with the centroid of the other. Two properties common to all **k**th-order convergent configuration, though not limited to them, is that (1) the set's homogeneity cannot be less than zero, and (2) no variable in the set has a negative projection on the set's centroid.

We could go on to define even more closely unidirectional types of configurations by considering covariances between the centroids of not-necessarily-dichotomous subsets of the variables, leading to the positive manifold as a limiting case. What is especially salient about **k**th-order convergences, however, is that these can be controlled by suitable reflection of the variables. In particular, *it is always possible to select orientations for the variables in a set which make their configuration strictly convergent.* Moreover, *a strictly convergent set has the maximal saturation which can be brought about by reflection of its variables.* To prove the second claim first, let variables $\mathbf{X}_1, \ldots, \mathbf{X}_n$ be arbitrarily divided into two groups G_a and G_b, and let $\mathbf{S}_a$ and $\mathbf{S}_b$ be the sums of the variables in groups G_a and G_b, respectively. Since $\overline{\mathbf{X}} = (\mathbf{S}_a + \mathbf{S}_b)/\mathbf{n}$,

$$\text{[7.188]} \qquad \text{Sat}_{\mathbf{X}} = \frac{\text{Var}(\mathbf{S}_a + \mathbf{S}_b)}{\mathbf{n}^2 \overline{\text{V}}_{\mathbf{X}}} = \frac{\text{V}_{\mathbf{S}_a} + \text{V}_{\mathbf{S}_b} + 2\text{C}_{\mathbf{S}_a\mathbf{S}_b}}{\mathbf{n}\text{V}_{\mathbf{X}}} .$$

If all the variables in one of the groups, say G_a, are now reflected, all terms in [7.188] remain the same except $\text{C}_{\mathbf{S}_a\mathbf{S}_b}$, which is replaced by $-\text{C}_{\mathbf{S}_a\mathbf{S}_b}$. But if the set $\mathbf{X}_1, \ldots, \mathbf{X}_n$ is strictly convergent, then by definition $\text{C}_{\mathbf{S}_a\mathbf{S}_b} \geqslant 0$; hence $-\text{C}_{\mathbf{S}_a\mathbf{S}_b} \leqslant 0$, and reflection of the variables in G_a would only lower the set's saturation or at best leave it unchanged. Since this argument holds for any partition of the $\mathbf{X}_i$ into a reflected group and an unreflected group, it is thus impossible to increase the saturation of a strictly convergent set by reflecting some of its variables. If the set $\mathbf{X}_1, \ldots, \mathbf{X}_n$ is not already strictly convergent, on the other hand, it can be reflected into being so as follows: Compute the covariance between the sums of the two subgroups in every different dichotomous partition of the $\mathbf{X}_i$, and select the partition (or one of them, if more than one qualifies) in which this between-group covariance has the largest negative value. Reflecting all the variables on one side of this partition while leaving the others as they are then makes the set strictly convergent and at the maximal saturation which can be achieved by reflection.[21] Unfortunately, while this can easily be done in practice for a set of five variables or less, and with only moderate effort for six or seven variables, the fact that there are $2^{\mathbf{n}-1} - 1$ different ways to dichotomize **n** variables makes direct computation of the saturation-maximizing reflections prohibitively tedious for more than a few variables unless the task is turned over to a computer.

Instead of attempting to maximize unidirectionality in a set of variables, it is also possible to select orientations which make for directional disagreement. Analogous to "**k**th-order convergence," let a configuration be said to be as "**k**th-order divergent" if the centroid of any selection of **k** or fewer variables from the set has a negative or at least nonpositive covariance with the centroid of the remainder, and "strictly divergent" if this is true for any dichotomous partition of the set. Then any set can be reflected into strict divergence by finding the partition for which the group-centroid covariance has the greatest positive value and reflecting the variables on one side of this partition. This also minimizes the set's saturation, and since the homogeneity of a divergent configuration is at most zero, it follows that saturation can always be reduced to a minimum no greater than $1/\mathbf{n}$ by suitable reflection of the variables. variables.

Finally, it may be noted that the quadratic mean magnitude of the proper covariances among the variables in a set, divided by their average variance, is an upper bound for the homogeneity which can be brought about in the set by reflecting its variables into strict convergence. Writing "$QM_{|C_{XX}|}$" for the quadratic mean magnitude of the off-diagonal entries in $\{C_{X_iX_j}\}$ as in [7.176], we have from principle [3.19] that

[7.189] $$\bar{C}_{XX} \leqslant QM_{|C_{XX}|}$$

and hence

[7.190] $$\text{Hom}_{X} \leqslant \frac{QM_{|C_{XX}|}}{\bar{V}_{X}} = \frac{\sqrt{\left(\frac{n}{n-1}\right) \sum_{i=1}^{n} \sum_{\substack{j=1 \\ i \neq j}}^{n} C^2_{X_iX_j}}}{\sum_{i=1}^{n} V_{X_i}}.$$

---

[21] *Proof:* (1) Let $G_1, G_2, \ldots$ be a list of all ways to select one or more variables from $\mathbf{X}_1, \ldots, \mathbf{X}_n$; (2) let C_i be the covariance between the sum of the variables in subgroup G_i and the sum of the $\mathbf{X}_j$ not in G_i; (3) let G_m be a subgroup of the $\mathbf{X}_i$ such that both $C_m \leqslant C_i$ for all subgroups i from $\mathbf{X}_1, \ldots, \mathbf{X}_n$ and $C_m < 0$; (4) let C_i' be the covariance between the sum of the variables in a subgroup $G_i (G_i \neq G_m)$ and the sum of the remaining $\mathbf{X}_i$ *after* the variables in subgroup G_m have been reflected; and finally, (5) let G_{mi} be the subgroup comprising those $\mathbf{X}_j$ which are either in both G_m and G_i or in neither of them, while C_{mi} is the covariance between the sum of variables in G_{mi} and the sum of the remaining $\mathbf{X}_j$. It is then readily seen that for any subgroup G_i other than G_m, $C_m + C_i' = C_{mi}$, so $C_i' = C_{mi} - C_m \geqslant 0$, where the inequality follows from stipulation (3). But since $C_m < 0$, also $C_m' > 0$. Hence all the covariances $C_1', C_2', \ldots$ are nonnegative, and reflection of the variables in G_m brings the $\mathbf{X}_j$-configuration into strict convergence.

Since the right-hand side of [7.190] remains unchanged under any reflections of the $\mathbf{X}_j$, it is thus an upper bound for the set's homogeneity under any choice of orientation for its variables. Correspondingly, an upper bound for the maximal saturation which can be achieved through reflection is

$$[7.191] \qquad \mathrm{Sat}_{\mathbf{X}} \leqslant \left(\frac{\mathbf{n}-1}{\mathbf{n}}\right)\frac{\mathrm{QM}_{|C_{\mathbf{X}\mathbf{X}}|}}{\overline{V}_{\mathbf{X}}} + \frac{1}{\mathbf{n}},$$

or more simply, though not quite so closely,

$$[7.192] \qquad \mathrm{Sat}_{\mathbf{X}} \leqslant \frac{\mathrm{QM}_{|C^*_{\mathbf{X}\mathbf{X}}|}}{\overline{V}_{\mathbf{X}}} = \frac{\sqrt{\sum_{i=1}^{n}\sum_{j=1}^{n} C^2_{X_iX_j}}}{\sum_{i=1}^{n} V_{X_i}},$$

where of course $\mathrm{QM}_{|C^*_{\mathbf{X}\mathbf{X}}|}$ is the quadratic mean magnitude of all entries in the set's covariance matrix. It can also be shown that

$$[7.193]^{22} \qquad \sum_{i=1}^{n}\sum_{j=1}^{n} C^2_{X_iX_j} = \sum_{i=1}^{n} \lambda_i^2,$$

where λ_i $(= V_{\mathbf{X}(P_i)})$ is the eigenvalue corresponding to the **i**th principal factor, $\mathbf{P}_i$, of the $\mathbf{X}_j$-configuration; hence from [7.192],

$$[7.194] \qquad \frac{\mathrm{QM}_{|C^*_{\mathbf{X}\mathbf{X}}|}}{V_{\mathbf{X}}} = \frac{V_{\mathbf{X}(P_1)}}{V_{\mathbf{X}}}\sqrt{\frac{\sum_{i=1}^{n}\lambda_i^2}{\lambda_1^2}} = P_{\mathbf{X}}(S_{P_1})\sqrt{1+\frac{\sum_{i=2}^{n}\lambda_i^2}{\lambda_1^2}} \geqslant P_{\mathbf{X}}(S_{P_1}),$$

where S_{P_1} is the space spanned by the first principal factor of the $\mathbf{X}_j$. Thus the upper bound for $\mathrm{Sat}_{\mathbf{X}}$ indicated in [7.192] is also an upper bound for the proportion of the set's variance accounted for by its first principal factor, and may be taken as an upper-bound approximation to the latter, the error of the approximation becoming increasingly small as the configuration becomes increasingly dominated by a single factor.[23] Since

---

[22] Briefly, the matrix-algebra proof runs as follows: The quantity $\sum_{i=1}^{n}\sum_{j=1}^{n} C^2_{X_iX_j}$ equals the trace of the squared covariance matrix $\{C_{X_iX_j}\}$. Now, if **A**, **B**, and **T** are $n \times n$ matrices such that **T** is orthonormal and $\mathbf{B} = \mathbf{TAT}'$, then $\mathbf{B}^2 = \mathbf{TAT}'\mathbf{TAT}' = \mathbf{TA}^2\mathbf{T}'$ and, since $\mathrm{Tr}(\mathbf{MN}) = \mathrm{Tr}(\mathbf{NM})$ for any two $n \times n$ matrices **M** and **N**, $\mathrm{Tr}(\mathbf{TA}^2\mathbf{T}') = \mathrm{Tr}(\mathbf{T}'\mathbf{TA}^2) = \mathrm{Tr}(\mathbf{A}^2)$. Hence the trace of the squared covariance matrix for variables $\mathbf{X}_1, \ldots, \mathbf{X}_n$ is invariant under orthogonal rotations of the set, while the principal components of the $\mathbf{X}_j$ are an orthogonal rotation thereof whose squared covariance matrix has the trace $\sum_{i=1}^{n} \lambda_i^2$.

[23] More specifically, it is easily seen that the term $\sum_{i=2}^{n} \lambda_i^2/\lambda_1^2$ in [7.174], which is the source of the approximation's error, has a maximum possible value of $(1/\lambda_1^2 - 1)^2$ and a minimum possible value equal to $(1/\mathbf{n})$th of this maximum. The maximum occurs when the second principal factor of the $\mathbf{X}_j$ accounts for all of their remaining variance, while the minimum occurs when all principal factors after the first are equally important (i.e., have equal eigenvalues).

$\mathrm{Sat}_{\mathbf{X}}$ is a lower bound for $P_{\mathbf{X}}(S_{\mathbf{P}_1})$ (see [7.96]), the bracketing inequalities

[7.195] $$\frac{\sum_{i=1}^{n}\sum_{j=1}^{n} C_{X_iX_j}}{n\sum_{i=1}^{n} V_{X_i}} \leqslant P_{\mathbf{X}}(S_{\mathbf{P}_1}) \leqslant \frac{\sqrt{\sum_{i=1}^{n}\sum_{j=1}^{n} C^2_{X_iX_j}}}{\sum_{i=1}^{n} V_{X_i}}$$

provides a quick way to learn something about the prominence of a single factor in a set of variables from the set's covariance matrix, the upper bound being useful even when the variables have arbitrary orientations. In particular, to consider a case which will later (p. 372) be seen to have some minor practical utility, we have from [7.66] that the quadratic mean magnitude of the covariances among the dispersion components of a set of variables is

[7.196] $$\begin{aligned} QM_{|C^*_{DD}|} &= \sqrt{QM^2_{|C^*_{XX}|} - \bar{C}^{*2}_{XX} - 2\sigma^2_{\bar{C}_X}} \\ &= \sqrt{\sigma^2_{C^*_{XX}} - 2\sigma^2_{\bar{C}_X}}, \end{aligned}$$

where $\sigma_{C^*_{XX}}$ and $\sigma_{\bar{C}_X}$ are the SD of all entries and the SD of column averages, respectively, in $\{C_{X_iX_j}\}$. Therefore, if $S_{P_{D1}}$ is the space spanned by the first principal factor of the $\mathbf{D}_i$, [7.195] shows that the penetrance of the dispersion configuration into the space of its first principal factor is at most

[7.197] $$P_{\mathbf{D}}(S_{P_{D1}}) \leqslant \frac{QM_{|C^*_{DD}|}}{\bar{V}_{\mathbf{D}}} = \frac{\sqrt{\sigma^2_{C^*_{XX}} - 2\sigma^2_{\bar{C}_X}}}{\bar{V}_X - \bar{C}^*_{XX}}.$$

**Variance Structure and Linear Transformations

One decision to be made when selecting a scale for a variable is its orientation. Another is the choice of reference point and unit of measurement. Together, these options compose the group of all linear transformations of the variable whose scale is under consideration. Since the scaling decision can be made separately for each variable in a set, a question which arises is how these choices affect the set's variance structure. In particular, if each variable $\mathbf{X}_i$ is subjected to its own linear transformation $\mathbf{W}_i = c_i + w_i\mathbf{X}_i$, how does the centroid $\overline{\mathbf{W}}$ of the transformed set compare with the original centroid $\overline{\mathbf{X}}$? The issue is important on at least two grounds: One is that since $\mathbf{X}_i = M_X + \sigma_{X_i} Z_{X_i}$, it subsumes the effect of normalization, or lack thereof, on the group properties of a set of variables. Secondly, any linear composite can be conceived as the centroid of a suitable rescaling of its constituent variables, so if useful relations exist between $\overline{\mathbf{W}}$ and $\overline{\mathbf{X}}$, the behavior of a set's centroid may reveal much about the behavior of linear functions on that set in general.

To minimize distractions once the main argument gets underway, we begin with some relationships which will be needed later. The first is a highly convenient formula which shows how closely the average product of a pair of variables is approximated by the product of their averages. Since by definition the covariance between two variables **X** and **Y** is

$$C_{\mathbf{XY}} = \frac{\sum_{i=1}^{n} (X_i - M_{\mathbf{X}})\ (Y_i - M_{\mathbf{Y}})}{n} = \frac{\sum_{i=1}^{n} X_i Y_i}{n} - M_{\mathbf{X}} M_{\mathbf{Y}} = M_{\mathbf{XY}} - M_{\mathbf{X}} M_{\mathbf{Y}}\ ,$$

a little rearrangement yields

[7.198] $$\frac{\sum_{i=1}^{n} X_i Y_i}{n} = M_{\mathbf{X}} M_{\mathbf{Y}} + C_{\mathbf{XY}}$$

or

[7.199] $$M_{\mathbf{XY}} = M_{\mathbf{X}} M_{\mathbf{Y}} + \sigma_{\mathbf{X}} \sigma_{\mathbf{Y}} r_{\mathbf{XY}}\ .$$

If one or both of the constituent means is appreciably different from zero, we may also usefully write

[7.200] $$\begin{aligned} M_{\mathbf{X}\,\mathbf{Y}} &= M_{\mathbf{X}}(M_{\mathbf{Y}} + \nu_{\mathbf{X}} \sigma_{\mathbf{Y}} r_{\mathbf{XY}}) \\ &= M_{\mathbf{X}} M_{\mathbf{Y}} (1 + \nu_{\mathbf{X}} \nu_{\mathbf{Y}} r_{\mathbf{XY}})\ , \end{aligned}$$

the second line of which reveals that the mean product is well approximated by the product of the means so long as the coefficient of variation for either variable or the correlation between them is sufficiently small. Our old friend [3.19] is the special instance of [7.199] in which $\mathbf{Y} = \mathbf{X}$, and like [7.200] may be written

[7.201] $$QM^2_{|\mathbf{X}|} = M_{\mathbf{X}^2} = M^2_{\mathbf{X}}(1 + \nu^2_{\mathbf{X}})\ .$$

It should be appreciated, incidently, that whenever we have an equation of form

[7.202] $$y = x(1 + e)\ ,$$

where x, y, and e are numbers (*not* variables), solving for e yields

[7.203] $$e = \frac{y - x}{x}\ ,$$

thus showing that e is the difference between y and x expressed as a proportion of the latter. Hence a term which plays the role of e in form [7.202] (as does, e.g., $\nu^2_{\mathbf{X}}$ in [7.201]) may be interpreted as an approximation-error coefficient which describes the proportionate error made by taking y as an approximation to x.

Next comes an important lemma concerning the correlation between a variable $\mathbf{X}$ and a linear composite, $\mathbf{L} = a_0 + a_1\mathbf{X} + a_2\mathbf{Y}$, of $\mathbf{X}$ with another variable $\mathbf{Y}$. As will be seen, the crucial parameter is the product of ratios $(a_2/a_1)(\sigma_{\mathsf{Y}}/\sigma_{\mathsf{X}})$; therefore we shall work with $\mathbf{L}$ in the form

[7.204] $$\mathbf{L} =_{\text{def}} a_0 + a_1(\mathbf{X} + c\mathbf{Y}) ,$$

where $c = a_2/a_1$, and introduce "q_{YX}" for the ratio of standard deviations —i.e.,

[7.205] $$\mathrm{q}_{\mathsf{YX}} =_{\text{def}} \frac{\sigma_{\mathsf{Y}}}{\sigma_{\mathsf{X}}} .$$

Then the covariance between $\mathbf{X}$ and $\mathbf{L}$ is

[7.206] $$\begin{aligned} \mathrm{C}_{\mathsf{XL}} &= a_1(\sigma^2_{\mathsf{X}} + c\mathrm{C}_{\mathsf{XY}}) \\ &= a_1\sigma^2_{\mathsf{X}}(1 + c\mathrm{q}_{\mathsf{YX}}\mathrm{r}_{\mathsf{XY}}) , \end{aligned} \qquad ([7.204])$$

which is positive so long as $c\mathrm{q}_{\mathsf{YX}} > -1$. To see the magnitude of the correlation, it is most convenient to look at $\mathrm{r}^2_{\mathsf{XL}}$. Since

[7.207] $$\begin{aligned} \sigma^2_{\mathsf{L}} &= a_1^2(\sigma^2_{\mathsf{X}} + 2c\mathrm{C}_{\mathsf{XY}} + c^2\sigma^2_{\mathsf{Y}}) \\ &= a_1^2\sigma^2_{\mathsf{X}}(1 + 2c\mathrm{q}_{\mathsf{YX}}\mathrm{r}_{\mathsf{XY}} + c^2\mathrm{q}^2_{\mathsf{YX}}) , \end{aligned} \qquad ([7.204])$$

we have

[7.208] $$\begin{aligned} \mathrm{r}^2_{\mathsf{XL}} &= \left(\frac{\mathrm{C}_{\mathsf{XL}}}{\sigma_{\mathsf{X}}\sigma_{\mathsf{L}}}\right)^2 \\ &= \frac{a_1^2\sigma^4_{\mathsf{X}}(1 + c\mathrm{q}_{\mathsf{YX}}\mathrm{r}_{\mathsf{XY}})^2}{a_1^2\sigma^4_{\mathsf{X}}(1 + 2c\mathrm{q}_{\mathsf{YX}}\mathrm{r}_{\mathsf{XY}} + c^2\mathrm{q}_{\mathsf{YX}})} \\ &= \frac{1 + 2c\mathrm{q}_{\mathsf{YX}}\mathrm{r}_{\mathsf{XY}} + c^2\mathrm{q}^2_{\mathsf{YX}}\mathrm{r}^2_{\mathsf{XY}}}{1 + 2c\mathrm{q}_{\mathsf{YX}}\mathrm{r}_{\mathsf{XY}} + c^2\mathrm{q}^2_{\mathsf{YX}}} \qquad ([7.204]) \\ &= 1 - \frac{c^2\mathrm{q}^2_{\mathsf{YX}}(1 - \mathrm{r}^2_{\mathsf{XY}})}{1 + 2c\mathrm{q}_{\mathsf{YX}}\mathrm{r}_{\mathsf{XY}} + c^2\mathrm{q}^2_{\mathsf{YX}}} . \end{aligned}$$

Using coefficients of alienation instead of correlation coefficients further simplifies [7.208] to

[7.209] $$\mathrm{k}^2_{\mathsf{XL}} = c^2\mathrm{q}^2_{\mathsf{YX}}\left[\frac{\mathrm{k}^2_{\mathsf{XY}}}{(\mathrm{r}_{\mathsf{XY}} + c\mathrm{q}_{\mathsf{YX}})^2 + \mathrm{k}^2_{\mathsf{XY}}}\right] \qquad ([7.204]) .$$

To avoid the nuisance of absolute-value signs, let us presuppose for the moment, without essential loss of generality, that c is positive. Then one immediate consequence of [7.209] is

[7.210] $$\mathrm{k}_{\mathsf{XL}} \leqslant c\mathrm{q}_{\mathsf{YX}} \qquad ([7.204];\ c \geqslant 0) ,$$

which is useful as an upper bound on k_{XL}—and hence when solved for r_{XL} as a *lower* bound on the latter—so long as $c\mathrm{q}_{\mathsf{YX}}$ is appreciably smaller than unity. Further, the denominator in [7.209] equals $1 + c^2 q^2_{\mathbf{YX}}$ when **X** and **Y** are uncorrelated, and lies between $(1 - c q_{\mathbf{YX}})^2$ and $(1 + c q_{\mathbf{YX}})^2$ no matter what $r_{\mathbf{XY}}$ may be. Hence $k_{\mathbf{XL}}$ falls within the limits

$$[7.211] \qquad \frac{c q_{\mathbf{YX}} k_{\mathbf{XY}}}{1 + c q_{\mathbf{YX}}} \leqslant k_{\mathbf{XL}} \leqslant \frac{c q_{\mathbf{YX}} k_{\mathbf{XY}}}{1 - c q_{\mathbf{YX}}} \qquad ([7.204];\ c \geqslant 0)\ ,$$

while if **X** and **Y** are uncorrelated,

$$[7.212] \qquad k_{\mathbf{XL}} = \frac{c q_{\mathbf{YX}}}{1 + c^2 q^2_{\mathbf{YX}}} \qquad ([7.204];\ c \geqslant 0;\ r_{\mathbf{XY}} = 0)\ .$$

By experimentation with various values for $r_{\mathbf{XY}}$ it may be seen that the approximation to $r^2_{\mathbf{XL}}$ suggested by [7.212], namely,

$$[7.213]^{24} \qquad r^2_{\mathbf{XL}} \simeq 1 - \frac{c^2 q^2_{\mathbf{YX}}}{1 + c^2 q^2_{\mathbf{YX}}} \qquad ([7.204])\ ,$$

is quite accurate when $c q_{\mathbf{YX}}$ is substantially smaller than unity (say $c q_{\mathbf{YX}} <$ .5) except when $r_{\mathbf{XY}}$ is large and positive, in which case [7.213] may seriously overestimate $r^2_{\mathbf{XL}}$ and the approximation

$$[7.214] \qquad r^2_{\mathbf{XL}} \simeq 1 - c^2 q^2_{\mathbf{YX}} (1 - r^2_{\mathbf{XY}}) \qquad ([7.204])$$

is better.

Finally, we shall have a fleeting desire to know the coefficient of variation for the distribution of squared values of a variable. By thoroughly routine computations, it can be shown that

$$\begin{aligned} [7.215] \qquad \mathrm{Var}(\mathbf{X}^2) &= \frac{\sum_{i=1}^{n} (X_i^2 - M_{\mathbf{X}^2})^2}{n} \\ &= M_{\mathbf{X}^4} - (M_{\mathbf{X}^2})^2 \\ &= \mu^{(4)}_{\mathbf{X}} + 4 M_{\mathbf{X}} \mu^{(3)}_{\mathbf{X}} + 4 M^2_{\mathbf{X}} \sigma^2_{\mathbf{X}} - \sigma^4_{\mathbf{X}} \\ &= 4 M^2_{\mathbf{X}} \sigma^2_{\mathbf{X}} (1 + 4 \nu_{\mathbf{X}}\ \mathrm{Sk}_{\mathbf{X}} + \nu^2_{\mathbf{X}}\ [2 + \mathrm{Kt}_{\mathbf{X}}])\ , \end{aligned}$$

where $\mu^{(3)}_{\mathbf{X}}$ and $\mu^{(4)}_{\mathbf{X}}$ are the third and fourth central moments (see p. 55) of the distribution of **X**, and $\mathrm{Sk}_{\mathbf{X}}$ and $\mathrm{Kt}_{\mathbf{X}}$ are its skew and kurtosis, respectively, as defined on pp. 50f. The coefficient of variation for $\mathbf{X}^2$ is hence

$$\begin{aligned} [7.216] \qquad \nu_{\mathbf{X}^2} &= \frac{\sigma_{\mathbf{X}^2}}{M_{\mathbf{X}^2}} \\ &= \frac{2 |M_{\mathbf{X}}| \sigma_{\mathbf{X}} \sqrt{1 + t_{\mathbf{X}}}}{M^2_{\mathbf{X}} + \sigma^2_{\mathbf{X}}} \\ &= \frac{2 |\nu_{\mathbf{X}}| \sqrt{1 + t_{\mathbf{X}}}}{1 + \nu^2_{\mathbf{X}}}\ , \end{aligned}$$

[24] The symbol "≃" means "is approximately equal to."

where t_X is the second-order quantity

[7.217] $$t_X =_{def} \nu_X(4Sk_X + 2\nu_X + \nu_X Kt_X) .$$

We are now properly armed to gun down our main quarry. Let $W_1, \ldots, W_n$ be the variables derived from $X_1, \ldots, X_n$, respectively, by the linear transformations

[7.218-i] (i = 1, . . . , n) $$W_i =_{def} c_i + w_i X_i .$$

The subscript "i" attached to the transformation coefficient for X_i in [7.219-i] serves notice that we have a distribution of these coefficients, namely, one for each X_i, and we may henceforth write "w" as a transformation-weight variable whose value for "individual" X_i is w_i, while $\bar{w}$, σ_W, and ν_W are the arithmetic mean, standard deviation, and coefficient of variation, respectively, for the transformation-weight distribution $w_1, \ldots, w_n$.

Now let $F_1, \ldots, F_m$ be an orthonormal factor basis for the set of variables $X_1, \ldots, X_n$ according to the factor pattern

[7.219-i] (i = 1, . . . , n) $$X_i = b_{io} + b_{i1}F_1 + \ldots + b_{im}F_m = b_{io} + \sum_{j=1}^{m} b_{ij}F_j .$$

As shown previously (see [7.39]), the corresponding factorial composition of the set's centroid is

[7.220] $$\bar{X} = \bar{b}_0 + \bar{b}_1 F + \ldots + \bar{b}_m F_m = \bar{b}_0 + \sum_{j=1}^{m} \bar{b}_j F_j ,$$

where b_j, it will be recalled, is the arithmetic mean of the factor loadings of the X_i on F_j. If the transformed variables $W_1, \ldots, W_n$ are also analyzed in terms of these same factors, it follows from [7.218] and [7.219] that

[7.221-i] (i = 1, . . . , n) $$W_i = c_i + w_i\left(b_{io} + \sum_{j=1}^{m} b_{ij}F_j\right) = c_i + w_i b_{io} + \sum_{j=1}^{m} w_i b_{ij} F_j$$

while the centroid of the W_i is hence

[7.222] $$\bar{W} = \bar{c} + \overline{wb_0} + \sum_{j=1}^{m} \overline{wb_j} F_j ,$$

where $\overline{wb}_j$ is the arithmetic mean of the products $w_i b_{ij}$ for variables $\mathbf{X}_1, \ldots, \mathbf{X}_n$ on factor $\mathbf{F}_j$. Writing "r_{wb_j}" for the correlation between the $\mathbf{n}$ transformation weights and the $\mathbf{n}$ pattern coefficients of the $\mathbf{X}_i$ on factor $\mathbf{F}_j$, we can draw upon principle [7.199] to convert [7.222] into

[7.223]
$$\begin{aligned}\overline{\mathbf{W}} &= \bar{c} + \overline{w}\bar{b}_0 + \sigma_w \sigma_{b_0} r_{wb_0} + \sum_{j=1}^{m} (\overline{w}\bar{b}_j + \sigma_w \sigma_{b_j} r_{wb_j}) \mathbf{F}_j \\ &= \bar{c} + \overline{w}\left(\bar{b}_0 + \sum_{j=1}^{m} \bar{b}_j \mathbf{F}_j\right) + \sigma_w \left(\sigma_{b_0} r_{wb_0} + \sum_{j=1}^{m} \sigma_{b_j} r_{wb_j} \mathbf{F}_j\right) \\ &= \bar{c} + \overline{w}\overline{\mathbf{X}} + \sigma_w \boldsymbol{\delta}_{wX} \\ &= \bar{c} + \overline{w}(\overline{\mathbf{X}} + \nu_w \boldsymbol{\delta}_{wX}) \ ,\end{aligned}$$

where

[7.224]
$$\boldsymbol{\delta}_{wX} =_{\text{def}} \sigma_{b_0} r_{wb_0} + \sum_{j=1}^{m} \sigma_{b_j} r_{wb_j} \mathbf{F}_j \ .$$

The nature of the variable $\boldsymbol{\delta}_{wX}$ which turns up along with $\overline{\mathbf{X}}$ in the composition of $\overline{\mathbf{W}}$ is clarified by observing it to be a linear combination of the dispersion components of the $\mathbf{X}_i$. Specifically, in view of [7.32],

[7.225]
$$\begin{aligned}\overline{\mathbf{W}} &=_{\text{def}} \frac{\sum_{i=1}^{n} \mathbf{W}_i}{\mathbf{n}} \\ &= \frac{\sum_{i=1}^{n} (c_i + w_i \mathbf{X}_i)}{\mathbf{n}} \\ &= \frac{\sum_{i=1}^{n} [c_i + w_i(\overline{\mathbf{X}} + \mathbf{D}_i)]}{\mathbf{n}} \\ &= \bar{c} + \overline{w}\overline{\mathbf{X}} + \frac{\sum_{i=1}^{n} w_i \mathbf{D}_i}{\mathbf{n}} \ ,\end{aligned}$$

so from [7.223],

[7.226]
$$\boldsymbol{\delta}_{wX} = \frac{\sum_{i=1}^{n} w_i \mathbf{D}_i}{\mathbf{n}\sigma_w} \ .$$

It is clear in [7.224] that $\boldsymbol{\delta}_{wX}$ is not influenced by the overall size or variability of the transformation weights, but only by their correlational affinities for the factor loadings of the $\mathbf{X}_i$. To make this explicit in [7.226], let z_{wi} be the standardized transformation coefficient corresponding to w_i—i.e.,

$$z_{wi} =_{\text{def}} \frac{w_i - \overline{w}}{\sigma_w} \qquad (\sigma_w > 0) ,$$

[7.227-i]
(i = 1, . . . , n)

which converts the w_i into a set of standardized weights whose mean is zero and whose SD is 1. Bearing in mind that $\sum_{i=1}^{n} \mathbf{D}_i = 0$ (see [7.33]), we may then continue [7.226] to obtain

[7.228]
$$\boldsymbol{\delta}_{wX} = \frac{\sum_{i=1}^{n} [(w_i - \overline{w})\mathbf{D}_i + \overline{w}\mathbf{D}_i]}{n\sigma_w}$$
$$= \frac{\sum_{i=1}^{n} (w_i - \overline{w})\mathbf{D}_i}{n\sigma_w} + \frac{\overline{w}}{n\sigma_w}\left(\sum_{i=1}^{n} \mathbf{D}_i\right) \qquad (\sigma_w > 0)$$
$$= \frac{\sum_{i=1}^{n} z_{wi}\mathbf{D}_i}{n} ,$$

which states that $\boldsymbol{\delta}_{wX}$ is the centroid of the dispersion components $\mathbf{D}_1, \ldots, \mathbf{D}_n$ after they have been weighted by the standardized transformation coefficients. Since the unweighted centroid of the $\mathbf{D}_i$ is identically zero, $\boldsymbol{\delta}_{wX}$ will itself differ from zero only insofar as the transformation weights impart emphasis to a particular direction of the dispersion configuration. Thus $\boldsymbol{\delta}_{wX}$ expresses in pure form the contribution to the transformed centroid of the selective association between transformation weights and the dispersion components of the variables being rescaled, while the effects of the average value and relative variability of these transformation weights are shown in [7.223] by $\overline{w}$ and ν_w, respectively.

An important interpretation of equation [7.223] is that when the variables in a set are individually rescaled, the centroid of the transformed variables is *approximately* a linear transformation of the original centroid in which the transformation constants are the arithmetic means of the corresponding transformation constants for the original variables. That is, if along with transformations [7.218] $\overline{\mathbf{X}}$ is subjected to the linear transformation

[7.229]
$$\mathbf{W}_{\overline{X}} =_{\text{def}} \overline{c} + \overline{w}\overline{\mathbf{X}} ,$$

we see from [7.223] that

[7.230]
$$\overline{\mathbf{W}} = \mathbf{W}_{\overline{X}} + \sigma_w \boldsymbol{\delta}_{wX} ,$$

which suggests that the approximation $\overline{\mathbf{W}} \simeq \mathbf{W}_{\overline{\mathbf{X}}}$ may be acceptable on many occasions. Just how accurate this approximation might be is next to be investigated.

While the raw means of variables are seldom of importance, we may begin comparison of $\overline{\mathbf{W}}$ and $\mathbf{W}_{\overline{\mathbf{X}}}$ by noting from [7.230] and [7.224], in view of general principle [4.45], that

[7.231]
$$\mathrm{M}_{\overline{\mathbf{W}}} - \mathrm{M}_{\mathbf{W}_{\overline{\mathbf{X}}}} = \sigma_{\mathbf{w}}\, \mathrm{M}_{\boldsymbol{\delta}_{\mathbf{w}\mathbf{X}}}$$
$$= \sigma_{\mathbf{w}}\, \sigma_{\mathbf{b}_0} \mathrm{r}_{\mathbf{w}\mathbf{b}_0} \, .$$

Since for normalized factors $b_{i0} = \mathrm{M}_{\mathbf{X}_i}$ for each $\mathbf{X}_i$, [7.231] shows that despite differences among the w_i, the means of $\overline{\mathbf{W}}$ and its approximation $\mathbf{W}_{\overline{\mathbf{X}}}$ differ only to the extent that the means of the $\mathbf{X}_i$ themselves differ and are also correlated with the transformation weights. Of greater interest when one variable is being approximated by another, however, is the correlation between them. Since $\mathbf{W}_{\overline{\mathbf{X}}}$ is a linear transformation of $\overline{\mathbf{X}}$, it will suffice to examine the correlational agreement between the old and new centroids $\overline{\mathbf{X}}$ and $\overline{\mathbf{W}}$—which is what commands primary interest anyway, since this tells how a linear composite is affected by differential item weights. Now, [7.223] states that $\overline{\mathbf{W}}$ is a linear composite of $\overline{\mathbf{X}}$ with a weight-standardized dispersion contribution $\boldsymbol{\delta}_{\mathbf{w}\mathbf{X}}$, and by a remarkable coincidence the last line of [7.223] is precisely of form [7.204], in terms of which the correlation between a part and the whole of a linear composite has already been analyzed. To apply this analysis, however, we first need the ratio of the standard deviation of $\boldsymbol{\delta}_{\mathbf{w}\mathbf{X}}$ to the standard deviation of $\overline{\mathbf{X}}$. From [7.224] and recollection that factors $\mathbf{F}_1, \ldots, \mathbf{F}_m$ were stipulated to be orthonormal, we have

[7.232]
$$\mathrm{Var}(\boldsymbol{\delta}_{\mathbf{w}\mathbf{X}}) = \sum_{j=1}^{m} \sigma^2_{\mathbf{b}_j} \mathrm{r}^2_{\mathbf{w}\mathbf{b}_j} \qquad \text{(orthonormal factors)}\, .$$

But from [7.43], $\sigma^2_{\mathbf{b}_j}$ is the average dispersion variance of $\mathbf{X}_1, \ldots, \mathbf{X}_n$ accounted for by factor $\mathbf{F}_j$, so we may continue

[7.233]
$$\mathrm{Var}(\boldsymbol{\delta}_{\mathbf{w}\mathbf{X}}) = \sum_{j=1}^{m} \overline{\mathrm{V}}_{\mathbf{D}(\mathbf{F}_j)} \mathrm{r}^2_{\mathbf{w}\mathbf{b}_j}$$
$$= \left[\sum_{j=1}^{m} \overline{\mathrm{V}}_{\mathbf{D}(\mathbf{F}_j)} \right] \frac{\sum_{j=1}^{m} \overline{\mathrm{V}}_{\mathbf{D}(\mathbf{F}_j)} \mathrm{r}^2_{\mathbf{w}\mathbf{b}_j}}{\sum_{j=1}^{m} \overline{\mathrm{V}}_{\mathbf{D}(\mathbf{F}_j)}} \qquad \text{(orthonormal factors)}$$
$$= \overline{\mathrm{V}}_{\mathbf{D}}\, \gamma_{\mathbf{w}\mathbf{X}} \, ,$$

where $\gamma_{\mathbf{wX}}$, which will be called the *selection coefficient* for transformations [7.218], is defined

$$[7.234] \qquad \gamma_{\mathbf{wX}} =_{\text{def}} \frac{\sum_{j=1}^{m} \bar{V}_{\mathbf{D}(F_j)} r^2_{\mathbf{wb}_j}}{\sum_{j=1}^{m} \bar{V}_{\mathbf{D}(F_j)}} \qquad \text{(orthonormal factors)} .$$

The nature of the selection coefficient will be examined in depth a little later. At present, we need only note that since $\gamma_{\mathbf{wX}}$ is a weighted average of the squared correlations $r^2_{\mathbf{wb}_j}$,

$$[7.235] \qquad 0 \leq \gamma_{\mathbf{wX}} \leq 1 ,$$

and also that $\gamma_{\mathbf{wX}}$, like $\boldsymbol{\delta}_{\mathbf{wX}}$, is independent of the particular choice of factor basis for the $\mathbf{X}_i$.[25]

From [7.233] and recollection of [7.78], the ratio of $\sigma_{\delta_{\mathbf{wX}}}$ to $\sigma_{\bar{\mathbf{X}}}$ is seen to be

$$[7.236] \qquad \begin{aligned} \rho_{\mathbf{wX}} &=_{\text{def}} q_{\delta_{\mathbf{wX}}\bar{\mathbf{X}}} \\ &= \sqrt{\frac{\text{Var}(\boldsymbol{\delta}_{\mathbf{wX}})}{\text{Var}(\bar{\mathbf{X}})}} \\ &= \sqrt{\gamma_{\mathbf{wX}} \frac{\bar{V}_{\mathbf{D}}}{V_{\bar{\mathbf{X}}}}} \\ &= \sqrt{\gamma_{\mathbf{wX}} \frac{\text{Disp}_{\mathbf{X}}}{\text{Sat}_{\mathbf{X}}}} \\ &= \sqrt{\gamma_{\mathbf{wX}} \text{DQ}_{\mathbf{X}}} , \end{aligned}$$

while the role of c in [7.204] is played in [7.223] by $\nu_{\mathbf{w}}$. Let us simplify subscripts a bit by writing "$\boldsymbol{\theta}_{\mathbf{wX}}$" for the correlation between $\bar{\mathbf{X}}$ and dispersion-contribution $\boldsymbol{\delta}_{\mathbf{wX}}$ —i.e.,

$$[7.237] \qquad \theta_{\mathbf{wX}} =_{\text{def}} r_{\bar{\mathbf{X}}\delta_{\mathbf{wX}}} .$$

Then from [7.208],

$$[7.238] \qquad r^2_{\bar{\mathbf{X}}\bar{\mathbf{W}}} = 1 - \frac{\nu^2_{\mathbf{w}} \rho^2_{\mathbf{wX}} (1 - \theta^2_{\mathbf{wX}})}{1 + 2\nu_{\mathbf{w}} \rho_{\mathbf{wX}} \theta_{\mathbf{wX}} + \nu^2_{\mathbf{w}} \rho^2_{\mathbf{wX}}} .$$

More simply, from [7.210] and [7.236],

[25] That $\delta_{\mathbf{wX}}$ is independent of the choice of factors in [7.219] is shown by [7.226], which assumes nothing about factors. That the same is true for $\gamma_{\mathbf{wX}}$ then follows by solving [7.233] for $\gamma_{\mathbf{wX}}$.

[7.239] $\kappa_{\overline{X}\overline{W}} \leqslant \nu_W \rho_{WX} = \nu_W \sqrt{\gamma_{WX} DQ_X}$ $(\overline{w} > 0)$,

or

[7.240] $r^2_{\overline{X}\overline{W}} \geqslant 1 - \nu^2_W \rho^2_{WX} = 1 - \nu^2_W \gamma_{WX} DQ_X$;

Inequality [7.240] is in fact a lower-bound approximation, since from [7.213] if the product $\nu^2_W \gamma_{WX} DQ_X$ is sufficiently small,

[7.241]
$$r^2_{\overline{X}\overline{W}} \simeq 1 - \frac{\nu^2_W \gamma_{WX} DQ_X}{1 + \nu^2_W \gamma_{WX} DQ_X} \simeq 1 - \nu^2_W \gamma_{WX} DQ_X. \qquad (\nu^2_W \gamma_{WX} DQ_X \ll 1)$$

Hence if the variation of weights is not extreme and the saturation of the $\mathbf{X}_i$ is high enough to keep the dispersion quotient on the order of 1 or less,[26] the correlation between $\overline{\mathbf{X}}$ and $\overline{\mathbf{W}}$ will be high if the numerical value of the selection coefficient is meager.

Next we shall investigate how rescaling-transformations [7.218] affect a set's saturation. From [7.223], the centroid variance of the transformed set is seen to be

[7.242] $V_{\overline{W}} = \overline{w}^2 V_{\overline{X}} (1 + 2\nu_W \rho_{WX} \theta_{WX} + \nu^2_W \rho^2_{WX})$,

which shows the variance of $\overline{\mathbf{W}}$ to lie somewhere in the range

[7.243] $\overline{w}^2 V_{\overline{X}} (1 - \nu_W \rho_{WX})^2 \leqslant V_{\overline{W}} \leqslant \overline{w}^2 V_{\overline{X}} (1 + \nu_W \rho_{WX})^2$ $(\overline{w} > 0)$.

To see what this implies about Sat_W we also need the average variance of the $\mathbf{W}_i$. From [7.217], the variance of each individual $\mathbf{W}_i$ is

[7.244-**i**] $V_{W_i} = w_i^2 V_{X_i}$,
(**i** = **1**, . . . , **n**)

so drawing upon [7.200], the average transformed variance may be written

[7.245]
$$\overline{V}_W = \frac{\sum_{i=1}^{n} w_i^2 V_{X_i}}{n} = \overline{w^2}\,\overline{V}_X (1 + \nu_{W^2} \nu_{V_X} r_{W^2 V_X}) ,$$

where $\overline{w}^2$ and ν_{W^2} are the mean and coefficient of variation for the set of squared transformation weights $w_1, \ldots, w_n$, $r_{W^2 V_X}$ is the correlation between the w_i^2 and the V_{X_i}, and ν_{V_X} is the coefficient of variation for the V_{X_i}. By applying first [7.201] and then [7.216] to $\mathbf{w}^2$, we may continue

[7.246]
$$\overline{V}_W = \overline{w}^2 \overline{V}_X (1 + \nu^2_W)(1 + \nu_{W^2} \nu_{V_X} r_{W^2 V_X}) = \overline{w}^2 \overline{V}_X (1 + \nu^2_W + 2|\nu_W| \nu_{V_X} r_{W^2 V_X} \sqrt{1 + t_W}) ,$$

[26] Since DQ_X is only 4 when Sat_X is as low as .2, a dispersion quotient on the order of 1 is not particularly difficult to attain.

where $t_{\mathbf{w}}$ is defined by substitution of "w" for "X" in [7.217]. The saturation of the $\mathbf{W_i}$ is hence

$$[7.247] \qquad \mathrm{Sat}_{\mathbf{W}} = \frac{V_{\overline{\mathbf{W}}}}{\overline{V}_{\mathbf{W}}}$$

$$= \frac{\overline{w}^2 V_{\overline{\mathbf{X}}}(1 + 2\nu_{\mathbf{w}}\rho_{\mathbf{wX}}\theta_{\mathbf{wX}} + \nu_{\mathbf{w}}^2\rho_{\mathbf{wX}}^2)}{\overline{w}^2\overline{V}_{\mathbf{X}}(1 + \nu_{\mathbf{w}}^2 + 2|\nu_{\mathbf{w}}|\nu_{V_{\mathbf{X}}} r_{\mathbf{w}^2 V_{\mathbf{X}}}\sqrt{1 + t_{\mathbf{w}}})}$$

or if $\overline{w} > 0$,

$$[7.248] \quad \mathrm{Sat}_{\mathbf{W}} = \mathrm{Sat}_{\mathbf{X}} \left[1 + \frac{2\nu_{\mathbf{w}}(\rho_{\mathbf{wX}}\theta_{\mathbf{wX}} - \nu_{V_{\mathbf{X}}} r_{\mathbf{w}^2 V_{\mathbf{X}}}\sqrt{1 + t_{\mathbf{w}}}) - \nu_{\mathbf{w}}^2(1 - \rho_{\mathbf{wX}}^2)}{1 + \nu_{\mathbf{w}}^2 + 2\nu_{\mathbf{w}}\nu_{V_{\mathbf{X}}} r_{\mathbf{w}^2 V_{\mathbf{X}}}\sqrt{1 + t_{\mathbf{w}}}} \right] \quad (\overline{w} > 0)\,.$$

Attempting to interpret [7.248] as it stands is not a rewarding experience. More can be learned by first examining the special case where the $\mathbf{X_i}$ have all been standardized to the same variance. In this instance $\nu_{V_{\mathbf{X}}}$ becomes zero and [7.247] simplifies to

$$[7.249] \quad \mathrm{Sat}_{\mathbf{W}} = \mathrm{Sat}_{\mathbf{X}} \left[1 + \frac{2\nu_{\mathbf{w}}\rho_{\mathbf{wX}}\theta_{\mathbf{wX}} - \nu_{\mathbf{w}}^2(1 - \rho_{\mathbf{wX}}^2)}{1 + \nu_{\mathbf{w}}^2} \right] \qquad (\nu_{V_{\mathbf{X}}} = 0)\,.$$

If the correlation term $\theta_{\mathbf{wX}}$, which can take negative values as readily as positive ones, is estimated to be about zero, this becomes

$$[7.250] \qquad \mathrm{Sat}_{\mathbf{W}} \simeq \mathrm{Sat}_{\mathbf{X}} \left[1 - \frac{\nu_{\mathbf{w}}^2(1 - \rho_{\mathbf{wX}}^2)}{1 + \nu_{\mathbf{w}}^2} \right] \qquad (\nu_{V_{\mathbf{X}}} = 0;\ \theta_{\mathbf{wX}} \simeq 0)\,.$$

Hence the prevailing effect of introducing inequalities among the individual variances in a set of variables is to decrease the set's saturation, though this trend can be hindered or even reversed by a sufficiently strong correlation between $\overline{\mathbf{X}}$ and $\boldsymbol{\delta}_{\mathbf{wX}}$. To examine this latter possibility in closer detail, let the big fraction after the + in [7.249] be called "A". In order for $\mathrm{Sat}_{\mathbf{W}}$ to be here larger than $\mathrm{Sat}_{\mathbf{X}}$, A must be positive. Solving for the conditions under which this can occur shows that if $\rho_{\mathbf{wX}}$ is less than 1 when $\nu_{V_{\mathbf{X}}} = 0$ and $\overline{w}$ is positive,[27] $\mathrm{Sat}_{\mathbf{W}}$ exceeds $\mathrm{Sat}_{\mathbf{X}}$ if and only if

$$\nu_{\mathbf{w}} < \frac{2\theta_{\mathbf{wX}}\rho_{\mathbf{wX}}}{1 - \rho_{\mathbf{wX}}^2}\,.$$

Thus it is generally possible to increase the saturation of a set of standardized variables by further rescalings if the variation among the trans-

[27] The condition $\rho_{\mathbf{wX}} \geqslant 1$ will be ignored, since as shown later this can occur only under highly extreme conditions for a set with a modicum of saturation, and not at all (cf. [7.236]) if $\mathrm{Sat}_{\mathbf{X}} > .5$. The possibility $\overline{w} < 0$ may likewise be disregarded, since in this case multiplying each w_i by -1 regains $\overline{w} > 0$ without changing any variance properties of the situation.

formation weights is kept sufficiently small. On the other hand, the increase cannot amount to much. While the precise maximum of A achieved by optimal choice of ν_{W} for fixed θ_{WX} and ρ_{WX} does not lend itself readily to insight, A is clearly no greater than its numerator, the maximum value of which is $\theta^2_{\mathsf{WX}}\rho^2_{\mathsf{WX}}/(1-\rho^2_{\mathsf{WX}})$. Hence

[7.251] $$\mathrm{Sat}_{\mathsf{W}} \leq \mathrm{Sat}_{\mathsf{X}}\left(1+\frac{\theta^2_{\mathsf{WX}}\rho^2_{\mathsf{WX}}}{1-\rho^2_{\mathsf{WX}}}\right) \qquad (\nu_{\mathsf{V_X}}=0;\ \rho_{\mathsf{WX}}<1)\ .$$

One reason for going into this much detail over the effect of rescaling on a set's saturation is that it is identical in mathematical form to the effect of rescaling on a centroid's penetrance quotient for similarity-space. To keep notation simple, this will be demonstrated only for the special case where similarity-space is common-factor space. When variable $\mathbf{X}_i$ is multiplied by w_i in transformation [7.218-**i**], its communal component $\mathbf{H}_i$ and unique component $\mathbf{U}_i$ are similarly multiplied by w_i—i.e.,

[7.252-**i**]
(**i** = **1**, . . . , **n**)
$$\begin{aligned}\mathbf{W}_i &= c_i + w_i\mathbf{X}_i\\ &= c_i + w_i(\mathbf{H}_i + \mathbf{U}_i)\\ &= (c_i + w_i\mathbf{H}_i) + w_i\mathbf{U}_i\ ,\end{aligned}$$

where $c_i + w_i\mathbf{H}_i$ and $w_i\mathbf{U}_i$ are the communal and unique components of $\mathbf{W}_i$ with respect to common-factor space S_{H} and unique-factor space S_{U}, respectively. Now, in view of [7.158], the ratio of $\overline{\mathbf{X}}$'s variance in common-factor space to its variance in unique-factor space is

[7.253] $$\begin{aligned}PQ_{\overline{\mathsf{X}}}(S_{\mathsf{H}}) &= \frac{V_{\overline{\mathsf{X}}(S_{\mathsf{H}})}}{V_{\overline{\mathsf{X}}(S_{\mathsf{U}})}}\\ &= \frac{V_{\overline{\mathsf{H}}}}{V_{\overline{\mathsf{U}}}}\\ &= \mathbf{n}\,\frac{V_{\overline{\mathsf{H}}}}{\overline{V}_{\mathsf{U}}}\ .\end{aligned}$$

Similarly, the penetrance quotient for $\overline{\mathbf{W}}$ in common-factor space is

[7.254] $$\begin{aligned}PQ_{\overline{\mathsf{W}}}(S_{\mathsf{H}}) &= \frac{V_{\overline{\mathsf{W}}(S_{\mathsf{H}})}}{V_{\overline{\mathsf{W}}(S_{\mathsf{U}})}}\\ &= \mathbf{n}\,\frac{V_{\overline{\mathsf{wH}}}}{\overline{V}_{\mathsf{wU}}}\ ,\end{aligned}$$

where $V_{\overline{\mathsf{wH}}}$ is the variance of the centroid of the transformed communal components $c_i + w_i\mathbf{H}_i$, and $\overline{V}_{\mathsf{wU}}$ is the average variance of the transformed unique components $w_i\mathbf{U}_i$. But the relation between $V_{\overline{\mathsf{H}}}$ and $V_{\overline{\mathsf{wH}}}$ follows directly from [7.242] by substituting "$\overline{\mathbf{wH}}$" and "$\overline{\mathbf{H}}$" for "$\overline{\mathbf{W}}$" and "$\overline{\mathbf{X}}$", respectively, while the relation between $\overline{V}_{\mathbf{WU}}$ and $\overline{V}_{\mathbf{U}}$ follows similarly from [7.246]. For the important special case where the unique components $\mathbf{U}_1, \ldots, \mathbf{U}_n$ all have the same variance, we have

[7.255]

$$PQ_{\overline{\mathbf{W}}}(S_{\mathbf{H}}) = \mathbf{n}\,\frac{\overline{w}^2 V_{\overline{\mathbf{H}}}\,(1 + 2\nu_{\mathbf{W}}\rho_{\mathbf{WH}}\theta_{\mathbf{WH}} + \nu_{\mathbf{W}}^2\rho_{\mathbf{WH}}^2)}{\overline{w}^2 \overline{V}_{\mathbf{U}}\,(1+\nu_{\mathbf{W}}^2)} \qquad (\nu_{V_{\mathbf{U}}} = 0)$$

$$= PQ_{\overline{\mathbf{X}}}(S_{\mathbf{H}})\left[1 + \frac{2\nu_{\mathbf{W}}\rho_{\mathbf{WH}}\theta_{\mathbf{WH}} - \nu_{\mathbf{W}}^2(1-\rho_{\mathbf{WH}}^2)}{1+\nu_{\mathbf{W}}^2}\right],$$

so assuming also $\rho_{\mathbf{WH}} < 1$ and $\overline{w} > 0$, the penetrance of $\overline{\mathbf{W}}$ into common-factor space is here greater than that of $\overline{\mathbf{X}}$ only if

$$\nu_{\mathbf{W}} < \frac{2\theta_{\mathbf{WH}}\rho_{\mathbf{WH}}}{1-\rho_{\mathbf{WH}}^2},$$

while an upper bound for the penetrance quotient of $\overline{\mathbf{W}}$ in $S_{\mathbf{H}}$ is

$$[7.256] \quad PQ_{\overline{\mathbf{W}}}(S_{\overline{\mathbf{H}}}) \leqslant PQ_{\mathbf{X}}(S_{\mathbf{H}})\left(1 + \frac{\theta_{\mathbf{WH}}^2\rho_{\mathbf{WH}}^2}{1-\rho_{\mathbf{WH}}^2}\right) \qquad (\nu_{V_{\mathbf{U}}} = 0;\ \rho_{\mathbf{WH}} < 1)\,.$$

A further algebraic consequence of [7.256] is that the difference between the penetrances of $\overline{\mathbf{W}}$ and $\overline{\mathbf{X}}$ into common-factor space, expressed as a proportion of the latter, cannot favor $\overline{\mathbf{W}}$ when the $\mathbf{X}_i$ have equal unique variances by more than

[7.257]

$$\frac{P_{\overline{\mathbf{W}}}(S_{\mathbf{H}}) - P_{\overline{\mathbf{X}}}(S_{\mathbf{H}})}{P_{\overline{\mathbf{X}}}(S_{\mathbf{H}})} \leqslant \frac{\theta_{\mathbf{WH}}^2\rho_{\mathbf{WH}}^2}{1-\rho_{\mathbf{WH}}^2}\,[1 - P_{\overline{\mathbf{W}}}(S_{\mathbf{H}})] \qquad (\nu_{V_{\mathbf{U}}} = 0;\ \rho_{\mathbf{WH}} < 1)\,,$$

or using [7.115], since $1 - P_{\overline{\mathbf{W}}}(S_{\mathbf{H}}) = P_{\overline{\mathbf{W}}}(S_{\mathbf{U}}) < P_{\overline{\mathbf{X}}}(S_{\mathbf{U}})$ when the left-hand side of [7.257] is positive,

$$[7.258] \quad \frac{P_{\overline{\mathbf{W}}}(S_{\mathbf{H}}) - P_{\overline{\mathbf{X}}}(S_{\mathbf{H}})}{P_{\overline{\mathbf{X}}}(S_{\mathbf{H}})} \leqslant \frac{\theta_{\mathbf{WH}}^2\rho_{\mathbf{WH}}^2}{1-\rho_{\mathbf{WH}}^2} \cdot \frac{P_{\mathbf{X}}(S_{\mathbf{U}})}{\mathbf{n}\ \mathrm{Sat}_{\mathbf{X}}} \qquad (\nu_{V_{\mathbf{U}}} = 0;\ \rho_{\mathbf{WH}} < 1)\,.$$

Looking ahead (pp. 369ff.) to the likely magnitude of $\theta_{\mathbf{WH}}\rho_{\mathbf{WH}}$ (i.e., $\theta_{\mathbf{WH}}\sqrt{DQ_{\mathbf{H}}\gamma_{\mathbf{WH}}}$) we may conclude that with the possible exception of sets comprising a small number of variables with little homogeneity (in which case, also, $\rho_{\mathbf{WH}}$ may exceed 1), the penetrance of the set's centroid into common-factor space will be only negligibly short of maximal when the unique-factor variances of the individual variables in the set are all equal.

Another way to analyze how transformations [7.218] affect the apportionment of a centroid's variance between common-factor and unique-factor space is to apply general principle [7.242] to both the $\mathbf{H}_i$-configuration and the $\mathbf{U}_i$-configuration, i.e.,

[7.259]

$$\frac{P_{\overline{\mathbf{W}}}(S_{\mathbf{H}})}{P_{\overline{\mathbf{W}}}(S_{\mathbf{U}})} = \frac{V_{\mathbf{w}\overline{\mathbf{H}}}}{V_{\mathbf{w}\overline{\mathbf{U}}}}$$

$$= \frac{\overline{w}^2 V_{\overline{\mathbf{H}}}\,(1 + 2\nu_{\mathbf{w}}\rho_{\mathbf{wH}}\theta_{\mathbf{wH}} + \nu_{\mathbf{w}}^2\rho_{\mathbf{wH}}^2)}{\overline{w}^2 V_{\overline{\mathbf{U}}}\,(1 + 2\nu_{\mathbf{w}}\rho_{\mathbf{wU}}\theta_{\mathbf{wU}} + \nu_{\mathbf{w}}^2\rho_{\mathbf{wU}}^2)}$$

$$= \frac{P_{\overline{\mathbf{W}}}(S_{\mathbf{U}})}{P_{\overline{\mathbf{X}}}(S_{\mathbf{U}})}\left[1 + \frac{2\nu_{\mathbf{w}}(\rho_{\mathbf{wH}}\theta_{\mathbf{wH}} - \rho_{\mathbf{wU}}\theta_{\mathbf{wU}}) + \nu_{\mathbf{w}}^2(\rho_{\mathbf{wH}}^2 - \rho_{\mathbf{wU}}^2)}{1 + 2\nu_{\mathbf{w}}\rho_{\mathbf{wU}}\theta_{\mathbf{wU}} + \nu_{\mathbf{w}}^2\rho_{\mathbf{wU}}^2}\right].$$

It can be shown that when all the $\mathbf{U}_i$ have equal variances, $\theta_{\mathbf{wU}} = 0$ and $\rho_{\mathbf{wU}} = 1$ for any set of transformation weights; hence [7.259] yields [7.255] as a special case. What is of primary interest about [7.259], however, is that its derivation draws upon no assumptions about the $\mathbf{H}_i$ and the $\mathbf{U}_i$ other than their having been rescaled by the same set of transformation weights. Hence [7.259] continues to hold if the $\mathbf{H}_i$ and $\mathbf{U}_i$ are redefined to be the projections of the $\mathbf{X}_i$ into any arbitrary pair of spaces $S_{\mathbf{H}}$ and $S_{\mathbf{U}}$. Temporarily liberalizing "H" and "U" in this way to avoid new notation, we see from [7.236] that if $\theta_{\mathbf{wH}}$ and $\theta_{\mathbf{wU}}$ are estimated to be about zero, [7.259] becomes

[7.260]

$$\frac{P_{\overline{\mathbf{W}}}(S_{\mathbf{H}})}{P_{\overline{\mathbf{W}}}(S_{\mathbf{U}})} \simeq \frac{P_{\overline{\mathbf{X}}}(S_{\mathbf{H}})}{P_{\overline{\mathbf{X}}}(S_{\mathbf{U}})}\left[1 + \frac{\nu_{\mathbf{w}}^2(\gamma_{\mathbf{wH}}\mathrm{DQ}_{\mathbf{H}} - \gamma_{\mathbf{wH}}\mathrm{DQ}_{\mathbf{U}})}{1 + \nu_{\mathbf{w}}^2\rho_{\mathbf{wU}}^2}\right] \quad (\theta_{\mathbf{wH}} \simeq \theta_{\mathbf{wU}} \simeq 0)\,.$$

If the selection coefficients $\gamma_{\mathbf{wH}}$ and $\gamma_{\mathbf{wU}}$ are also approximately equal, as would be expected for an arbitrary choice of the w_i, it follows that $P_{\overline{\mathbf{W}}}(S_{\mathbf{H}})/P_{\overline{\mathbf{W}}}(S_{\mathbf{U}})$ is larger or smaller than $P_{\overline{\mathbf{X}}}(S_{\mathbf{H}})/P_{\overline{\mathbf{X}}}(S_{\mathbf{U}})$, respectively, according to whether $\mathrm{DQ}_{\mathbf{H}}$ is larger or smaller than $\mathrm{DQ}_{\mathbf{U}}$. Hence while the relative importance of a given space in the variance composition of a set's centroid can in general be either increased or decreased by a suitable assignment of transformation weights, the prevailing effect of an arbitrary selection of weights is to increase the centroid's penetrance into spaces in which the set's saturation is lowest and correspondingly decrease the centroid's penetrance into spaces in which the set's saturation is highest.

In similar fashion, it may be seen from [7.245] that the effect of transformations [7.218] upon the set-penetrance ratio $P_X(S_H)/P_X(S_U)$ for two arbitrary spaces S_H and S_U is

$$[7.261] \quad \frac{P_W(S_H)}{P_W(S_U)} = \frac{\overline{w^2}\overline{V}_H(1+\nu_{w^2}\nu_{V_H} r_{w^2 V_H})}{\overline{w^2}\overline{V}_U(1+\nu_{w^2}\nu_{V_U} r_{w^2 V_U})}$$

$$= \frac{P_X(S_H)}{P_X(S_U)}\left[1+\frac{\nu_{w^2}(\nu_{V_H} r_{w^2 V_H} - \nu_{V_U} r_{w^2 V_U})}{1+\nu_{w^2}\nu_{V_U} r_{w^2 V_U}}\right].$$

Hence in contrast to the effect on centroid penetrance, there is no tendency for rescaling the variables in a set to alter the set's own penetrance properties in any systematic fashion. In particular, if the projections of $\mathbf{X}_1, \ldots, \mathbf{X}_n$ into S_H are all of equal length and the same is true of the $\mathbf{X}_i$-projections into S_U, then the set's penetrance into S_H compared to its penetrance into S_U is unaffected by any (linear) rescalings of its variables.

While equation [7.259] in full bloom is not an altogether charming sight, it has interesting implications about a set's component configurations in two spaces S_H and S_U when the dominance of $P_{\overline{X}}(S_H)$ over $P_{\overline{X}}(S_U)$ has been maximized. It will be recalled that the "index of radial irregularity" (see pp. 313f.) for the set $\mathbf{X}_1, \ldots, \mathbf{X}_n$ may be written

$$[7.262] \quad \nu_{c_X} = \frac{\sigma_{c_X}}{\overline{c}_X} = \frac{\sigma_{c_X}}{V_{\overline{X}}} = \frac{\sigma_{c_X}}{\overline{V}_X \, \mathrm{Sat}_X},$$

where

$$c_{X_i} =_{\text{def}} C_{X_i \overline{X}}$$

as in [7.59], and

$$[7.263] \quad \overline{c}_X =_{\text{def}} \frac{\sum_{i=1}^{n} C_{X_i \overline{X}}}{n} = V_{\overline{X}}.$$

The statistic ν_{c_X} is the coefficient of variation for both the covariances of the individual $\mathbf{X}_i$ with their centroid and for the lengths of the $\mathbf{X}_i$-projections on $\overline{\mathbf{X}}$ (cf. [7.60]). Since $C_{D_i \overline{X}}$ differs from c_{X_i} only by the constant $\overline{c}_X$ (see [7.64]), σ_{c_X} is also the standard deviation of the covariances of the dispersion components $\mathbf{D}_1, \ldots, \mathbf{D}_n$ with $\overline{\mathbf{X}}$, and in the special case that $\sigma_{c_X} = \nu_{c_X} = 0$, the $\mathbf{D}_i$ are all orthogonal to $\overline{\mathbf{X}}$. We now observe from

[7.236], [7.237], and [7.228], bearing [7.227] in mind, that

$$[7.264] \qquad \rho_{\mathbf{wX}}\theta_{\mathbf{wX}} = \frac{\mathrm{Cov}(\overline{\mathbf{X}}, \boldsymbol{\delta}_{\mathbf{wX}})}{V_{\overline{\mathbf{X}}}}$$

$$= \frac{\sum_{i=1}^{n} z_{wi} C_{D_i\overline{X}}}{nV_{\overline{X}}}$$

$$= \frac{\sum_{i=1}^{n} z_{wi}(c_{X_i} - \bar{c}_X)}{nV_{\overline{X}}}$$

$$= \frac{\sigma_{cX} r_{z_w c_X}}{\bar{c}_X}$$

$$= \nu_{c_X} r_{z_w c_X},$$

where $r_{z_w c_X}$ (or equivalently r_{wc_X}) is the correlation between the $C_{X_i\overline{X}}$ and the transformation weights $w_1, \ldots, w_n$ in [7.218]. In view of [7.264], [7.259] may be rewritten as

$$[7.265] \qquad \frac{P_{\overline{W}}(S_H)}{P_{\overline{W}}(S_U)} = \frac{P_{\overline{X}}(S_H)}{P_{\overline{X}}(S_U)}(1 + \nu_w A_{wHU}),$$

where

$$[7.266] \quad A_{wHU} =_{\text{def}} \frac{2(\nu_{c_H} r_{z_w c_H} - \nu_{c_U} r_{z_w c_U}) + \nu_w(\rho^2_{wH} - \rho^2_{wU})}{1 + 2\nu_w \rho_{wU}\theta_{wU} + \nu^2_w \rho^2_{wU}},$$

where as before we are temporarily letting "S_H" and "S_U" designate any arbitrary pair of spaces. Suppose, now, that $P_{\overline{X}}(S_H)/P_{\overline{X}}(S_U)$ is at a maximum—i.e., the scaling of $\mathbf{X}_1, \ldots, \mathbf{X}_n$ is such that this ratio cannot be further increased by any transformation of form [7.218]. If the dimensionality of $\mathbf{U}_1, \ldots, \mathbf{U}_n$ is less than $\mathbf{n}$, then $P_{\overline{X}}(S_U) = 0$ in this case and no conclusions can be drawn about the $\mathbf{H}_i$-configuration. If there exists no linear combination of the $\mathbf{U}_i$ which is identically zero, however, then $P_{\overline{X}}(S_U) > 0$ when $P_{\overline{X}}(S_H)/P_{\overline{X}}(S_U)$ is maximal and the $\mathbf{H}_i$- and $\mathbf{U}_i$-configurations must be such that the term $\nu_w A_{wHU}$ in [7.265] is zero or negative for any choice of $w_1, \ldots, w_n$. Now, since $r_{z_w c_H}$ and $r_{z_w c_U}$ are independent of w and σ_w, the w_i can be chosen to set ν_w equal to any positive or negative value we wish without changing the value of $\nu_{c_H} r_{z_w c_H} - \nu_{c_U} r_{z_w c_U}$ in A_{wHU}. Hence by choosing ν_w sufficiently small and of appropriate sign, the term $\nu_w A_{wHU}$ can always be made positive unless $\nu_{c_H} r_{z_w c_H} = \nu_{c_U} r_{z_w c_U}$ for any assignment of transformation weights. This condition is satisfied if and only if

$$[7.267] \qquad \nu_{c_H} = \nu_{c_U}, \quad r_{c_H c_U} = 1 \qquad \left(\frac{P_{\overline{X}}(S_H)}{P_{\overline{X}}(S_U)} = \text{maximum} < \infty\right),$$

where the condition on $r_{C_H C_U}$ is vacuous if $\nu_{C_H} = \nu_{C_U} = 0$. Conditions [7.267],in turn, obtain if and only if there exists some constant λ such that

[7.628-**i**] (**i** = **1**, . . . , **n**)
$$C_{H_i\bar{H}} = \lambda C_{U_i\bar{U}} \qquad \left(\frac{P_{\bar{X}}(S_H)}{P_{\bar{X}}(S_U)} = \text{maximum} < \infty\right),$$

while for any such λ it follows from [7.268] that

[7.269]
$$\lambda = \frac{V_{\bar{H}}}{V_{\bar{U}}} \qquad ([7.267])$$
$$= \frac{P_{\bar{X}}(S_H)}{P_{\bar{X}}(S_U)} .$$

From [7.268] and [7.269] it also obtains that

[7.270-**i**]
(**i** = **1**, . . . , **n**)
$$\sigma_{H_i} r_{H_i\bar{H}} = \left(\frac{\sigma_{\bar{H}}}{\sigma_{\bar{U}}}\right) \sigma_{U_i} r_{U_i\bar{U}} \qquad \left(\frac{P_{\bar{X}}(S_H)}{P_{\bar{X}}(S_U)} = \text{maximum} < \infty\right),$$

where $\sigma_{H_i} r_{H_i\bar{H}}$ and $\sigma_{U_i} r_{U_i\bar{U}}$ are the lengths of the projections of $\mathbf{H}_i$ on $\bar{\mathbf{H}}$ and $\mathbf{U}_i$ on $\bar{\mathbf{U}}$, respectively. Hence for any two arbitrary spaces S_H and S_U, if the variables in the set $\mathbf{X}_1, \ldots, \mathbf{X}_n$ have been scaled to maximize the ratio of $P_{\bar{X}}(S_H)$ to $P_{\bar{X}}(S_U)$ while the latter cannot be reduced to zero, the configuration of $\mathbf{X}_i$-projections in S_H has the same degree of radial irregularity as does the configuration of $\mathbf{X}_i$-projections in S_U; while the length of the projection of each $\mathbf{X}_i$ on the component of $\bar{\mathbf{X}}$ lying in S_H (i.e., the projection of $\mathbf{H}_i$ on $\bar{\mathbf{H}}$) is proportional to the length of $\mathbf{X}_i$'s projection on the component of $\bar{\mathbf{X}}$ lying in S_U.

Similar conclusions can be derived about the shape of a configuration whose variables have been scaled either to maximize or to minimize the set's saturation. Using [7.264], [7.248] can be rewritten

[7.271]
$$\text{Sat}_W = \text{Sat}_X (1 + \nu_W B_{WX})$$

where

[7.272]
$$B_{WX} =_{\text{def}} \frac{2(\nu_{C_X} r_{z_W C_X} - \nu_{V_X} r_{w^2 V_X} \sqrt{1 + t_W}) - \nu_W(1 + \rho^2_{WX})}{1 + \nu^2_W + 2\nu_W \nu_{V_X} r_{w^2 V_X} \sqrt{1 + t_W}} \qquad (\bar{w} > 0) .$$

With $\bar{w}$ held constant at any given positive value, $r_{w^2 V_X}$ approaches $r_{z_W V_X}$ and t_W approaches zero as σ_W approaches zero. Hence with fixed positive $\bar{w}$ and a sufficiently small choice of ν_W, $\nu_W B_{WX}$ is positive, zero, or negative according to whether $\nu_{C_X} r_{z_W C_X} - \nu_{V_X} r_{z_W V_X}$ is positive, zero, or negative. The latter quantity, moreover, can be reversed in sign without changing $\bar{w}$ or σ_W by reversing the signs of all the z_{Wi}. Hence $\nu_W B_{WX} \lessgtr$

0 for all choices of the w_i when Sat_X is maximal (or $\nu_W B_{WX} \geq 0$ for all choices of the w_i when Sat_X is minimal) only if $\nu_{C_X} r_{Z_w C_X} = \nu_{V_X} r_{Z_w V_X}$ under any assignment of transformation weights. This occurs when and only when

$$[7.273] \qquad \nu_{C_X} = \nu_{V_X}, \quad r_{C_X V_X} = 1 \qquad (\text{Sat}_X = \text{maximum or minimum}),$$

which in turn is equivalent to

$$[7.274\text{-}\mathbf{i}] \quad (\mathbf{i} = \mathbf{1}, \ldots, \mathbf{n}) \qquad C_{X_i \bar{X}} = V_{X_i} \text{Sat}_X \qquad (\text{Sat}_X = \text{maximum or minimum})$$

and to

$$[7.275\text{-}\mathbf{i}] \quad (\mathbf{i} = \mathbf{1}, \ldots, \mathbf{n}) \qquad r_{X_i \bar{X}} \geq 0, \quad r^2_{X_i \bar{X}} = \left(\frac{V_{X_i}}{V_{\bar{X}}}\right) \text{Sat}_X \qquad \left(\begin{array}{c}\text{Sat}_X = \text{maximum} \\ \text{or minimum}\end{array}\right),$$

and to

$$[7.276\text{-}\mathbf{i}] \quad (\mathbf{i} = \mathbf{1}, \ldots, \mathbf{n}) \qquad b_{\bar{X} X_i} = \text{Sat}_X \qquad (\text{Sat}_X = \text{maximum or minimum}),$$

where $b_{\bar{X}X_i}$ is the b-coefficient for the regression of $\bar{\mathbf{X}}$ upon $\mathbf{X}_i$.

Actually, with the exception of [7.264], the relationships derived in the preceding two paragraphs have little mathematical importance for multivariate analysis, especially since these properties are not restricted to the indicated conditions. (E.g., [7.272] can be satisfied even though Sat_X is neither maximal nor minimal.) They do, however, enrich our comprehension of what a configuration is like when its variables have been scaled to have maximal saturation, or to have maximal centroid penetrance in one space as compared to another, and such configurations *are* important, insomuch as when the coefficients in a linear composite $\mathbf{L}_X = w_0 + \sum_{i=1}^{n} w_i \mathbf{X}_i$ are chosen to optimize some feature of $\mathbf{L}_X$, it usually turns out that the configuration of weighted items $\mathbf{W}_i = w_i \mathbf{X}_i$ ($\mathbf{i} = \mathbf{1}, \ldots, \mathbf{n}$) is of this sort (see Chapter 9, pp. 468 ff.). In particular, if S_X is the space spanned by variables $\mathbf{X}_1, \ldots, \mathbf{X}_n$, then $P_{\bar{W}}(S)/P_{\bar{W}}(S_X) = P_{L_X}(S)$ for any arbitrary space S, so the theory of maximal centroid-penetrance ratios subsumes canonical factoring and—when S is spanned by a single criterion variable—multiple regression.

The demonstration on p. 359 f., that a set's centroid penetrance into common-factor space is essentially maximized by scaling the variables to have equal unique-factor variances, raises a further question about how much difference alternative scalings for the $\mathbf{X}$ actually make for $P_{\bar{X}}(S_H)$. More generally, to what extent do transformations [7.218] alter the penetrance of the set's centroid into an arbitrary space S? While analysis of this problem specifically in terms of equations [7.218] does not seem to work out very effectively, useful results are available along broader lines. Let s_1 and s_2 be the standard deviations of the projections into space S of the normalized scales $\mathbf{Z_1}$ and $\mathbf{Z_2}$ of two variables $\mathbf{X_1}$ and $\mathbf{X_2}$, respectively, while s_1^* and s_2^* are the standard deviations of the projections of $\mathbf{Z_1}$ and $\mathbf{Z_2}$ in the complement, S^*, of S. Similarly, let p_1, p_2, p_1^*, and p_2^* be the penetrances of $\mathbf{X_1}$ and $\mathbf{X_2}$ into spaces S and S^*, respectively. Then

$$p_1 =_{\text{def}} P_{\mathbf{X}_1}(S) = \frac{\mathrm{V}_{\mathbf{X}_1(S)}}{\mathrm{V}_{\mathbf{X}_1}} = \mathrm{V}_{\mathbf{Z}_1(S)} = S_1^2 \ ,$$

while similarly $p_1^* = s_1^{*2}$, $p_2 = s_2^2$, and $p_2^* = s_2^{*2}$. Also, since by definition $\mathrm{V}_{\mathbf{X}_1 \bullet SS^*} = \mathrm{V}_{\mathbf{X}_2 \bullet SS^*} = 0$,

$$p_1 + p_1^* = p_2 + p_2^* = 1 \ ,$$

so $s_1^{*2} = 1 - p_1$ and $s_2^{*2} = 1 - p_2$. Writing "r" for the correlation between the projections of variables $\mathbf{X_1}$ and $\mathbf{X_2}$ in space S and "r^*" for the correlation between their projections in S^*, we have from [7.14]

$$\text{[7.277]} \qquad \begin{aligned} \mathrm{r}_{12} &= \mathrm{r}_{\mathbf{Z}_1\mathbf{Z}_2} \\ &= \mathrm{C}_{\mathbf{Z}_1\mathbf{Z}_2(S)} + \mathrm{C}_{\mathbf{Z}_1\mathbf{Z}_2(S^*)} \\ &= s_1 s_2 r + s_1^* s_2^* r^* \\ &= (s_1 s_2 + s_1^* s_2^*)\tilde{r} \ , \end{aligned}$$

where $\tilde{r}$ is a weighted average of r and r^*, namely,

$$\text{[7.278]} \qquad \tilde{r} =_{\text{def}} \frac{s_1 s_2 r + s_1^* s_2^* r_2^*}{s_1 s_2 + s_1^* s_2^*} \ .$$

Squaring and rearranging [7.277] yields

$$\text{[7.279]} \qquad \begin{aligned} 1 - (s_1 s_2 + s_1^* s_2^*)^2 &= 1 - \frac{\mathrm{r}_{12}^2}{\tilde{r}^2} \\ &= 1 - \mathrm{r}_{12}^2 - \mathrm{r}_{12}^2\left(\frac{1}{\tilde{r}^2} - 1\right) \\ &= \mathrm{k}_{12}^2 - \mathrm{r}_{12}^2\left(\frac{1-\tilde{r}^2}{\tilde{r}^2}\right) . \end{aligned}$$

But also,

$$\text{[7.280]} \qquad \begin{aligned} 1 - (s_1 s_2 + s_1^* s_2^*)^2 &= 1 - s_1^2 s_2^2 - s_1^{*2} s_2^{*2} - 2 s_1 s_1^* s_2 s_2^* \\ &= 1 - p_1 p_2 - (1 - p_1)(1 - p_2) - 2 s_1 s_1^* s_2 s_2^* \end{aligned}$$

$$= p_1 + p_2 - 2p_1 p_2 - 2s_1 s_1^* s_2 s_2^*$$
$$= p_1^2 + p_2^2 - 2p_1 p_2 + p_1 (1 - p_1) + p_2 (1 - p_2) - 2s_1 s_1^* s_2 s_2^*$$
$$= (p_1 - p_2)^2 + (s_1 s_1^*)^2 + (s_2 s_2^*)^2 - 2s_1 s_1^* s_2 s_2^*$$
$$= (p_1 - p_2)^2 + (s_1 s_1^* - s_2 s_2^*)^2 .$$

Hence from [7.279] and [7.280],

[7.281] $$(p_1 - p_2)^2 = \mathrm{k}_{12}^2 - \mathrm{r}_{12}^2\left(\frac{1-\bar{r}^2}{\bar{r}^2}\right) - (s_1 s_1^* - s_2 s_2^*)^2 \leq \mathrm{k}_{12}^2 ,$$

which shows that the coefficient of alienation for two variables is a generous upper bound on the difference between their penetrances into any space S. That is, in less abbreviated notation,

[7.282] $$|P_{X_1}(S) - P_{X_2}(S)| \leq \mathrm{k}_{X_1X_2}$$

or equivalently,

[7.282a] $$|\mathrm{R}^2_{X_1(\boldsymbol{\mu})} - \mathrm{R}^2_{X_2(\boldsymbol{\mu})}| \leq \mathrm{k}_{X_1X_2} ,$$

where $\boldsymbol{\mu}$ is any set of predictor variables.

In particular, the change in a centroid's penetrance into a space S effected by rescaling its constituent variables is seen from [7.282] and [7.239] to be generously bounded by

[7.283] $$|P_{\overline{W}}(S) - P_{\overline{X}}(S)| \leq \nu_W \sqrt{\gamma_{WX} \mathrm{DQ}_X}$$

The Transformation Parameters. We have seen that how rescaling, or "weighting," the variables in a set affects the variance properties of the set's centroid depends upon three major parameters, ν_W, DQ_X, and γ_{WX}, which interact multiplicatively, and a minor parameter θ_{WX} (or alternatively ν_{c_X}). The interpretation of ν_W and DQ_X should require little further comment, since the dispersion quotient is readily understood as a simple decreasing function of the set's saturation (see [7.78]), while the nature of ν_W, which carries the impact of the degree of variability among the transformation weights, has already been covered by the generic discussion of the coefficient of variation in Chapter 3 (p. 47). Fully as important as these, however, and so far more enigmatic, is the selection coefficient γ_{WX}. For even in the teeth of low saturation (i.e., high DQ_X) and extreme transformation-weight variability, $\mathrm{r}^2_{\overline{W}\overline{X}}$ still approaches unity as γ_{WX} approaches zero; and the centroid of the rescaled variables hence escapes being merely a linear transformation of the original centroid only to the extent that the transformation weights are correlated with the factor-pattern coefficients of the original variables. It is thus desirable to look more deeply into the meaning of $\gamma_{\mathbf{wX}}$ and especially to get a feel for its likely magnitude.

As before, let $\mathbf{F_1}, \ldots, \mathbf{F_m}$ be a set of orthonormal factors for variables $\mathbf{X_1}, \ldots, \mathbf{X_n}$ according to factor pattern [7.219], and let $\mathbf{b_j}$ be a factor-pattern variable whose value for individual variable $\mathbf{X_i}$ is the loading, b_{ij}, of $\mathbf{X_i}$ on factor $\mathbf{F_j}$. We have already discussed (pp. 304 ff.) how the **m**-dimensional scattergram for the joint distribution of the $\mathbf{b_j}$ in the population of "individuals" $\mathbf{X_1}, \ldots, \mathbf{X_n}$ gives rise to the (simple) vector model for the joint distribution of the $\mathbf{X_i}$. Now, however, we wish to attend to the configuration of the set $\mathbf{b_1}, \ldots, \mathbf{b_m}$ in its own right with its own factor structure. Since there is one transformation weight w_i for each "individual" $\mathbf{X_i}$, we have a transformation-weight variable **w** as well as factor-pattern variables $\mathbf{b_1}, \ldots, \mathbf{b_m}$ over the population of the $\mathbf{X_i}$, and **w** accounts for a certain amount of the variance of each **b** in virtue of its correlation, $r_{\mathbf{wb_j}}$, with the latter. Specifically,

[7.284-j] (j = 1, . . . , m)

$$V_{\mathbf{b_j(w)}} = \sigma^2_{\mathbf{b_j}} r^2_{\mathbf{wb_j}} = \bar{V}_{\mathbf{D(F_j)}} r^2_{\mathbf{wb_j}}$$

(from [7.43] and general principle [6.9]). Hence from [7.234],

[7.285]

$$\gamma_{\mathbf{wX}} = \frac{\sum_{\mathbf{j=1}}^{\mathbf{m}} V_{\mathbf{b_j(w)}}}{\sum_{\mathbf{j=1}}^{\mathbf{m}} V_{\mathbf{b_j}}} = \frac{V_{\mathbf{b(w)}}}{V_{\mathbf{b}}} = P_{\mathbf{b}}(S_{\mathbf{w}}) \, ,$$

where $S_{\mathbf{w}}$ is the one-dimensional space of variables over population $\mathbf{X_1}, \ldots, \mathbf{X_n}$ spanned by **w**. That is, the selection coefficient for transformations [7.218] equals the proportion of the total variance of the factor-pattern variables $\mathbf{b_1}, \ldots, \mathbf{b_m}$ accounted for by the transformation-weight variable **w**. Now, over a population of n individuals, it is possible to have a maximum of only $n - 1$ linearly independent variables;[28] so variables $\mathbf{b_1}, \ldots, \mathbf{b_m}$ span a space whose dimensionality is at most $\mathbf{n} - 1$. Let us assume, as will generally be the case, that the dimensionality of the $\mathbf{b_j}$ is at this maximum. (What happens when this is not so

[28] While this cannot be conveniently proved here, it may be seen from the fact that a vector model of a multivariate distribution can always be constructed in an orthogonal coordinate system whose reference axes correspond to the various individuals in the population on which the distribution is based, while one dimension of this system accommodates the means of the variables.

can subsequently be derived from the results reached under this assumption by letting the penetrance of the $\mathbf{b}_j$ approach zero in one or more directions.) Then $\mathbf{w}$ must lie in the space of the $\mathbf{b}_j$ and may be treated as a (nonnormalized) basis factor of the $\mathbf{b}_j$, while conversely, any basis factor of the $\mathbf{b}_j$ defines a set of possible values for the transformation weights $w_1, \ldots, w_n$; so the maximum, minimum, and expected values of the selection coefficient are seen from [7.285] to be determined by the shape of the joint distribution of factor-pattern coefficients. Specifically, the value of γ_{wX} – i.e., the proportion of V_b accounted for by $\mathbf{w}$ – is the proportion of V_b lying in some one direction of the space spanned by the $\mathbf{b}_j$. Obviously the proportion of a set's variance lying in a single dimension of the $\mathbf{m}$-dimensional space which it spans averages $1/\mathbf{m}$, while any departure above or below this average is possible only if the configuration has greater spread along some of its principal axes than along others. Consequently, we may expect that for an arbitrarily chosen set of transformation weights,

[7.286] $$\gamma_{wX} \simeq \frac{1}{\mathbf{n}-1},$$

while no matter how the weights are selected, the maximum and minimum values possible for γ_{wX} are the proportions of the variance of the $\mathbf{b}_j$ accounted for, respectively, by their first and their $(\mathbf{n}-1)$th principal axes, as exhibited in the factor-pattern scattergram by its degree of ellipticality.

The nature of γ_{wX} and δ_{wX} can also be usefully visualized in terms of the dispersion configuration of the $\mathbf{X}_i$. (Recall that the vector model for the $\mathbf{D}_i$ differs from that for the $\mathbf{X}_i$ only by a translation of origin.) Suppose that we have a scattergram – *scattergram,* mind you, not vector model – of the joint distribution of $\mathbf{D}_1, \ldots, \mathbf{D}_n$ and we now contemplate an orthogonal rotation of axes (see pp. 240f.) which carries the original axis variables $\mathbf{D}_1, \ldots, \mathbf{D}_n$ into a new set $\mathbf{D}'_1, \ldots, \mathbf{D}'_n$ by transformations

[7.287-i] $(\mathbf{i}=1, \ldots, \mathbf{n})$ $$\mathbf{D}'_i = \sum_{j=1}^{n} c_{ij}\,\mathbf{D}_j .$$

It is an important theorem of analytic geometry that transformations [7.287] are an *orthogonal* rotation if and only if the c_{ij} satisfy the relations

[7.288-ij] $(\mathbf{i},\mathbf{j}=1, \ldots, \mathbf{n})$ $$\sum_{k=1}^{n} c_{ij}c_{jk} = \begin{cases} 1 \text{ if } \mathbf{i}=\mathbf{j} \\ 0 \text{ if } \mathbf{i}\neq\mathbf{j}, \end{cases}$$

one immediate consequence of which is that if the rotation weights are all equal for one rotated axis $\mathbf{D}'_j$ – i.e., if $c_{j1} = c_{j2} = \ldots = c_{jn} = 1/\sqrt{\mathbf{n}}$ – then $\sum_{k=1}^{n} c_{ik} = 0$ for every rotated axis $\mathbf{D}'_i$ orthogonal to $\mathbf{D}'_j$. Now let one of the rotated dispersion-scattergram axes, say $\mathbf{D}'_n$, be defined by the transformation

$$\mathbf{D}'_n =_{\text{def}} \sum_{i=1}^{n} \left(\frac{1}{\sqrt{\mathbf{n}}}\right) \mathbf{D}_i = \frac{\sum_{i=1}^{n} \mathbf{D}_i}{\sqrt{\mathbf{n}}} . \qquad [7.289]$$

Since the variance of $\mathbf{D}'_n$ is zero (see [7.33]), $\mathbf{D}'_n$ is the $\mathbf{n}$th principal component of the configuration $\mathbf{D}_1, \ldots, \mathbf{D}_n$.[29] Moreover, equation [7.228] may be rewritten

$$\sqrt{\mathbf{n}}\,\boldsymbol{\delta}_{wX} = \sum_{i=1}^{n} \left(\frac{z_{wi}}{\sqrt{\mathbf{n}}}\right) \mathbf{D}_i \qquad (\sigma_w > 0) , \qquad [7.290]$$

where in view of [7.227],

$$\sum_{i=1}^{n} \left(\frac{z_{wi}}{\sqrt{\mathbf{n}}}\right)^2 = 1 , \quad \sum_{i=1}^{n} \frac{z_{wi}}{\sqrt{\mathbf{n}}} = 0 \qquad (\sigma_w > 0) . \qquad [7.291]$$

Hence excluding the degenerate case in which the rescaling weights in [7.218] are all equal, the variable $\sqrt{\mathbf{n}}\boldsymbol{\delta}_{wX}$ corresponds to some rotated axis in the $\mathbf{D}_i$-scattergram orthogonal to the scattergram's $\mathbf{n}$th principal axis. In particular, if the rescaling weights $w_1, \ldots, w_n$ maximize $\text{Var}(\sqrt{\mathbf{n}}\boldsymbol{\delta}_{wX})$, then $\sqrt{\mathbf{n}}\boldsymbol{\delta}_{wX}$ is the first principal component of the dispersion configuration, while if the w_i minimize $\text{Var}(\sqrt{\mathbf{n}}\,\boldsymbol{\delta}_{wX})$, $\sqrt{\mathbf{n}}\,\boldsymbol{\delta}_{wX}$ is the $(\mathbf{n}-1)$th principal component of the $\mathbf{D}_i$. From [7.233], it is further seen that

$$\gamma_{wX} = \frac{\text{Var}(\boldsymbol{\delta}_{wX})}{\overline{V}_D} = \frac{\mathbf{n}\text{Var}(\boldsymbol{\delta}_{wX})}{V_D} = \frac{\text{Var}(\sqrt{\mathbf{n}}\,\boldsymbol{\delta}_{wX})}{\sum_{i=1}^{n} V_{D_i}} \qquad [7.292]$$

Since as just observed $\text{Var}(\sqrt{\mathbf{n}}\;\boldsymbol{\delta}_{wX})$ is bounded above and below, respectively, by the variance of the first and the $(\mathbf{n}-1)$th principal components of the $\mathbf{D}_i$, and since the variance of a set of variables accounted

[29] This follows from the fact that the *last* principal component of a set of variables is the rotated axis variable whose variance is *minimal*, and variances don't come more minimal than zero.

for by their **k**th principal factor equals the variance of their **k**th principal component, it follows from [7.292] that *the value of the selection coefficient for rescaling-transformations* [7.218] *must lie between the proportions of the dispersion variance accounted for by the first and by the* $(\mathbf{n}-1)$*th principal factors, respectively, of the dispersion configuration of the* $\mathbf{X}_i$.

More generally, $\mathrm{Var}(\sqrt{\mathbf{n}}\,\boldsymbol{\delta}_{WX})$ cannot be greater than the total variance of the dispersion configuration accounted for by $\boldsymbol{\delta}_{WX}$, with equality being attained when and only when $\boldsymbol{\delta}_{WX}$ coincides up to a linear transformation with one of the principal factors of the $\mathbf{D}_i$.[30] Hence

$$[7.293] \qquad \gamma_{WX} \leqslant \frac{V_{D(\delta_{WX})}}{V_D} = P_D(S_{\delta_{WX}}),$$

where $S_{\delta_{WX}}$ is the one-dimensional space spanned by $\boldsymbol{\delta}_{WX}$.

From [7.241] and our present conclusions about the magnitude of γ_{WX}, the anticipated correlation between an original centroid $\overline{\mathbf{X}}$ and the centroid $\overline{\mathbf{W}}$ which results from rescaling-transformations [7.218] is seen to be on the order of

$$[7.294] \qquad r^2_{\overline{W}\overline{X}} \simeq 1 - \frac{\nu_W^2 DQ_X}{\mathbf{n} - 1 + \nu_W^2 DQ_X}$$
$$\simeq 1 - \frac{\nu_W^2 DQ_X}{\mathbf{n}},$$

where the approximation is a serious overestimate of $r^2_{\overline{W}\overline{X}}$ only if the dispersion configuration of the $\mathbf{X}_i$ has a pronounced first principal axis and the transformation weights have been assigned to take advantage of this.

It will be recalled that in all above formulas concerning the effect of transformations [7.218] on the variance properties of the weighted centroid $\overline{\mathbf{W}}$, the selection coefficient occurs only as part of a more inclusive statistic ρ_{WX} $(= \sqrt{\gamma_{WX} DQ_X})$, while it is the maximum value which can be given to ρ_{WX} that is most critical for determining the extent to which $\overline{\mathbf{W}}$ can be made to differ from $\overline{\mathbf{X}}$ without resorting to extreme variation among the w_i. An important interpretation is found for ρ^2_{WX} by observing that the maximum value it can attain under alternative choices of rescaling weights is

$$[7.295] \qquad \mathrm{Max}(\rho^2_{WX}) = DQ_X \cdot \mathrm{Max}(\gamma_{WX})$$
$$= \frac{V_D \cdot \mathrm{Max}(\gamma_{WX})}{\mathbf{n} V_{\overline{X}}}$$
$$= \frac{V_{D(P_{D1})}}{\mathbf{n} V_{\overline{X}}}$$

[30] *Proof*: If $\mathbf{D}'_1, \ldots, \mathbf{D}'_n$ are an orthogonal rotation of $\mathbf{D}_1, \ldots, \mathbf{D}_n$ as in [7.287,8], then $V_{D(F)} = V_{D'(F)}$ for any factor $\mathbf{F}$ (see p. 580, Appendix B). Hence if $\mathbf{D}'_1 = \sqrt{\mathbf{n}}\,\boldsymbol{\delta}_{WX}$, $V_{D(\delta_{WX})} = \sum_{i=1}^{n} V_{D'_1(\delta_{WX})} = \mathrm{Var}(\sqrt{\mathbf{n}}\,\boldsymbol{\delta}_{WX}) + \sum_{i=2}^{n} V_{D'_i} r^2_{D'_i\,\delta_{WX}}$.

where $\mathbf{P_{D1}}$ is the first principal factor of the dispersion components of the $\mathbf{X_i}$, and $\mathbf{n}V_{\bar{\mathbf{X}}}$, it will be recalled (p. 304), is the saturation variance of the $\mathbf{X_i}$-configuration. Hence the maximal value that can be given to $\rho^2_{\mathbf{WX}}$ for a set of variables $\mathbf{X_1}, \ldots, \mathbf{X_n}$ through optimal choice of the rescaling weights in [7.218] equals the ratio of the maximal amount of the set's dispersion variance which can be accounted for by a single factor to the set's saturation variance. Let a configuration of variables be said to be "well-balanced" when its saturation variance is at least as great as its dispersion variance lying in any one direction – i.e., when $\rho^2_{\mathbf{WX}} \leqslant 1$ for any choice of the w_i. It may be discerned from [7.271,2] by allowing $\nu_{\mathbf{W}}$ to become arbitrarily large that if the $\mathbf{X_i}$ have been scaled to have maximal saturation, then the $\mathbf{X_i}$-configuration must be well-balanced. Hence no matter how small the homogeneity of a set of variables may be, it is always possible to find scalings for these variables such that the set is well-balanced – i.e., to be such that its saturation variance is at least as great as any one dimension's worth of its dispersion variance. It is also worth mention that when $\nu_{\mathbf{C_X}} = 0$ for a well-balanced configuration,

[7.296][31]

$$\mathrm{Max}(\rho^2_{\mathbf{WX}}) = \frac{\mathrm{P}_{\mathbf{X}}(S_{\mathbf{P_{X2}}})}{\mathrm{P}_{\mathbf{X}}(S_{\mathbf{P_{X1}}})} = \frac{V_{\mathbf{X}(\mathbf{P_{X2}})}}{V_{\mathbf{X}(\mathbf{P_{X1}})}} = \frac{\lambda_2}{\lambda_1} \qquad (\nu_{\mathbf{C_X}} = 0,\ \ \mathrm{Max}(\rho^2_{\mathbf{WX}}) \leqslant 1)\,,$$

where $\mathbf{P_{X1}}$ and $\mathbf{P_{X2}}$ are respectively the first and second principal factors of the $\mathbf{X_i}$-configuration with corresponding eigenvalues λ_1 and λ_2. Hence in general, the value of Max $(\rho^2_{\mathbf{WX}})$ is approximated for a configuration $\mathbf{X_1}, \ldots, \mathbf{X_n}$ by the importance of its second principal factor (as assessed by accounted-for variance) in comparison to its first principal factor, though the approximation becomes more and more an underestimate as $\nu_{\mathbf{C_X}}$ grows large. The chief virtue of this approximation is conceptual, rather than computational, for when facilities for ready extraction of principal factors are available, the exact value of Max $(\rho^2_{\mathbf{WX}})$ can be determined by computing the eigenvalue of the first principal factor of the dispersion configuration and dividing by $\mathbf{n}V_{\bar{\mathbf{X}}}$. Fast estimates of Max $(\rho^2_{\mathbf{WX}})$ by desk computer are also available; notably, the upper-bound approximation

[7.297] $$\mathrm{Max}(\rho^2_{\mathbf{WX}}) = \mathrm{DQ}_{\mathbf{X}} \cdot \mathrm{P}_{\mathbf{D}}(S_{\mathbf{P_{D1}}}) \leqslant \frac{\sqrt{\sigma^2_{\mathbf{C^*_{XX}}} - 2\sigma^2_{\mathbf{C_X}}}}{\bar{\mathrm{C}}^*_{\mathbf{XX}}}$$

(from [7.295] and [7.197]), which is little trouble to compute from the set's covariance matrix. Since the upper bound in [7.297] may be con-

[31] It is shown in Appendix B, p. 588, that $\bar{\mathbf{X}}$ coincides (up to a linear transformation) with one of the principal factors of the $\mathbf{X_i}$-configuration if and, when there are no linear dependencies among the $\mathbf{X_i}$, only if $\nu_{\mathbf{C_X}} = 0$. Further, if the set is well-balanced, this coincidence is with $\mathbf{P_1}$. Hence in this case $V_{\mathbf{X}(\mathbf{P_1})} = V_{\mathbf{X}(\bar{\mathbf{X}})} = \mathbf{n}V_{\bar{\mathbf{X}}}$ (cf. [7.62]), while each $\mathbf{D_i}$ differs from the residual of $\mathbf{X_i}$ left by $\mathbf{P_1}$ only by the constant $M_{\mathbf{X_i}} - M_{\bar{\mathbf{X}}}$ so $V_{\mathbf{D}(\mathbf{P_{D1}})} = V_{\mathbf{X}(\mathbf{P_{X2}})}$.

siderably in excess of $\text{Max}(\rho^2_{\mathbf{wX}})$ if the first principal factor of the dispersion configuration is weak, it is also useful when the value of Max $(\rho^2_{\mathbf{wX}})$ is of interest to look at the lower-bound approximation to this quantity obtained by substituting $V_{\mathbf{X}(\mathbf{F}_2)}$ for $V_{\mathbf{D}(\mathbf{P}_{\mathbf{D}1})}$ in [7.295], where $\mathbf{F_2}$ is a second centroid factor of the $\mathbf{X}_i$-configuration.[32]

While parameter $\theta_{\mathbf{wX}}$, the correlation between $\overline{\mathbf{X}}$ and $\boldsymbol{\delta}_{\mathbf{wX}}$, is perhaps of secondary interest, its expected order of magnitude should not pass unheeded. Since by [7.228] $\boldsymbol{\delta}_{\mathbf{wX}}$ is a linear combination of the $\mathbf{D}_i$, we have

[7.298] $$\theta^2_{\mathbf{wX}} = P_{\overline{\mathbf{X}}}(S_{\mathbf{D}}) \cdot r^2,$$

where $S_{\mathbf{D}}$ is the space spanned by the $\mathbf{D}_i$ and r is the correlation between $\boldsymbol{\delta}_{\mathbf{wX}}$ and the component of $\overline{\mathbf{X}}$ lying in $S_{\mathbf{D}}$. Since in general the dimensionality of $S_{\mathbf{D}}$ is $\mathbf{n}-1$, the proportion of $\text{Var}(\boldsymbol{\delta}_{\mathbf{wX}})$ lying in any one dimension of $S_{\mathbf{D}}$ is on the average $1/(\mathbf{n}-1)$; so r^2 may be expected to be on the order of $1/(\mathbf{n}-1)$. Hence for an arbitrary assignment of weights in transformations [7.218],

[7.299] $$\theta_{\mathbf{wX}} \simeq \sqrt{\frac{P_{\overline{\mathbf{X}}}(S_{\mathbf{D}})}{\mathbf{n}-1}} = \frac{R_{\overline{\mathbf{X}}(S_{\mathbf{D}})}}{\sqrt{\mathbf{n}-1}},$$

while no matter how the w_i are chosen $\theta_{\mathbf{wX}}$ cannot be greater in magnitude than the multiple correlation of $\overline{\mathbf{X}}$ with the $\mathbf{D}_i$.

It may be observed from [7.264], [7.236], and [7.298] that when the w_i are chosen to have a correlation of unity with the $\mathbf{C}_{\mathbf{X}_i\overline{\mathbf{X}}}$,

[7.300] $$\nu^2_{\mathbf{C_X}} = \rho^2_{\mathbf{wX}}\theta^2_{\mathbf{wX}} \qquad (r_{\mathbf{wC_X}} = 1)$$
$$= \gamma_{\mathbf{wX}} \cdot r^2 \cdot P_{\overline{\mathbf{X}}}(S_{\mathbf{D}}) \cdot \text{DQ}_{\mathbf{X}}$$

This suggests that $\nu_{\mathbf{C_X}}$ should generally be on the order of $1/\mathbf{n}$. Further, [7.300] generates a succession of upper bounds for $\nu_{\mathbf{C_X}}$:

[7.301] $$\nu^2_{\mathbf{C_X}} \leqslant \text{DQ}_{\mathbf{X}} \cdot P_{\overline{\mathbf{X}}}(S_{\mathbf{D}}) \cdot \text{Max}(\gamma_{\mathbf{wX}}) \leqslant \text{DQ}_{\mathbf{X}} \cdot P_{\overline{\mathbf{X}}}(S_{\mathbf{D}}) \leqslant \text{DQ}_{\mathbf{X}},$$

where as we have seen, $\text{Max}(\gamma_{\mathbf{wX}})$ equals the penetrance of the dispersion configuration into the space of its first principal factor. Hence there is a systematic tendency for a configuration's radial irregularity to become smaller as the set's saturation is increased. This is not a consequence merely of the fact that the denominator in the last line of [7.262] is proportional to $\text{Sat}_{\mathbf{X}}$, for inequalities [7.301] also imply that

[7.302] $$\sigma_{\mathbf{C_X}} \leqslant \overline{V}_{\mathbf{X}}\sqrt{\text{Sat}_{\mathbf{X}}\,(1-\text{Sat}_{\mathbf{X}}) \cdot P_{\overline{\mathbf{X}}}(S_{\mathbf{D}}) \cdot \text{Max}(\gamma_{\mathbf{wX}})}$$
$$\leqslant \overline{V}_{\mathbf{X}}\sqrt{\text{Sat}_{\mathbf{X}}\,(1-\text{Sat}_{\mathbf{X}}) \cdot P_{\overline{\mathbf{X}}}(S_{\mathbf{D}})}$$
$$\leqslant \overline{V}_{\mathbf{X}}\sqrt{\text{Sat}_{\mathbf{X}}\,(1-\text{Sat}_{\mathbf{X}})}\,.$$

[32] From [7.45], we have that for any factor $\mathbf{F}$ orthogonal to $\mathbf{X}$, $V_{\mathbf{X}(\mathbf{F})} = V_{\mathbf{D}(\mathbf{F})}$; hence $V_{\mathbf{X}(\mathbf{F}_2)} \leqslant V_{\mathbf{D}(\mathbf{P}_{\mathbf{D}1})}$.

Thus with fixed $\overline{V}_X$, the differences among the $C_{X_i\overline{X}}$ approach zero as Sat_X approaches either extreme.

Finally, it is possibly of theoretical interest to note that since [7.61] implies

[7.303] $$\nu^2_{C_X} = DQ_X \cdot P_D(S_{\overline{X}}) ,$$

a relation between (1) the penetrance of the dispersion configuration into centroid space and (2) the penetrance of the centroid into dispersion space which follows from [7.301] is

[7.304] $$P_D(S_{\overline{X}}) \leq P_{\overline{X}}(S_D) \cdot P_D(S_{P_{D1}}) ,$$

where as before, $\mathbf{P}_{D1}$ is the first principal factor of the $\mathbf{D}_i$.

Chapter 8. **Reliability**

Of all the technical concepts which have issued from meditations on the statistical principles of prediction, none has proved quite so beloved to mathematically inclined test theorists as the notion of "reliability." Much of this affection can undoubtedly be traced to the demure simplicity of the basic reliability equations which, like Hayden's Theme in the history of musical composition, have persistently challenged the test theorist to display his technical virtuosity in some new variation on their development. Also influential in the burgeoning of reliability theory, however, has been a more earthy incentive: While empirical validation of tests is an expensive, time-consuming, and experimentally treacherous undertaking even when it can be done at all, empirical reliability estimates can readily be harvested in abundant supply. Since reliability does have a certain relevance to objective validity,[1] industrious attention to questions about reliability has made it possible for commercial psychological tests to be served to their consumers with such a scientifically dignified dressing of quantitative reliability ratings that it seems boorish to raise any doubts about the test's ultimate practical utility.

In brief, the "reliability" of a test is a measure of the *consistency* with which the test procedure establishes the scores by which it differentiates among testees. The operational thrust of the concept is toward repetitive observation: If a subject were to be assessed not just once but several times by the test, how closely would his test scores agree? A straightforward operational definition of "reliability" as empirical test-retest agreement, however, turns out to be not wholly satisfactory; instead, reliability concepts appeal in one way or another to hypothesized determinants which, like the source variables postulated by inferential factor analysis, are held to account for certain kinds of observed regu-

[1] Measures of reliability might be called "the poor man's validity coefficient," or—to use a cliché of more recent coinage—"instant validity."

larities. The plural form, "reliability concepts," is here used advisedly, for as a number of test theorists have somewhat grimly pointed out, "reliability" has meant various things to various people—subtle differences to be sure, but enough to make one man's theorem another man's fallacy.

The fundamental tenet of reliability theory in all its varied formulations (though the particular route by which this commitment makes its appearance differs greatly from one version to another) is that a score X_i actually observed for an individual i on a given test **X** is the sum of two components: (1) the individual's *true score*, T_i, on that test plus (2) an "observation error" or *error of measurement*, E_i, which contaminates the observed X_i as a perfect reproduction of T_i. It is further maintained (either by definition or by postulation) that measurement errors have an expected value of zero and are uncorrelated with true scores. That is,

[8.1] $$\mathbf{X} = \mathbf{T} + \mathbf{E} \, ,$$

[8.2] $$M_{\mathbf{E}} = 0 \, ,$$

[8.3] $$r_{\mathbf{TE}} = 0 \, .$$

More generally, when observations are made on a set of **n** variables $\mathbf{X_i}$, . . . , $\mathbf{X_n}$, it is assumed, one way or another, that each variable $\mathbf{X_j}$ is composed of true-score and measurement-error components in such fashion that

[8.4-**j**] (**j** = **1**, . . . , **n**) $$\mathbf{X_j} = \mathbf{T_j} + \mathbf{E_j} \, ,$$

[8.5-**j**] (**j** = **1**, . . . , **n**) $$M_{\mathbf{E_j}} = 0 \, ,$$

[8.6-**jk**] (**j**,**k** = **1**, . . . , **n**) $$r_{\mathbf{T_j E_k}} = 0 \, .$$

Despite the superficially stern requirements imposed by equations [8.4]–[8.6] on hypothesized components $\mathbf{T_1}, \ldots, \mathbf{T_n}$ and $\mathbf{E_1}, \ldots, \mathbf{E_n}$ (note that [8.6] stipulates that no true-score variable correlates with any measurement-error variable), these postulates are actually quite promiscuous in the alternative interpretations to which they will submit. This is because if $\mathbf{T_j}$ ($\mathbf{j} = \mathbf{1}, \ldots, \mathbf{n}$) is taken to be the linear regression of $\mathbf{X_j}$ upon any particular set of predictors $\mathbf{F_1}, \ldots, \mathbf{F_m}$, then $\mathbf{E_j} = \mathbf{e}_{\mathbf{X_j} \cdot \mathbf{F_1} \ldots \mathbf{F_m}}$ and equations [8.4]–[8.6] are all satisfied no matter what variables we have chosen for $\mathbf{F_1}, \ldots, \mathbf{F_m}$. This has two interesting consequences for the methodological status of reliability theory: (1) The *mathematical form* of reliability theory is simply a portion of multivariate analysis capable of widespread applications under many different interpretations of its axiomatic terms, while (2) what gives reliability theory its distinctive substantive flavor is the special sort of meaning with which it imbues the notion of "true score." As might be expected, it is the conceptual basis of the theory which has been most controversial, and we shall examine this aspect of the matter first.

As already observed, the notion of "reliability" originates in the bothersome fact that when we "observe" the value of a given variable for a particular individual, repetition of the observation rarely yields a result which is altogether consistent with the previous one. For example, if Henry Jones weighs 173 pounds, the pointer of our pound-calibrated weighing scale should ideally indicate 173 every time Jones steps on its platform; whereas in fact, three successive weighings of Jones might yield pointer readings of, say, 174, 175, and 172. Similarly, if we test Jones's ability to work a certain multiplication problem by presenting it to him on four consecutive days, he might get the correct answer in 36 seconds on the first occasion, the wrong answer in 24 seconds on the second, the correct answer in 17 seconds on the third, and the correct answer in two seconds on the fourth. Part of the explanation for these observational discrepancies may be that the subject's status on the variable being measured does, in fact, change from observation to observation, possibly as a direct causal consequence of the previous measurement. (This is why an operational definition of reliability as test-retest consistency is inadequate.) In general, however, intrasubject differences under repeated measurement are too large and irregular to be plausibly regarded as the subject's temporal progress on the measured variable. If so, we are driven to conclude that the numerical scores obtained by this technique are not literally scores on the variable we construe them to measure, but are only imperfect approximations to the latter. And to be sure, once one stops to think about the matter, it is obvious that instrument readings are not logically identical with what they supposedly inform us about. Jones's weight in pounds is not at all the same thing as the pointer position of any weighing device on which he may or may not happen to be standing, nor can the degree of his *ability* to work a given multiplication problem at a particular moment be equated with any feature of his overt behavior at that time (see pp. 206 f.). A measurement technique, in short, defines an observation variable to which the variable *of* which this is a measurement is related as criterion to predictor, with the attendant margin of inferential uncertainty which always intrudes between two logically distinct variables.

On the face of it, therefore, the phenomenon of measurement error, in which the concept of "reliability" has its origin, is nothing more than an instance of imperfect predictability, to which we have already given detailed consideration in terms of correlation and regression. However, while we shall indeed eventually subsume reliability under correlation, the measurement situation envisioned in reliability theory involves special complications which prevent reliability from being construed as merely an empirical relationship between test scores and what they measure. If we but knew, e.g., the joint distribution of scale-pointer readings and the corresponding weights of objects placed upon the scale, estimation of an object's weight given its scale reading would readily follow, along with the likely error of that estimate, by the regression principles developed in Chapter 4. To learn this joint distribution, however, we must first be able to measure weight, *and this we can do only by inference from readings on the very measuring instrument, or others like it, whose accuracy we are hoping to establish in the first place.* Similarly, the closest we can come to observing a person's ability at some task is to confront him with it and see what he does, even though no aspect of the resulting behavior may reasonably be assumed to correlate perfectly with the ability hypothesized to account for it. In general, the question of reliability arises when we have a test procedure which at first impression seems explicitly to *define* a certain concept (as we might at first think to define, e.g., a person's "weight" as his effect on a certain spring balance's pointer reading, or his Stanford-Binet IQ as the IQ score he obtains upon taking the Stanford-Binet intelligence test), but where closer analysis of that concept's usage reveals it to presume an underlying condition, logically distinct from the literal test result, which is postulated specifically to account for whatever tendency there may be for subjects to have characteristically different effects upon the test procedure's outcome. How to make—and to justify—inferences of this sort is precisely the problem which generates transempirical conceptions of test validity (see pp. 205ff.), and so reliability theory turns out to be a form of construct validation.

Hypothetical Test Results and the Concept of "True Score"

While any definition of "reliability," with its partition of observed scores into true-score and measurement-error components, must inevitably assume unobserved variables of one sort or another, there are numerous ways in which this can be conceptually accomplished, and some versions are decidedly more presumptuous in their demands upon reality than are others. We shall here develop an approach which not only clings tightly to the intuitive presuppositions which are inescapable in an actual test situation no matter what official theory of reliability is adopted, but which almost avoids postulation of theoretical variables altogether.

A "test" may be described as some distinctive way to assign a numerical score[2] to a person or object at a particular time. A test's definition includes not merely identification of test materials but also stipulation of a particular way in which these materials are to be applied, the conditions under which the test is to be administered, and how a single test score (or set of test scores in case of a multidimensional assessment) is to be abstracted from the events which ensue from the testing operation. For

---

[2] It is not actually necessary for a test to yield *numerical* scores, so long as it generates scale values of *some* sort. These values can always be represented by numerals, however, and in practice virtually always are.

example, a certain test of a person's weight might stipulate (*a*) that a scale conforming to such-and-such physical specifications is to be used (test material); (*b*) that the subject is to step or be placed on the scale's platform and remain there until the scale's pointer has shown no perceptible movement for at least two seconds (test application); (*c*) that the scale's platform be devoid of visible encumbrances just before and, apart from the subject, during weighing, that the scale's pointer remain motionless on zero for at least two seconds just before the subject mounts, and that while on the scale the subject is to be in contact with no physical object other than the scale's platform and the ambient air (test conditions); and (*d*) that at any moment when stipulations (*a*)–(*c*) are all fulfilled, the number indicated by the scale's pointer is the weight score assigned by this procedure to the person on the scale for this moment of his life (scoring procedure). Similarly, a particular IQ test might be defined as (*a*) a certain sheet of questions printed in such-and-such standard fashion (*b*) put into the possession of the subject for a period of exactly 30 minutes after the subject has been read a standard set of instructions, where (*c*) the subject has normal vision and hearing, can understand English, has been equipped with a usable pencil, a writing surface, adequate illumination, and freedom from external distractions; and where (*d*) the number computed by a stated procedure from the pencil marks found on the subject's test sheet after conditions (*a*)–(*c*) have been fulfilled is the IQ score assigned by this test to the subject for the 30-minute period while he was taking it.

Despite the superficiality of these examples, their intent is wholly serious. An accurate description of even the simplest of tests would require thousands of words which, no matter how carefully chosen, would still fail to capture all the conditions implicitly assumed by most of the test's users. An enormous number of difficult methodological problems become conspicuous when one makes a *really* serious attempt to describe a test procedure in detail, hints of which will perhaps be discerned in the examples as given. For present purposes, it suffices to observe that at various junctures in space and time there occur episodes which might be called "score-marking" events, such as the writing of a numeral on a record form or the alignment of a dial pointer with a dial character or the congruence of an object's edge with a position along a calibrated rod, etc., and that what differentiates one test from another is (1) which of these score-marking events qualify, by virtue of their attendant circumstances, as instances of the test and (2) to what subject during what temporal interval the score indicated by a qualifying event is assigned. Thus in the preceding weight-test example it was stipulated that the scale pointer has to remain stationary for at least two seconds prior to the scale reading if the latter is to count as an instance of the test. Another slightly different test of weight might be identical to this one except for requiring that the scale pointer be motionless for only one second before the reading counts. Then every weighing event which qualifies as an instance of the second test also qualifies as an instance of the first, but not conversely. To appreciate that tests may also be differentiated by how they allocate the score determined by a score-marking event, reflect that since a test procedure can usually be applied repeatedly to a subject, the score assigned to him on any one testing occasion is considered to hold only for a certain brief segment of his life, and it needs to be decided just what that interval is—e.g., when a test performance has been graded, does this score apply to the subject at just the instant the score was computed, at just the instant the performance was completed, throughout the entire interval during which the performance took place, or perhaps to some other moment or interval of the subject's life? There may even be room for decision about what *subject* to assign the score to—e.g., if one person performs while another person rates the performance, the resultant score could be ascribed to the performer by one test and to the judge by another.

Although this abbreviated survey of the methodology of testing is admittedly crude, it serves to highlight two technical curiosities which complicate the interpretation of test scores. The first is that the score actually assigned to a subject on a given test occasion is determined not merely by the subject's own attributes, but by a great many details of the surrounding circumstances as well. Thus the precise position of a weighing scale's pointer when a person is standing upon its platform is influenced not only by the physical properties of that person's body, but also by the amount of clothing he is wearing, how dirty his hands and feet are, the accuracy of the scale's zero-adjustment prior to weighing, the presence or absence of dust, gum, mice, or other contaminants at critical points in the scale's internal mechanism, the velocity and direction of air currents impinging upon the scale's platform, the temperature of the surrounding air, and many, many other environmental variables which are responsible for some variation—in most instances negligible, but variation nonetheless—in the pointer-reading variable. Similarly, the score a person obtains on an intelligence test is sensitive not merely to the psychological attributes he brings with him to the testing situation, but also to details of how the test is administered (the particular wording and intonation of instructions, time allowances on the various items, etc.), the full array of stimuli impinging upon him as he works on it (the view through the window, hardness of chair, degree to which neighboring answer sheets are exposed, etc.), the accuracy with which his performance is subsequently scored, and so forth. A good test attempts to delete the differential contributions of the more influential extraneous variables by stipulating that they be held constant at certain standard values, but no matter how extensively the test's conditions of application have been standardized, there will always persist uncontrolled nuisance factors such that for any particular test outcome, had such-and-such an extraneous detail been different, as permissible under the test's definition, then the subject would have received a somewhat different score – e.g., had John not bounced so hard when he stepped on the scale, had he placed his feet a little differently on the platform, or had the ambient air temperature been a few degrees cooler, then the scale's pointer would have come to rest on the numeral 163 rather than the 162 actually observed; or had Jim not poked himself in the eye with his pencil halfway through the IQ test, he would have answered several more questions correctly. Consequently if we presume, *as we inevitably do*, that a person's test score reveals something about him which is independent of the uncontrolled details of the testing situation – e.g., that there is something about a person which affects the score he is assigned by a weighing episode but which is not a function of how he places his feet on the scale's platform; or that a person's score on an IQ test reflects some psychological attribute which holds steady while ocular irritations come and go – then there cannot be perfect correlation (linear or otherwise) between test scores as actually obtained and whatever it is that they are interpreted to signify.

Moreover, while a hard-nosed empiricist might legitimately insist that we do not *have* to regard an obtained test score as indicative of anything which is independent of the uncontrolled details of the test circumstances, it must also be unflinchingly recognized that in general, the test in question *fails to assign any test score at all to the overwhelming majority of subjects for the overwhelming preponderance of their life histories.* Many persons have gone their entire lives without ever having been weighed, or tested for IQ, or evaluated by any other particular testing procedure we might name, not to mention the even greater proportion of nonhuman subjects (animals, plants, rocks, etc.) which have not and never will be weighed, IQed, etc. And even a person who manages to get assessed repeatedly by a given test will still be assigned scores on this test for only a vanishingly small proportion of his total temporal duration. (What proportion of his day, for example, does even a diet-conscious human spend getting weighed, and how many days a year does a person ordinarily take an IQ test?) If "**X**" designates the variable whose values are the alternatively possible scores yielded by a given test procedure, and by the phrase "individual i" we understand the temporal cross section of a particular person or object o at a particular time t, so that "X_i" designates the score assigned by **X** to o at t, we are forced to conclude that most individuals to whom test **X** is in principle applicable simply do not, in literal fact, have any score on **X** at all.[3] But with few if any exceptions, our concept of a test carries with it the notion that the test somehow defines, reveals, circumscribes, or otherwise manages to make cognitively

[3] That is, unless we include in the set of values for **X** a "no-results" score which cannot be meaningfully interpreted or scaled along with proper values of **X**.

accessible certain attributes of individuals to whom the test is applicable which hold for these individuals whether they are actually tested or not. It would be intolerable, for example, to regard a person's "weight" as an attribute which comes into existence only as he steps upon a weighing device and vanishes as he dismounts, nor should we look with favor on the suggestion that the only people in the world who have ever had any intelligence are those persons who have taken an intelligence test. Thus we find ourselves pressed to extend the notion of "score on test **X**" *in some sense* to a class of individuals much wider than those who have literally received a test score by procedure **X**.

Now, an operationist who would like to define, say, "weight" as the score assigned to an individual by a certain weighing procedure **W**, yet who does not wish to deny weight to the vast majority of individuals who have not in fact been weighed by this procedure, can point out that while, e.g., Henry Jones was not actually weighed by procedure **W** at 2:35 P.M. yesterday and hence does not have an actual score on **W** for that time, Jones nevertheless *could* have been weighed then. It might be proposed, therefore that Henry Jones's weight at 2:35 P.M. yesterday is the weight score he *would have* received if he *had* been tested by procedure **W** at that time. Certainly subjunctive ("What would happen if such-and-such were to be the case?") and counterfactual ("What would have happened had such-and-such been so?") queries are an integral part of science and everyday life, even if definite answers to such questions are not so easy to come by as are answers to questions about what is actually the case; and once a test procedure **X** has been defined, it becomes meaningful to ask for each individual i to which **X** might be, or might have been, applied what score i would receive, or would have received, if i were to be, or were to have been, tested by **X**. Occasionally i actually does have an **X**-score, whereas in most instances i's score on **X** remains only an unrealized possibility. Either way, the concept of a test **X** inevitably gives parthenogenetic birth to thought of an individual's test *potential,* or *disposition* to receive one score rather than another on **X**, where the value of this **X**-potential or **X**-disposition variable for an individual i is to be defined in terms of what, subjunctively, would happen, or would have happened, were i to be, or to have been, tested by **X**. It is this intuitive distinction between actual and potential test outcomes which has been the most compelling goad to the development of a theory of measurement in which "observed" scores are contrasted with "true" scores, and any interpretation of a test's "reliability" which does justice to the commonsense roots of this concept must correspondingly grow directly from the considerations, whatever they may be, which underlie judgments about the score an individual *would* receive on the test *were* he to be evaluated by it.

Now as philosophers of science have become acutely aware, analysis of the meaning and truth conditions of subjunctive and counterfactual conditionals[4] is a treacherous business which is still far from complete,[5] and an honest effort to make sense out of the notion of "potential" scores would require a lengthy and still not fully satisfactory technical argument quite impractical here. We can, however, note the *form* of conclusion which appears to be implicated, and develop its mathematical consequences without regard for how a more penetrating analysis may eventually fill in the details. The (schematic) interpretation which will be adopted here is that *the definition of a particular testing procedure* **X** *may be considered to determine a specific probability distribution over potential scores on* **X** *for each individual i to whom the test is applicable, while the* **X**-*score, if any, actually received by i is a sampling of this distribution.* That is, the subjunctive query, "If individual *i were* tested by procedure **X**, what score *would i* receive?" does not, in general, have any single determinate answer. Rather, for each possible score on **X** there is a certain probability (or probability density) that individual *i* would receive that particular score were *i* to be tested by **X**, and where the probability of this score differs from one individual to another. This form of thought is thoroughly commonplace—e.g., "There's a much better chance that Harry will loan me $5 for the weekend than will Dick, so I'll try Harry first," or "Don't use that adding machine, because the answers it gives are usually wrong," or "I forgot to invite Tom to go with us, but he'd almost certainly have declined anyway." The assumption behind such remarks is that the outcome of a situation involving individual *i* is a lawful consequence (whether the laws are strictly deterministic or only probabilistic does not here matter) jointly of the attributes that *i* brings to the situation and the nature of the circumstances acting upon *i*, so that if we but knew the relevant laws and attributes of *i*, we could deduce for each possible detailed circumstance C_j what the outcome (or, if the laws are probabilistic, the probability distribution over alternative outcomes) would be if C_j were to act upon *i*. Now, to define a testing procedure is *partially* to identify the causally relevant circumstances which are operative when individuals are assigned scores by that test, and hence to ask what score *would* a particular individual *i* receive on test **X** if *i were* to be tested by **X** is to speculate about what could be deduced from the laws governing such situations given exhaustive information about what *i* is like, but only so much information about the test circumstances as is included in the definition of the test. Then the distribution of probabilities for the alternative unspecified details of the testing situation, considered in light of *i*'s particular attributes and the laws determining test scores as a func-

---

[4] A subjunctive conditional is a proposition of form, "If *P* were to be the case then *Q* would also be the case," wherein nothing is implied about the truth of *P*. A counterfactual conditional is like a subjunctive conditional except that *P* is further recognized to be not so—e.g., "If I had applied the brakes a half-second later, we would have gone over the cliff."

[5] To appreciate some of the problems involved, see Goodman (33) and Rescher (66).

tion of the subject's attributes and the test-circumstance details, generates a corresponding distribution of probabilities for the score that i would receive were i to be tested on **X**. (Of course we don't actually *know* this probability distribution of **X** for i because we don't have the requisite background information, but this is a different problem from making meaningful the notion that i *has* a probability distribution on **X**.)

This line of reasoning may be illustrated in somewhat oversimplified fashion as follows: Suppose that what happens when an individual i is tested by procedure **X** is governed by deterministic laws such that if sufficient details about i and the circumstances under which **X** is administered were known, then the score which eventuates when i is tested by **X** could be predicted exactly. Further, let $C_1, \ldots, C_p$ be a list of all the alternatively possible detailed circumstances in which i might be found such that each C_j (*a*) meets the conditions to be counted as an application of test **X** and (*b*) specifies a particular set of values for all the circumstance-variables which are causally relevant to the outcome of testing by **X**.[6] For example, suppose that **X** is a weighing procedure in which the subject's bodily activity and clothing worn at the moment the scale reading is taken are standardized, but the ambient air temperature and subject's foot position on the scale's platform are not. Then each test-circumstance description C_j would include specification of, among other relevant factors, the subject's degree of activity, amount of clothing worn, stance on platform, and the ambient air temperature; but while the degree of subject's activity and amount of clothing worn agree for all C_j with the values (say, motionless and nude) set by the test's standardization, different C_j will specify different platform stances and ambient air temperatures. Then given the attributes which are in fact possessed by an individual i independently of the test circumstances, if any, i may be in—e.g., i's physical mass, which is independent of air temperature and of the particular placement of i's feet—the hypothesis that i is in the set of specific test circumstances C_j causally implies that i receives a certain score X_{ij} on test **X**; so even if i is *not* actually in C_j, it could still meaningfully be said that if i *were* in C_j, i's score on **X** *would* be X_{ij}. Then the various potential scores X_{ij} for an individual i corresponding to the alternative test-circumstance possibilities C_j together with the distribution of conditional probabilities over the C_j, given testing by **X**—i.e., for each C_j, the probability that C_j is the set of conditions which are present when **X** is administered—imply a probability distribution over values of **X** for i under the hypothesis that i is tested by procedure **X**. Specifically, the probability that i would receive score X if i were tested on **X** is the sum over j of all probabilities $\Pr(C_j|i \textit{ tested on } \mathbf{X})$ such that $X_{ij} = X_i$.

If the ideas developed in the preceding two paragraphs seem distres-

[6] What is particularly artificial about this assumption is the pretense that all possible alternative test circumstances could be enumerated in a finite list.

singly incomplete—as indeed they are—it must be remembered that they do not attempt to *prove* anything, but merely try to convey some feeling for how sense can be made of the notion that a given testing procedure determines a probability distribution over potential test scores specific to each individual who might be so tested. While the present suggestions gloss over some exceedingly nasty questions,[7] these belong in one guise or another to a heritage of unresolved foundational problems common to the whole of science. Starting with the conviction that propositions of form "If such-and-such were to be the case, then . . . ," however these are to be eventually analyzed, have a legitimate and indeed indispensable place in science, we go on to posit that in general, subjunctive or counterfactual conditionals can properly assert a categorical consequent only probabilistically, and that with respect to hypothetical testings of factual individuals, the probability of a given test result depends in part upon the particular individual being considered.[8] From these meager premises the classic theory of reliability follows immediately.

Suppose that we have a population P of individuals (i.e., persons or objects at specific times) who may be, or might have been, tested by a procedure **X**. According to our basic assumption, each member i of P has a probability distribution over potential scores on **X**, namely, the probabilities of the various alternative test outcomes were i to be, or to have been, tested on **X**. Accordingly, let us define the "true score," T_i, of individual i on test **X** to be *the score expected for i were i to be tested on* **X**, where "expectation" is understood statistically. That is, i's true score on test **X** is the arithmetic mean over i's probability distribution of potential scores on **X**. Also, let the algebraic difference between a potential score

[7]One is the nature of *unknown probabilities*, an issue which cuts to the heart of unsolved problems in probability theory. Another is distinguishing between the test-circumstance details, independent of individual i, to be included in the alternatives C_j, and the test-event details which follow from the interaction between i and C_j. Most troublesome of all in many respects is deciding whether a given detail of the total complex of facts involving an individual i should be regarded as an independent attribute of i, and hence to be preserved when contemplating the distribution of potential test scores for i, or whether it should be attributed to the circumstances in which i is now involved and hence not to be preserved as an "independent attribute" of i. For example, if John Smith happened to suffer from migraine all day yesterday, and we say that his IQ yesterday is to be defined in terms of the probable IQ score he would have received had he been tested then, do we insist, when counterfactually envisioning the circumstances in which he might have taken the test yesterday, that he retain his headache, or can this be regarded as one of the uncontrolled test-circumstance details? It appears that the concept of "test potential" remains importantly ambiguous in application to an extant test unless the concept of the test procedure not only specifies what test conditions *are* to be held constant, but also implies, somehow, what sorts of further conditions it would *like* to standardize were it practical to do so.

[8] It is worth mention that much of contemporary psychology is based upon concepts, such as "habit," "preference," etc., which are implicitly or explicitly characterized in terms of probabilities over what an organism *would* do at a given moment *were* it to be confronted with certain stimuli, and where these dispositional probabilities vary from organism to organism and from time to time even in the same organism.

X_i and i's true score on **X** be called the (potential) "error of measurement," E_i, corresponding to the potential observation X_i—i.e.,

$$[8.7] \qquad E_i =_{\text{def}} X_i - T_i \ .$$

Equation [8.7] is to be interpreted as saying that if X_i *were* to be the score observed by test procedure **X** for individual i, then the error of measurement for this observation *would* be $X_i - T_i$, or E_i; while if X_i *is*, in fact, a score on **X** obtained for i, then E_i *is* the error of this measurement. To the probability distribution over potential scores on **X** implicated for each individual i by the query, "What score would i receive if i were tested on **X**?", there thus corresponds a probability distribution over potential errors **E** for i implicated by "What would the error of measurement be for i if i were tested on **X**?" Now: What can we say about the relations among true scores, observed scores, and measurement errors on test **X** for members of population P? If by "observed scores" we restrict ourselves to scores on **X** which have actually been obtained, the question has no meaning for P as a whole, since in general only a vanishingly small proportion of members of P will in fact have been tested on **X**. We can, however, inquire subjunctively about joint probabilities on **X**, **T**, and **E** in P—i.e., for each combination of possible values on **X**, **T**, and **E**, what is the likelihood of obtaining that combination if a random member of P were to be tested on **X**? The numerical details of this joint distribution depend of course upon empirical facts about **X** and P, but it has two important mathematical properties which follow directly from the definition of "true score": (1) *the error of measurement expected on a test observation for any particular individual i in P is zero*, and (2) *the observed score expected to result from testing an individual drawn randomly from among those members of P whose true scores on the test are T, is T*. While these conclusions are intuitively obvious, they cannot strictly be proved here insomuch as they expressly concern *probability* distributions, whereas we have restricted our statistical mathematics to frequency distributions over finite populations. We circumvented this difficulty in Chapter 4, however, by deriving formulas for hypothetical frequency distributions, and the same tactic will put us in business here, even though the reader will have to take on faith that the conclusions so reached also apply to probabilities.

Suppose, then, that for each individual i in population P we have a set of potential observed scores $X_{i1}, X_{i2}, \ldots, X_{ip}$ on test **X** such that the frequency of a particular value X among the X_{ij} for i is essentially equal to the probability that X would be the score observed for i were i tested on **X**.[9] Each double subscript ij stands for a "potential testing-on-**X** event"

[9] More precisely, we let the cumulative frequency function for the distribution $X_{i1}, \ldots, X_{ip}$ approximate the cumulative probability function for i's potential scores on **X**. The approximation may be made as close as we please if p is sufficiently large.

comprising a score X_{ij} potentially observed on **X** for individual i, a score T_{ij} equal to i's true score on **X**, namely,

$$T_{ij} =_{\text{def}} T_i \ , \tag{8.8}$$

and the corresponding potential measurement error E_{ij}, namely,

$$E_{ij} =_{\text{def}} X_{ij} - T_{ij} \ . \tag{8.9}$$

It may be heuristically helpful to think of each subscript j in the pair ij as designating one of p equiprobable detailed test circumstances C_j such that if individual i were tested on **X** under circumstance C_j, then i would receive score X_{ij}. Or we may fantasize an experiment with a matter duplicator in which each member i of P has been replicated p times and each replica ij is tested on **X**, so that if p is large the frequency of a particular observed value X among i's replicas approaches the probability of this observed score for i. In any case, we have constructed our (hypothetical) joint frequency distribution of **X**, **T**, and **E** in the population, P^*, of potential testing-on-**X** events to be equivalent in statistical properties to the joint probability distribution for **X**, **T**, and **E** were a randomly selected member of P to be tested on **X**, and formulas computed for the former hold for the latter as well. In particular, since T_i is defined as the expected value of **X** for individual i,

$$T_i =_{\text{def}} \frac{\sum_{j=1}^{p} X_{ij}}{p} \ , \tag{8.10}$$

and the expected error of measurement for i is

$$\begin{aligned} \frac{\sum_{j=1}^{p} E_{ij}}{p} &= \frac{\sum_{j=1}^{p} (X_{ij} - T_{ij})}{p} \\ &= \frac{\sum_{j=1}^{p} X_{ij}}{p} - T_i \\ &= 0 \ , \end{aligned} \tag{8.11}$$

as claimed previously. Now consider the average value of **X** among all potential testing-on-**X** events in P^* which have the same true score T. Writing "$\sum_{i}^{P_T}$" for summation over all individuals i in P such that $T_i = T$, where n_T is the number of such individuals, it follows from [8.8] and [8.10] that the average value of **X** among potential testing-on-**X** events

ij for which $T_{ij} = T$—and correspondingly the observed score on **X** expected for individuals i such that $T_i = T$—is

[8.12]
$$M_{\mathbf{X}|T} =_{\text{def}} \frac{\sum_i^{P_T} \sum_{j=1}^{p} X_{ij}}{n_T \bullet p} = \frac{\sum_i^{P_T} p \bullet T}{n_T \bullet p} = T \, .$$

This may be put by saying that the true-score variable **T** is identical with the curvilinear regression of **X** upon **T** in P^* (frequency-wise) and in P (probability-wise), while **E**, which by [8.7] and [8.12] equals $\mathbf{X} - M_{\mathbf{X}|\mathbf{T}}$, is hence the residual left by the curvilinear regression of **X** upon **T**. Moreover, since **T** and hence $M_{\mathbf{X}|\mathbf{T}}$ is obviously a linear function of **T**, the linear and curvilinear regressions of **X** upon **T** coincide and we may write

[8.13]
$$\dot{\mathbf{X}}_{(\mathbf{T})} = M_{\mathbf{X}|\mathbf{T}} = \mathbf{T} \, ,$$

[8.14]
$$\mathbf{e}_{\mathbf{X}\bullet\mathbf{T}} = \mathbf{e}_{\mathbf{X}|\mathbf{T}} = \mathbf{E} \, ,$$

while in view of the general properties of residuals under linear regression (see [4.87]),

[8.15]
$$\text{Cov}(\mathbf{T}, \mathbf{E}) = 0 \, ,$$

[8.16]
$$M_{\mathbf{E}} = 0 \, ,$$

and of course

[8.17]
$$M_{\mathbf{T}} = M_{\mathbf{X}} \, .$$

These results may readily be generalized to the multivariate relations among true scores and potential observed scores on a number of tests. Let $\mathbf{X}_1, \ldots, \mathbf{X}_\mathbf{m}$ be **m** different testing procedures—or better, to make provision for the fact that the way in which $\mathbf{X}_1, \ldots, \mathbf{X}_\mathbf{m}$ are co-administered may make a difference for the joint distribution of scores on the $\mathbf{X}_i$,[10] let $\mathbf{X}_1, \ldots, \mathbf{X}_\mathbf{m}$ be **m** different aspects, or "items," of a single complex testing procedure—and consider the probability distribution over simultaneous values of $\mathbf{X}_1, \ldots, \mathbf{X}_\mathbf{m}$, respectively, for the potential outcome of testing a random member of population P. Cast in terms of our hypothetical frequency model, we have a population P^* of potential testing events ij, where as before, i ranges over members of P and j may be thought to run over p replications of each i, each of which is tested on $\mathbf{X}_1, \ldots, \mathbf{X}_\mathbf{m}$. The true score, $T_{\mathbf{k}i}$, of a particular individual i on test

[10] It is well known to psychometricians that the response elicited by a particular item on a compound test is frequently influenced by the nature and perhaps the order of other items on the test. An extreme example of this possibility would be an item reading "My answer to the preceding question was ________."

item $\mathbf{X_k}$ is the value of $\mathbf{X_k}$ expected for i were i to be tested, so the true score on $\mathbf{X_k}$ for potential testing event ij is

[8.18-**k**] (**k** = **1**, . . . , **m**)

$$T_{\mathbf{k}ij} =_{\text{def}} T_{\mathbf{k}i} = \frac{\sum_{j=1}^{p} X_{\mathbf{k}ij}}{p},$$

while the error of measurement on item $\mathbf{X_k}$ for potential testing event ij is

[8.19-**k**] (**k** = **1**, . . . , **m**)

$$E_{\mathbf{k}ij} =_{\text{def}} X_{\mathbf{k}ij} - T_{\mathbf{k}ij},$$

or simply

[8.20-**k**] (**k** = **1**, . . . , **m**)

$$\mathbf{E_k} =_{\text{def}} \mathbf{X_k} - \mathbf{T_k},$$

where the latter form is also applicable to the probability distribution over potential scores on $\mathbf{X_k}$ for members of P. Let "$\sum_{i}^{P_{T_1,\ldots,T_m}}$" designate summation over all members of P having the same set of true scores $T_1, \ldots, T_m$ on test items $\mathbf{X_1}, \ldots, \mathbf{X_m}$, respectively, while $n_{T_1 \ldots T_m}$ is the number of such individuals. Then the mean value of $\mathbf{X_k}$ among potential testing events in P^* which share the same set $T_1, \ldots, T_m$ of true scores on test items $\mathbf{X_1}, \ldots, \mathbf{X_m}$—and correspondingly the value of $\mathbf{X_k}$ expected for an individual randomly selected from members of P whose true scores on the $\mathbf{X_k}$ are $T_1, \ldots, T_m$, respectively—is

[8.21-**k**] (**k** = **1**, . . . , **m**)

$$\mathrm{M}_{\mathbf{X_k} T_1 \ldots T_m} =_{\text{def}} \frac{\sum_{i}^{P_{T_1 \ldots T_m}} \sum_{j=1}^{p} X_{\mathbf{k}ij}}{p \cdot n_{T_1 \ldots T_m}} = \frac{\sum_{i}^{P_{T_1 \ldots T_m}} p \cdot T_{\mathbf{k}}}{p \cdot n_{T_1 \ldots T_m}} = T_{\mathbf{k}}.$$

Thus,

[8.22-**k**] (**k** = **1**, . . . , **m**)

$$\dot{\mathbf{X}}_{\mathbf{k}(\mathbf{T_1} \ldots \mathbf{T_m})} = \mathrm{M}_{\mathbf{X_k} | \mathbf{T_1} \ldots \mathbf{T_m}} = \mathbf{T_k},$$

[8.23-**k**] (**k** = **1**, . . . , **m**)

$$\mathbf{e}_{\mathbf{X_k} \cdot \mathbf{T_1} \ldots \mathbf{T_m}} = \mathbf{e}_{\mathbf{X_k} | \mathbf{T_1} \ldots \mathbf{T_m}} = \mathbf{E_k},$$

which say that the true-score component, $\mathbf{T_k}$, of potential observed scores on item $\mathbf{X_k}$ is identical with both the linear and the curvilinear multiple regression of $\mathbf{X_k}$ upon $\mathbf{T_1}, \ldots, \mathbf{T_m}$, while $\mathbf{E_k}$ is the residual of $\mathbf{X_k}$ left by these regressions. Consequently, from [4.87],

[8.24-**k**] (**k** = **1**, . . . , **m**) $$M_{\mathbf{E_k}} = 0 ,$$

[8.25-**hk**] (**h**,**k** = **1**, . . . , **m**) $$\mathrm{Cov}(\mathbf{T_h}, \mathbf{E_k}) = 0 ,$$

and our present partition of potential observed scores on test items $\mathbf{X_1}, \ldots, \mathbf{X_m}$ into true scores and measurement errors is seen to yield the basic reliability equations ([8.4]–[8.6]) set forth at the beginning of this chapter.

The Dispositional Interpretation of "True Scores": A Review. An individual's score on a test is customarily interpreted to reveal a "tendency," "propensity," "disposition," or "potential" of that individual to respond one way rather than another to the test situation, this being not the same thing as the subject's manifest test behavior and whose possession does not require that the subject be tested at all. This distinction between test achievement (i.e., test scores actually attained) and test potential is logically inescapable for anyone, no matter how ruthlessly operationistic he may believe himself to be, who concedes that definition of a testing procedure allows us to conceptualize test differences of *some* sort among individuals who have not actually been so tested. When we attempt to characterize the test potential of an individual *i* in terms of the score that *i would* receive if *i were* tested, however, the fact that test scores are influenced not only by the attributes of the testee but also by uncontrolled details of the test circumstances implies that an individual's test potential must be described not as a single test score but as a probability distribution over potential scores. Hence even if individual *i* has, in fact, been tested, his obtained score is only a sample from his distribution of possibilities and cannot reveal all there is to know about his test potential. To represent *i*'s distribution of potential scores on the test by a single "most typical" value, we choose the distribution's arithmetic mean and call it *i*'s "true score" on this test. Then a score actually observed on the test provides an approximation to the subject's true score, but differs from it by an amount called the "error of measurement" for that observation. This intrusion of measurement error between true and observed scores gives rise to the concept of a test's "reliability," which concerns the accuracy with which true scores can be inferred from obtained scores. As the statistical foundation on which an articulated theory of reliability will subsequently be erected, we have observed that the joint probability distribution for observed scores and true scores on a test in any population of potential subjects is such that the unrestricted regression of observed scores upon true scores is identical with the latter, one important consequence of which is that true scores and errors of measurement are linearly uncorrelated.

Alternative Approaches

If much in the preceding remarks about "potential" test scores has seemed a bit mysterious, it is only because we have attempted openly to confront—not to solve, but at least to make our discomfiture explicit—certain fundamental conceptual problems of test theory which lie unrecognizably smothered in the more ornate flourishes of most traditional accounts of reliability. Before proceeding to elaborate upon the basic equations, it is appropriate to touch briefly upon alternative approaches by which reliability theory has been developed. Historically, these have taken three major forms: (*a*) axiomatic theory, (*b*) "parallel forms" (also known as "equivalent forms") theory, and (*c*) "item sampling" theory.[11]

The most ingenuously convenient way to do reliability theory is by the *axiomatic* approach. This is simply to postulate that given a test **X**, there exist components **T** and **E** of **X** which satisfy equations [8.1]–[8.3], or more generally that given a set of tests $\mathbf{X}_1, \ldots, \mathbf{X}_n$, these have true-score and measurement-error components which behave according to equations [8.4]–[8.6]. (Additional postulates are also sometimes adopted for special purposes.) The strain of trying to clarify what "true scores" may be is held to a minimum, for in axiomatic theories (whether of reliability or of other matters) the postulated entities are said to be "implicitly defined" by the postulates. Thus for axiomatic reliability theory, "true scores" are whatever satisfy the conditions demanded of true scores by the reliability equations. It may be protested, however, that this is having it *too* easy. As observed earlier (p. 376), there are innumerably many ways in which the basic reliability equations can be satisfied, whereas the distinctive empirical applications which are in fact made of reliability theory reveal that the concept of "reliability" intends not just a set of abstract formal relations, but carries a specific substantive interpretation. A bare axiomatic approach is thus deficient in leaving the substantive aspects of the theory wholly to intuition, and in providing no rationale by which the theory's *de facto* applications are justified. A further criticism which applies not merely to axiomatic reliability but to all traditional versions is that it makes no explicit provision for individuals who have not actually received a score on the test. If the theory is thought to apply in some sense to untested individuals as well as to the fortunate tested few, then the notion of an individual's distribution of potential test scores must be

[11] A comprehensive exposition of axiomatic and parallel-form arguments may be found in Gulliksen (36), which contains the most extensive coverage of reliability theory currently available in a single source. Item-sampling theory has been developed in some detail by Lord (54) and Cronbach, *et al.* (22), while a hybrid between item-sampling and parallel-forms approaches sometimes known as "rationally equivalent forms" is vigorously championed in preference to other approaches by Tryon (80).

introduced. But the latter notion suffices to generate the desired reliability concepts and equations, while additional hypotheses or constructions to secure these same results are then only so much dead weight.

In the *parallel forms* or *equivalent forms* versions of reliability theory, it is assumed that we have a large number of tests $\mathbf{X_1}, \ldots, \mathbf{X_n}$, all of which have equal means, standard deviations, and intercorrelations—i.e., that $M_{\mathbf{X_i}} = M$, $\sigma_{\mathbf{X_i}} = s$, and $r_{\mathbf{X_i X_j}} = r(\mathbf{i,j} = \mathbf{1}, \ldots, \mathbf{n}; \mathbf{i} \neq \mathbf{j})$ for some constants M, s, and r. A set of tests satisfying these requirements are said to be "equivalent" or "parallel" forms,[12] the (questionable) thought behind this phrase being that any one test in a set of parallel forms is interchangeable for most purposes with any other. An individual i's "true score" on each test in a set of parallel forms is defined as the limiting value reached by the average of i's scores across all $\mathbf{n}$ forms—i.e.,

$$T_i = \frac{\sum_{\mathbf{j}=1}^{\mathbf{n}} X_{\mathbf{j}i}}{\mathbf{n}}$$

as $\mathbf{n}$ grows indefinitely large—while the measurement error for i on form $\mathbf{X_j}$ is the difference between X_i and T_i. The most objectionable feature to this approach is its heavy-handed reliance on fictitious entities. In practice, we seldom if ever encounter a set of tests which even approximates the parallel-forms strictures, while in any event we wish to be able to consider the reliability of a single test without presupposing that it has many parallel forms. Application of the parallel-forms argument is wholly hypothetical: It says that to develop reliability theory for an extant test **X** let us proceed *as though* **X** were just one of a number of parallel forms. But not only does this raise the problem of test scores for untested individuals with a vengeance (What score would individual i have received had i taken imaginary test **X**?), it also fails abjectly to define a unique true-score component for **X**. For there are innumerably many different sets of parallel forms which might include a given test, and to hypothesize that parallel forms might in principle be found for test **X** does not specify which factorial component of **X** is to be the basis for the construction.[13]

The *item sampling* version of reliability theory assumes that the test whose reliability is being assessed is a composite of number of items which have been drawn more or less at random from a large domain of

---

[12] Cureton (23) has proposed that tests meeting these conditions be called "equivalent forms" and that a weaker definition be adopted for "parallel forms."

[13] The reader who has studied Chapter 6 will readily see by choosing r for all communalities that a set of parallel forms contains a single common factor, this being the "true-score" variable (or at least a linear transformation thereof) defined by the set. Thus to hypothesize that a given test **X** might be developed into a set of parallel forms is merely to speculate that **X** may contain some unspecified component such that a set of tests may be imagined having only this component in common.

items. An individual *i*'s "true score" on the test is defined as the composite score that would be expected for *i* on this number of items randomly drawn from the sampled domain. This approach to test reliability is a close kin to the concept of "content validity" (see pp. 197 ff.), and in fact there is little difference between the composite criterion envisioned by the theory of content validity and an item-sampling true score. The item-sampling approach is rather powerful mathematically in the inferences it allows to be drawn from the statistical properties of the individual items on the test, since the distribution of an individual's scores on the constituent items may be taken as a sampling approximation to his distribution of scores over the entire domain. Mathematical potency is something which can be achieved only at the expense of postulational risk, however, and how legitimate the sampling assumptions are in any given application is always questionable. Further limitations of this approach are its failure to provide a satisfactory definition for the reliability of noncomposite tests or single items, and the difficulties which arise in attempting to specify the domain of which the test items are to be regarded as a sample. And of course the item-sampling consideration of individual probability distributions for the score a given subject *would* receive on a sample of items selected randomly from the test domain makes an even more extensive and problematic commitment to dispositional probabilities than the approach advocated here.

The Accuracy of Test Observations: The Reliability Index and the Reliability Coefficient

The linear correlation, r_{XT}, between (potential) observed scores and true scores on a test **X** in a population P is known as the *reliability index* for test **X** in population P. Since an immediate consequence of [8.1] and [8.3] by principle [4.36] is that

[8.26] $$\mathrm{Cov}(\mathbf{X}, \mathbf{T}) = \mathrm{Var}(\mathbf{T}) ,$$

the correlation index is seen to be

[8.27] $$r_{XT} = \frac{\mathrm{Cov}(\mathbf{X},\mathbf{T})}{\sigma_X \sigma_T} = \frac{\sigma_T^2}{\sigma_X \sigma_T} = \frac{\sigma_T}{\sigma_X} ,$$

a result which may also be obtained directly from [8.13] by [4.79]. To make clear how errors of measurement affect the reliability index, we may substitute

$$\sigma^2_{\mathbf{X}} = \sigma^2_{\mathbf{T}} + \sigma^2_{\mathbf{E}} \qquad [8.28]$$

(from [8.1] and [8.3] by [4.40] or from [8.13] by [4.80]) into [8.27] to obtain

$$r_{\mathbf{XT}} = \sqrt{\frac{\sigma^2_{\mathbf{T}}}{\sigma^2_{\mathbf{T}} + \sigma^2_{\mathbf{E}}}} \qquad [8.29]$$

While the reliability index crisply states the correlational accuracy with which true scores on text **X** can be linearly[14] predicted from observed scores, however, nothing in our reliability equations so far do a thing to suggest how we might attach a numerical value to this statistic for an actual test. No matter how urgently our test concepts plead for a distinction between true scores and observed scores, the theory of reliability must remain otiose until the apportionment of observed test variance between true-score and measurement-error components can be rooted in quantitative empirical data of some sort. Thus it is comforting to recall that our reflections on reliability did, in fact, begin with a distinctive and important empirical phenomenon, namely, intrasubject consistency under repeated testing. To appreciate the relevance of reliability theory for the interpretation of repeated measurements, let us begin with an idealized case. Suppose, contrary to literal possibility, that each individual i in population P were to be tested twice under different selections of detailed test circumstances which count as instances of test procedure **X**. (The reason why this is literally impossible is that we have defined an "individual" to be a particular person or object at a particular moment in time, so that the two testings would have to occur simultaneously. To avoid this logical complication, we may suppose that each individual i is actually a pair of identical individuals i and i', perhaps the same person at two moments from an interval of time during which he undergoes no changes relevant to his test potential.) Letting one of the two observed scores for individual i be labeled $X_{\mathbf{a}i}$ and the other $X_{\mathbf{b}i}$, we then have two observed-score variables $\mathbf{X_a}$ and $\mathbf{X_b}$ over population P together with the true-score-on-**X** variable **T** and corresponding measurement-error variables $\mathbf{E_a}$ $(=_{\text{def}} \mathbf{X_a} - \mathbf{T})$ and $\mathbf{E_b}$ $(=_{\text{def}} \mathbf{X_b} - \mathbf{T})$. Without any

[14] Note that while [8.13] asserts that the regression of **X** upon **T** is perfectly linear, the converse is not necessarily true. Hence it is possible that linear estimation of true scores from observed scores is not the optimal prediction policy. Even so, the linearity of $M_{\mathbf{X}|\mathbf{T}}$ makes a serious departure of $M_{\mathbf{T}|\mathbf{X}}$ from linearity extremely unlikely if $r_{\mathbf{XT}}$ is appreciable.

consideration of the special connection between the two sets of observed scores $\mathbf{X_a}$ and $\mathbf{X_b}$ we can write

[8.30]

$$\begin{aligned} r_{\mathbf{X_a X_b}} &= \frac{\mathrm{Cov}(\mathbf{X_a}, \mathbf{X_b})}{\sigma_{\mathbf{X_a}} \sigma_{\mathbf{X_b}}} \\ &= \frac{\mathrm{Cov}(\mathbf{T} + \mathbf{E_a}, \mathbf{T} + \mathbf{E_b})}{\sigma_{\mathbf{X_a}} \sigma_{\mathbf{X_b}}} \\ &= \frac{\mathrm{Var}(\mathbf{T}) + \mathrm{Cov}(\mathbf{T}, \mathbf{E_a}) + \mathrm{Cov}(\mathbf{T}, \mathbf{E_b}) + \mathrm{Cov}(\mathbf{E_a}, \mathbf{E_b})}{\sigma_{\mathbf{X_a}} \sigma_{\mathbf{X_b}}} . \end{aligned}$$

Now the measurement error $E_{\mathbf{a}i}$ for each tested individual i is a sample drawn from the probability distribution of $\mathbf{E}$ for i, the expected value of which is zero for each i. It is difficult to think of a sampling procedure which would make the measurement errors $\mathbf{E_a}$ actually obtained vary systematically with the true scores of the tested individuals. Hence $\mathrm{Cov}(\mathbf{T}, \mathbf{E_a})$, and similarly $\mathrm{Cov}(\mathbf{T}, \mathbf{E_b})$, should differ from zero only negligibly if the number of individuals tested is sufficiently large, in which case [8.30] reduces to

$$[8.31] \qquad r_{\mathbf{X_a X_b}} = \frac{\mathrm{Var}(\mathbf{T}) + \mathrm{Cov}(\mathbf{E_a}, \mathbf{E_b})}{\sigma_{\mathbf{X_a}} \sigma_{\mathbf{X_b}}} \qquad (r_{\mathbf{TE_a}} = r_{\mathbf{TE_b}} = 0) ,$$

or using [8.27]

$$[8.32] \quad r_{\mathbf{X_a X_b}} = \left(\frac{\sigma_{\mathbf{X}}}{\sigma_{\mathbf{X_a}}}\right)\left(\frac{\sigma_{\mathbf{X}}}{\sigma_{\mathbf{X_b}}}\right) r^2_{\mathbf{XT}} + \left(\frac{\sigma_{\mathbf{E_a}}}{\sigma_{\mathbf{X_a}}}\right)\left(\frac{\sigma_{\mathbf{E_b}}}{\sigma_{\mathbf{X_b}}}\right) r_{\mathbf{E_a E_b}} \qquad (r_{\mathbf{TE_a}} = r_{\mathbf{TE_b}} = 0) .$$

Consequently, if the test observations $\mathbf{X_a}$ and $\mathbf{X_b}$ have sampled the full range of variation in the uncontrolled test-circumstance details leading to measurement error, so that $\sigma_{\mathbf{E_a}} = \sigma_{\mathbf{E_b}} = \sigma_{\mathbf{E}}$ and hence $\sigma_{\mathbf{X_a}} = \sigma_{\mathbf{X_b}} = \sigma_{\mathbf{X}}$, and if moreover the uncontrolled details of the test circumstances are subject-wise unrelated between the two sets of observations so that $r_{\mathbf{E_a E_b}} = 0$, then [8.32] becomes simply

$$[8.33] \qquad r_{\mathbf{X_a X_b}} = r^2_{\mathbf{XT}} \qquad \begin{pmatrix} r_{\mathbf{E_a E_b}} = r_{\mathbf{TE_a}} = r_{\mathbf{TE_b}} = 0 , \\ \sigma_{\mathbf{X_a}} = \sigma_{\mathbf{X_b}} = \sigma_{\mathbf{X}} \end{pmatrix} .$$

Let two sets of test scores $X_{\mathbf{a}1}, \ldots, X_{\mathbf{a}i}, \ldots, X_{\mathbf{a}n}$ and $X_{\mathbf{b}1}, \ldots, X_{\mathbf{b}i}, \ldots, X_{\mathbf{b}n}$ obtained by administration of test $\mathbf{X}$ to a sample of individuals from population P be said to be *ideal repetitions* of test $\mathbf{X}$ in population P if the following conditions obtain: (*A*) for each i, the observed scores $X_{\mathbf{a}i}$ and $X_{\mathbf{b}i}$ are obtained by giving test $\mathbf{X}$ to individuals i and i', respectively, where i and i' are a matched pair (e.g., the same person at slightly different moments in time) which have the same probability distribution over potential scores on $\mathbf{X}$; (*B*) the joint frequency distribution of observed scores $\mathbf{X_a}$ and true scores $\mathbf{T}$ on test $\mathbf{X}$ for tested individuals i $(i = 1, \ldots, n)$ differs at most negligibly from the joint probability distribution for $\mathbf{X}$ and $\mathbf{T}$ in population P, and similarly for the joint frequency distribution of $\mathbf{X_b}$ and $\mathbf{T}$; and (C) the linear correlation between the two sets of measurement errors actually obtained is zero—i.e., $r_{\mathbf{E_a E_b}} = 0$, where $E_{\mathbf{a}i} =_{\text{def}} X_{\mathbf{a}i} - T_i$ and $E_{\mathbf{b}i} =_{\text{def}} X_{\mathbf{b}i} - T_i$ $(i = 1, \ldots, n)$. Then the "reliability coefficient" $r_{\mathbf{X}}$,[15] or simply "the reliability," of test $\mathbf{X}$ in population P may be defined as *the linear correlation between ideal repetitions of test* $\mathbf{X}$ *in population* P. Since condition B in our definition of "ideal repetitions" implies that $\sigma_{\mathbf{T}}$ is the same in the sample of subjects actually tested as it is in population P as a whole, that $\sigma_{\mathbf{X_a}} = \sigma_{\mathbf{X_b}} = \sigma_{\mathbf{X}}$ (where $\sigma_{\mathbf{X}}$ is the SD of the probability distribution over potential observed scores on test $\mathbf{X}$ in population P), and that $r_{\mathbf{TE_a}} = r_{\mathbf{TE_b}} = 0$, it follows that if $\mathbf{X_a}$ and $\mathbf{X_b}$ are ideal repetitions of test $\mathbf{X}$, they satisfy the conditions presumed by equation [8.33] and hence

$$[8.34] \qquad r_{\mathbf{X}} = r^2_{\mathbf{XT}} \,,$$

which may be taken as the mathematical definition of $r_{\mathbf{X}}$. That is, *a test's reliability coefficient equals the square of its reliability index*, or otherwise put, the correlation between ideal repetitions of test $\mathbf{X}$ in a population P equals the square of the correlation between potential observed scores and true scores on test $\mathbf{X}$ in P. From [8.34] and [8.27] we also have

$$[8.35] \qquad r_{\mathbf{X}} = \frac{\sigma^2_{\mathbf{T}}}{\sigma^2_{\mathbf{X}}} = \frac{\sigma^2_{\mathbf{T}}}{\sigma^2_{\mathbf{T}} + \sigma^2_{\mathbf{E}}} \,,$$

so *a test's reliability (i.e., reliability coefficient) is the proportion of the test's observed-score variance which is contributed by the variance in true scores on the test.*[16] It is the reliability coefficient which prepares reliability theory for intercourse with empirical data, for while we can never realistically expect to obtain repetitive test observations which are *exactly* ideal, it is not

[15] Since notation for the reliability coefficient is not fully standardized, we here adopt the convention that the correlation symbol "r" with a *single* subscript designates the reliability coefficient of the test indicated by the subscript. A frequently used alternative notation for $r_{\mathbf{X}}$ is "$r_{\mathbf{XX}}$." However, this makes for confusion with a variable's self-correlation (i.e., unity), a complication which becomes notationally serious when the intercorrelations within a set of variables are examined analytically.

[16] It may be observed from [8.27] and [8.35] that the reliability *index*, $r_{\mathbf{XT}}$, for test $\mathbf{X}$ is the ratio of the standard deviation of true scores to the standard deviation of observed scores on the test, while the test's reliability *coefficient*, $r_{\mathbf{X}}$, is the corresponding ratio of variances. Cureton (23) has proposed that this distinction between the terms "index" and "coefficient" by systematically generalized, so that statistics which analyze as ratios of standard deviations are to be called *indices* while variance ratios are to be called *coefficients*. This usage would entail that the correlation, $r_{\mathbf{XY}}$, between two variables would have to be renamed the "correlation index," while $r^2_{\mathbf{XY}}$ would then become the correlation "coefficient."

unreasonable to hope that perhaps we can at least obtain estimates of the test's reliability through repetitions which are approximately so.

Empirical Approximations to Reliability

Historically, there have emerged four major procedures for empirical estimation of test reliability: (1) test-retest correlation, (2) alternate (equivalent, parallel) form correlation, (3) the split-halves method, and (4) internal consistency measures, of which (3) turns out to be a special case. These correspond rather interestingly to a conceptual evolution in which the primitive notion of "true score" passes over into a factorial hypothesis until in the higher reaches of internal-consistency theory, factor-analytic and reliability considerations are inextricably fused.

As the name implies, the test-retest method for ascertaining a test's reliability is literally to give the test twice to each subject in a (hopefully) representative sample drawn from the population of interest, and to compute the correlation between the two sets of observed scores. This procedure clearly corresponds as closely as is practically possible to the definition of reliability as ideal repetitive consistency, and for tests on which a subject's probability distribution over potential test scores is not likely to be appreciably modified either by the testing operation itself or by the passage of events during the test-retest interval, it has no peer. Most tests of elementary physical properties—height, weight, electrical resistance (in inorganic objects), elasticity (ditto), etc.—appear to qualify in this regard,[17] and for this reason the physical sciences are usually able to assess the reliability of their test procedures to a high degree of precision. Even for repeated measurements $\mathbf{X_a}$ and $\mathbf{X_b}$ which meet condition *A* stipulated above (p. 395 f.) for ideal repetitions, however, conditions *B* and *C* demand a certain wariness. So long as the number of tested subjects is reasonably large, there is probably little danger that measurement errors will be appreciably correlated with true scores. On the other hand, if the conditions under which the various subjects are tested on either occasion do not adequately sample the uncontrolled test-circumstance details, then the error variance in the observed sample of test scores will be less than the variance of the probability distribution over potential values of **E**, and $\sigma_{\mathbf{X_a}}\sigma_{\mathbf{X_b}}$ will be less than $\sigma^2_{\mathbf{X}}$ in [8.32]. For example, if readings on a certain weighing scale vary somewhat with the ambient air temperature (due, say, to differential thermal expansion in parts of its mechanism) while standardization of temperature is not included in the definition of the weighing procedure with this scale, then a test-retest assessment of the scale's reliability in which all subjects in the study were weighed on each occasion in such rapid succession that the ambient air temperature did not have time to change from one subject to another would fail to include in $\mathbf{X_a}$ and $\mathbf{X_b}$ the variability in **X** due

[17] At least this seems to be true of macroscopic physical properties. The subatomic physicist has a different story to tell.

to uncontrolled temperature fluctuations. Further, the repetition ideal of uncorrelated measurement errors is far from a practical certainty. Quite the contrary: If the two test observations for each subject are taken close together in time, then it is altogether possible that some of the particular test-circumstance details which were responsible for a subject's measurement error on the first testing will be present on the second test-occasion as well, thereby inducing a positive correlation between $\mathbf{E_a}$ and $\mathbf{E_b}$. Thus in our weighing-scale example, if the uncontrolled variation in ambient air temperature were adequately sampled by distributing the weighings of different subjects throughout an extended period of time, but the test-retest observations on each subject were made in immediate succession (i.e., as soon as the subject dismounts from the scale after his first weighing, he hops back up for his second try), whatever deviation of $X_{\mathbf{a}i}$ from T_i resulted from the particular air temperature under which this reading was obtained would persist in the deviation of $X_{\mathbf{b}i}$ from T_i as well. From [8.32], we see that if $\sigma_{\mathbf{X_a}}$ or $\sigma_{\mathbf{X_b}}$ underestimates $\sigma_{\mathbf{X}}$, or if $r_{\mathbf{E_a E_b}}$ is positive, $r_{\mathbf{X_a X_b}}$ will exceed $r_{\mathbf{X}}$. Hence failure to allow sufficient variation in the uncontrolled test circumstances either between subjects or within subjects (i.e., between successive observations on the same subject) will dispose an empirical test-retest correlation to overestimate the test's reliability.

For many tests, moreover, especially in the behavioral sciences, the accuracy with which a test's reliability can be determined by test-retest procedures is seriously complicated by the fact that it *cannot* reasonably be assumed that a subject's distribution of potential scores on the test is unaffected by the first testing operation—i.e., that there are no "practice effects." Just the opposite: It is well known that practice effects, frequently large ones, are the rule for psychological tests rather than the exception. Since the nature of such effects is a rather complicated business around which has burgeoned an extensive body of data and theory,[18] we shall not elaborate on this point except for the commonsense observation that on tests involving a cognitive factor, the subject's memory of his previous test responses will almost certainly modify his retest performance in ways dependent upon the type of test (e.g., of intelligence, personality dimensions, sensory acuity, perceptual reactions, etc.) but in each case readily envisioned by the reader. To be sure, the effect of prior test experience tends to dissipate with the passage of time. However, the longer the interval between test and retest, the more certain it also becomes that intervening events will have produced some change in the subject's test potential. Thus whether the test-retest interval be made short or long, it may well prove impossible, for a particular test in whose reliability we are interested, to work out a test-retest procedure which satisfactorily approximates condition *A* (p. 395) for ideal repe-

[18] Namely, learning theory.

titions. In this case, we should look upon test and retest as two different testing procedures, one of which includes in its defining conditions that the subject has *not* been previously so tested while prior test exposure is a prerequisite of the other, and which may differ to a greater or lesser extent both in their reliabilities and in their true-score components. (Thus a problem-solving test might assess a subject's reasoning ability upon its first application, but upon repetition become primarily a test of memory.) But then equations [8.30]–[8.33] no longer apply to the test-retest correlation; instead, the problem has become that of inferring something about a test's reliability from its correlation with another test.

In a thoughtful comparison of different conceptions of reliability and measurement error, Cronbach (17) has proposed that the test-retest correlation for a particular interval t of elapsed time between test and retest be called the test's "coefficient of stability" for that interval. This useful concept (which might better be phrased the "stability function" to make clear its dependence on t) gives explicit recognition to the modifications which occur in a testable attribute through the passage of time, and calls attention to the need for distinguishing between intrasubject variation in test scores due to changes in the tested attribute itself (i.e., the temporal instability of true scores) and variation due to uncontrolled test-circumstance details (i.e., the unreliability of observed scores at a given moment in time). It should be noted, though, that the interpretation of empirical test-retest correlations in terms of true-score stability involves several complications. For one, the computed correlation reflects observed-score unreliability as well as changes in true scores (see equation [8.38], below). Secondly, as discussed previously (pp. 131 f.), a correlation coefficient cannot assess change as such, but only the degree to which the altered values of the variable fail to be a linear transformation of their initial values. Finally, subjects in a test-retest study have necessarily had their retest true-scores exposed to modification through prior experience on the test, so the computed stability coefficient need not reveal the stability of true scores among the vastly larger number of potential subjects who have not been tested. (It can however, be argued that an empirical stability coefficient is generally a lower bound to what it would be could practice effects be partialled out.)

To evade—or rather, to try to evade—the difficulties in test-score interpretation which arise for subjects who have had prior experience with the test, psychometricians frequently resort to use of *alternate forms* of the test. The concept of "alternate forms" is readily comprehended from specific examples, but is surprisingly troublesome to define abstractly. Perhaps we can say that a test $\mathbf{X}$ comes in $\mathbf{m}$ alternate forms when it is defined $\mathbf{m}$-disjunctively—i.e., its definition states that an event counts as an application of test $\mathbf{X}$ if the testee is treated in fashion $\mathbf{F_1}$, or in fashion $\mathbf{F_2}$, or . . . , or in fashion $\mathbf{F_m}$, where each specific "fashion" or "alternate form" of treatment could if desired be regarded as a distinctive test procedure in its own right. In psychological testing, alternate forms of a test usually consist of options among test-stimulus materials. Thus intelligence tests frequently specify two or more alternative sets of test problems, leaving it to the discretion of the test administrator which set is to be given to any particular subject. Similarly, an optometrist who has two different eye charts which he uses interchangeably is, in effect, employing an alternate-form test of visual acuity. Although in principle there need be no similarity among the various disjuncts of an alternate-form test, considerable standardization effort is normally expended in practice to make equal scores on the various forms also equivalent in interpretation as well. Ideally, alternate forms of a test would be such that each individual to whom the test might be applied has the same distribution of potential scores on each form[19] while at the same time the specific content differs sufficiently from one form to another that a subject's previous experience with one has little or no influence on his distribution of potential scores on the others. Consequently, testing subjects first on one and then on another ideal alternate form of a test **X** satisfies condition *A* for ideal repetitions (see p. 395) of **X** (at least if the interval between testings is insufficient to allow appreciable changes in a subject's test potential), and so long as care is taken to approximate ideal repetition conditions *B* and *C*, the correlation between observed scores on two ideal alternate forms of a test will then approximate the test's reliability.

As the reader must already have reflexively surmised, however, test reliability estimated from the actual empirical correlation between alternate forms of a test is of no greater guaranteed accuracy than is the estimate obtained by test-retest correlation using a single form. For one, it cannot be trusted that a subject's experience on one form of the test makes no difference for his subsequent potential on another. While the cross-form practice effect is not generally as large as the same-form effect, it is apt to be present in some degree just the same. To be sure, it is perhaps questionable whether a small cross-form practice effect is anything to fret about.[20] However, another doubt which always looms large

[19] If test **X** consists of alternate forms $\mathbf{X}_1, \ldots, \mathbf{X}_m$, then the true score T_i of individual i on test **X** is a weighted average of his true scores $T_{1i}, \ldots, T_{mi}$ on the alternate forms. There is no logical requirement that $T_{1i}, \ldots, T_{mi}$ be all equal for each i, but to the extent that this is not so, the test-form alternatives contribute additional variance to the distribution of potential scores on **X** for i and hence decrease the test's reliability.

[20] The most obvious manifestations of practice effects are in fact irrelevant to reliability estimation, though not to the interpretation of test scores for individual subjects. Empirically, we recognize practice effects of form $\mathbf{X}_1$ upon form $\mathbf{X}_2$ (or of $\mathbf{X}_1$ upon a repetition of $\mathbf{X}_1$) by comparing scores on $\mathbf{X}_2$ made by a group of subjects who have taken $\mathbf{X}_1$ previously with the scores made by control subjects who have not taken $\mathbf{X}_1$. Practice effects due to experience with $\mathbf{X}_1$ are then manifested if the means and perhaps SDs on $\mathbf{X}_2$ in the two groups show greater discrepancies than can plausibly be ascribed to chance. But to the extent that practice on form $\mathbf{X}_1$ merely works a linear transformation on true $\mathbf{X}_2$-scores (which would suffice to bring about a shift in mean and/or standard deviation of observed $\mathbf{X}_2$-scores), the correlation between scores on form $\mathbf{X}_1$ and subsequent scores on form $\mathbf{X}_2$ will be the same as it would be were there no practice effect at all.

concerns the extent to which alternate forms really are altogether equivalent in the sense of each prospective subject's having the same distribution of potential scores on all forms. What happens to alternate-forms reliability estimates when this equivalence is violated will not be discussed here, since this would require attention to some tricky but not overly important niceties in the logic of alternate-form tests. Instead, we may observe that the distinction between, on the one hand, a single test **X** which comes in **m** alternate forms, and on the other, a set of **m** different tests $\mathbf{X}_1, \ldots, \mathbf{X}_m$ corresponding to the alternate forms of **X**, is a distinction so fine as to be almost nonexistent.[21] In practice, alternate forms are almost always treated as different tests, albeit hopefully as ones with the same true-score component, and so again (see p. 399), this time more conspicuously, our original concept of "reliability" as a measure of a test's repetitive consistency becomes driven under the press of empirical estimation procedures toward reanalysis in terms of between-test correlations. We shall defer serious mathematical exploration of this development until later, but since the applicability of equations [8.30]–[8.33] is becoming increasingly remote as we proceed, it is time to examine the connection between a test's reliability and its correlation with another test.

Let $\mathbf{X}_1$ and $\mathbf{X}_2$ be two tests such that it is possible to obtain scores on both for a sample of individuals from a population P, and let it also be assumed that this sample is large and representative enough that the joint frequency distribution of observed and true scores on $\mathbf{X}_1$ and $\mathbf{X}_2$ in the sample differs at most negligibly from the joint probability distribution over potential observed scores and true scores on $\mathbf{X}_1$ and $\mathbf{X}_2$ in P.[22] (This approximation of sample frequencies to dispositional probabilities will be henceforth assumed in all subsequent formulas without further mention.) Then equations [8.4]–[8.6] with $\mathbf{n} = 2$ hold for the observed scores on $\mathbf{X}_1$ and $\mathbf{X}_2$, and the observed covariance between $\mathbf{X}_1$ and $\mathbf{X}_2$ is

$$[8.36] \qquad \begin{aligned} \mathrm{Cov}(\mathbf{X}_1, \mathbf{X}_2) &= \mathrm{Cov}(\mathbf{T}_1 + \mathbf{E}_1, \mathbf{T}_2 + \mathbf{E}_2) \\ &= \mathrm{Cov}(\mathbf{T}_1, \mathbf{T}_2) + \mathrm{Cov}(\mathbf{E}_1, \mathbf{E}_2) \\ &= \sigma_{\mathbf{T}_1}\sigma_{\mathbf{T}_2}r_{\mathbf{T}_1\mathbf{T}_2} + \sigma_{\mathbf{E}_1}\sigma_{\mathbf{E}_2}r_{\mathbf{E}_1\mathbf{E}_2}. \end{aligned}$$

[21] In brief, the difference lies in whether or not when recording and interpreting an observed score on **X** we keep track of the particular form on which it was obtained. If we do, then we are in practice treating the different forms as separate tests.

[22] These assumptions are straightforward enough if tests $\mathbf{X}_1$ and $\mathbf{X}_2$ are defined as two dimensions of a joint testing procedure—e.g., if the definition of test $\mathbf{X}_2$ stipulates that it is to be administered after the subject has taken $\mathbf{X}_1$. On the other hand, if $\mathbf{X}_1$ and $\mathbf{X}_2$ are defined in such fashion that neither presupposes prior or coincident administration of the other, then joint-distribution theory for $\mathbf{X}_1$ and $\mathbf{X}_2$ gets into some rather esoteric logical complexities which will not be discussed here but which are not wholly without issue if experience with the one test makes a difference for a subject's potential performance on the other.

Hence in view of [8.35] and [8.28], the observed correlation between $\mathbf{X_1}$ and $\mathbf{X_2}$ in a representative sample from P is

[8.37]

$$\begin{aligned}
r_{X_1 X_2} &= \frac{\text{Cov}(\mathbf{X_1}, \mathbf{X_2})}{\sigma_{X_1}\sigma_{X_2}} \\
&= \frac{\sigma_{T_1}\sigma_{T_2}}{\sigma_{X_1}\sigma_{X_2}} r_{T_1 T_2} + \left(\frac{\sqrt{\sigma^2_{X_1} - \sigma^2_{T_1}}}{\sigma_{X_1}}\right)\left(\frac{\sqrt{\sigma^2_{X_2} - \sigma^2_{T_2}}}{\sigma_{X_2}}\right) r_{E_1 E_2} \\
&= r_{T_1 T_2}\sqrt{r_{X_1} r_{X_2}} + r_{E_1 E_2}\sqrt{(1 - r_{X_1})(1 - r_{X_2})}
\end{aligned}$$

If measurement errors on the two tests are uncorrelated, this simplifies to

[8.38] $$r_{X_1 X_2} = r_{T_1 T_2}\sqrt{r_{X_1} r_{X_2}} \qquad (r_{E_1 E_2} = 0) \; ,$$

which states that the observed between-test correlation is the product of the correlation between true scores on the two tests with the geometric mean of the tests' reliabilities. Finally, if true scores on $\mathbf{X_1}$ and $\mathbf{X_2}$ are perfectly correlated – i.e., if tests $\mathbf{X_1}$ and $\mathbf{X_2}$ measure the same true-score variable – and measurement errors contribute the same proportion of variance to $\mathbf{X_1}$ and $\mathbf{X_2}$, [8.38] becomes simply

[8.39] $$r_{X_1 X_2} = r_{X_1} = r_{X_2} \qquad (r_{E_1 E_2} = 0,\ r_{T_1 T_2} = 1,\ r_{X_1} = r_{X_2}) \; .$$

Since the construction of alternate forms of a test usually endeavors to achieve the conditions assumed in [8.39], it follows that the observed correlation between well-constructed alternate forms should approximate the reliability of each form. Moreover, while designing alternate forms with perfectly (or almost perfectly) correlated true-score components is a technical problem of extraordinary difficulty, it follows from [8.38] that even if $\mathbf{X_1}$ and $\mathbf{X_2}$ measure somewhat different true-score dimensions,

[8.40] $$|r_{X_1 X_2}| \leqslant \sqrt{r_{X_1} r_{X_2}} \qquad (r_{E_1 E_2} = 0) \; .$$

Hence the magnitude of correlation between two tests administered under sufficiently different circumstances to warrant an assumption of uncorrelated measurement errors is a lower bound on the geometric mean of the two tests' reliabilities. If there is reason to think that the reliability of test $\mathbf{X_2}$ is equal to or lower than that of test $\mathbf{X_1}$, then it may also be concluded that $r_{X_1} \geqslant \sqrt{r_{X_1} r_{X_2}}$ and $|r_{X_1 X_2}|$ may be taken as a lower bound for r_{X_1}. In any event, $r_{X_2} \leqslant 1$, so from [8.40],

[8.41] $$r_{X_1} \geqslant r^2_{X_1 X_2} \qquad (r_{E_1 E_2} = 0) \; .$$

That is, even if two tests do not satisfy the requirements for ideal alternate forms, their squared correlation is always a lower bound for the reliability of each so long as their measurement errors are unrelated.

The next stage in the evolution of reliability theory is associated with the once popular but now obsolescent[23] *split-halves* procedure for computing test reliability. Whatever advantages may accrue from alternate-forms reliability estimates, a practical complication of the method is the need actually to prepare and administer a second form of the test. Suppose, however, that the test whose reliability interests us is a sum of parts, e.g., as when the test consists of a list of questions and a subject's score on the test is the sum of his scores on the constituent items. Then by grouping these parts into two comparable halves, each of which yields a part-score, we may regard the test as simultaneous administration of two alternate forms, and the correlation between these two halves should then provide information about the reliability of the full test. Specifically, if we assume that the test halves satisfy the conditions stipulated for $\mathbf{X}_1$ and $\mathbf{X}_2$ in [8.39], then the correlation between them equals the reliability of each half. What we want, however, is the reliability of the whole test—i.e., the sum of the halves—so further computations are called for.

It is a basic theorem of probability theory, corresponding to our frequency theorem [4.45], that the expected value of a linear combination of variables, given any particular joint probability distribution for its constituents, is equal to that same linear combination of the expected values of those variables in that distribution. Consequently, if $\mathbf{L_X}$ is a compound testing procedure comprising a number of test items $\mathbf{X}_1, \ldots, \mathbf{X}_n$ such that the score on $\mathbf{L_X}$ for an individual i is defined as a given linear combination of i's scores on $\mathbf{X}_1, \ldots, \mathbf{X}_n$, it follows that i's true score, $T_{\mathbf{L_X}i}$, on $\mathbf{L_X}$ is equal to this same linear combination of i's true scores, $T_{1i}, \ldots, T_{ni}$, on $\mathbf{X}_1, \ldots, \mathbf{X}_n$. That is,

$$[8.42]^{24} \qquad \mathbf{T}_{\mathbf{L_X}} = a_0 + \sum_{i=1}^{n} a_i \mathbf{T}_i \qquad \left(\mathbf{L_X} = a_0 + \sum_{i=1}^{n} a_i \mathbf{X}_i\right).$$

[23] Prematurely so (see p. 455).

[24] To prove this in terms of our frequency approximation to probabilities wherein the joint distribution of potential scores on variables $\mathbf{X}_1, \ldots, \mathbf{X}_n$ for an individual i is conceived as the joint distribution of these variables in a set of potential testing-on-$\mathbf{X}$ events ij ($j = 1, \ldots, p$), observe that i's true score on $\mathbf{L_X}$ is

$$T_{\mathbf{L_X}i} =_{\text{def}} \frac{\sum_{j=1}^{p} L_{\mathbf{X}ij}}{p} = \frac{\sum_{j=1}^{p} (a_0 + a_1 X_{1ij} + \ldots + a_n X_{nij})}{p}$$

$$= a_0 + a_1 \frac{\sum_{j=1}^{p} X_{1ij}}{p} + \ldots + a_n \frac{\sum_{j=1}^{p} X_{nij}}{p} = a_0 + a_1 T_{1i} + \ldots + a_n T_{ni}.$$

In particular, if test **S** is the sum of two halves or "subtests" $\mathbf{X_1}$ and $\mathbf{X_2}$, an individual's true score on the whole test is the sum of his true scores on the two subtests. That is, if

$$\mathbf{S} = \mathbf{X_1} + \mathbf{X_2} \qquad \text{(assumed)}, \tag{8.43}$$

then

$$\mathbf{T_S} = \mathbf{T_1} + \mathbf{T_2} \qquad ([8.43]) \tag{8.44}$$

and the reliability of test **S** is hence

$$\begin{aligned} r_S &= \frac{\mathrm{Var}(\mathbf{T_S})}{\mathrm{Var}(\mathbf{S})} \\ &= \frac{\mathrm{Var}(\mathbf{T_1} + \mathbf{T_2})}{\mathrm{Var}(\mathbf{X_1} + \mathbf{X_2})} \\ &= \frac{\sigma^2_{T_1} + \sigma^2_{T_2} + 2\sigma_{T_1}\sigma_{T_2} r_{T_1T_2}}{\sigma^2_{X_1} + \sigma^2_{X_2} + 2\sigma_{X_1}\sigma_{X_2} r_{X_1X_2}} \qquad ([8.43]) \\ &= \frac{\sigma^2_{X_1} r_{X_1} + \sigma^2_{X_2} r_{X_1} + 2\sigma_{X_1}\sigma_{X_2} r_{T_1T_2}\sqrt{r_{X_1} r_{X_2}}}{\sigma^2_{X_1} + \sigma^2_{X_2} + 2\,\sigma_{X_1}\sigma_{X_2} r_{X_1X_2}}, \end{aligned} \tag{8.45}$$

since by [8.35], $\sigma_{T_i} = \sigma_{X_i}\sqrt{r_{X_i}}$. If the two subtests have equal variances, this simplifies to

$$r_S = \frac{r_{X_1} + r_{X_2} + 2r_{T_1T_2}\sqrt{r_{X_1} r_{X_2}}}{2 + 2\,r_{X_1X_2}} \qquad ([8.43],\ \sigma_{X_1} = \sigma_{X_2}). \tag{8.46}$$

Suppose further that the two subtests $\mathbf{X_1}$ and $\mathbf{X_2}$ measure the same true-score variable (i.e., that $r_{T_1T_2} = 1$), that their reliabilities are equal, and that their measurement errors are uncorrelated. Then $r_{X_1} = r_{X_2} = r_{X_1X_2}$ by [8.39], and [8.46] further reduces to

$$r_S = \frac{2\,r_{X_1X_2}}{1 + r_{X_1X_2}} \qquad \left(\begin{matrix}[8.43],\ \sigma_{X_1} = \sigma_{X_2},\ r_{X_1} = r_{X_2}, \\ r_{T_1T_2} = 1,\ r_{E_1E_2} = 0.\end{matrix}\right) \tag{8.47}$$

Equation [8.47] is known as the "Spearman-Brown" formula for split-half reliability. It states that if scores on a test **S** can be analyzed as the sum of scores on two equivalent halves $\mathbf{X_1}$ and $\mathbf{X_2}$ – i.e., $\mathbf{X_1}$ and $\mathbf{X_2}$ have equal variances, equal reliabilities, and perfectly correlated true scores – and measurement errors on the two halves are unrelated, then the reliability of the full test can be computed as shown from the correlation between the halves.

Various alternatives to formula [8.47] have been devised for split-half reliability estimation, some being mathematically equivalent to

[8.47] while others are slightly less demanding of subtest equivalence.[25] One of these which is particularly worthy of mention as the simplest instance of an important relationship which we shall later explore in considerable generality is

$$[8.48] \qquad r_{\mathbf{S}} = 2\left(1 - \frac{\sigma^2_{\mathbf{X}_1} + \sigma^2_{\mathbf{X}_2}}{\sigma^2_{\mathbf{S}}}\right) \qquad \left(\begin{array}{c}[8.43],\ \sigma_{\mathbf{T}_1} = \sigma_{\mathbf{T}_2},\\ r_{\mathbf{T}_1\mathbf{T}_2} = 1,\ r_{\mathbf{E}_1\mathbf{E}_2} = 0\end{array}\right)$$

which the reader may derive either by substitution of the stipulated conditions into [8.36] and the second line of [8.45] and combining, or by setting **n** = **2** in [8.68], below. Formula [8.48] computes the reliability of test **S** from a comparison of **S**'s variance to the summed variances of the two halves. It will be observed that [8.48] is mathematically equivalent to

$$[8.49]^{26} \qquad r_{\mathbf{S}} = \frac{4\sigma_{\mathbf{X}_1}\sigma_{\mathbf{X}_2}r_{\mathbf{X}_1\mathbf{X}_2}}{\sigma^2_{\mathbf{S}}} \qquad \left(\begin{array}{c}[8.43],\ \sigma_{\mathbf{T}_1} = \sigma_{\mathbf{T}_2},\\ r_{\mathbf{T}_1\mathbf{T}_2} = 1,\ r_{\mathbf{E}_1\mathbf{E}_2} = 0\end{array}\right)$$

which makes clear that like formula [8.47], the reliability computed for test **S** by formula [8.48] is determined substantially by the correlational agreement between the two test halves. The assumptions of [8.48] are weaker than those of [8.47] in that while both require that $\sigma_{\mathbf{T}_1} = \sigma_{\mathbf{T}_2}$ (which follows for [8.47] from its stipulation of equal subtest SDs and reliabilities), [8.48] allows the subtests to have unequal standard deviations. It will be seen later that an additional virtue of formula [8.48] is that so long as measurement errors on the two subtests remain uncorrelated, the value it computes for $r_{\mathbf{S}}$ is a lower bound on the correct value no matter how true scores on the two test halves are related.

In addition to computational procedures, other topics which have been prominent in the voluminous literature on split-half reliability are (*a*) what split to choose when the test is composed of many items which can be dichotomized in numerous different ways, and (*b*) the method's inapplicability to "speeded" tests—i.e., tests where the time a subject spends on one test item makes a difference for how much time he has available to work on another.[27] The how-to-split issue is a practical detail which need not detain us here. Later, though, it will be shown (pp. 451 ff.) that the optimal split is the one which maximizes the covariance between the two test halves, and that this split used with formula [8.48] is probably the most powerful of all reliability-estimation procedures based on a test's internal statistics. Discussion of the unsuitability of split-half reliability estimates for speeded tests will also be deferred until later (pp. 437 f.), since this is merely one of many ways in which the rather unrealistic assumption of uncorrelated measurement errors on the two halves may be violated.

[25] See Cronbach (18) for a summary of the major variants.

[26] Since $\sigma^2_{\mathbf{S}} = \sigma^2_{\mathbf{X}_1} + \sigma^2_{\mathbf{X}_2} + 2\sigma_{\mathbf{X}_1}\sigma_{\mathbf{X}_2}r_{\mathbf{X}_1\mathbf{X}_2}$.

[27] See Gulliksen (36, chaps. 15 and 17) for discussion of these and related matters.

Actually, split-half reliability procedures constitute but the opening scene in the latest act of reliability theory's unfolding drama. It will be recalled that split-half reliability estimates may just as well be described as measures of between-halves similarity. But if the test is in actuality a composite of not just two subtests but of a considerably larger number, **n**, of items, so that before split-half formulas can be applied it is necessary to select one of the many alternative ways in which the items can be sorted into two groups, why should we not be able to extend the split-halves rationale to derive split-**n**ths reliability formulas which bypass the grouping problem? That is, if a test's reliability can be judged from the consistency of its parts when dichotomized, it becomes apparent that split-half formulas should be merely special instances of more general relations between the reliability of a compound test and its interitem similarity, or *internal consistency*.

Suppose that an individual's score on test **S** may be analyzed as the sum of his scores on **n** subtests $\mathbf{X}_1, \ldots, \mathbf{X}_n$. (It does not matter if one or more subtests $\mathbf{X}_i$ can be further analyzed as a composite of sub-subtests, though we shall have something to say about this possibility later.) Then by definition,

$$[8.50] \qquad \mathbf{S} = \mathbf{X}_1 + \ldots + \mathbf{X}_n \qquad \text{(assumed)}$$

$$= \sum_{i=1}^{n} \mathbf{X}_i \,,$$

while from [8.42], the true-score component, $\mathbf{T_S}$, of **S** correspondingly analyzes as

$$[8.51] \qquad \mathbf{T_S} = \mathbf{T}_1 + \ldots + \mathbf{T}_n \qquad ([8.50])$$

$$= \sum_{i=1}^{n} \mathbf{T}_i \,,$$

where $\mathbf{T}_i$ is the true-score component of subtest $\mathbf{X}_i$. Since from [8.35] the reliability of test **S** is

$$[8.52] \qquad r_{\mathbf{S}} = \frac{\mathrm{Var}\,(\mathbf{T_S})}{\mathrm{Var}\,(\mathbf{S})}$$

$$= \frac{\mathrm{Var}\left(\sum_{i=1}^{n} \mathbf{T}_i\right)}{\mathrm{Var}\left(\sum_{i=1}^{n} \mathbf{X}_i\right)} \qquad ([8.50])\,,$$

which may be further expanded by principle [4.40] into a function of the variances and covariances among the $\mathbf{T_i}$ and the $\mathbf{X_i}$, we are thus able to analyze the reliability of a compound test into the reliabilities and interrelations of its constituent items. The composition of $r_{\mathbf{S}}$ will be developed in complete generality in Chapter 9. At present, we shall assume whatever special conditions are needed to arrive at conceptually simple results, notably perfect homogeneity among the true-score components of the test items and uncorrelated measurement errors.

Assume, then, that test **S** is composed of items $\mathbf{X_1}, \ldots, \mathbf{X_n}$ all of which have the same true-score component, so that a person's score on one item differs from his score on another only as a result of measurement errors which we also assume to be uncorrelated. That is,

[8.53][28] $$\mathbf{T_1} = \mathbf{T_2} = \ldots = \mathbf{T_n} = \mathbf{T_X} \qquad \text{(assumed)}$$

[8.54-**ij**] (**i**,**j** = **1**, . . . , **n**; **i** ≠ **j**) $$r_{\mathbf{E_i E_j}} = 0 \qquad \text{(assumed)}$$

where we write "$\mathbf{T_X}$" for the true-score component common to all the $\mathbf{X_i}$. Then from [8.51] and [8.53],

[8.55] $$\begin{aligned} \mathrm{Var}(\mathbf{T_S}) &= \mathrm{Var}(\mathbf{nT_X}) \\ &= \mathbf{n}^2\sigma^2_{\mathbf{T_X}} \end{aligned} \qquad ([8.50], [8.53])$$

while from [8.53] and [8.54] by [4.39], in view of [8.25],

[8.56-**ij**] (**i**,**j** = **1**, . . . , **n**; **i** ≠ **j**) $$\begin{aligned} \mathrm{Cov}(\mathbf{X_i}, \mathbf{X_j}) &= \mathrm{Cov}(\mathbf{T_i} + \mathbf{E_i}, \mathbf{T_j} + \mathbf{E_j}) \\ &= \sigma^2_{\mathbf{T_X}}, \end{aligned} \qquad ([8.53], [8.54])$$

and hence from [8.50] by [4.40],

[8.57] $$\begin{aligned} \mathrm{Var}(\mathbf{S}) &= \sum_{i=1}^{n} \mathrm{Var}(\mathbf{X_i}) + \sum_{i=1}^{n}\sum_{\substack{j=1 \\ i \neq j}}^{n} \mathrm{Cov}(\mathbf{X_i}, \mathbf{X_j}) \\ &= \sum_{i=1}^{n} \sigma^2_{\mathbf{X_i}} + \mathbf{n}(\mathbf{n}-1)\sigma^2_{\mathbf{T_X}} \end{aligned} \qquad ([8.50], [8.53], [8.54])$$

For the moment, let us assume even further that the individual test items all have the same reliability, namely,

[8.58] $$r_{\mathbf{X_1}} = r_{\mathbf{X_2}} = \ldots = r_{\mathbf{X_n}} = r_{\mathbf{X}} \qquad \text{(assumed)},$$

[28] This requires not only that the $\mathbf{T_i}$ are all perfectly correlated but also that their variances are identical. It likewise entails that the $\mathbf{T_i}$ and hence the $\mathbf{X_i}$ all have the same mean, but as a restriction, this is both trivial and irrelevant.

from which it follows by [8.35] and [8.53] that the variances of the $\mathbf{X}_i$ are all equal to a common value $\sigma_{\mathbf{X}}^2$ – i.e.,

$$\sigma_{\mathbf{X}_1} = \sigma_{\mathbf{X}_2} = \ldots = \sigma_{\mathbf{X}_n} = \sigma_{\mathbf{X}} \qquad [8.59] \quad ([8.53], [8.58]) .$$

Then the true-score variance, $\sigma_{\mathbf{T_X}}^2$, common to all the individual items is

$$\sigma_{\mathbf{T_X}}^2 = \sigma_{\mathbf{X}}^2 r_{\mathbf{X}} \qquad [8.60] \quad ([8.53], [8.58])$$

and substitution of [8.59] and [8.60] into [8.55] and [8.57] reveals that under these conditions the reliability of the total test **S** analyzes as

$$[8.61] \qquad r_{\mathbf{S}} = \frac{\mathrm{Var}(\mathbf{T_S})}{\mathrm{Var}(\mathbf{S})}$$

$$= \frac{\mathbf{n}^2\sigma_{\mathbf{X}}^2 r_{\mathbf{X}}}{\mathbf{n}\sigma_{\mathbf{X}}^2 + \mathbf{n}(\mathbf{n}-1)\sigma_{\mathbf{X}}^2 r_{\mathbf{X}}} \qquad \begin{pmatrix}[8.50], [8.53],\\ [8.54], [8.58]\end{pmatrix}$$

$$= \frac{\mathbf{n} r_{\mathbf{X}}}{1 + (\mathbf{n}-1) r_{\mathbf{X}}}$$

Equation [8.61] (with the intermediate steps omitted) is the classical *Spearman-Brown "prophecy" formula*[29] relating a test's reliability to its length. It states that if a test is constructed as a sum of equivalent items whose measurement errors are all uncorrelated, then the reliability of the total test is determined by the number of items and the reliability of a single item in the manner shown. Other mathematically equivalent ways to write [8.61] which bring out more clearly the manner in which $r_{\mathbf{S}}$ varies with **n** and $r_{\mathbf{X}}$ are

$$[8.62] \qquad r_{\mathbf{S}} = \frac{1}{1 + \frac{1}{\mathbf{n}}\left(\frac{1 - r_{\mathbf{X}}}{r_{\mathbf{X}}}\right)} \qquad \begin{pmatrix}[8.50], [8.53],\\ [8.54], [8.58]\end{pmatrix}.$$

and

$$[8.63] \qquad \frac{1 - r_{\mathbf{S}}}{r_{\mathbf{S}}} = \frac{1}{\mathbf{n}}\left(\frac{1 - r_{\mathbf{X}}}{r_{\mathbf{X}}}\right) \qquad \begin{pmatrix}[8.50], [8.53],\\ [8.54], [8.58]\end{pmatrix}.$$

or

$$[8.64] \qquad \frac{\sigma_{\mathbf{E_S}}^2}{\sigma_{\mathbf{T_S}}^2} = \frac{1}{\mathbf{n}}\left(\frac{\sigma_{\mathbf{E_X}}^2}{\sigma_{\mathbf{T_X}}^2}\right) \qquad \begin{pmatrix}[8.50], [8.53],\\ [8.54], [8.58]\end{pmatrix},$$

where $\sigma_{\mathbf{E_S}}^2/\sigma_{\mathbf{T_S}}^2$ and $\sigma_{\mathbf{E_X}}^2/\sigma_{\mathbf{T_X}}^2$ are the ratios of error variance to true-score variance for, respectively, the total test and for an individual test item. It

[29] In 1910, Charles Spearman and William Brown independently authored back-to-back articles in the *British Journal of Psychology* describing this relationship.

will be seen that under the assumed conditions, a test's reliability rapidly approaches perfection as the number of test items increases, even if the individual item reliability is relatively low. The nature of this relationship may be further appreciated by reading "$r_{\mathbf{S}}$" for "α" and "$r_{\mathbf{X}}$" for "H" in Figure 8.1.

Written in form [8.61], the Spearman-Brown formula is traditionally interpreted as showing what the reliability of a test **X** would become were the test to be increased to **n** times its present length by adding suitably equivalent items—which is why it has been called the "prophecy" formula. To appreciate its significance as an internal-consistency measure of reliability, on the other hand, note that [8.56] and [8.59] imply that the correlation between any two items $\mathbf{X_i}$ and $\mathbf{X_j}$ $(\mathbf{i} \neq \mathbf{j})$ on test **S** is the same, namely $\sigma^2_{\mathbf{T_X}}/\sigma^2_{\mathbf{X}}$, or $r_{\mathbf{X}}$. Writing "$r_{\mathbf{XX}}$" for this common interitem correlation, we then have from [8.61]

$$[8.65] \qquad r_{\mathbf{S}} = \frac{\mathbf{n} r_{\mathbf{XX}}}{1 + (\mathbf{n} - 1) r_{\mathbf{XX}}} \qquad \begin{pmatrix}[8.50], [8.53],\\ [8.54], [8.58]\end{pmatrix},$$

which differs importantly from [8.61] in showing an empirical interitem correlation where [8.61] contains the theoretical term $r_{\mathbf{X}}$, and of which [8.47] is the special case where $\mathbf{n} = 2$. Equation [8.65] suggests that we can estimate the reliability of an extant compound test **S** composed of

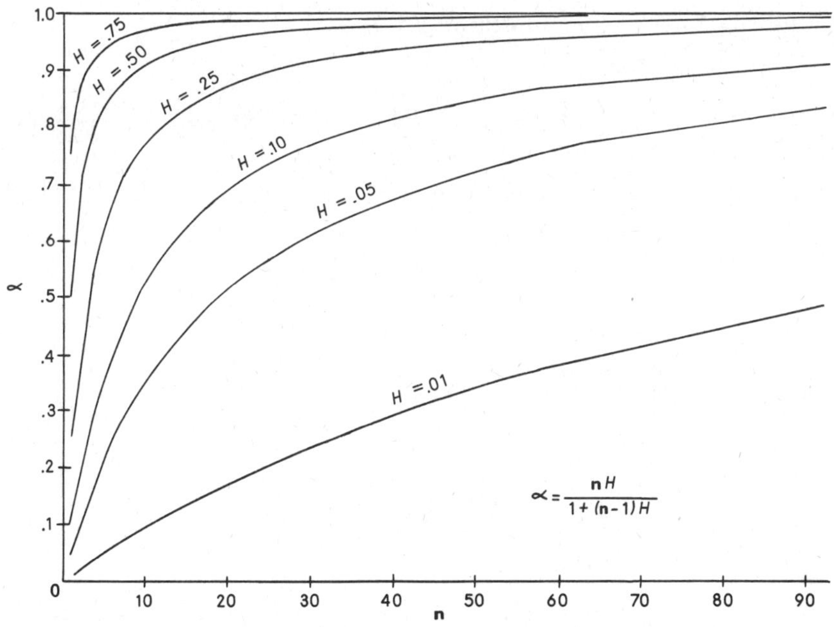

Figure 8.1. **The Alpha Function**

reasonably equivalent items by plugging the correlation between any two single items on the test into the formula along with the test's length. To be sure, a literal application of this procedure would be complicated by the fact that the stipulated ideal of equal interitem correlations will virtually never be realized in practice for $\mathbf{n} > \mathbf{2}$, in most instances not even approximately so, and to select one such correlation rather than another for estimation of $r_{\mathbf{S}}$ by [8.65] would be both to ignore most of the available internal-consistency data and to introduce an element of arbitrary choice into what should be a computational algorithm. The obvious way to avoid this difficulty would be to use an average interitem correlation for $r_{\mathbf{XX}}$ in [8.65]. For practical purposes, however, the question of how to estimate a test's reliability from its internal statistics by application of the Spearman-Brown formula is pointless, for there is a much better way to go about it.

The Alpha Coefficient. Suppose that as before we assume perfect true-score homogeneity ([8.53]) and uncorrelated measurement errors ([8.54]) for the items composing test **S**, but this time do *not* require the additional Spearman-Brown condition that the individual test items are all equally reliable. As consequences of our present assumptions we still have [8.55] and [8.57], while a direct consequence of the latter is

$$[8.66] \quad \sigma^2_{\mathbf{S}} - \sum_{i=1}^{\mathbf{n}} \sigma^2_{\mathbf{X}_i} = \mathbf{n}(\mathbf{n}-1)\sigma^2_{\mathbf{T_X}} \qquad ([8.50], [8.53], [8.54]),$$

or solving for $\sigma^2_{\mathbf{T_X}}$ and substituting into [8.55],

$$[8.67] \quad \sigma^2_{\mathbf{T_S}} = \left(\frac{\mathbf{n}}{\mathbf{n}-1}\right)\left(\sigma^2_{\mathbf{S}} - \sum_{i=1}^{\mathbf{n}} \sigma^2_{\mathbf{X}_i}\right) \qquad ([8.50], [8.53], [8.54]).$$

Hence the reliability of test **S** under these conditions is

$$[8.68] \quad r_{\mathbf{S}} = \frac{\sigma^2_{\mathbf{T_S}}}{\sigma^2_{\mathbf{S}}}$$

$$= \left(\frac{\mathbf{n}}{\mathbf{n}-1}\right)\left(\frac{\sigma^2_{\mathbf{S}} - \sum_{i=1}^{\mathbf{n}} \sigma^2_{\mathbf{X}_i}}{\sigma^2_{\mathbf{S}}}\right) \qquad ([8.50], [8.53], [8.54])$$

$$= \left(\frac{\mathbf{n}}{\mathbf{n}-1}\right)\left(1 - \frac{\sum_{i=1}^{\mathbf{n}} \sigma^2_{\mathbf{X}_i}}{\sigma^2_{\mathbf{S}}}\right).$$

Equation [8.68] is frequently known as *Kuder-Richardson formula #20* in honor of the two men who jointly in 1937 first introduced this development, though equation #20 in Kuder and Richardson's historic paper (49) was actually a special instance of [8.68].

It will be observed that while equation [8.68] is literally true for the reliability of a compound test **S** only under certain ideal conditions as specified, the quantity on the right-hand side of [8.68] is determined entirely by the observable variance properties of the test and its constituent items, and can be computed as an empirical statistic for any sum of test items no matter how arbitrarily these have been chosen. This statistic turns out to have important properties in test theory even when conditions [8.53,4] are not satisfied, and Cronbach (18) has proposed that it be identified by the term "coefficient alpha." Having no reason to take offense at this usage (which is certainly an improvement on calling it "K-R_{20}" or the like, as many post-Kuder-Richardson articles have done), we shall follow Cronbach's lead and define the *alpha coefficient*, $\alpha_{\mathbf{X}}$, for a set of variables $\mathbf{X}_1, \ldots, \mathbf{X}_n$ to be

[8.69] $$\alpha_{\mathbf{X}} =_{\text{def}} \left(\frac{\mathbf{n}}{\mathbf{n}-1}\right)\left(1 - \frac{\sum_{i=1}^{n} \sigma^2_{\mathbf{X}_i}}{\sigma^2_{\mathbf{S}}}\right) \qquad \left(\mathbf{S} = \sum_{i=1}^{n} \mathbf{X}_i\right) .$$

in which the subscript "**X**" in "$\alpha_{\mathbf{X}}$" designates the set of items $\mathbf{X}_1, \ldots, \mathbf{X}_n$. While we may also speak loosely of $\alpha_{\mathbf{X}}$ as the alpha coefficient for test **S**, it should be appreciated that α is primarily a statistic on a *set* of variables rather than on the set's sum, and that when in a secondary sense the alpha coefficient is ascribed to a compound test, its value is relative to the particular way the test is analyzed into parts. Thus if test **S** is the sum of **n** items $\mathbf{X}_1, \ldots, \mathbf{X}_n$, **S** can also be regarded as the sum of **m** subtests $\mathbf{Y}_1, \ldots, \mathbf{Y}_m$ where each $\mathbf{Y}_j$ is the sum of the items in one of **m** groups among which the $\mathbf{X}_i$ have been partitioned, and the alpha coefficient for the set $\mathbf{Y}_1, \ldots, \mathbf{Y}_m$ is not necessarily identical with the alpha coefficient for the set $\mathbf{X}_1, \ldots, \mathbf{X}_n$ even though $\sum_{i=1}^{n} \mathbf{X}_i = \sum_{i=1}^{m} \mathbf{Y}_i = \mathbf{S}$.

Since we have been led to the alpha coefficient through consideration of "internal consistency" reliability estimates, it is seemly that we pause to examine the sense in which $\alpha_{\mathbf{X}}$ is such a measure. As defined in [7.23] and [7.24], let $\overline{\mathbf{C}}_{\mathbf{XX}}$ and $\overline{\mathbf{V}}_{\mathbf{X}}$ be the average interitem covariance and average variance, respectively, among test items $\mathbf{X}_1, \ldots, \mathbf{X}_n$. Then in view of principle [4.41], definition [8.69] expands into

[8.70] $$\alpha_{\mathbf{X}} = \left(\frac{\mathbf{n}}{\mathbf{n}-1}\right)\left[\frac{\mathbf{n}\overline{\mathbf{V}}_{\mathbf{X}} + \mathbf{n}(\mathbf{n}-1)\overline{\mathbf{C}}_{\mathbf{XX}} - \mathbf{n}\overline{\mathbf{V}}_{\mathbf{X}}}{\mathbf{n}\overline{\mathbf{V}}_{\mathbf{X}} + \mathbf{n}(\mathbf{n}-1)\overline{\mathbf{C}}_{\mathbf{XX}}}\right]$$
$$= \frac{\mathbf{n}\overline{\mathbf{C}}_{\mathbf{XX}}}{\overline{\mathbf{V}}_{\mathbf{X}} + (\mathbf{n}-1)\overline{\mathbf{C}}_{\mathbf{XX}}} .$$

If the "homogeneity," $\text{Hom}_{\mathbf{X}}$, of items $\mathbf{X}_1, \ldots, \mathbf{X}_n$ is defined as the ratio of their average interitem covariance to their average variance (cf. [7.85]), then dividing numerator and denominator of the right-hand side of [8.70] by $\overline{V}_{\mathbf{X}}$ yields

[8.71]
$$\alpha_{\mathbf{X}} = \frac{\mathbf{n}\,\text{Hom}_{\mathbf{X}}}{1 + (\mathbf{n} - 1)\,\text{Hom}_{\mathbf{X}}},$$

which is identical with Spearman-Brown formula [8.65] except for replacement of $r_{\mathbf{S}}$ and $r_{\mathbf{XX}}$ by $\alpha_{\mathbf{X}}$ and $\text{Hom}_{\mathbf{X}}$, respectively, and deletion of the parenthetically recorded restrictive assumptions. The meaning of $\text{Hom}_{\mathbf{X}}$ as a measure of interitem similarity has been discussed previously (pp. 320ff.) and we need mention here only that $\text{Hom}_{\mathbf{X}}$ is approximately the average interitem correlation (see [7.90]) and is so exactly if the individual items all have the same variance. The alpha coefficient for a compound test is thus seen to be a generalization of the Spearman-Brown formula which, in contrast to the latter (which presupposes identical item variances and intercorrelations), can be computed for any arbitrary analysis of a compound test into a sum of parts. The magnitude of $\alpha_{\mathbf{X}}$ as a joint function of the number and homogeneity of test items is illustrated in Figure 8.1. It will be seen that for any fixed value of $\text{Hom}_{\mathbf{X}}$ above zero, $\alpha_{\mathbf{X}}$ approaches unity as $\mathbf{n}$ increases, though the rapidity of this approach decreases with decreasing $\text{Hom}_{\mathbf{X}}$. This asymptotic approach of $\alpha_{\mathbf{X}}$ to unity should help drive home the realization that—in contrast to a misinterpretation which occasionally appears in the literature—$\alpha_{\mathbf{X}}$ is *not* a measure of item homogeneity. Rather, $\alpha_{\mathbf{X}}$ is an estimate of reliability based on both the test's internal consistency and the number of test items,[30] whereas the corresponding statistic which represents interitem similarity is $\text{Hom}_{\mathbf{X}}$.

Not the least of the alpha coefficient's virtues is the ease with which it can be computed—all that is required by formula [8.69] in addition to the number of test items is the sum of the item variances and the variance of the total test. For tests consisting of dichotomous items, moreover, this computational convenience verges on sheer indolence. Specifically, let a test item be said to be a *unit-dichotomous* variable if it takes only two values, 0 or 1. Unit-dichotomous items are common in psychological testing where, e.g., a subject's raw score on a test is frequently defined as the number of items he answers in agreement with a certain scoring key. It is customary to designate the proportion of test subjects in a population P whose scores on unit-dichotomous item $\mathbf{X}_i$ are 1 by "p_i," and the proportion of subjects in P whose scores on $\mathbf{X}_i$ are 0 by "q_i." Thus, by definition,

[8.72]
$$p_i + q_i = 1 \qquad \text{(unit-dichotomous } \mathbf{X}_i\text{)}.$$

[30] A more detailed analysis of the nature of the alpha coefficient will be found in Chapter 9 (pp. 445ff.).

The proportion-correct, p_i, on $\mathbf{X}_i$ is also known as this item's "difficulty" in population P. Now the arithmetic mean of a unit-dichotomous variable $\mathbf{X}_i$ in population P is obviously

$$\text{[8.73]} \qquad M_{\mathbf{X}_i} = p_i \qquad \text{(unit-dichotomous } \mathbf{X}_i\text{)} ,$$

while the variance of $\mathbf{X}_i$ in P in this case is

$$\text{[8.74][31]} \qquad \begin{aligned} \sigma^2_{\mathbf{X}_i} &= p_i - p_i^2 \\ &= p_i(1-p_i) \qquad \text{(unit-dichotomous } \mathbf{X}_i\text{)} \\ &= p_i q_i \, . \end{aligned}$$

Hence the alpha coefficient for a set of unit-dichotomous items whose sum defines a test **S** is

$$\text{[8.75]} \qquad \alpha_{\mathbf{X}} = \left(\frac{\mathbf{n}}{\mathbf{n}-1}\right)\left(1 - \frac{\sum_{i=1}^{n} p_i q_i}{\sigma^2_{\mathbf{S}}}\right) \qquad (\mathbf{S} = \sum_{i=1}^{n} \text{unit-dichotomous } \mathbf{X}_i)$$

which, incidentally, becomes the original Kuder-Richardson formula #20 if $\alpha_{\mathbf{X}}$ is replaced by $r_{\mathbf{S}}$. All that is needed to compute $\alpha_{\mathbf{X}}$ by formula [8.75] in addition to the test's variance and number of items is the difficulty (i.e., p_i, or $M_{\mathbf{X}_i}$) of each test item. Moreover, the calculations can be simplified even further. Let $\bar{p}$ be the average difficulty of the items on test **S**, i.e.,

$$\text{[8.76]} \qquad \bar{p} =_{\text{def}} \frac{\sum_{i=1}^{n} p_i}{\mathbf{n}}$$

while $\bar{q}$ is similarly defined

$$\text{[8.77]} \qquad \begin{aligned} \bar{q} &=_{\text{def}} \frac{\sum_{i=1}^{n} q_i}{\mathbf{n}} \\ &= 1 - \bar{p} \, . \end{aligned}$$

Also, let $\sigma^2_{\mathbf{p}}$ be the variance of the item difficulties $p_1, \ldots, p_n$—i.e.,

$$\text{[8.78]} \qquad \sigma^2_{\mathbf{p}} =_{\text{def}} \frac{\sum_{i=1}^{n} p_i^2}{\mathbf{n}} - \bar{p}^2 \, .$$

Then the sum $\sum_{i=1}^{n} p_i q_i$ in [8.75] may be written

[31] *Proof:* The variance of any variable **X** may be written as the mean of $\mathbf{X}^2$ less the squared mean of **X** (cf. [3.21]). But the square of 1 is 1 and the square of 0 is 0; hence for a unit-dichotomous variable $\mathbf{X}_i$, $M_{(\mathbf{X}_i^2)} = M_{\mathbf{X}_i}$ and $\text{Var}(\mathbf{X}_i) = M_{\mathbf{X}_i} - M^2_{\mathbf{X}_i} = p_i - p_i^2$.

[8.79][32]
$$\sum_{i=1}^{n} p_i q_i = \mathbf{n}(\overline{pq} - \sigma_{\mathbf{p}}^2) = \mathbf{n}\overline{pq}(1-\iota) ,$$

where

[8.80]
$$\iota =_{\text{def}} \frac{\sigma_{\mathbf{p}}^2}{\overline{pq}} ,$$

and [8.75] correspondingly becomes

[8.81]
$$\alpha_{\mathbf{X}} = \left(\frac{\mathbf{n}}{\mathbf{n}-1}\right)\left[1 - \frac{\mathbf{n}\overline{pq}}{\sigma_{\mathbf{S}}^2}(1-\iota)\right] \qquad \left(\mathbf{S} = \sum_{i=1}^{n} \text{unit-dichotomous } \mathbf{X}_i\right) .$$

Except for tests on which item difficulty is unusually variable, the term ι will be much smaller than 1. (E.g., if $\bar{p} = .5$ and $\sigma_{\mathbf{p}} = .2$, ι is only .16.) If we assume ι to be negligible, [8.81] then becomes

[8.82][33]
$$\alpha_{\mathbf{X}} = \left(\frac{\mathbf{n}}{\mathbf{n}-1}\right)\left(1 - \frac{\mathbf{n}\overline{pq}}{\sigma_{\mathbf{S}}^2}\right) \qquad \left(\mathbf{S} = \sum_{i=1}^{n} \text{unit-dichotomous } \mathbf{X}_i,\ \sigma_{\mathbf{p}} = 0\right)$$

a formula which requires only the average item difficulty in addition to the total-test variance and number of items. Further, by [4.45],

[8.83]
$$\mathrm{M}_{\mathbf{S}} = \sum_{i=1}^{n} \mathrm{M}_{\mathbf{X}_i} = \mathbf{n}\bar{p} , \qquad \left(\mathbf{S} = \sum_{i=1}^{n} \text{unit-dichotomous } \mathbf{X}_i\right)$$

so [8.83] may also be written

[8.84]
$$\alpha_{\mathbf{X}} = \left(\frac{\mathbf{n}}{\mathbf{n}-1}\right)\left(1 - \frac{\mathrm{M}_{\mathbf{S}}(1-\mathrm{M}_{\mathbf{S}}/\mathbf{n})}{\sigma_{\mathbf{S}}^2}\right) = \left(\frac{\mathbf{n}}{\mathbf{n}-1}\right)\left(1 - \frac{\mathbf{n}\mathrm{M}_{\mathbf{S}} - \mathrm{M}_{\mathbf{S}}^2}{\mathbf{n}\sigma_{\mathbf{S}}^2}\right) \qquad \left(\mathbf{S} = \sum_{i=1}^{n} \text{unit-dichotomous } \mathbf{X}_i,\ \sigma_{\mathbf{p}} = 0\right)$$

Equation [8.84] says that the alpha coefficient for a test composed of equi-difficult dichotomous items can be computed simply from the test's mean, standard deviation, and number of items. Study of the contri-

[32] *Proof:* $\sum_{i=1}^{n} p_i q_i = \sum_{i=1}^{n} p_i - \sum_{i=1}^{n} p_i^2 = \mathbf{n}\bar{p} - \mathbf{n}\left(\sum_{i=1}^{n} p_i^2 / \mathbf{n} - \bar{p}^2 + \bar{p}^2\right) = \mathbf{n}(\bar{p} - \bar{p}^2 - \sigma_{\mathbf{p}}^2) = \mathbf{n}(\overline{pq} - \sigma_{\mathbf{p}}^2)$.

[33] With $r_{\mathbf{S}}$ in place of $\alpha_{\mathbf{X}}$, equation [8.82] is known as *Kuder-Richardson formula* #21.

bution of ι in [8.81] also shows that the value computed for $\alpha_{\mathbf{X}}$ by [8.84] is a lower bound for and normally a satisfactorily close approximation to the correct value of $\alpha_{\mathbf{X}}$ even when the assumption of equal item difficulty is not altogether correct.

We have seen that under certain conditions, a test's internal consistency as measured by its alpha coefficient is equal to its reliability—i.e., from [8.68] and [8.69],

$$[8.85] \qquad r_{\mathbf{S}} = \alpha_{\mathbf{X}} \qquad ([8.50], [8.53], [8.54]) .$$

What happens when these conditions are violated will be explored later (pp. 434ff.), at which time it will be seen that a test's alpha coefficient is a lower bound for and generally a very close approximation to its reliability so long as the measurement-error components of the individual test items are uncorrelated. Distressingly, however, this is a most unrealistic assumption. When the individual items on a test are administered at one sitting it is inevitable—or at least we have no reason to think otherwise—that a substantial proportion of the uncontrolled extraneous conditions which are presumably responsible for measurement error will persist from one item to the next, thus inducing positive error correlations which may well be substantial. If so, then the reliability estimated for a test from its internal consistency will generally be in excess of the test's true reliability—perhaps greatly so, since a given degree of interitem agreement can be due just as well to correlated errors as to correlated true scores. Hence the apparent power of internal-consistency reliability estimates is largely illusory, and however pleasant a mathematical pastime it may be to shuffle through the internal statistics of a compound test in search of a formula which gives the closest estimate of the test's reliability under conditions of uncorrelated errors, this is for practical applications like putting on a clean shirt to rassle a hog. No matter how mathematically sophisticated internal consistency measures may be, they cannot substitute for reliability estimates which draw independent samples of error factors. To be sure, traditional methods which offer the best prospect for accomplishing this, namely, test-retest and alternate-forms procedures, have presuppositional problems of their own. It will be shown in Chapter 9, however, that suitable modifications of these approaches can establish useful lower bounds on a test's reliability and, perhaps of greater ultimate importance, point the way to research assessing the quantitative significance of correlated-error effects.

The Standard Error of Measurement and the Estimation of True Scores

As the name implies,[34] the "standard error of measurement" for a test **X** in a population P is the *quadratic mean magnitude of potential measurement errors on* **X** *in* P. Since $M_{\mathbf{E}} = 0$,

$$[8.86] \qquad QM_{|\mathbf{E}|} = \sigma_{\mathbf{E}}$$

[34] It will be recalled that just as the "expected" value of a variable is its arithmetic mean, its "standard" value is its quadratic mean magnitude.

(cf. [3.19]), so the standard error of measurement may also be described as the standard deviation of measurement errors. The relation between a test's standard error of measurement and its reliability index or reliability coefficient is readily seen from [8.28] to be

[8.87]
$$\begin{aligned}\sigma_{\mathbf{E}} &= \sqrt{\sigma_{\mathbf{X}}^2 - \sigma_{\mathbf{T}}^2} \\ &= \sigma_{\mathbf{X}}\sqrt{1 - \left(\frac{\sigma_{\mathbf{T}}}{\sigma_{\mathbf{X}}}\right)^2} \\ &= \sigma_{\mathbf{X}}\sqrt{1 - r_{\mathbf{XT}}^2} \\ &= \sigma_{\mathbf{X}}\sqrt{1 - r_{\mathbf{X}}}\,,\end{aligned}$$

the last line of which is the most familiar formula for $\sigma_{\mathbf{E}}$.

A test's standard error of measurement is frequently said to be the standard error of estimate for inferring true scores on the test from observed scores—and indeed it is, but in more complex and devious ways than is usually appreciated. To begin with, we may note from [8.14] that

[8.88]
$$\begin{aligned}\sigma_{\mathbf{E}} = \sigma_{\mathbf{X|T}} &= \mathrm{SE}_{\mathbf{X,T}}[\hat{\mathbf{X}} = \mathrm{M}_{\mathbf{X|T}}] \\ = \sigma_{\mathbf{X\bullet T}} &= \mathrm{SE}_{\mathbf{X,T}}\,[\hat{\mathbf{X}} = \dot{\mathbf{X}}_{(\mathbf{T})}]\;.\end{aligned}$$

That is, $\sigma_{\mathbf{E}}$ is the (absolute) standard error of **X**, given **T**, under both linear and curvilinear regression—i.e., $\sigma_{\mathbf{E}}$ is the standard error of estimate for predicting observed scores from true scores on test **X** under either regression policy. *This* sense in which the standard error of measurement for test **X** is a standard error of estimate has little if any practical importance, however, since our problem is to infer not **X** from **T** but the converse.

Suppose, then, that scores actually observed on test **X** are taken at face value as approximations to the corresponding true scores. That is, consider the commonsense inference

[8.89]
$$\hat{T}_i = X_i\,,$$

which we shall call the "equivalence" policy, in which the test score X_i observed for an individual i is taken simply and straightforwardly, without qualms or statistical adjustments, as the estimate of i's true score on **X**. The estimate error made in predicting T_i from X_i under the equivalence policy is obviously $T_i - X_i$ (see definition [4.10]), or $-E_i$, so the (absolute) standard error of estimate under this policy is

[8.90]
$$\begin{aligned}\mathrm{SE}_{\mathbf{T,X}}\,[\hat{\mathbf{T}} = \mathbf{X}] &= \mathrm{QM}_{|-\mathbf{E}|} \\ &= \sigma_{\mathbf{E}}\;.\end{aligned}$$

Hence *a test's standard error of measurement in a population P is the standard error which results from taking the scores observed for members of P on this test as estimates of their true scores on it.*

The body of statistical considerations attendant to inferring true scores by equivalence policy $\hat{\mathbf{T}} = \mathbf{X}$ is sometimes called the *theory of measurement*, in contrast to the "theory of estimates" whose concern is with regression relationships.[35] In many respects the equivalence policy is the natural way to interpret test scores. In the first place, it is what we inadvertently do when we fail to distinguish between observed scores and true scores on a test; while no matter how exquisitely our test-theoretical sensibilities have been refined, it still remains our only rational policy when no information about the test's reliability is available. Moreover, since a score X_i observed on test $\mathbf{X}$ for an individual i is the mean of a sample of size 1 drawn from i's distribution of potential scores on $\mathbf{X}$, the expected value of which is T_i, the estimate $\hat{T}_i = X_i$ is an orthodox application of statistical sampling theory, which favors the mean of a sample for its estimate of the variable's expected value in the distribution sampled. Yet despite the spontaneity with which the equivalence policy is apt to be adopted, it does *not* convert observed test scores into the most accurate linear estimates of true scores. For the linear regression of $\mathbf{T}$ upon $\mathbf{X}$ in population P is seen by application of principle [4.56] to be

[8.91]
$$\begin{aligned} \dot{\mathrm{T}}_{(\mathbf{X})} &= \mathrm{r}_{\mathbf{TX}} \frac{\sigma_{\mathbf{T}}}{\sigma_{\mathbf{X}}} (\mathbf{X} - \mathrm{M}_{\mathbf{X}}) + \mathrm{M}_{\mathbf{T}} \\ &= \mathrm{r}^2_{\mathbf{TX}}(\mathbf{X} - \mathrm{M}_{\mathbf{X}}) + \mathrm{M}_{\mathbf{X}} \\ &= \mathrm{r}_{\mathbf{X}}\mathbf{X} + (1 - \mathrm{r}_{\mathbf{X}})\mathrm{M}_{\mathbf{X}} , \end{aligned}$$

the standard error which is only

[8.92]
$$\begin{aligned} \sigma_{\mathbf{T \cdot X}} &= \sigma_{\mathbf{T}}\sqrt{1 - \mathrm{r}^2_{\mathbf{TX}}} \\ &= \sigma_{\mathbf{X}}\mathrm{r}_{\mathbf{TX}}\sqrt{1 - \mathrm{r}^2_{\mathbf{TX}}} \\ &= \sigma_{\mathbf{X}}\sqrt{\mathrm{r}_{\mathbf{X}}(1 - \mathrm{r}_{\mathbf{X}})} \\ &= \sigma_{\mathbf{E}}\sqrt{\mathrm{r}_{\mathbf{X}}} . \end{aligned}$$

Thus when a test's reliability is known, the standard error for *optimal* (utility-free) linear estimation of true scores from observed scores is only a fraction of the test's standard error of measurement. It turns out, therefore, that inference from observed scores to true scores on a test is a more delicate matter than might at first be anticipated, insomuch as the "theory of measurement" (i.e., prediction of true scores by the equiv-

[35] See Guttman (38).

alence policy) and the "theory of estimates" (i.e., prediction of true scores by regression principles) lead to different results with different accuracies.

Moreover, neither equivalence policy [8.89] nor regression policy [8.91] do justice to the complications in true-score inference introduced by the *standardization* of test scores. The partitioning of observed scores on **X** into true-score and measurement-error components is wholly indifferent to whether the scale of values for **X** reports the raw scores in which performances on the test are initially recorded or a standardized transformation of these; for any transformation of scores from, say, **X** to **X**′ correspondingly transforms the probability distribution over potential scores on **X** for an individual *i* into a distribution over potential scores on **X**′, the expected value of which is *i*'s true score on **X**′. In particular, a linear transformation of observed scores effects the same linear transformation upon true scores—i.e., if $\mathbf{X}' = a\mathbf{X} + b$ and $\mathbf{T}_{\mathbf{X}}$ and $\mathbf{T}_{\mathbf{X}'}$ are the true-score components of **X** and **X**′, respectively, then from [8.42],

$$[8.93] \qquad \mathbf{T}_{\mathbf{X}'} = a\mathbf{T}_{\mathbf{X}} + b \qquad (\mathbf{X}' = a\mathbf{X} + b)\ .$$

Hence

$$[8.94] \qquad \mathrm{r}_{\mathbf{X}} = \left(\frac{\sigma_{\mathbf{T}_{\mathbf{X}}}}{\sigma_{\mathbf{X}}}\right)^2 = \left(\frac{\sigma_{\mathbf{T}_{\mathbf{X}'}}}{\sigma_{\mathbf{X}'}}\right)^2 = \mathrm{r}_{\mathbf{X}'} \qquad (\mathbf{X}' = a\mathbf{X} + b)\ ,$$

which makes clear that linear standardization of test scores does not affect the test's reliability. It also makes clear, however, that the *inequality* (unless $\mathrm{r}_{\mathbf{X}} = 1$) between the variances of observed and true scores on a test is unaffected by such standardization, since the ratio of one to the other remains unchanged. But when scores on a test are deliberately given a built-in statistical meaning by standardizing them to a preselected mean and standard deviation, *it is inevitable that thinking about true scores on the test will presuppose these very same norms,* especially if the definition of the norms does not explicitly stipulate otherwise. For example, the long evolution of the IQ concept has now settled upon a definition of "Deviation IQ" as a standard score (i.e., a linear transformation of raw scores) whose mean and standard deviation are set at 100 and (approximately) 15, respectively, at each normative age level.[36] A guidance counselor who has been informed that Johnny's observed Deviation IQ is 115 thus knows (or should know) that Johnny's observed test performance was one SD above the mean of performances to which his is being compared—and if the counselor were told that Johnny's *true* Deviation IQ were estimated to be

[36]Deviation IQs were first introduced in 1939 with a stipulated SD of 14.8 by the Wechsler-Bellevue test of adult intelligence, on which the older age-ratio IQ concept (mental age divided by chronological age, times 100) was inapplicable, and has now been adopted by the 1960 edition of the Stanford-Binet with the SD set at 16. Deviation IQs are determined by partitioning the total normative population into successive age groups, and raw scores on the test are linearly transformed for each age group into the assigned distribution of Deviation IQs.

115, he would *also* undoubtedly assume that Johnny's true Deviation IQ is estimated to be one SD above the mean. But while standardizing observed scores to a given mean confers this same mean on the test's true scores (see [8.17]), the SDs of observed scores and true scores on an imperfectly reliable test cannot simultaneously assume the same value. Consequently, what scores on a test with standardized norms are implicitly construed to measure is not literally the true-score component, **T**, of the standardized observed-score variable **X**, but a transformation of **T** which has the same mean and standard deviation as **X**.

Let the "sigma-corrected" true-score variable **T*** for a test **X** whose true-score component is **T** be defined as the linear transformation of **T** whose mean and SD are the same as the mean and SD, respectively, of observed scores on the test. That is,

[8.95] $$\mathbf{T}^* =_{\text{def}} \frac{\mathbf{T} - (1 - r_{XT})M_X}{r_{XT}}$$

which is readily seen to yield

[8.96] $$\sigma_{T^*} = \frac{\sigma_T}{r_{XT}} = \sigma_X,$$

[8.97] $$M_{T^*} = \frac{M_T - (1 - r_{XT})M_X}{r_{XT}} = M_X .$$

The analysis of observed scores on test **X** as a linear combination of sigma-corrected true scores and measurement errors is then

[8.98] $$\mathbf{X} = r_{XT}\mathbf{T}^* + \mathbf{E} + (1 - r_{XT})M_X = \sqrt{r_X}\,\mathbf{T}^* + \mathbf{E} + (1 - \sqrt{r_X})M_X .$$

The correlation between **X** and **T*** of course remains

[8.99] $$r_{XT^*} = r_{XT} = \sqrt{r_X},$$

so the linear regression of sigma-corrected true scores upon observed scores is

[8.100] $$\dot{\mathbf{T}}^*_{(X)} = r_{XT}\mathbf{X} + (1 - r_{XT})M_X = \sqrt{r_X}\,\mathbf{X} + (1 - \sqrt{r_X})M_X$$

with a corresponding standard error of

[8.101]
$$\begin{aligned}\sigma_{\mathbf{T}^*\cdot\mathbf{X}} &= \sigma_{\mathbf{T}^*}\sqrt{1-r^2_{\mathbf{XT}^*}}\\ &= \sigma_{\mathbf{X}}\sqrt{1-r^2_{\mathbf{XT}}}\\ &= \sigma_{\mathbf{X}}\sqrt{1-r_{\mathbf{X}}}\\ &= \sigma_{\mathbf{E}}\,.\end{aligned}$$

Hence *a test's standard error of measurement is also the standard error for estimating sigma-corrected true scores on the test from their linear regression on observed scores.* On the other hand, if we follow the equivalence policy of inferring that an individual's sigma-corrected true score is equal to his observed score, our standard error of estimate is

[8.102][37]
$$\begin{aligned}\mathrm{SE}_{\mathbf{T}^*;\mathbf{X}}[\hat{\mathbf{T}}^* = \mathbf{X}] &= \mathrm{QM}_{|\mathbf{T}^*-\mathbf{X}|}\\ &= \sigma_{\mathbf{X}}\sqrt{2(1-r_{\mathbf{XT}})}\\ &= \sigma_{\mathbf{X}}\sqrt{2(1-\sqrt{r_{\mathbf{X}}})}\\ &= \sigma_{\mathbf{E}}\sqrt{\frac{2}{1+\sqrt{r_{\mathbf{X}}}}}\,,\end{aligned}$$

which shows that the standard error of the "theory-of-measurement" estimate of sigma-corrected true scores on a test is *larger* than the test's standard error of measurement, though not seriously so unless the test has low reliability. It may also be seen by comparing the ratio of [8.90] to [8.92] to the ratio of [8.102] to [8.101] that the relative inefficiency of equivalence estimates over regression estimates is less for sigma-corrected true scores than for unadjusted true scores. Hence application of the traditional theory-of-measurement and theory-of-estimates formulas [8.90]–[8.92] to tests on which the same standardized norms are assumed for both observed scores and true scores exaggerates not only (1) the accuracy with which either policy estimates true scores, but also (2) the superiority of regression estimates over equivalence estimates.

Example. Suppose that **X** is an intelligence test whose scores are standardized as Deviation IQs, so that $M_{\mathbf{X}} = 100.0$ and $\sigma_{\mathbf{X}} = 15.0$ in the relevant populations, and suppose also that the reliability coefficient of **X** has been discovered to be about $r_{\mathbf{X}} = .64$ (which, incidentally, is an unusually poor reliability for a test of this sort). The correlation between observed scores and true scores on the test—i.e., the test's reliability index—is hence $r_{\mathbf{XT}} = \sqrt{.64} = .80$, while the test's standard error of measurement is $\sigma_{\mathbf{E}} = 15\sqrt{1-.64} = 9.0$. From [8.90], this means that there is a quadratic mean discrepancy of 9.0 points between a subject's

[37] *Proof:* Since the mean of **T*** − **X** is zero, $\mathrm{QM}^2_{|\mathbf{T}^*-\mathbf{X}|} = \mathrm{Var}(\mathbf{T}^*-\mathbf{X}) = \sigma^2_{\mathbf{T}^*}+\sigma^2_{\mathbf{X}}-2\sigma_{\mathbf{T}^*}\sigma_{\mathbf{X}}r_{\mathbf{XT}^*} = 2\sigma^2_{\mathbf{X}}(1-r_{\mathbf{XT}})$ (from [8.96] and [8.99]), while $\sigma^2_{\mathbf{X}} = \sigma^2_{\mathbf{E}}/(1-r^2_{\mathbf{XT}}) = \sigma^2_{\mathbf{E}}/(1+r_{\mathbf{XT}})(1-r_{\mathbf{XT}})$.

observed IQ and his score on the true-score component of **X**. On the other hand, if we estimate this true-score component by its regression, $\dot{\mathbf{T}}_{(\mathbf{X})} = .64\mathbf{X} + 36.0$ (from [8.91]) on observed IQ, so that e.g. if a subject's observed IQ is 130 the regression estimate of his true score is only 119.2, the quadratic mean discrepancy between observed and true scores is reduced to $\sigma_{\mathbf{T}\cdot\mathbf{X}} = 15\sqrt{.64 \times .36} = 7.2$ points. It must also be appreciated, however, that while an observed Deviation IQ of 130 corresponds to a test performance two SDs above the mean, a true score of 130 does *not* signify a true IQ two SDs above the mean. Rather, since here $\sigma_{\mathbf{T}} = 15 \times .80 = 12.0$ (using [8.27]), a true score of 130 on this test is superior to the mean by 2.5 SDs. That is, the true-score component of observed Deviation IQ is not itself a Deviation IQ, and the concept of "true score" on this test is systematically misleading unless we pass over to sigma-corrected true scores which, like observed scores, have in this instance a mean of 100 and standard deviation of 15 and are hence also Deviation IQs. The regression of true Deviation IQ upon observed Deviation IQ for the present example is $\dot{\mathbf{T}}^*_{(\mathbf{X})} = .80\mathbf{X} + 20.0$ (from [8.100]), which yields estimated true Deviation IQs which typically (i.e., standardly) differ from their correct values by $\sigma_{\mathbf{E}} = 9.0$ points (from [8.101]). The best linear estimate of true Deviation IQ on this test for a subject whose observed Deviation IQ is 130 is then 124—i.e., the observed value of 2.0 SDs above the mean is regressed to an estimated 1.6 SDs above the mean. On the other hand, if we take unregressed observed Deviation IQs for our estimates of true Deviation IQs, the quadratic mean estimate error is 9.5 points (from [8.102]), which is not seriously inferior to the accuracy of regression estimates.

Interval Estimates of True Scores. It should be appreciated that the standard errors of estimate discussed in the preceding paragraphs are *absolute,* not contingent, standard errors. That is, they state what the quadratic mean error is for a particular estimation policy applied to *all* members of the relevant population. This leaves open a possibility that the *contingent* standard error of estimate under this policy among subjects with a given observed test score may vary from one score level to another. For example, alternate-forms reliability data on the 1937 Stanford-Binet scale suggest that the quadratic mean measurement error among subjects with a given true score on the test (which we may call the *contingent* standard error of measurement in contrast to the *absolute* standard error of measurement defined by [8.86]) is larger for high IQs than for low, so that true IQ on this test can be determined with greater precision for low values than for high ones. For equivalence-policy estimation of true scores, moreover, there is a systematic tendency for estimates based on observed scores at extremes of the distribution to be less accurate than those based on observations closer to the mean.[38]

[38] This is because the discrepancy between $\hat{T}_i = X_i$ or $\hat{T}^* = X_i$ and $\hat{T}_i = \dot{T}_{(\mathbf{X})i}$ is zero when $X_i = \mathrm{M}_{\mathbf{X}}$ and grows larger as X_i diverges in either direction from $\mathrm{M}_{\mathbf{X}}$.

Even so, the absolute standard error of estimate for regression policy [8.91] or [8.100] should usually be an acceptable approximation to the contingent standard error at each value of the observed-score variable. If we are also willing to assume that the contingent distributions of true scores, given observed scores, are reasonably normal in shape and that the unrestricted regression of true scores on observed scores is approximately linear (since the linearity of $M_{\mathbf{X}|\mathbf{T}}$ does not guarantee linearity of $M_{\mathbf{T}|\mathbf{X}}$), we can define confidence intervals (see pp. 75f.) which contain an individual's true score or sigma-corrected true score on the test, given his observed score, with a stipulated likelihood. Thus if the regression of **T** on **X** is linear and the contingent distributions of **T**, given **X**, are homoscedastic and normal, there is a 95% chance that a person whose test score has been observed to be X_i has a sigma-corrected true score somewhere in the interval

$$\sqrt{r_{\mathbf{X}}}X_i + (1-\sqrt{r_{\mathbf{X}}})M_{\mathbf{X}} \pm 2\sigma_{\mathbf{X}}\sqrt{1-r_{\mathbf{X}}}\,.$$

For example, if **X** is the IQ test previously hypothesized with $r_{\mathbf{X}} = .64$, an observed Deviation IQ of 130 would imply (under the stated assumptions) a 95% certainty that the subject's true Deviation IQ lies somewhere between 106 and 142, a spread which vividly betrays the effect of low reliability. On the other hand, if the test's reliability were increased to $r_{\mathbf{X}} = .90$ (a good but not unreasonable figure for an intelligence test), its standard error of measurement would shrink to 4.74 and 95% of subjects whose observed Deviation IQs are 130 would have true Deviation IQs between 119 and 138.

Reliability and Validity

It may have occurred to the reader that while we have devoted considerable attention to *how* reliability and true scores are estimated, the discussion has so far remained oddly taciturn about *why* these inferences should be a subject for concern. Actually, this question is somewhat embarrassing, for it is debatable whether the practical benefits of reliability theory are sufficiently bountiful to recompense the labor that test theorists have invested in it. The primary justification of reliability theory lies in abstract curiosity: If we are driven—as inexorably we are—to postulate a realm of true scores at all, then we may as well learn as much about them as we can. Even so, reliability concepts do find occasional application, one of which, in particular, merits respect. Specifically, for most criteria in which a test's user is likely to be interested, *the test's reliability index is an upper limit to its validity.* Let a variable **Y** whose value for an individual i is independent of the uncontrolled test-circumstance details responsible for errors of measurement on test **X** be called a "test-stable" criterion for **X**. Thus attributes which a subject brings with him to the testing situation, such as his weight, intelligence, sociability, blood type, financial indebtedness, etc., are unrelated to chance influences which disturb his test performance, though what he is like during or after the test may in some ways be so affected. Now, a test-stable criterion by definition has zero correlation with measurement errors on the test. Hence the correlation between a test-stable criterion **Y** and observed scores on **X** is

[8.103][39]
$$\begin{aligned} r_{XY} &= \frac{\mathrm{Cov}(\mathbf{X},\mathbf{Y})}{\sigma_X \sigma_Y} \\ &= \frac{\mathrm{Cov}(\mathbf{T},\mathbf{Y})}{\sigma_X \sigma_Y} \qquad\qquad (r_{EY}=0) \\ &= \frac{\sigma_T}{\sigma_X} r_{TY} \\ &= r_{XT} r_{TY} , \end{aligned}$$

which says that the objective validity of test **X** for predicting a test-stable criterion **Y** is the product of the test's reliability index with the validity that true scores on **X** would have for prediction of **Y**. Since the magnitude of r_{TY} cannot exceed unity, this shows, in turn, that

[8.104] $$|r_{XY}| \leqslant r_{XT} \qquad (r_{EY}=0)$$

or equivalently,

[8.105] $$|r_{XY}| \leqslant \sqrt{r_X} \qquad (r_{EY}=0) .$$

Consequently, while high reliability in a test does not insure that it is good for predicting anything beyond its own true-score component, we do know, conversely, that if a test does *not* have high reliability then it has little chance at having much validity for the predictive purposes for which it is intended. In particular, considering the nonlinear relationship between correlation and predictive efficiency (see pp. 123f.), the prospect for discovering practical utility in a test whose reliability is not in the .80s or .90s is pretty bleak. Thus reliability theory implies certain minimal standards for the development and consumption of applied tests: If direct data are available on a test's validity for its intended purpose, then in that context of usage the test's reliability is a matter of indifference. However, if validity estimates are *not* available, then the test should not be published commercially or, if released, should be spurned by test consumers unless its reliability is demonstrably high enough to give it at least a fighting chance at usefulness.[40] A parallel moral for the economics of test development is that it is generally a waste of resources

---

[39] Since $\mathrm{Cov}(\mathbf{X},\mathbf{Y}) = \mathrm{Cov}(\mathbf{T}+\mathbf{E},\mathbf{Y}) = \mathrm{Cov}(\mathbf{T},\mathbf{Y}) + \mathrm{Cov}(\mathbf{E},\mathbf{Y})$ while $\mathrm{Cov}(\mathbf{E},\mathbf{Y}) = 0$.

[40] This moral assumes, of course, that what the test user is trying to predict is a criterion which is reasonably test-stable. This will generally be the case in practical applications, but is not necessarily so for scientific research, wherein a test with low reliability might be just what is needed for the study of process-variables such as muscular tonus, perceptual vigilance, etc., which *are* dependent upon the momentary details of the testing situation.

to carry out expensive validation studies on a test before it has been brought to a high level of reliability, though as will be observed shortly, a combination of validity and reliability data for a test in the process of development may help to decide what should be done with it.

The limitations on a test's usefulness implied by equation [8.105] also gives some practical justification to computation of regression estimates of true scores rather than simply reporting a subject's observed score. Standardizing **X**, **T**, and **Y** as Z-scales to simplify the regression equation, we have from [8.103] by [4.58] that

[8.106]
$$\begin{aligned} \dot{Z}_{Y(X)} &= r_{YX} Z_X \\ &= r_{YT}\, r_{TX}\, Z_X \qquad (r_{YE} = 0) \\ &= r_{YT} \dot{Z}_{T(X)} \,. \end{aligned}$$

That is, the best linear estimate of an individual's Z-score on criterion **Y**, given his observed score on test **X**, is his estimated true Z-score on the test, attenuated by the correlation between true test-scores and the criterion. In particular, since r_{YT} can never be larger in magnitude than unity,

[8.107]
$$|\dot{Z}_{Y(X)}| \leq |\dot{Z}_{T(X)}| \qquad (r_{YE} = 0) \,.$$

Hence the best linear estimate of an individual's score on a test-stable criterion based on his observed test score can be no more extreme than his regression-estimated true score on the test. Since there is a strong tendency for test users to ignore regression principles when interpreting test scores, with a testee's superiority or inferiority on the test being taken at face value as his predicted status on the criterion, conversion from observed test scores to regressed sigma-corrected true scores helps to discourage the reading of unrealistic significance into the extremity of a particular test performance. Still better is to report the true-score estimate in the form of a confidence interval, even when the distributional assumptions behind the computation may be somewhat suspect, since this serves to infuse the test result with an appropriate feeling of uncertainty about the conclusions which can be drawn from it.

Another practical, if somewhat specialized, application of reliability theory is suggested by solving equation [8.103] for r_{TX}:

[8.108]
$$\begin{aligned} r_{TY} &= \frac{r_{XY}}{r_{XT}} \\ &= \frac{r_{XY}}{\sqrt{r_X}} \,. \end{aligned} \qquad (r_{YE} = 0)$$

This states that if both a test's reliability and its validity for a given test-stable criterion are known, then the correlation of true scores on the test with that criterion can also be computed. Now, r_{TY} is the validity that test **X** *would* have for criterion **Y** if it were possible to eliminate all measurement error from the test, and may hence be thought of as the test's *theoretical validity* for predicting **Y**. When a test is being developed specifically with an eye to a given criterion, its theoretical validity for that criterion assumes considerable importance; for if r_{TY} is high even though the test's present empirical validity is unsatisfactorily low, then there is reason to hope that the test's predictive efficiency can be substantially improved by increased standardization of the test-circumstance details. Conversely, if the theoretical validity of the test is estimated by [8.108] to be poor (say $|r_{TY}| < .8$), then the main thrust of test development should go into search for improved test content, such as new or revised test items, which raise r_{TY} to a more promising level.

An extension of formula [8.108] which recognizes measurement errors in the criterion as well as in the predictor is known as the *correction for attenuation.* Let $\mathbf{X_1}$ and $\mathbf{X_2}$ be two tests on which observed scores analyze into true-score and measurement-error components $\mathbf{T_1}$, $\mathbf{E_1}$, and $\mathbf{T_2}$, $\mathbf{E_2}$, respectively, and assume that the two error components are uncorrelated. Then from [8.38],

[8.109][41] $$r_{T_1T_2} = \frac{r_{X_1X_2}}{\sqrt{r_{X_1}r_{X_2}}} \qquad (r_{E_1E_2} = 0)\ .$$

If—repeat, *if*—observations on tests $\mathbf{X_1}$ and $\mathbf{X_2}$ are made in such fashion as to justify the assumption of uncorrelated errors, then formula [8.109] discloses the "true" correlation between the variables measured by tests $\mathbf{X_1}$ and $\mathbf{X_2}$, unsullied by the attenuating distractions which arise from our inability to observe $\mathbf{T_1}$ and $\mathbf{T_2}$ with perfect accuracy. Whether there is any legitimate end to which an estimated "true" correlation can be put which cannot better be served by factor-analytic procedures, however, is problematic—especially since empirical approximations to a test's reliability tend to be underestimates (at least when measurement errors in the reliability study are uncorrelated) with the result that correlation coefficients corrected for attenuation by formula [8.109] are likely to be excessive. In particular, one unfortunately common application of equation [8.109] which should *not* be made is to upgrade empirical correlations in research reports and public information documents (e.g., test manuals), since to state no more than that the correlation between variables **X** and **Y**, "corrected for attenuation," is such-and-such too easily leaves the impression that this is the accuracy with which **Y** can actually be predicted from **X**, while the empirical relation between **X** and **Y** remains suppressed.

[41] Like many other basic theorems of reliability theory, the "correction for attenutation" originated in the work of Charles Spearman in the early 1900's.

Coda: The Concept of "Test Potential"

It was argued at the beginning of this chapter that reliability theory is founded upon the notion that each individual i who could be tested by a certain procedure **X** has a characteristic "potential" or "disposition" to have the test come out one way rather than another for him, and that this disposition cannot in generally be properly conceived as a single determinate score but only as a distribution of probabilities over the various scores that i might receive were he to be so tested. This distribution of probabilities on **X** for i presumably arises from the attributes that i brings with him to the test situation and may itself be thought of as a complex attribute which is independent of i's momentary surroundings, while the particular score (if any) that i actually receives on **X** is a joint function of this **X**-potential attribute and the more or less chancy details of the test circumstances.

Now, by distinguishing between "true" scores and observed scores on test **X**, reliability theory intends to recognize precisely this distinction between a subject's test potential and something which happens as a *result* of that attribute. But strictly speaking, a distribution of probabilities can only be described by a *function,* not by a single number, even though a distribution's expectation is, to be sure, generally its most important single feature. Hence abstracting a subject's "true score"—i.e., his test expectation—from his total test potential disregards additional aspects of the latter which in principle may also be significant, notably, its dispersion and shape. In the special case that the **X**-potentials of prospective testees differ only in their expectations, then the marginal distribution of the error component of **X** in this population is the same as the distribution of potential errors for each subject i, with the result that i's true score here conveys all that is distinctive about his test potential. However, if there are appreciable intersubject differences in test potentials beyond their expectations—e.g., if one subject's score on **X** is virtually unaffected by chance aspects of the test situation while another's **X**-score has violent transituational instability, or if measurement errors on two tests $\mathbf{X}_1$ and $\mathbf{X}_2$ are uncorrelated for one subject but not for another—then these are further distinguishing attributes of subjects which are tapped by the test and which in principle could have as much predictive importance as true scores. So far, test-potential moments higher than the first have been profoundly (though understandably) neglected in test theory, and while these may not be altogether bursting with promise for practical applications, they nonetheless constitute a frontier for further research.

*Chapter 9. The Variance Structure of Composite Tests

IN THE PRECEDING chapter, several formulas relating the reliability of a multiple-item test to the correlational consistency of its constituents were derived under the classical presuppositions of uncorrelated inter-item measurement errors and a single true-score component common to all the test items. But these assumptions are thoroughly implausible for tests actually in use, especially the part about true-score homogeneity. Factor analysis of interitem covariances generally fails to support even the assumption of a single common factor, much less that the variance attributable to this factor is the same for all test items, and we have already scoffed at the thought that measurement errors for multiple items included on the same testing occasion would remain undefiled by correlational agreement. If the internal-consistency developments of reliability theory are to be taken seriously, therefore, it becomes important to make clear the manner in which they are affected by true-score heterogeneity and correlated errors. More generically, the fact that many tests are linear combinations of several subtests or "items" raises the question of how the variance properties of a composite test are related to the factorial composition of its constituents. Happily, many aspects of this question have a surprisingly simple answer.

The General Composition Theorem

Suppose that $\mathbf{S}$ is a test which can be analyzed as the sum of subtests or items $\mathbf{X_1}, \ldots, \mathbf{X_n}$. (This does not preclude the possibility that an individual "item" $\mathbf{X_i}$ is itself a linear function of one or more subitems. We shall attend to such further complexities in due course.) Then

[9.1] $$\mathbf{S} =_{\text{def}} \mathbf{X_1} + \ldots + \mathbf{X_n} = \mathbf{n}\,\frac{\sum_{i=1}^{n} \mathbf{X_i}}{\mathbf{n}} = \mathbf{n}\overline{\mathbf{X}}\,,$$

which says that **S** differs from the centroid of its constituent items only by a shift in unit of measurement. This apparently trivial conclusion actually has rather profound consequences. For one, it makes immediately apparent the relation between **S** and the factorial composition of its constituents. Specifically, *no matter how factorially complex a set of items may be, a test defined as the sum of those items is simply a linear resealing of the first centroid factor of that set.* More generally, Chapter 7 has already explored the variance structure of a centroid in some detail and these conclusions now have an immediate interpretation as the variance structure of a compound test. In what follows, we shall be explicit about $\overline{\mathbf{X}}$ rather than about **S**; in virtually all formulas of interest, the two terms are interchangeable.

According to the basic reliability equations, each item $\mathbf{X}_i$ in a set of test items $\mathbf{X}_1, \ldots, \mathbf{X}_n$ may be analyzed as the sum of a true-score component on that item and a corresponding measurement-error component —i.e., to repeat [8.4],

[9.2-i] (i = 1, . . . , n)
$$\mathbf{X}_i = \mathbf{T}_i + \mathbf{E}_i \, .$$

The true-score components $\mathbf{T}_1, \ldots, \mathbf{T}_n$ together span a true-score space $S_\mathbf{T}$, namely, the set of all variables which are linear combinations of the $\mathbf{T}_i$, while error components $\mathbf{E}_1, \ldots, \mathbf{E}_n$ similarly span an error space $S_\mathbf{E}$. We know from [8.6] by way of principle [4.39] that any linear combination of the $\mathbf{T}_i$ has zero covariance with any linear combination of the $\mathbf{E}_i$, so we may write

[9.3]
$$\perp (S_\mathbf{T}, S_\mathbf{E}) \, ,$$

which says that true-score space and error space are orthogonal to each other (see p. 293). It is further clear from [8.22,3] that $\mathbf{E}_i$ is the "projection" (see p. 294) of item $\mathbf{X}_i$ into error space, while the projection of $\mathbf{X}_i$ into true-score space differs from $\mathbf{T}_i$ only by an additive constant (specifically, $\mathbf{T}_i = \mathrm{M}_{\mathbf{X}_i} + \mathbf{e}_{\mathbf{X}_i(S_\mathbf{T})}$), so

[9.4-i] (i = 1, . . . , n)
$$\mathrm{V}_{\mathbf{X}_i(S_\mathbf{T})} = \mathrm{V}_{\mathbf{T}_i} \, ,$$

[9.5-i] (i = 1, . . . , n)
$$\mathrm{V}_{\mathbf{X}_i(S_\mathbf{E})} = \mathrm{V}_{\mathbf{E}_i} \, .$$

Thus the total configuration of the set of test items $\mathbf{X}_1, \ldots, \mathbf{X}_n$ is partitioned between true-score space and error space in the neatly additive fashion presumed by the fundamental partitioning theorem (p. 295) and its consequences. In particular, the observed-score variance of each item analyzes as

[9.6-i] (i = 1, . . . , n)
$$\mathrm{V}_{\mathbf{X}_i} = \mathrm{V}_{\mathbf{T}_i} + \mathrm{V}_{\mathbf{E}_i} \, ,$$

while the total variance and average variance in the set $\mathbf{X}_1, \ldots, \mathbf{X}_n$ analyze as

[9.7] $$V_{\mathbf{X}} = V_{\mathbf{T}} + V_{\mathbf{E}} ,$$

[9.8] $$\overline{V}_{\mathbf{X}} = \overline{V}_{\mathbf{T}} + \overline{V}_{\mathbf{E}} ,$$

where $V_{\mathbf{X}}$, $V_{\mathbf{T}}$, $V_{\mathbf{E}}$ and $\overline{V}_{\mathbf{X}}$, $\overline{V}_{\mathbf{T}}$, $\overline{V}_{\mathbf{E}}$ are the total and average variances of the $\mathbf{X}_i$, $\mathbf{T}_i$, and $\mathbf{E}_i$, respectively (cf. [6.38] and [7.24]). Similarly, the centroid of the test items analyzes as

[9.9] $$\overline{\mathbf{X}} = \overline{\mathbf{T}} + \overline{\mathbf{E}} ,$$

[9.10] $$V_{\overline{\mathbf{X}}} = V_{\overline{\mathbf{T}}} + V_{\overline{\mathbf{E}}} ,$$

where of course $\overline{\mathbf{T}}$ and $\overline{\mathbf{E}}$ are respectively the centroids of the true-score and the error components. We also know from [8.42] that $\overline{\mathbf{T}}$ and $\overline{\mathbf{E}}$ are the true-score and measurement-error components, respectively, of $\overline{\mathbf{X}}$—i.e.,

[9.11] $$\mathbf{T}_{\overline{\mathbf{X}}} = \overline{\mathbf{T}} ,$$

[9.12] $$\mathbf{E}_{\overline{\mathbf{X}}} = \overline{\mathbf{E}} .$$

Hence

[9.13] $$\mathrm{Var}(\mathbf{T}_{\overline{\mathbf{X}}}) = V_{\overline{\mathbf{T}}} = V_{\overline{\mathbf{X}}(S_{\mathbf{E}})} ,$$

[9.14] $$\mathrm{Var}(\mathbf{E}_{\overline{\mathbf{X}}}) = V_{\overline{\mathbf{E}}} = V_{\overline{\mathbf{X}}(S_{\mathbf{E}})} ,$$

and the reliability, $r_{\overline{\mathbf{X}}}$, of the test-item centroid is

[9.15] $$\begin{aligned} r_{\overline{\mathbf{X}}} &=_{\text{def}} \frac{\mathrm{Var}(\mathbf{T}_{\overline{\mathbf{X}}})}{\mathrm{Var}(\overline{\mathbf{X}})} \\ &= \frac{V_{\overline{\mathbf{T}}}}{V_{\overline{\mathbf{X}}}} \\ &= \frac{V_{\overline{\mathbf{T}}}}{V_{\overline{\mathbf{T}}} + V_{\overline{\mathbf{E}}}} \\ &= P_{\overline{\mathbf{X}}}(S_{\mathbf{T}}) , \end{aligned}$$

which are various ways to say that a centroid's reliability is its penetrance into the true-score space of its constituent items. The reliability of each individual test item is likewise its penetrance into true-score space, i.e.,

[9.16-**i**]
($\mathbf{i} = \mathbf{1}, \ldots, \mathbf{n}$)
$$\begin{aligned} r_{\mathbf{X}_i} &=_{\text{def}} \frac{V_{\mathbf{T}_i}}{V_{\mathbf{X}_i}} \\ &= \frac{V_{\mathbf{X}_i(S_{\mathbf{T}})}}{V_{\mathbf{X}_i}} \\ &= P_{\mathbf{X}_i}(S_{\mathbf{T}}) , \end{aligned}$$

while the penetrance into true-score space of the total configuration of test items may variously be written

[9.17]
$$P_{\mathbf{X}}(S_{\mathbf{T}}) =_{\text{def}} \frac{V_{\mathbf{X}(S_{\mathbf{T}})}}{V_{\mathbf{X}}} = \frac{V_{\mathbf{T}}}{V_{\mathbf{X}}} = \frac{\overline{V}_{\mathbf{T}}}{\overline{V}_{\mathbf{X}}} = \frac{\sum_{i=1}^{n} V_{\mathbf{X}_i} P_{\mathbf{X}_i}(S_{\mathbf{T}})}{\sum_{i=1}^{n} V_{\mathbf{X}_i}} = \frac{\sum_{i=1}^{n} V_{\mathbf{X}_i} r_{\mathbf{X}_i}}{\sum_{i=1}^{n} V_{\mathbf{X}_i}},$$

or writing "$\tilde{r}_{\mathbf{X}}$" for the variance-weighted average reliability of items $\mathbf{X}_1, \ldots, \mathbf{X}_n$,

[9.18]
$$\tilde{r}_{\mathbf{X}} =_{\text{def}} \frac{\sum_{j=1}^{n} V_{\mathbf{X}_i} r_{\mathbf{X}_i}}{\sum_{i=1}^{n} V_{\mathbf{X}_i}} = P_{\mathbf{X}}(S_{\mathbf{T}}) .$$

The corresponding penetrances into error space are of course

[9.19]
$$P_{\overline{\mathbf{X}}}(S_{\mathbf{E}}) = 1 - r_{\overline{\mathbf{X}}},$$

[9.20] (**i = 1, . . . , n**)
$$P_{\mathbf{X}_i}(S_{\mathbf{E}}) = 1 - r_{\mathbf{X}_i},$$

[9.21]
$$P_{\mathbf{X}}(S_{\mathbf{E}}) = 1 - \tilde{r}_{\mathbf{X}} .$$

In view of principles [7.102] and [7.105], equations [9.15] and [9.18] show that analysis of the reliability of a compound test $\overline{\mathbf{X}}$ reduces to stating how the centroid variance of the test items is partitioned between true-score space and error space by (1) the item-reliability apportionment of the total item variance between these spaces and (2) the shapes of the item configurations projected into them. In previous internal-consistency formulas (e.g., [8.65], [8.68]), these configurations were assumed to be at opposite extremes, with all the test items having identical projections into S_T while their projections into S_E are mutually orthogonal. Now, however, we wish to consider more general possibilities in which the true-score components of the test items are factorially complex while their error components have some degree of correlational agreement. It might be thought that in order to carry through the general analysis it becomes necessary to study the factor pattern of the $\mathbf{T}_i$ and the $\mathbf{E}_i$. Actually, the theory of saturation and dispersion components precludes the need for this, since all the relevant mathematical properties of the true-score and error configurations can be abstracted without requiring an explicit factorial decomposition of the test items. Even so, it is additionally instructive to further analyze each set of primary components into common-factor and unique-factor contributions. Let us, therefore, suppose that true-score components $\mathbf{T}_1, \ldots, \mathbf{T}_n$ can be factored into communal components $\boldsymbol{\tau}_1, \ldots, \boldsymbol{\tau}_n$ and unique components $\mathbf{t}_1, \ldots, \mathbf{t}_n$,[1] so that

[9.22-i] $\quad \mathbf{T}_i = \boldsymbol{\tau}_i + \mathbf{t}_i ,$
$(\mathbf{i} = \mathbf{1}, \ldots, \mathbf{n})$

[9.23-ij] $\quad C_{\boldsymbol{\tau}_i \mathbf{t}_j} = 0 ,$
$(\mathbf{i},\mathbf{j} = \mathbf{1}, \ldots, \mathbf{n})$

[9.24-ij] $\quad C_{\mathbf{t}_i \mathbf{t}_j} = 0 .$
$(\mathbf{i},\mathbf{j} = \mathbf{1}, \ldots, \mathbf{n};\ \mathbf{i} \neq \mathbf{j})$

Then $\boldsymbol{\tau}_1, \ldots, \boldsymbol{\tau}_n$ span a common-factor space S_τ of true scores, orthogonal to which is the unique-factor space S_t of true scores spanned by the mutually orthogonal $\mathbf{t}_1, \ldots, \mathbf{t}_n$. Unique true-score component $\mathbf{t}_i$, or its normalized equivalent, is frequently called the *specific factor* in test item $\mathbf{X}_i$ (which for increased clarity we shall expand to "specific true-factor") in contrast to the one or more common true-score factors into which $\boldsymbol{\tau}_i$ may be analyzed given a choice of factor basis for space S_τ. In like manner, if there are any nonzero covariances among the error components of the $\mathbf{X}_i$, the $\mathbf{E}_i$ may be factored into common-error components $\boldsymbol{\epsilon}_1, \ldots, \boldsymbol{\epsilon}_n$ which span a common-error space S_ϵ and unique-error components $\mathbf{e}_1, \ldots, \mathbf{e}_n$ which span unique-error space S_e —i.e.,

[9.25-i] $\quad \mathbf{E}_i = \boldsymbol{\epsilon}_i + \mathbf{e}_i ,$
$(\mathbf{i} = \mathbf{1}, \ldots, \mathbf{n})$

[1] The present use of "$\boldsymbol{\tau}_i$" for the communal component of $\mathbf{T}_i$ has no connection with the previous employment of this symbol (pp. 252 ff.) to denote a hypothetical source variable. No significance attaches to the introduction of Greek letters in the present context other than a shortage of different styles of notation for the same letter.

[9.26-**ij**] $$C_{\epsilon_i e_j} = 0 \,,$$
(**i**,**j** = **1**, . . . , **n**)

[9.27-**ij**] $$C_{e_i e_j} = 0 \,.$$
(**i**,**j** = **1**, . . . , **n**; **i** ≠ **j**)

The configuration of test items $\mathbf{X_1}, \ldots, \mathbf{X_n}$ is thus partitioned among four mutually orthogonal inferred spaces: common true-factor space S_τ, specific true-factor space S_t, common-error space S_ϵ, and unique-error space S_e. Correspondingly, the variance of each item $\mathbf{X_i}$ analyzes as

[9.28-**i**] $$V_{X_i} = V_{\tau_i} + V_{t_i} + V_{\epsilon_i} + V_{e_i} \,,$$
(**i** = **1**, . . . , **n**)

or averaging over all test items,

[9.29] $$\overline{V}_X = \overline{V}_\tau + \overline{V}_t + \overline{V}_\epsilon + \overline{V}_e \,.$$

Similarly, the test-item centroid has composition

[9.30] $$\overline{\mathbf{X}} = \overline{\tau} + \overline{\mathbf{t}} + \overline{\epsilon} + \overline{\mathbf{e}}$$

with a variance partition of

[9.31] $$V_{\overline{X}} = V_{\overline{\tau}} + V_{\overline{t}} + V_{\overline{\epsilon}} + V_{\overline{e}}$$

or using [7.97],

[9.32] $$V_{\overline{X}} = \overline{V}_\tau \,\mathrm{Sat}_\tau + \overline{V}_t \,\mathrm{Sat}_t + \overline{V}_\epsilon \,\mathrm{Sat}_\epsilon + \overline{V}_e \,\mathrm{Sat}_e \,.$$

There is nothing special about equation [9.32] as it stands, since an analysis of V_X in this form can be derived from [7.105] for any arbitrary partition of the test items among orthogonal spaces. What is of more than ordinary interest about the particular fourfold partition selected here, however, is that division of each primary configuration $\mathbf{T_1}, \ldots, \mathbf{T_n}$ and $\mathbf{E_1}, \ldots, \mathbf{E_n}$ into common-factor and unique-factor subconfigurations makes maximally articulate what is mathematically relevant in the total factor structure of a set of test items to the composition of their centroid. Specifically, the homogeneity of a configuration of unique components is necessarily zero and its saturation therefore $1/\mathbf{n}$. Hence

[9.33] $$\mathrm{Hom}_t = \mathrm{Hom}_e = 0 \,,$$

[9.34] $$\mathrm{Sat}_t = \mathrm{Sat}_e = \frac{1}{\mathbf{n}} \,,$$

so using [7.86], the variance of compound test $\overline{\mathbf{X}}$ lying in common true-factor space, specific true-factor space, common-error space, and unique-error space, respectively, is

[9.35]
$$
\begin{aligned}
V_{\bar{\mathbf{X}}(S_{\mathcal{T}})} &= V_{\bar{\mathcal{T}}} \\
&= \bar{V}_{\mathcal{T}}\ \mathrm{Sat}_{\mathcal{T}} \\
&= \bar{V}_{\mathcal{T}} \left[\left(\frac{\mathbf{n}-1}{\mathbf{n}}\right) \mathrm{Hom}_{\mathcal{T}} + \frac{1}{\mathbf{n}}\right] \\
&= \bar{V}_{\mathcal{T}} \left(\mathrm{Hom}_{\mathcal{T}} + \frac{1-\mathrm{Hom}_{\mathcal{T}}}{\mathbf{n}}\right),
\end{aligned}
$$

[9.36]
$$
\begin{aligned}
V_{\bar{\mathbf{X}}(S_{\mathbf{t}})} &= V_{\bar{\mathbf{t}}} \\
&= \bar{V}_{\mathbf{t}}\ \mathrm{Sat}_{\mathbf{t}} \\
&= \frac{\bar{V}_{\mathbf{t}}}{\mathbf{n}},
\end{aligned}
$$

[9.37]
$$
\begin{aligned}
V_{\bar{\mathbf{X}}(S_{\epsilon})} &= V_{\bar{\epsilon}} \\
&= \bar{V}_{\epsilon}\ \mathrm{Sat}_{\epsilon} \\
&= \bar{V}_{\epsilon} \left[\left(\frac{\mathbf{n}-1}{\mathbf{n}}\right) \mathrm{Hom}_{\epsilon} + \frac{1}{\mathbf{n}}\right] \\
&= \bar{V}_{\epsilon} \left(\mathrm{Hom}_{\epsilon} + \frac{1-\mathrm{Hom}_{\epsilon}}{\mathbf{n}}\right),
\end{aligned}
$$

[9.38]
$$
\begin{aligned}
V_{\bar{\mathbf{X}}(S_{\mathbf{e}})} &= V_{\bar{\mathbf{e}}} \\
&= \bar{V}_{\mathbf{e}}\ \mathrm{Sat}_{\mathbf{e}} \\
&= \frac{\bar{V}_{\mathbf{e}}}{\mathbf{n}}.
\end{aligned}
$$

Equations [9.29]–[9.38] may be called the *general composition theorem*, since they show how the variance of a compound test is apportioned by the factorial composition of its constituent items. An immediate corollary is that the reliability of $\bar{\mathbf{X}}$ analyzes as

[9.39]
$$
\begin{aligned}
r_{\bar{\mathbf{X}}} &= \frac{V_{\bar{\mathcal{T}}} + V_{\bar{\mathbf{t}}}}{V_{\bar{\mathcal{T}}} + V_{\bar{\mathbf{t}}} + V_{\bar{\mathbf{e}}} + V_{\bar{\epsilon}}} \\
&= \frac{\bar{V}_{\mathcal{T}}\ [(\mathbf{n}-1)\ \mathrm{Hom}_{\mathcal{T}} + 1] + \bar{V}_{\mathbf{t}}}{\bar{V}_{\mathcal{T}}\ [(\mathbf{n}-1)\ \mathrm{Hom}_{\mathcal{T}} + 1] + \bar{V}_{\mathbf{t}} + \bar{V}_{\mathbf{e}}\ [(\mathbf{n}-1)\ \mathrm{Hom}_{\mathbf{e}} + 1] + \bar{V}_{\mathbf{e}}} \\
&= \frac{\bar{V}_{\mathcal{T}}\ \mathrm{Hom}_{\mathcal{T}} + (\bar{V}_{\mathcal{T}} + \bar{V}_{\mathbf{t}})/(\mathbf{n}-1)}{\bar{V}_{\mathcal{T}}\ \mathrm{Hom}_{\mathcal{T}} + \bar{V}_{\mathbf{e}}\ \mathrm{Hom}_{\mathbf{e}} + (\bar{V}_{\mathcal{T}} + \bar{V}_{\mathbf{t}} + \bar{V}_{\mathbf{e}} + \bar{V}_{\mathbf{e}})/(\mathbf{n}-1)}.
\end{aligned}
$$

If for simplicity we write

$$\mathrm{P}_{\mathcal{T}} =_{\text{def}} \mathrm{P}_{\mathbf{X}}(S_{\mathcal{T}}) = \frac{\overline{\mathrm{V}}_{\mathcal{T}}}{\overline{\mathrm{V}}_{\mathbf{X}}}, \tag{9.40}$$

$$\mathrm{P}_{\mathbf{t}} =_{\text{def}} \mathrm{P}_{\mathbf{X}}(S_{\mathbf{t}}) = \frac{\overline{\mathrm{V}}_{\mathbf{t}}}{\overline{\mathrm{V}}_{\mathbf{X}}}, \tag{9.41}$$

$$\mathrm{P}_{\epsilon} =_{\text{def}} \mathrm{P}_{\mathbf{X}}(S_{\epsilon}) = \frac{\overline{\mathrm{V}}_{\epsilon}}{\overline{\mathrm{V}}_{\mathbf{X}}}, \tag{9.42}$$

$$\mathrm{P}_{\mathbf{e}} =_{\text{def}} \mathrm{P}_{\mathbf{X}}(S_{\mathbf{e}}) = \frac{\overline{\mathrm{V}}_{\mathbf{e}}}{\overline{\mathrm{V}}_{\mathbf{X}}}, \tag{9.43}$$

for the penetrances of the set of test items into the various spaces under consideration, equation [9.39] simplifies upon division of numerator and denominator by $\overline{\mathrm{V}}_{\mathbf{X}}$ and use of [9.31] to

$$\mathrm{r}_{\overline{\mathbf{X}}} = \frac{\mathrm{P}_{\mathcal{T}}\ \mathrm{Hom}_{\mathcal{T}} + (\mathrm{P}_{\mathcal{T}} + \mathrm{P}_{\mathbf{t}})/(\mathbf{n}-1)}{\mathrm{P}_{\mathcal{T}}\ \mathrm{Hom}_{\mathcal{T}} + \mathrm{P}_{\epsilon}\ \mathrm{Hom}_{\epsilon} + 1/(\mathbf{n}-1)}. \tag{9.44}$$

Since from [9.22] and [9.18]

$$\begin{aligned} \mathrm{P}_{\mathcal{T}} + \mathrm{P}_{\mathbf{t}} &= \mathrm{P}_{\mathbf{X}}(S_{\mathbf{T}}) \\ &= \tilde{\mathrm{r}}_{\mathbf{X}}, \end{aligned} \tag{9.45}$$

[9.44] may also be rewritten as

$$\mathrm{r}_{\overline{\mathbf{X}}} = \frac{(\tilde{\mathrm{r}}_{\mathbf{X}} - \mathrm{P}_{\mathbf{t}})\ \mathrm{Hom}_{\mathcal{T}} + \tilde{\mathrm{r}}_{\mathbf{X}}/(\mathbf{n}-1)}{(\tilde{\mathrm{r}}_{\mathbf{X}} - \mathrm{P}_{\mathbf{t}})\ \mathrm{Hom}_{\mathcal{T}} + \mathrm{P}_{\epsilon}\ \mathrm{Hom}_{\epsilon} + 1/(\mathbf{n}-1)}. \tag{9.46}$$

Equations [9.44] and [9.46] analyze the reliability of the centroid of an arbitrary set of test items unfettered by any restrictive assumptions. Before drawing out the significance of these results, however, let us first examine a case of intermediate generality.

Heterogeneous Test Items with Uncorrelated Errors. While it is unreasonable to expect that the measurement-error components of the individual items on a compound test administered at a single sitting will be uncorrelated, it is nonetheless useful to examine the reliability of the centroid of a set of items $\mathbf{X}_1, \ldots, \mathbf{X}_n$ whose configuration in true-score space is arbitrary but whose error components are mutually orthogonal. This makes clear how classical internal-consistency formulas are restricted specifically by their assumption of perfect true-score homogeneity, and also derives results which have practical application to composites of variables on which the various observations for each subject are sufficiently scattered to comprise essentially independent samplings of error effects.

Let us, therefore, assume at present that $C_{\mathbf{E_i E_j}} = 0$ for $\mathbf{i,j} = \mathbf{1}, \ldots, \mathbf{n}$; $\mathbf{i} \neq \mathbf{j}$. Then partition [9.2] of the $\mathbf{X_i}$ into true-score and error components may be construed as a factoring of each $\mathbf{X_i}$ into a communal component $\mathbf{T_i}$ and a unique component $\mathbf{E_i}$, so that $S_{\mathbf{T}}$ is a common-factor space and $S_{\mathbf{E}}$ the complementary unique-factor space for the set of test items. (That additional unique factors might be taken out of the $\mathbf{T_i}$, as made explicit in [9.22], does not interfere with regarding $S_{\mathbf{T}}$ as common-factor space, since as emphasized previously, there are many different ways in which a set of variables can be analyzed into communal and unique components, and common-factor space is simply what is left over after extraction of some unique-factor space.) Correspondingly, the reliabilities of test items $\mathbf{X_1}, \ldots, \mathbf{X_n}$ and their centroid $\overline{\mathbf{X}}$ are the respective penetrances of these variables into common-factor space $S_{\mathbf{T}}$; and equations [7.139]–[7.162] for the apportionment of centroid variance between common-factor space and unique-factor space may be applied directly to the present case by writing "T" for "H", "E" for "U", "$\tilde{r}_{\mathbf{X}}$" for "$\widetilde{h^2}$", and "$r_{\overline{\mathbf{X}}}$" for "$h^2_{\overline{\mathbf{X}}}$".

To generalize Spearman-Brown "prophecy" formula [8.61] to a set of imperfectly homogeneous test items with uncorrelated errors, we obtain from [7.167] that

$$[9.47] \qquad r_{\overline{\mathbf{X}}} = \frac{\mathbf{n}\,\tilde{r}_{\mathbf{X}}\,\mathrm{Sat}_{\mathbf{T}}}{(\mathbf{n}-1)\tilde{r}_{\mathbf{X}}\mathrm{Hom}_{\mathbf{T}}+1} \qquad (\mathrm{Hom}_{\mathbf{E}} = 0)\ .$$

If we take the variance-weighted average item reliability, $\tilde{r}_{\mathbf{X}}$, for our measure of single-item reliability, this reduces to the Spearman-Brown formula in the special case that the set of true-score components is perfectly homogeneous, since $\mathrm{Sat}_{\mathbf{T}} = \mathrm{Hom}_{\mathbf{T}} = 1$ when all the $\mathbf{T_i}$ are identical as assumed in [8.61]. Since the Spearman-Brown equation has frequently been published as a statement of how the reliability of a compound test depends upon its length and its single-item reliability, it is of some interest to obtain from [7.162] that

$$[9.48] \qquad r_{\overline{\mathbf{X}}} = \frac{\mathbf{n}\,\tilde{r}_{\mathbf{X}}}{(\mathbf{n}-1)\tilde{r}_{\mathbf{X}}+1}\left[1-\left(\frac{1}{\mathbf{n}}\right)\left(\frac{1-\tilde{r}_{\mathbf{X}}}{\tilde{r}_{\mathbf{X}}}\right)\left(\frac{1-\mathrm{Hom}_{\mathbf{T}}}{\mathrm{Hom}_{\mathbf{T}}}\right)\left(1-\frac{1}{\mathbf{n}\,\mathrm{Sat}_{\mathbf{X}}}\right)\right] \qquad (\mathrm{Hom}_{\mathbf{E}} = 0)\ ,$$

in which the unbracketed portion of the right-hand side is the Spearman-Brown estimate of $r_{\overline{\mathbf{X}}}$, while the complex expression to the right of the first minus within the brackets shows the proportion by which the Spearman-Brown formula is in error and what brings this error about. It will be observed that even when uncorrelated errors are assumed (or the slightly weaker assumption that $\mathrm{Hom}_{\mathbf{E}} = 0$), the Spearman-Brown estimate of the gain in reliability to be achieved by increasing test length is excessive unless perfect true-score homogeneity is maintained. On the other hand, when the Spearman-Brown formula is used to estimate total-test reliability from the correlations among subtests, as in split-halves formula [8.47] or more generally [8.65], the nature of its inaccuracy is more complex, since with uncorrelated errors, the subtest correlations are generally an underestimate of subtest reliability. This may be appreciated most easily by observing from [7.152] that the arithmetic mean proper correlation among test items $\mathbf{X}_1, \ldots, \mathbf{X}_n$ is

$$\bar{r}_{XX} = \bar{r}_X \, \mathrm{Hom}_{T'} \qquad (\mathrm{Hom}_{E'} = 0) \,, \tag{9.49}$$

where $\bar{r}_X$ is the aritnmetic mean reliability of the individual items and $\mathrm{Hom}_{T'}$ is their true-score homogeneity after they have been standardized to the same variance. It can be shown that substituting the average interitem correlation for r_{XX} in [8.65] tends to underestimate the total test's reliability when $\mathrm{Hom}_E = 0$. However, since the formula is messy and the issue not awesomely important, we shall not pursue the matter.

Although equations [9.47] and [9.48] enrich our perspective on the Spearman-Brown formula, they do not readily submit to insightful understanding of the relationship there expressed. A more revealing way to exhibit the apportionment of test variance between true-score and error components is to show how large one of these is in proportion to the other. From [7.156], after inverting,

$$\frac{1 - r_{\bar{X}}}{r_{\bar{X}}} = \frac{1}{\mathbf{n}\,\mathrm{Sat}_T}\left(\frac{1 - \tilde{r}_X}{\tilde{r}_X}\right) \qquad (\mathrm{Hom}_E = 0) \,, \tag{9.50}$$

of which [8.63] is the limiting case in which $\mathrm{Sat}_T = 1$. Equation [9.50] shows that the effect of true-score heterogeneity among the test items comprised by $\bar{\mathbf{X}}$ is to retard the *rate* at which the test's ratio of error to true-score variance decreases with increasing test length. Perhaps simplest of all is to observe from [7.159] that

$$r_{\bar{X}} \simeq 1 - \frac{1}{\mathbf{n}\,\mathrm{Sat}_T}\left(\frac{1 - \tilde{r}_X}{\tilde{r}_X}\right) \qquad (\mathrm{Hom}_E = 0) \,, \tag{9.51}$$

where the approximation is highly accurate except perhaps for very low values of $\mathbf{n}$, Sat_T, or $\tilde{r}_X$, and is a lower bound for $r_{\bar{X}}$ in any case.

Finally, a fact of considerable importance for internal-consistency estimation of reliability is that while equivalence between a test's reliability and alpha coefficient (see [8.85]) requires that the test items have perfect true-score homogeneity, moderate violation of this condition turns out for most purposes to be not very serious so long as $\mathrm{Hom}_E = 0$ is retained. Dividing numerator and denominator of the right-hand side of [8.71] by $\mathbf{n}$ and applying [7.86] shows that for any set of variables $\mathbf{X}_1, \ldots, \mathbf{X}_n$,

$$\alpha_X = \frac{\mathrm{Hom}_X}{\mathrm{Sat}_X} = 1 - \frac{\mathrm{DQ}_X}{\mathbf{n} - 1} \tag{9.52}$$

Hence from [7.167],

[9.53] $$\alpha_{\mathbf{T}} r_{\overline{\mathbf{X}}} = \alpha_{\mathbf{X}} \qquad (\mathrm{Hom}_{\mathbf{E}} = 0)$$

or

[9.54] $$\alpha_{\mathbf{X}} = r_{\overline{\mathbf{X}}}\left(1 - \frac{\mathrm{DQ}_{\mathbf{T}}}{\mathbf{n} - 1}\right) \qquad (\mathrm{Hom}_{\mathbf{E}} = 0) \; .$$

Hence

[9.55] $$\alpha_{\mathbf{X}} \leqslant r_{\overline{\mathbf{X}}} \qquad (\mathrm{Hom}_{\mathbf{E}} = 0) \; ,$$

where the difference between these two terms is seen from [9.54] to be generally on the order of $1/\mathbf{n}$. Thus given $\mathrm{Hom}_{\mathbf{E}} = 0$, a test's alpha coefficient is a lower bound for its reliability as well as being a close approximation to the latter except perhaps when the number of test items or their true-score homogeneity is very small. More detailed evaluation of the accuracy with which $\alpha_{\mathbf{X}}$ approximates $r_{\overline{\mathbf{X}}}$ when item errors are uncorrelated, as well as other internal-consistency estimates of reliability which are also appropriate in this case, follow from the considerations on pp. 330ff.

Heterogeneous Test Items with Correlated Errors. It was remarked previously (p. 405) that discussions of split-half and other internal-consistency estimates of reliability frequently include an admonition that these should not be applied to speeded tests. The basis for this warning may be appreciated by observing that one determinant of scores on a test item $\mathbf{X}_i$ is how much time is spent on it, especially whether or not the item is attempted at all. It is also to be expected that the time a potential testee *would* spend on item $\mathbf{X}_i$ were this subject to take the test depends in part upon the detailed test circumstances, so that the variance in a subject's distribution of potential values on the time-factor component of $\mathbf{X}_i$ contributes to the distribution of potential measurement errors on this item. But on speeded tests (or for that matter, due to fatigue or other motivational effects, even to some extent on "power"—i.e., unspeeded—tests) extra time spent on one item generally decreases the time the subject is willing or able to spend on another. Just how this causes a subject's performance on one item to influence his score on another depends rather critically on the importance of deliberation over an item and the overall pacing with which the items are taken up, since on tests where time limits prevent all items from being attempted, the deficit in remaining available time produced by an excess of time spent on a particular item $\mathbf{X}_i$ can result either in a decrease in time spent on other attempted items, a decrease in the number of other items attempted, or a combination thereof. The first of these two effects would tend to induce negative correlation between the measurement errors on $\mathbf{X}_i$ and other test items, and could be relatively important if the likelihood of success on an attempted item is significantly influenced by the time spent on it. As a result of the second time-limit effect, on the other hand, items tend to be attempted or not to be attempted together (i.e., what increases the opportunity for one item to be attempted similarly favors other items as well), which works for positive correlations among their error components. Whatever the net outcome of these influences, the vicissitudes of internal-consistency reliability estimates in application to speeded tests turn out to be an anticipated violation of the $\text{Hom}_{\mathbf{E}} = 0$ stipulation in equations [9.47]–[9.55]. But quite apart from time-limit details, responsible test theorists have repeatedly pointed out that it is madness to expect the measurement-error components of test items administered on the same testing occasion to be untainted by correlation. To cringe from internal-consistency estimates of reliability for speeded tests while voicing no qualms about other applications of such measures thus appears somewhat parochial—if speeded tests are to be so stigmatized, it should be stated only that internal-consistency statistics are probably *more* misleading about a test's reliability if the test is speeded than if it is not. Actually, the problem is generic: If internal-consistency measures are to attain stature in reliability theory by honest merit rather than by irrelevant mathematical elegance, explicit provision must be made for the effects of correlated measurement errors. And of course it is desirable to know what $\text{Hom}_{\mathbf{E}} > 0$ does to a test's reliability regardless of what schemes we may have to assess this reliability empirically.

The reliability of a compound test $\overline{\mathbf{X}}$ under completely general conditions of true-score heterogeneity and correlated errors has already been analyzed in formulas [9.44] and [9.46]. An equation in six independent variables is not likely to be comprehended at a glance, however, and it is worth a few paragraphs to tease out more deftly what these and general composition equations [9.29]–[9.38] say about the variance structure of $\overline{\mathbf{X}}$, especially in regard to how this is affected by the number of test items. In so doing, we shall see that the alpha coefficient, which first made its appearance on p. 411 as an internal-consistency estimate of reliability, turns out to be importantly involved in the mathematics of centroid variance.

Let the alpha coefficient, $\alpha_{\mathbf{X}}(S)$, for the projection of a set $\mathbf{X}_1, \ldots, \mathbf{X}_n$ into an arbitrary space S be defined as the alpha coefficient for the components of the $\mathbf{X}_i$ lying in S—i.e., from [9.52]

[9.56]
$$\alpha_{\mathbf{X}}(S) =_{\text{def}} \alpha_{\mathbf{e}_{\mathbf{X}(S)}} = \frac{\text{Hom}_{\mathbf{X}}(S)}{\text{Sat}_{\mathbf{X}}(S)} = \frac{\mathbf{n}\,\text{Hom}_{\mathbf{X}}(S)}{(\mathbf{n}-1)\,\text{Hom}_{\mathbf{X}}(S)+1}.$$

From [7.102], the penetrance of the set's centroid into space S may then be written

[9.57] $$P_{\bar{\mathbf{X}}}(S) = \frac{\alpha_{\mathbf{X}}}{\alpha_{\mathbf{X}}(S)} \cdot \frac{\mathrm{P}_{\mathbf{X}}(S)\ \mathrm{Hom}_{\mathbf{X}}(S)}{\mathrm{Hom}_{\mathbf{X}}} .$$

Equation [9.57] becomes indeterminate in case $\mathrm{Hom}_{\mathbf{X}}(S) = 0$. However, the penetrance of $\bar{\mathbf{X}}$ into any neuter-space S_0 is seen from [7.102], [7.106], and [9.56] to be

[9.58] $$P_{\bar{\mathbf{X}}}(S_0) = \frac{\alpha_{\mathbf{X}}}{\mathbf{n}} \cdot \frac{\mathrm{P}_{\mathbf{X}}(S_0)}{\mathrm{Hom}_{\mathbf{X}}} \qquad (\mathrm{Hom}_{\mathbf{X}}(S_0) = 0) .$$

Since there appears to be no mathematical reason why a set's penetrance and homogeneity in a given space should systematically vary with the number of variables in the set so long as $\mathrm{Hom}_{\mathbf{X}}(S) \geqslant 0$,[2] equations [9.57] and [9.58] may be interpreted as a function relating a set's centroid penetrance into a given space to the number of variables in the set, with the set's penetrances and homogeneities in the relevant spaces taken as parameters. As is visually apparent in Figure 8.1, an alpha coefficient increases to an asymptotic value of unity with increasing **n** so long as the corresponding homogeneity is positive. Hence it is clear from [9.57,8] that with increasing **n**, the penetrance of $\bar{\mathbf{X}}$ into space S asymptotically approaches

[9.59] $$\lim_{\mathbf{n}\to\infty} P_{\bar{\mathbf{X}}}(S) = \frac{\mathrm{P}_{\mathbf{X}}(S)\ \mathrm{Hom}_{\mathbf{X}}(S)}{\mathrm{Hom}_{\mathbf{X}}} \qquad \text{(fixed parameters)}$$
$$= \frac{\mathrm{P}_{\mathbf{X}}(S)\ \mathrm{Hom}_{\mathbf{X}}(S)}{\mathrm{P}_{\mathbf{X}}(S)\ \mathrm{Hom}_{\mathbf{X}}(S) + \mathrm{P}_{\mathbf{X}}(S^*)\ \mathrm{Hom}_{\mathbf{X}}(S^*)}$$

where the second line of [9.59] follows by [7.112]. To see explicitly the manner in which $P_{\bar{\mathbf{X}}}(S)$ approaches this limit as a function of **n**, we may observe that

[9.60] $$\frac{\alpha_{\mathbf{X}}}{\alpha_{\mathbf{X}}(S)} = 1 + \alpha_{\mathbf{X}}\left[\frac{1}{\alpha_{\mathbf{X}}(S)} - \frac{1}{\alpha_{\mathbf{X}}}\right] = 1 + \frac{\alpha_{\mathbf{X}}}{\mathbf{n}}\left[\frac{\mathrm{Hom}_{\mathbf{X}} - \mathrm{Hom}_{\mathbf{X}}(S)}{\mathrm{Hom}_{\mathbf{X}} \cdot \mathrm{Hom}_{\mathbf{X}}(S)}\right] .$$

Hence from [9.57], [9.59], and [9.60], the divergence of $P_{\bar{\mathbf{X}}}(S)$ from its asymptotic limit is

[9.61] $$P_{\bar{\mathbf{X}}}(S) - \lim_{\mathbf{n}\to\infty} P_{\bar{\mathbf{X}}}(S) = \frac{\alpha_{\mathbf{X}}}{\mathbf{n}} \cdot \frac{\mathrm{P}_{\mathbf{X}}(S)}{\mathrm{Hom}_{\mathbf{X}}}\left[1 - \frac{\mathrm{Hom}_{\mathbf{X}}(S)}{\mathrm{Hom}_{\mathbf{X}}}\right] \qquad \text{(fixed parameters)}$$
$$= \frac{\alpha_{\mathbf{X}}}{\mathbf{n}\ \mathrm{Hom}_{\mathbf{X}}}\left[\mathrm{P}_{\mathbf{X}}(S) - \lim_{\mathbf{n}\to\infty} P_{\bar{\mathbf{X}}}(S)\right] .$$

[2] By [7.93], homogeneity cannot remain at any fixed negative value as **n** grows indefinitely large.

Since $P_{\overline{\mathbf{X}}}(S) = P_{\mathbf{X}}(S)$ when $\mathbf{n} = \mathbf{1}$, the second line of [9.61] says that the rate at which $P_{\overline{\mathbf{X}}}(S)$ approaches its asymptote with increasing $\mathbf{n}$ is essentially inversely proportional to $\text{Hom}_{\mathbf{X}}$ and directly proportional to the maximum difference in $P_{\overline{\mathbf{X}}}(S)$ that a difference in $\mathbf{n}$ can make.

To apply these results to the reliability of a set's centroid, we have from [9.15], [9.18], and [9.57]–[9.61], since $\alpha_{\mathbf{X}}(S_{\mathbf{T}}) = \alpha_{\mathbf{T}}$,

[9.62]
$$r_{\overline{\mathbf{X}}} = \frac{\alpha_{\mathbf{X}}}{\alpha_{\mathbf{T}}} \cdot \frac{\tilde{r}_{\mathbf{X}} \text{Hom}_{\mathbf{T}}}{\text{Hom}_{\mathbf{X}}}$$
$$= \frac{\tilde{r}_{\mathbf{X}} \text{Hom}_{\mathbf{T}}}{\tilde{r}_{\mathbf{X}} \text{Hom}_{\mathbf{T}} + (1 - \tilde{r}_{\mathbf{X}}) \text{Hom}_{\mathbf{E}}} - \frac{\alpha_{\mathbf{X}} \tilde{r}_{\mathbf{X}}}{\mathbf{n} \text{Hom}_{\mathbf{X}}} \left(\frac{\text{Hom}_{\mathbf{T}}}{\text{Hom}_{\mathbf{X}}} - 1 \right),$$

where by [7.122],

[9.63]
$$\text{Hom}_{\mathbf{X}} = \tilde{r}_{\mathbf{X}} \text{Hom}_{\mathbf{T}} + (1 - \tilde{r}_{\mathbf{X}}) \text{Hom}_{\mathbf{E}} .$$

It is thus apparent that as the number of items on a compound test $\overline{\mathbf{X}}$ increases, its reliability goes asymptotically to

[9.64]
$$\lim_{\mathbf{n} \to \infty} r_{\overline{\mathbf{X}}} = \frac{\tilde{r}_{\mathbf{X}} \text{Hom}_{\mathbf{T}}}{\tilde{r}_{\mathbf{X}} \text{Hom}_{\mathbf{T}} + (1 - \tilde{r}_{\mathbf{X}}) \text{Hom}_{\mathbf{E}}} \quad \text{(fixed parameters)} .$$

Some algebraic reorganization of the second major term in [9.62], using [9.63], also shows that

[9.65]
$$\frac{\alpha_{\mathbf{X}} \tilde{r}_{\mathbf{X}}}{\mathbf{n} \text{Hom}_{\mathbf{X}}} \left(\frac{\text{Hom}_{\mathbf{T}}}{\text{Hom}_{\mathbf{X}}} - 1 \right) = \frac{\alpha_{\mathbf{X}}}{\mathbf{n} \text{Hom}_{\mathbf{T}}} \left(\frac{1 - \tilde{r}_{\mathbf{X}}}{\tilde{r}_{\mathbf{X}}} \right) \left\{ \frac{1 - \dfrac{\text{Hom}_{\mathbf{E}}}{\text{Hom}_{\mathbf{T}}}}{\left[1 + \left(\dfrac{1 - \tilde{r}_{\mathbf{X}}}{\tilde{r}_{\mathbf{X}}} \right) \dfrac{\text{Hom}_{\mathbf{E}}}{\text{Hom}_{\mathbf{T}}} \right]^2} \right\},$$

in which the messy-looking expression within braces is between zero and unity so long as $\text{Hom}_{\mathbf{E}}$ is neither negative nor greater than $\text{Hom}_{\mathbf{T}}$, and approaches unity if $\text{Hom}_{\mathbf{E}}$ is small in comparison to $\text{Hom}_{\mathbf{T}}$. Hence if $0 \leqslant \text{Hom}_{\mathbf{E}} \leqslant \text{Hom}_{\mathbf{T}}$, the discrepancy between $r_{\overline{\mathbf{X}}}$ and its asymptotic value is bounded by

[9.66]
$$0 \leqslant \frac{\tilde{r}_{\mathbf{X}} \text{Hom}_{\mathbf{T}}}{\tilde{r}_{\mathbf{X}} \text{Hom}_{\mathbf{T}} + (1 - \tilde{r}_{\mathbf{X}}) \text{Hom}_{\mathbf{E}}} - r_{\overline{\mathbf{X}}} \leqslant \frac{\alpha_{\mathbf{X}}}{\mathbf{n} \text{Hom}_{\mathbf{T}}} \left(\frac{1 - \tilde{r}_{\mathbf{X}}}{\tilde{r}_{\mathbf{X}}} \right)$$
$$(0 \leqslant \text{Hom}_{\mathbf{E}} \leqslant \text{Hom}_{\mathbf{T}}) .$$

where the inequality on the right approaches an identity as $\text{Hom}_{\mathbf{E}}/\text{Hom}_{\mathbf{T}}$ approaches zero.

It is clear from equations [9.62]–[9.66] that the only factor-structure properties of the items composing a compound test $\overline{\mathbf{X}}$ relevant to the test's reliability are the variance-weighted average reliability of the individual test items and their homogeneities in true-score space and error space, respectively. In particular, the factorial complexity of the $\mathbf{T_i}$ or the $\mathbf{E_i}$ is as such irrelevant to $r_{\overline{X}}$ (though much factorial diversity among the $\mathbf{T_i}$ will tend to be associated with relatively low $\text{Hom}_{\mathbf{T}}$), nor does it matter in the slightest how the true-score configuration orthogonal to $\overline{\mathbf{T}}$ is partitioned between common-factor and unique-factor space. Just the same, we know that the proportion of variance a set of variables invests in unique-factor space places a limit on the homogeneity which that set can achieve through its behavior in common-factor space (cf. [7.151]), and it is of some interest to make this explicit in the general reliability equations. From principle [7.108] we have

[9.67]
$$\tilde{r}_{\mathbf{X}}\,\text{Hom}_{\mathbf{T}} = P_{\tau}\,\text{Hom}_{\tau} + P_{\mathbf{t}}\,\text{Hom}_{\mathbf{t}} = P_{\tau}\,\text{Hom}_{\tau}\,,$$

[9.68]
$$(1-\tilde{r}_{\mathbf{X}})\,\text{Hom}_{\mathbf{X}} = P_{\epsilon}\,\text{Hom}_{\epsilon} + P_{\mathbf{e}}\,\text{Hom}_{\mathbf{e}} = P_{\epsilon}\,\text{Hom}_{\epsilon}\,,$$

and

[9.69]
$$\text{Hom}_{\mathbf{X}} = P_{\tau}\,\text{Hom}_{\tau} + P_{\epsilon}\,\text{Hom}_{\epsilon}$$

Hence equation [9.62] may also be written

[9.70]
$$r_{\overline{\mathbf{X}}} = \frac{\alpha_{\mathbf{X}}}{\alpha_{\mathbf{T}}} \cdot \frac{P_{\tau}\,\text{Hom}_{\tau}}{P_{\tau}\,\text{Hom}_{\tau} + P_{\epsilon}\,\text{Hom}_{\epsilon}}$$
$$= \frac{P_{\tau}\,\text{Hom}_{\tau}}{P_{\tau}\,\text{Hom}_{\tau} + P_{\epsilon}\,\text{Hom}_{\epsilon}} - \frac{\alpha_{\mathbf{X}}}{\mathbf{n}\,\text{Hom}_{\mathbf{X}}}\left(\frac{P_{\tau}\,\text{Hom}_{\tau}}{P_{\tau}\,\text{Hom}_{\tau} + P_{\epsilon}\,\text{Hom}_{\epsilon}} - \tilde{r}_{\mathbf{X}}\right),$$

while

[9.71]
$$\lim_{\mathbf{n}\to\infty} r_{\overline{\mathbf{X}}} = \frac{P_{\tau}\,\text{Hom}_{\tau}}{P_{\tau}\,\text{Hom}_{\tau} + P_{\epsilon}\,\text{Hom}_{\epsilon}} \qquad \text{(fixed parameters)}\,.$$

To summarize the general case, then, we see that the reliability of a compound test $\overline{\mathbf{X}}$ grows with the number of test items from an initial value of $\tilde{r}_{\mathbf{X}}$ when $\mathbf{n} = \mathbf{1}$ to an asymptotic value determined by the balance between the penetrance and homogeneity of the configuration of test items in common true-factor space and common-error space, respectively. It is clear from [9.66] or [9.70], moreover, that unless the number of test items is quite small, $r_{\overline{\mathbf{X}}}$ will generally be well approximated by its asymptote—which also shows that the Spearman-Brown "prophecy" formula is in general grossly misleading. Specifically, the Spearman-Brown formula and its internal-consistency variants lead one to assume that the most important determinants of a compound test's reliability are the number of test items and their single-item reliability, whereas neither of these quantities are directly involved in [9.71]. As made explicit by rewriting [9.71] as

$$[9.72] \qquad \lim_{n \to \infty} r_{\bar{X}} = \frac{(\tilde{r}_X - P_t)\,\mathrm{Hom}_\tau}{(\tilde{r}_X - P_t)\,\mathrm{Hom}_\tau + P_\epsilon\,\mathrm{Hom}_\epsilon} \qquad \text{(fixed parameters)},$$

the reliabilities of the individual items contribute little to their composite reliability if the single-item reliabilities are dispersed through specific true-factor space. Further, the behavior of the test items in error space turns out to be critical for $r_{\bar{X}}$. No matter how homogeneous the $\mathbf{X}_i$ may be in true-factor space or how large the number of items, $r_{\bar{X}}$ cannot exceed the limit

$$[9.73]^{3} \qquad r_{\bar{X}} \leqslant \frac{1 - P_\epsilon}{1 - P_\epsilon + P_\epsilon\,\mathrm{Hom}_\epsilon} \leqslant 1 - \frac{P_\epsilon}{1 - P_\epsilon}\,\mathrm{Hom}_\epsilon\,.$$

In fact, if the homogeneity of the test items in error space exceeds their true-score homogeneity (i.e., if $\mathrm{Hom}_E > \mathrm{Hom}_T$), the asymptotic value of $r_{\bar{X}}$ is below $\tilde{r}_X$, and assuming fixed parameters, increasing the length of the test in this case actually *decreases* its reliability. Hopefully, this situation is rare. But even so, inequality [9.73] has the important practical implication that if high test reliability is desired (and principle [8.105] gives ample justification for desiring it), then research is needed on the extent to which item errors on a compound test do, in fact, tend to be correlated, and what, if anything, can be done to mitigate this effect if it turns out to be appreciable.

Validity and Test Length

While we have here followed in test theory's noble tradition of allocating first concern to reliability analysis, it is perhaps not altogether inappropriate to see what import the length and factor structure of a composite test have for its *validity*. To begin, since a given test $\bar{\mathbf{X}}$ may be used to predict not just one specific criterion but perhaps many different criteria of a certain kind (e.g., using IQ scores to forecast success in various occupations), it is helpful to think of a test's validity for a certain general purpose as being its correlation with whatever criterion of the relevant sort it predicts best. In particular, if the concept of "validity" is generalized from predicting a single criterion to predicting within a *space*, S_Y, of criterion variables, the validity of $\bar{\mathbf{X}}$ for S_Y is then the maximal correlation that $\bar{\mathbf{X}}$ has with any variable in S_Y, namely, the square root of $\bar{\mathbf{X}}$'s penetrance into S_Y, where the variables in S_Y with which $\bar{\mathbf{X}}$ has this

[3] Since $\mathrm{Hom}_T \leqslant 1$ and $P_T \leqslant 1 - P_\epsilon$. The first inequality in [9.73] may be stated more elegantly as

$$PQ_{\bar{X}}(S_E) \geqslant PQ_X(S_\epsilon) \cdot \mathrm{Hom}_\epsilon\,.$$

maximal correlation coincide up to a linear transformation with $\overline{\mathbf{X}}$'s projection into $S_{\mathbf{Y}}$. In the limiting case where $S_{\mathbf{Y}}$ is a one-dimensional space spanned by variable $\mathbf{Y}$, $P_{\overline{\mathbf{X}}}(S_{\mathbf{Y}}) = \mathrm{r}^2_{\overline{\mathbf{X}}\mathbf{Y}}$ – which makes clear that the concept of test penetrance into criterion space is a natural generalization of single-criterion validity theory.

Once validity (or more precisely its square) is assimilated to penetrance, moreover, the effect of a test's length and structural parameters upon its validity can be read directly from the equations for $P_{\overline{\mathbf{X}}}(S)$ developed above. Specifically, if $S^*_{\mathbf{Y}}$ is the complement of criterion space $S_{\mathbf{Y}}$ – i.e., $S^*_{\mathbf{Y}}$ is the space of all variables orthogonal to $S_{\mathbf{Y}}$ – then the asymptotic limit of $\overline{\mathbf{X}}$'s squared correlation with the criterion it predicts best in $S_{\mathbf{Y}}$ is

[9.74]

$$\lim_{\mathbf{n}\to\infty} P_{\overline{\mathbf{X}}}(S_{\mathbf{Y}}) = \frac{\mathrm{P}_{\mathbf{X}}(S_{\mathbf{Y}})\ \mathrm{Hom}_{\mathbf{X}}(S_{\mathbf{Y}})}{\mathrm{P}_{\mathbf{X}}(S_{\mathbf{Y}})\ \mathrm{Hom}_{\mathbf{X}}(S_{\mathbf{Y}}) + \mathrm{P}_{\mathbf{X}}(S^*_{\mathbf{Y}})\,\mathrm{Hom}_{\mathbf{X}}(S^*_{\mathbf{Y}})}$$

(fixed parameters)

$$= \frac{\mathrm{P}_{\mathbf{X}}(S_{\mathbf{Y}})\ \mathrm{Hom}_{\mathbf{X}}(S_{\mathbf{Y}})}{\mathrm{P}_{\mathbf{X}}(S_{\mathbf{Y}})\ \mathrm{Hom}_{\mathbf{X}}(S_{\mathbf{Y}}) + [1 - \mathrm{P}_{\mathbf{X}}(S_{\mathbf{Y}})]\ \mathrm{Hom}_{\mathbf{X}}(S^*_{\mathbf{Y}})},$$

while the rate at which $P_{\overline{\mathbf{X}}}(S_{\mathbf{Y}})$ approaches this limit may be obtained by reading "$S_{\mathbf{Y}}$" for "S" in [9.61]. The mathematical relations here are identical with those holding in general for a centroid's reliability, except that in the analysis of $\mathrm{r}_{\overline{\mathbf{X}}}$ we can hope that $\mathrm{Hom}_{\mathbf{X}}(S_{\mathbf{E}})$ will be negligible in comparison to $\mathrm{Hom}_{\mathbf{X}}(S_{\mathbf{T}})$, whereas for validity, $\mathrm{Hom}_{\mathbf{X}}(S^*_{\mathbf{Y}})$ and $\mathrm{Hom}_{\mathbf{X}}(S_{\mathbf{Y}})$ may easily be on the same order of magnitude. It may be seen that if length (i.e., numerosity of items) is to be much of an asset for promoting validity in a test, it is necessary for the homogeneity of the item projections into criterion space to be substantially greater than the homogeneity of the item components orthogonal to criterion space. This is shown most vividly by the test's penetrance quotient in the complement of criterion space, namely,

$$[9.75]\quad PQ_{\overline{\mathbf{X}}}(S^*_{\mathbf{Y}}) = \frac{P_{\overline{\mathbf{X}}}(S^*_{\mathbf{Y}})}{P_{\overline{\mathbf{X}}}(S_{\mathbf{Y}})} = \mathrm{PQ}_{\mathbf{X}}(S^*_{\mathbf{Y}})\,\frac{\mathrm{Sat}_{\mathbf{X}}(S^*_{\mathbf{Y}})}{\mathrm{Sat}_{\mathbf{X}}(S_{\mathbf{Y}})}$$

$$= \frac{\alpha_{\mathbf{X}}(S_{\mathbf{Y}})}{\alpha_{\mathbf{X}}(S^*_{\mathbf{Y}})}\left[\mathrm{PQ}_{\mathbf{X}}(S^*_{\mathbf{Y}})\,\frac{\mathrm{Hom}_{\mathbf{X}}(S^*_{\mathbf{Y}})}{\mathrm{Hom}_{\mathbf{X}}(S_{\mathbf{Y}})}\right],$$

in which the saturation ratio lies between unity and the corresponding ratio of homogeneities. (We examine $PQ_{\overline{\mathbf{X}}}(S^*_{\mathbf{Y}})$ rather than $PQ_{\overline{\mathbf{X}}}(S_{\mathbf{Y}})$ since as shown by reading $S^*_{\mathbf{Y}}$ for S and $S_{\mathbf{Y}}$ for S^* in [7.126], $P_{\overline{\mathbf{X}}}(S_{\mathbf{Y}}) \simeq 1 - PQ_{\overline{\mathbf{X}}}(S^*_{\mathbf{Y}})$ when $PQ_{\overline{\mathbf{X}}}(S^*_{\mathbf{Y}})$ is small.) Since $PQ_{\overline{\mathbf{X}}}(S^*_{\mathbf{Y}}) = \mathrm{PQ}_{\mathbf{X}}(S^*_{\mathbf{Y}})$ when $\mathbf{n} = \mathbf{1}$, the effect of $\mathbf{n} > \mathbf{1}$ is to place $PQ_{\overline{\mathbf{X}}}(S^*_{\mathbf{Y}})$ somewhere between the extremes $\mathrm{PQ}_{\mathbf{X}}(S^*_{\mathbf{Y}})$ and $\mathrm{PQ}_{\mathbf{X}}(S^*_{\mathbf{Y}})\cdot[\mathrm{Hom}_{\mathbf{X}}(S^*_{\mathbf{Y}})/\mathrm{Hom}_{\mathbf{X}}(S_{\mathbf{Y}})]$. Further, the alpha-coefficient ratio in [9.75] will be very close to unity, and $PQ_{\overline{\mathbf{X}}}(S^*_{\mathbf{Y}})$

hence very close to the latter extreme, unless $\mathbf{n}$ is small and the difference between $\text{Hom}_{\mathbf{X}}(S_{\mathbf{Y}})$ and $\text{Hom}_{\mathbf{H}}(S^*_{\mathbf{Y}})$ is rather large. The potential effect on $PQ_{\bar{\mathbf{X}}}(S^*_{\mathbf{Y}})$ of increased test length, virtually all of which is generally achieved by only modest $\mathbf{n}$, is thus represented by the factor $[\text{Hom}_{\mathbf{X}}(S^*_{\mathbf{Y}})/\text{Hom}_{\mathbf{X}}(S_{\mathbf{Y}})]$, which diminishes $PQ_{\bar{\mathbf{X}}}(S^*_{\mathbf{Y}})$ and hence benefits $P_{\bar{\mathbf{X}}}(S_{\mathbf{Y}})$ only to the extent that $\text{Hom}_{\mathbf{X}}(S_{\mathbf{Y}})$ exceeds $\text{Hom}_{\mathbf{X}}(S^*_{\mathbf{Y}})$. In fact, if this inequality is reversed, the longer the test the *lower* is its validity.

When criterion space is one-dimensional—i.e., when $S_{\mathbf{Y}}$ is spanned by a single criterion $\mathbf{Y}$—the general relationship stated in [9.75] has a striking expression in terms of partial correlation. Let the "sigma-weighted" statistics $\tilde{r}_{\mathbf{XY}}$, $\tilde{k}_{\mathbf{XY}}$, and $\tilde{r}^*_{\mathbf{XX}\bullet\mathbf{Y}}$ be defined

[9.76] $$\tilde{r}_{\mathbf{XY}} =_{\text{def}} \frac{\sum_{i=1}^{n} \sigma_{\mathbf{X}_i}\sigma_{\mathbf{Y}} r_{\mathbf{X}_i\mathbf{Y}}}{\sum_{i=1}^{n} \sigma_{\mathbf{X}_i}\sigma_{\mathbf{Y}}} = \frac{\sum_{i=1}^{n} \sigma_{\mathbf{X}_i} r_{\mathbf{X}_i\mathbf{Y}}}{\sum_{i=1}^{n} \sigma_{\mathbf{X}_i}},$$

[9.77] $$\tilde{k}_{\mathbf{XY}} =_{\text{def}} \frac{\sum_{i=1}^{n} \sigma_{\mathbf{X}_i}\sigma_{\mathbf{Y}} k_{\mathbf{X}_i\mathbf{Y}}}{\sum_{i=1}^{n} \sigma_{\mathbf{X}_i}\sigma_{\mathbf{Y}}} = \frac{\sum_{i=1}^{n} \sigma_{\mathbf{X}_i} k_{\mathbf{X}_i\mathbf{Y}}}{\sum_{i=1}^{n} \sigma_{\mathbf{X}_i}},$$

[9.78] $$\tilde{r}^*_{\mathbf{XX}\bullet\mathbf{Y}} =_{\text{def}} \frac{\sum_{i=1}^{n}\sum_{j=1}^{n} \sigma_{\mathbf{X}_i\bullet\mathbf{Y}}\sigma_{\mathbf{X}_j\bullet\mathbf{Y}} r_{\mathbf{X}_i\mathbf{X}_j\bullet\mathbf{Y}}}{\sum_{i=1}^{n}\sum_{j=1}^{n} \sigma_{\mathbf{X}_i\bullet\mathbf{Y}}\sigma_{\mathbf{X}_j\bullet\mathbf{Y}}}.$$

$\tilde{r}_{\mathbf{XY}}$ is simply a weighted average of the correlations between criterion $\mathbf{Y}$ and the individual test items while $\tilde{k}_{\mathbf{XY}}$ is a weighted average of the corresponding coefficients of alienation and $\tilde{r}^*_{\mathbf{XX}\bullet\mathbf{Y}}$ is a weighted average of the correlations, including self-correlations, among the test items after $\mathbf{Y}$ is partialled out. Now when space $S_{\mathbf{Y}}$ is spanned by $\mathbf{Y}$, $C_{\mathbf{X}_i\mathbf{X}_j(S_{\mathbf{Y}})} = C_{\mathbf{X}_i\mathbf{Y}}C_{\mathbf{X}_j\mathbf{Y}}/V_{\mathbf{Y}}$ (see [6.15]) and hence

$$\begin{aligned} V_{\bar{\mathbf{X}}(S_{\mathbf{Y}})} &= (1/\mathbf{n}^2)\sum_{i=1}^{n}\sum_{j=1}^{n} C_{\mathbf{X}_i\mathbf{X}_j(S_{\mathbf{Y}})} = (1/\mathbf{n}^2)\sum_{i=1}^{n}\sum_{j=1}^{n} \sigma_{\mathbf{X}_i}\sigma_{\mathbf{X}_j} r_{\mathbf{X}_i\mathbf{Y}} r_{\mathbf{X}_j\mathbf{Y}} \\ &= (1/\mathbf{n}^2)\left(\sum_{i=1}^{n} \sigma_{\mathbf{X}_i} r_{\mathbf{X}_i\mathbf{Y}}\right)^2 = (1/\mathbf{n}^2)\left(\sum_{i=1}^{n} \sigma_{\mathbf{X}_i}\right)^2 \tilde{r}^2_{\mathbf{XY}} \end{aligned}$$

while

$$V_{\bar{\mathbf{X}}(S^*_{\mathbf{Y}})} = (1/\mathbf{n}^2)\sum_{i=1}^{n}\sum_{j=1}^{n} C_{\mathbf{X}_i\mathbf{X}_j\bullet\mathbf{Y}} = (1/\mathbf{n}^2)\sum_{i=1}^{n}\sum_{j=1}^{n} \sigma_{\mathbf{X}_i}\sigma_{\mathbf{X}_j} k_{\mathbf{X}_i\mathbf{Y}} k_{\mathbf{X}_j\mathbf{Y}} r_{\mathbf{X}_i\mathbf{X}_j\bullet\mathbf{Y}}$$

$$= (1/\mathbf{n}^2)\ \tilde{r}^*_{\mathbf{XX\bullet Y}} \sum_{i=1}^{\mathbf{n}} \sum_{j=1}^{\mathbf{n}} \sigma_{\mathbf{X}_i}\sigma_{\mathbf{X}_j} k_{\mathbf{X}_i\mathbf{Y}} k_{\mathbf{X}_j\mathbf{Y}} = (1/\mathbf{n}^2)\ \tilde{r}^*_{\mathbf{XX\bullet Y}} \left(\sum_{i=1}^{\mathbf{n}} \sigma_{\mathbf{X}_i}\right)^2 \tilde{k}^2_{\mathbf{XY}} .$$

Consequently, the penetrance quotient for $\overline{\mathbf{X}}$ in the space orthogonal to criterion **Y** is

[9.79]

$$\left(\frac{k_{\overline{\mathbf{X}}\mathbf{Y}}}{r_{\overline{\mathbf{X}}\mathbf{Y}}}\right)^2 = PQ_{\overline{\mathbf{X}}}(S^*_{\mathbf{Y}}) = \frac{V_{\overline{\mathbf{X}}(S^*_{\mathbf{Y}})}}{V_{\overline{\mathbf{X}}(S_{\mathbf{Y}})}} = \left(\frac{\tilde{k}_{\mathbf{XY}}}{\tilde{r}_{\mathbf{XY}}}\right)^2 \tilde{r}^*_{\mathbf{XX\bullet Y}} \qquad (\mathrm{Span}(S_{\mathbf{Y}};\ \mathbf{Y}))\ ,$$

or using [7.124] when the penetrance of **X** into $S_{\mathbf{Y}}$ is greater than into $S^*_{\mathbf{Y}}$,

[9.80]

$$r^2_{\overline{\mathbf{X}}\mathbf{Y}} = 1 - \left(\frac{\tilde{k}_{\mathbf{XY}}}{\tilde{r}_{\mathbf{XY}}}\right)^2 \tilde{r}^*_{\mathbf{XX\bullet Y}} + \left[\left(\frac{\tilde{k}_{\mathbf{XY}}}{\tilde{r}_{\mathbf{XY}}}\right)^2 \tilde{r}^*_{\mathbf{XX\bullet Y}}\right]^2 - [\ \cdots\ ]^3 + [\ \cdots\ ]^4 - \ldots .$$

Although the term $\tilde{r}^*_{\mathbf{XX\bullet Y}}$ contains self-correlations as well as partial intercorrelations, $\tilde{r}^*_{\mathbf{XX\bullet Y}}$ approaches the corresponding sigma-weighted average intercorrelation $\tilde{r}_{\mathbf{XX\bullet Y}}$ among the $\mathbf{X}_i$ after **Y** is partialled out even faster with increasing **n** than $\mathrm{Sat}_{\mathbf{X}}(S^*_{\mathbf{Y}})$ approaches $\mathrm{Hom}_{\mathbf{X}}(S^*_{\mathbf{Y}})$, since from [7.84] and [7.90],

$$[9.81] \qquad \alpha_{\mathbf{X}}(S^*_{\mathbf{Y}}) = \frac{\tilde{r}_{\mathbf{XX\bullet Y}}}{\tilde{r}^*_{\mathbf{XX\bullet Y}}}\left(1 - \frac{\nu^2_{\tilde{\sigma}_{\mathbf{X\bullet Y}}}}{\mathbf{n}-1}\right) \qquad (\mathrm{Span}(S_{\mathbf{Y}};\ \mathbf{Y}))$$

or

$$[9.82] \qquad \alpha_{\mathbf{X}}(S^*_{\mathbf{Y}}) \cdot r^*_{\overline{\mathbf{X}}\mathbf{X\bullet Y}} \leqslant \tilde{r}_{\mathbf{XX\bullet Y}} \leqslant \tilde{r}^*_{\mathbf{XX\bullet Y}} \qquad (\mathrm{Span}\ (S_{\mathbf{Y}};\ \mathbf{Y}))\ .$$

Equation [9.79] makes vividly apparent that the crucial determinants of a test's validity for a given criterion are the validities of its constituent items for that criterion and their residual correlations when the criterion is partialled out. For an extremely short (i.e., very small **n**) test, the number of items is also influential if the homogeneity of the test-item configuration orthogonal to the criterion is sufficiently low, but the ability to increase validity merely by lengthening the test with more items of the same sort is rapidly exhausted.

Internal-Consistency Theory and the Alpha Coefficient

Since the alpha coefficient for the items in any compound test $\overline{\mathbf{X}}$ approaches unity with increasing **n** so long as $\mathrm{Hom}_{\mathbf{X}} > 0$, whereas this is *not* generally true for the test's reliability, it is clear that not only the equivalence between $\alpha_{\mathbf{X}}$ and $r_{\overline{\mathbf{X}}}$ (i.e., $r_{\mathbf{S}}$) stated in [8.85] but also the weaker inequality [9.55] depends critically on the assumption of uncorrelated errors. In view of the prominence the alpha coefficient has attained in contemporary reliability theory, it is desirable to examine what its significance may be when the factor structure of the test is less ideal than classically presupposed.

Despite the apparent complexity of its original definition in [8.69], the alpha coefficient for a set of variables actually abstracts a very simple property of the set's covariance structure, namely, the ratio of the set's homogeneity to its saturation (see [9.52]). Specifically, from [8.69] and [4.40],

[9.83]
$$\begin{aligned}\alpha_{\mathbf{X}} &= \left(\frac{\mathbf{n}}{\mathbf{n}-1}\right)\left(1-\frac{V_{\mathbf{X}}}{C^*_{\mathbf{XX}}}\right)\\ &= \left(\frac{\mathbf{n}}{\mathbf{n}-1}\right)\frac{C_{\mathbf{XX}}}{C^*_{\mathbf{XX}}}\\ &= \frac{\bar{C}_{\mathbf{XX}}}{\bar{C}^*_{\mathbf{XX}}},\end{aligned}$$

which says that $\alpha_{\mathbf{X}}$ is the average proper covariance in the set $\mathbf{X}_1, \ldots, \mathbf{X}_n$ compared to the average covariance when self-covariances are included, and from which [9.52] follows by division of numerator and denominator by $\bar{V}_{\mathbf{X}}$. To appreciate what $\alpha_{\mathbf{X}}$ implies about the set's factor structure, let the $\mathbf{X}_i$ be factored into communal components $\mathbf{H}_i$ and unique components $\mathbf{U}_i$ as in [7.138], while as defined in [7.147,8], $\widetilde{h^2}$ and $h^2_{\bar{\mathbf{X}}}$ are the respective penetrances of the set and its centroid into common-factor space. Then [7.168] may be rewritten

[9.84]
$$\alpha_{\mathbf{X}} = h^2_{\bar{\mathbf{X}}}\left(1-\frac{DQ_{\mathbf{H}}}{\mathbf{n}-1}\right)$$

or

[9.85]
$$\alpha_{\mathbf{X}} = h^2_{\bar{\mathbf{X}}}\,\alpha_{\mathbf{H}} \leqslant h^2_{\bar{\mathbf{X}}},$$

the mathematical form of which is pleasingly parallel to that of

[9.86]
$$\mathrm{Hom}_{\mathbf{X}} = \widetilde{h^2}\ \mathrm{Hom}_{\mathbf{H}} \leqslant \widetilde{h^2}$$

(from [7.151]). That is, just as $\mathrm{Hom}_{\mathbf{X}}$ is a lower bound for the proportion of a set's variance lying in common-factor space, so is $\alpha_{\mathbf{X}}$ a lower bound for the proportion of common-factor variance in the set's centroid—in fact, from [7.170],

[9.87]
$$\alpha_{\mathbf{X}} = \mathrm{Est}_\alpha(h^2_{\bar{\mathbf{X}}}),$$

which shows that $\alpha_{\mathbf{X}}$ equals the estimate of $h^2_{\bar{\mathbf{X}}}$ which results from taking $\mathrm{Hom}_{\mathbf{X}}$ for the estimate of $\widetilde{h^2}$ in [7.155]. Moreover, the proportionate error of $\mathrm{Est}_\alpha(h^2_{\bar{\mathbf{X}}})$ is

[9.88]
$$\frac{\alpha_{\bar{\mathbf{X}}} - h^2_{\bar{\mathbf{X}}}}{h^2_{\bar{\mathbf{X}}}} = -\frac{DQ_{\mathbf{H}}}{\mathbf{n}-1},$$

which is negligible for most combinations of **n** and $\text{Hom}_{\mathbf{H}}$ (see [7.171]). Hence *the alpha coefficient for a set of variables is a lower bound for and usually a close approximation to the penetrance of the set's centroid into common-factor space.* Since there is an infinitude of ways in which a set of variables can be analyzed into communal and unique components, the alpha coefficient's factorial interpretation can be sharpened by adding that the common-factor space in which a set's penetrance is most closely approximated by its alpha coefficient is the one in which the set has maximal homogeneity.

This conclusion about the significance of $\alpha_{\mathbf{X}}$ holds for internal-consistency estimates of reliability in general. While the class of "internal-consistency" measures has never been clearly defined, nor have any reliability estimates of this sort other than $\alpha_{\mathbf{X}}$ and Spearman-Brown split-half formula [8.47] received widespread application, other formulas described as similar in intent and in some cases superior to $\alpha_{\mathbf{X}}$ have occasionally appeared in the literature.[4] These are derived under the assumption of uncorrelated errors, and turn out to be approximations to $h^2_{\overline{\mathbf{X}}}$. That internal consistency estimates of reliability should essentially be measures of the test's penetrance into common-factor space is inherent in the fact that while the covariances among the test items imply lower bounds for $h^2_{\overline{\mathbf{X}}}$ (as well as for the individual $h^2_{\mathbf{i}}$) no matter how common-factor space is defined, true-score factors are not distinguished from error factors by any formal variance properties, and the distinction has no import as such for $\{C_{\mathbf{X_iX_j}}\}$. When the configuration of error components is orthogonal, however, $S_{\mathbf{T}}$ qualifies as a common-factor space for the $\mathbf{X}_{\mathbf{i}}$ and lower-bound approximations to $h^2_{\overline{\mathbf{X}}}$ become lower-bound approximations to $r_{\overline{\mathbf{X}}}$ as well. The root problem for internal-consistency approaches to reliability is hence analysis of the relationship between a test's reliability and its penetrance into the common-factor space of its test items.

To see how $h^2_{\overline{\mathbf{X}}}$ and $\alpha_{\mathbf{X}}$ are related to $r_{\overline{\mathbf{X}}}$ in the general case, observe that decompositions [9.22] and [9.25] of the $\mathbf{T}_{\mathbf{i}}$ and the $\mathbf{E}_{\mathbf{i}}$ into common true-factor, specific true-factor, common-error and unique-error components determine a corresponding partition of the $\mathbf{X}_{\mathbf{i}}$ into communal and unique components, namely,

[9.89-**i**]
(**i** = **1**, . . . , **n**)

$$\mathbf{H}_{\mathbf{i}} = \boldsymbol{\tau}_{\mathbf{i}} + \boldsymbol{\epsilon}_{\mathbf{i}},$$

[9.90-**i**]
(**i** = **1**, . . . , **n**)

$$\mathbf{U}_{\mathbf{i}} = \mathbf{t}_{\mathbf{i}} + \mathbf{e}_{\mathbf{i}},$$

where the $\mathbf{H}_{\mathbf{i}}$ and $\mathbf{U}_{\mathbf{i}}$ satisfy [7.139]. Similar to definitions [9.40]–[9.43], let the penetrances of $\overline{\mathbf{X}}$ into spaces $S_{\boldsymbol{\tau}}$, $S_{\mathbf{t}}$, $S_{\boldsymbol{\epsilon}}$ and $S_{\mathbf{e}}$ be abbreviated

[4] Notably, in (37) and (49).

"$p_{\bar{\tau}}$", "$p_{\bar{t}}$", "$p_{\bar{\epsilon}}$", and "$p_{\bar{e}}$", respectively—i.e., considering also [9.57,8,9], [9.69], and [9.61],

[9.91]

$$\begin{aligned} p_{\bar{\tau}} &=_{\text{def}} P_{\bar{\mathbf{X}}}(S_\tau) \\ &= \frac{\alpha_{\mathbf{X}}}{\alpha_\tau}\left(\frac{P_\tau \operatorname{Hom}_\tau}{P_\tau \operatorname{Hom}_\tau + P_\epsilon \operatorname{Hom}_\epsilon}\right) \\ &= \frac{P_\tau \operatorname{Hom}_\tau}{P_\tau \operatorname{Hom}_\tau + P_\epsilon \operatorname{Hom}_\epsilon} - \frac{\alpha_{\mathbf{X}}}{\mathbf{n} \operatorname{Hom}_{\mathbf{X}}}\left(\frac{P_\tau \operatorname{Hom}_\tau}{P_\tau \operatorname{Hom}_\tau + P_\epsilon \operatorname{Hom}_\epsilon} - P_\tau\right), \end{aligned}$$

[9.92]

$$\begin{aligned} p_{\bar{t}} &=_{\text{def}} P_{\bar{\mathbf{X}}}(S_{\mathbf{t}}) \\ &= \frac{\alpha_{\mathbf{X}}}{\mathbf{n} \operatorname{Hom}_{\mathbf{X}}} P_{\mathbf{t}}, \end{aligned}$$

[9.93]

$$\begin{aligned} p_{\bar{\epsilon}} &=_{\text{def}} P_{\bar{\mathbf{X}}}(S_\epsilon) \\ &= \frac{\alpha_{\mathbf{X}}}{\alpha_\epsilon}\left(\frac{P_\epsilon \operatorname{Hom}_\epsilon}{P_\tau \operatorname{Hom}_\tau + P_\epsilon \operatorname{Hom}_\epsilon}\right) \\ &= \frac{P_\epsilon \operatorname{Hom}_\epsilon}{P_\tau \operatorname{Hom}_\tau + P_\epsilon \operatorname{Hom}_\epsilon} - \frac{\alpha_{\mathbf{X}}}{\mathbf{n} \operatorname{Hom}_{\mathbf{X}}}\left(\frac{P_\epsilon \operatorname{Hom}_\epsilon}{P_\tau \operatorname{Hom}_\tau + P_\epsilon \operatorname{Hom}_\epsilon} - P_\epsilon\right), \end{aligned}$$

[9.94]

$$\begin{aligned} p_{\bar{e}} &=_{\text{def}} P_{\bar{\mathbf{X}}}(S_{\mathbf{e}}) \\ &= \frac{\alpha_{\mathbf{X}}}{\mathbf{n} \operatorname{Hom}_{\mathbf{X}}} P_{\mathbf{e}}, \end{aligned}$$

while of course

[9.95]

$$p_{\bar{\tau}} + p_{\bar{t}} + p_{\bar{\epsilon}} + p_{\bar{e}} = 1 .$$

Equations [9.91]–[9.94] are a standardized equivalent to general composition equations [9.35]–[9.38].[5] Now, the penetrance of centroid $\bar{\mathbf{X}}$ into common-factor space $S_{\mathbf{H}}$ (i.e., $S_\tau S_\epsilon$) is

[9.96]

$$\begin{aligned} h^2_{\bar{\mathbf{X}}} &= P_{\bar{\mathbf{X}}}(S_\tau S_\epsilon) \\ &= p_{\bar{\tau}} + p_{\bar{\epsilon}} \end{aligned}$$

whereas the reliability of $\bar{\mathbf{X}}$ is

[9.97]

$$\begin{aligned} r_{\bar{\mathbf{X}}} &= P_{\bar{\mathbf{X}}}(S_\tau S_{\mathbf{t}}) \\ &= p_{\bar{\tau}} + p_{\bar{t}} . \end{aligned}$$

[5] The reader will find it instructive to visualize equations [9.91]–[9.95] simultaneously shown on a graph whose abscissa is **n**.

Hence the difference between centroid communality and centroid reliability is

$$h^2_{\bar{\mathbf{X}}} - r_{\bar{\mathbf{X}}} = p_{\bar{\epsilon}} - p_{\bar{t}} = \frac{\alpha_{\mathbf{X}}}{\mathrm{Hom}_{\mathbf{X}}}\left(\frac{P_{\epsilon}\ \mathrm{Hom}_{\epsilon}}{\alpha_{\epsilon}} - \frac{P_t}{\mathbf{n}}\right), \tag{9.98}$$

the details of which do not appear conducive to many useful insights other than that numerical similarity between $h^2_{\bar{\mathbf{X}}}$ and $r_{\bar{\mathbf{X}}}$ is rather precariously balanced on the length of the test. Given fixed parameters of item composition, $p_{\bar{\epsilon}}$ begins ($\mathbf{n} = \mathbf{1}$) at the value P_{ϵ} and goes asymptotically to the fractional value $P_{\epsilon}\,\mathrm{Hom}_{\epsilon}/(P_{\mathcal{T}}\,\mathrm{Hom}_{\mathcal{T}} + P_{\epsilon}\,\mathrm{Hom}_{\epsilon})$, while $p_{\bar{t}}$ begins at P_t and goes asymptotically to zero. If $P_t > P_{\epsilon}$, then $p_{\bar{\epsilon}}$ and $p_{\bar{t}}$ will coincide at some value of $\mathbf{n}$ (or approximately so, since $\mathbf{n}$ is restricted to integers) and $h^2_{\bar{\mathbf{X}}}$ will correspondingly equal $r_{\bar{\mathbf{X}}}$. Specifically, solving equation [9.98] for $\mathbf{n}$ shows that centroid communality and centroid reliability are equal when

$$\mathbf{n} = 1 + \frac{P_t - P_{\epsilon}}{P_{\epsilon}\ \mathrm{Hom}_{\epsilon}} \qquad (h^2_{\bar{\mathbf{X}}} = r_{\bar{\mathbf{X}}})\ . \tag{9.99}$$

For $\mathbf{n}$ smaller than this,

$$h^2_{\bar{\mathbf{X}}} < r_{\bar{\mathbf{X}}} \qquad \left(\mathbf{n} < 1 + \frac{P_t - P_{\epsilon}}{P_{\epsilon}\ \mathrm{Hom}_{\epsilon}}\right). \tag{9.100}$$

whereas as $\mathbf{n}$ grows large,

[9.101]

$$\lim_{\mathbf{n}\to\infty} (h^2_{\bar{\mathbf{X}}} - r_{\bar{\mathbf{X}}}) = \frac{P_{\epsilon}\ \mathrm{Hom}_{\epsilon}}{P_{\mathcal{T}}\ \mathrm{Hom}_{\mathcal{T}} + P_{\epsilon}\ \mathrm{Hom}_{\epsilon}} \qquad \text{(fixed parameters)}\ .$$

Hence an internal-consistency estimate of reliability may be seriously in excess of the correct value for a many-itemed test if measurement-error homogeneity is not negligible. Even so, [9.100] shows that any lower-bound estimate of $h^2_{\bar{\mathbf{X}}}$ will also underestimate $r_{\bar{\mathbf{X}}}$ for at least the smaller test lengths so long as the penetrance of the set of test items into common-error space is sufficiently small.

These general conclusions about internal-consistency estimates of reliability may be made more specific for the alpha coefficient by observing from [9.62] that

$$\begin{aligned} \alpha_{\mathbf{X}} - r_{\bar{\mathbf{X}}} &= \alpha_{\mathbf{X}}\left(1 - \frac{\tilde{r}_{\mathbf{X}}\ \mathrm{Hom}_{\mathbf{T}}}{\alpha_{\mathbf{T}}\ \mathrm{Hom}_{\mathbf{X}}}\right) \\ &= \frac{\alpha_{\mathbf{X}}}{\mathrm{Hom}_{\mathbf{X}}}\left[(1 - \tilde{r}_{\mathbf{X}})\ \mathrm{Hom}_{\mathbf{E}} - \frac{\tilde{r}_{\mathbf{X}}(1 - \mathrm{Hom}_{\mathbf{T}})}{\mathbf{n}}\right] \\ &= \frac{\alpha_{\mathbf{X}}}{\mathrm{Hom}_{\mathbf{X}}}\left[P_{\epsilon}\ \mathrm{Hom}_{\epsilon} - \frac{P_t + P_{\mathcal{T}}(1 - \mathrm{Hom}_{\mathcal{T}})}{\mathbf{n}}\right], \end{aligned} \tag{9.102}$$

a difference which increases as test length increases (assuming fixed parameters) until α_X asymptotically exceeds $r_{\bar{X}}$ by the amount to which the asymptotic value of $r_{\bar{X}}$ falls short of unity. For α_X to be less than $r_{\bar{X}}$ it is necessary that $[P_t + P_\tau(1 - Hom_\tau)]/\mathbf{n}$ exceed $P_\epsilon\ Hom_\epsilon$, with equality being attained when

$$[9.103] \qquad \mathbf{n} = \frac{P_t + P_\tau(1 - Hom_\tau)}{P_\epsilon\ Hom_\epsilon} = \frac{\tilde{r}_X}{1 - \tilde{r}_X}\left(\frac{1 - Hom_T}{Hom_E}\right). \qquad (\alpha_X = r_{\bar{X}})$$

Hence $\alpha_X \leqslant r_{\bar{X}}$ if and only if either $Hom_E \leqslant 0$ or

$$\mathbf{n} \leqslant \frac{\tilde{r}_X}{1 - \tilde{r}_X}\left(\frac{1 - Hom_T}{Hom_E}\right).$$

Since $(1 - Hom_T) = [\mathbf{n}/(\mathbf{n} - 1)]\ Disp_T \simeq Disp_T$ (see [7.133]) while $\tilde{r}_X/(1 - \tilde{r}_X)$ should generally be on the order of 1, this may be read as saying that for a test's alpha coefficient to be a lower bound on the test's reliability, the dispersion of the test items in true-score space must roughly be at least as many times larger than their homogeneity in error space as there are items on the test. If this condition is violated, then α_X will exceed $r_{\bar{X}}$ by an amount no greater than

$$[9.104] \qquad \alpha_X - r_{\bar{X}} \leqslant \alpha_X \left(\frac{P_\epsilon\ Hom_\epsilon}{P_\tau\ Hom_\tau + P_\epsilon\ Hom_\epsilon}\right),$$

while assuming nonnegative error homogeneity, α_X underestimates $r_{\bar{X}}$ in the lower-bound region by no more than

$$[9.105] \qquad r_{\bar{X}} - \alpha_X \leqslant \frac{\alpha_X \tilde{r}_X (1 - Hom_T)}{\mathbf{n}\ Hom_X} \leqslant \frac{\alpha_X}{\mathbf{n}}\left(\frac{1 - Hom_T}{Hom_T}\right) \qquad (Hom_E \geqslant 0).$$

In summary, we can say that for fixed values of the parameters $\tilde{r}_X$, Hom_T, and Hom_E, the closer to zero and unity are Hom_E and Hom_T, respectively, the closer does the curve for α_X as a function of $\mathbf{n}$ approximate the curve for $r_{\bar{X}}$. While α_X always rises asymptotically to unity if $Hom_X > 0$, the effect of positive error homogeneity is to drop the asymptote of the reliability curve below this, the degree of terminal discrepancy being determined by the balance between Hom_T and Hom_E weighted by $\tilde{r}_X$. On the other hand, imperfect homogeneity among the true-score components of the test items displaces the first (i.e., small-$\mathbf{n}$) part of the α_X-curve below the $r_{\bar{X}}$-curve by a gap which is rapidly closed with increasing $\mathbf{n}$. If both $Hom_E > 0$ and $Hom_T < 1$, as is to be generally expected, there will exist a crossover value of $\mathbf{n}$ (not necessarily an integer) at which $r_{\bar{X}} = \alpha_X$, while the difference between the two increases as $\mathbf{n}$ diverges in either direction from this point. All in all, a test's alpha coefficient would seem to have the best prospects for making a fairly accurate appraisal of the test's reliability when the number of test items is moderately small, whereas the value of α_X must be viewed with suspicion as an approximation to $r_{\overline{X}}$ when **n** is either large or very small unless there is reason to think that Hom_E is extremely low in the large-**n** case, or, when **n** is tiny, that Hom_T is rather high. Just what the proper interpretation of "moderately small" is, however, must await evidence about the general magnitude of correlated-error effects.

Actually, if it were possible to set even a rough numerical value on the number of test items at which a test's alpha coefficient best approximates its reliability, there would be a straightforward procedure by which tests containing more than the optimal number of items could be brought to the desired **n** without altering the test in any way. It was emphasized earlier (p. 411) that properly speaking, the alpha coefficient is a property of a set of variables and only derivatively of their sum, while the alpha value assigned to a compound test **S** is relative to how **S** is analyzed as a sum of parts. In particular, if $\mathbf{S} = \sum_{i=1}^{n} \mathbf{X}_i$ and the $\mathbf{X}_i$ are sorted into **m** groups $G_1, \ldots, G_m$ where $\mathbf{Y}_j$ is the sum of the $\mathbf{X}_i$ in group G_j, then also $\mathbf{S} = \sum_{j=1}^{m} \mathbf{Y}_j$ and α_Y is just as much an alpha coefficient for test **S** as is α_X . Hence if test **S** can be analyzed as a sum of **n** items, it can also be analyzed as a sum of any given smaller number **m** of parts simply by combining items, and if the significance of a test's alpha coefficient for reliability theory is to be fully understood it is necessary to investigate the manner in which the numerical value of this statistic is influenced by how the test is analyzed into parts.

Let the set of variables $\mathbf{X}_1, \ldots, \mathbf{X}_n$ be divided into **m** groups $G_1, \ldots, G_m$ such that each $\mathbf{X}_i$ is in one and only one of the G_j, and let variables $\mathbf{Y}_1, \ldots, \mathbf{Y}_m$ be defined as

[9.106-j] $$\mathbf{Y}_j =_{\text{def}} \sum_{i}^{G_j} \mathbf{X}_i \,,$$
$(\mathbf{j} = 1, \ldots, \mathbf{m})$

where "$\sum_{i}^{G_j}$" denotes summation over the variables in G_j. Then

[9.107] $$\sum_{j=1}^{m} \mathbf{Y}_j = \sum_{i=1}^{n} \mathbf{X}_i \qquad ([9.106])$$

or

[9.108] $$\mathbf{m}\overline{\mathbf{Y}} = \mathbf{n}\overline{\mathbf{X}} \qquad ([9.106]) \,.$$

Writing "g_j" for the number of $\mathbf{X}_i$ in group G_j we have

[9.109] $$\sum_{j=1}^{m} g_j = \mathbf{n}$$

while the average number, $\bar{g}$, of the $\mathbf{X}_i$ in a G_j is

[9.110]
$$\bar{g} =_{\text{def}} \frac{\sum_{j=1}^{m} g_j}{m} = \frac{n}{m}$$

Finally, let C_{G_j} be the total proper covariance among the variables in group G_j, i.e.,

[9.111-j] (j = 1, . . . , m)
$$C_{G_j} =_{\text{def}} \sum_{i \neq j}^{G_j}\sum C_{X_iX_j}$$

while $\overline{C}_G$ is the average of those $C_{X_iX_j}$ which are also included in the within-group covariances, namely, since the total number of the $C_{X_iX_k}$ included in group total C_{G_j} is $g_j(g_j - 1)$,

[9.112]
$$\overline{C}_G =_{\text{def}} \frac{\sum_{j=1}^{m} C_{G_j}}{\sum_{j=1}^{m} g_j(g_j - 1)} .$$

As in [9.83], the alpha coefficient for the set of items $\mathbf{X}_1, \ldots, \mathbf{X}_n$ may be written

[9.113]
$$\alpha_X = \left(\frac{n}{n-1}\right)\frac{C_{XX}}{C^*_{XX}} .$$

Since $C^*_{YY} = \text{Var}\left(\sum_{j=1}^{m} Y_j\right) = \text{Var}\left(\sum_{i=1}^{n} X_i\right) = C^*_{XX}$ (from [9.107] by [4.40]), we have

[9.114]
$$C_{YY} = C^*_{YY} - V_Y = C^*_{XX} - V_Y = C_{XX} + V_X - V_Y \qquad ([9.106]) .$$

Hence the alpha coefficient for the set of group sums $\mathbf{Y}_1, \ldots, \mathbf{Y}_m$ has the value

[9.115]
$$\alpha_Y = \left(\frac{m}{m-1}\right)\frac{C_{YY}}{C^*_{YY}}$$
$$= \left(\frac{m}{m-1}\right)\left(\frac{C_{XX} + V_X - V_Y}{C^*_{XX}}\right) \qquad ([9.106])$$

and the ratio of α_Y to α_X is

[9.116] $$\frac{\alpha_Y}{\alpha_X} = \frac{m(n-1)}{n(m-1)}\left(\frac{C_{XX} + V_X - V_Y}{C_{XX}}\right) \qquad ([9.106])$$

$$= \frac{mn(n-1)\bar{C}_{XX} - m(V_Y - V_X)}{n^2(m-1)\bar{C}_{XX}} .$$

Now,

[9.117] $$V_Y - V_X = \sum_{j=1}^{m} V_{Y_j} - V_X$$

$$= \sum_{j=1}^{m} \mathrm{Var}\left(\sum_{i}^{G_j} X_i\right) - V_X \qquad ([9.106])$$

$$= \sum_{j=1}^{m}\left(C_{G_j} + \sum_{i}^{G_j} V_{X_i}\right) - V_X$$

$$= \bar{C}_G \sum_{j=1}^{m} g_j(g_j - 1) ,$$

since $\sum_{j=1}^{m}\sum_{i}^{G_j} V_{X_i} = \sum_{i=1}^{n} V_{X_i} = V_X$. Also, in light of [7.201] and [9.110],

[9.118] $$\sum_{j=1}^{m} g_j(g_j - 1) = m\left(\frac{\sum_{j=1}^{m} g_j^2}{m}\right) - \sum_{j=1}^{m} g_j$$

$$= m\bar{g}^2(1 + \nu_g^2) - n$$

$$= \frac{n}{m}(n + n\nu_g^2 - m) ,$$

where ν_g is the coefficient of variation for the array of group sizes g_1, . . . , g_m. Substitution of [9.118] into [9.117] and the result, in turn, into [9.116] then yields, after collection of terms,

[9.119] $$\frac{\alpha_Y}{\alpha_X} = 1 + \frac{n-m}{n(m-1)}\left(1 - \frac{\bar{C}_G}{\bar{C}_{XX}}\right) - \frac{\nu_g^2\bar{C}_G}{(m-1)\bar{C}_{XX}} \qquad ([9.106]) ,$$

or

[9.120] $$\frac{\alpha_Y - \alpha_X}{\alpha_X} = \frac{n-m}{n(m-1)}\left(\frac{\bar{C}_{XX} - \bar{C}_G}{\bar{C}_{XX}}\right) - \frac{\nu_g^2\bar{C}_G}{(m-1)\bar{C}_{XX}} \qquad ([9.106]) .$$

This is a remarkably informative result. First of all, it makes explicit that the alpha coefficient for a set of variables $\mathbf{X}_1$, . . . , $\mathbf{X}_n$ does, in fact, generally differ to some extent from the alpha coefficient for a set $\mathbf{Y}_1$,

. . . , $\mathbf{Y_m}$ of group sums of these variables. Secondly, it shows that what determines how α_Y differs from α_X are (1) the number of original items and the number of groups into which they are partitioned, (2) the degree and direction to which the average interitem covariance, $\overline{C}_G$, included within the groups differs from the average proper covariance, $\overline{C}_{XX}$, among all the $\mathbf{X_i}$, and (3) the relative variability, ν_g, of the group sizes. The most critical of these determinants is the ratio of $\overline{C}_G$ to $\overline{C}_{XX}$; for if ν_g^2 is negligible, then α_Y is larger or smaller than α_X according to whether $\overline{C}_G$ is smaller or larger, respectively, than $\overline{C}_{XX}$, while the effect of $\mathbf{m}$ is to amplify or attenuate the effect of $\overline{C}_G$. If there are differences among the group sizes, then $\nu_g > 0$, which works to drag α_Y below α_X. If the significance of the ratio $\overline{C}_G/\overline{C}_{XX}$ is to be properly understood, it must be clear that $\overline{C}_G$ is an average of *part* of the $C_{X_iX_j}$ which are averaged in $\overline{C}_{XX}$. Specifically, the difference between the two is that $\overline{C}_G$ includes a covariance $C_{X_iX_j}$ ($\mathbf{i} \neq \mathbf{j}$) if and only if $\mathbf{X_i}$ and $\mathbf{X_j}$ are included in the same group. If the $\mathbf{X_i}$ are assigned to the various groups $G_1, \ldots, G_m$ randomly, then the expected value of $\overline{C}_G$ equals $\overline{C}_{XX}$, which shows that there is no *systematic* tendency for grouping items on a test before computing its alpha coefficient to influence the value of this statistic if the groups are kept equal in size. However, if there is appreciable variation among the interitem covariances $C_{X_iX_j}$, then it will generally be possible to find a group-sum alpha coefficient α_Y larger than α_X by so partitioning the $\mathbf{X_i}$ that the within-group covariances are less, on the average, than the overall average—i.e., by *minimizing* the within-group homogeneity of the items.

Since for reasons to be discussed shortly it is of considerable interest, given a test analyzable as a sum of items $\mathbf{X_1}, \ldots, \mathbf{X_n}$, to find a grouping of these items which yields the largest possible group-sum alpha coefficient, it is worth a moment's reflection on equation [9.119] to see what conditions are likely to obtain when α_Y is maximal. Since increasing ν_g decreases α_Y/α_X, we may expect first of all that when α_Y is at maximum the groups $G_1, \ldots, G_m$ will all contain close to the same number of $\mathbf{X_i}$. Secondly, with $\nu_g = 0$, the number of covariances $C_{X_iX_j}$ averaged in $\overline{C}_G$ is $\mathbf{m}\bar{g}(\bar{g} - 1) = \mathbf{n}(\mathbf{n} - \mathbf{m})/\mathbf{m}$, the ratio of which to the number, $\mathbf{n}(\mathbf{n} - 1)$, of $C_{X_iX_j}$ averaged in $\overline{C}_{XX}$ is $(\mathbf{n} - \mathbf{m})/\mathbf{m}(\mathbf{n} - 1)$, or approximately $1/\mathbf{m}$ for large $\mathbf{n}$. Thus by choosing $\mathbf{m}$ for the number of groups among which the $\mathbf{X_i}$ are partitioned we allow ourselves to include in $\overline{C}_G$ only about $1/\mathbf{m}$th of the $C_{X_iX_j}$, and the smaller is this proportion the more extreme a selection will be possible. Accordingly, the larger the number of groups into which the $\mathbf{X_i}$ are partitioned, the smaller will it be possible to make the ratio $\overline{C}_G/\overline{C}_{XX}$ in [9.119]. However, the multiplying fraction $(\mathbf{n} - \mathbf{m})/\mathbf{n}(\mathbf{m} - 1)$ in [9.119] decreases rapidly as $\mathbf{m}$ increases, being approximately equal to $1/(\mathbf{m} - 1)$ for large $\mathbf{n}$. It seems unlikely that the largest increase in $(1 - \overline{C}_G/\overline{C}_{XX})$ accomplished by a given increase in $\mathbf{m}$ would compensate for the corresponding decrease in $(\mathbf{n} - \mathbf{m})/\mathbf{n}(\mathbf{m} - 1)$, and the best prospect for maximizing $\alpha_{\mathbf{Y}}$ would thus appear to occur when the $\mathbf{X}_i$ are split into two groups of about equal size. In this case, [9.120] becomes

$$[9.121] \qquad \frac{\alpha_{\mathbf{Y}} - \alpha_{\mathbf{X}}}{\alpha_{\mathbf{X}}} = \left(1 - \frac{2}{\mathbf{n}}\right)\left(\frac{\bar{C}_{\mathbf{XX}} - \bar{C}_G}{\bar{C}_{\mathbf{XX}}}\right) \qquad \left(\begin{matrix}[9.106], \mathbf{m} = 2, \\ \nu_{\mathbf{g}} = 0\end{matrix}\right),$$

which says that the proportionate increase in $\alpha_{\mathbf{Y}}$ over $\alpha_{\mathbf{X}}$ is slightly less than the proportionate decrease in the average within-group proper covariance under the average proper covariance for all the $\mathbf{X}_i$. Since when $\mathbf{m} = 2$, $C^*_{\mathbf{XX}} = \text{Var}\left(\sum_{i=1}^{n} \mathbf{X}_i\right) = \text{Var}(\mathbf{Y}_1 + \mathbf{Y}_2) = V_{\mathbf{Y}} + 2C_{\mathbf{Y}_1\mathbf{Y}_2}$, we also have from [9.116]

$$[9.122] \qquad \frac{\alpha_{\mathbf{Y}}}{\alpha_{\mathbf{X}}} = \frac{2(\mathbf{n}-1)}{\mathbf{n}(2-1)}\left(\frac{V_{\mathbf{Y}} + 2C_{\mathbf{Y}_1\mathbf{Y}_2} - V_{\mathbf{Y}}}{C_{\mathbf{XX}}}\right) = 4\left(\frac{\mathbf{n}-1}{\mathbf{n}}\right)\frac{C_{\mathbf{Y}_1\mathbf{Y}_2}}{C_{\mathbf{XX}}}. \qquad ([9.106], \mathbf{m} = 2)$$

Let the statistic $\alpha_{\mathbf{Y}}$ for a test analyzed as a sum of **m** parts $\mathbf{Y}_1, \ldots, \mathbf{Y}_{\mathbf{m}}$ be called a "split-**m**th" alpha coefficient for that test. Then equation [9.122] shows that a test's split-half alpha coefficient is maximal when the test has been split (i.e., its test items sorted into two halves) in such fashion that the covariance between the halves is maximal. Our reflections on the effect of **m** upon $\alpha_{\mathbf{Y}}/\alpha_{\mathbf{X}}$ indicate that a test's maximal split-half alpha coefficient is also likely to be its maximal split-**m**th alpha coefficient for any **m**. Whether there are, in fact, covariance matrices which yield split-**m**th alpha coefficients substantially larger than the split-half maximum is a question for further research.[6]

The reason why finding a test's maximal split-**m**th alpha coefficient is of prospective importance is that as proved earlier (p. 341), the centroid communality of group sums $\mathbf{Y}_1, \ldots, \mathbf{Y}_{\mathbf{m}}$ defined as in [9.106] is equal to the centroid communality of the set $\mathbf{X}_1, \ldots, \mathbf{X}_{\mathbf{n}}$; hence from [9.85],

$$[9.123] \qquad \alpha_{\mathbf{Y}} = h^2_{\bar{\mathbf{X}}}\, \text{Hom}_{\mathbf{Y}}(S_{\mathbf{H}}) \qquad ([9.106])$$

That is, any split-**m**th alpha coefficient for a test $\bar{\mathbf{X}}$ is a lower bound on the test's penetrance into any common-factor space of its constituent items. Moreover, even when the homogeneity of the $\mathbf{X}_i$ in common-factor space is low—which will be recalled from pp. 336ff. to be the condition under which estimates of $h^2_{\bar{\mathbf{X}}}$ do most poorly—it is possible

[6] If test **S** consists of **n** groups of items such that (1) each group contains the same number, **g**, of items where **g** is a prime number, (2) the items in each group have the same common-factor component, and (3) the minimal common-factor dimensionality of the full set of items is **n**, then the test's maximal split-**g**th alpha coefficient is larger than any of its split-**m**th ($\mathbf{m} < \mathbf{g}$) alpha coefficients. Whether the superiority of the maximal split-**g**th alpha over the maximal split-half alpha could be made appreciable even in this contrived case, however, is uncertain.

that there will be a split of the $\mathbf{X}_i$ for which the common-factor homogeneity of the $\mathbf{Y}_j$ is very high and for which $\alpha_{\mathbf{Y}}$ is hence a very close approximation to $h^2_{\bar{\mathbf{X}}}$. This possibility derives from the fact that all that is required for variables $\mathbf{X}_1, \ldots, \mathbf{X}_n$ to have, say, a split-half $\alpha_{\mathbf{Y}}$ equal to $h^2_{\bar{\mathbf{X}}}$ is for the $\mathbf{X}_i$ to be sortable into two groups G_1 and G_2 such that the sum, $\mathbf{Y}_1$, of the $\mathbf{X}_i$ in G_1 has the same projection into common-factor space as does the sum, $\mathbf{Y}_2$, of the $\mathbf{X}_i$ in G_2. No further resemblance of the items in the two groups is relevant—their common-factor dispersion configurations can assume any degree of similarity or dissimilarity without affecting $\text{Hom}_{\mathbf{Y}}(S_{\mathbf{H}})$. In particular, it is unnecessary to match the two halves item by item as is frequently attempted in practice. The best matching occurs when the between-half covariance is maximal, and additional equivalence between individual items accomplishes nothing. However, pending efficient computational techniques for discovering the split which maximizes $C_{\mathbf{Y}_1\mathbf{Y}_2}$, matching more or less equivalent items should provide a reasonable approximation to the optimal split.

And why should we wish to estimate $h^2_{\bar{\mathbf{X}}}$ so closely? Well, we know that $r_{\bar{\mathbf{X}}} = h^2_{\bar{\mathbf{X}}} + p_{\bar{t}} - p_{\bar{\epsilon}}$, so when measurement errors on the test items are uncorrelated the best lower bound for $h^2_{\bar{\mathbf{X}}}$ is also the best lower bound on the test's reliability which can be derived from the test's internal statistics. In cases where $\text{Hom}_{\mathbf{E}}$ is appreciably positive, on the other hand, pressing closer to $h^2_{\bar{\mathbf{X}}}$ with the test's maximal split-**m**th alpha coefficient may only serve to overestimate $r_{\bar{\mathbf{X}}}$ more grossly than would be done by remaining content with $\alpha_{\mathbf{X}}$. Even so, the move to maximal $\alpha_{\mathbf{Y}}$ is still to be recommended: As we have seen (p. 446), an alpha coefficient's primary factorial significance is as a lower-bound approximation to the set's centroid communality, and it is desirable to recognize openly and unflinchingly that the alpha coefficient and other internal-consistency measures are germane to a test's reliability only insofar as $h^2_{\bar{\mathbf{X}}}$ is relevant to $r_{\bar{\mathbf{X}}}$. If so, then whatever uses can be found for internal-consistency statistics should be accomplished most successfully if estimates of $h^2_{\bar{\mathbf{X}}}$ strive for maximal precision. In particular, if it becomes possible to develop an empirically supported theory of correlated-error effects, then correction of $\alpha_{\mathbf{X}}$ for estimated error homogeneity will bring us once again into the realm of estimated lower bounds for $r_{\bar{\mathbf{X}}}$, and the more closely $\alpha_{\mathbf{Y}}$ approaches $h^2_{\bar{\mathbf{X}}}$, the less uncertain will our ultimate reliability judgement be.

Empirical Estimation of Error Homogeneity

There is little hope that practical methods will ever be developed for accurate assessment of a test's reliability which do not presume unrealistic special conditions of one sort or another. To estimate $r_{\bar{\mathbf{X}}}$ by the correlation of observed scores on test $\mathbf{X}$ with a second set of scores obtained in some rationally similar fashion $\mathbf{X}'$, as is done in test-retest and alternate-forms methods, is sound only insofar as we genuinely have reason to believe that **X** and **X**′ have approximately equal reliabilities and the same true-score component, while internal-consistency approximations to reliability are haunted by the specter of correlated item errors. To be sure, we know that the *squared* correlation of test **X** with any other variable **X**′ whose measurement errors can plausibly be assumed to be independent of errors on **X** may be taken as a lower bound for $r_{\bar{\mathbf{X}}}$ (cf. [8.41]), and perhaps this is all the accuracy we really need for practical applications of reliability data. Still, with internal-consistency statistics available at virtually no cost beyond the gathering of test-performance data which are needed to establish test norms in any case, it seems indecently wasteful to ignore them completely, especially when the possibility exists that the test's error homogeneity may be negligible after all. One of the most pressing needs now confronting reliability theory is thus for a body of empirical knowledge about error homogeneity. Quite aside from its claim on scientific interest for its own sake, data on the predisposing circumstances and general order of magnitude of correlated-error effects should have a useful practical payoff in at least two ways: (1) While it is to be expected that the error homogeneity of a compound test will vary considerably with the nature of the test material, the manner of item presentation, the character of the population tested, etc., it may well turn out to be possible to combine background information of this sort with a test's alpha coefficient or other internal-consistency measure to yield an improved estimate of the test's reliability. (2) More importantly, error homogeneity is a source of test invalidity which cannot be eliminated simply by increasing the number of test items.[7] If $p_{\bar{\boldsymbol{\epsilon}}}$ turns out to be frequently appreciable under present methods of test construction and administration, efforts to increase test validity should include search for ways to minimize this component.

In the next few paragraphs we shall briefly consider two procedures by which data on correlated-error effects might in principle be acquired. The purpose of these reflections is to plot the major compass bearings for such an endeavor, not to chart its course through the shoals of practical details nor even to make book on its successful completion, and the discussion will be largely schematic. In particular, we shall remain mute about problems in statistical sampling, even though these seriously complicate multivariate analysis unless the sample population is very large (cf. Chapter 10, pp. 504 ff.).

In an investigation of the role of correlated errors in the variance structure of a compound test, there are a variety of relevant quantities to which attention can be directed. The one which most directly carries the sting for reliability theory is $p_{\bar{\boldsymbol{\epsilon}}}$, the proportion of test variance lying in common-error space, since for reasonably large **n**, $1 - p_{\bar{\boldsymbol{\epsilon}}}$ is an upper-

[7] This consideration, incidentally, implies that other things equal, power tests should have greater validity than speeded tests, since as discussed previously there is good reason to believe that error homogeneity may be far from negligible on the latter.

bound approximation to $r_{\overline{X}}$. However, as shown by [9.93], $p_{\overline{\epsilon}}$ is jointly determined by several more fundamental quantities, namely P_τ, Hom_τ, P_ϵ, Hom_ϵ, and $\mathbf{n}$, which leave correlated-error effects in $p_{\overline{\epsilon}}$ severely confounded with the behavior of the test items in common true-factor space. Considerably more informative than $p_{\overline{\epsilon}}$ alone would be separate quantitative estimates of P_ϵ and Hom_ϵ. To obtain such estimates by the factorial method, we need in addition to test items $\mathbf{X}_1, \ldots, \mathbf{X}_n$ a set of external predictors $\mathbf{Y}_1, \ldots, \mathbf{Y}_m$ which as closely as possible approximate the conditions that (1) the error components of $\mathbf{Y}_1, \ldots, \mathbf{Y}_m$ are orthogonal to each other and to the error components of the test items, and (2) the common true-factor component τ_i of each $\mathbf{X}_i$ lies in the space spanned by the common true-factor components of $\mathbf{Y}_1, \ldots, \mathbf{Y}_m$. While items $\mathbf{X}_1, \ldots, \mathbf{X}_n$ are administered together in a single compound test $\overline{\mathbf{X}}$, condition (1) can presumably be brought about by making the observations for each subject on the set of variables $\overline{\mathbf{X}}, \mathbf{Y}_1, \ldots, \mathbf{Y}_m$ sufficiently well-spaced to be essentially independent selections of the uncontrolled test-circumstance details. (We shall here consider the primary source of correlated errors to be close temporal proximity between observations on the items in question. Actually, the story is more complex than this, perhaps importantly so.) Condition (2) can hopefully be attained by including among the $\mathbf{Y}_j$ a sufficiently large and redundant number of variables of the same general kind as the $\mathbf{X}_i$.

Given conditions (1) and (2), the entire common true-factor component τ_i and perhaps a portion of the specific true-factor component $\mathbf{t}_i$ of each test item $\mathbf{X}_i$ lies in the common-factor space of the external predictors $\mathbf{Y}_1, \ldots, \mathbf{Y}_m$, while $\mathbf{X}_i$'s error component $\mathbf{E}_i$ is orthogonal to both the common-factor and unique-factor spaces of the $\mathbf{Y}_j$. Operationally, this means that inferential factoring of $\mathbf{Y}_1, \ldots, \mathbf{Y}_m$ should disclose a common-factor solution which remains unchanged when alternatively, for each test item $\mathbf{X}_i$, the set of factored variables is augmented to $\mathbf{X}_i, \mathbf{Y}_1, \ldots, \mathbf{Y}_m$.[8] This would substantiate the assumption that $\mathbf{X}_i$ and each $\mathbf{Y}_j$ are related only through their components lying in the common-factor space of $\mathbf{Y}_1, \ldots, \mathbf{Y}_m$ while simultaneously permitting computation of the covariances among the $\mathbf{X}_i$-components in this space. Since the matrix of these covariances differs from $\{C_{\tau_i\tau_j}\}$ only in possible inclusion of portions of the specific true-factor variances V_{t_i} in the diagonal elements of the former, solving this matrix for communalities yields $\{C_{\tau_i\tau_j}\}$, from which we can compute Hom_τ and P_τ $(= V_\tau / V_{\overline{X}})$. More importantly,

[8] For greatest convenience, let the common-factor space of $\mathbf{Y}_1, \ldots, \mathbf{Y}_m$ be spanned by their communal components, the covariance matrix for which follows immediately from $\{C_{Y_iY_j}\}$ and the $\mathbf{Y}_j$-communalities. Since under assumptions (1) and (2) the covariance between each $\mathbf{X}_i$ and the communal component of each $\mathbf{Y}_j$ is equal to $C_{X_iY_j}$, we can thus compute the regression of each $\mathbf{X}_i$ upon the communal components of the $\mathbf{Y}_j$, without need for further factoring, as soon as the external predictors have been solved for communalities. Partialling these components out of $\mathbf{X}_1, \ldots, \mathbf{X}_n$ then confirms (or, more likely, disconfirms) that the common-factor space of the $\mathbf{Y}_j$ accounts for essentially all of the between-set covariances $C_{X_iY_j}$.

the matrix of residual $\mathbf{X}_i$-covariances unaccounted for by the common factors of the $\mathbf{Y}_j$ differs from $\{C_{E_i E_j}\}$ only in that the diagonal elements of the former also presumably include portions of the $\mathbf{t}_i$-variances. Hence solving this residual covariance matrix for communalities should give us the factor structure of the common-error components $\epsilon_1, \ldots, \epsilon_n$ as well as Hom_ϵ and P_ϵ. Thus in principle, the factorial procedure yields a complete analysis of how the common-factor configuration of test items $\mathbf{X}_1, \ldots, \mathbf{X}_n$ is partitioned between common true-factor space and common-error space. All that is left indeterminate is how the unique variances of the $\mathbf{X}_i$ are apportioned between specific true-factor and unique-error components.

An outstanding difficulty with the factorial approach to correlated-error research, however, is that it requires such ideal conditions to come off effectively. It is not merely that the identity of τ_i with its regression on the communal components of the $\mathbf{Y}_j$ will in practice be no more than an approximation, but we have also spoken of inferential factoring as though this were an unambiguous computational procedure which arrives at a sharply defined solution, whereas in fact extraction of common-factor space involves important subjective decisions—notably in the solution for communalities[9] and judging when the residual off-diagonal covariances are "essentially" zero—which may cause the solution finally arrived at to seem unpleasantly arbitrary. Hence even if the test items and the external predictors do, in fact, have components which are related in precisely the fashion presupposed, the factoring routine used may not come up with just that solution. To obtain a convincing decomposition into inferred components it is necessary that the common factors be strongly overdetermined, which means that the number of external predictors required for factorial studies of error homogeneity would undoubtedly have to be quite large, larger than could conveniently be combined with the stipulation that data on the $\mathbf{Y}_j$ be gathered in such fashion as to make plausible the assumption of uncorrelated measurement errors. As a basis for empirical research on correlated-error effects, therefore, the practical prospects for the factorial method are not overly bright. Even so, the principles of such an approach are worth thinking through if only for the heightened appreciation they afford for the logical connections between reliability theory and factor analysis. In particular, this emphasizes that relative to a particular operational criterion for "independent observations" in the sense of statistically independent selections of uncontrolled test-circumstance details, a test's reliability may be thought of as the limiting proportion of the test's variance which can be accounted for by its regression on other variables whose values are observed independently of the test observations.

---

[9] It will be recalled (see p. 262) that even when the intent is to find rank-minimizing communalities, the initial choice of trial communalities may make a difference for what final common-factor space is eventually extracted.

For some tests, there is an especially simple way to estimate $\tilde{r}_{\mathbf{X}}$, $\mathrm{Hom}_{\mathbf{T}}$, and $\mathrm{Hom}_{\mathbf{E}}$ which, despite its implausibly strong presuppositions, may turn out to be the most practical method for investigation of correlated-error effects. Suppose that it is possible to assemble two matched sets of items $\mathbf{X}_1, \ldots, \mathbf{X}_n$ and $\mathbf{X}'_1, \ldots, \mathbf{X}'_n$ composing tests $\overline{\mathbf{X}}$ and $\overline{\mathbf{X}}'$, respectively, such that when first test $\overline{\mathbf{X}}$ and then test $\overline{\mathbf{X}}'$ are administered with a between-test alteration of test-circumstance details adequate to break down error correlations, the true-score component $\mathbf{T}_i$ of each item $\mathbf{X}_i$ ($\mathbf{i} = \mathbf{1}, \ldots, \mathbf{n}$) on the first test is identical with the true-score component $\mathbf{T}'_i$ of the matching item $\mathbf{X}'_i$ on the second test. Specifically, we assume that

[9.124-i] ($\mathbf{i} = \mathbf{1}, \ldots, \mathbf{n}$)
$$\mathbf{X}_i = \mathbf{T}_i + \mathbf{E}_i \qquad \text{(assumed)},$$

[9.125-i] ($\mathbf{i} = \mathbf{1}, \ldots, \mathbf{n}$)
$$\mathbf{X}'_i = \mathbf{T}_i + \mathbf{E}'_i \qquad \text{(assumed)},$$

and that the two configurations of error components are orthogonal to each other and to the configuration of true scores—i.e., that

[9.126]
$$\perp(S_{\mathbf{T}}, S_{\mathbf{E}}, S'_{\mathbf{E}}) \qquad \text{(assumed)},$$

where $S_{\mathbf{T}}$, $S_{\mathbf{E}}$, and $S_{\mathbf{E}}'$ are the spaces spanned by the $\mathbf{T}_i$, the $\mathbf{E}_i$, and the $\mathbf{E}'_i$, respectively. It is an obvious consequence of these assumptions that

[9.127-ij] ($\mathbf{i,j} = \mathbf{1}, \ldots, \mathbf{n}$)
$$C_{\mathbf{X}_i\mathbf{X}'_j} = C_{\mathbf{T}_i\mathbf{T}_j} \qquad ([9.124,5,6]),$$

and

[9.128-ij] ($\mathbf{i,j} = \mathbf{1}, \ldots, \mathbf{n}$)
$$C_{\mathbf{X}_i\mathbf{X}_j} - C_{\mathbf{X}_i\mathbf{X}'_j} = C_{\mathbf{E}_i\mathbf{E}_j} \qquad ([9.124,5,6]),$$

so

[9.129]
$$\begin{aligned}\overline{C}_{\mathbf{XX}'} &=_{\text{def}} \frac{\sum\limits_{\substack{\mathbf{i}=1\\ \mathbf{i}\neq\mathbf{j}}}^{\mathbf{n}}\sum\limits_{\mathbf{j}=1}^{\mathbf{n}} C_{\mathbf{X}_i\mathbf{X}'_j}}{\mathbf{n}(\mathbf{n}-1)} \\ &= \overline{C}_{\mathbf{TT}} \\ &= \overline{V}_{\mathbf{T}}\,\mathrm{Hom}_{\mathbf{T}} \qquad ([9.124,5,6]) \\ &= \overline{V}_{\mathbf{X}}\,\tilde{r}_{\mathbf{X}}\,\mathrm{Hom}_{\mathbf{T}},\end{aligned}$$

[9.130] $$\overline{V}_{XX'} =_{\text{def}} \frac{\sum_{i=1}^{n} C_{X_iX_i'}}{n}$$

$$= \overline{V}_T \qquad ([9.124,5,6])$$

$$= \overline{V}_X \tilde{r}_X ,$$

and

[9.131] $$\overline{C}_{XX} - \overline{C}_{XX'} = \overline{C}_{EE}$$
$$= \overline{V}_X \,\text{Hom}_X - \overline{V}_T \,\text{Hom}_T \qquad ([9.124,5,6])$$
$$= \overline{V}_X (1 - \tilde{r}_X) \,\text{Hom}_E .$$

or

[9.132] $$\tilde{r}_X = \frac{\overline{V}_{XX'}}{\overline{V}_X} \qquad ([9.124,5,6]) ,$$

[9.133] $$\text{Hom}_T = \frac{\overline{C}_{XX'}}{\overline{V}_{XX'}} \qquad ([9.124,5,6]) ,$$

and

[9.134] $$\text{Hom}_E = \frac{\overline{C}_{XX} - \overline{C}_{XX'}}{\overline{V}_X - \overline{V}_{XX'}} \qquad ([9.124,5,6]) .$$

Hence under the conditions stipulated, $\tilde{r}_X$, Hom_T, and Hom_E can easily be computed from the within-test covariance matrix $\{C_{X_iX_j}\}$ and the between-test covariance matrix $\{C_{X_iX_j'}\}$, while the detailed factor structure of the true-score and error configurations can be examined by inferential factoring of the covariances matrices $\{C_{T_iT_j}\}$ and $\{C_{E_iE_j}\}$ determined by [9.127] and [9.128], respectively.

The power of the matched-items method for correlated-error research seems too good to be true, however, and unfortunately it is. The assumption that each test item $\mathbf{X}_i$ has exactly the same true-score component as its mate, $\mathbf{X}_i'$, on the second test is critical, and the degree to which this can be achieved in practice is highly uncertain. Ideally, conditions [9.124,5,6] should result when the second test $\overline{\mathbf{X}}'$ is a repetition of test $\overline{\mathbf{X}}$, so that the $C_{X_iX_i'}$ are test-retest covariances. As observed previously (p. 398), however, we can have little confidence that the factorial composition of an item upon retest is the same as its composition the first time around, at least in the area of psychological assessment. And if we (hopefully) reduce practice effects from $\overline{\mathbf{X}}$ to $\overline{\mathbf{X}}'$ by choosing the stimulus material in each item $\mathbf{X}_i'$ to differ from the detail of $\mathbf{X}_i$ in what seem like unimportant respects, we may nonetheless expect, however reluctantly, that the difference in content will produce some difference in true-factor composition as well. Even so, the matched-items method should be a source of useful data. In the first place, it may be possible to find certain types of test items where assumptions [9.124,5] seem reasonable (e.g., where practice effects are not believed to be appreciable, permitting a test-retest procedure). Further, even when it is not plausible that matched items $\mathbf{X}_i$ and $\mathbf{X}'_i$ have essentially the same true-score component it may still be possible to regard the items on tests $\overline{\mathbf{X}}$ and $\overline{\mathbf{X}}'$ as two samples of size $\mathbf{n}$ from the same more inclusive domain of items, so that the $\overline{C}_{XX'}$-estimate of $\overline{C}_{TT'}$ differs from the average proper true-score covariance in this domain only by sampling error. Then while the $\overline{V}_{XX'}$-estimate of $\overline{V}_T$ will inevitably be too low,[10] perhaps seriously so, $\overline{C}_{XX'}$ will be approximately correct as an estimate of $\overline{C}_{TT}$, and the computed estimates of $\tilde{r}_X$, Hom_E, and Hom_T, respectively, provide lower bounds on the values of $\tilde{r}_X$ and Hom_E, and an upper bound for Hom_T. Further, from [9.62],

[9.135]
$$\lim_{n\to\infty} \tilde{r}_{\overline{X}} = \frac{r_{\overline{X}}\,\mathrm{Hom}_T}{\mathrm{Hom}_X} = \frac{\overline{C}_{TT}}{\overline{C}_{XX}} \qquad \left(\begin{matrix}[9.124,5,6];\ \text{fixed}\\ \text{parameters}\end{matrix}\right) = \frac{\overline{C}_{XX'}}{\overline{\overline{C}}_{XX}},$$

so using $\overline{C}_{XX'}$ (which, it will be appreciated, does not include the covariances between matched items) it is possible to estimate the limiting proportion of true-factor variance in $\overline{\mathbf{X}}$ without making use of the questionable estimate [9.130].

More generally, even if the true-factor structure of the second set of items $\mathbf{X}'_1, \ldots, \mathbf{X}'_n$ does, in fact, differ somewhat from that of items $\mathbf{X}_1, \ldots, \mathbf{X}_n$, it can be shown that violations of conditions [9.124,5] almost certainly eventuate in $\overline{C}_{XX'}$ being proportionately more accurate as an estimate of $\overline{C}_{TT}$ than is $\overline{V}_{XX'}$ of $\overline{V}_T$, so given [9.126], the matched-forms method can be used with considerable assurance to determine an upper bound for Hom_T and a lower bound for $\tilde{r}_X$. The error in the corresponding estimate of Hom_E, unfortunately, is somewhat more problematic. Writing

[9.136]
$$\Delta_1 =_{\text{def}} \frac{\overline{C}_{TT} - \overline{C}_{XX'}}{\overline{C}_{TT}},$$

[9.137]
$$\Delta_2 =_{\text{def}} \frac{\overline{V}_T - \overline{V}_{XX'}}{\overline{V}_T},$$

[10] For simplicity, assume that $V_{T'_i} = V_{T_i}$. Then $C_{T_iT'_i} = V_{T_i}\,r_{T_iT'_i}$, which shows that apart from complications due to unequal true-score variances, violation of conditions [9.124,5] causes $\overline{V}_{XX'}$ systematically to underestimate $\overline{V}_T$.

for the proportionate amounts by which $\bar{C}_{XX'}$ and $\bar{V}_{XX'}$ underestimate $\bar{C}_{TT}$ and $\bar{V}_{T}$, respectively, the estimate

[9.138] $$\text{Est}\,(\text{Hom}_E) =_{\text{def}} \frac{\bar{C}_{XX} - \bar{C}_{XX'}}{\bar{V}_X - \bar{V}_{XX'}}$$

is found to be in error by the amount

[9.139] $$\text{Est}\,(\text{Hom}_E) - \text{Hom}_E = \frac{P_T(\Delta_1\,\text{Hom}_T - \Delta_2\,\text{Hom}_E)}{P_E + \Delta_2 P_T} \qquad ([9.126])\,.$$

Using principle [4.39], it may be seen that assuming [9.126] and approximately equal true-score variance in the two sets of test items, $\bar{C}_{XX'}$ approximates $\bar{C}_{TT}$ essentially to the degree that the true-score centroid of the $\mathbf{X}_i$ coincides with the true-score centroid of the $\mathbf{X}_i'$, whereas $\bar{V}_{XX'}$ approximates $\bar{V}_T$ only to the degree that the true-score component of each item $\mathbf{X}_i$ coincides with that of matched item $\mathbf{X}_i'$. It should not prove overly difficult in practice to work out sets of test items whose centroid congruence in true-score space is high enough to bring Δ_1 close to vanishing. Then according to [9.139], the matched-items estimate of Hom_E should be a lower bound for the correct value except perhaps when Hom_E, too, is negligible.

**Item Weighting[11]

At first thought, the preceding analysis of composite reliability might seem to be excessively constricted in that it applies only to centroids, whereas in practice we are free to define a compound test as any composite of its constituent items that we choose. Actually, centroid theory subsumes all linear functions of test items, since any linear composite

$$\mathbf{L}_X = a_0 + a_1\mathbf{X}_1 + \ldots + a_n\mathbf{X}_n$$

of items $\mathbf{X}_1, \ldots, \mathbf{X}_n$ is brought within the comprehension of centroid analysis by setting

$$\mathbf{W}_i =_{\text{def}} \mathbf{n}a_i\mathbf{X}_i$$

($\mathbf{i} = \mathbf{1}, \ldots, \mathbf{n}$), whence $\bar{\mathbf{W}}$ differs from $\mathbf{L}_X$ only by an additive constant which could also be absorbed into $\bar{\mathbf{W}}$ were there any point in doing so. Even so, the fact remains that given a set of items $\mathbf{X}_1, \ldots, \mathbf{X}_n$ and the desire to fuse these into a single final-outcome variable, we may select the combining function in innumerably many different ways, and it would be comforting to develop some standards against which to assess the merits or demerits of a particular alternative. In what follows, we shall be concerned with linear composites only—whatever promise (if any) nonlinear combinations of test items may have for the future of test theory, it is still a fact of contemporary test practice that nonlinear

[11] Before studying this section, the reader is advised to review pp. 352–373, especially pp. 367ff.

constructions are virtually nonexistent, and sufficient unto the day are the mathematical complexities thereof.

The problem at hand, then, is the following: Given a set of test items $\mathbf{X}_1, \ldots, \mathbf{X}_n$ which may or may not be standardized, we contemplate transforming the $\mathbf{X}_i$ into a weighted set $\mathbf{W}_1, \ldots, \mathbf{W}_n$, where

[9.140-**i**] (**i** = **1**, . . . , **n**)

$$\mathbf{W}_i =_{\text{def}} w_i \mathbf{X}_i \, ,$$

and wish to consider what effect these weights may have on the variance properties of the configuration, with especial concern for the statistical behavior of the weighted centroid $\overline{\mathbf{W}}$, namely,

[9.141]

$$\overline{\mathbf{W}} =_{\text{def}} \frac{\sum_{i=1}^{n} \mathbf{W}_i}{\mathbf{n}} = \left(\frac{1}{\mathbf{n}}\right) \sum_{i=1}^{n} w_i \mathbf{X}_i \, .$$

In particular, it is our intent to inspect various objectives which might be realized through proper choice of item weights and to judge what benefits or liabilities might accrue to these. Generally speaking, there are two major types of such objectives: external and internal. An "external" objective for item weighting is one which seeks to bring $\overline{\mathbf{W}}$ into some stipulated relation with variables defined independently of the test items. For example, it might be desired that $\overline{\mathbf{W}}$ be maximally effective at predicting a certain known criterion **Y**, or that $\overline{\mathbf{W}}$ be minimally redundant with a given array of other tests. An "internal" objective, on the other hand, is one which can be defined wholly in terms of the test's own constituents, such as maximizing $\overline{\mathbf{W}}$'s penetrance into common-factor space, or bringing the set of weighted items $\mathbf{W}_1, \ldots, \mathbf{W}_n$ into some ideal configuration. Of the two, internal objectives pose the greater intellectual challenge, both at conceiving of singular mathematical properties which might be sought through item weighting and in finding reasons why we should or should not actually seek them. Moreover, selection of item weights according to internal standards has considerably greater practical importance than might at first be anticipated, for construction of tests specifically to meet a precisely specified need is much more the exception than the rule. Most commonly, a battery of items is assembled in hopes of servicing a general area of application without foreknowledge of the manifold detailed uses to which the test may eventually be put. For the commercial test producer, in particular, it is most strategic to develop a repertory of different tests from which the consumer may select those which are best adapted to his aims, in which case it may be less important that a given composite of test items be engineered to meet a specific preassigned end than for the test to do well at whatever it can do best.

Of course, discussion of *alternative* objectives for selecting item weights should not be thought to imply that it is illicit to define more than one composite on the same set of test items. If anything is felt to be gained by doing so, there is no reason why the data obtained by a multiple-itemed testing procedure cannot be combined in various ways to yield a multidimensional assessment of each subject rather than just a single score. In fact, contemporary practice has turned more and more to development of test "profiles" in which a given item may contribute to several different composite scales.[12] The problem of weighting persists, however, for it is not possible to report a subject's scores on *all* variables which lie in the space of the test items, and hence grounds on which to prefer one selection over another are still needed. Any particular objective which might be sought through item weighting can as readily be used to define one of the several scales in a test-outcome profile as to collapse an **n**-dimensional observation into a one-dimensional report. In particular, a given objective can usually be employed to define as many different orthogonal composites $\overline{\mathbf{W}}_{(1)}, \ldots, \overline{\mathbf{W}}_{(n)}$ of the test items as there are items, namely, by applying this same objective to selection of the weights in each $\overline{\mathbf{W}}_{(i)}$ under the restriction that $\overline{\mathbf{W}}_{(i)}$ is orthogonal to $\overline{\mathbf{W}}_{(1)}, \ldots, \overline{\mathbf{W}}_{(i-1)}$. Such an iterative routine yields a set of orthogonal basis factors for the configuration of test items, thus showing that selecting standards for item weights is equivalent to developing a taste for one style of basis factoring in preference to another.

Before turning to specific considerations of what can be accomplished through item weighting, it is useful to look first at the weighting process itself to see what is involved. Since $w_1, \ldots, w_n$ in [9.140] can be any set of real numbers, including zero and negative values as well as positive ones, it is useful to think of the magnitude, $|w_i|$, of the weight given to $\mathbf{X}_i$ in weighted composite $\overline{\mathbf{W}}$ as the *stress* placed therein upon this item, while the sign of w_i is the item's *orientation.* Accordingly, selection of item weights comprises both a choice of differential stresses and a choice of orientations. Assigning a particular stress to $\mathbf{X}_i$ is equivalent to adjusting its unit of measurement, while reversing an orientation—i.e., choosing w_i to be negative—is the operation known as "reflection."

A further, more powerful, conceptualization of the weighting process follows from decomposition of $\overline{\mathbf{W}}$ into a linear combination of the unweighted centroid $\overline{\mathbf{X}}$ with a weight-standardized dispersion contribution $\boldsymbol{\delta}_{\mathbf{WX}}$. According to this analysis (see [7.223] and [7.228]), $\overline{\mathbf{W}}$ is consti-

[12] Partly for technical convenience and partly, perhaps, through lack of imagination, profile tests which allow a constituent item to have nonzero weight on more than one scale are still relatively uncommon. Even so, such tests still illustrate the general principle that more than one test-outcome dimension may be abstracted from the full set of test items.

tuted from the $\mathbf{X}_i$ by two primary decisions about the item weights: (1) a particular plane of the $\mathbf{X}_i$-configuration, spanned by $\overline{\mathbf{X}}$ and $\boldsymbol{\delta}_{WX}$, is determined by selecting (1*a*) a certain shape of distribution for the standardized weights $z_{W1}, \ldots, z_{Wn}$ and (1*b*) a particular coordination of the z_{Wi} with the dispersion components, $\mathbf{D}_1, \ldots, \mathbf{D}_n$, of the test items; while (2) $\overline{\mathbf{W}}$ is then positioned in the $\overline{\mathbf{X}}$–$\boldsymbol{\delta}_{WX}$ plane by the relative variability, ν_W (i.e., $\sigma_W/\bar{w}$), which is allowed among the item weights $w_1, \ldots, w_n$ derived by a linear transformation $w_i = \sigma_W z_{Wi} + \bar{w}$ from the standardized weights assigned in $\boldsymbol{\delta}_{WX}$ to the $\mathbf{D}_i$. The extent to which $\overline{\mathbf{W}}$ differs from $\overline{\mathbf{X}}$ is then seen to depend most crucially on the coefficient of variation for the weights, though the placement of $\boldsymbol{\delta}_{WX}$ is also important. In particular, if the $\mathbf{X}_i$-configuration is "well-balanced" (see p. 372), as will almost surely be the case if the initial orientations given to the $\mathbf{X}_i$ make some attempt to maximize the set's convergence, it follows from [7.240] that a lower bound for the correlational agreement between the weighted and unweighted centroids $\overline{\mathbf{W}}$ and $\overline{\mathbf{X}}$ is

[9.142] $$r^2_{\overline{X}\overline{W}} \geq 1 - \nu_W^2 \qquad \text{(well-balanced } \mathbf{X}_i\text{-configuration)},$$

while the difference between $\overline{\mathbf{W}}$ and $\overline{\mathbf{X}}$ in their penetrance into any factor space S is bounded by

[9.143] $$|P_{\overline{W}}(S) - P_{\overline{X}}(S)| \leq \nu_W \qquad \text{(well-balanced } \mathbf{X}_i\text{-configuration)}$$

(from [7.283]).

Actually, we know from [7.238] and [7.283] and our previous discussion of selection coefficient γ_{WX} (see pp. 367ff., especially [7.293]) that unless a large proportion of the dispersion variance in the test-item configuration lies on the $\boldsymbol{\delta}_{WX}$-axis, the similarity between $\overline{\mathbf{W}}$ and $\overline{\mathbf{X}}$ will almost certainly be much greater than suggested by inequalities [9.142] and [9.143]. More generally, [7.238]–[7.241] show that for a given choice of $\boldsymbol{\delta}_{WX}$, the coefficient of alienation between $\overline{\mathbf{X}}$ and $\overline{\mathbf{W}}$ is roughly proportional to ν_W, while unless Hom_X is diminutive, ν_W's multiplier—approximately ρ_{WX}, or $\sqrt{\gamma_{WX}\text{DQ}_X}$—is usually much smaller than unity, especially if $\mathbf{n}$ is large. The maximum value which can be given to ρ^2_{WX} by an assignment of item weights may be thought of as the *sensitivity* of the set $\mathbf{X}_1, \ldots, \mathbf{X}_n$ to differential weighting.[13]

We see, therefore, that if differential item weighting is to have much effect on a test, it is generally necessary (though by no means sufficient) for the variation among the weights to be extreme—i.e., for ν_W to be on the order of 1 or greater. This is at least an order of magnitude greater than what can be accomplished merely by adjusting the stress (with no reflections) given to the various test items unless a large proportion of

[13] Since $\rho^2_{WX} = \lambda_{Di}/\mathbf{n}V_{\overline{X}}$ when $\boldsymbol{\delta}_{WX}$ coincides (up to a linear transformation) with the $\mathbf{i}$th principal factor of the test-items' dispersion configuration, the eigenvalue of which is λ_{Di}, a more detailed description of the sensitivity of items $\mathbf{X}_1, \ldots, \mathbf{X}_n$ to weighting is provided by the set of statistics $\lambda_{Di}/\mathbf{n}V_{\overline{X}}$ $(\mathbf{i} = \mathbf{1}, \ldots, \mathbf{n} - \mathbf{1})$.

the $\mathbf{X}_i$ receive essentially zero weight. For example, if a proportion p of the weights are equal to the same positive value a while the remaining weights are zero (which is at the most extreme form of weighting possible when the w_i make no reflections), the coefficient of variation for the distribution of weights is

$$\nu_{\mathsf{W}} = \frac{\sigma_{\mathsf{W}}}{\overline{w}} = \frac{a\sqrt{p(1-p)}}{ap} = \sqrt{\frac{1-p}{p}}\,,$$

which surpasses unity only if $p < .5$ and reaches a value of merely 3 when $p = .1$.[14] But setting $w_i = 0$ (or essentially so) amounts simply to excluding $\mathbf{X}_i$ from the set of items which constitute $\overline{\mathbf{W}}$, and while rejection of irrelevant items is certainly an important part of test construction, what is normally at issue in discussion of item weighting is the effect of differences among the weights given to nonexcluded items. To take a less extreme example of differential stress, it can be shown that if the w_i are all positive and are uniformly distributed between a maximum weight which is m times as large as the minimum weight, then

$$\nu_{\mathsf{W}} = \frac{1}{\sqrt{3}}\left(\frac{m-1}{m+1}\right) < .6\,.$$

Our first conclusion about item weighting, then, is: *If weights are restricted to positive values only, then differential weighting of the items in a compound test generally makes little difference unless a substantial proportion of test items are in effect discarded. In particular, differential stressing of included items will have negligible effect on the composite test except perhaps when the items have low homogeneity and their dispersion configuration has a strong first factor.* A composite test's sensitivity to item weighting can usually be discerned from the quick approximations to $\mathrm{Max}(\rho^2_{\mathsf{WX}})$ described on pp. 372f. Unless $\mathrm{Max}(\rho^2_{\mathsf{WX}})$ is on the order of 1 or greater, there is probably little practical reason to consider varying the stresses assigned to the retained test items.

On the other hand, if changes in orientation as well as in stress are countenanced in the weighting process, then ν_{W} may be made as large as desired by setting the average item weight, $\overline{w}$, sufficiently close to zero. It is instructive to visualize adjustment of $\overline{w}$ as a shift in position of a distribution of weights with fixed shape and SD, starting with $\overline{w}$ large enough to have all the w_i positive. As $\overline{w}$ is decreased, the weights in the

[14] More generally, if a proportion p of the $\mathbf{X}_i$ are given weight w_a and the remainder are given weight w_b, where both are positive and w_a is m times as large as w_b, then

$$\nu_{\mathsf{W}} = \frac{(m-1)\sqrt{p(1-p)}}{(m-1)p+1} = \frac{(m-1)p}{(m-1)p+1}\sqrt{\left(\frac{1-p}{p}\right)}\,.$$

While this equation is not the easiest to interpret, careful study will show it to substantiate the claim that w_b must be minute in comparison to w_a if ν_{W} is to be appreciably larger than unity.

lower end of the distribution first decrease, pass through zero, and then increase negatively. If the w_i-distribution is approximately symmetric, then ν_W becomes infinitely large (i.e., $\bar{w}=0$) at a point where approximately half of the w_i are negative. Thus when $\overline{\mathbf{W}}$ has low correlation with $\overline{\mathbf{X}}$—and $\overline{\mathbf{W}}$ can be made to lie anywhere in the space spanned by the $\mathbf{X}_i$, most of which is orthogonal to $\overline{\mathbf{X}}$—roughly half of the weights are negative.[15]

Let us now turn to the ends which may be served by an appropriate choice of stresses and orientations for the variables in a set $\mathbf{X}_1, \ldots, \mathbf{X}_n$, beginning with internal objectives. These can be defined in terms of the configuration's behavior either in observation space (i.e., the space spanned by the $\mathbf{X}_i$) or in the space of some set of factors inferred from the $\mathbf{X}_i$-covariances. Of these, observation-space objectives are by far the easiest to achieve and also turn out to provide surprisingly powerful approximations to other major goals of weighting.

Although our primary interest in item weighting concerns the effect of this upon the weighted composite $\overline{\mathbf{W}}$, realization that meaningful comparisons can seldom be made between numerical scores on different raw-score scales and that personal whim in selection of an initial unit of measurement (e.g., measuring length in millimeters rather than miles) can affect a variable's standard deviation by several orders of magnitude, suggests that prior to final choice of item weights it may be useful—at least conceptually if not actually in computational practice—to begin with the items scaled according to some standardized procedure which minimizes the effect on their configuration of the original statistically arbitrary choice of raw-score scales. The obvious response to such an urge for uniformity is to equate all variables in the set for means and variances, and this is, in fact, usually presupposed in multivariate analysis (where, e.g., virtually no one would think to factor raw covariances rather than correlations), though it is much less common in applied test construction. Let us therefore call a set of variables which have all been standardized to the same mean and variance a *standard configuration.*[16] Since fixing a scale's reference point and unit of measurement leaves unspecified the scale's direction, a standard configuration remains so under any choice of orientations for its variables. However, it is commonly felt that whatever correlational consistency there may be in a set of variables should not be masked by arbitrary misalignment of scale directions, and in particular, that if the configuration is latently a positive manifold (see p. 343) then the variables should be oriented to make this manifest. A second desideratum for the initial scalings of the variables in a set, therefore, is that they be reflected (if needed) into as convergent a configura-

---

[15] This is best appreciated from the third line of [7.223], whence it is clear that if $\boldsymbol{\delta}_{WX}$ is orthogonal to $\overline{\mathbf{X}}$, then $\bar{w}$ must approach zero for $r_{\overline{W}\overline{X}}$ to approach zero.

[16] We could just as well omit standardization of the means, since this is irrelevant for any variance properties of the configuration and it is the latter that are almost exclusively our point of concern.

tion as is practical with the computational means at hand (see pp. 345f.). In particular, a *strictly convergent standard configuration*, whose variables all have the same variance and whose average intercorrelation cannot be further increased by reflection,[17] would appear to be the intuitively ideal choice of initial scales for the variables in this set.

Recognition that unidirectionality among the variables in a set is a "natural" objective for the scalings of these variables, and that the choice of orientations which maximizes the set's directional agreement is coincident with the maximum saturation which can be reflected into the set (see p. 345), suggests that it may be of interest to consider saturation as a criterion for allocating stresses as well as orientations. Specifically, let a set of variables be said to be in *MaxSat* configuration when the set's saturation cannot be further increased by linear rescalings of its constituent variables. Then one internal objective which may be set for the item weights $w_i, \ldots, w_n$ in [9.140] is for the resulting set of weighted items $\mathbf{W}_1, \ldots, \mathbf{W}_n$ to be in MaxSat configuration. (How to compute MaxSat weights—i.e., those which yield a MaxSat configuration—will be discussed later.) Similarly, a "MinSat" configuration may be defined as one whose item scalings minimize the set's saturation. However, while MaxSat weights will shortly be seen to have an impressive array of useful properties, MinSat weights have little if anything to offer beyond theoretical interest.

Before examining what virtues might be possessed by the centroid of a MaxSat configuration, let us first ask what other internal observation-space objectives might be set for selection of item weights. With respect to special properties of the $\mathbf{W}_i$-configuration and its relation to $\overline{\mathbf{W}}$, standardization of variance and/or control of saturation appear to subsume all the interesting alternatives. For example, the $\mathbf{W}_i$-configuration has maximal (minimal) homogeneity if and only if it has maximal (minimal) saturation, while maximizing (minimizing) the average intercorrelation among the $\mathbf{W}_i$ is achieved by maximizing (minimizing) $\text{Sat}_{\mathbf{W}}$ under the restriction that $\nu_{V_{\mathbf{W}}} = 0$—i.e., by putting the $\mathbf{W}_i$ into strictly convergent (divergent) standard configuration. There are, to be sure, still other properties of $\overline{\mathbf{W}}$ and the $\mathbf{W}_i$—e.g., $\nu_{C_{\mathbf{W}}}$, $\text{Max}(\gamma_{\mathbf{WW}})$, $P_{\mathbf{W}}(S_{\overline{\mathbf{W}}})$, etc.—which we could seek to extremetize, but the solutions for these are either prohibitively difficult while achieving no useful end, or give degenerate results. (E.g., if the penetrance of the $\mathbf{W}_i$-configuration into the space of its centroid is maximized, in general all items but one receive zero weight.) Comparison of $\overline{\mathbf{W}}$ to the initial unweighted $\mathbf{X}_i$-configuration, on the other hand, is more provocative; for if the $\mathbf{X}_i$ call special attention to any one direction in observation space, a selection of item weights is also thereby singled out, namely, those w_i such that $\overline{\mathbf{W}}$ lies on the directional axis so identified.

---

[17] When the $V_{\mathbf{X}_i}$ are all equal, a choice of orientations for the $\mathbf{X}_i$ maximizes $\text{Sat}_{\mathbf{X}}$ if and only if it maximizes the average interitem correlation among the $\mathbf{X}_i$.

Now, to ask whether a distribution of variables $\mathbf{X}_1, \ldots, \mathbf{X}_n$ somehow manages to distinguish one direction in observation space more conspicuously than the others is essentially to ask whether any variable in this space may be thought to have priority as the first basis factor of the set. It is also evident that whatever may be described as a set's outstanding direction or first basis factor also qualifies intuitively as the factor which "best represents" or is "most typical" of the set as a whole. Of course, the notion of "typicality" is no less ambiguous in application to a set of variables than to scores on a single variable, and in principle we can think of many different ways to define "most representative factor," just as there are innumerably many interpretations of "most representative score."[18] There is, however, one direction in a set's observation space which has repeatedly claimed first honors in mathematical analysis of multivariate relations and which, even more than the centroid, is strongest pretender to the title of "dominant direction"—namely, the configuration's *first principal axis.* By definition, the first principal axis of variables $\mathbf{X}_1, \ldots, \mathbf{X}_n$ is the direction in which the joint distribution of the $\mathbf{X}_i$ has the greatest variability, and which also accounts for at least as much of the total variance of the $\mathbf{X}_i$ as does any other direction. As will now be shown, it is the latter property which wins the prize for "best representative."

In previous discussion of prediction and regression, we have considered only cases wherein scores on a single criterion variable are estimated from data on one or more predictor variables. Suppose, however, that we have a set of criteria $\mathbf{X}_1, \ldots, \mathbf{X}_n$, scores on *all* of which are to be linearly estimated from a single predictor **F**. If **F** can be any variable we wish, what choice of **F** will give us the greatest accuracy at simultaneous prediction of $\mathbf{X}_1, \ldots, \mathbf{X}_n$? The answer is straightforward enough if we continue to take the standard error of estimate as our measure of predictive accuracy. Suppose that from data on **F** in a population P we linearly estimate scores on $\mathbf{X}_1$ for f_1 members of P, scores on $\mathbf{X}_2$ for f_2 members of $P, \ldots,$ and scores on $\mathbf{X}_n$ for f_n members of P. (This leaves open the possibility that when using **F** to predict the $\mathbf{X}_i$ we may wish to predict scores on only some of the criteria for a given subject—e.g., sometimes **F** may be used to predict $\mathbf{X}_1$, other times to predict $\mathbf{X}_2$, etc.)

[18] Thus in analogy to defining a measure of central tendency in a distribution as the variable's value around which the scores in the distribution are in some respect least discrepant, the "central tendency" of variables $\mathbf{X}_1, \ldots, \mathbf{X}_n$ may be defined as that variable χ such that the configuration of discrepancy-variables $\Delta_i =_{\text{def}} \mathbf{X}_i - \chi$ is minimized in some respect. In this connection, it is of interest that in analogy to $\sum \left(X_i - c\right) = 0$ and $\sum_i (X_i - c)^2 = \textit{minimum}$ when $c = \mathrm{M}_{\mathbf{X}}$ for the distribution of scores on a single variable **X**, we have $\sum_{i=1}^{n} \Delta_i = 0$ and $\sum_{i=1}^{n} \mathrm{V}_{\Delta_i} = \textit{minimum}$ for configuration $\mathbf{X}_1, \ldots, \mathbf{X}_n$ when $\chi = \overline{\mathbf{X}}$.

Then the overall standard error of estimate in this situation is given by

[9.144]
$$\mathrm{SE}^2_{\mathbf{X}_1 \cdots \mathbf{X}_n \cdot \mathbf{F}}[\hat{\mathbf{X}}_i = \dot{\mathbf{X}}_{i(\mathbf{F})}] = \frac{\sum_{i=1}^{n} \sum_{j=1}^{f_i} (X_{ij} - \dot{X}_{ij(\mathbf{F})})^2}{\sum_{i=1}^{n} f_i} = \sum_{i=1}^{n} a_i^2 \frac{\sum_{j=1}^{f_i} e_{\mathbf{X}_i j \bullet \mathbf{F}}}{f_i},$$

where

[9.145-**i**] (**i** = **1**, . . . , **n**)
$$a_i =_{\text{def}} \sqrt{\frac{f_i}{\sum_{j=1}^{n} f_j}}\,.$$

But if the f_i subjects for whom $\mathbf{X}_i$ is estimated from **F** are a sufficiently large random selection from P, then

[9.146-**i**] (**i** = **1**, . . . , **n**)
$$\frac{\sum_{j=1}^{f_i} e_{\mathbf{X}_i j \bullet \mathbf{F}}}{f_i} = \sigma^2_{\mathbf{X}_i \bullet \mathbf{F}} = \mathrm{V}_{\mathbf{X}_i} - \mathrm{V}_{\mathbf{X}_i(\mathbf{F})},$$

and [9.144] becomes

[9.147]
$$\mathrm{SE}^2_{\mathbf{X}_1 \cdots \mathbf{X}_n \cdot \mathbf{F}}[\hat{\mathbf{X}}_i = \dot{\mathbf{X}}_{i(\mathbf{F})}] = \sum_{i=1}^{n} a_i^2 \sigma^2_{\mathbf{X}_i \bullet \mathbf{F}} = \sum_{i=1}^{n} a_i^2 \mathrm{V}_{\mathbf{X}_i} - \sum_{i=1}^{n} a_i^2 \mathrm{V}_{\mathbf{X}_i(\mathbf{F})} = \sum_{i=1}^{n} \mathrm{V}_{a_i \mathbf{X}_i} - \sum_{i=1}^{n} \mathrm{V}_{a_i \mathbf{X}_i(\mathbf{F})} = \mathrm{V}_{a\mathbf{X}} - \mathrm{V}_{a\mathbf{X}(\mathbf{F})}\,.$$

Hence the predictor **F** which has the smallest standard error at estimating scores on all the variables $\mathbf{X}_1, \ldots, \mathbf{X}_n$ in respective proportions $a_1^2, \ldots, a_n^2$ (given also the randomness assumption noted) is the variable which accounts for the largest total variance of the weighted set $a_1\mathbf{X}_1, \ldots, a_n\mathbf{X}_n$—namely, the first principal factor (or a linear transformation thereof) of the $a_i\mathbf{X}_i$-configuration. Since the multiplier a_i in [9.147] may be thought of simply as a weight which combines with whatever differential emphasis has been built into $\mathbf{X}_i$ by choice of its SD to determine the importance of predicting $\mathbf{X}_i$ in this set, we may conclude that *if the* *units of measurement for variables* $\mathbf{X}_1, \ldots, \mathbf{X}_n$ *have been adjusted to represent the relative importance of these variables as criteria, the best (i.e., standard-error minimizing) single variable for predicting scores on all the* $\mathbf{X}_i$ *is the first principal factor (or a linear transformation thereof) of the* $\mathbf{X}_i$*-configuration.* It is in this sense, more than in any other, that a set's first principal axis may be considered to be its most representative direction, and why selection of item weights in [9.140] to make $\overline{\mathbf{W}}$ coincide (u.l.t.)[19] with the first principal factor of the $\mathbf{X}_i$-configuration has a special appeal in the absence of external objectives which can be attained by choosing the weights otherwise.

It must be appreciated, however, that the principal-axis solution for item weights remains unpleasantly arbitrary unless the variances of the $\mathbf{X}_i$ have first been attuned to some standard of item importance extraneous to the principal-axis concept. For example, if the $\mathbf{X}_i$ are in an original raw-score form whose scalings happen to give $\mathbf{X}_1$ a grossly larger standard deviation than any of the other variables in the set, the principal-axis solution for $\overline{\mathbf{W}}$ in this case will nearly coincide with $\mathbf{X}_1$. Hence in the absence of external justification for emphasizing one item over another, assignment of item weights to yield the set's first principal factor makes intuitive sense only if the set is in standard configuration. And now saturation considerations leap in with a powerful reinforcement for this intuition. For as shown in Appendix B, *the centroid of a set of variables in MaxSat configuration coincides (u.l.t.) with the first principal factor of the set in standard configuration.* That is, given arbitrarily scaled variables $\mathbf{X}_1, \ldots, \mathbf{X}_n$, the set of weights $w_1, \ldots, w_n$ which maximizes the saturation of the set $w_1\mathbf{X}_1, \ldots, w_n\mathbf{X}_n$ is also a set of weights such that $\sum_{i=1}^{n} w_i\mathbf{X}_i$ coincides (u.l.t.) with the first principal factor of the standardized items $\mathbf{z}_{\mathbf{X}_1}, \ldots, \mathbf{z}_{\mathbf{X}_n}$. Hence if the constituent items in a composite test $\overline{\mathbf{W}}$ are to be weighted on the basis of observation-space objectives alone, the outstanding choice, upon which considerations of interitem similarity, standardization of item scales, and factorial primacy all converge, is the MaxSat solution.

Unfortunately, as is true in general for extraction of principal factors, computation of MaxSat weights is a forbiddingly difficult task unless computer services are available or the number of items is very small. It is encouraging to recall, therefore, that the first principal factor of a set of variables will usually be well approximated (u.l.t.) by the set's centroid, especially if the set is in convergent standard configuration. In particular, if the set $\mathbf{X}_1, \ldots, \mathbf{X}_n$ is well-balanced (as will almost certainly be the case if the $\mathbf{X}_i$ have been suitably oriented) and in standard configuration, it follows from [7.240] and [7.264] by putting $\overline{\mathbf{W}}$ into coincidence

[19] Here and henceforth, the letters "u.l.t." abbreviate the qualification "up to a linear transformation." That is, two variables coincide (u.l.t.) if and only if one is a linear transformation of the other.

(u.l.t.) with the first principal factor, $\mathbf{P}_1$, of the $\mathbf{X}_i$ and using the upper bound for $\nu_{\mathbf{W}}$ which follows in this case from the considerations on p. 358, that

$$[9.149] \qquad r^2_{\mathbf{P}_1\bar{\mathbf{X}}} \geqslant 1 - \left[\frac{2\nu_{\mathbf{C_X}} \operatorname{Max}(\rho^2_{\mathbf{WX}})}{1 - \operatorname{Max}(\rho^2_{\mathbf{WX}})}\right]^2 \qquad \left(\begin{matrix} \nu_{\mathbf{V_X}} = 0; \\ \operatorname{Max}(\rho^2_{\mathbf{WX}}) \leqslant 1 \end{matrix}\right).$$

Since maximizing a set's convergence strongly tends also to minimize $\nu_{\mathbf{C_X}}$,[20] we may expect that the bracketed expression on the right-hand side of [9.149] will be on the order of 10^{-1} or possibly less for variables whose orientations attempt to maximize convergence. Hence if $\mathbf{X}_1, \ldots,$ $\mathbf{X}_n$ are in strictly convergent standard configuration or a reasonably good approximation thereto, the set's centroid, $\bar{\mathbf{X}}$, should not seriously differ from its first principal factor unless the importance of the set's second principal factor approaches that of its first. Using [9.149], the acceptability of $\bar{\mathbf{X}}$ as an approximation (u.l.t.) to $\mathbf{P}_1$ can quickly be tested by computing $\nu_{\mathbf{C_X}}$ and the approximations to $\operatorname{Max}(\rho^2_{\mathbf{WX}})$ described on p. 372f. from the array of item correlations $\{r_{\mathbf{X}_i\mathbf{X}_j}\}$, which is what $\{C_{\mathbf{X}_i\mathbf{X}_j}\}$ becomes for a standard configuration if we set $\bar{V}_{\mathbf{X}} = 1$.

If MaxSat weights are desired when the possibility that $r_{\mathbf{P}_1\bar{\mathbf{X}}}$ is unsatisfactorily small cannot be ruled out by lower bound [9.149], the following iterated-approximation procedure is known to converge (u.l.t.) upon the first principal factor of the set $\mathbf{X}_1, \ldots, \mathbf{X}_n$: Starting with $\mathbf{L}_1 = \bar{\mathbf{X}}$ as our first approximation (u.l.t.) to $\mathbf{P}_1$, let $\mathbf{L}_2$ be defined as

$$[9.150\text{-}\mathbf{2}] \qquad \mathbf{L}_2 =_{\text{def}} \sum_{i=1}^{n} C_{\mathbf{X}_i\mathbf{L}_1}\mathbf{X}_i$$

$$= \sum_{i=1}^{n} C_{\mathbf{X}_i\bar{\mathbf{X}}}\mathbf{X}_i,$$

which is then our second approximation (u.l.t.) to $\mathbf{P}_1$. The third approximation is $\mathbf{L}_3 = \sum_{i=1}^{n} C_{\mathbf{X}_i\mathbf{L}_2}\mathbf{X}_i$, and more generally, the **m**th approximation to $\mathbf{P}_1$ (u.l.t.) is

$$[9.150\text{-}\mathbf{m}] \qquad \mathbf{L}_m =_{\text{def}} \sum_{i=1}^{n} C_{\mathbf{X}_i\mathbf{L}_{m-1}}\mathbf{X}_i,$$

where

$$[9.151\text{-}\mathbf{im}] \; (\mathbf{i} = \mathbf{1}, \ldots, \mathbf{n}) \qquad C_{\mathbf{X}_i\mathbf{L}_{m-1}} = \sum_{j=1}^{n} C_{\mathbf{X}_i\mathbf{X}_j}C_{\mathbf{X}_j\mathbf{L}_{m-2}}.$$

[20] Since $QM^2_{|\mathbf{C}^*_{\mathbf{X}}|}$ in [7.66] is constant under any reflections of the $\mathbf{X}_i$, an increase in $V^2_{\bar{\mathbf{X}}}$ (i.e., $\bar{C}^{*2}_{\mathbf{XX}}$) through reflections can be attained only by an equal decrease in $QM^2_{|\mathbf{C}^*_{\mathbf{DD}}|} + 2\sigma^2_{\mathbf{C_X}}$. Hence saturation-increasing reflections should tend to decrease the numerator of $\sigma_{\mathbf{C_X}}/V_{\bar{\mathbf{X}}}$ $(= \nu_{\mathbf{C_X}})$ as well as to increase its denominator.

Since literal application of [9.150-**m**] to $\mathbf{L}_{m-1}$ increases the average item weight at each iteration, it is more convenient to divide all the $C_{X_i L_{n-1}}$ by a suitable normalizing constant before the next iteration. The series may be terminated whenever desired—in particular, when the weights begin to show no appreciable change from one iteration to the next or when whoever is carrying out the computations begins to complain.[21]

It yet remains to examine whether weighting test items by the MaxSat principle accomplishes anything beyond the attainment of mathematical singularity. In particular, it is certainly relevant for speculations about a composite test's ultimate utility to ask where MaxSat weights cause $\overline{\mathbf{W}}$ to be positioned in inferred-factor space. It turns out that MaxSat weights provide a surprisingly powerful approximation to the major inferred-space objectives which might be set for $\overline{\mathbf{W}}$. From [7.115], the penetrance of $\overline{\mathbf{W}}$ into any unique-factor space S_U of the test items is seen to be

$$[9.152] \qquad P_{\overline{W}}(S_U) = \frac{P_W(S_U)}{\mathbf{n}\ \mathrm{Sat}_W} .$$

Thus with $P_W(S_U)$ held constant, the penetrance of $\overline{\mathbf{W}}$ into the complementary common-factor space S_H is a monotonic increasing function of Sat_W. Also, interpreting "S_H" and "S_U" in [7.261] (which there denote any arbitrary pair of spaces) to be unique-factor space and observation space, respectively, in the present case, and for simplicity starting with the $\mathbf{X}_i$ in standard configuration, we have

$$[9.153] \qquad P_W(S_U) = P_X(S_U) \bullet [1 + \nu_{W^2}\nu_{V_U} r_{W^2 V_U}] \qquad (\nu_{V_X} = 0) .$$

If further $V_{U_i} = V_{X_i}(1 - h_i^2) = \bar{V}_X(1 - \bar{h}^2)$ for $\mathbf{i} = \mathbf{1}, \ldots, \mathbf{n}$—i.e., if the $\mathbf{X}_i$ have equal communalities as well as equal variances—we also have $\nu_{V_U} = 0$ and hence from [9.153] $P_W(S_U) = P_X(S_U)$ irrespective of how the w_i are chosen. Hence *if variables* $\mathbf{X}_1, \ldots, \mathbf{X}_n$ *all have the same communality, a choice of weights in* [9.140] *which maximizes* Sat_W *also maximizes the penetrance of* $\overline{\mathbf{W}}$ *into common-factor space.* To be sure, if the h_i^2 differ, item weights make a difference for $P_W(S_U)$ as well as for Sat_W, and the selection of weights which strikes the balance between low $P_W(S_U)$ and high Sat_W which is optimal to maximize $P_{\overline{W}}(S_H)$ may not agree entirely with the MaxSat weights. Even so, we know from [7.111], since $\mathrm{Sat}_W(S_U) = 1/\mathbf{n}$, that

$$\mathrm{Sat}_W = [1 - P_W(S_U)]\ \mathrm{Sat}_W(S_H) + \frac{P_W(S_U)}{\mathbf{n}} ,$$

so maximization of Sat_W tends to minimize $P_W(S_U)$ as well as to maximize $\mathrm{Sat}_W(S_H)$. Hence even when the $\mathbf{X}_i$ have different communalities, we

[21] There are also faster ways to compute $\mathbf{P}_1$ based on the repeated squaring of the covariance matrix $\{C_{X_i X_j}\}$. For details, consult the section on principal factors in most any text on factor analysis, e.g., Harmon (44), p. 160 ff.

may expect the MaxSat-weighted composite $\overline{\mathbf{W}}$ to have very close to the maximum penetrance into common-factor space possible for any linear combination of these $\mathbf{X}_i$.

This argument can be generalized to the effect of MaxSat weights on the penetrance of $\overline{\mathbf{W}}$ into any factor space S in which the maximum value which $\text{Sat}_{\mathbf{W}}(S)$ can attain through optimal weighting is large in comparison to the maximum for $\text{Sat}_{\mathbf{W}}(S^*)$ in the space S^* complementary to S. Using principle [7.102], the penetrance quotient for $\overline{\mathbf{W}}$ in S is seen to be

[9.154] $$PQ_{\overline{\mathbf{W}}}(S) = \frac{\text{P}_{\mathbf{W}}(S)\ \text{Sat}_{\mathbf{W}}\ (S)}{\text{P}_{\mathbf{W}}(S^*)\ \text{Sat}_{\mathbf{W}}\ (S^*)}\ ,$$

while transcribing [7.111],

[9.155] $$\text{Sat}_{\mathbf{W}} = \text{P}_{\mathbf{W}}(S)\ \text{Sat}_{\mathbf{W}}(S) + \text{P}_{\mathbf{W}}(S^*)\ \text{Sat}_{\mathbf{W}}(S^*)\ .$$

Now in general, the term on one side of "+" in the right-hand side of [9.155] can be increased only at the expense of decreasing the other—since $\text{P}_{\mathbf{W}}(S) + \text{P}_{\mathbf{W}}(S^*) = 1$, obviously increasing $\text{P}_{\mathbf{W}}(S)$ decreases $\text{P}_{\mathbf{W}}(S^*)$ and conversely, while since arbitrary weighting tends to reduce saturation to the order $1/\mathbf{n}$,[22] maximizing $\text{P}_{\mathbf{W}}(S)\ \text{Sat}_{\mathbf{W}}(S)$ should tend to reduce $\text{Sat}_{\mathbf{W}}(S^*)$ to a negligible value, at least if $\mathbf{n}$ is reasonably large. Hence if the maximum value which can be given to $\text{P}_{\mathbf{W}}(S)\ \text{Sat}_{\mathbf{W}}(S)$ by choice of the w_i is much greater than the maximum for $\text{P}_{\mathbf{W}}(S^*)\ \text{Sat}_{\mathbf{W}}(S^*)$, the weights which maximize the former should also be virtually the same as those which maximize $\text{Sat}_{\mathbf{W}}$. Consequently, maximizing $\text{Sat}_{\mathbf{W}}$ in this case should bring the numerator in [9.154] very close to maximal while tending to minimize the denominator as well, especially when $\text{Sat}_{\mathbf{W}}\ (S^*)$ cannot be much affected by differential weighting—the upshot of which is that $PQ_{\overline{\mathbf{W}}}(S)$ also tends toward its maximum. Just how close MaxSat weights come to maximizing $PQ_{\overline{\mathbf{W}}}(S)$ when $\text{Max}[\text{Sat}_{\mathbf{W}}(S)] \gg \text{Max}[\text{Sat}_{\mathbf{W}}(S^*)]$ turns rather critically upon additional details of the configurations of test-item projections in S and S^*, respectively, discussion of which would require more elaboration than seems profitable here. Even so, if by the "first-factor concentration" of a set of variables we mean the proportion of the set's standard-configuration variance accounted for by its first principal factor—which, as shown in Appendix B, is equal to the set's saturation in MaxSat configuration—it may be concluded that *in general, if the first-factor concentration of the components of test items* $\mathbf{X}_1, \ldots, \mathbf{X}_n$ *lying in a space S is considerably greater than the first-factor concentration of their components orthogonal to S, then the penetrance into S of the MaxSat-weighted composite* $\overline{\mathbf{W}}$ *is also a first approximation to the*

[22] When orientations are assigned randomly, $\bar{w}$ is expected to be about zero, and it may be seen from [7.248] that as $\nu_{\mathbf{W}}$ grows very large (i.e., as $\bar{w}$ approaches zero), $\text{Sat}_{\mathbf{W}}$ approaches $\text{Sat}_{\mathbf{X}}\ \rho^2_{\mathbf{WX}}$, or $\gamma_{\mathbf{WX}}\ \text{Disp}_{\mathbf{X}}$. Since the expected value of $\gamma_{\mathbf{WX}}$ for an arbitrary assignment of weights is $1/(\mathbf{n}-1)$, random weighting which includes arbitrary choice of orientations as well as of stresses may hence be expected to produce a saturation of order $1/\mathbf{n}$.

maximal penetrance into S which can be attained by any linear composite of the $\mathbf{X}_i$. *In particular, if S is a common-factor space for the* $\mathbf{X}_i$, *the approximation is likely to be excellent.*

Contemplating the possibility that test-item weights might be selected with an eye to how these influence the composite test's penetrance into a space S directs our attention to the inferred-space objectives which might be set for item weighting. Without groping for unnatural interests, these would appear to be mainly a question of how $P_{\overline{\mathbf{W}}}(S)$ can be maximized or perhaps minimized in some particular factor space inferred from the observed interitem covariances. Whenever the loadings of items $\mathbf{X}_1, \ldots, \mathbf{X}_n$ on an orthonormal factor basis for a space S have been determined, the matrix $\{C_{\mathbf{X}_i\mathbf{X}_j(S)}\}$ of covariances among the test-item projections into S also readily follows, from which together with $\{C_{\mathbf{X}_i\mathbf{X}_j}\}$ the weights which maximize (or minimize) $P_{\mathbf{W}}(S)$ can be derived by methods formally equivalent to solving a correlation matrix for principal factors (see Appendix B). This is a consequence of the interesting theorem that *if factors* $\mathbf{F}_1, \ldots, \mathbf{F}_m$ *are an orthonormal basis for space S, then the penetrance,* $P_{\mathbf{L_X}}(S)$, *of any linear composite* $\mathbf{L_X}$ *of variables* $\mathbf{X}_1, \ldots, \mathbf{X}_n$ *into space S equals the total variance of the set of* $\mathbf{F}_j$*-projections into* $\mathbf{X}$*-space accounted for by* $\mathbf{L_X}$.[23] Hence if $\mathbf{L_X}$ has maximal penetrance into S, $\mathbf{L_X}$ coincides (u.l.t.) with the first principal factor of the configuration of $\mathbf{F}_j$-projections into the space of the $\mathbf{X}_i$.

Since there is no limit to the number of different ways in which a set of data variables can be partitioned between an inferred-factor space S and its complement S^*, singling out one such S rather than another within which to maximize $P_{\overline{\mathbf{W}}}(S)$ is difficult to justify on internal grounds alone unless the factor solution manifests some special pattern which urges us to consider the space spanned by a particular subset of the extracted factors a likely lair of scientifically meaningful source variables. What a computed factor pattern must be like to merit such esteem is difficult to say (see pp. 280ff.). One form of partition respected by all styles of terminal factoring, however, is the distinction between common-factor space and unique-factor space; and if we have been fortunate enough to discover provocative communalities (e.g., which yield a common-factor space of small dimensionality, or which provide an outstanding fit to an a priori factor pattern), we may also find ourselves desirous of item weights which maximize the penetrance of $\overline{\mathbf{W}}$ into the

[23] *Proof*: It is easily seen from [4.90] and [4.98] that if $\mathbf{F}_1, \ldots, \mathbf{F}_m$ are orthonormal

$$P_{\mathbf{L_x}}(S) = R^2_{\mathbf{L_x}(\mathbf{F}_1 \cdots \mathbf{F}_m)} = \sum_{j=1}^{m} r^2_{\mathbf{L_x}\mathbf{F}_j} = \sum_{j=1}^{m} V_{\mathbf{F}_j(\mathbf{L_x})} = V_{\mathbf{F}(\mathbf{L_x})},$$

which says that the penetrance of $\mathbf{L_X}$ into S equals the total variance of an orthonormal basis for S accounted for by $\mathbf{L_X}$. But since $\mathbf{F}_j$ ($\mathbf{j} = \mathbf{1}, \ldots, \mathbf{m}$) may be analyzed as a component lying in $S_{\mathbf{X}}$ plus a residual which is orthogonal to any linear combination of the $\mathbf{X}_i$, the variance of the $\mathbf{F}_j$ accounted for by $\mathbf{L_X}$, and hence $P_{\mathbf{L_X}}(S)$, equals the total variance of the $\mathbf{F}_j$-projections into $S_{\mathbf{X}}$ accounted for by $\mathbf{L_X}$.

common-factor space so implicated. It has already been shown that MaxSat weights will yield an approximation to maximal $P_{\overline{\mathbf{W}}}(S_{\mathbf{H}})$ which should be more than adequate for most purposes, and this without requiring any inferential factoring at all. On the other hand, if communalities (and hence the covariances $\{C_{\mathbf{X}_i\mathbf{X}_j(S_{\mathbf{H}})}\}$) are actually at hand, we can either compute the exact weights which maximize $P_{\overline{\mathbf{W}}}(S_{\mathbf{H}})$ or, if iterated matrix manipulations grow wearisome, avail ourselves of the following approximation which is probably at least as good as the MaxSat approximation and requires virtually no computational labor at all.

Let the weighted variables $\mathbf{W}_1, \ldots, \mathbf{W}_n$ derived as in [9.140] from test items $\mathbf{X}_1, \ldots, \mathbf{X}_n$, respectively, be said to be in "UniStan"[24] configuration relative to a unique-factor space $S_{\mathbf{U}}$ when the projections of the $\mathbf{W}_i$ into $S_{\mathbf{U}}$ are all the same length—i.e.,

[9.156-**i**] $$V_{\mathbf{W}_i(S_{\mathbf{U}})} = V_{\mathbf{W}_i}(1 - h_i^2) = \overline{V}_{\mathbf{W}(S_{\mathbf{U}})} \quad \text{(UniStan configuration)} .$$
(**i** = **1**, . . . , **n**)

Then weights $w_1, \ldots, w_n$ yield a UniStan configuration (with respect to $S_{\mathbf{U}}$) if and only if they satisfy

$$V_{w_i\mathbf{X}_i}(1 - h_i^2) = w_i^2 V_{\mathbf{X}_i}(1 - h_i^2) = c$$

for **i** = **1**, . . . , **n** and some constant c—i.e., if and only if

[9.157-**i**]
(**i** = **1**, . . . , **n**)
$$w_i = \frac{c}{\sigma_{\mathbf{X}_i}\sqrt{1 - h_i^2}} = \frac{c}{\sigma_{\mathbf{U}_i}} . \quad \text{(UniStan weights)}$$

Thus to put a set of test items into UniStan configuration, each item is divided by the square root of its unique variance. To let the virtues of the UniStan condition be appreciated without further complications of notation, suppose that the set of items $\mathbf{X}_1, \ldots, \mathbf{X}_n$ is already in UniStan configuration while the communal-component configuration $\mathbf{H}_1, \ldots, \mathbf{H}_n$, of the $\mathbf{X}_i$ is well-balanced. Then if $\overline{\mathbf{W}}$ is any further weighted composite of the $\mathbf{X}_i$—in particular, if $\overline{\mathbf{W}}$ is the one whose penetrance into common-factor space is maximal—we have from [7.258] and [7.264] that the relative superiority of $\overline{\mathbf{W}}$ over $\overline{\mathbf{X}}$ in common-factor penetrance is no greater than

[9.158]
$$\frac{P_{\overline{\mathbf{W}}}(S_{\mathbf{H}}) - P_{\overline{\mathbf{X}}}(S_{\mathbf{H}})}{P_{\overline{\mathbf{X}}}(S_{\mathbf{H}})} \leqslant \frac{P_{\mathbf{X}}(S_{\mathbf{U}})}{\mathbf{n}\ \mathrm{Sat}_{\mathbf{X}}} \left[\frac{\nu^2_{\mathbf{C}_{\mathbf{H}}}\,\mathrm{Max}(\rho^2_{\mathbf{WH}})}{1 - \mathrm{Max}(\rho^2_{\mathbf{WH}})}\right] \quad (\nu_{\mathbf{V}_{\mathbf{U}}} = 0;\ \rho_{\mathbf{WH}} \leqslant 1) ,$$

where $\nu_{\mathbf{C}_{\mathbf{H}}}$ is the radial irregularity of the communal-component configuration and $\mathrm{Max}(\rho^2_{\mathbf{WH}})$ equals the maximum dispersion variance of

[24] From "*uni*que variances *stan*dardized."

the $\mathbf{H}_i$ lying in a single dimension compared to the saturation variance of the $\mathbf{H}_i$-configuration (cf. [7.295]. If orientations have been chosen for the $\mathbf{X}_i$ to bring their configuration (and hence also the $\mathbf{H}_i$-configuration, since there is a strict monotonic relation between $\text{Sat}_{\mathbf{X}}$ and $\text{Sat}_{\mathbf{H}}$ under changes of orientation) as close to strict convergence as is practically possible, we may expect the bracketed expression in [9.158] to be on the order of 10^{-1} or less, in which case the degree to which the UniStan centroid approaches maximal penetrance into common-factor space should be more than ample for any practical purpose unless $\mathbf{n}\,\text{Sat}_{\mathbf{X}}$ is unusually small.

And why might we wish to maximize a composite test's penetrance into common-factor space? One powerful reason follows from the assumption of uncorrelated item errors in classical approaches to reliability theory. If the measurement-error components, $\mathbf{E}_1, \ldots, \mathbf{E}_n$, of the $\mathbf{X}_i$ are all mutually orthogonal, then error space $S_{\mathbf{E}}$ and true-score space $S_{\mathbf{T}}$ are, respectively, a unique-factor space and complementary common-factor space for the set of test items, and the composite test $\overline{\mathbf{W}}$ which has maximal penetrance into common-factor space $S_{\mathbf{T}}$ likewise has the maximum reliability which can be given to $\overline{\mathbf{W}}$ through optimal choice of weights. Also in this case $\sigma_{\mathbf{X}_i}\sqrt{1-h_i^2} = \sigma_{\mathbf{X}_i}\sqrt{1-r_{\mathbf{X}_i}} = \sigma_{\mathbf{E}_i}$, so to put the test items into UniStan configuration with respect to error space, each item is divided by its error of measurement. Thus *if measurement errors on test items* $\mathbf{X}_1, \ldots, \mathbf{X}_n$ *are uncorrelated and the item configuration has been brought into strict convergence or nearly so, then weighting each item by the reciprocal of its error of measurement will usually provide an extremely close approximation to the maximum reliability which can be achieved by any linear combination of these items.*

Of course to determine reliability-maximizing weights either by exact computation or by UniStan approximation, it is first of all necessary to have information about the individual item reliabilities, which is something that can be procured only by correlating scores on the $\mathbf{X}_i$ with some additional set of measurements. Hence contemplation of how to control test reliability through item weighting moves beyond internal analysis of the test-item configuration into concern for the external objectives which might be set for choice of weights. Before looking more critically into the effect of weighting upon composite reliability, let us first consider what general opportunities may present themselves for external selection of weights.

The ultimate standard for weighting test items, in competition with which all others fade into irrelevance, is to have some specific criterion $\mathbf{Y}$, prediction of which is the sole purpose of the test and whose correlation with each test item $\mathbf{X}_i$ is known. In such an ideal case, the weight to be given to item $\mathbf{X}_i$ is obviously

$$w_i = b_{\mathbf{Y}\mathbf{X}_i \cdot \mathbf{X}_1 \cdots \mathbf{X}_{i-1}\mathbf{X}_{i+1} \cdots \mathbf{X}_n},$$

or some fixed multiple thereof, since then $\overline{\mathbf{W}}$ coincides (u.l.t.) with the regression of $\mathbf{Y}$ upon $\mathbf{X}_1, \ldots, \mathbf{X}_n$ and the (linear) accuracy with which $\overline{\mathbf{W}}$ predicts $\mathbf{Y}$ is the greatest which can be squeezed out of this set of test items. However, such an extreme specificity of criterion is neither very demanding theoretically nor very typical of actual test practice. Of greater challenge is to ask how item weights might be found which maximize a test's overall usefulness at a certain *kind* of application, of which single-criterion prediction is merely a limiting case.

Suppose, for example, we wish to use the test comprising items $\mathbf{X}_1, \ldots, \mathbf{X}_n$ to predict not just a single criterion, but a whole set of criteria $\mathbf{Y}_1, \ldots, \mathbf{Y}_m$. The optimal use of the test data in this case would be to derive each criterion's regression upon the test items separately and report the test result as an **m**-scale profile. However, to keep the problem interesting let us suppose that for some reason, say practical simplicity if **m** is large, we wish to find a single weighted composite $\overline{\mathbf{W}}$ of the $\mathbf{X}_i$ which has maximal combined efficiency at predicting all the $\mathbf{Y}_j$. Now, the standard error of estimate for simultaneous prediction of $\mathbf{Y}_1, \ldots, \mathbf{Y}_m$ from $\overline{\mathbf{W}}$ is

$$[9.159] \quad SE_{\mathbf{Y}_1 \ldots \mathbf{Y}_m, \overline{\mathbf{W}}}[\hat{\mathbf{Y}}_j = \dot{\mathbf{Y}}_{j(\overline{\mathbf{W}})}] = \sqrt{\sum_{j=1}^{m} a_j^2 V_{\mathbf{Y}_j \bullet \overline{\mathbf{W}}}}$$

$$= \sqrt{\sum_{j=1}^{m} V_{a_j \mathbf{Y}_j} - \sum_{j=1}^{m} V_{a_j \mathbf{Y}_j(\overline{\mathbf{W}})}}\,,$$

where $a_1^2, \ldots, a_m^2$ are the relative frequencies with which the $\mathbf{Y}_j$ are predicted from $\overline{\mathbf{W}}$ and where the SDs of the $\mathbf{Y}_j$ may be adjusted to represent other aspects of the comparative importance of the $\mathbf{Y}_i$ as criteria (see p. 471). Hence if by "maximal predictive efficiency" in this case we mean minimal combined standard error, the weights in $\overline{\mathbf{W}}$ which yield maximal efficiency at simultaneous prediction of $\mathbf{Y}_1, \ldots, \mathbf{Y}_m$ are the w_i which maximize $\sum_{j=1}^{m} V_{a_j \mathbf{Y}_j(\overline{\mathbf{W}})}$. Let $\mathbf{X}_j^*$ be the projection of the importance-weighted criterion $a_j\mathbf{Y}_j$ into test-item space—i.e.,

$$[9.160\text{-j}] \quad (\mathbf{j} = 1, \ldots, \mathbf{m}) \qquad \mathbf{X}_j^* =_{\text{def}} a_j \hat{\mathbf{Y}}_{j(\mathbf{X}_1 \ldots \mathbf{X}_n)}\,.$$

Then weighted criterion $a_j\mathbf{Y}_j$ equals $\mathbf{X}_j^*$ plus a residual which is orthogonal to all the $\mathbf{X}_i$ and hence also to $\overline{\mathbf{W}}$; so

$$[9.161\text{-j}] \quad (\mathbf{j} = 1, \ldots, \mathbf{m}) \qquad V_{a_j \mathbf{Y}_j(\overline{\mathbf{W}})} = V_{\mathbf{X}_j^*(\overline{\mathbf{W}})}$$

and minimizing $SE_{\mathbf{Y}_1 \ldots \mathbf{Y}_m, \overline{\mathbf{W}}}$ in [9.159] is equivalent to maximizing

$\sum_{j=1}^{m} V_{X_j^*(\overline{W})}$. But the latter is maximal when $\overline{\mathbf{W}}$ coincides (u.l.t.) with the first principal factor of the set $\mathbf{X}_1^*, \ldots, \mathbf{X}_m^*$ – as it can always be made to do by proper choice of weights since the $\mathbf{X}_j^*$ all lie in test-item space. Hence *the linear combination of test items* $\mathbf{X}_1, \ldots, \mathbf{X}_n$ *which is the best single predictor for simultaneous estimation of several importance-weighted criteria coincides (u.l.t.) with the first principal factor of the configuration of criterion projections into the space spanned by the* $\mathbf{X}_i$.

While optimizing a composite test's efficiency at predicting multiple criteria is an interesting theoretical extension of regression analysis, however, it is not likely to find much application in actual test practice, if only because a specific set of exclusively intended criteria of known relative importance and relation to the test items will seldom if ever be available. A slightly more realistic possibility is that test $\overline{\mathbf{W}}$ is being developed to predict as best it can within a certain space of criteria. For example, it might be intended that $\overline{\mathbf{W}}$ is to be a test of "intelligence," even though whatever it is that we mean by this term apparently includes a great many different dimensions of mental ability. Now roughly speaking, no matter how optimally $\overline{\mathbf{W}}$ is weighted, it can still be used effectively to predict only one dimension of criterion space (i.e., if criterion space $S_{\mathbf{Y}}$ has $\mathbf{m}$ dimensions, $\overline{\mathbf{W}}$ has zero validity for all criteria lying in the $\mathbf{m} - 1$ dimensional subspace of $S_{\mathbf{Y}}$ orthogonal to the projection of $\overline{\mathbf{W}}$ into $S_{\mathbf{Y}}$), while $\sqrt{P_{\overline{\mathbf{W}}}(S_{\mathbf{Y}})}$ is the maximum validity of $\overline{\mathbf{W}}$ for any criterion in $S_{\mathbf{Y}}$. Hence if it really is the case that we desire to predict wherever we can in criterion space, and are not preoccupied just with certain favored dimensions thereof, it seems most sensible to weigh the test items in such fashion that $\overline{\mathbf{W}}$ has the maximum validity possible in $S_{\mathbf{Y}}$ for a test composed of these items, irrespective of where this may position $\overline{\mathbf{W}}$'s projection in $S_{\mathbf{Y}}$. According to this line of reasoning, *the item weights which optimize the efficiency of a composite test* $\overline{\mathbf{W}}$ *at predictions within a space* $S_{\mathbf{Y}}$ *of criterion variables are those which maximize the penetrance of* $\overline{\mathbf{W}}$ *into* $S_{\mathbf{Y}}$.

If we are willing to report test results as a profile, rather than just a single score, the maximum-validity principle can be extended to generate a series of test-item composites, each of which has maximum penetrance into the portion of criterion space orthogonal to the predictor composites defined previously. The profile scales so defined respectively coincide (u.l.t.) with the canonical factors of the test items with respect to any set of variables which span criterion space, while the squared **k**th canonical correlation so generated equals the penetrance of the **k**th profile scale (i.e., **k**th canonical factor of the test items) into criterion space.

A third possibility for defining item weights with respect to multiple criteria, conceptually intermediate to the previous two and subsuming them mathematically, is that we are interested in predicting throughout criterion space $S_{\mathbf{Y}}$, but attach greater importance to some directions in

S_Y than to others. To find the best test-item composite in this case, let $\mathbf{Y}_1, \ldots, \mathbf{Y}_m$ be any set of criteria which span S_Y in such fashion that the proportion of $\sum_{j=1}^{m} V_{Y_j}$ lying in a given dimension of S_Y corresponds to the importance we attach to predicting that dimension. Then the optimal item weights are the w_i which make $\overline{\mathbf{W}}$ coincide (u.l.t.) with the first principal factor of the $\mathbf{Y}_j$-projections into test-item space. The solution is invariant for different choices of the $\mathbf{Y}_j$ so long as the marginal conditions on the total variance of the $\mathbf{Y}_j$-configuration are preserved. In the limiting case where the $\mathbf{Y}_j$-configuration has the same variance in all directions of S_Y, it follows from the theorem cited on p. 476 that the item weights which minimize the standard error of $\overline{\mathbf{W}}$ at simultaneous prediction of $\mathbf{Y}_1, \ldots, \mathbf{Y}_m$—i.e., which bring $\overline{\mathbf{W}}$ into coincidence with the first principal factor of the $\mathbf{Y}_j$-projections in test-item space—are identical with the weights which maximize the penetrance of $\overline{\mathbf{W}}$ into S_Y. (For mathematical details see Appendix B.)

To be sure, in order actually to compute item weights which maximize the predictive efficiency of $\overline{\mathbf{W}}$ for criterion-space S_Y, it does not suffice just to know S_Y by name; a set of variables which span S_Y and whose correlations with the test items are accessible must also be procured. And even in the unlikely case that this requirement is actually fulfilled, it is still quite possible that the maximum validity of $\overline{\mathbf{W}}$ for a criterion in S_Y is poor in comparison to the maximum validity which, when properly weighted, it can attain for criteria not included in S_Y—in which case it might seem most prudent to weigh $\overline{\mathbf{W}}$ in accord with whatever it can do best and to search for another set of test items whose command of S_Y is more satisfactory. Or if the items in $\overline{\mathbf{W}}$ are the best we have been able to come up with for prediction in S_Y, even though they are considerably more effective elsewhere, it would be commendable also to make the best-criterion item weights available in addition to those which are most useful for S_Y. But if the realm of potential criteria for $\overline{\mathbf{W}}$ is construed to comprise all variables unrelated to $\overline{\mathbf{W}}$'s error component, then the criterion which $\overline{\mathbf{W}}$ predicts best is its own true-score component, while the correlation of $\overline{\mathbf{W}}$ with the latter—i.e., $\overline{\mathbf{W}}$'s reliability index—is an upper limit to $\overline{\mathbf{W}}$'s validity for any test-stable criterion. Consequently, when the intent is to optimize the general predictive utility of a composite test when the prospective criteria are vaguely conceived or whose correlations with the test items cannot be determined, the most reasonable objective to adopt for selection of item weights is maximization of the test's reliability.

**Item Weighting and Composite Reliability

Since $r_{\overline{W}}$ is $\overline{\mathbf{W}}$'s penetrance into the true-score space of its test items, maximizing the reliability of $\overline{\mathbf{W}}$ through optimal choice of item weights in the general case where no special assumptions are made about the error configuration requires the matrix procedures outlined in Appendix B. Also needed for these computations, however, is the matrix of covariances among the true-score components (or alternatively, among the error components) of the test items, and it is seldom if ever that this information will actually be available. The best we can hope for in practice is to approximate the reliability-maximizing item weights by simplified procedures which at least yield the desired solution under special conditions and which hopefully will not lead us seriously astray so long as these conditions are not violated too flagrantly. The most useful of these approximations have already been cited in prior discussion of internal weighting objectives, but before reviewing these results, let us first consider a special case whose mathematical structure is exceptionally appealing even though its presuppositions are far too strong to make it a serious contender for practical application.

Suppose that test items $\mathbf{X_1}, \ldots, \mathbf{X_n}$ have but a single factor, $\mathbf{F}$, in common, so that

[9.162-**i**,**j**] (**ij** = **1**, . . . , **n**; **i** ≠ **j**)
$$r_{X_iX_j \bullet F} = 0 \qquad \text{(assumed)},$$

or in view of principle [4.122],

[9.163-**i**,**j**] (**ij** = **1**, . . . , **n**; **i** ≠ **j**)
$$r_{X_iX_j} = r_{X_iF}\, r_{X_jF} \qquad ([9.162]).$$

Then the normal equations (see [4.90]) for the regression of $\mathbf{F}$ upon $\mathbf{X_1}, \ldots, \mathbf{X_n}$ in this special case become

[9.164-**i**] (**i** = **1**, . . . , **n**)
$$\begin{aligned} r_{X_iF} &= \sum_{j=1}^{n} \beta_{FX_j} r_{X_iX_j} \\ &= \sum_{j=1}^{n} \beta_{FX_j} r_{X_iF} r_{X_jF} + \beta_{FX_i}(1 - r^2_{X_iF}) \\ &= r_{X_iF}\left(\sum_{j=1}^{n} \beta_{FX_j} r_{X_jF}\right) + \beta_{FX_i} k^2_{X_iF} \\ &= r_{X_iF} R^2_{F(X_1\cdots X_n)} + \beta_{FX_i} k^2_{X_iF}, \end{aligned} \qquad ([9.162])$$

where for simplicity we write "β_{FX_i}" for "$\beta_{FX_i \bullet X_1 \cdots X_{i-1} X_{i+1} \cdots X_n}$". Solving for the β-weights, we have

[9.165-**i**] (**i** = **1**, . . . , **n**)
$$\begin{aligned} \beta_{FX_i} &= \frac{r_{X_iF}(1 - R^2_{F(X_1\cdots X_n)})}{k^2_{X_iF}} \\ &= K^2_{F(X_1\cdots X_n)} \frac{r_{X_iF}}{k^2_{X_iF}} \end{aligned} \qquad ([9.162])$$

so the regression of **F** upon the normalized $\mathbf{X_i}$ is

[9.166] $$\dot{z}_{F(X_1 \ldots X_n)} = K^2_{F(X_1 \ldots X_n)} \sum_{i=1}^{n} \frac{r_{X_iF}}{k^2_{X_iF}} z_{X_i} \qquad ([9.162])$$

while the accuracy of the relationship is given by

[9.167] $$R^2_{F(X_1 \ldots X_n)} = \sum_{i=1}^{n} \beta_{FX_i} r_{X_iF}$$

$$= K^2_{F(X_1 \ldots X_n)} \sum_{i=1}^{n} \frac{r^2_{X_iF}}{k^2_{X_iF}}, \qquad ([9.162])$$

which can be put into the esthetically pleasing form

[9.168] $$\left(\frac{R_{F(X_1 \ldots X_n)}}{K_{F(X_1 \ldots X_n)}}\right)^2 = \sum_{i=1}^{n} \left(\frac{r_{X_iF}}{k_{X_iF}}\right)^2 \qquad ([9.162]),$$

or

[9.169] $$\frac{R^2_{F(X_1 \ldots X_n)}}{1 - R^2_{F(X_1 \ldots X_n)}} = \sum_{i=1}^{n} \frac{r^2_{X_iF}}{1 - r^2_{X_iF}} \qquad ([9.162]).$$

Now suppose further that this single factor **F** shared by the test items coincides (u.l.t. with positive coefficient) with the true-score component of each $\mathbf{X_i}$—i.e., that

[9.170-**i**] (**i** = **1**, . . . , **n**) $$r_{T_iF} = 1 \qquad \text{(assumed)}.$$

That is, we assume (1) that the true-score space of the test items is one-dimensional, (2) that the measurement-error components of the items are mutually orthogonal, and (3) that the test items are in convergent configuration. Then r_{X_iF} is the reliability index of test item $\mathbf{X_i}$ and from [9.166] the linear regression of **F** upon the $\mathbf{X_i}$ is

[9.171]

$$\dot{z}_{F(X_1 \ldots X_n)} = K^2_{F(X_1 \ldots X_n)} \sum_{i=1}^{n} \frac{\sqrt{r_{X_i}}}{1 - r_{X_i}} z_{X_i} \qquad ([9.162], [9.170])$$

$$= K^2_{F(X_1 \ldots X_n)} \sum_{i=1}^{n} \frac{\sqrt{r_{X_i}}}{\sigma_{X_i}(1 - r_{X_i})} (X_i - M_{X_i}).$$

Also in this case the true-score component of any weighted composite $\overline{\mathbf{W}}$ of the $\mathbf{X_i}$ coincides (u.l.t.) with true-score factor **F** while $\overline{\mathbf{W}}$'s reliability is its squared correlation with **F**. Since this correlation is maximal when **W** coincides (u.l.t.) with the regression of **F** upon the $\mathbf{X_i}$, the coefficients of the $\mathbf{X_i}$ in equation [9.171] are the weights which maximize the reliability of $\overline{\mathbf{W}}$. That is,

[9.172-**i**]
(**i** = **1**, . . . , **n**)

$$w_i = c \frac{\sqrt{r_{X_i}}}{\sigma_{X_i}(1 - r_{X_i})} = \frac{c}{\sigma_{E_i}} \sqrt{\frac{r_{X_i}}{1 - r_{X_i}}}, \qquad \left(\begin{matrix}[9.162], [9.170], \\ r_{\overline{W}} = \text{maximum}\end{matrix}\right)$$

where c is an arbitrary constant and the second line of [9.172] invites comparison to UniStan weights (see [9.157]) when S_U is error space. The reliability of $\overline{\mathbf{W}}$ under optimal item weighting in the present case may be found by solving for $r_{\overline{W}}$ in

[9.173]

$$r_{\overline{W}} = R^2_{F(X_1 \cdots X_n)} = (1 - r_{\overline{W}}) \sum_{i=1}^{n} \frac{r_{X_i}}{1 - r_{X_i}}, \qquad \left(\begin{matrix}[9.162], [9.170], \\ r_{\overline{W}} = \text{maximum}\end{matrix}\right)$$

the most elegant form of which is

[9.174]

$$PQ_{\overline{W}}(S_T) = \sum_{i=1}^{n} PQ_{X_i}(S_T) \qquad \left(\begin{matrix}[9.162], [9.170], \\ r_{\overline{W}} = \text{maximum}\end{matrix}\right).$$

While equations [9.170]–[9.174] charmingly round out the classical theory of uncorrelated errors and a single true-score dimension, it is not clear how well maximum reliability is approximated by weights [9.172] when—as is inevitable—the assumed conditions are violated. We have already seen (pp. 477f.) however, that when item errors are uncorrelated, simply weighting each test item by the reciprocal of its measurement error generally gives so close an approximation to maximal reliability that further improvements would be trivial at best, at least if the $\mathbf{X_i}$-configuration is in or near strict convergence. Moreover, while both [9.172] and the UniStan approximation to maximal reliability require that the reliability of each individual test item be known, we have also shown (p. 474) that MaxSat weights, which can be computed solely from the interitem covariances, generally yield an excellent approximation to maximum penetrance into common-factor space and hence also to maximum reliability when item errors are uncorrelated. An additional convenience of MaxSat weights is that although their calculation may involve considerable labor when computer services are not available, they automatically solve the orientation problem, since the

MaxSat-weighted item configuration $\mathbf{W}_1, \ldots, \mathbf{W}_n$ is of necessity strictly convergent.

How well these approximations hold up in the more likely case that item errors are not orthogonal is not easy to judge. We have, however, seen (p. 475) that if the first-factor concentration of the items' error configuration is small in comparison to the first-factor concentration of their true-score configuration, MaxSat weights should still afford a useful approximation to maximal test penetrance into true-score space. Since we have no reason to believe that the other approximations described here are any more accurate under correlated errors than is the MaxSat approximation, nor are we likely to have the true-score (or error) covariances requisite to computation of the exact reliability-maximizing weights, it may be concluded that *by far and away the most practical method for attempting to maximize the reliability of a composite test through differential item weighting, and probably a highly accurate one at that, is to use weights which maximize the saturation of the resulting configuration of weighted test items—i.e., which bring the weighted test into coincidence (u.l.t.) with the first principal factor of the standardized items.* Moreover, if the initial (i.e., unweighted) item configuration has been brought reasonably close to strict convergence and the coefficient of variation for the item variances is not excessive, our earlier conclusions about a test's sensitivity to differential item stressing would lead us to expect that the MaxSat-weighted composite should differ (u.l.t.) only negligibly from the simple unweighted sum of the test items, especially if these are numerous and have a respectable homogeneity. This last observation is particularly important for the design of commercial tests, since item weights other than 0 and 1 intolerably magnify the time and effort required to score a test unless the number of differentially weighted items or subtests is rather small. The practical moral, then, is that so long as the item configuration is near strict convergence—and if the items do not obviously form a positive manifold, it may be worth the effort to compute MaxSat weights just to learn what orientations they prescribe[25]—there is little likelihood that the test's reliability can be substantially improved by differential weighting of included items except perhaps under precisely the circumstances in which weighting is easiest to implement, namely, when there are only a few items or subtests to be so treated.

Our discussion of item weighting has laid increasing emphasis upon test reliability as a major objective for selection of weights, and we shall close with a more detailed analysis of why this should command such high priority. The obvious justification, that reliability is a prerequisite for

[25] While reflecting just those items whose MaxSat weights are negative does not necessarily yield a strictly convergent configuration of unweighted items, it should do so in most cases, or at worst result in a configuration which differs from strict convergence only negligibly.

validity, is inadequate because it says nothing about the extent to which a composite's reliability is likely to suffer when its item weights are chosen on other grounds. In order to judge how important it is to approximate the maximum-reliability composite, we need to know how sensitive $r_{\overline{W}}$ is to displacement of $\overline{\mathbf{W}}$ from its position of maximum reliability.[26]

Suppose that test items $\mathbf{X}_1, \ldots, \mathbf{X}_n$ have been so scaled that the reliability of their centroid cannot be increased by further weighting. Then if $S_{\mathbf{X}}$ is the space spanned by the $\mathbf{X}_i$, so that $P_{\overline{\mathbf{X}}}(S_{\mathbf{X}}) = 1$, the penetrance ratio $P_{\overline{\mathbf{X}}}(S_{\mathbf{T}})/P_{\overline{\mathbf{X}}}(S_{\mathbf{X}}) = P_{\overline{\mathbf{X}}}(S_{\mathbf{T}}) = r_{\overline{\mathbf{X}}}$ is at a maximum, and for any weighted composite $\overline{\mathbf{W}}$ of the $\mathbf{X}_i$, substitution of "**T**" and "**X**" for "**H**" and "**U**", respectively, in [7.265,6] while recalling (p. 363) that $\nu_{\mathbf{c_T}} r_{\mathbf{z_w c_T}} = \nu_{\mathbf{c_X}} r_{\mathbf{z_w c_X}}$ for any choice of item weights if $P_{\overline{\mathbf{X}}}(S_{\mathbf{T}})/P_{\overline{\mathbf{X}}}(S_{\mathbf{X}}) = \text{maximum} < \infty$ shows that

$$[9.175] \qquad r_{\overline{\mathbf{W}}} = P_{\overline{\mathbf{W}}}(S_{\mathbf{T}}) = r_{\overline{\mathbf{X}}}\left[1 - \frac{\nu_{\mathbf{W}}^2(\rho_{\mathbf{WX}}^2 - \rho_{\mathbf{WT}}^2)}{1 + 2\nu_{\mathbf{W}}\rho_{\mathbf{WX}}\theta_{\mathbf{WX}} + \nu_{\mathbf{W}}^2\rho_{\mathbf{WX}}^2}\right]. \qquad (r_{\overline{\mathbf{X}}} = \text{maximum})$$

Actually, equation [9.175] holds not only when $r_{\overline{\mathbf{X}}}$ is maximal but also when it is minimal and for many other scalings of the $\mathbf{X}_i$ as well. It is apparent from [9.175] that if $r_{\overline{\mathbf{X}}}$ really is maximal, it must also be the case that $\rho_{\mathbf{WX}}^2 \geqslant \rho_{\mathbf{WT}}^2$ for any choice of weights—i.e., that

$$[9.176] \qquad \frac{\gamma_{\mathbf{WT}}}{\gamma_{\mathbf{WX}}} \leqslant \frac{\mathrm{DQ}_{\mathbf{X}}}{\mathrm{DQ}_{\mathbf{T}}} \qquad (r_{\overline{\mathbf{X}}} = \text{maximum}) .$$

Through consideration of principle [7.292] and its attendant discussion, it may be seen that the maximum value which can be given to the selection-coefficient ratio in [9.176] by a choice of weights is at the very least unity and should be considerably larger than this unless the shapes of the dispersion configurations of the $\mathbf{X}_i$ and the $\mathbf{T}_i$ respectively, are so coordinated that for any choice of weights, the proportion of $\mathbf{X}_i$-dispersion variance lying on the $\boldsymbol{\delta}_{\mathbf{WX}}$-axis is about the same as the proportion of $\mathbf{T}_i$-dispersion variance which lies on the $\boldsymbol{\delta}_{\mathbf{WT}}$-axis. Hence when the $\mathbf{X}_i$ have been scaled to yield maximum centroid reliability, the dispersion quotient of the test items must be at least as large as, and will likely be considerably larger than, the dispersion quotient of their true-score components. Thus in particular, since $\mathrm{Hom}_{\mathbf{X}}$ is a weighted average of $\mathrm{Hom}_{\mathbf{T}}$ and $\mathrm{Hom}_{\mathbf{E}}$,

$$[9.177] \qquad \mathrm{Hom}_{\mathbf{T}} \geqslant \mathrm{Hom}_{\mathbf{X}} \geqslant \mathrm{Hom}_{\mathbf{E}} \qquad (r_{\overline{\mathbf{X}}} = \text{maximum}) .$$

To see how the reliability of a weighted composite $\overline{\mathbf{W}}$ of the $\mathbf{X}_i$ is attenuated by $\overline{\mathbf{W}}$'s dissimilarity to $\overline{\mathbf{X}}$, we can solve for $\nu_{\mathbf{W}}^2/(1 + 2\nu_{\mathbf{W}}\rho_{\mathbf{WX}}\theta_{\mathbf{WX}} +$

[26] With appropriate revisions of notation, the equations which follow apply equally well to the effect of item weights upon a composite variable's penetrance into any arbitrary space S.

$\nu^2_{\mathbf{W}}\rho^2_{\mathbf{WX}}$) in [7.238] and substitute into [9.175], thereby disclosing that

[9.178] $$r_{\overline{\mathbf{W}}} = r_{\overline{\mathbf{X}}}\left[1 - \frac{(1 - r^2_{\overline{\mathbf{X}}\overline{\mathbf{W}}})(\rho^2_{\mathbf{WX}} - \rho^2_{\mathbf{WT}})}{(1-\theta^2_{\mathbf{WX}})\rho^2_{\mathbf{WX}}}\right] \qquad \left(r_{\overline{\mathbf{X}}} = \text{max-imum}\right),$$

or

[9.179] $$\frac{r_{\overline{\mathbf{X}}} - r_{\overline{\mathbf{W}}}}{r_{\overline{\mathbf{X}}}} = \left(\frac{1 - r^2_{\overline{\mathbf{X}}\overline{\mathbf{W}}}}{1-\theta^2_{\mathbf{WX}}}\right)\left(\frac{\rho^2_{\mathbf{WX}} - \rho^2_{\mathbf{WT}}}{\rho^2_{\mathbf{WX}}}\right)$$
$$= \left(\frac{1 - r^2_{\overline{\mathbf{X}}\overline{\mathbf{W}}}}{1-\theta^2_{\mathbf{WX}}}\right)\left(1 - \frac{\gamma_{\mathbf{WT}}\,DQ_{\mathbf{T}}}{\gamma_{\mathbf{WX}}\,DQ_{\mathbf{X}}}\right) \qquad \left(r_{\overline{\mathbf{X}}} = \text{max-imum}\right)$$
$$= \left(\frac{1 - r^2_{\overline{\mathbf{X}}\overline{\mathbf{W}}}}{1-\theta^2_{\mathbf{WX}}}\right)\left[1 - \left(\frac{\gamma_{\mathbf{WT}}}{\gamma_{\mathbf{WX}}}\right)\left(\frac{\text{Sat}_{\mathbf{X}}}{\text{Sat}_{\mathbf{T}}}\right)\left(\frac{1-\text{Sat}_{\mathbf{T}}}{1-\text{Sat}_{\mathbf{X}}}\right)\right].$$

Further rearrangement of the bracketed expression in the last line of [9.179] finally brings the equation into form

[9.180] $$\frac{r_{\overline{\mathbf{X}}} - r_{\overline{\mathbf{W}}}}{r_{\overline{\mathbf{X}}}} = \Lambda_{\mathbf{WX}}[1 - (1 - B_{\mathbf{WX}})(1 - \Gamma_{\mathbf{WX}})]$$
$$= \Lambda_{\mathbf{WX}}(B_{\mathbf{WX}} + \Gamma_{\mathbf{WX}} - B_{\mathbf{WX}}\Gamma_{\mathbf{WX}}), \qquad \left(r_{\overline{\mathbf{X}}} = \text{max-imum}\right)$$

where

[9.181] $$\Lambda_{\mathbf{WX}} =_{\text{def}} \frac{1 - r^2_{\overline{\mathbf{X}}\overline{\mathbf{W}}}}{1-\theta^2_{\mathbf{WX}}},$$
$$= \left(\frac{k_{\overline{\mathbf{X}}\overline{\mathbf{W}}}}{k_{\overline{\mathbf{X}}}\delta_{\mathbf{WX}}}\right)^2$$

[9.182] $$B_{\mathbf{WX}} =_{\text{def}} \frac{\text{Sat}_{\mathbf{T}} - \text{Sat}_{\mathbf{X}}}{\text{Sat}_{\mathbf{T}}\,(1 - \text{Sat}_{\mathbf{X}})},$$

and

[9.183] $$\Gamma_{\mathbf{WX}} =_{\text{def}} 1 - \frac{\gamma_{\mathbf{WT}}}{\gamma_{\mathbf{WX}}}$$
$$= \frac{\gamma_{\mathbf{WX}} - \gamma_{\mathbf{WT}}}{\gamma_{\mathbf{WX}}},$$

in which it is readily seen that $\Lambda_{\mathbf{WX}}$ has a lower bound of 0, and $B_{\mathbf{WX}}$ and $\Gamma_{\mathbf{WX}}$ both have an upper bound of 1. Also, from [9.177], $B_{\mathbf{WX}}$ has a lower bound of 0 when $r_{\overline{\mathbf{X}}}$ is maximal.

Equation [9.180] provides a powerfully detailed analysis of how $\overline{\mathbf{W}}$'s reliability is jointly determined by three separate effects: (1) the degree to which $\overline{\mathbf{W}}$ is displaced from the position of maximal reliability (represented in [9.180] by Λ_{WX}), (2) the degree to which the maximum-reliability item-configuration's saturation in true-score space differs from its saturation in observation space (represented by B_{WX}), and (3) the degree to which the selection coefficient implicated by $\overline{W}$ for the maximum-reliability configuration in true-score space differs from the corresponding selection coefficient for the configuration in observation space (represented by Γ_{WX}). Since the left-hand side of [9.180] is the amount by which the reliability of $\overline{W}$ falls short of maximal, expressed as a proportion of the latter, the right-hand side of [9.180] ranges between 0 and 1, with increasingly large values signifying increasingly poor reliability until $\Lambda_{WX}(B_{WX}+\Gamma_{WX}-B_{WX}\Gamma_{WX})=1$ implies that $r_{\overline{W}}=0$. Given the bounds noted above on Λ_{WX}, B_{WX}, and Γ_{WX}, the quantity $\Lambda_{WX}(B_{WX}+\Gamma_{WX}-B_{WX}\Gamma_{WX})$ is a monotonic increasing function of both B_{WX} and Γ_{WX}, and the reliability of $\mathbf{W}$ thus suffers acutely if either B_{WX} or Γ_{WX} has an appreciably positive value, though a vigorous negative value for Γ_{WX} can do much to curtail the ravages of large positive B_{WX}.

It will be recalled that positioning the weighted composite $\overline{\mathbf{W}}$ may be conceived as a two-stage process in which a direction $\boldsymbol{\delta}_{WX}$ in dispersion space is first selected by an assignment of standardized weights to the dispersion components of the $\mathbf{X}_i$, and $\overline{\mathbf{W}}$ is then located in the $\overline{\mathbf{X}}$–$\boldsymbol{\delta}_{WX}$ plane by choice of ν_W. As ν_W begins at zero and becomes increasingly large in magnitude, $\overline{\mathbf{W}}$ begins at the position of $\overline{\mathbf{X}}$ and rotates toward the position of either $\boldsymbol{\delta}_{WX}$ or $-\boldsymbol{\delta}_{WX}$, depending upon whether $\overline{w}$ is positive or negative. If by the "divergence" between two variables we mean the acute angle formed by the vectors representing these variables in a vector model of the configuration (so that, e.g., two vectors at an angle of 170° have a divergence of 10°), then the term Λ_{WX} in [9.180] is seen to measure the extent to which the divergence of $\overline{\mathbf{W}}$ from $\overline{\mathbf{X}}$ approaches that of $\boldsymbol{\delta}_{WX}$ from $\overline{\mathbf{X}}$. Specifically, $\Lambda_{WX}=1$ implies that $\overline{\mathbf{W}}$ coincides (u.l.t.) with $\boldsymbol{\delta}_{WX}$, while Λ_{WX} is greater or less than 1, respectively, according to whether $\overline{\mathbf{W}}$ diverges from $\overline{\mathbf{X}}$ more or less than does $\boldsymbol{\delta}_{WX}$. This shows that apart from the possibility of a systematic effect of θ_{WX} upon Γ_{WX} (note that B_{WX} is invariant under different choices of $\boldsymbol{\delta}_{WX}$), the smaller is the divergence of $\boldsymbol{\delta}_{WX}$ from $\overline{\mathbf{X}}$ the more will a given divergence of $\overline{\mathbf{W}}$ from $\overline{\mathbf{X}}$ sacrifice the reliability of $\overline{\mathbf{W}}$. However, equations [7.298] and [7.299] reassure us that the divergence between $\boldsymbol{\delta}_{WX}$ and $\overline{\mathbf{X}}$ will usually be close to maximal, and that no matter how item weights are chosen, $\boldsymbol{\delta}_{WX}$ cannot get closer to $\overline{\mathbf{X}}$ than a certain lower limit which is likely to be substantial. If for simplicity we assume that $\theta_{WX}=0$, then from [9.180] and the upper bounds on B_{WX} and Γ_{WX},

$$\frac{r_{\overline{X}}-r_{\overline{W}}}{r_{\overline{X}}} \leqslant 1-r^2_{\overline{X}\overline{W}} \qquad (\theta_{WX}=0,\ r_{\overline{X}}=\text{maximum})\ , \tag{9.184}$$

or

$$r_{\overline{W}} \geqslant r_{\overline{X}} r^2_{\overline{X}\overline{W}} \qquad (\theta_{WX}=0,\ r_{\overline{X}}=\text{maximum})\ . \tag{9.185}$$

Hence a small displacement of $\overline{\mathbf{W}}$ from the position of maximal reliability need not be very detrimental to $r_{\overline{\mathbf{W}}}$. But this was intuitively obvious at the outset. What we really want to know is what happens to $r_{\overline{\mathbf{W}}}$ as the divergence of $\overline{\mathbf{W}}$ from its maximum-reliability position becomes large—e.g., if $\overline{\mathbf{W}}$ lies somewhere in the $\mathbf{n}-1$ dimensions of observation space orthogonal to $\overline{\mathbf{X}}$. In those cases which are of primary interest, then, $\Lambda_{\mathbf{WX}}$ may be expected to be about 1, and the burden of determining $r_{\overline{\mathbf{W}}}$ falls on $B_{\mathbf{WX}}$ and $\Gamma_{\mathbf{WX}}$.

Since the value of $B_{\mathbf{WX}}$ in [9.180] depends only on the variance properties of the $\mathbf{X}_i$-configuration, it represents a debilitating influence on $r_{\overline{\mathbf{W}}}$ which is independent of how the item weights in $\overline{\mathbf{W}}$ are chosen. What its order of magnitude may be is not easy to discern in [9.182]; however,

$$\frac{\text{Sat}_{\mathbf{T}}-\text{Sat}_{\mathbf{X}}}{\text{Sat}_{\mathbf{T}}}=\frac{\alpha_{\mathbf{T}}}{\text{Hom}_{\mathbf{T}}}(\text{Sat}_{\mathbf{T}}-\text{Sat}_{\mathbf{X}})=\frac{\alpha_{\mathbf{T}}}{\text{Hom}_{\mathbf{T}}}\left(\frac{\mathbf{n}-1}{\mathbf{n}}\right)(\text{Hom}_{\mathbf{T}}-\text{Hom}_{\mathbf{X}})$$

$$=\left(\frac{\mathbf{n}-1}{\mathbf{n}}\right)\frac{\alpha_{\mathbf{T}}}{\text{Hom}_{\mathbf{T}}}[\text{Hom}_{\mathbf{T}}-\tilde{r}_{\mathbf{X}}\,\text{Hom}_{\mathbf{T}}-(1-\tilde{r}_{\mathbf{X}})\,\text{Hom}_{\mathbf{E}}]$$

$$=\left(\frac{\mathbf{n}-1}{\mathbf{n}}\right)\alpha_{\mathbf{T}}\,(1-\tilde{r}_{\mathbf{X}})\left(1-\frac{\text{Hom}_{\mathbf{E}}}{\text{Hom}_{\mathbf{T}}}\right)$$

while

$$1-\text{Sat}_{\mathbf{X}}=1-\left(\frac{\mathbf{n}-1}{\mathbf{n}}\right)\text{Hom}_{\mathbf{X}}-\frac{1}{\mathbf{n}}$$

$$=\left(\frac{\mathbf{n}-1}{\mathbf{n}}\right)[1-\tilde{r}_{\mathbf{X}}\,\text{Hom}_{\mathbf{T}}-(1-\tilde{r}_{\mathbf{X}})\,\text{Hom}_{\mathbf{E}}]\,,$$

so from [9.183],

$$[9.186]\quad B_{\mathbf{WX}}=\frac{\alpha_{\mathbf{T}}\,(1-\tilde{r}_{\mathbf{X}})\left(1-\frac{\text{Hom}_{\mathbf{E}}}{\text{Hom}_{\mathbf{T}}}\right)}{1-\tilde{r}_{\mathbf{X}}\,\text{Hom}_{\mathbf{T}}-(1-\tilde{r}_{\mathbf{X}})\,\text{Hom}_{\mathbf{E}}}$$

$$=\alpha_{\mathbf{T}}\frac{1-\tilde{r}_{\mathbf{X}}}{1-\tilde{r}_{\mathbf{X}}\,\text{Hom}_{\mathbf{T}}}\left(1-\frac{\text{Hom}_{\mathbf{E}}}{\text{Hom}_{\mathbf{T}}}\right)\left\{1+\frac{\text{Hom}_{\mathbf{E}}}{1-\text{Hom}_{\mathbf{E}}}\left[\frac{(1-\tilde{r}_{\mathbf{X}})(1-\text{Hom}_{\mathbf{E}})}{\tilde{r}_{\mathbf{X}}\,(1-\text{Hom}_{\mathbf{T}})+(1-\tilde{r}_{\mathbf{X}})\,(1-\text{Hom}_{\mathbf{E}})}\right]\right\}$$

$$=\alpha_{\mathbf{T}}\frac{1-\tilde{r}_{\mathbf{X}}}{1-\tilde{r}_{\mathbf{X}}\,\text{Hom}_{\mathbf{T}}}\left(1-\frac{\text{Hom}_{\mathbf{E}}}{\text{Hom}_{\mathbf{T}}}\,t\right),$$

where

$$\frac{1-\text{Hom}_{\mathbf{T}}}{1-\text{Hom}_{\mathbf{E}}}\leqslant t\leqslant 1\qquad\qquad(\text{Hom}_{\mathbf{E}}\leqslant\text{Hom}_{\mathbf{T}})\,,$$

or using 0 as a more liberal lower bound for t,

$$[9.187]\quad \alpha_{\mathbf{T}}\frac{1-\tilde{r}_{\mathbf{X}}}{1-\tilde{r}_{\mathbf{X}}\,\text{Hom}_{\mathbf{T}}}\left(1-\frac{\text{Hom}_{\mathbf{E}}}{\text{Hom}_{\mathbf{T}}}\right)\leqslant B_{\mathbf{WX}}\leqslant\alpha_{\mathbf{T}}\frac{1-\tilde{r}_{\mathbf{X}}}{1-\tilde{r}_{\mathbf{X}}\,\text{Hom}_{\mathbf{T}}}\qquad(0\leqslant\text{Hom}_{\mathbf{E}}\leqslant\text{Hom}_{\mathbf{T}})\,.$$

If $\text{Hom}_{\mathbf{E}}$ is small in comparison to $\text{Hom}_{\mathbf{T}}$, as occurs when the error configuration approaches orthogonality, we can write simply

$$[9.188] \qquad B_{\mathbf{wX}} \simeq \alpha_{\mathbf{T}} \frac{1-\tilde{r}_{\mathbf{X}}}{1-\tilde{r}_{\mathbf{X}}\,\text{Hom}_{\mathbf{T}}} \qquad (0 \leqslant \text{Hom}_{\mathbf{E}} \ll \text{Hom}_{\mathbf{T}}),$$

where the approximation becomes exact as $\text{Hom}_{\mathbf{E}}$ approaches zero, and is likely to be reasonably accurate even when $\text{Hom}_{\mathbf{E}}$ is appreciable. To illustrate the general magnitude of $B_{\mathbf{wX}}$, it may be seen from [9.188] that if $\tilde{r}_{\mathbf{X}} \simeq .5$, $B_{\mathbf{wX}} \simeq \alpha_{\mathbf{T}}/(2-\text{Hom}_{\mathbf{T}})$, which sinks below .5 only when $\mathbf{n}$ or $\text{Hom}_{\mathbf{T}}$ is quite small.

Of the three reliability-attenuating influences in [9.180], $\Gamma_{\mathbf{wX}}$ is the most difficult to evaluate cleanly. Since the anticipated value of a selection coefficient under an arbitrary choice of item weights is $1/(\mathbf{n}-1)$ (see pp. 369 ff.), which is the same for both $\gamma_{\mathbf{wX}}$ and $\gamma_{\mathbf{wT}}$, there is no systematic tendency for $\gamma_{\mathbf{wX}}$ to be larger than $\gamma_{\mathbf{wT}}$ or conversely, and hence in general $\Gamma_{\mathbf{wX}}$ should have a value around zero. To see more precisely what is involved in $\Gamma_{\mathbf{wX}}$, we note first of all from [7.252] that since $\mathbf{D_i} = \mathbf{D_{T_i}} + \mathbf{D_{E_i}}$ $(\mathbf{i}=\mathbf{1},\ldots,\mathbf{n})$, where $\mathbf{D_i}$, $\mathbf{D_{Ti}}$, and $\mathbf{D_{Ei}}$ are the dispersion components of $\mathbf{X_i}$, $\mathbf{T_i}$, and $\mathbf{E_i}$, respectively,

$$[9.189] \qquad \boldsymbol{\delta}_{\mathbf{wX}} = \frac{\sum_{\mathbf{i=1}}^{\mathbf{n}} z_{\mathbf{wi}}\mathbf{D_i}}{\mathbf{n}} = \frac{\sum_{\mathbf{i=1}}^{\mathbf{n}} z_{\mathbf{wi}}\mathbf{D_{Ti}}}{\mathbf{n}} + \frac{\sum_{\mathbf{i=1}}^{\mathbf{n}} z_{\mathbf{wi}}\mathbf{D_{Ei}}}{\mathbf{n}} = \boldsymbol{\delta}_{\mathbf{wT}} + \boldsymbol{\delta}_{\mathbf{wE}}.$$

Hence

$$[9.190] \qquad \gamma_{\mathbf{wX}}\,\text{Disp}_{\mathbf{X}} = \frac{\text{Var}(\boldsymbol{\delta}_{\mathbf{wX}})}{\overline{V}_{\mathbf{D}}} \cdot \frac{\overline{V}_{\mathbf{D}}}{\overline{V}_{\mathbf{X}}} = \frac{\text{Var}(\boldsymbol{\delta}_{\mathbf{wT}}) + \text{Var}(\boldsymbol{\delta}_{\mathbf{wE}})}{\overline{V}_{\mathbf{X}}} = \frac{\overline{V}_{\mathbf{D_T}}\gamma_{\mathbf{wT}} + \overline{V}_{\mathbf{D_E}}\gamma_{\mathbf{wE}}}{\overline{V}_{\mathbf{X}}} = \tilde{r}_{\mathbf{X}}\gamma_{\mathbf{wT}}\,\text{Disp}_{\mathbf{T}} + (1-\tilde{r}_{\mathbf{X}})\,\gamma_{\mathbf{wE}}\,\text{Disp}_{\mathbf{E}},$$

or since

$$[9.191] \qquad \text{Disp}_{\mathbf{X}} = \tilde{r}_{\mathbf{X}}\,\text{Disp}_{\mathbf{T}} + (1-\tilde{r}_{\mathbf{X}})\,\text{Disp}_{\mathbf{E}},$$

[9.192] $$\gamma_{\mathbf{WX}} = \frac{\tilde{r}_{\mathbf{X}}\,\mathrm{Disp}_{\mathbf{T}}\gamma_{\mathbf{WT}} + (1-\tilde{r}_{\mathbf{X}})\,\mathrm{Disp}_{\mathbf{E}}\gamma_{\mathbf{WE}}}{\tilde{r}_{\mathbf{X}}\,\mathrm{Disp}_{\mathbf{T}} + (1-\tilde{r}_{\mathbf{X}})\,\mathrm{Disp}_{\mathbf{E}}}$$

Thus the selection coefficient determined by a given set of weights for the test items in observation space is a weighted average of the corresponding selection coefficients for the item-projections in true-score space and error space, respectively. Substituting [9.192] into [9.183], we have

[9.193] $$\begin{aligned}\Gamma_{\mathbf{WX}} &= \frac{(1-\tilde{r}_{\mathbf{X}})\,\mathrm{Disp}_{\mathbf{E}}}{\mathrm{Disp}_{\mathbf{X}}}\left(\frac{\gamma_{\mathbf{WE}}-\gamma_{\mathbf{WT}}}{\gamma_{\mathbf{WX}}}\right)\\ &= \frac{\gamma_{\mathbf{WE}}-\gamma_{\mathbf{WT}}}{\gamma_{\mathbf{WE}}+\left(\dfrac{\tilde{r}_{\mathbf{X}}}{1-\tilde{r}_{\mathbf{X}}}\right)\left(\dfrac{\mathrm{Disp}_{\mathbf{T}}}{\mathrm{Disp}_{\mathbf{E}}}\right)\gamma_{\mathbf{WT}}}\\ &\geqslant -\left(\frac{1-\tilde{r}_{\mathbf{X}}}{\tilde{r}_{\mathbf{X}}}\right)\frac{\mathrm{Disp}_{\mathbf{E}}}{\mathrm{Disp}_{\mathbf{T}}},\end{aligned}$$

where the inequality approaches an identity if $\gamma_{\mathbf{WE}}$ manages to become very small in comparison to $\gamma_{\mathbf{WT}}$. This shows that if the dispersion configurations of the item projections in true-score space and error space, respectively, are sufficiently eccentric and out of phase, there may be positions for $\boldsymbol{\delta}_{\mathbf{WX}}$ at which $\Gamma_{\mathbf{WX}}$ is appreciably negative, enough so to thwart the depredations by $B_{\mathbf{WX}}$ on $r_{\overline{\mathbf{W}}}$. Specifically, this will occur when the dispersion configuration in true-score space is substantially elongated in the direction of the component of $\boldsymbol{\delta}_{\mathbf{WX}}$ lying in $S_{\mathbf{T}}$ while the component of $\boldsymbol{\delta}_{\mathbf{WX}}$ lying in $S_{\mathbf{E}}$ cuts through the dispersion configuration of error components in a direction where the latter is especially thin. When the configuration of item errors is orthogonal, $\gamma_{\mathbf{WE}}$ will as a rule differ only negligibly from $1/(\mathbf{n}-1)$ irrespective of the position of $\boldsymbol{\delta}_{\mathbf{WE}}$; hence with uncorrelated errors, $\Gamma_{\mathbf{WX}}$ will be most strongly negative and $r_{\overline{\mathbf{W}}}$ least impaired by divergence of $\overline{\mathbf{W}}$ from the maximum-reliability position when $\boldsymbol{\delta}_{\mathbf{WT}}$ is at or near the position of the first principal factor of the dispersion configuration in true-score space.

To summarize, then, if item weights are chosen without regard for the dispersion configuration of the test items, the proportion of maximum reliability sacrificed by this weighting should more often than not be at least as large as

[9.194][27] $$\frac{r_{\overline{\mathbf{X}}}-r_{\overline{\mathbf{W}}}}{r_{\overline{\mathbf{X}}}} \geqslant \alpha_{\mathbf{T}}\,(1-r^2_{\overline{\mathbf{X}}\overline{\mathbf{W}}})\left(\frac{1-\tilde{r}_{\mathbf{X}}}{1-\tilde{r}_{\mathbf{X}}\,\mathrm{Hom}_{\mathbf{T}}}\right)\left(1-\frac{\mathrm{Hom}_{\mathbf{E}}}{\mathrm{Hom}_{\mathbf{T}}}\right)$$
$$(\gamma_{\mathbf{WE}} \geqslant \gamma_{\mathbf{WT}},\ r_{\overline{\mathbf{X}}} = \text{maximum})$$

[27] Since $\Lambda_{\mathbf{WX}} \geqslant 1 - r^2_{\overline{\mathbf{W}}\overline{\mathbf{X}}}$ and $\Gamma_{\mathbf{WX}} \geqslant 0$ when $\gamma_{\mathbf{WE}} \geqslant \gamma_{\mathbf{WT}}$ (where the latter is as likely as not under random selection of weights.

while if the weighting is vigorous enough to rotate $\overline{\mathbf{W}}$ well away from the maximum-reliability position when $\alpha_{\mathbf{T}}$ is high and $\mathrm{Hom}_{\mathbf{E}}$ is small compared to $\mathrm{Hom}_{\mathbf{T}}$,

$$[9.195] \quad r_{\overline{\mathbf{W}}} \simeq r_{\overline{\mathbf{X}}} \left[\frac{\tilde{r}_{\mathbf{X}}(1-\mathrm{Hom}_{\mathbf{T}})}{1-\tilde{r}_{\mathbf{X}}\,\mathrm{Hom}_{\mathbf{T}}}\right] \quad \left(\begin{array}{c}\alpha_{\mathbf{T}} \simeq 1,\ r^2_{\overline{\mathbf{X}}\overline{\mathbf{W}}} \simeq \theta^2_{\mathbf{WX}},\ \gamma_{\mathbf{WT}} \simeq \gamma_{\mathbf{WE}},\\ 0 \leqslant \mathrm{Hom}_{\mathbf{E}} \ll \mathrm{Hom}_{\mathbf{T}},\\ r_{\overline{\mathbf{X}}} = \text{maximum.}\end{array}\right)$$

To be sure, if the dispersion configuration of the test items in true-score space is strongly dominated by one (or possibly more than one) direction which can be picked up by $\boldsymbol{\delta}_{\mathbf{WX}}$ without hitting a correspondingly strong concentration of the dispersion configuration in error space, then it may be possible to put $\overline{\mathbf{W}}$ anywhere in the plane spanned by this $\boldsymbol{\delta}_{\mathbf{WX}}$ and the maximum-reliability $\overline{\mathbf{X}}$ without seriously impairing $\overline{\mathbf{W}}$'s reliability. How likely it is that $\boldsymbol{\delta}_{\mathbf{WX}}$ would strike such a position when item weights are determined by external criteria which do not explicitly consider test reliability, however, is problematic. Hence on the whole, formula [9.195] (which tends to err on the side of pessimism but has the virtue of simplicity) warns us what to expect of a composite test's reliability if we try to adapt it to purposes other than the one for which it is best suited by maximum-reliability weights. Since for small $r_{\overline{\mathbf{X}}\overline{\mathbf{W}}}$ and realistic values of $\tilde{r}_{\mathbf{X}}$ the attenuation of $r_{\overline{\mathbf{X}}}$ indicated by [9.195] (or somewhat more accurately by [9.194]) is large—generally well over a half—while a test with a reliability no greater than this is virtually worthless for predicting a test-stable criterion, we may conclude that for a set of test items whose true-score homogeneity in maximum-reliability configuration is appreciable, unless a weighted composite $\overline{\mathbf{W}}$ of these items lies rather close to the maximum-reliability position, the prospect for $\overline{\mathbf{W}}$'s having much predictive utility is not in general very encouraging.

Of course, this general conclusion about composite reliability should not be construed to imply that anything is amiss with locating $\overline{\mathbf{W}}$ in secondary zones of high reliability if these can be found. Admittedly, such a prospect is easier to recommend than to implement. But we do have a way to estimate the reliability of a composite test which is generally quite accurate so long as error homogeneity is not too pronounced. Specifically, we know that if $\overline{\mathbf{W}}$ is a weighted composite of test items $\mathbf{X}_1, \ldots,$ $\mathbf{X}_n$, then the alpha coefficient for the set of weighted items $\mathbf{W}_1, \ldots, \mathbf{W}_n$ is a lower bound on the penetrance of $\overline{\mathbf{W}}$ into common-factor space, most of which, hopefully, is penetrance into common true-factor space. In fact, it may be seen from the discussion on p. 449 f. that so long as the error homogeneity of the $\mathbf{W}_i$ remains small (and the first-factor concentration of the $\mathbf{E}_i$ is an upper bound for $\mathrm{Hom}_{w\mathbf{E}}$ no matter how item weights are chosen) and the number of test items is not very large, $r_{\overline{\mathbf{W}}}$ has a good chance at surpassing $\alpha_{\mathbf{W}}$. This is especially true when the true-score homogeneity of the $\mathbf{W_i}$ is small, which is precisely the circumstance in which $\overline{\mathbf{W}}$'s reliability is least likely to be satisfactory and hence where a lower bound for $r_{\overline{\mathbf{W}}}$ is most important.

So long as we are willing to treat lower-bound approximations to common-factor penetrance as at least rough estimates of reliability, moreover, there is a simple and effective procedure by which the total space spanned by a set of test items can be stratified into zones of decreasing estimated reliability. As shown in Appendix B (p. 592), *if test items* $\mathbf{X_1}$, . . . , $\mathbf{X_n}$ *have all been standardized to unit variance while* $\overline{\mathbf{W}}_{(\mathbf{k})}$ *is a weighted composite*

$$\overline{\mathbf{W}}_{(\mathbf{k})} = \left(\frac{1}{\mathbf{n}}\right)\sum_{\mathbf{i}=1}^{\mathbf{n}} \mathbf{W}_{(\mathbf{k})\mathbf{i}} \ , \quad \mathbf{W}_{(\mathbf{k})\mathbf{i}} =_{\text{def}} w_{(\mathbf{k})\mathbf{i}}\mathbf{X_i} \ ,$$

of the $\mathbf{X_i}$ *which coincides (u.l.t.) with their* **k***th principal factor* $\mathbf{P_k}$,[28] *then the proportion of* $V_{\mathbf{X}}$ *accounted for by* $\mathbf{P_k}$ *equals the saturation of the set of weighted items* $\mathbf{W}_{(\mathbf{k})1}$, . . . , $\mathbf{W}_{(\mathbf{k})\mathbf{n}}$. That is, if $\lambda_{\mathbf{k}}$ is the eigenvalue (see [6.44]) of $\mathbf{P_k}$ and the $\mathbf{X_i}$ all have unit variance so that $V_{\mathbf{X}} = \mathbf{n}$, then

$$[9.196] \qquad \text{Sat}_{\mathbf{W}_{(\mathbf{k})}} = \frac{\lambda_{\mathbf{k}}}{\mathbf{n}} \qquad (r^2_{\mathbf{P_k}\overline{\mathbf{W}}_{(\mathbf{k})}} = 1, \ \overline{V}_{\mathbf{X}} = 1, \ \nu_{V_{\mathbf{X}}} = 0) \ .$$

Since from [9.52] and [7.87*a*] the alpha coefficient may be written

$$[9.197] \qquad \alpha_{\mathbf{X}} = \frac{\mathbf{n}\ \text{Sat}_{\mathbf{X}} - 1}{(\mathbf{n}-1)\ \text{Sat}_{\mathbf{X}}} = \left(\frac{\mathbf{n}}{\mathbf{n}-1}\right)\left(1 - \frac{1}{\mathbf{n}\ \text{Sat}_{\mathbf{X}}}\right) ,$$

it follows from [9.196] and [9.84] that

$$[9.198] \qquad \left(\frac{\mathbf{n}}{\mathbf{n}-1}\right)\left(1 - \frac{1}{\lambda_{\mathbf{k}}}\right) = \alpha_{\mathbf{W}_{(\mathbf{k})}} = \left[1 - \frac{DQ_{\mathbf{W}_{(\mathbf{k})}}(S_{\mathbf{H}})}{\mathbf{n}-1}\right] P_{\mathbf{P_k}}(S_{\mathbf{H}}) \qquad (r^2_{\mathbf{P_k}\overline{\mathbf{W}}_{(\mathbf{k})}} = 1, \ \overline{V}_{\mathbf{X}} = 1, \ \nu_{V_{\mathbf{X}}} = 0) \ .$$

Hence

$$[9.199] \qquad 1 - \frac{1}{\lambda_{\mathbf{k}}} < \left(\frac{\mathbf{n}-1}{\mathbf{n}}\right) P_{\mathbf{P_k}}(S_{\mathbf{H}}) < P_{\mathbf{P_k}}(S_{\mathbf{H}}) \qquad (\overline{V}_{\mathbf{X}} = 1, \ \nu_{V_{\mathbf{X}}} = 0) \ ,$$

---

[28] More technically, weights $w_{(\mathbf{k})1}$, . . . , $w_{(\mathbf{k})\mathbf{n}}$ must constitute a **k**th eigenvector of covariance matrix $\{C_{\mathbf{X_i}\mathbf{X_j}}\}$.

or

$$[9.200] \qquad P_{\mathbf{P_k}}(S_{\mathbf{U}}) < \frac{1}{\lambda_{\mathbf{k}}} \qquad (\overline{V}_{\mathbf{X}} = 1, \nu_{V_{\mathbf{X}}} = 0) \ ,$$

where the inequalities are close to identities unless **n** or $\mathrm{Hom}_{\mathbf{W}_{(k)}}(S_{\mathbf{H}})$ is quite small. Thus when the $\mathbf{X}_i$ have all been standardized to unit variance, the reciprocal of the eigenvalue of their **k**th principal factor is an upper-bound approximation to that factor's penetrance into unique-factor space. Further, every weighted[29] composite $\overline{\mathbf{W}} = (1/\mathbf{n}) \sum_{i=1}^{n} w_i \mathbf{X}_i$ of the test items is identical with some linear combination $\sum_{i=1}^{n} a_i \mathbf{C}_i$ of the principal components $\mathbf{C}_1, \ldots, \mathbf{C}_n$ of the $\mathbf{X}_i$-configuration, and as shown in Appendix B (p. 591 f.), the saturation of the weighted set $\mathbf{W}_1, \ldots, \mathbf{W}_n$ (where $\mathbf{W}_i = w_i \mathbf{X}_i$ as before) is then

$$[9.201]^{30} \qquad \mathrm{Sat}_{\mathbf{W}} = \frac{\sum_{i=1}^{n} a_i^2 \lambda_i}{\mathbf{n} \sum_{i=1}^{n} a_i^2} \qquad \left(\begin{array}{c} \overline{\mathbf{W}} = \sum_{i=1}^{n} a_i \mathbf{C}_i, \; r^2_{\mathbf{C}_i \overline{\mathbf{W}}_{(i)}} = 1, \\ \overline{V}_{\mathbf{X}} = 1, \nu_{V_{\mathbf{X}}} = 0 \end{array} \right)$$

$$= \frac{\sum_{i=1}^{n} a_i^2 \, \mathrm{Sat}_{\mathbf{W}_{(i)}}}{\sum_{i=1}^{n} a_i^2} \ .$$

[29] Since the centroid of a set of unstandardized variables may always be regarded as a weighted composite of Z-scales, the following theorems apply to any unweighted set of extant raw-score variables just as much as to a configuration which *could* be produced by weighting standardized items.

[30] If the dimensionality of $\mathbf{X}_1, \ldots, \mathbf{X}_n$ is less than **n**, the set of coefficients $a_1, \ldots, a_n$ is not uniquely determined (since the coefficient of any principal component whose variance is zero can be arbitrarily chosen). In this case, theorem [9.201] stipulates that the a_i are defined from the w_i as in [B.63], p. 591.

Hence from [9.84], [9.197] and the first line of [9.201],

[9.202]

$$\left(\frac{\mathbf{n}}{\mathbf{n}-1}\right)\left(1-\frac{\sum_{i=1}^{n} a_i^2}{\sum_{i=1}^{n} a_i^2\lambda_i}\right) = \alpha_{\mathbf{W}} \leqslant P_{\overline{\mathbf{W}}}(S_{\mathbf{H}}) \qquad \begin{pmatrix} \overline{\mathbf{W}} = \sum_{i=1}^{n} a_i\mathbf{C}_i, \\ \overline{\mathbf{V}}_{\mathbf{X}} = 1,\ \nu_{\mathbf{V_X}} = 0 \end{pmatrix}.$$

or more simply

[9.203]

$$P_{\overline{\mathbf{W}}}(S_{\mathbf{U}}) < \frac{\sum_{i=1}^{n} a_i^2}{\sum_{i=1}^{n} a_i^2\lambda_i} \qquad \begin{pmatrix} \overline{\mathbf{W}} = \sum_{i=1}^{n} a_i\mathbf{C}_i, \\ \overline{\mathbf{V}}_{\mathbf{X}} = 1,\ \nu_{\mathbf{V_X}} = 0 \end{pmatrix}.$$

In particular, if $a_{k+1} = a_{k+2} = \ldots = a_n = 0$, so that $\overline{\mathbf{W}}$ lies in the space of the first **k** principal factors of the $\mathbf{X}_i$, [9.202] implies that

[9.204]

$$P_{\overline{\mathbf{W}}}(S_{\mathbf{U}}) < \frac{1}{\lambda_k} \qquad \begin{pmatrix} \overline{\mathbf{W}} = \sum_{i=1}^{k} a_i\mathbf{C}_i, \\ \overline{\mathbf{V}}_{\mathbf{X}} = 1,\ \nu_{\mathbf{V_X}} = 0) \end{pmatrix},$$

which shows that *if variables* $\mathbf{X}_1, \ldots, \mathbf{X}_n$ *have all been standardized to unit variance, the reciprocal of the eigenvalue of their* **k***th principal factor is an upper bound for the penetrance of any linear combination of the first* **k** *principal factors of the* $\mathbf{X}_i$ *into any unique-factor space for the* $\mathbf{X}_i$.

More incisively, it follows from [9.201] that if $\overline{\mathbf{W}}$ is any weighted composite of the $\mathbf{X}_i$ confined to the subspace of their consecutive principal factors $\mathbf{P}_j, \mathbf{P}_{j+1}, \ldots, \mathbf{P}_{k-1}, \mathbf{P}_k$ ($j \leqslant k$),

[9.205]

$$\alpha_{\mathbf{W}_{(k)}} \leqslant \alpha_{\mathbf{W}} \leqslant \alpha_{\mathbf{W}_{(j)}} \qquad \begin{pmatrix} V_{\overline{\mathbf{W}}\bullet \mathbf{P}_j\ldots\mathbf{P}_k} = 0,\ r^2_{\mathbf{P}_j\mathbf{W}_{(j)}} = 1, \\ r^2_{\mathbf{P}_k\overline{\mathbf{W}}_{(k)}} = 1,\ \ \overline{\mathbf{V}}_{\mathbf{X}} = 1,\ \nu_{\mathbf{V_X}} = 0 \end{pmatrix}$$

and hence from [9.198],

[9.206]

$$\left(\frac{\mathbf{n}}{\mathbf{n}-1}\right)\left(1-\frac{1}{\lambda_k}\right) \leqslant \alpha_{\mathbf{W}} \leqslant \left(\frac{\mathbf{n}}{\mathbf{n}-1}\right)\left(1-\frac{1}{\lambda_j}\right) \qquad \begin{pmatrix} V_{\overline{\mathbf{W}}\bullet \mathbf{P}_j\ldots\mathbf{P}_k} = 0, \\ \overline{\mathbf{V}}_{\mathbf{X}} = 1,\ \nu_{\mathbf{V_X}} = 0 \end{pmatrix},$$

where $\alpha_{\mathbf{W}}$ ranges throughout the full interval indicated as $\overline{\mathbf{W}}$ assumes different positions in the space of $\mathbf{P}_j, \ldots, \mathbf{P}_k$. If $\alpha_{\mathbf{W}}$ is accepted as an approximation to the reliability of composite test $\overline{\mathbf{W}}$, then [9.206] shows how the space comprising all linear combinations of a set of test items can be effectively partitioned into approximate reliability strata. Specifically, if $V_{\mathbf{X}_i} = 1$ ($\mathbf{i} = \mathbf{1}, \ldots, \mathbf{n}$), the region of observation space spanned by the successive principal factors from $\mathbf{P}_j$ to $\mathbf{P}_k$, inclusive, of variables $\mathbf{X}_1, \ldots, \mathbf{X}_n$ contains exactly those linear composites of the $\mathbf{X}_i$ whose alpha-estimated reliabilities range from $[\mathbf{n}/(\mathbf{n}-1)](1 - 1/\lambda_k)$ to $[\mathbf{n}/(\mathbf{n}-1)](1 - 1/\lambda_j)$. In particular, [9.206] has the important consequence that while the alpha-estimate of $r_{\overline{\mathbf{W}}}$ can always be computed for any linear composite $\overline{\mathbf{W}}$ of the $\mathbf{X}_i$ which happens to interest us, we can also extract all principal factors of the (normalized) $\mathbf{X}_i$ whose eigenvalues are larger than a preassigned lower limit λ_0 and know in advance that any linear combination of these factors has an alpha-estimated reliability greater than $1 - 1/\lambda_0$. The moral for practical test construction is obvious: If a standard of minimal reliability, r_0, can be agreed upon such that a test whose reliability is no greater than r_0 cannot be taken seriously as an instrument having predictive utility, and it is desired to report the outcome of a given multi-itemed test as a profile in anticipation that the several test-outcome dimensions may subsequently be united in various weighted combinations for a variety of predictive purposes, the profile scales so defined should be restricted to test-item composites which lie only in the space spanned by those principal factors of the normalized test items whose eigenvalues exceed $1/(1-r_0)$. We can then differentially weight the reduced test dimensions with abandon, secure from the menace of [9.195].

*Chapter 10. **Epilog**

WHILE the preceding chapters have attempted to develop the theory of prediction in sufficient depth to lay bare its conceptual foundations and mathematical structure, it would be unfortunate were the reader to be left with the illusion that he has now become conversant with all phases of the subject. As a lesson in humility and, hopefully, a goad to further study, we shall close with an embarrassingly superficial survey of several important problem areas which we have not attempted to explore.

Sampling: The Problem of Probabilities

From time to time, the reader has been admonished that while the statistical concepts developed in this book have been here formally derived only from relative frequencies in finite populations of real or hypothetical entities, they are actually intended to apply primarily to distributions of *probabilities* for which real or hypothetical frequency distributions are only simplifying surrogates. In developing policies for making specific predictions, moreover, it was suavely assumed that the relevant probabilities are actually known. These expository tactics have been far from guileless, for in fact, adequate appreciation of the complexities thus simplified moves into immediate confrontation with more advanced problems and intellectual demands on a number of research frontiers. To begin with, there is the question of how the mathematics of probability differs from a mere calculus of frequencies, study of which quickly leads to the theory of measures on transfinite sets. Secondly, there is the achingly unresolved issue of what probabilities *are*. This is a perplexity which is largely neglected in mathematical treatises on probability and statistics, but it has never ceased to harrass serious researchers in the foundations of these fields. Nor is this "philosophical" uncertainty devoid of substantial import for applications of probability theory to practical affairs, for just how the concept of "probability" is to be interpreted (and it may well be that we need to admit several different *kinds* of "probability") makes a difference for how numerical judgments about specific probabilities are to be distilled from accumulated experience. In particular, the recent thrust of development in Bayesian statistics and "subjective" probability[1] urges a thorough rethinking of the foundations and practical recommendations of traditional sampling theory, especially the status of its commitment to the existence of objective probabilities about which we have only uncertain knowledge. Finally, assuming that the axiomatic framework of currently established belief about the relations between sample frequencies and underlying population parameters will not likely be seriously shaken by future revisions of the theory's substantive interpretation, it remains for the reader to learn something of what has been worked out about how, in practice, we *can* discover the probability distributions presupposed by the prediction policies described in previous chapters, and what additional complications and cautions may be introjected by our having only sampling approximations to these. Because this last question is so obviously critical to any enterprise in which prediction theory is actually applied, a few of the most salient conclusions about multivariate sampling will be summarized here, though in so brief a description it will not be possible even to explain their significance adequately, much less to indicate their derivations. (The reader who has had no prior exposure to sampling theory at all will not likely be able to make much sense out of this section, but he should at least read the qualitative summarizing passages.)

The core assumption upon which sampling theory (i.e., inferential statistics) is grounded is that it is generally possible to conceive scores actually observed on certain variables as being jointly determined by (1) certain known or hypothesized attributes of the observed events, the systematic quantitative influences of which are to be estimated from the observations at hand; and (2) one or more "random" or "stochastic" processes whose specific numerical contributions vary unpredictably from one observation to another but which are governed by probabilities with a determinate albeit partially unknown distribution. A particular pattern of such hypotheses applied to a given body of data is known as a "model" of these observations, and by describing the model algebraically —i.e., writing symbols for the unknown numerical constants or "population parameters"—it becomes possible to find corresponding algebraic expressions in the parametric unknowns for the probabilities (or probability densities) of the variously possible observational outcomes, where these "observational outcomes" may include the values of functions (e.g., the sample mean) defined on the array of raw observations.

[1] See especially the work of L. J. Savage. A useful introduction to this development is available in Edwards, *et al.* (25), while the less enthusiastic review by Binder (7) is also worth consultation.

In particular, for each set of possible numerical values for the parameters of the model, the likelihood conferred by that particular parametric hypothesis upon a given constellation of data can be determined. While the derivation of these parameter-dependent probabilities of observation—i.e., the distribution of probabilities over the various possible values of the data variables implicated by a particular parameteric hypothesis—is in principle (though by no means always so simply in practice) a straightforward piece of logical deduction, how to reason backward from them to what values the parameters probably have in view of the data actually obtained is not so clear. In Bayesian statistics, one attempts ultimately to arrive at a distribution of probabilities over the parametric possibilities, whereas in more traditional approaches, "estimator functions" are defined which convert the observed values of the data variables into point or interval estimates of the parameters in question—e.g., as when the sample mean is taken as an estimate of the mean of the population from which the sample is drawn. By studying the parameter-dependent probability distributions of different estimator functions it becomes possible to single out those whose statistical properties are optimal according to accepted standards of desirability. In particular, a "maximum likelihood" estimator of a certain parameter is one which takes as its estimate the value of the parameter under which the obtained observations have the greatest probability of occurrence, while an "unbiased, minimum-variance" estimator is one whose parameter-dependent probability distribution under the model has an expected value equal to the parameter being estimated no matter what this value may be (which is what "unbiased" here means) and a variance no larger than that of any other unbiased estimator of this parameter. The variance of an unbiased estimator—or better, the square root of the variance, since for an unbiased estimator the standard deviation of its probability distribution is its "standard error," or quadratic mean deviation from the parameter's correct value—is a useful measure of how strongly the estimates so yielded can be trusted, though how this information about the accuracy of estimation is utilized in non-Bayesian statistics is a rather subtle and precarious venture not readily summarized in a sentence or two.

Since we will shortly be considering unbiased, minimum-variance estimators of statistical parameters to be those which in general yield the greatest accuracy which can be anticipated for such an estimate, it is worth a moment's effort to clarify the sense in which this is so. Suppose that an observation variable **O** (which in general will take alternatively possible *sets* of data as its values but may for the moment just as well be considered to comprise a single observation) has a probability distribution which is in part a function of an unknown parameter θ (e.g., θ might be **O**'s expected value), and that we wish to find a function $\phi(\mathbf{O})$ of **O** such that the discrepancy between $\phi(O)$ and θ for a to-be-obtained value O° of **O** is as small as we are able to make it. That is, we contemplate estimating θ by observing a sample value of **O**, plugging this observed number into the estimator function $\phi(\mathbf{O})$, and using the result as an approximation to the unknown θ; while to maximize our confidence in the efficacy of this approximation, the estimator function $\hat{\boldsymbol{\theta}} = \phi(\mathbf{O})$ is to be so chosen that the anticipated error of estimate is as small as possible, namely, by minimizing some measure of the likely deviation of $\phi(\mathbf{O})$ from θ. Taking the quadratic mean magnitude of this discrepancy—i.e., the "standard error" of the estimator—as the measure to be minimized, we have from [3.19],

$$[10.1] \qquad \mathrm{QM}_{|\hat{\boldsymbol{\theta}}-\theta|} = \sqrt{Var\{\hat{\boldsymbol{\theta}} - \theta\} + Exp\{\hat{\boldsymbol{\theta}} - \theta\}^2} \qquad (\hat{\boldsymbol{\theta}} = \phi(\mathbf{O}))$$

$$= \sqrt{Var\{\phi(\mathbf{O})\} + [Exp\{\phi(\mathbf{O})\} - \theta]^2}\ ,$$

where we write "*Exp*" and "*Var*" for the mean (i.e., expectation) and variance, respectively, of the distribution of probabilities over the various possible values of $\phi(\mathbf{O})$, and the change from previous notation is to emphasize that we are *not* pretending that this is a frequency distribution of scores in some finite population of extant entities. The probability distribution for $\phi(\mathbf{O})$ is determined by the corresponding distribution over **O** and is dependent upon the same unknown parameters as is the latter, θ in particular. The expected difference,

$$[10.2] \qquad d_{\phi} =_{\mathrm{def}} Exp\{\hat{\boldsymbol{\theta}} - \theta\} \qquad (\hat{\boldsymbol{\theta}} = \phi(\mathbf{O}))$$

$$= Exp\{\phi(\mathbf{O})\} - \theta\ ,$$

between the estimate of θ so obtained and its correct value is called the *bias* of the estimator $\hat{\boldsymbol{\theta}} = \phi(\mathbf{O})$ and represents whatever tendency this function may have to err systematically, while if $d_{\phi} = 0$—i.e., if $Exp\{\phi(\mathbf{O})\} = \theta$—for all possible values of the unknown parameters, $\phi(\mathbf{O})$ is said to be an *unbiased* estimator of θ. According to [10.1], the standard error of $\phi(\mathbf{O})$ as an estimator of θ is an increasing function of both $\phi(\mathbf{O})$'s variance and the magnitude of its bias. Suppose now that d_{ϕ}, though not zero, is not a function of any unknowns. Then d_{ϕ} can be determined numerically and the revised estimator function $\hat{\boldsymbol{\theta}} = \phi(\mathbf{O}) - d_{\phi}$ is unbiased, has a variance equal to that of $\phi(\mathbf{O})$, and has hence a smaller standard error than does $\hat{\boldsymbol{\theta}} = \phi(\mathbf{O})$. On the other hand, suppose that the bias of $\hat{\boldsymbol{\theta}} = \phi(\mathbf{O})$ is a function of unknown parameters while another estimator $\psi(\mathbf{O})$ of θ is unbiased. Then in almost all cases there will be possible values of the parameters which make d_{ϕ} so large that the standard error of

$\phi(\mathbf{O})$ is very much larger than that of $\psi(\mathbf{O})$ even though the latter may have the larger variance of the two estimators; and if our a priori beliefs about the unknown parameters cannot discount these large-d_ϕ possibilities as serious contenders, we will have greater confidence in the estimate of θ yielded by the unbiased estimator $\psi(\mathbf{O})$ than in the biased estimate from $\phi(\mathbf{O})$. (A Bayesian argument from an a priori distribution of probabilities over the alternative parameter possibilities makes this point more explicitly than we need to consider here.) Hence except for unusual circumstances, an unbiased estimator has greater anticipated accuracy than any biased one, while within the class of unbiased estimators of a given parameter, the one with minimum variance also has the smallest standard error (cf. [10.1] with $Exp\{\phi(\mathbf{O})\}$ set equal to θ) and hence enjoys the greatest anticipated accuracy of all.

For making inferences to underlying probabilities from the joint frequency distribution on predictor variables $\mathbf{X}_1, \ldots, \mathbf{X}_m$ and criterion $\mathbf{Y}$ observed in a sample of n individuals selected under conditions P (i.e., P defines the "population" from which the sample is drawn), three major models have been studied by mathematical statisticians: the "correlation model," the "regression model," and "structural equations" (sometimes known as "functional relations"). In the *correlation model*, all the variables $\mathbf{Y}, \mathbf{X}_1, \ldots, \mathbf{X}_m$ are construed to be stochastic with a joint probability distribution in P whose means and covariance matrix are unknown but whose shape is presumed to be normal, while each set of joint scores $Y_j, X_{1j}, \ldots, X_{mj}$ manifested by a member j of the observed sample is assumed to be an independent random selection from this distribution. The nature of the stochastic process envisioned by the correlation model may be clarified by stating that in theory, the joint probability distribution of $\mathbf{Y}, \mathbf{X}_1, \ldots, \mathbf{X}_m$ in population P (i.e., under conditions P) is what the joint frequency distribution on these variables in a random sample of n individuals from P should converge to as n becomes very large. The parameters to which primary attention is directed in applications of the correlation model are the means and covariances among $\mathbf{Y}, \mathbf{X}_1, \ldots, \mathbf{X}_m$, thus recognizing no distinction among the variables *vis-à-vis* criterion versus predictors. When our intent is to estimate scores on $\mathbf{Y}$ from scores on the $\mathbf{X}_i$, however, our first concern is for the regression coefficients $b_{\mathbf{YX}_i \cdot \mathbf{X}_1 \cdots \mathbf{X}_{i-1}\mathbf{X}_{i+1} \cdots \mathbf{X}_m}$ (henceforth abbreviated to b_i), and so long as normality is assumed for all stochastic effects, the correlation model yields the same maximum-likelihood and unbiased, minimum-variance estimates of the b_i and the residual criterion variance as does the regression model—which is especially convenient for prediction theory insomuch as the regression model not only depends upon weaker stochastic assumptions and has correspondingly greater applicability than does the correlation model, but is also exceptionally tractable mathematically.

In the *regression model* of sample observations $Y_j, X_{1j}, \ldots, X_{mj}$ $(j = 1, \ldots, n)$, it is postulated that each score Y_j observed on criterion **Y** for an individual j from population P has the regression composition

$$[10.3] \qquad Y_j = b_0 + \sum_{i=1}^{m} b_i X_{ij} + e_j ,$$

in which $b_0, b_1, \ldots, b_m$ are parameters which are the same for all members of P, X_{ij} is individual j's score on predictor $\mathbf{X}_i$, and e_j is j's score on a random variable **e** whose probability distribution in P is normal with an expected value of zero, an algebraically specified variance of $\sigma^2_{\mathbf{e}}$, and is statistically independent of $\mathbf{X}_1, \ldots, \mathbf{X}_m$. That is, the contingent distribution of **e** in P, given any constellation of joint scores on $\mathbf{X}_1, \ldots, \mathbf{X}_m$ is identical with **e**'s unconditional distribution in P. It is also assumed that each e_j $(j = 1, \ldots, n)$ in the sample is an independent random selection from the distribution of **e**.[2] Thus the regression model requires only that the contingent probability distribution of **Y** in P, given scores $X_1, \ldots, X_m$ on $\mathbf{X}_1, \ldots, \mathbf{X}_m$, respectively, be normal with variance $\sigma^2_{\mathbf{e}}$ and an expected value of $b_0 + \sum_{i=1}^{m} b_i X_i$, and that the departure from expectation for one observed **Y**-score in the sample does not affect the **Y**-probabilities for another. If it were to be additionally assumed that the scores on $\mathbf{X}_1, \ldots, \mathbf{X}_m$ obtained for the members of the observed sample were drawn randomly from the joint probability distribution of these variables in P and that this distribution is normal, we would be back in the correlation model. However, by presuming stochastic behavior only for the criterion residual **e**, the regression model is indifferent to what shape the predictor distribution has in P and to how the sample distribution of predictor scores arises so long as the method of selection does not disturb the contingent distributions of **Y**, given $\mathbf{X}_1, \ldots, \mathbf{X}_m$, in P. (E.g., the n individuals whose scores on **Y** are observed in the sample may have been deliberately chosen by the experimentor to have a distribution on the $\mathbf{X}_i$ with preassigned characteristics such as orthogonality, even though this may be quite different from the predictor distribution which would be expected under random selection of subjects from P.) The regression model yields estimates of the regression coefficients $b_0, \ldots, b_m$ in [10.3] and of the residual criterion variance $\sigma^2_{\mathbf{e}}$, which are precisely the statistics of primary importance for practical applications of prediction theory insomuch as the b-parameters determine the ideal policy for predicting **Y** from $\mathbf{X}_1, \ldots, \mathbf{X}_m$ in P while $\sigma_{\mathbf{Y} \cdot \mathbf{X}_1 \ldots \mathbf{X}_m} = \sigma_{\mathbf{Y}|\mathbf{X}_1 \ldots \mathbf{X}_m} = \sigma_{\mathbf{e}}$ is its standard error. What the regression model does *not* properly esti-

[2] More precisely, the model conceives of **n** random variables $\mathbf{e}_1, \ldots, \mathbf{e}_n$, one for each observation on **Y** in the sample, whose joint probability distribution is taken to be normal with zero means, equal variances σ^2, and zero intercorrelations. These assumptions can be relaxed, but only by complicating the model's conclusions.

mate without the additional assumptions of the correlation model, however, is the joint probability distribution of $\mathbf{X}_1, \ldots, \mathbf{X}_m$ in P. Neither does it give the multiple and partial correlations between $\mathbf{Y}$ and the predictors, or the total variance of $\mathbf{Y}$ in P, since these statistics also depend in part upon the distribution of the $\mathbf{X}_i$.

Before summarizing the findings of the regression model, we should also mention the third major stochastic approach to multivariate models, *structural equations* (or *functional relations*). This model postulates that an exact relationship of a certain stated form, say linear, would hold between criterion $\mathbf{Y}$ and predictors $\mathbf{X}_1, \ldots, \mathbf{X}_m$ in population P were it not for error components in $\mathbf{Y}$ *and also* in $\mathbf{X}_1, \ldots, \mathbf{X}_m$. That is, it is assumed that

$$\mathbf{Y} = \boldsymbol{\tau}_Y + \mathbf{e}_Y ,$$

$$\mathbf{X}_i = \boldsymbol{\tau}_i + \mathbf{e}_i \quad (\mathbf{i} = 1, \ldots, \mathbf{m}) ,$$

$$\boldsymbol{\tau}_Y = b_0 + \sum_{i=1}^{m} b_i \boldsymbol{\tau}_i ,$$

where $\mathbf{e}_Y, \mathbf{e}_1, \ldots, \mathbf{e}_m$ are random variables with an algebraically specified joint probability distribution which virtually always includes stipulation of orthogonality but not necessarily equal variances or normality. The sampling problem is to convert joint scores actually observed on $\mathbf{Y}, \mathbf{X}_1, \ldots, \mathbf{X}_m$ into estimates of the b_i. However, structural-equations analysis has conceptual difficulties which extend far beyond those of inferring probabilities from sample frequencies. Even were it possible to observe scores on $\mathbf{Y}, \mathbf{X}_1, \ldots, \mathbf{X}_m$ in an indefinitely large random sample of population P (which for correlation and regression models removes all uncertainty about the underlying parameters), the structural-equations model is still unable to solve for the postulated coefficients $b_0, \ldots, b_m$ without the aid of additional assumptions. For the structural equations model is no more than a special case of inferential factor analysis (with $\boldsymbol{\tau}_Y, \boldsymbol{\tau}_1, \ldots, \boldsymbol{\tau}_m$ as the communal components of $\mathbf{Y}, \mathbf{X}_1, \ldots, \mathbf{X}_m$ respectively) in which the common-factor dimensionality is presupposed to be only one less than the number of data variables. But it is easily seen (e.g., by partialling $\boldsymbol{\tau}_2, \ldots, \boldsymbol{\tau}_m$ out of $\boldsymbol{\tau}_Y$ and $\boldsymbol{\tau}_1$) that this case fulfills the conditions described on p. 262 under which the minimum-rank solution for communal components is indeterminate. That is, the proper covariances among $\mathbf{m} + 1$ data variables can be reproduced by communal components in infinitely many different $\mathbf{m}$-dimensional common-factor spaces unless additional restrictions are imposed on the inferred components. One such supplementary stricture is to hypothesize that the unique variances stand in a given relationship such as equality. Another is to make assumptions about the shapes of the inferred-component distributions which interact with the b-parameters to have algebraic implications for the shapes of the observed distributions—except that only nonnormality is of any help for ajudicating among alternative solutions for the $b_{\mathbf{i}}$. Not only do these additional assumptions tend to be rather unconvincing, the fact that $\mathbf{e_Y}, \mathbf{e_1}, \ldots, \mathbf{e_m}$ are usually construed to be or to include errors of measurement make their postulated orthogonality likewise suspect. All in all, the structural-equations model conceives of no prospects in multivariate relationships which are not already addressed with greater comprehension by more general approaches to inferential factoring, and there seems to be little reason why this model should have any special priority over other factorial hypotheses.

We now return to the problem of estimating regression parameters from sample statistics. Assuming regression model [10.3], let us contemplate selecting n subjects from population P, observing the score of each on variables $\mathbf{Y}, \mathbf{X_1}, \ldots, \mathbf{X_m}$, and condensing the data from these $(\mathbf{m}+1)n$ observations into estimates of the parameters $b_0, b_1, \ldots, b_{\mathbf{m}}$ and $\sigma^2_{\mathbf{e}}$. We shall write "O_n" for the set of observations $\langle Y_1, \ldots, Y_n; X_{1_1}, \ldots, X_{1_n}; \ldots; X_{\mathbf{m}_1}, \ldots, X_{\mathbf{m}_n}\rangle$ obtained on variables $\mathbf{Y}, \mathbf{X_1}, \ldots, \mathbf{X_m}$ for a particular sample of n individuals drawn from P, and "$\mathbf{O}_n$" for the corresponding complex variable whose value for a given sample of size n from P is O_n. That is, $\mathbf{O}_n$ is a variable whose subjects are samples of size n from P and whose value for such a sample is the joint (absolute) frequency distribution on $\mathbf{Y}, \mathbf{X_1}, \ldots, \mathbf{X_m}$ in the sample. We intend to select certain functions $\mathrm{f}_0(\mathbf{O}_n)$, $\mathrm{f}_1(\mathbf{O}_n), \ldots, \mathrm{f}_{\mathbf{m}}(\mathbf{O}_n)$, and $\mathrm{f}_{\mathbf{e}}(\mathbf{O}_n)$ of this sample-distribution variable and figure out how much error should result if, when O_n is the configuration of joint scores on $\mathbf{Y}$ and the $\mathbf{X_i}$ actually observed in a sample from P, the quantities $\hat{b}_0 = \mathrm{f}_0(O_n)$, $\hat{b}_1 = \mathrm{f}_1(O_n), \ldots, \hat{b}_{\mathbf{m}} = \mathrm{f}_{\mathbf{m}}(O_n)$, and $\hat{\sigma}^2_{\mathbf{e}} = \mathrm{f}_{\mathbf{e}}(O_n)$ are adopted as estimates of the indicated parameters.

According to the regression model, the value taken by any given function $\phi(\mathbf{O}_n)$ for a particular sample from P is determined jointly by the $\mathbf{m}n$ scores on predictor variables $\mathbf{X_1}, \ldots, \mathbf{X_m}$ for the n individuals in the sample, together with n independent chance events respectively responsible for the $\mathbf{e}$-scores of the sample members. Hence $\phi(\mathbf{O}_n)$ is a random variable whose probability distribution is a function both of the probabilities for the alternative distributions of joint scores on $\mathbf{X_1}, \ldots, \mathbf{X_m}$ that may occur in the sample and of the probability distribution over the various combinations of scores on $\mathbf{e}$ possible for the n sample members. Let us write "χ_n" for the (absolute) frequency distribution of just the predictor variables in the sample—i.e.,

$$\chi_n =_{\text{def}} \langle X_{1_1}, \ldots, X_{1_n}; \ldots; X_{\mathbf{m}_1}, \ldots, X_{\mathbf{m}_n}\rangle \ ,$$

so that $O_n = \langle Y_1, \ldots, Y_n; \chi_n\rangle$. Then while determination of the unconditional (parameter-dependent) probabilities for the various possible values of a function $\phi(\mathbf{O}_n)$ of the sample observations requires an assumption about the probability distribution for $\boldsymbol{\chi}_n$ which the regression model (in contrast to the correlation model) does not make, the regression model does permit calculation of the *contingent* probability distribution of $\phi(\mathbf{O}_n)$, given a specific sample distribution χ_n of the predictors. The unconditional probability distribution of $\phi(\mathbf{O}_n)$ *relative to the particular method by which the sample is obtained* is then a weighted average of these contingent distributions, the weight of each being the probability conferred upon its sample predictor-distribution by the method of sampling. Writing "$Exp\ \{\phi(\mathbf{O}_n)|\chi_n\}$" and "$Var\ \{\phi(\mathbf{O}_n)|\chi_n\}$" for the expectation and variance of the contingent probabilities for $\phi(\mathbf{O}_n)$ given that the predictor scores in the sample have the distribution χ_n, and "$Exp\ \{\phi(\mathbf{O}_n)\}$" and "$Var\{\phi(\mathbf{O}_n)\}$" for the corresponding properties of the unconditional probabilities for $\phi(\mathbf{O}_n)$ under this method of sampling the predictors, we then have that if, for some parameter θ, $Exp\{\phi(\mathbf{O}_n)|\chi_n\} = \theta$ for all χ_n, then also $Exp\{\phi(\mathbf{O}_n)\} = \theta$, while if further $Var\{\phi(\mathbf{O}_n)|\chi_n\} \leqslant Var\{\psi(\mathbf{O}_n)|\chi_n\}$ for all χ_n, then $Var\{\phi(\mathbf{O}_n)\} \leqslant Var\{\psi(\mathbf{O}_n)\}$. That is, if the contingent probabilities for $\phi(\mathbf{O}_n)$ are such that $\phi(\mathbf{O}_n)$ is an unbiased, minimum-variance estimator of θ given any particular distribution of predictor scores in the sample, then $\phi(\mathbf{O}_n)$ is also unconditionally an unbiased, minimum-variance estimator of θ under this method for obtaining the sample predictor-distribution, whether this be random selection or not. (In fact, it is then unconditionally an unbiased, minimum-variance estimator of θ under *any* particular method for obtaining the predictor sample which does not alter the contingent distribution of $\mathbf{Y}$, given the $\mathbf{X}_\mathbf{i}$.)

Let "$b_0(O_n)$", "$b_1(O_n)$", . . . , "$b_\mathbf{m}(O_n)$", and "$\sigma^2_{\mathbf{Y}\cdot\mathbf{X}_1\cdots\mathbf{X}_\mathbf{m}}(O_n)$" designate, respectively, the b-coefficients and residual criterion variance for the linear regression of $\mathbf{Y}$ upon $\mathbf{X}_1$, . . . , $\mathbf{X}_\mathbf{m}$ in an n-member population whose joint frequency distribution on $\mathbf{Y}, \mathbf{X}_1, \ldots, \mathbf{X}_\mathbf{m}$ is O_n. More generally, we will write "$s(O_n)$" for any statistical property s (means, correlations, etc.) of the joint frequency distribution of sample observations O_n, while "$s(P)$" designates the value of this same statistic for the joint probability distribution of $\mathbf{Y}, \mathbf{X}_1, \ldots, \mathbf{X}_\mathbf{m}$ in the population P from which the sample is drawn. Then it can be shown that given the assumptions of the regression model, the quantities

[10.4-**i**] $\hat{b}_\mathbf{i} =_{\text{def}} b_\mathbf{i}(O_n)$
($\mathbf{i} = 0, 1, \ldots, \mathbf{m}$)

are both maximum-likelihood and unbiased, minimum-variance estimates of the population parameters $b_0, \ldots, b_\mathbf{m}$ (i.e., $b_0(P), \ldots, b_\mathbf{m}(P)$) in [10.3] based on the sample data O_n, and that

[10.5]
$$\hat{\sigma}^2_\mathbf{e} =_{\text{def}} \left(\frac{n}{n-\mathbf{m}-1}\right) \sigma^2_{\mathbf{Y}\cdot\mathbf{X}_1\cdots\mathbf{X}_\mathbf{m}}(O_n)$$
$$= \left(\frac{n}{n-\mathbf{m}-1}\right) \sigma^2_\mathbf{Y}(O_n)\ [1 - \mathrm{R}^2_{\mathbf{Y}(\mathbf{X}_1\cdots\mathbf{X}_\mathbf{m})}(O_n)]$$

is an unbiased estimate of $\sigma^2_{\mathbf{e}}$ (i.e., of $\sigma^2_{\mathbf{Y}\cdot\mathbf{X}_1\cdots\mathbf{X}_m}(P)$).[3] That is, for any sample predictor-distribution X_n,

[10.6-i] $$Exp\{b_i(\mathbf{O}_n)|X_n\} = Exp\{b_i(\mathbf{O}_n)\} = b_i\ ,$$
($\mathbf{i} = 0, 1, \ldots, \mathbf{m}$)

and

[10.7] $$Exp\left\{\left(\frac{n}{n-\mathbf{m}-1}\right)\sigma^2_{\mathbf{Y}\cdot\mathbf{X}_1\cdots\mathbf{X}_m}(\mathbf{O}_n)|X_n\right\} = Exp\left\{\left(\frac{n}{n-\mathbf{m}-1}\right)\sigma^2_{\mathbf{Y}\cdot\mathbf{X}_1\cdots\mathbf{X}_m}(\mathbf{O}_n)\right\} = \sigma^2_{\mathbf{e}}\ .$$

The variances of these estimators contingent upon the observed sample distribution of predictor scores are

[10.8-0] $$Var\{b_0(\mathbf{O}_n)|X_n\} = \frac{\sigma^2_{\mathbf{e}}}{n}\ ,$$

[10.8-i] $$Var\{b_i(\mathbf{O}_n)|X_n\} = \frac{\sigma^2_{\mathbf{e}}}{n}\,C^{ii}(X_n)\ ,$$
($\mathbf{i} = 1, \ldots, \mathbf{m}$)

where the quantities $C^{ij}(X_n)$ ($\mathbf{i,j} = 1, \ldots, \mathbf{m}$) are properties of the predictor distribution X_n which will be defined in a moment, and

[10.9] $$Var\left\{\left(\frac{n}{n-\mathbf{m}-1}\right)\sigma^2_{\mathbf{Y}\cdot\mathbf{X}_1\cdots\mathbf{X}_m}(\mathbf{O}_n)|X_n\right\} = \frac{2\sigma^4_{\mathbf{e}}}{n-\mathbf{m}-1}\ .$$

More completely, under the normality assumption for **e**, the probabilities for $[n\sigma^2_{\mathbf{Y}\cdot\mathbf{X}_1\cdots\mathbf{X}_m}(\mathbf{O}_n)]/\sigma^2_{\mathbf{e}}$ are independent of X_n and have a Chi-square distribution with $n - \mathbf{m} - 1$ degrees of freedom, while the joint distribution of $b_0(\mathbf{O}_n), \ldots, b_m(\mathbf{O}_n)$ contingent upon X_n is normal with expectations and variances as stated in [10.6,8] and covariances

[10.10-0i] $$Cov\{b_0(\mathbf{O}_n),\ b_i(\mathbf{O}_n)|X_n\} = 0\ ,$$
($\mathbf{i} = 1, \ldots, \mathbf{m}$)

[10.10-ij] $$Cov\{b_i(\mathbf{O}_n),\ b_j(\mathbf{O}_n)|X_n\} = \frac{\sigma^2_{\mathbf{e}}}{n}\,C^{ij}(X_n)\ .$$
($\mathbf{i,j} = 1, \ldots, \mathbf{m}$)

The meaning of these contingent expectations, variances, etc., for $b_0(\mathbf{O}_n), \ldots, b_m(\mathbf{O}_n)$ may be clarified by saying that if we were to draw

[3] See, e.g., Chapter 1 of Scheffé (73) or Chapter 12 of Wilks (86). For simplicity of exposition, it is frequently claimed only that estimators [10.4] are unbiased, minimum-variance *linear* estimators, meaning that they have minimum variance in the class of all estimators of the b_i which are linear functions of the sample scores on **Y**. However, under the complete regression model with normality this restriction is unnecessary.

an indefinitely large number of samples of size n from parent population P, each of which has its own joint frequency distribution on $\mathbf{Y}, \mathbf{X}_1, \ldots, \mathbf{X}_\mathbf{m}$ and corresponding b-statistics determined by the linear regression of $\mathbf{Y}$ upon the $\mathbf{X}_\mathbf{i}$ therein, and we now look at the joint frequency distribution of these b-statistics among just those samples in which the distribution of predictor scores is χ_n, then the means of the bs in this class of samples should respectively equal the corresponding b-parameters for the regression of $\mathbf{Y}$ upon the $\mathbf{X}_\mathbf{i}$ in P, while their covariance matrix should be as given by [10.8] and [10.10].

It will be observed that the expectations for estimates $\hat{b}_0, \ldots, \hat{b}_\mathbf{m}$ and $\sigma^2_{\mathbf{e}}$ contingent on sample distribution χ_n are actually independent of χ_n. Hence the regression coefficients and $n/(n - \mathbf{m} - 1)$ times the residual criterion variance in a sample of size n drawn from population P are expected to equal $b_0, b_1, \ldots, b_\mathbf{m}$ and $\sigma^2_{\mathbf{e}}$, respectively, even before the sample's predictor distribution is known, nor are these expectations influenced by how the sample of predictor scores is obtained (always assuming, of course, that the sampling method does not modify the contingent probabilities for $\mathbf{Y}$, given the $\mathbf{X}_\mathbf{i}$). The same is true of the variances of the estimates $\hat{b}_0$ and $\hat{\sigma}^2_{\mathbf{e}}$. However, the contingent joint probability distribution for the estimates $\hat{b}_1, \ldots, \hat{b}_\mathbf{m}$ given that the sample predictor distribution is χ_n does, in fact, depend on χ_n. The unconditional covariance matrix for these estimates relative to a particular method of sampling from P is given by

$$[10.11\text{-}\mathbf{ij}] \qquad Cov\{b_\mathbf{i}(\mathbf{O}_n), b_\mathbf{j}(\mathbf{O}_n)\} = \frac{\sigma^2_{\mathbf{e}}}{n} Exp\{\mathbf{C}^{\mathbf{ij}}(\chi_n)\}, \quad (\mathbf{i},\mathbf{j} = 1, \ldots, \mathbf{m})$$

where $Exp\{\mathbf{C}^{\mathbf{ij}}(\chi_n)\}$ is the value of the statistic $\mathbf{C}^{\mathbf{ij}}$ expected for a sample of size n drawn in this fashion from P. If sampling is random on the predictor variables as well as on the criterion residual $\mathbf{e}$, then the value of $\mathbf{C}^{\mathbf{ij}}$ expected for a sample from P is approximately the value of $\mathbf{C}^{\mathbf{ij}}$ in P. The approximation is annoyingly not an identity for finite n, but it approaches one as n becomes large. Hence for simplicity we may write

$$[10.12\text{-}\mathbf{ij}] \quad Cov\{b_\mathbf{i}(\mathbf{O}_n), b_\mathbf{j}(\mathbf{O}_n)\} \simeq \frac{\sigma^2_{\mathbf{e}}}{n} \mathbf{C}^{\mathbf{ij}}(P) \qquad \begin{pmatrix}\text{fully random} \\ \text{sampling from } P\end{pmatrix}, \quad (\mathbf{i},\mathbf{j} = 1, \ldots, \mathbf{m})$$

where the approximation is more than adequate if the sample is at all reasonable in size.

And what are these statistics $\mathbf{C}^{\mathbf{ij}}$ which have come to our attention? They cannot be fully explained without resorting to matrix algebra, but we shall list enough of their mathematical properties to convey some comprehension of their nature. By definition, the value of $\mathbf{C}^{\mathbf{ij}}$ ($\mathbf{i},\mathbf{j} = 1, \ldots, \mathbf{m}$) for a given joint distribution of $\mathbf{X}_1, \ldots, \mathbf{X}_\mathbf{m}$ is the entry in the $\mathbf{i}$th row and **j**th column of the *inverse* of the covariance matrix $\{C_{X_iX_j}\}$ for this distribution. The numerical value of C^{ij} is determined by the factor structure of $\mathbf{X}_1, \ldots, \mathbf{X}_m$ in the relevant distribution as follows: Let the loadings of variable $\mathbf{X}_i$ ($\mathbf{i} = 1, \ldots, \mathbf{m}$) on the *principal factors,* $\mathbf{P}_1, \ldots, \mathbf{P}_m$, of the $\mathbf{X}_i$-configuration be $a_{i1}, \ldots, a_{im}$, respectively, so that

[10.13-i]
($\mathbf{i} = 1, \ldots, \mathbf{m}$)

$$X_i = M_{X_i} + \sum_{j=1}^{m} a_{ij}\mathbf{P}_j \,,$$

where the $\mathbf{P}_j$ are those normalized orthogonal linear combinations of $\mathbf{X}_1, \ldots, \mathbf{X}_m$ which successively maximize the total variance of the $\mathbf{X}_i$ for which they account (see p. 237). Then if λ_j is the eigenvalue corresponding to $\mathbf{P}_j$, i.e.,

[10.14-j]
($\mathbf{i} = 1, \ldots, \mathbf{m}$)

$$\lambda_j = \sum_{i=1}^{m} V_{X_i(P_j)} = \sum_{i=1}^{m} a_{ij}^2 \,,$$

we have

[10.15-ij]
($\mathbf{i,j} = 1, \ldots, \mathbf{m}$)

$$C^{ij} = \sum_{k=1}^{m} \frac{a_{ik}a_{jk}}{\lambda_k^2} \,.$$

The relation between C^{ij} and the corresponding covariance $C_{X_iX_j}$ of which C^{ij} is the inverse counterpart is brought out by the fact that

[10.16-ij]
($\mathbf{i,j} = 1, \ldots, \mathbf{m}$)

$$\sum_{k=1}^{m} \left(\frac{a_{ik}a_{jk}}{\lambda_k}\right) t_k = \begin{cases} C_{X_iX_j} & \text{if } t_k = \lambda_k \quad (\mathbf{k} = 1, \ldots, \mathbf{m}) \\ \delta_{ij} & \text{if } t_k = 1 \quad (\mathbf{k} = 1, \ldots, \mathbf{m}) \\ C^{ij} & \text{if } t_k = \lambda_k^{-1} \quad (\mathbf{k} = 1, \ldots, \mathbf{m}) \end{cases}$$

where δ_{ij} ("Kronecker's delta") by definition equals 1 when $\mathbf{i} = \mathbf{j}$ and 0 when $\mathbf{i} \neq \mathbf{j}$. A little study of [10.16] will show that $C_{X_iX_j}$ and C^{ij} tend to be roughly symmetric around the pivot 1 when $\mathbf{i} = \mathbf{j}$ or 0 when $\mathbf{i} \neq \mathbf{j}$. That is, $C_{X_iX_j}$ and C^{ij} tend to be on opposite sides of δ_{ij} while the greater is the deviation of $C_{X_iX_j}$ in one direction from δ_{ij}, the more C^{ij} tends to deviate from δ_{ij} in the other.

Even better, if we let $\boldsymbol{\mu}_i$ be the set of variables $\mathbf{X}_1, \ldots, \mathbf{X}_m$ less $\mathbf{X}_i$ while $\boldsymbol{\mu}_{ij}$ is the set which remains after $\mathbf{X}_i$ and $\mathbf{X}_j$ ($\mathbf{i} \neq \mathbf{j}$) are both dropped from $\mathbf{X}_1, \ldots, \mathbf{X}_m$, it can be shown (see pp. 577f., Appendix B) that the diagonal elements of $\{C^{ii}\}$ (i.e., of $\{C_{X_iX_j}\}^{-1}$) have the values

[10.17-ii]
(i = 1, . . . , m)

$$C^{ii} = \frac{1}{V_{X_i \bullet \mu_i}}$$

$$= \frac{1}{V_{X_i}(1 - R^2_{X_i(\mu_i)})}$$

$$= \frac{1}{V_{X_i} K^2_{X_i(\mu_i)}}$$

while its off-diagonal elements are

[10.17-ij]
(i,j = 1, . . . , m; i ≠ j)

$$C^{ij} = -\frac{b_{X_iX_j \bullet \mu_{ij}}}{V_{X_i \bullet \mu_i}}$$

$$= -\frac{C_{X_iX_j \bullet \mu_{ij}}}{V_{X_i \bullet \mu_i} V_{X_j \bullet \mu_{ij}}}$$

$$= -\left(\frac{1}{\sigma_{X_i}\sigma_{X_j} K_{X_i(\mu_{ij})} K_{X_j(\mu_{ij})}}\right)\left(\frac{r_{X_iX_j \bullet \mu_{ij}}}{k^2_{X_iX_j \bullet \mu_{ij}}}\right).$$

An important practical consequence of [10.17], incidentally, is that the regression weights for predicting variable $\mathbf{X_i}$ from the other variables in the set $\mathbf{X_1}, \ldots, \mathbf{X_m}$ are given by

[10.18-ij]
(i,j = 1, . . . , m; i ≠ j)

$$b_{X_iX_j \bullet \mu_{ij}} = -\frac{C^{ij}}{C^{ii}},$$

while the multiple correlation of $\mathbf{X_i}$ with the remainder of the set $\mathbf{X_1}$, . . . , $\mathbf{X_m}$ follows by

[10.19-i]
(i = 1, . . . , m)

$$R^2_{X_i(\mu_i)} = 1 - \frac{1}{V_{X_i} C^{ii}}.$$

It is also of theoretical interest, perhaps, that in view of [10.17] and [B.16], Appendix B, the β-weight of $\mathbf{X_i}$ in the linear regression of a criterion **Y** upon predictors $\mathbf{X_1}, \ldots, \mathbf{X_m}$ can be written explicitly as

[10.20-i]
(i = 1, . . . , m)

$$\beta_{YX_i \bullet \mu_i} = \sum_{j=1}^{m} r_{YX_j} r^{ij}$$

$$= \frac{r_{YX_i}}{K^2_{X_i(\mu_i)}} - \sum_{\substack{j=1 \\ j \neq i}}^{m} \frac{r_{YX_j} r_{X_iX_j \bullet \mu_{ij}}}{K_{X_i(\mu_{ij})} K_{X_j(\mu_{ij})} k^2_{X_iX_j \bullet \mu_{ij}}},$$

where $\mathbf{r}^{\mathbf{ij}}$ is what $\mathbf{C}^{\mathbf{ij}}$ becomes when $\sigma_{\mathbf{X}_i} = \sigma_{\mathbf{X}_j} = 1$. It is easily verified that [10.20] reduces to [4.93] when $\mathbf{n} = 2$.

With these facts about the estimation of regression parameters at our disposal, we may now ask what implications they have for practical applications of regression principles. Specifically, suppose that endeavors to learn the joint probability distribution for criterion $\mathbf{Y}$ and predictors $\mathbf{X}_1, \ldots, \mathbf{X}_m$ in population P have resulted in acquisition of a joint frequency distribution O_n observed among n members of P, where the sampling on $\mathbf{Y}$, given any particular set of joint scores on $\mathbf{X}_1, \ldots, \mathbf{X}_m$, is presumably random though the sampling of the predictor scores need not be so. Our intent is to estimate the regression parameters b_0, b_1, $\ldots, b_m$ in P from the data O_n and then use the equation

$$[10.21] \qquad \hat{\mathbf{Y}} = \hat{b}_0 + \sum_{i=1}^{m} \hat{b}_i \mathbf{X}_i$$

(where the $\hat{b}_i$ are the estimates of the $b_i(P)$ computed from O_n) to predict scores on $\mathbf{Y}$ for additional members of P as their scores on $\mathbf{X}_1, \ldots, \mathbf{X}_m$ become known. What the regression model tells us is that so long as the joint distribution of $\mathbf{Y}, \mathbf{X}_1, \ldots, \mathbf{X}_m$ has the properties assumed, *the estimates of $b_0, b_1, \ldots, b_m$ which have the greatest anticipated accuracy are simply the corresponding constants computed for the linear regression of* $\mathbf{Y}$ *upon* $\mathbf{X}_1, \ldots, \mathbf{X}_m$ *in the observed distribution O_n. Moreover, these are also the parameter estimates which afford the greatest anticipated accuracy when the estimated regression equation* [10.21] *is subsequently used to predict scores on* $\mathbf{Y}$ *for additional members of P.*[4]

On the other hand, [10.7] shows that the residual criterion variance in an observed sample is misleadingly small if taken without correction as an estimate of the parametric residual criterion variance unless the sample size is very much larger than the number of predictor variables. The nature of this bias can be most easily appreciated intuitively by considering the case of a single predictor (i.e., $\mathbf{m} = 1$) and observing that when scores are observed on $\mathbf{X}_1$ and $\mathbf{Y}$ in a sample of size $n = 2$, the two scattergram points will always lie *exactly* on the sample regression line irrespective of the correlation between $\mathbf{X}_1$ and $\mathbf{Y}$ in the parent population. Moreover, the parametric error variance $\sigma^2_{\mathbf{e}}$ (i.e., $\sigma^2_{\mathbf{Y}\cdot\mathbf{X}_1\cdots\mathbf{X}_m}(P)$) unbiasedly esti-

[4] It is a simple extension of the Gauss-Markov theorem (see Scheffé 73, p. 14; or Wilks, 86, p. 285) that if $\hat{b}_0, \ldots, \hat{b}_m$ are unbiased, minimum-variance estimates of the regression parameters, then $\hat{Y}_j = \hat{b}_0 + \sum_{i=1}^{m} \hat{b}_i X_{ij}$ is an unbiased, minimum-variance estimator of the (unknown) score on $\mathbf{Y}$ for an additional member j of P whose predictor scores are $X_{1j}, \ldots, X_{mj}$, respectively.

mated by $[n/(n-\mathbf{m}-1)]\sigma^2_{\dot{\mathbf{Y}}\bullet\mathbf{X}_1\ldots\mathbf{X}_m}(O_n)$ is the error variance in P of the ideal regression policy

$$[10.22] \qquad \dot{\mathbf{Y}}_{(\mathbf{X}_1\ldots\mathbf{X}_m)} = b_0 + \sum_{i=1}^{m} b_i\mathbf{X}_i\,,$$

not of the practical policy [10.21] in which we are able to use only estimates of the regression parameters. The difference between the theoretically optimal regression estimate $\dot{Y}_{(\mathbf{X}_1\ldots\mathbf{X}_m)}$ and the practical estimate $\hat{Y}$ defined by [10.21] for a member of P whose scores on the predictors are known to be $X_1, \ldots, X_m$, respectively, is obviously

$$[10.23] \qquad \hat{Y} - \dot{Y}_{(\mathbf{X}_1\ldots\mathbf{X}_m)} = (\hat{b}_0 - b_0) + \sum_{i=1}^{m} (\hat{b}_i - b_i)\mathbf{X}_i\,,$$

from which it follows that the contingent standard error for predicting $\mathbf{Y}$ by policy [10.21] for members of P whose scores on $\mathbf{X}_1, \ldots, \mathbf{X}_m$ are given to be $X_1, \ldots, X_m$, respectively, is

[10.24]

$$\mathrm{SE}_{\mathbf{Y}|X_1\ldots X_m}\left[\hat{\mathbf{Y}} = \hat{b}_0 + \sum_{i=1}^{m} \hat{b}_i\mathbf{X}_i\right] = \sqrt{\sigma^2_{\mathbf{e}} + \left[(\hat{b}_0 - b_0) + \sum_{i=1}^{m} (\hat{b}_i - b_i)X_i\right]^2}\,.$$

It is of interest to observe from [10.24] that the additional prediction error introjected by errors of parameter estimation does not affect all predictions equally. While the contingent distributions of $\mathbf{Y}$, given $\mathbf{X}_1$, $\ldots$, $\mathbf{X}_m$ are assumed to be homoscedastic in P, the contingent distributions of prediction errors under policy [10.21] are seen to be a function of the subject's predictor scores. There is, of course, no way for the regression model to say definitely what the standard error of policy [10.21] at a given predictor position actually is, since this depends upon the unknown stochastically generated errors $\hat{b}_i - b_i$ $(\mathbf{i} = 0, \mathbf{1}, \ldots, \mathbf{m})$. It is, however, possible to reason from the joint probability distribution for the parameter errors to an expectation for the squared prediction-error variable $(\mathbf{Y} - \hat{\mathbf{Y}})^2$ when parameters are estimated from a sample in which the predictor distribution is $\mathcal{X}_n$: Let $\mathbf{F}_1, \ldots, \mathbf{F}_1$ be any orthonormal factor basis for the distribution $\mathcal{X}_n$ of predictor scores in the sample from which the $\hat{b}_i$ have been computed. That is, each $\mathbf{F}_i$ is a linear combination of $\mathbf{X}_1, \ldots, \mathbf{X}_m$ so chosen that within the observed sample, the $\mathbf{F}_1$ have zero means, unit variances, and zero intercorrelations. Then if $F_1, \ldots, F_m$, respectively, are the scores on these factors corresponding to a particular set of scores $X_1, \ldots, X_m$ on predictors $\mathbf{X}_1, \ldots, \mathbf{X}_m$, it can be shown that the expected squared deviation of $\hat{Y}$ from the ideal regression estimate $\dot{Y}$ for a member of P with predictor scores $X_1, \ldots, X_m$ is

$$[10.25] \quad Exp\{(\hat{\mathbf{Y}} - \dot{\mathbf{Y}})^2 | \chi_n; X_1, \ldots, X_m\} = \frac{\sigma_e^2}{n}\left(1 + \sum_{i=1}^{m} F_i^2\right),$$

and hence that the expected error square for estimating $\mathbf{Y}$ for a member of P whose scores on the predictors are given to be $X_1, \ldots, X_m$ is

$$[10.26] \quad Exp\{(\mathbf{Y} - \hat{\mathbf{Y}})^2 | \chi_n; X_1, \ldots, X_m\} = \sigma_e^2\left(1 + \frac{1 + \sum_{i=1}^{m} F_i^2}{n}\right).$$

(The notation "$\chi_n; X_1, \ldots, X_m$" in [10.25,6] indicates that the expectation is contingent upon the predictor scores from which $\hat{\mathbf{Y}}$ is computed being $X_1, \ldots, X_m$, and also upon the parameter-estimates $\hat{b}_0, \hat{b}_1, \ldots, \hat{b}_m$ being obtained from a sample in which the distribution of predictor scores is χ_n.) Expectation [10.26] contains the unknown parameter σ_e^2, but this can be unbiasedly estimated by $\hat{\sigma}_e^2$, defined in [10.5]. When this substitution is made into [10.26], it is found that contingent upon χ_n and $X_1, \ldots, X_m$, the statistic

$$\frac{\mathbf{Y} - \hat{\mathbf{Y}}}{\sigma_{\mathbf{Y}}(\mathbf{O}_n)\, \mathrm{K}_{\mathbf{Y}(\mathbf{X}_1 \cdots \mathbf{X}_m)}(\mathbf{O}_n)} \sqrt{\frac{n - \mathbf{m} - 1}{n + 1 + \sum_{i=1}^{m} F_i^2}}$$

has a t-distribution with $n - \mathbf{m} - 1$ degrees of freedom, from which confidence intervals for a predictee's score on $\mathbf{Y}$ can readily be obtained. Specifically, writing "$t_{p(d.f.)}$" for that number which is such that $100p\%$ of a t-distribution with $d.f.$ degrees of freedom lies within a distance of $t_{p(d.f.)}$ units from zero (tabled values of which for selected p and $d.f.$ can be found in the appendix of any modern statistics text), a confidence interval at the $100p\%$ level for the $\mathbf{Y}$-score of a member of P whose predictor scores $X_1, \ldots, X_m$ respectively correspond to orthonormal factor scores $F_1, \ldots, F_m$ is

$$[10.27] \quad Y \pm t_{p\,(n-\mathbf{m}-1)}\, \sigma_{\mathbf{Y}}(O_n)\, \mathrm{K}_{\mathbf{Y}(\mathbf{X}_1 \ldots \mathbf{X}_m)}(O_n) \sqrt{\frac{n + 1 + \sum_{i=1}^{m} F_i^2}{n - \mathbf{m} - 1}}.$$

For all but very small d.f., the value of $t_{p(d.f.)}$ for $p = .95$ is approximately 2.0, while the quantity $\sum_{i=1}^{m} F_i^2$ can be determined without need for explicit factoring of the observed predictor covariances through application of

$$[10.28] \qquad \sum_{i=1}^{m} F_i^2 = \sum_{i=1}^{m} \sum_{j=1}^{m} [X_i - M_{X_i}(\chi_n)][X_j - M_{X_j}(\chi_n)]\, C^{ij}(\chi_n)\,,$$

in which the quantities X_i and X_j are the scores on predictor variables $\mathbf{X}_i$ and $\mathbf{X}_j$, respectively, for the individual in question, and $M_{X_i}(\chi_n)$ is the mean of $\mathbf{X}_i$ in the observed sample.

While [10.26] legitimately states the squared discrepancy which is statistically "expected" between a subject's predicted **Y**-score and his actual **Y**-score relative to certain indicated background conditions, this important formula and the confidence intervals which follow from it must be interpreted with care if they are to be properly understood. [10.26] does *not* give the expectation of the probability distribution for $(\mathbf{Y} - \hat{\mathbf{Y}})^2$ that would be approximated by the frequency distribution of squared errors obtained by using the *same* estimated regression policy [10.21] to predict scores on **Y** for a great many members of P who have the same array $X_1, \ldots, X_m$ of predictor scores. Rather, the probability distribution whose expectation is given by [10.26] is the one that would be approximated by the frequency distribution of $(\mathbf{Y} - \hat{\mathbf{Y}})^2$ generated by repeatedly drawing from P a sample of size n in which the predictor distribution is χ_n and then using the regression-parameter estimates computed from that sample to predict **Y** for an additional member of P whose scores on the predictors are $X_1, \ldots, X_m$. That is, [10.26] and the probability statistics which follow from it envision repeated estimation of the regression parameters as well as repeated applications of the estimated regression policy to subjects with this same array of predictor scores. scores.

The quantity $\sum_{i=1}^{m} F_i^2$ which appears in [10.26] and [10.27] represents the total deviation from the center of the sample predictor distribution of a person whose status on the predictor variables correspond to factor coordinates $F_1, \ldots, F_m$ (in a scattergram of $\mathbf{F}_1, \ldots, \mathbf{F}_m$, $\sum_{i=1}^{m} F_i^2$ is the squared distance from the origin to a point with coordinates $F_1, \ldots, F_m$), and may be called the subject's "predictor extremity" relative to the predictor distribution in the sample from which the regression parameters are estimated. Formulas [10.26] and [10.27] show that the greater a subject's predictor extremity, the worse is the uncertainty with which his criterion score can be estimated in practice—which is all the more unfortunate in that it is only when predictor extremity is substantial that the criterion estimate is likely to be usefully divergent from the mean. However, if the sample predictor-distribution χ_n is reasonably representative of the joint probability distribution of the $\mathbf{X}_i$ in parent population P (so that $\mathbf{F}_1, \ldots, \mathbf{F}_m$ are approximately orthonormal in P as well as so by definition in the observed sample) the probability distribution for $\sum_{i=1}^{m} \mathbf{F}_i^2$ in P should be approximately Chi-square with **m** degrees of freedom, in which case, roughly speaking, less than one member of P in ten has a predictor extremity greater than 2**m** while fewer than one in a hundred are more extreme than 3**m**. Hence if the size of the sample population from which the regression parameters are estimated is, say, at least an order of magnitude larger than the number of predictor variables, the uncertainty component in [10.26] and [10.27] due to inaccuracy in the parameter estimates may generally be ignored.

While it has already been pointed out that the squared standard error of the criterion in an observed sample distribution is *not*, in general, a satisfactory estimate of the parametric residual criterion variance, the bias is of sufficient importance to warrant further examination. By [10.7], the error variance $\sigma^2_{\mathbf{Y}\bullet \mathbf{X}_1\cdots\mathbf{X}_m}(O_n)$ expected in a sample of size n is only a fraction, namely, $(n - \mathbf{m} - 1)/n = 1 - (\mathbf{m} + 1)/n$, of the parametric error variance $\sigma^2_{\mathbf{e}}$. The magnitude of this effect, like that of the sampling uncertainty in [10.27], is seen to depend on the ratio of the number of regression parameters to the size of the sample. To interpret what the error variance in the sample implies about the parametric relation between the criterion and the predictors, it is helpful to convert [10.7] into a statement about the connection between sample and parametric multiple correlation. To be sure, no conclusions about correlations in P can properly be drawn from the regression model, and even with the additional assumptions of the correlation model the exact expectation for $R^2_{\mathbf{Y}(\mathbf{X}_1\cdots\mathbf{X}_m)}(\mathbf{O}_n)$ is messy. Still, [10.7] is equivalent to

[10.29]
$$Exp\,\{\sigma^2_{\mathbf{Y}}(\mathbf{O}_n)\,K^2_{\mathbf{Y}(\mathbf{X}_1\cdots\mathbf{X}_m)}(\mathbf{O}_n)\} = \left(\frac{n-\mathbf{m}-1}{n}\right)\sigma^2_{\mathbf{Y}}(P)\,K^2_{\mathbf{Y}(\mathbf{X}_1\cdots\mathbf{X}_m)}(P)\ ,$$

where the expectation is relative to the sampling method used but is not contingent upon a particular sample distribution $\mathcal{X}_n$ on the predictors. Further, the expectation of a product is approximately equal to the product of the expectations for the product's constituents, and becomes so exactly as the coefficient of variation for either constituent or their correlation approaches zero (see [7.200]). Hence $Exp\,\{\sigma^2_{\mathbf{Y}}(\mathbf{O}_n)K^2_{\mathbf{Y}(\mathbf{X}_1\cdots\mathbf{X}_m)}(\mathbf{O}_n)\} \simeq Exp\,\{\sigma^2_{\mathbf{Y}}(\mathbf{O}_n)\} \times Exp\,\{K^2_{\mathbf{Y}(\mathbf{X}_1\ldots\mathbf{X}_m)}(\mathbf{O}_n)\} = Exp\,\{\sigma^2_{\mathbf{Y}}(\mathbf{O}_n)\} \times [1 - Exp\,\{R^2_{\mathbf{Y}(\mathbf{X}_1\cdots\mathbf{X}_m)}(\mathbf{O}_n)\}]$, and so from [10.29]

[10.30]
$$Exp\,\{R^2_{\mathbf{Y}(\mathbf{X}_1\cdots\mathbf{X}_m)}(\mathbf{O}_n)\} \simeq 1 - \left(\frac{n-\mathbf{m}-1}{n}\right)\frac{\sigma^2_{\mathbf{Y}}(P)}{Exp\,\{\sigma^2_{\mathbf{Y}}(\mathbf{O}_n)\}} \times [1 - R^2_{\mathbf{Y}(\mathbf{X}_1\cdots\mathbf{X}_m)}(P)]\ ,$$

where the approximation is virtually indistinguishable from an identity except perhaps when n is very small. In particular, if $\mathbf{Y}$ is randomly sampled—i.e., if sampling from P is random on the predictors as well as on the criterion residual—then $Exp\{\sigma^2_{\mathbf{Y}}(\mathbf{O}_n)\} = [(n-1)/n]\sigma^2_{\mathbf{Y}}(P)$ (from [10.7], letting $\mathbf{m} = 0$), whence substitution into [10.30] yields

[10.31]

$$Exp\{R^2_{\mathbf{Y}(\mathbf{X}_1\cdots\mathbf{X}_\mathbf{m})}(\mathbf{O}_n)\} \simeq R^2_{\mathbf{Y}(\mathbf{X}_1\cdots\mathbf{X}_\mathbf{m})}(P) + \frac{\mathbf{m}}{n-1}[1 - R^2_{\mathbf{Y}(\mathbf{X}_1\cdots\mathbf{X}_\mathbf{m})}(P)]$$

(fully random sampling) ,

where again the error of the approximation is negligible except for at most small n. This shows clearly that the sample $R^2_{\mathbf{Y}(\mathbf{X}_1\cdots\mathbf{X}_\mathbf{m})}$ is expected to be greater than the value of this statistic in the parent population P, perhaps grotesquely so if $\mathbf{m}$ is on the same order as n. To be sure, when $n > 10\mathbf{m}$, say, the second term on the right-hand side of [10.31] becomes very small, so if the sample size is at least an order of magnitude greater than the number of predictors, it is probably safe to disregard the systematic tendency for sample correlations to be inflated. Even so, a better estimate of the parametric correlation is indicated by

[10.32]

$$R^2_{\mathbf{Y}(\mathbf{X}_1\cdots\mathbf{X}_\mathbf{m})}(P) \simeq Exp\{R^2_{\mathbf{Y}(\mathbf{X}_1\cdots\mathbf{X}_\mathbf{m})}(\mathbf{O}_n) - \left(\frac{\mathbf{m}+1}{n-\mathbf{m}-1}\right)[1 - R^2_{\mathbf{Y}(\mathbf{X}_1\cdots\mathbf{X}_\mathbf{m})}(\mathbf{O}_n)]\}$$

(fully random sampling) ,

(from [10.31]), which shows that under fully random sampling an essentially unbiased estimate of the parametric squared multiple correlation of $\mathbf{Y}$ with predictors $\mathbf{X}_1, \ldots, \mathbf{X}_\mathbf{m}$ is given by the sample statistic following the "*Exp*" in [10.32].

We have yet to comment upon the sampling behavior of the regression-parameter estimates [10.4]. While the most vital facts are given by [10.6], which tells us what to take from the sample data for subsequent prediction of the criterion, and by [10.26] or [10.27], which assess the extent to which errors in the parameter estimates are likely to further contaminate the accuracy with which the criterion can be predicted, the amount of sampling error in the $\hat{b}_\mathbf{i}$ also has some import for applied test theory. The primary statistics which describe this are the standard errors of the $\hat{b}_\mathbf{i}$, namely, the square roots of the sampling variances $Var\{b_\mathbf{i}(\mathbf{O}_n)\}$ ($\mathbf{i} = 0, \mathbf{1}, \ldots, \mathbf{m}$), though for determining confidence intervals for several regression parameters simultaneously, the sampling covariances among the $\hat{b}_\mathbf{i}$ are also important. Since the numerical values of these errors, like those of the regression coefficients themselves, are in part a function of whatever more or less arbitrary units of measurement have been chosen for the variables, we shall assume whenever it is clarifying to do so that variables $\mathbf{Y}, \mathbf{X}_1, \ldots, \mathbf{X}_m$ have been so standardized from the observed sample data O_n that $\sigma_{\mathbf{Y}}(O_n) = \sigma_{\mathbf{X}_1}(O_n) = \ldots = \sigma_{\mathbf{X}_m}(O_n) = 1$. (This is not, of course, the same as standardizing all the variables to unit variance in the parent population P, though it is essentially the best approximation we can make thereto,[5] nor does it guarantee that any variable so standardized will have precisely unit variance in another sample from P.) It is also most convenient to leave the analysis contingent upon the observed predictor distribution $\mathcal{X}_n$ as in [10.10], since what is learned about the general magnitude of sampling-error effects in the contingent distributions of the $b_i(\mathbf{O}_n)$ is readily generalized by [10.11] and [10.12] to the unconditional sampling errors.

According to [10.8], the variance of $b_i(\mathbf{O}_n)$ among samples from parent population P in which the sample predictor distribution is $\mathcal{X}_n$ equals $\sigma_{\mathbf{e}}^2/n$ times a multiplier which is unity for $b_0(\mathbf{O}_n)$ and $C^{ii}(\mathcal{X}_n)$ for the predictor coefficients. To see what the magnitude of $\sigma_{\mathbf{e}}^2/n$ looks like with standardized variables, we note from [10.5] that when the sample criterion variance is unity, an unbiased estimate of $\sigma_{\mathbf{e}}^2/n$ is given by

[10.33] $$\frac{\hat{\sigma}_{\mathbf{e}}^2}{n} = \frac{1 - R^2_{\mathbf{Y}(\mathbf{X}_1 \ldots \mathbf{X}_m)}(O_n)}{n - \mathbf{m} - 1} \qquad (\sigma_{\mathbf{Y}}(O_n) = 1) ,$$

which begins to get comfortably small if $n - \mathbf{m}$ is well into the hundreds.[6] Turning to the $C^{ii}(\mathcal{X}_n)$, however, we discover that the sampling behavior of the individual $\hat{b}_i$ $(\mathbf{i} \neq 0)$ is considerably wilder than [10.26] would lead one to suspect. With the predictor variances standardized at unity, [10.17-**ii**] becomes

[10.34-**i**] ($\mathbf{i} = \mathbf{1}, \ldots, \mathbf{m}$) $$C^{ii} = \frac{1}{1 - R^2_{\mathbf{X}_i(\boldsymbol{\mu}_i)}} = K^{-2}_{\mathbf{X}_i(\boldsymbol{\mu}_i)} , \qquad (\sigma_{\mathbf{X}_i} = 1)$$

where $\boldsymbol{\mu}_i$, it will be recalled, is the set of predictors $\mathbf{X}_1, \ldots, \mathbf{X}_{i-1}, \mathbf{X}_{i+1}, \ldots, \mathbf{X}_m$. It is clear from [10.34-**i**] that with $\sigma_{\mathbf{X}_i} = 1$, the value of C^{ii} cannot possibly be lower than unity, a limit which occurs when and only when $\mathbf{X}_i$ has no linear correlation with the other predictors, and can be-

[5] More precisely, if the sample is fully random from P and we want the unbiased estimate of a standardized variable's variance in the parent population to be unity, the standard deviation of that variable in the observed sample has to be set equal to $\sqrt{(n-1)/n}$.

[6] Observe, though, that the standard error of $b_0(\mathbf{O}_n)$ is $\sigma_{\mathbf{e}}/\sqrt{n}$, *not* $\hat{\sigma}_{\mathbf{e}}^2/n$, so it is the square root of [10.33] which most directly represents the anticipated magnitude of error in b_0. Similarly, the standard error of $b_i(\mathbf{O}_n)$ $(\mathbf{i} = \mathbf{1}, \ldots, \mathbf{m})$ contingent upon $\mathcal{X}_n$ is $\sigma_{\mathbf{e}}\sqrt{C^{ii}(\mathcal{X}_n)/n}$.

come very large if $\mathbf{X_i}$ is severely redundant with the other predictors. Moreover, while it is perfectly possible for some of the C^{ii} to remain in the vicinity of unity while others ascend to more awesome levels, any excess of one $R^2_{X_i(\mu_i)}$ over zero is symptomatic of a general correlational consistency among the predictors which must be reflected by some of the other $R^2_{X_i(\mu_i)}$ as well. The average value of C^{ii} for $\mathbf{X_1}, \ldots, \mathbf{X_m}$ may be analyzed by averaging over **ii** in [10.15] while heeding [10.14]:

$$\text{[10.35]} \qquad \frac{\sum_{i=1} C^{ii}}{\mathbf{m}} = \left(\frac{1}{\mathbf{m}}\right) \sum_{j=1}^{\mathbf{m}} \frac{1}{\lambda_j} .$$

That is, the average value of C^{ii} for predictors $\mathbf{X_1}, \ldots, \mathbf{X_m}$ in a given population equals the average reciprocal eigenvalue of the predictor configuration therein. It is not difficult to show that the average reciprocal of a set of numbers is at least as great as the reciprocal of the average of those numbers, with this lower limit being attained only when the numbers are all equal. Hence $(1/\mathbf{m}) \sum_{i=1}^{n} C^{ii}$ has a lower bound of $1/\overline{V}_X$ and can become very much larger than this if any of the principal factors of the $\mathbf{X_i}$-configuration are trivial in importance—i.e., if λ_m and any of the eigenvalues which precede it are close to vanishing and hence contribute large reciprocals to [10.35]. But small tail-end eigenvalues are an inevitable consequence of prominent first factors. Thus *in general, the stronger the factorial agreement within a set of predictors, the greater is the sampling error for estimating the regression weights of these predictors for any criterion,* though to be sure, it is not the dominant factors as such which are responsible for this error, but the manner in which they emasculate the terminal factors. As a rough guide to the magnitude of this effect, let the principal factors of the $\mathbf{X_i}$ be sorted into two groups $\mathbf{P_1}, \ldots, \mathbf{P_k}$ and $\mathbf{P_{k+1}}, \ldots, \mathbf{P_m}$ where the proportion of factors in the first group is $p_F =_{\text{def}} \mathbf{k}/\mathbf{m}$ and the proportion of the total $\mathbf{X_i}$-variance collectively accounted for by the factors in the first group is

$$p_V =_{\text{def}} \frac{V_{X(P_1 \ldots P_k)}}{V_X} = \frac{\sum_{i=1}^{k} \lambda_i}{\sum_{i=1}^{m} \lambda_i} .$$

Then assuming that $\overline{V}_X = 1$, it is not difficult to compute from [10.35] that

$$\text{[10.36]} \qquad \frac{\sum_{i=1}^{\mathbf{m}} C^{ii}}{\mathbf{m}} \geqslant \frac{p_F^2}{p_V} + \frac{(1-p_F)^2}{1-p_V} = 1 + \frac{(p_V - p_F)^2}{p_V(1-p_V)} \qquad (\overline{V}_X = 1) ,$$

with equality being attained when each factor has the same eigenvalue as the others in its group. (To drop the restriction that $\overline{V}_X = 1$, divide the right-hand side of [10.36] by $\overline{V}_{\mathbf{X}}$.) Thus if 50% of the factors account for 90% of the predictor variance, the average C^{ii} is at least 2.8 if the average predictor variance is unity, while if 90% of the predictor variance is accounted for by only 10% of the factors, the average C^{ii} when $\overline{V}_{\mathbf{X}} = 1$ is greater than 7.1. As a rule of thumb, we may state that to achieve a given level of overall accuracy in estimating regression coefficients from sample data in which the predictors are strongly correlated, the sample size must be an order of magnitude larger than the sample size required for that level of accuracy with uncorrelated predictors.

It might at first seem puzzling—though reassuring—to observe from [10.26] or [10.27] that this excessive uncertainty in the $\hat{b}_i$ for strongly intercorrelated predictors has no effect at all on the anticipated inaccuracy of the actual predictions which are derived from the estimated regression equation. The explanation for this may be gleaned from [10.17-**ij**], which shows that the more highly are $\mathbf{X}_i$ and $\mathbf{X}_j$ correlated with the other predictors and with each other independently of the rest, the more strongly is C^{ij} negative. Thus when the predictors are redundant, the sampling errors in the $\hat{b}_i$ are on the whole negatively correlated (see [10.10]), with the result that these errors tend to cancel one another and leave no more combined uncertainty in the estimated regression surface than would occur for that size of sample with uncorrelated predictors. Where the sampling eccentricities of the $\hat{b}_i$ do wreak havoc, however, is with efforts to be sophisticated about item selection and item weighting in test construction. Most multiple-item tests strive industriously to achieve a fairly high level of interitem consistency. But with the sample variances standardized at unity, a confidence interval for $b_i(P)$ at the 100p% level of confidence, contingent upon the predictor distribution χ_n in O_n, is

[10.37-**i**] (**i** = **1**, . . . , **m**)

$$b_i(O_n) \pm t_{p(n-\mathbf{m}-1)} \sqrt{\frac{1 - R^2_{\mathbf{Y}(\mathbf{X}_1 \ldots \mathbf{X}_m)}(O_n)}{(n - \mathbf{m} - 1)[1 - R^2_{\mathbf{X}_i(\boldsymbol{\mu}_i)}(O_n)]}} \qquad (\sigma_{\mathbf{Y}}(O_n) = \sigma_{\mathbf{X}_i}(O_n) = 1)$$

or, more elegantly,

[10.37*a*-**i**] (**i** = **1**, . . . , **m**)

$$b_i(O_n) \pm \frac{t_{p(n-\mathbf{m}-1)}}{\sqrt{n - \mathbf{m} - 1}} \, \frac{K_{\mathbf{Y}(\mathbf{X}_1 \ldots \mathbf{X}_m)}(O_n)}{K_{\mathbf{X}_i(\boldsymbol{\mu}_i)}(O_n)} \qquad (\sigma_{\mathbf{Y}}(O_n) = \sigma_{\mathbf{X}_i}(O_n) = 1) ,$$

where for a confidence level of 95%, $t_{p(n-\mathbf{m}-1)} \simeq 2.0$ if $n - \mathbf{m} - 1 > 10$. Even when $R^2_{\mathbf{X}_i(\boldsymbol{\mu}_i)}(O_n)$ is at its minimum of zero, $n - \mathbf{m}$ must be in the hundreds if the uncertainty in $\hat{b}_i$ is to be confined essentially to the second decimal; and while $R_{\mathbf{X}_i(\boldsymbol{\mu}_i)}(O_n)$ can tolerate moderate values without lowering $K_{\mathbf{X}_i(\boldsymbol{\mu}_i)}(O_n)$ appreciably below unity (see Figure 4.6), if $R_{\mathbf{X}_i(\boldsymbol{\mu}_i)}(O_n)$ becomes substantial $n - \mathbf{m}$ is required to be at least a thousand and perhaps considerably more in order to give $\hat{b}_i$ firm first-decimal precision. Only when empirical studies are conducted on a grand scale, therefore, can we feel reasonably sure (presuming there to be no doubt about the applicability of the regression model in the first place) that an item whose sample regression coefficient for a given criterion is essentially zero is really useless in combination with the other predictors for estimating that criterion in the population from which the sample was drawn, or that the relative magnitudes of two sample regression weights properly reflect the differential stress these items should optimally receive. Since composite tests with a modicum of interitem homogeneity are remarkably insensitive to moderate adjustments of the individual item weights anyway (see pp. 466f.), the gain in predictive efficiency achieved by use of ultra-refined techniques of item analysis in preference to relatively crude methods would appear to be nominal at best.

Nonlinearity and Other Problems of Presuppositions

Apart from some mention of unrestricted curvilinear regression, which is ideal in principle but hopelessly unmanageable in practice, all the prediction theory developed in this book has been restricted to linear equations. Admittedly, linearity of relationships, together with joint normality of all stochastic processes in more advanced problems such as the estimation of population parameters, permit an extraordinarily powerful mathematical development of multivariate analysis, much more so than can be achieved under less obliging circumstances. Yet while linearity and stochastic normality are frequently observed to obtain at least approximately in natural phenomena, they are far from universal. A question which naturally arises, then, is what should be said or done about phenomena that do not concur in all the presuppositions of the analysis which we would like to impose upon them? By rights, this problem should be subsumed under a general *theory of approximations,* but unfortunately, no such theory yet exists. It is, to be sure, frequently possible to discover how flagrantly the results of a computational algorithm deviate from correct values when the conditions which would make this method exact are not altogether satisfied. (Equation [9.48] is a minor illustration of the genre.) But this merely analyzes the efficiency of certain tools at performing tasks whose nature is not in question. Useful as this may be, it does little to illuminate the cognitive status of conceptual schemes—"models," hypotheses, theories, idealizations, even percepts—which on the face of it are shot through and through with propositional commitments which, taken literally, are implausible or demonstrably false, yet for which our only workable intellectual substitutes are alternative theories, etc., bearing similar epistemological stigmata. As a requisite to understanding the relation between a complex reality and the simplified statistical models which to a greater or lesser extent are inappropriate to it, we need something like an ontological theory of *almost-being* and a semantical account of *near-truth*, nothing of which will be ventured here. The present remarks attempt no more than to alert the reader to some possible limitations of linear models and to cite certain alternative approaches.

For application of regression principles to predictive situations in which the criterion is empirically accessible, nonlinearity need not be much of a hardship either in theory or in practice. In the first place, when all that is at stake is predictive accuracy, philosophical or methodological anxieties about inappropriate models are quite irrelevant—the issue is purely a pragmatic assessment of the benefits to be harvested through use of a certain equation in a certain way. No matter how complex the functional association between variables **X** and **Y** may be, nothing prevents us from using a linear prediction policy to estimate scores on **Y** from scores on **X**, and if we choose the linear regression of **Y** upon **X** in population *P* for this purpose, then no matter how far $\dot{\mathbf{Y}}_{(\mathbf{X})}$ may stray from the expected value of **Y**, given **X**, for specific values of the predictor, the linear correlation between **X** and **Y** in *P* informs us primly and uncontrovertably what degree of predictive control over **Y** we have acquired through this policy. Thus if **Y** is curvilinearly related to **X** in degree $\eta_{\mathbf{YX}} = .99$ by a function far too intimately wrinkled for its course to be accurately charted empirically, but which also shows a general upward trend at, say, $r_{\mathbf{YX}} = .60$, then optimal linear prediction of **Y** from **X** will still reduce errors by 20% from what they would be under optimal estimation of **Y** without regard for data on **X**. On the other hand, if the unrestricted regression of **Y** upon **X** does depart conspicuously from linearity, as is by no means unheard of in empirical reality, then there is no reason why we should not try to improve our predictions by use of a more complex formula. As discussed in Chapter 4 (pp. 154f.), it is not at all difficult to compute regression surfaces in one or more predictors with as lively a shape as desired, without abandoning any of the mathematical conveniences of linearity, simply by treating higher-degree polynomic terms in the predictors (or other nonlinear functions thereof if desired) as additional independent variables whose regression coefficients occur linearly and are computed just like those of the first-degree terms. The only major caution is to keep the number of fitted parameters from becoming absurdly large in comparison to the precision with which they can be estimated from the available sample data. For if "Pm(d, **m**)" designates the number of parametric coefficients in the complete polynomial regression form of degree d in **m** predictor variables, it can be shown that

$$\mathrm{Pm}(d,\mathbf{m}) = \frac{(d+\mathbf{m})!}{d!\mathbf{m}!} = (1+\mathbf{m})\left(1+\frac{\mathbf{m}}{2}\right)\left(1+\frac{\mathbf{m}}{3}\right)\cdots\left(1+\frac{\mathbf{m}}{d}\right),$$

which quickly grows enormous as **m** and d both become much larger than unity. (E.g., Pm(2, **3**) = 10 for a second degree polynomial in three predictors, while for a third degree polynomial in five predictors, Pm(3,

5) = 56.) When higher powers of the predictors are fitted in practice, it is standard procedure to build up in complexity by a sequential procedure which begins with linear components and adds terms of successively higher degree only if these pass certain tests of statistical significance—e.g., if a reasonably stringent confidence interval computed from the sample data for their regression coefficients does not include zero.[7]

This is not to suggest that practical applications of regression principles are home free *vis-à-vis* shaky presuppositions. If the inferences drawn from predictor data are more than just point estimates of the criterion, then the contingent distributions of the criterion, given scores on the predictors, may well bring grief to the unwary. Most practical predictions actually take the form of interval judgments, and if joint normality or the somewhat weaker premises of the normal regression model are assumed where they do not in fact obtain, then it is possible to end up with interval inferences to which quite inappropriate degrees of confidence are attached, especially if there is any systematic nonlinearity or tendency for the criterion's contingent standard deviation to vary with the predictor scores. There is no methodological problem here, however, but only a technical demand (though it may not be easily met) for enough sampling data to give a clear picture of what the joint distribution of criterion and predictors in the relevant population is like, and enough professional acumen to judge whether the criterion's departure from linearity of regression and contingent homoscedastic normality is severe enough to be of any real consequence.

When predictive evaluations go beyond the sampling-determinable relations among empirical variables, on the other hand, the threat of inappropriate presuppositions is more ominously enigmatic. Even in unabashedly pragmatic contexts of diagnosis and forecast it is seldom that the empirical criteria, if any, by which validity in this setting is operationally assessed are truly the ultimate targets of inference. For example, an employer judging the effectiveness of his personnel selection procedures by examining the statistical relations between his screening variables and, say, some measure of productivity or supervisor ratings at the end of a year on the job does not care about the supervisor ratings or even that particular productivity measure *as such,* but only insofar as these are felt to be symptomatic of some more or less vaguely conceived underlying job-efficiency factor, evidence for the existence of which would be found in suitable consistencies among a variety of productivity

[7] The methodology of curve-fitting is considerably more involved than suggested by the present remarks. For example, taken literally, the regression model implies that the greatest anticipated predictive accuracy is achieved when as many parameters are fitted as possible, the result of which would be that the computed curve would faithfully follow all the digressions of the individual sample points from what undoubtedly is in reality a much simpler trend. In practice, we find ourselves modifying the unbiased, minimum-variance policies promulgated by the regression model to take into account intuitive opinions about the a priori likelihood of higher-order components. For a technical survey of curve-fitting methods, see Ezekiel and Fox (26).

measures (e.g., not just on one occasion but day after day). Similarly, while the grade-point averages of college students may be taken to validate the effectiveness of college entrance-board examinations, it is not a candidate's eventual grade-point average with which the admissions staff is primarily concerned, but such obscure desiderata as "academic potential," "intellectual creativity," and the like, so that ultimate questions of test validity would remain even for an errorless forecaster of grade-point average. Statistical models which seek to explain the suggestions of regularity lurking within observed multivariate distributions by fitting to them postulated patterns of underlying processes, as assayed, e.g., by inferential factor analysis and reliability theory, only exercise with technical rigor a major mode of interpretive thinking which is at least as old as human reason and probably considerably older. And here is where the problem of presuppositions begins to get sticky, for while a statistical model fills in its details by estimating parameters from the observed data, the framework of the model, such as linearity of relationships or normality of stochastic ingredients, within which the algebraically specified parameters are imbedded is not subject to this sort of a posteriori empirical monitoring. Only when the model entails some observable property (e.g., joint normality of the data variables) which cannot be accommodated by proper tuning of the parameters is it possible to discredit the model on empirical grounds, while the control over the model such a property affords is only an option between toleration and rejection. All that contemporary model methodology can suggest for finding the "right" model is to try a variety of a priori conceptions and see which one feels least uncomfortable when its parameters are optimally fitted. In principle, moreover, there is always an abundance of incompatible or at least nonequivalent models which will satisfactorily fit the same array of data. If we wished to stir this witches' brew of perplexities, we could probe into such questions as why should one model be favored over another which fits the data just as well, or what reason have we to think that there is some model which not merely "fits" but is actually correct, or what is wrong with using a model whose observable implications are not fully borne out in the data. As it is, we shall settle for some observations on what happens when linear models are imposed upon a more curvaceous reality.

The fundamental premise of any *explanatory model* of a multivariate array of data, whether it be a linear hypothesis of the sort which characterizes inferential factor analysis or some other postulated mathematical structure, is that all the variables $\mathbf{X}_1, \ldots, \mathbf{X}_n$ whose joint distribution has actually been observed are simultaneously determined by a number of underlying influences or "source" variables $\boldsymbol{\tau}_1, \ldots, \boldsymbol{\tau}_m$.[8] That is, an

[8] Note that not all statistical models are "explanatory" in this sense. For example, neither the correlation model nor the regression model of a multivariate configuration postulates underlying sources. (At first impression, the stochastic component $\mathbf{e}$ in the regression model looks like a theoretical variable, but mathematically it is only the criterion resid-

explanatory model has the general form

$$\mathbf{X}_i = \phi_i(\tau_1, \ldots, \tau_m), \quad [10.38\text{-}\mathbf{i}]$$

$(\mathbf{i} = \mathbf{1}, \ldots, \mathbf{n})$

where the number of source variables may be an adjustable parameter and it is not required that every τ_j occur nontrivially in each function ϕ_i. (In particular, an explanatory model usually includes for each data variable $\mathbf{X}_i$ a "unique" source which occurs nontrivially only in ϕ_i, the role of which is to account for discrepancies between the actual behavior of $\mathbf{X}_i$ and the behavior ideally determined by the source variables nontrivially common to $\mathbf{X}_1, \ldots, \mathbf{X}_n$.) Given a joint probability distribution, or sampling approximation thereto, for variables $\mathbf{X}_1, \ldots, \mathbf{X}_n$ in some population *P*, the mathematical problem of the model is to solve for composition functions $\phi_1, \ldots, \phi_m$ and a joint probability distribution for $\tau_1, \ldots, \tau_m$ which reproduce the observed distribution of the $\mathbf{X}_i$; and what differentiates one such model from another are the restrictions which a particular model imposes on the forms that $\phi_1, \ldots, \phi_n$ and, perhaps, the joint distribution of $\tau_1, \ldots, \tau_m$, are allowed to take.[9] In inferential factor analysis, the major restriction is that the ϕ_i are all linear in $\tau_1, \ldots, \tau_m$. An additional postulate which is sometimes appended to the factor-analytic model is that the unique components of the $\mathbf{X}_i$ are not merely orthogonal, but are independent of each other and of the common factors in the strongest statistical sense of this term. While this further assumption of statistical independence for the unique components does little if anything to reduce the class of admissible common-factor solutions for a given distribution of data variables, it is sometimes felt to be a necessary condition if the common factors are to be regarded as "real." However, there are important cases of data variables for which fully independent unique components are a mathematical impossibility (see fn. 12, p. 527), yet which are perfectly good candidates for inferential factoring.

The most challenging problem of nonlinearity for factor analysis is what, if anything, can be learned about underlying processes through imposition of a linear model when there are indeed common sources which govern the data variables in accord with general form [10.38], but for which the composition functions ϕ_i are distinctly curvilinear. This question is imparted special urgency by the fact that well-substantiated explanations of phenomena in the physical sciences find nonlinearity with depressing frequency. It is thus gratifying, if perhaps surprising, to learn that studies in which the covariances among data variables of known nonlinear composition have been factored linearly

---

ual in the joint probability distribution of the criterion and predictors.) The assumptions in these cases are not ontological but distributional, namely, that the discrepancy between the observed frequency distribution and the probability distribution postulated for the data variables is only a sampling artefact.

[9] See Anderson (4) for a useful summary of certain basic theorems applicable to all explanatory models.

and rotated to simple structure have shown excellent recapture of the original sources.[10] How this is possible can be appreciated most readily with the aid of an example. Suppose that data variables $\mathbf{X}_1, \ldots, \mathbf{X}_n$ derive entirely from two common sources τ_1 and τ_2 and that while the dependence of each $\mathbf{X}_i$ upon these sources is nonlinear, the relation is adequately written as a second-degree polynomial. Then

$$\mathbf{X}_i = b_{i0} + b_{i1}\tau_1 + b_{i2}\tau_2 + b_{i11}\tau_1^2 + b_{i22}\tau_2^2 + b_{i12}\tau_1\tau_2\,, \qquad [10.39\text{-}\mathbf{i}]\ (\mathbf{i} = 1, \ldots, \mathbf{n})$$

where the bs are to-be-discovered parameters. By treating the components τ_1^2, τ_2^2, and $\tau_1\tau_2$ as separate variables and partialling τ_1 and τ_2 out of them, [10.39] can alternatively be rewritten as

$$\mathbf{X}_i = b_{i0} + b_{i1}\tau_1 + b_{i2}\tau_2 + b_{i3}\mathbf{F}_3 + b_{i4}\mathbf{F}_4 + b_{i5}\mathbf{F}_5\,, \qquad [10.40\text{-}\mathbf{i}]\ (\mathbf{i} = 1, \ldots, \mathbf{n})$$

where $\mathbf{F}_3$, $\mathbf{F}_4$, and $\mathbf{F}_5$ are second-degree polynomials in τ_1 and τ_2 whose covariances with τ_1 and τ_2 are zero. (Making $\mathbf{F}_3$, $\mathbf{F}_4$, and $\mathbf{F}_5$ orthogonal to τ_1 and τ_2 is actually unnecessary, but it expedites thinking about what the higher-degree components in τ_1 and τ_2 contribute to the covariance structure of the $\mathbf{X}_i$.) Now, equations [10.40] analyze data configuration $\mathbf{X}_1, \ldots, \mathbf{X}_n$ in a linear factor space of five dimensions which would be disclosed (assuming $\mathbf{n} > 5$) by any routine for basis factoring the data variables' covariance matrix. Moreover, if the coefficients b_{i3}, b_{i4}, b_{i5} $(\mathbf{i} = 1, \ldots, \mathbf{n})$ in [10.40] are small in comparison to the b_{i1} and b_{i2}, as is especially likely if the scores on the data variables have been gathered over a rather restricted range of the τ_i, and if the method of factoring attempts to maximize the data variance accounted for by each successive factor, the space spanned by the first two factors should closely approximate the space spanned by τ_1 and τ_2, while the remaining data variance might well be discarded as negligible. The evidence would thus implicate two major common sources, while if a number of the $\mathbf{X}_j$ load only on one of these sources, a search for simple structure in the two-dimensional space so extracted should be able to settle on a factor pattern that closely approximates the coefficients b_{i1} and b_{i2} in [10.39] and [10.40], with a corresponding factor structure which then approximates the covariances between the $\mathbf{X}_i$ and the τ_j. (In fact, a simple-structure solution might well be able to arrive at factors which are closely congruent to τ_1 and τ_2 even when the full five-dimensional factor space is searched if enough of the higher-degree components in [10.39] or [10.40] have

[10] See Cattell and Dickman (11) for a recent experiment of this sort, together with additional references.

near-zero coefficients.) Moreover, the fact that the data variables have a nonlinear composition in their sources does not prevent the latter from being successfully estimated by linear functions of the former. Thus in the present example, given a solution for the coefficients b_{i1} and b_{i2} ($\mathbf{i} = 1, \ldots, \mathbf{n}$) of the first-degree components in τ_1 and τ_2, together with the remaining coefficients for any choice of additional factors $\mathbf{F}_3$, $\mathbf{F}_4$, and $\mathbf{F}_5$ which along with τ_1 and τ_2 span the five-dimensional space of $\mathbf{X}_1, \ldots, \mathbf{X}_n$ (assuming $\mathbf{n} \geqslant 5$), we can solve equations [10.40] to yield both τ_1 and τ_2 as exact linear functions of the $\mathbf{X}_i$. This example is, to be sure, highly idealized, but it illustrates the general principle that except for extraordinarily complex relationships, the ϕ_i in [10.38] should be adequately approximated by functions of functions of the τ_j in which the parameters occur linearly and where the coefficients of the first-degree components in the τ_j may turn out empirically to be dominant. Hence even when data variables derive nonlinearly from their common sources, factor analysis of the data-variable covariance matrix still has a good chance of coming up with evidence for those sources, as well as, perhaps, with linear functions of the data variables which usefully approximate them.

However, while it is reassuring to know that causal nonlinearity need not hopelessly cripple the usefulness of linear explanatory models, a more basic conclusion which follows from the present considerations is that *factor analysis of observed covariances is unable to distinguish between cases in which a relatively large number of source variables determine the data variables linearly and cases in which the data variables are more complexly governed by a smaller number of sources.* When data-variable covariances have been factored down to a common-factor space of large dimensionality, it is altogether possible that many of these dimensions simply represent nonlinear components in curvilinear dependencies of the data variables upon their common sources. Thus when observed covariances result from a nonlinear underlying causal structure, factor analysis is disposed to come up with spurious factors—spurious, that is, in that they do not in fact correspond to additional source variables. Which raises a nice point: Given a successful decomposition of covariance matrix $\{C_{X_iX_j}\}$ into a factor pattern $\{b_{ij}\}$, which columns of the latter should be interpreted as data-variable loadings on causally distinct source variables and which should more properly be regarded as the coefficients of higher powers and cross-products (or other nonlinear functions) of sources already represented by other columns in the factor-pattern matrix? Since there is nothing in the data-variable covariances or their factorial decomposition upon which the distinction between these two kinds of factorial components leaves any identifying traces, our only hope for separating them lies in examination of the higher moments of the data-variable distribution.[11] This is an important extension of factor theory which has as yet received very little development, though study of higher moments has been gathering momentum in closely allied areas. Another possibility for the future (though not an especially promising one) is development of techniques for extracting simple-structure factor spaces which still leave appreciable residual covariances among the factored variables – i.e., discovering ways to cut through the obscuring haze introduced into the factored covariances by higher-degree components of the source variables, comparable to the elimination of distraction now attempted by factoring with communality-reduced variances. Meanwhile, that many of the factors which emerge in empirical factor-analytic research may be no more than nonlinear shadows of the same primary source variables, like "ghost" images on a television screen, is a possibility which has received far too little recognition by most practitioners of the art.

Multivariate systems for which it is especially tempting to posit nonlinear dependencies occur frequently in psychological testing, notably when the data variables are dichotomous. Consider a test item **X** which by definition has only two possible values, such as when the item is scored as either right or wrong, or when the subject indicates whether he agrees or disagrees with the statement made by the item. How might the observed distribution of **X**-scores arise as a resultant of underlying influences? To begin with, it is clear that if a dichotomous variable **X** is to be analyzed as a linear combination

$$\mathbf{X} = b_0 + \sum_{j=1}^{m-1} b_j \mathbf{F}_j \qquad [10.41]$$

of factors $\mathbf{F}_1, \ldots, \mathbf{F}_m$, where some of the $\mathbf{F}_j$ may or may not be different functions of the same source variables, the joint distribution of $\mathbf{F}_1, \ldots, \mathbf{F}_m$ cannot be multivariate normal or even a reasonable approximation thereto. For [10.41] may alternatively be written as, say,

$$\mathbf{F}_m = \frac{1}{b_m}\left(\mathbf{X} - b_0 - \sum_{j=1}^{m} b_j \mathbf{F}_j\right), \qquad [10.42]$$

[11] With suitable assumptions (e.g., statistical independence) about the unique components in a linear explanatory model, all the mixed rth-order moments ($r = 1, 2, 3, \ldots$) of the joint data-variable distribution are linear combinations of the rth-order moments of their common factors. Moreover, the coefficients of these factor moments are strictly determined by the factor-pattern coefficients, while if there are sufficiently fewer common factors than there are data variables, there are more distinct rth-order mixed data-variable moments than there are distinct unknown rth-order common-factor moments. Hence given a common-factor pattern extracted from the data-variable covariances, it is in principle generally possible to convert the higher-order data-variable moments into a solution for the corresponding moments of the factor distribution. The numerical values of these moments, in turn, provide clues to which of the factors in the pattern are causally distinct and which are but nonlinear functions of one or more of the other factors.

from which it is easily seen that the contingent distribution of $\mathbf{F_m}$ (and similarly for any other of the $\mathbf{F_j}$), given any particular combination F_1, . . . , F_{m-1} of values on the other factors, differs from the contingent distribution of **X**, given $F_1, \ldots, F_{m-1}$, only by a linear transformation. In particular, if **X** is dichotomous, so must the contingent distributions of each factor in [10.41], given scores on the other factors, likewise be dichotomous, while moreover the particular pair of values that $\mathbf{F_m}$ may take given $F_1, \ldots, F_{m-1}$ is a function of $\sum_{j=1}^{m-1} b_j F_j$.[12] If $\mathbf{F_1}, \ldots, \mathbf{F_m}$ are, or are functions of, genuine causal sources of $\mathbf{X_i}$, the only remotely possible way in which such strong mathematical constraints could hold on the joint distribution of $\mathbf{F_1}, \ldots, \mathbf{F_m}$ is for the $\mathbf{F_j}$ to include nonlinear components of the source variables.

More substantial insight into the nonlinear composition of dichotomous items is proffered by their reliability theory. Consider the relation between true scores and observed scores on a unit-dichotomous variable **X** (i.e., the two possible values for **X** are scaled 0 and 1). The probability distribution over potential scores on **X** for a given subject i is completely specified in this case by the probability, $p_{\mathbf{X}i}$, of i's receiving a score of 1 on **X**, while $p_{\mathbf{X}i}$ is also the expected value of **X** for i and is hence by definition i's "true score" on **X**. Now: How is it possible for a complex of underlying determinants, including sources of measurement error, to so interact that their result is always a score of either 0 or 1 on **X**? Without attempting to survey the logical possibilities, let it be stated dogmatically that about the only plausible models are those which posit a more or less continuous process $\mathbf{X}^*$ (which need be conceived only as a mathematical abstraction from the joint distribution of more fundamental source variables) on which each subject has his own individual probability distribution and for which there exists a certain threshold value or "difficulty level" c such that a subject receives a score of 1 on **X** if and only if his score on $\mathbf{X}^*$ exceeds c. Then the probability $p_{\mathbf{X}i}$ that a particular subject i receives a score of 1 on **X** is the proportion of his probability distribution on $\mathbf{X}^*$ which lies above c, and to express the true-score component of **X** as a function of one or more source variables the model must specify the individual $\mathbf{X}^*$-distributions in terms of the subjects' scores on the hypothesized sources. For example, if it be hypothesized that the individual probability distributions on $\mathbf{X}^*$ are identical for all members of population P except in their expectations—e.g., normal in shape with constant

[12] Hence in particular, $\mathbf{F_m}$ cannot be a unique component of **X** which is statistically independent of $\mathbf{F_1}, \ldots, \mathbf{F_{m-1}}$ (unless $\mathrm{Var}\left(\sum_{j=1}^{m-1} b_j \mathbf{F_j}\right) = 0$, in which case $\mathbf{F_1}, \ldots, \mathbf{F_{m-1}}$ occur vacuously in **X**). Whenever a variable which can take only a finite number of discrete values is (nontrivially) analyzed according to pattern [10.41], it is mathematically impossible for any one of the constituent factors to be fully independent of the rest.

variance s^2 and mean T_i^* for each subject i, where by definition T_i^* is also i's "true score" on $\mathbf{X}^*$ – then for each i in P,

$$[10.43] \qquad p_{\mathbf{X}i} = 1 - \Phi\left(\frac{c - T_i^*}{s}\right) = \Phi\left(\frac{T_i^* - c}{s}\right),$$

where $\Phi(z)$ is the cumulative proportion of a normal distribution at sigma-distance z above the mean. In this case, the true-score component $\mathbf{p_X}$ of the observed unit-dichotomous item $\mathbf{X}$ is an errorless increasing function of the true-score component $\mathbf{T}^*$ of the underlying process $\mathbf{X}^*$, but the function is S-shaped, not linear. A further consequence of model [10.43] is that if $\mathbf{X}_1, \ldots, \mathbf{X}_n$ are a set of dichotomies whose true-score components all result from precisely the same immediate determinant $\mathbf{T}^*$ but which have different difficulty levels $c_1, \ldots, c_n$, the true-score components $\mathbf{p}_{\mathbf{X}_j}$ and $\mathbf{p}_{\mathbf{X}_k}$ of each pair of items $\mathbf{X}_j$ and $\mathbf{X}_k$ in the set will be curvilinearly though perfectly related and inferential factoring of the observed covariances will be unable to account for the relations among these items by a single common factor. To complicate matters further, if the probability distributions for individual subjects on the process $\mathbf{X}^*$ underlying an observed dichotomy $\mathbf{X}$, while still normal, differ in their standard deviations as well as in their expectations, then for each i in P,

$$p_{\mathbf{X}i} = \Phi\left(\frac{T_i^* - c}{s_i}\right),$$

which gives $\mathbf{p_X}$ as a nonlinear function of two immediate determinants, $\mathbf{T}^*$ and $\mathbf{s}$.

The fact that the true-score components of dichotomous test items (and hence also the items as observed) almost certainly communicate nonlinearly with their most immediate causal sources means that there is especially good reason for factor analysis of dichotomous variables to be viewed with apprehension about whatever interpretive dangers may lurk in linear models. One common ploy for coaxing the factor-analytic model to seem less inappropriate is to operate not upon the linear correlations actually observed among the data variables (these correlations being known as "Phi coefficients" when both variables are dichotomous) but upon their "tetrachoric" correlations, which are estimates of the linear correlations between the continuous processes $\mathbf{X}_i^*$ and $\mathbf{X}_j^*$ presumed to underlie each pair of observed dichotomies $\mathbf{X}_i$ and $\mathbf{X}_j$. However, this is helpful only insofar as the strong presupposition of the tetrachoric estimate, namely, bivariate normality for $\mathbf{X}_i^*$ and $\mathbf{X}_j^*$, is acceptable.[13]

[13] Lest this seem like no more than what is already assumed by inferential factoring, it should be thoroughly understood that, contrary to frequent misimpression, the theory of factor analysis depends in no way upon assumptions about the shapes of the data-variable or factor distributions. In particular, nothing is gained by postulation of joint normality for the factors except the implication that no further information can be obtained about

(Statisticians have also been known to grumble that no sampling theory is available for treating results obtained from data so transformed, though this is perhaps a burden that one could learn to live with.) On the other hand, whatever the precise composition pattern may be by which a unit-dichotomous variable **X** arises from its sources, the dependence of **X**'s true-score component $\mathbf{p_X}$ upon its closest determinants (e.g., **T***, or **T*** and **s**, in the models cited above) will almost surely be well-approximated by a low-degree polynomial in which the linear components are dominant. Further, it can readily be shown that if measurement errors on two dichotomous items $\mathbf{X_i}$ and $\mathbf{X_j}$ are statistically independent for each subject—i.e., if there is no relation between $\mathbf{X_i}$ and $\mathbf{X_j}$ within their joint probability distribution for an individual testee—then the observed covariance $C_{\mathbf{X_i X_j}}$ equals the covariance between the true-score components, $\mathbf{p_{X_i}}$ and $\mathbf{p_{X_j}}$, of $\mathbf{X_i}$ and $\mathbf{X_j}$.[14] Hence if the sources of within-subject error variance are reasonably independent from one item to another, the off-diagonal entries in the data-covariance matrix $\{C_{\mathbf{X_i X_j}}\}$ will be essentially the same as the corresponding elements in $\{C_{\mathbf{p_{X_i} p_{X_j}}}\}$, and inferential factoring of $\{C_{\mathbf{X_i X_j}}\}$ with a shrewd choice of communalities should provide powerful clues to the common sources of the $\mathbf{X_i}$ even if an occasional higher-degree function of these sources manages to pass as an independent factor. (To the extent that the within-subject errors are *not* fully independent from one item to another, the error components $\mathbf{E_i} = \mathbf{X_i} - \mathbf{p_{X_i}}$ of the observed items will also have nonzero covariances that add additional dimensionality to the set's factor structure—which, however, is no different from what correlated errors do when the data variables are determined linearly by their common sources.)

When arguing for the legitimacy of factoring Phi coefficients or other worrisome cases of correlation, it should, of course, also be emphasized that there is nothing *wrong* with replacing such measures with some prearranged transformation thereof. Quite the contrary: If mathematical operations of any sort upon the data can bring to light regularities therein whose presence is not a logically necessary consequence of the method of manipulation, then we have discovered something lawful about these data which becomes a brute empirical fact demanding interpretation and explanation.

---

the factorial composition of the data variables by examining the higher moments of the latter. For further comments on the use of tetrachoric correlations and other data transformations when the nature of the data lead one to feel uneasy about factoring linear correlations, see Carroll (10).

[14] More generally, this freedom from error contributions when each subject's measurement errors are statistically independent of one another is true of all the mixed moments of a distribution of dichotomous items $\mathbf{X_1}, \ldots, \mathbf{X_n}$. It is important to appreciate that within-subject independence of errors can occur even though the error components of $\mathbf{X_1}, \ldots, \mathbf{X_n}$ cannot be statistically independent of the true-score components $\mathbf{p_{X_1}}, \ldots, \mathbf{p_{X_n}}$ of the $\mathbf{X_i}$ within a population comprising subjects whose true scores on these items differ.

While by and large, spurious factors notwithstanding, factor analysis of empirical covariances is probably still the most mathematically powerful and least assumption-ridden method yet available for detecting underlying determinants in multivariate data configurations, the reader should be apprised that efforts have been made to develop explanatory models for observed multivariate distributions which do not presuppose linear structures. The oldest and most comprehensive of these is the *latent structure analysis* originated by Lazarsfeld (see, e.g., 52). Generically, latent structure theory postulates that behind data variables $\mathbf{X}_1, \ldots, \mathbf{X}_n$ there dwell sources $\tau_1, \ldots, \tau_m$ such that in the contingent joint distributions of $\mathbf{X}_1, \ldots, \mathbf{X}_n$ given any constellation of values on the τ_j, the $\mathbf{X}_i$ are fully independent of one another—i.e., that there is no relationship among the $\mathbf{X}_i$ which is not wholly accounted for by $\tau_1, \ldots, \tau_m$. In order to make any model-fitting possible at all, latent structure theory finds it necessary to try various specific patterns by which the τ_j determine the $\mathbf{X}_i$, but there is no special insistence on linearity nor do the covariances among the $\mathbf{X}_i$ have in principle any greater priority for fitting a model than do other moments of the joint $\mathbf{X}_i$-distribution. The most conspicuous technical limitation to latent structure analysis is that in its present state of development, it is restricted to dichotomous data variables or at least to data which can be recast into the equivalent of dichotomies. (However, see Gibson, 32.)

More recently, Coombs and Kao (15) have investigated nonlinear factor models with composition patterns based on combinatorial concepts ("either-or" and "both-and") rather than on the traditional mathematics of continuous functions. Actually, this is only one development in Coombs' monumental efforts to subsume all data processing in the behavioral sciences under a single comprehensive formal theory (14). While Coombs' models unfortunately tend toward triviality in their conceptualization of problem areas in which traditional quantitative methods have been most successful, they provide illuminating new ways to think about inferential decomposition of data on subject/stimulus interactions, especially classificatory behaviors and choice reactions in which the data variables cannot in any meaningful sense be thought of as metrical.

Finally, it is appropriate in this context to record that Lord (e.g., 55) has liberated reliability theory from total commitment to linear thinking by his pioneer studies of how such interesting details of the joint distribution of observed and true scores as the possible dependence of contingent error variance upon true score and the shape of the unrestricted regression of true scores upon observed scores (which, it will be recalled, need not be precisely linear even though the converse regression must be) can be inferred from the higher moments of the observed joint distribution of test items.

Problems of Scaling

On various occasions in the preceding pages, we skirmished with the fact that choice of a numerical scale for the values of a variable is to a high degree arbitrary. Whatever conveniences may lead us to prefer one scale over another, it is still perfectly within our option to represent the various alternative attributes which compose the variable by any set of labels, numerical or not, which can be put into one-one correspondence with them.[15] It will also be recalled, however, that the prediction policies which have been developed here are based upon arithmetic operations whose outcomes are of necessity critically dependent upon the particular numerical scale values to which they are applied—which should evoke an uneasy concern about the extent to which the predictions so made are influenced by caprice in the selection of scales. Specifically, the problem which now confronts us is the following: Suppose that according to some given standard S of predictive excellence, $\hat{\mathbf{Y}} = f_S(\mathbf{X}_1, \ldots, \mathbf{X}_n)$ is the optimal policy for estimating scores on a numerically scaled criterion $\mathbf{Y}$ from numerically scaled predictors $\mathbf{X}_1, \ldots, \mathbf{X}_n$ (e.g., S might stipulate that $\hat{\mathbf{Y}}$ is a regression estimate of a certain form), while according to this same standard, $\hat{\mathbf{Y}}' = f'_S(\mathbf{X}'_1, \ldots, \mathbf{X}'_n)$ is the best policy for predicting $\mathbf{Y}'$ from $\mathbf{X}'_1, \ldots, \mathbf{X}'_n$ when $\mathbf{Y}', \mathbf{X}'_1, \ldots, \mathbf{X}'_n$ are alternative scales for $\mathbf{Y}, \mathbf{X}_1, \ldots, \mathbf{X}_n$, respectively, defined by the transformations $\mathbf{Y}' = \psi(\mathbf{Y})$, $\mathbf{X}'_1 = \phi_1(\mathbf{X}_1), \ldots, \mathbf{X}'_n = \phi_n(\mathbf{X}_n)$. Then to predict that an individual has value $\hat{Y}$ of $\mathbf{Y}$ is logically equivalent to predicting that his score on $\mathbf{Y}'$ is $\psi(\hat{Y})$, and the question of how predictions under best-estimation standard S are affected by the choice of scales is whether $f'_S[\phi_1(\mathbf{X}_1), \ldots, \phi(\mathbf{X})]$ (i.e., $\hat{\mathbf{Y}}'$) ever differs from $\psi[f_S(\mathbf{X}_1, \ldots, \mathbf{X}_n)]$ (i.e., $\psi(\hat{\mathbf{Y}})$) and if so, in what fashion is the discrepancy related to the nature of the rescaling transformations $\psi, \phi_1, \ldots, \phi_n$.

When the best estimate of $\mathbf{Y}$ given scores on predictors $\mathbf{X}_1, \ldots, \mathbf{X}_n$ maximizes the utility expected from the prediction, which of course is the ultimate desire of a prediction policy, it (generally) makes no difference how either the criterion or the predictors are scaled. That is, if both $\hat{Y} = f_S(X_1, \ldots, X_n)$ and $\hat{Y}' = f'_S(X'_1, \ldots, X'_n)$ minimize the expected loss of utility when the predictor variables have values $X_1, \ldots, X_n$, respectively, then $\hat{Y}' = \psi(\hat{Y})$ no matter what the transformations $\psi, \phi_1, \ldots, \phi_n$ may be. This may be seen by reflecting first of all that the role of $X_1, \ldots, X_n$ in the prediction is to determine a contingent probability distribution for the criterion, which is unaffected by how the predictors are scaled, and then recalling (pp. 62ff.) that derivation of the loss-minimizing prediction does not consider the criterion's scale values as such, but only

[15] There are a number of current myths about scale "types" which allegedly constrain the scaling alternatives which are to be countenanced for a given variable. However, these restrictions only preserve certain scaling conveniences and are in no way an inherent requirement (see Rozeboom, 70).

the loss associated with each possible combination of prediction and criterion outcome, this being (in general[16]) independent of the choice of criterion scale. Unfortunately, it will also be recalled (p. 68) that explicit computation of utilities is not really very feasible. The most practical, powerful, and prevalent standard for optimizing a prediction policy is to seek minimal standard error under whatever constraints may be in force. This includes, in particular, all forms of regression estimation, and regrettably, prediction policies derived from considerations of error distributions are not so untainted by problems of scaling as are predictions based wholly on utilities. Since these problems are rather different in character according to whether it is the criterion or the predictors whose scaling is in question, we shall examine these two cases separately.

Consider, then, a regression policy $\hat{\mathbf{Y}} = \mathrm{f}_F(\mathbf{X}_1, \ldots, \mathbf{X}_n)$ defined to minimize the standard error of estimate for members of a given population P when f_F has the stipulated mathematical form F. (As a limiting case, F may be unrestricted.) If the predictors are rescaled as $\mathbf{X}'_i = \phi_i(\mathbf{X}_i)$ $(\mathbf{i} = \mathbf{1}, \ldots, \mathbf{n})$ and the same regression form is used to estimate $\mathbf{Y}$ (the same scale as before) from $\mathbf{X}'_1, \ldots, \mathbf{X}'_n$, to what extent will the two estimates differ and what methodological significance do such differences have? If $\mathbf{Y} = \mathrm{f}'_F(\mathbf{X}'_1, \ldots, \mathbf{X}'_n)$ is the F-form regression of $\mathbf{Y}$ upon the rescaled predictors, we have

$$\mathrm{f}'_F(\mathbf{X}'_1, \ldots, \mathbf{X}'_n) = \mathrm{f}'_F[\phi_1(\mathbf{X}_1), \ldots, \phi_n(\mathbf{X}_n)] ,$$

where $\mathrm{f}'_F[\phi_1(\mathbf{X}_1), \ldots, \phi_n(\mathbf{X}_n)]$, like $\mathrm{f}_F(\mathbf{X}_1, \ldots, \mathbf{X}_n)$, is a function of the originally scaled predictors $\mathbf{X}_1, \ldots, \mathbf{X}_n$ and also selects the values of its parameters to minimize the standard error of $\mathbf{Y}$. The difference between the regression equations $\hat{\mathbf{Y}} = \mathrm{f}_F(\mathbf{X}_1, \ldots, \mathbf{X}_n)$ and $\hat{\mathbf{Y}} = \mathrm{f}'_F[\phi_1(\mathbf{X}_1), \ldots, \phi_n(\mathbf{X}_n)]$ is that in general, the rescaling transformations $\phi_1, \ldots, \phi_n$ imbedded in the latter prevent it from having form F. For example, suppose that F is the full linear form so that $\mathrm{f}_F(\mathbf{X}_1, \ldots, \mathbf{X}\ )$ and $\mathrm{f}'_F(\mathbf{X}'_1, \ldots, \mathbf{X}'_n)$ are the linear regressions of $\mathbf{Y}$ upon $\mathbf{X}_1, \ldots, \mathbf{X}_n$ and $\mathbf{X}'_1, \ldots, \mathbf{X}'_n$, respectively, and that the $\mathbf{X}'_i$ are obtained from the $\mathbf{X}_i$ by rescaling transformations $\mathbf{X}'_i =_{\mathrm{def}} \mathbf{X}^3_i$ $(\mathbf{i} = \mathbf{1}, \ldots, \mathbf{n})$. Then $\mathrm{f}_F(\mathbf{X}_1, \ldots, \mathbf{X}_n)$ has the form $b_0 + \sum_{i=1}^{n} b_i\mathbf{X}_i$ whereas $\mathrm{f}'_F(\mathbf{X}'_1, \ldots, \mathbf{X}'_r)$ has the form $b'_0 + \sum_{i=1} b'_i\mathbf{X}'_i = b'_0 + \sum_{i=1}^{n} b'_i\mathbf{X}^3_i$, the latter being a restricted cubic surface in the original predictor scales. In short, *for regression estimation of a criterion whose scale is fixed, selection among alternative scales for the predictor variables is mathematically indistinguishable from selecting from among certain alternative regression forms given fixed predictor scales.* More precisely, if F is a given re-

---

[16] It is possible for this independence to be violated, however, in complex cases where the act of prediction itself has causal repercussions for the ensuing criterion outcome.

gression form and $\mathbf{X}'_1, \ldots, \mathbf{X}'_n$ are rescalings of variables $\mathbf{X}_1, \ldots, \mathbf{X}_n$, respectively, then another regression form F^* always exists such that the F-form regression of any criterion $\mathbf{Y}$ upon the rescaled predictors $\mathbf{X}'_1, \ldots, \mathbf{X}'_n$ is identical with (i.e., gives the same criterion estimates as) the F^*-form regression of $\mathbf{Y}$ upon the original scales $\mathbf{X}_1, \ldots, \mathbf{X}_n$. In special cases the two forms F and F^* may be equivalent, notably when F is the full polynomic form of any degree m while the $\mathbf{X}'_i$ are linear rescalings of the $\mathbf{X}_i$, and when F is the unrestricted curvilinear form while the $\mathbf{X}'_i$ are *any* rescalings of the $\mathbf{X}_i$. In such instances, estimation of $\mathbf{Y}$ by its F-form regression on the predictors is indifferent to whether the latter are scaled as $\mathbf{X}_1, \ldots, \mathbf{X}_n$ or as $\mathbf{X}'_1, \ldots, \mathbf{X}'_n$. In particular, for predicting the criterion by an unabridged mth degree polynomic regression, it makes no difference what reference point, orientation, and unit of measurement (i.e., what linear scale) we choose for the predictors, while the unrestricted curvilinear estimates of the criterion are altogether unaffected by how the predictors are scaled.

Of course, even when the F-form regression of $\mathbf{Y}$ upon different scalings of the predictors yield the same estimates, choice of predictor scales makes a difference for the numerical details of the regression parameters. In particular, when $M_{\mathbf{Y}|\mathbf{X}_1 \ldots \mathbf{X}_n} = f(\mathbf{X}_1, \ldots, \mathbf{X}_n)$ is the unrestricted curvilinear regression of $\mathbf{Y}$ upon $\mathbf{X}_1, \ldots, \mathbf{X}_n$ and the predictors are rescaled by transformations $\mathbf{X}'_i = \phi_i(\mathbf{X}_i)$ $(\mathbf{i} = \mathbf{1}, \ldots, \mathbf{n})$, then

$$M_{\mathbf{Y}|\mathbf{X}'_1 \ldots \mathbf{X}'_n} = f[\phi_1^{-1}(\mathbf{X}'_1), \ldots, \phi_n^{-1}(\mathbf{X}'_n)] ,$$

and within rather wide limits, the latter surface can be made to assume any desired shape by suitable choice of the ϕ_i. Thus options among predictor scales allow us to accomplish through a predictor function of given form the same criterion estimates that would be obtained from a differently shaped predictor function applied to other scalings of the predictors, and the total complexity of mathematical operations in passing from original predictor raw scores to final criterion estimates can be partitioned more or less at will between the form of the predictor equation and adjustments of the predictor scales.

We may conclude, then, that the availability of alternative predictor scales raises no methodological problems for prediction theory which differ in kind from questions about choice of a regression form. Since ideally we want our regression estimates to coincide as closely as possible with the criterion's contingent expectation, given the predictor data, but are obliged in practice to work with regression forms in a small number of parameters, the optimal choice of predictor scales from among the practical alternatives is the one which, with respect to the criterion of concern, eventuates in an unrestricted curvilinear regression surface of the simplest possible form, hopefully linear. (By the "practical alternatives" for the predictor scales, we recognize that while any one-one transformation of the scale in which a variable initially arises is admissible in principle, in practice we will be able or willing to consider only a few of the simpler transformations.) More generally, if there exist scalings for a set of predictors which simultaneously reduce the unrestricted curvilinear regressions of a large number of different criteria upon these predictors to what, on the whole, are simpler forms than what can be achieved through any other scalings of the predictors, then on statistical grounds, at least, these are the "natural" scales for these variables. If this "simple-surface" standard for selecting scales is to be properly implemented, however, the effect of the criterion's scale on its regression curvature must also be considered, and this raises difficulties which are not so easy to resolve.

The reason why the scaling of criteria poses special problems for error-minimizing prediction policies is simply that the predictions so derived do, in fact, generally differ according to the manner in which the criterion is scaled, while there is nothing in the concept of minimal error which also favors one scale on which these errors can be minimized over another. To show this it will suffice to consider the simplest case where the available predictor data is only that the to-be-predicted score is randomly drawn from a population P in which the criterion's distribution is known, and where the "best" estimate is stipulated to be the one which minimizes standard error. Under this policy and with respect to this information, the best estimate $\hat{Y}$ of scaled criterion score Y is the arithmetic mean of **Y**'s distribution in P. Suppose, however, that **Y** were to be alternatively scaled as $\mathbf{Y}' = \psi(\mathbf{Y})$. Then this same policy applied to the distribution of $\mathbf{Y}'$ in P selects the arithmetic mean of $\mathbf{Y}'$ (which is equivalent to the ψ-mean—see Chapter 3, pp. 30f.—of **Y**) in P for its best estimate of the criterion, and the two predictions $\hat{Y}$ and $\hat{Y}'$ agree if and only if $\hat{Y}' = \psi(\hat{Y})$, i.e., if and only if $M_{\mathbf{Y}'} = \psi(M_{\mathbf{Y}})$. It is easily seen that $M_{\mathbf{Y}'} = \psi(M_{\mathbf{Y}})$ holds for any arbitrary distribution of **Y** if and only if the transformation $\mathbf{Y}' = \psi(\mathbf{Y})$ has form $\mathbf{Y}' = a + b\mathbf{Y}$. Hence except for fluke couplings of a particular ψ with just the right **Y**-distribution, the error-minimizing estimate of the criterion based on its **Y**-scale agrees with the corresponding estimate computed from its $\mathbf{Y}'$-scale if and only if the one is a linear transformation of the other. The cause of this effect, about which we shall have more to say in a moment, is that prediction errors which are equal on one scale of the criterion are in general no longer equal after a nonlinear transformation of that scale. That is, nonlinear rescalings alter the relative importance of the various possible combinations of prediction and outcome.

But if, apart from adjustments in reference point and unit of measurement, a change in the criterion's scale also modifies the error-minimizing predictions we make thereof, what scale *should* we choose? For example, suppose that we wish to forecast a man's income just prior to retirement from his grades in high school. Should we simply scale income in dollars or might we not feel more comfortable in using a nonlinear transformation of the dollar scale which gives a little less weight to the upper extremity of this highly skewed distribution? Or in sensory-discrimination research on, say, the relation between the sound level to which a person is adapted and the minimal increment in noise which he can detect, why should we measure this increment as a difference on the customary decibel scale rather than on the original scale of physical energy from which the decibel rating is derived logarithmically? Or when computing a student's grade-point average, what are the proper conversions from letter grades to numerical equivalents—should, e.g., the numerical difference between C^+ and B^- be less than, equal to, or greater than the difference between C^+ and straight C? Unfortunately, the theory of scaling has not as yet progressed to the point where such uncertainties can be comfortably resolved, and here we can do no more than to offer a glimpse of the problem's nature.

Let $\boldsymbol{\alpha}$ be a set of attributes which are mutually exclusive and exhaustive over some population P while variable **A** is a scaled counterpart of set $\boldsymbol{\alpha}$ such that for each attribute α in $\boldsymbol{\alpha}$, there is a numerical value A of **A** which represents α. (For example, $\boldsymbol{\alpha}$ might be the set of all possible heights while **A** is the Height-in-inches variable on which a value of, say, 60 represents the height attribute which can variously be described as "being 60 inches tall," "being 5.0 feet tall," "being twice as tall as 30 inches," etc.) Let it also be supposed that there is some meaningful sense in which all possible pairs of attributes from $\boldsymbol{\alpha}$ can be ranked (ties permissible) according to the degree of similarity or approximity between the elements in the pair. (E.g., a height of 62.0 inches more closely resembles a height of 5.0 feet than a height of 3.0 inches resembles a height of 3.0 yards.) Then variable **A** may be said to be a "metrical scale," or more briefly a *metric*, for the set $\boldsymbol{\alpha}$ if for any attributes α_h, α_i, α_j, and α_k in $\boldsymbol{\alpha}$ represented by scale values A_h, A_i, A_j, and A_k, respectively, the similarity between α_h and α_i is greater than that between α_j and α_k if and only if the numerical difference between A_h and A_i is greater in magnitude than that between A_j and A_k.[17] Any linear transformation of a metrical scale for $\boldsymbol{\alpha}$ is likewise a metric for $\boldsymbol{\alpha}$, while if the attributes in $\boldsymbol{\alpha}$ are sufficiently numerous (to be technically precise, if they are densely ordered), one metric for $\boldsymbol{\alpha}$ with respect to the given similarity rankings can be transformed into another *only* by a linear transformation.

Now, the procedure by which regression theory or any similar approach to estimation derives its prediction policies is to survey the array of predictive inaccuracies anticipated under each of the policies in the

[17] This introduction of the notion of "metric" scarcely begins to do it justice. While the application of this term has no precisely established boundaries, it must be considered to extend at least to multidimensional scales with non-Euclidian distance measures.

class from which selection is to be made and to choose the one whose overall prospective inaccuracy is least. For assessing this, moreover, the degree of inaccuracy for a particular combination of prediction $\hat{Y}$ and outcome Y on scaled criterion $\mathbf{Y}$ is represented by the magnitude of the numerical difference between these scale values in such fashion that the smaller the difference $|\mathbf{Y}-\hat{\mathbf{Y}}|$ for a particular prediction, the more adequate the estimate is judged to be as an approximation. (Specifically, the inaccuracy rating assigned to each alternative prediction policy is a function only of the distribution of errors $|\mathbf{Y}-\hat{\mathbf{Y}}|$ under that policy, while any decrease in the probability of one or more larger values of $|\mathbf{Y}-\hat{\mathbf{Y}}|$ at the expense of increasing the probabilities of smaller values decreases the inaccuracy measure.[18]) Thus error-minimizing prediction policies, regression estimates in particular, are based on a dissimilarity ordering of pairs of criterion values in accord with the magnitude of their numerical scale differences and hence in effect treat this scale as a metric for the criterion. That is, confronted with the need to select one particular scale for the criterion from among all the available alternatives, the internal logic of regression theory dictates that numerical differences on the chosen scale have a metrical interpretation not (in general) possessed by scale differences on nonlinear transformations thereof.

However, regression analysis only *presupposes* that the adopted criterion scale is a metric with respect to predictive inaccuracy. It authorizes no decisions about which of various nonlinearly related alternative scales may in fact have this property. The trouble is, no firm standards for this judgment are available elsewhere, either. What is needed is a way to assess the relative similarity between any two attributes in the criterion set regardless of how these may have been scaled, and this, in turn, requires that we have first of all some idea of what we *mean* by such a comparison of similarities among values of this particular criterion. (It is, of course, quite possible for the sense of similarity to differ from one variable to another, or to be lacking altogether in some cases. Moreover, while differences among a variable's values can readily be ranked by psychophysical methods in which human judges exhibit their intuitive reactions, it may well be questioned whether the claim that the difference between attributes α_h and α_i is greater than the difference between attributes α_j and α_k is properly to be equated with the claim that over 50% of the persons in a certain group of judges think this to be so.) Actually, this fundamental question of what it is that confers metrical meaning is one which, with a few exceptions,[19] has been profoundly neglected in the

[18] Actually, it would not affect the argument if the measure of overall inaccuracy were a function of the direction of the differences $Y-\hat{Y}$ as well as of their magnitude. The essential point is that it is scale differences alone which determine the solution for the "best" prediction policy.

[19] The metricization of time and space has been argued extensively by philosophers and physicists, though still not to any well-accepted resolution. For a recent comprehensive discussion, see Grünbaum (34).

literature and we shall not attempt to redress the deficiency here. What usually happens in practice is that certain scales turn out for one reason or another (perhaps no more than the inertia of tradition) to be more convenient than their alternatives, and we proceed to work with these preferred scales *as though* they are metrics. One such "convenience," in particular, is sufficiently provocative to warrant special attention. This occurs when a scale **Y** can be found for the criterion which reduces its joint distribution with other variables to a more orderly form than is achieved by nonlinear alternatives to the **Y**-scale. Contrary to first expectation, the most impressive simplicity feature is not the shape of **Y**'s regression upon the other variables (since this is influenced by the scalings of the latter as well), but regularity in the contingent distributions of **Y**. In particular, whatever marginal distribution **Y** may have, if its contingent distributions given the various possible combinations of predictor scores more and more approach homoscedastic normality (or possibly some other constant shape and variance) as more and more predictors are considered—a condition which, if it exists, would be spoiled by replacing **Y** with a nonlinear transformation thereof—then we have a powerful statistical inducement to regard the **Y**-scale as "natural" for the criterion. The reasoning is rather similar to that behind inferential factoring: A scaling of the criterion which exhibits a striking regularity for which there is no mathematical necessity must surely reflect some special feature of reality which is obscured by scalings which do not preserve this orderliness. What contingent homoscedastic normality (or other contingent regularities) may signify about the attributes so scaled, and the relevance of this for the possible metrical properties of the scale, are matters which we must leave to the reader's own brooding.

Actually, it is altogether possible that no scale which is metrical even by the most liberal intuitive standards can be found for the criterion with which we are concerned. One can still make regression estimates of the scaled criterion in such a case, but there is then no meaningful sense in which these are systematically "better" than estimates obtained in any other way. This unpleasant prospect is conspicuously realized when, in particular, the criterion is a *categorical* ("qualitative") variable—i.e., a variable which has a finite (usually small) number of values which, moreover, do not fall into any significant one-dimensional order. Suppose, for example, that we wish to make prenatal predictions of an infant's sex and blood type based on, say, interuterine activity, X-ray observations of the foetal skeleton, biological traits of the parents, and other possibly relevant data. How might these variables be estimated by regression principles? The primary obstacle is not, as one might at first suppose, that we normally list the values of the Sex variable as *male* and *female*, and the values of the Blood-type variable as A, B, AB, and O,[20] none

[20] We disregard the rare cases of intersexes and the fact that in medical practice the concept of "blood type" includes a great many more dimensions of agglutination behavior than the familiar classification recognized here.

of which remotely resembles anything that can be cranked out of an algebraic equation. With spotless propriety, we can simply stipulate that variable **S** is a numerical scale for Sex on which, say, values of 1 and 0 represent *male* and *female*, respectively, while **T** is a numerical scale for Blood-type on which a value of 1 corresponds to type *O*, 2 corresponds to type *A*, 3 to type *B*, and 4 to type *AB*. Then regression estimates of **S** and **T** can be computed just as readily from numerically scaled predictor data as this can be done for estimates of, say, Birth-weight-in-grams.

There are, however, two complications which arise for the interpretation of such estimates. The first, which is surmountable, also affects indisputably quantitative scales such as Birth-order and Number-of-toes on which numbers that actually signify possible values of the variable are scattered discretely along the real-number continuum. This is that the criterion's regression estimate will seldom be a number which actually represents any criterion attribute. For example, the arithmetic means of Sex scale **S**, Blood-type scale **T**, and the Number-of-toes variable among children of mothers who were 38 years old at the time of conception might be .61, 3.12, and 9.87, respectively. It seems unreasonable to predict for the unborn child of a 38-year-old mother that its sex will have an **S**-scale value of .61, its blood type a **T**-scale value of 3.12, and that it will have 9.87 toes, since we cannot imagine what it would be like for any of these predictions to come literally true. In practice, we would implicitly or explicitly round off these and similar regression estimates to the numerically nearest occurrent value—e.g., the unborn child of a 38-year-old mother would be predicted to have an **S**-scale score of 1 (*male*), a **T**-scale score of 3 (blood-type *B*), and to have ten toes—and it is easily seen that this procedure minimizes the standard error of estimate when predictions are restricted to genuinely possible values of the criterion. (That is, this is easily seen for unrestricted curvilinear regression. The argument is somewhat more complicated when restricted regression forms are involved, though the conclusion is essentially the same. This *de facto* adjustment to occurrent values, incidentally, also implies that the effective standard error in such cases is somewhat greater than regression theory computes.) Moreover, a regression estimate's failure to correspond to any genuine criterion possibility does not at all interfere with treating that number as the center of an interval estimate, though of course a precise interval estimate at a known confidence level requires more information about the joint distribution of criterion and predictors than just the regression equation.

However, while application of regression principles to prediction of discrete-valued criteria requires only minor technical adjustments, regression estimates of numerically scaled categorical variables such as **S** and **T** also suffer from a fundamental conceptual absurdity in that there is no meaningful connection between anticipated predictive accuracy and the scaled categorical criterion's standard error of estimate. Of our two present examples, the **T**-scale illustrates this most clearly, since **S** has the important property, unique to dichotomies, that all its alternative scales are linear transformations of one another, one consequence of which is that for any orthodox regression form F, a dichotomous criterion's F-form regression estimates, rounded off to the numerically nearest occurrent value, are unaffected by how the criterion is scaled. If minimizing standard error is a suitable procedure for selecting a **T**-scale prediction policy, then predicting a blood type of, say, O (i.e., a **T**-scale value of 1) must be more accurate when the subject's actual blood type is A (**T**-scale value 2) than when it is B (**T**-scale value 3), while predicting a blood type of A for a person whose correct type is AB has precisely the same inaccuracy as predicting type B for a type-O subject (i.e., a **T**-scale error of 2 in both cases). But while there is no reason *in principle* why discrepancies between blood types might not be so rankable (this could, for example, reflect the transfusion danger of mistaking one blood type for another), there is in fact no operational significance that we are currently able to bestow upon a claim that the difference between two given blood types is less than, equal to, or greater than the difference between two others (or at least no such comparisons are known which can be represented by numerical differences on a one-dimensional scale). To put the objection more abstractly, we can arbitrarily choose any four different numbers n_O, n_A, n_B, and n_{AB} and define a blood-type scale $\mathbf{T}^*$ on which blood type $t (t = O, A, B, AB)$ is represented by scale value n_t. Let "$\{\mathbf{T}^*\}$" designate the class of all such possible blood-type scales. Then for any blood type t, any set of scores $X_1, \ldots, X_n$ on predictor variables $\mathbf{X}_1, \ldots, \mathbf{X}_n$, respectively, and a given (nondegenerate) regression form F, there is a scale in $\{\mathbf{T}^*\}$ (in fact, an infinitude of them) whose F-form regres. sion on the predictors has value n_t at data-point $X_1, \ldots, X_n$.[21] Thus regression theory will convert a given constellation of predictor data into any estimate of blood type we choose, dependent on how we elect to scale the criterion—and there are no grounds other than personal whim on which to prefer one of these scales to another. Clearly, then, while procedures designed to minimize the prospective error of estimate are technically applicable to numerically scaled categorical criteria, it makes no sense to use them when differences among the scale values are arbitrary.

Even so, there are ways in which categorical variables can be usefully treated by regression analysis. Specifically, there exist at least two mean-

[21] For all but the more bizarre regression forms, the F-form regression estimate of $\mathbf{T}^*$ at data-point $X_1, \ldots, X_n$ is a continuous, unbounded function of the scale value n_t assigned to each occurrent (i.e., nonzero frequency) blood type t. Hence so long as there are at least three occurrent blood types, one can be given a fixed scale value while the scale values are adjusted to put the F-form regression estimate of $\mathbf{T}^*$ at $X_1, \ldots, X_n$ equal to the former. (Three occurrent values are needed to prevent the solution from possibly demanding the same scale value for different blood types.)

ingful interpretations of the regressed components of unit-dichotomous criteria, which interpretations can also be extended to the more general case by replacing an m-valued categorical variable with a set of $m - 1$ unit-dichotomies or, more symmetrically, with m unit-dichotomous variables whose dimensionality is $m - 1$.[22] The first of these interpretations is suggested by reliability theory and requires a pair of suppositions. Let $\mathbf{Y}$ be a unit-dichotomous variable whose true-score component is $\mathbf{p_Y}$. That is, we assume that each subject i who can be assessed on $\mathbf{Y}$ has his own individual probability p_{Y_i} of receiving a score of 1 on $\mathbf{Y}$, which is also the value of $\mathbf{Y}$ statistically expected for i and is hence i's true score on $\mathbf{Y}$. Then if it is also assumed that $\mathbf{Y}$ is statistically independent of predictors $\mathbf{X_1}, \ldots, \mathbf{X_n}$ within each subject's joint probability distribution for these variables—that is, if measurement errors on $\mathbf{Y}$ are fully independent of measurement errors on $\mathbf{X_1}, \ldots, \mathbf{X_n}$ for each subject so that $\mathbf{E_Y}$ $(= \mathbf{Y} - \mathbf{p_Y})$ has a contingent expectation of zero at every combination of predictor scores—then for any F, the F-form regression of $\mathbf{Y}$ upon $\mathbf{X_1}, \ldots, \mathbf{X_n}$ is identical with the F-form regression of $\mathbf{p_Y}$ upon $\mathbf{X_1}, \ldots, \mathbf{X_n}$. Hence if we are not dismayed by the assumptions noted, a regression estimate of a subject's score on a unit-dichotomous criterion $\mathbf{Y}$ may be interpreted as the corresponding regression estimate of his true score on $\mathbf{Y}$. Of course it may still be questioned whether the $\mathbf{p_Y}$-scale should properly be considered a metric, but at least the prospect of a metrical interpretation for the numerical differences among probabilities is not absurd at the outset. The accuracy with which $\mathbf{p_Y}$ is so predicted can also be computed if the reliability of $\mathbf{Y}$ is known, for it follows from principle [8.108] and the assumption about measurement errors that

$$r^2_{\mathbf{p_Y}\hat{\mathbf{Y}}} = \frac{r^2_{\mathbf{Y}\hat{\mathbf{Y}}}}{r_{\mathbf{Y}}},$$

where $\hat{\mathbf{Y}}$ is the F-form regression estimate of $\mathbf{Y}$ and $r_{\mathbf{Y}}$, it will be recalled, is the reliability of $\mathbf{Y}$. The reliability of $\mathbf{Y}$ also yields the variance of $\mathbf{p_Y}$, namely,

$$\begin{aligned} \sigma^2_{\mathbf{p_Y}} &= r_{\mathbf{Y}}\sigma^2_{\mathbf{Y}} \\ &= r_{\mathbf{Y}}(M_{\mathbf{Y}} - M^2_{\mathbf{Y}}) \end{aligned}$$

(from [8.35] and the stipulation that $\mathbf{Y}$ is unit-dichotomous) while of course $M_{\mathbf{p_Y}} = M_{\mathbf{Y}}$. Thus in particular, the unrestricted curvilinear regression of a unit-dichotomous criterion upon a given set of predictors, together with the criterion's reliability, provides us with a usefully detailed

---

[22] If the alternative values of categorical variable $\mathbf{Y}$ are $Y_1, \ldots, Y_m$, then $\mathbf{Y}$ is equivalent to the set of unit-dichotomous variables $\mathbf{Y_1}, \ldots, \mathbf{Y_m}$ where the value of a subject's score on $\mathbf{Y_i}$ is 1 or 0 according to whether or not his $\mathbf{Y}$-category is Y_i. Since each subject belongs to exactly one of the categories $Y_1, \ldots, Y_m$, it then also follows that $\sum_{i=1}^{m} \mathbf{Y_i} = 1$.

picture of how individual response probabilities on **Y** are related to these predictors. All that remains unspecified, in fact, are the shapes of the contingent distributions of $\mathbf{p}_Y$, given $\mathbf{X}_1, \ldots, \mathbf{X}_n$, and the extent of their homoscedasticity.

For an even more seemly interpretation of a dichotomous criterion's regressed component, we recall that in principle, prediction is a two-stage process which first converts the available information into a probability distribution for the to-be-predicted score and then decides what course of predictive action is most desirable in light of these probabilities. Only the derivation of the criterion's contingent probability distribution is purely a cognitive judgment—the final decision about what to predict depends critically upon the personal interests of whoever happens to be making the prediction. To establish some semblance of interpersonal predictive accord, it is convenient to adopt the standard error of estimate as a more or less conventional measure of anticipated predictive accuracy and to define the "best" (utility-free) estimate of the criterion as that choice of prediction which minimizes this measure. Not only is this convention especially felicitous mathematically, it also derives predictions which are generally close approximations to the optimal decision-theoretical results so long as the loss of utility due to an incorrect prediction is a function only of the magnitude of error (see pp. 69f.). It is also possible, however, to reserve predictive judgment and attend merely to the cognitive operation of converting predictor data into contingent criterion probabilities—which is precisely what regression theory amounts to in its purely statistical conception: The arithmetic mean of criterion **Y**, given scores $X_1, \ldots, X_n$ on predictors $\mathbf{X}_1, \ldots, \mathbf{X}_n$, respectively, is given by the value of the unrestricted curvilinear regression of **Y** upon the $\mathbf{X}_i$ at data-point $X_1, \ldots, X_n$, while the (absolute curvilinear) standard error of estimate $\sigma_{Y,X_1 \ldots X_n}$ is an approximation to the contingent standard deviation of **Y**, given $X_1, \ldots, X_n$ which becomes exact as the contingent distributions approach homoscedasticity. Further, if $\hat{\mathbf{Y}} = f_F(\mathbf{X}_1, \ldots, \mathbf{X}_n)$ is the F-form regression of **Y** upon the $\mathbf{X}_i$, $f_F(X_1, \ldots, X_n)$ approximates the contingent mean of **Y**, given data-constellation $X_1, \ldots, X_n$, and is so exactly if the unrestricted curvilinear regression of **Y** upon the $\mathbf{X}_i$ happens to be of form F. This still leaves open the shapes of the contingent criterion distributions, but in most cases where regression analysis makes sense at all these should be approximately normal or perhaps some other shape whose specification can be added to the regression information. Likewise, if the contingent distributions stray appreciably from homoscedasticity, it may be possible to find a convenient approximation to the equation $\sigma_{Y|X_1 \ldots X_n} = \phi(\mathbf{X}_1, \ldots, \mathbf{X}_n)$ whose value for a data-point $X_1, \ldots, X_n$ is the contingent standard deviation of **Y**, given these data. Thus if the joint distribution of criterion and predictors is sufficiently orderly, regression theory shows how the contingent probabilities of the criterion, given the predictor data, can be extracted (or at least approximated) from the latter by a few simple calculations.

When regression theory is relieved of responsibility for making final predictions (i.e., decisions), moreover, the problem of scaling becomes much less formidable. If **Y** and **Y**′ are alternative numerical scales for the same criterion, then the contingent distribution of **Y**′ given any constellation of predictor scores is fully determined by the distribution of **Y** given these same data, and conversely. Hence it makes no difference in principle which scale we adopt, and the choice can be dictated wholly by convenience. Since variation in the shapes of the contingent distributions is the most awkward irregularity for regression analysis to cope with, the most desirable scale for the criterion is one on which the criterion's contingent distributions have the same shape for every combination of predictor scores. Excluding degenerate cases, if such a scale exists it is unique up to a linear transformation. An alternative possibility, not necessarily incompatible with the first and likewise generally unique up to a linear transformation if it can be realized at all, is a scale on which the criterion's contingent distributions are homoscedastic. (In practice, equality of contingent variances is considerably easier to search for than sameness of contingent shapes, while if the former can be found it is not unlikely that the latter will also hold at least approximately.) To be sure, remission of the requirement that the criterion's scale be a metric does not much improve the generic applicability of regression analysis to polychotomous categorical criteria, since when the criterion has three or more cateories which fall into no metrically significant order, it is exceedingly unlikely that a criterion scale can be found on which the contingent means and SDs, given the predictor data, reveal much about the contingent probabilities of the various criterion categories. However, in the special case of dichotomous criteria (and derivatively for m-valued categorical variables when these are made over into a set of dichotomies), the contingent distribution of the criterion, given the predictor data, is completely specified by the probability of one designated value of the criterion (either one will do), given these data, while if the criterion is scaled numerically, this probability is a linear function of the criterion's contingent expectation. In particular, if the two categories of dichotomy **Y** are scored 1 and 0, respectively (i.e., if **Y** is unit-dichotomous), then the value $M_{\mathbf{Y}|X_1 \ldots X_n}$ of **Y**'s curvilinear regression upon predictors $\mathbf{X_1}, \ldots, \mathbf{X_n}$ at data-point $X_1, \ldots, X_n$ equals the contingent probability that **Y** has the value 1, given data $X_1, \ldots, X_n$, while the probability that **Y** has value 0 given these data is $1 - M_{\mathbf{Y}|X_1 \ldots X_n}$. Thus the (unrestricted) curvilinear regression of a dichotomous criterion upon its predictors tells all there is to know about the criterion's contingent distributions given these predictors, while the criterion's F-form regression on these predictors approximates this information to the extent that the unrestricted regression surface approximates form F.

The Varieties of Relational Analysis

The fact that not all data arrays are prima facie amenable to analysis by regression techniques has by no means gone unheeded by scientists and statisticians. A number of conceptual schemes for dissecting multivariate configurations have arisen during the past few decades, the differences among which originate largely, though by no means entirely, in the scaling distinction between metrical and categorical variables—or, as it is commonly but obscurely put, between "quantitative" and "qualitative" variables. The major varieties of these analytic procedures (not to be confused with explanatory models) are classified in Table 10.1 according to the types of scales to which they are most appropriate, though none is rigidly restricted to the category in which it is tabled. We have already discussed regression analysis at length. The descriptions which follow attempt to convey some perspective on the overall methodological character of the remainder of these methods, but make no consistent effort to develop technical detail.

Analysis of Variance and Analysis of Covariance.[23] While in a broad sense the phrase "analysis of variance" subsumes any technique by which the variance of a dependent variable is partitioned into components attributed to various sources, this title is most commonly reserved for certain specialized albeit extraordinarily versatile methods of experimental design and statistical analysis introduced in the 1920s by R. A. Fisher. Fisherian Analysis of Variance and Analysis of Covariance are species of the same generic mathematical theory that also subsumes regression

		Dependent Variables	
		Metrical criteria	Categorical criteria
Independent Variables	Metrical predictors	Regression analysis (including descriptive factor analysis)	Discriminant analysis
		Analysis of Covariance	
Independent Variables	Categorical predictors	Analysis of Variance	Information theory (i.e., Uncertainty analysis)

Table 10.1. The major varieties of relational analysis, listed according to the types of scales to which they are most directly applicable. These methods of *analysis*, which are purely descriptive techniques for examining what patterns of relationship there may be within a multivariate configuration, should not be confused with *explanatory models*, which are interpretive hypotheses about these distributions.

[23] A definitive theoretical treatment of Analysis of Variance and Analysis of Covariance is available in Scheffé (73), while Winer (87) provides a handbook of operationally detailed designs covering an exceptionally wide variety of specific applications.

analysis.[24] The fact that the former deal primarily with categorical rather than metrical predictors (see Table 10.1) is only a superficial distinction, since as observed a few pages back, the independent variables in a regression analysis can be scaled in whatever fashion is most pleasing to the investigator, so that in principle, regression theory can assimilate categorical predictors as readily as it can process predictors whose scales are obviously metrics. (That is, while regression analysis requires that the independent variables be scaled numerically if regression surfaces of restricted form are to be computed, it does not make use of any metrical properties these scales may possess.) However, Analysis-of-Variance designs differ from ordinary regression analysis in several important respects. Contrary to the latter, Analysis of Variance has no need to scale the independent variables numerically—even when the predictors do, in fact, have quantitative values (which, though irrelevant, is perfectly permissible), Analysis of Variance makes no use of these numbers as such. Further, instead of addressing itself to predictor distributions as they arise naturally, as is common though not essential in regression analysis, Analysis of Variance restricts itself to a (usually) controlled number of observations under each of a small finite selection of the possible combinations of predictor values, where the latter are (usually) so chosen that within the observed distribution, each predictor variable is statistically independent of the others. Finally, Analysis of Variance introduces a concept of "interaction" among predictors in their effect on the dependent variable which is not found as such in regression analysis, though there is a close connection between interaction terms in a Fisherian variance partition and the cross-product components of a nonlinear regression surface.

To illustrate the pattern of Analysis-of-Variance thinking, suppose that we wish to investigate the possible relevance of an infant's sex and racial type for his weight at birth. While the concept of "race" has never been clearly defined, there is no special trouble in devising operational procedures which will allow us to label some babies as "caucasoid," some as "negroid," and still others as "mongoloid," which, let us say, are considered to be a sufficient number of racial distinctions for our study. These three categories need not be so defined that every human is forced into one of them, for typically an Analysis-of-Variance design investigates only a few of the (generally many) values of each predictor included in the analysis. Let the studied values of the Racial-type variable be denoted "*a*" (caucasoid), "*b*" (negroid), and "*c*" (mongoloid), while the two values of the Sex variable are designated "♂" (male) and "♀" (female). (In the algebraic development of Analysis of Variance, values of the predictors are normally designated by consecutive integers, but here we do otherwise to illustrate that numerical scaling is irrelevant.) These two

[24] See Scheffé (73), especially chapters 1 and 6.

predictor variables, one with three studied values and the other with two, jointly determine $3 \times 2 = 6$ conditions of observation, namely, ♂*a*, ♂*b*, ♂*c*, ♀*a*, ♀*b*, and ♀*c* (i.e., male caucasoid, etc.). We now identify the population *P* (here infants born in, say, a certain conveniently located hospital) within which we hope to learn the effect of our independent variables upon the criterion variable **Y** (here Birth-weight-in-grams), and contemplate sampling from *P* under each predictor combination $ij (i = ♂, ♀; j = a,b,c)$ in order to estimate the expected criterion score among members of *P* who are also in joint predictor category *ij*. This expectation is designated "μ_{ij}," i.e.,

$$[10.44\text{-}ij][25] \quad (i = ♂, ♀; j = a, b, c) \qquad \mu_{ij} =_{\text{def}} Exp\{Y \mid ij\} \ ,$$

where the expectation is for random choice of a member of *P* of sex *i* and racial type *j*, and is likewise the expected value of the mean on **Y** of a sample of size *n* randomly selected under these conditions.

So far, Analysis of Variance is conceptually no different from regression analysis, since the quantity μ_{ij}, considered as a function of the joint predictor categories, is equivalent to the unrestricted curvilinear regression of Birth-weight upon Sex and Racial-type in population *P*. What happens next, however, is tricky. Quantities $\mu_{..}$, $\mu_{i.}$, $\mu_{.j}$, and I_{ij} $(i = ♂, ♀; j = a, b, c)$ are introduced which in all cases stand in the relation

$$[10.45\text{-}ij] \quad (i = ♂, ♀; j = a, b, c) \qquad \mu_{ij} = \mu_{..} + (\mu_{i.} - \mu_{..}) + (\mu_{.j} - \mu_{..}) + I_{ij} \ ,$$

but the definitions of these terms (which, as components of **Y**'s contingent expectation, are also analytic components of **Y**) can be accomplished in a variety of ways. Most commonly by far, $\mu_{..}$ is taken to be the arithmetic mean of μ_{ij} over all predictor combinations *ij* included in the study (i.e., here $\mu_{..} = (1/6)(\mu_{♂a} + \mu_{♂b} + \mu_{♂c} + \mu_{♀a} + \mu_{♀b} + \mu_{♀c})$), $\mu_{i.}$ is taken to be the mean μ_{ij} over all studied *j* with *i* fixed (i.e., here $\mu_{♂.} = (1/3)(\mu_{♂a} + \mu_{♂b} + \mu_{♂c})$ and $\mu_{♀.} = (1/3)(\mu_{♀a} + \mu_{♀b} + \mu_{♀c})$) and similarly for $\mu_{.j}$, while $\mathbf{I}_{ij}$ is defined to be what remains in μ_{ij} unaccounted for by the other components, i.e., from [10.45],

$$[10.46\text{-}ij] \quad (i = ♂, ♀; j = a, b, c) \qquad I_{ij} =_{\text{def}} \mu_{ij} - (\mu_{i.} - \mu_{..}) - (\mu_{.j} - \mu_{..}) - \mu_{..} \ .$$

The constant $\mu_{..}$ is known as the criterion's *general mean* under this predictor layout, the quantities $(\mu_{i.} - \mu_{..})$ for the studied values of the first

[25] This notation, with at times some other symbol in place of "μ," is by now well established. It should be noted that while "μ_{ij}" designates the parametric mean of a criterion variable **Y** in a certain restricted population, the subscripts in Analysis-of-Variance notation refer *not* to the variable of which μ_{ij} is the expectation but to the population to which the expectation is restricted.

predictor (here Sex) are the *main effects* upon the criterion of this variable, the $(\mu_{.j} - \mu_{..})$ are similarly the "main effects" of the second predictor (Racial-type), and the I_{ij} are the predictors' joint *interaction effects.* In Analysis-of-Variance designs involving three or more independent variables, moreover, the joint interaction effects of all predictors are further partitioned into interaction components of various levels of complexity too intricate to be discussed here. The sampling theory of Analysis of Variance, which has attained a formidable degree of sophistication, undertakes to make judgments about the numerical values of these various "effects," especially in regard to whether the effects of a given kind are all the same. It is easily seen from the standard definitions of $\mu_{..}$, $\mu_{i.}$, $\mu_{.j}$, and I_{ij} just cited that the average $\mu_{i.}$ across the studied first-predictor conditions i and the average $\mu_{.j}$ across the studied second-predictor conditions j both equal $\mu_{..}$, while the average I_{ij} across all studied predictor combinations ij is zero; hence if the effects of a given kind—i.e., the main effects of either predictor or their interaction effects—all have a common value, that value must be zero. This property of zero effects is always built into Analysis-of-Variance components even when the latter are not defined by the simple unweighted averaging described here.

The mathematical significance of the "effect"-components of μ_{ij} in [10.45] can best be understood by considering their implications for the shape of the criterion's unrestricted regression upon Sex and Racial-type at the studied combinations of predictor values when the latter have been scaled numerically to yield the simplest possible regression surface. Suppose to begin with that the numerical values of the $\mu_{i.}$ are all different, and similarly for the $\mu_{.j}$. Also, let population P^* consist of just those members of P whose sex is either male or female and who meet the operational definition for being classified as either caucasoid, negroid, or mongoloid. That is, population P^* is a pruning of our base population P to exclude individuals who have predictor values not included in our study. Then we can define variables $\mathbf{X_1}$ and $\mathbf{X_2}$ as numerical scales for Sex and Racial-type, respectively, for members of P^* such that sex i (= ♂, ♀) is represented by the numerical value $\mu_{i.} - \mu_{..}$ on $\mathbf{X_1}$, and racial type j $(= a, b, c)$ is represented by score $\mu_{.j} - \mu_{..}$; while a numerical function $f_I(\mathbf{X_1}, \mathbf{X_2})$ of the scaled predictors can always be found such that $I_{ij} = f_I(\mu_{i.} - \mu_{..}, \mu_{.j} - \mu_{..})$ for all studied i and j. (In fact, $f_I(\mathbf{X_1}, \mathbf{X_2})$ can be chosen to be a low-degree polynomial, the chief requirement for this being that the fitted function contain as many parameters as there are predictor combinations ij.) Equation [10.45] is then equivalent to

$$[10.47] \qquad M_{\mathbf{Y}|\mathbf{X_1}\mathbf{X_2}} = \mu_{..} + \mathbf{X_1} + \mathbf{X_2} + f_I(\mathbf{X_1}, \mathbf{X_2}),$$

the applicability of which, however, is restricted to members of P^*, since no sexes other than ♂ and ♀, and no racial types other than a, b, and c, have been assigned representation by values of $\mathbf{X}_1$ and $\mathbf{X}_2$. If all the interaction terms I_{ij} are zero, the function $f_I(\mathbf{X}_1, \mathbf{X}_2)$ in [10.47] equals zero for all occurrent values of $\mathbf{X}_1$ and $\mathbf{X}_2$ in P^* and may be omitted—in which case $M_{\mathbf{Y}|\mathbf{X}_1\mathbf{X}_2}$ is a linear function of $\mathbf{X}_1$ and $\mathbf{X}_2$. Conversely, it can be shown that numerical scalings $\mathbf{X}_1'$ and $\mathbf{X}_2'$ exist for the two predictor variables in [10.45] such that $M_{\mathbf{Y}|\mathbf{X}_1'\mathbf{X}_2'} = b_0 + b_1\mathbf{X}_1' + b_2\mathbf{X}_2'$ in P^* only if the interactions I_{ij} are all zero.[26] Thus if the main effects of each predictor are all distinct, scales can be found for the predictors upon which the criterion's unrestricted regression in P^* is linear if and only if all the interaction effects of the predictors upon the criterion in P^* are zero.

To be sure, if the $\mu_{i.}$ (or similarly the $\mu_{.j}$) are *not* all distinct, they cannot be used to define a numerical scale for this predictor and it is then likewise impossible to find scales $\mathbf{X}_1'$ and $\mathbf{X}_2'$ for the predictor variables such that $M_{\mathbf{Y}|\mathbf{X}_1'\mathbf{X}_2'}$ is linear in $\mathbf{X}_1'$ and $\mathbf{X}_2'$ unless the coefficient of $\mathbf{X}_1'$ is zero. In the more general case, it may be shown that the interaction effects are all zero if and only if numerical scalings $\mathbf{X}_1$ and $\mathbf{X}_2$ exist for the occurrent predictor values in P^* such that

$$M_{\mathbf{Y}|\mathbf{X}_1\mathbf{X}_2} = \mu_{..} + f_1(\mathbf{X}_1) + f_2(\mathbf{X}_2) ,$$

where $f_k(\mathbf{X}_k)$ ($\mathbf{k} = 1,2$) is a polynomial in $\mathbf{X}_k$ whose degree equals the largest number of different occurrent values of $\mathbf{X}_k$ in P^* with the same main effect, and where $f_k(X_k)$ equals the main effect of predictor $\mathbf{X}_k$ at occurrent value X_k. If the interactions are *not* all zero (or even, as a special case, when they are), [10.45] may be put into regression form

$$[10.48] \qquad M_{\mathbf{Y}|\mathbf{X}_1\mathbf{X}_2} = \mu_{..} + f_1(\mathbf{X}_1) + f_2(\mathbf{X}_2) + f_{12}(\mathbf{X}_1, \mathbf{X}_2) ,$$

where f_1, f_2, $\mathbf{X}_1$, and $\mathbf{X}_2$ are as just described and f_{12} is a polynomial such that $f_{12}(X_1, X_2)$ equals the interaction effect of occurrent predictor combination X_1, X_2. It may further be seen from [10.48] in this two-predictor case that the criterion's unrestricted regression upon the predictors is independent of one of them, say Sex, if and only if both the main effects of Sex *and* all the interaction terms are zero. When more than two predictors are included in an Analysis-of-Variance design, the conditions of unrelatedness are somewhat more complicated, since for the criterion to be independent of predictor $\mathbf{X}_k$ it is unnecessary for the interaction effects not involving $\mathbf{X}_k$ to be zero.

However, while the parallel between polynomic regression components and the various types of "effects" in an Analysis-of-Variance partition of the criterion is straightforward enough once these effects have been

[26] Using the standard definitions of $\mu_{..}$, $\mu_{i.}$ and $\mu_{.j}$ given above, it is easily computed that if $M_{\mathbf{Y}|\mathbf{X}_1'\mathbf{X}_2'}$ is linear in $\mathbf{X}_1'$ and $\mathbf{X}_2'$, then $\mu_{ij} = b_0 + b_1X_{1\,i}' + b_2X_{2\,j}'$. $\mu_{..} = b_0 + b_2\bar{X}_2' + b_2\bar{X}_2'$, $\mu_{i.} = b_0 + b_1X_{1\,i}' + b_2\bar{X}_2'$ and $\mu_{.j} = b_0 + b_1\bar{X}_1' + b_2X_{2\,j}'$, where $X_{1\,i}'$ is the value of $\mathbf{X}_1'$ representing Sex category i, $\bar{X}_1'$ is the average value of the X_{1i}', and similarly for X_{2j}' and $\bar{X}_2'$. Substitution into [10.46] then yields $I_{ij} = 0$.

defined, it does not appear to be sufficiently realized by devotees of Analysis of Variance that the statistical and/or causal interpretation of Analysis-of-Variance components is still methodologically obscure, especially when nonzero interactions are present in the data. For example, the docile student is encouraged, both by notation and by the usual context of presentation, to think that general mean $\mu_{..}$ is the unconditional expectation of criterion **Y** in base population P while $\mu_{i.}$ (and similarly for $\mu_{.j}$) is **Y**'s contingent expectation among members of P who also belong to category i of the first predictor—which in general just isn't so, not even if P is replaced by the more restricted population P^* defined above. Rather, let population P^{**} be formed from the natural base population P by a twofold adjustment: (1) P^{**} contains only members of P who belong to one of the joint predictor categories included in the study (i.e., P includes only members of P^*), *and* (2) these categories are made equiprobable in P^{**}. That is, the contingent criterion distributions, given each combination of joint predictor scores, are the same in P^{**} as in P, but the probability in P^{**} of a particular predictor combination is $1/N$ if that combination is one of those included in the study, where N is the number of such combinations (six in our present example), and is zero otherwise.[27] (From this it follows that the predictors are fully independent of one another in P^{**} and that the frequency of each occurrent value of a given predictor in P^{**} equals one over the number of alternatives on this variable included in P^{**}.) Then $\mu_{..}$ is the unconditional expectation of **Y** in P^{**}, $\mu_{i.}$ is **Y**'s expectation among members of P^{**} in category i of the first predictor, and similarly for $\mu_{.j}$. It can further be shown that the total variance of **Y** in P^{**} partitions as a sum of three component variances corresponding to the three components of $\mathrm{M}_{\mathbf{Y}|\mathbf{X}_1\mathbf{X}_2}$ indicated in [10.48] plus a residual—i.e.,

$$\mathrm{Var}(\mathbf{Y}) = \mathrm{Var}[\mathrm{f}_1(\mathbf{X}_1)] + \mathrm{Var}[\mathrm{f}_2(\mathbf{X}_2)] + \mathrm{Var}[\mathrm{f}_{12}(\mathbf{X}_1, \mathbf{X}_2)] + \mathrm{Var}(\mathbf{e}_{\mathbf{Y}|\mathbf{X}_1\mathbf{X}_2})$$

in P^{**} (though *not*, in general, in P or P^*), which is why "Analysis of Variance" is so-named.

Now, interpreting Analysis-of-Variance "effects" as properties merely of the criterion's behavior in an artificially constructed population P^{**}, rather than in the natural base population P, is unsatisfactory on at least two counts. For one, if the predictor combinations which have nonzero incidence in P^{**} do not include all possible joint values on these predictors—i.e., if the Analysis-of-Variance layout does not include *all* possible alternatives on each predictor studied—then the numerical values of all effects $\mu_{..}$, $(\mu_{i.} - \mu_{..})$, $(\mu_{.j} - \mu_{..})$, and I_{ij} (and similarly when

[27] The equiprobability of occurrent predictor combinations in P^{**} can be relaxed so long as full independence among the predictors is maintained, but then the definitions for $\mu_{..}$, $\mu_{i.}$ and $\mu_{.j}$ given earlier have to be modified.

more than two predictors are involved) are in general influenced by the particular selection of predictor categories which has been adopted, in which case the Analysis-of-Variance components do not have a unique objective definition but remain ambiguously dependent upon conflicting tastes in predictor values from one investigator to another. This might not appear to be a serious complication in the setting of our present example, since only for rare purposes need sex be treated as more than a dichotomy, and we can always devise a caste system for pigeonholing all of humanity among a few racial categories even if occasional qualms arise about the classifications of persons with mixed ancestry or about the biological significance of the categories in the first place. In most Analysis-of-Variance research, however, the number of predictor categories which can actually be investigated in a single experiment is but a minor fraction of that variable's full array of possibilities, especially when the variable is basically quantitative in nature. One way to resolve these ambiguities in the definition of Analysis-of-Variance "effects" is to stipulate that in principle, P^{**} is an ideal modification of natural population P in which *all* logically possible predictor combinations occur with equal probability, while we then try to learn what we can about the values of these ideally defined effects by sampling on the predictor values. For example, it is easily seen that if all the interactions I_{ij} are zero in the ideal population P^{**}, they are also zero in a reduced population $P^{**\prime}$ formed by discarding some of the alternatives on one or more of the predictor variables, while in this case the algebraic differences among the main effects for retained values of a given predictor are the same in $P^{**\prime}$ as in P^{**}. However, while there are also other ways in which interaction effects may be sufficiently well-behaved to permit some judgments about the criterion's Analysis-of-Variance components in P^{**} from what is observed in a reduced $P^{**\prime}$, nonzero interactions present a formidable obstacle to inferences from a practical $P^{**\prime}$ to the ideal P^{**}.[28]

Further, even if the definitional ambiguity of Analysis-of-Variance effects is diminished by stipulating that the idealized population P^{**} in terms of which these effects are interpreted is to include all possible values of the studied predictors, major technical difficulties still bedevil the attempted definition of P^{**},[29] and in any event, if these components are to have any scientifically significant meaning, it should be possible to abstract them from the criterion's relation to the predictors in the natural

[28] In a recent symposium on the interpretation of interaction, Lubin (57) observes that "as the interaction decreases, the anxiety of the statistician diminishes at an ever-increasing rate." This goes double for the methodologist.

[29] An obvious complication arises if one or more of the studied predictors has an infinitude of alternative values. Also, the criterion's distribution in P^{**} is not unambiguously specified unless stipulations are made about the distribution in P^{**} of all variables additional to the ones explicitly recognized in the study—attempts at which, however, eventuate in some really horrendous conceptual snarls.

population P rather than in just the artificial construction P^{**}. That is, it is highly desirable that we find definitions for $\mu_{..}$, $(\mu_{i.} - \mu_{..})$, I_{ij}, etc., which identify them with properties of the joint distribution of criterion and predictors irrespective of what form the predictor distribution may take. Unfortunately, this desire has yet to be fully consummated. The most appealing prospect is to equate Analysis-of-Variance effects with the values of curvilinear regression components after the pattern of [10.48]. Given three arbitrarily scaled finite-valued predictors $\mathbf{X}_1$, $\mathbf{X}_2$, and $\mathbf{X}_3$, for example, a constant c and functions $f_1, \ldots, f_{123}$ can always be found for the joint distribution of $\mathbf{Y}$, $\mathbf{X}_1$, $\mathbf{X}_2$, and $\mathbf{X}_3$ in an arbitrary population P such that

[10.49]
$$M_{\mathbf{Y}|\mathbf{X}_1\mathbf{X}_2\mathbf{X}_3} = c + f_1(\mathbf{X}_1) + f_2(\mathbf{X}_2) + f_3(\mathbf{X}_3) + f_{12}(\mathbf{X}_1, \mathbf{X}_2) + f_{13}(\mathbf{X}_1, \mathbf{X}_3) + f_{23}(\mathbf{X}_2, \mathbf{X}_3) + f_{123}(\mathbf{X}_1, \mathbf{X}_2, \mathbf{X}_3),$$

which suggests that we should set general mean $\mu_{...}$ equal to c, main effect $(\mu_{i..} - \mu_{...})$ equal to the value of $f_1(\mathbf{X}_1)$ for the ith value of $\mathbf{X}_1$, and so on. To accomplish this, however, it is necessary to place additional restrictions on $c, f_1, \ldots, f_{123}$ in order that these be uniquely determined. One such restriction which has much to recommend it is that the criterion's residuals are to be minimized at each ascending level of complexity—i.e., that c is to minimize the standard error of $\hat{Y} = c$, that c, f_1, f_2, and f_3 are to minimize the standard error of $\hat{Y} = c + f_1(\mathbf{X}_1) + f_2(\mathbf{X}_2) + f_3(\mathbf{X}_3)$, etc. But this still leaves a plurality of alternative solutions for the f_i at each complexity level, and except for the ideal Fisherian case in which the predictors are fully independent of one another, a satisfactory standard for selecting a particular one of these solutions is still wanting.

Analysis-of-Variance designs have climbed to extraordinary heights of popularity within the past few decades of research in the behavioral sciences, in some areas to the near exclusion of other statistical methods. Whether the net scientific accomplishment of this development has been more gain than loss, however, is seriously debatable. Despite the haze which still lingers around its conceptual foundations, Analysis of Variance is an enormously powerful research tool when exploited wisely, but the indiscriminate applicability of its sophisticated veneer too readily abets slovenly thinking that could otherwise be shaping up under the press of critical scientific standards into more incisive research habits. Probably the most flagrant abuse of Analysis of Variance has been to mobilize its sampling-theoretical appurtenances for testing the "null hypothesis" that the main effects or interactions associated with certain predictors in which the investigator is interested are all zero in order to conclude with shrieks of delight that the null hypothesis is probably false, while making little if any attempt to estimate the numerical values of these apparently nonzero effects or to assess their scientific importance in the criterion's causal composition.[30] In fact, it is by no means unknown for "statistically significant" effects to be reported without even a concommitant description of the apparent nature of the relationship so implicated.

A more subtle danger from overindulgence in Analysis-of-Variance designed research is the potentially disastrous effect of this upon an empirical discipline's conceptual growth. One of the primal requisites for developing scientific knowledge which strikes through the confusion and uncertainty of commonsense belief is for the vague, coarsely drawn conceptual categories of everyday thought to be superceded by precise distinctions of much finer grain. With overwhelming regularity the history of science shows that research leading to novel phenomena, improved theories, and deepened understanding builds upon the tightly controlled exploration of small, carefully identified details. Rather than promoting attention to minutiae in the predictor variables, however, Analysis-of-Variance methodology actually discourages it. In the first place, research can be conducted under an Analysis-of-Variance layout just as readily when the predictor categories have been crudely and arbitrarily defined as when the nature of the predictor's values has been carefully thought out. Consequently, once a metricized criterion is available, Analysis of Variance places no demands on the researcher to increase the acuity with which he conceives his variables. Everyday distinctions will do, and no matter if it is not clear what to do with borderline cases, or what the full range of predictor alternatives may be, or whether our intuitive classifications under a given heading may not in fact be inconsistent or cut across and perhaps confound several importantly distinct dimensions of differentiation—we need simply make sure that the predictor categories included in the study are restricted to paradigm cases about which we feel minimal uncertainty, while anomalies which might otherwise shake our confidence in the whole conceptual scheme can then be shrugged off as lying outside the scope of the design. (Thus the three racial-type categories in our preceding example can stipulate pure blood lines without concern for what additional categories might be required to accommodate persons of mixed ancestry.) Worse, Analysis of Variance becomes increasingly unwieldy as the number of predictor categories grows large, both through the increasing scarcity of subjects available in any one category and through the enormous expenditure of effort required for simultaneous investigation of several predictors unless each is restricted to a very few studied values. Practical demands of Analysis-of-Variance methods thus urge the researcher to be frugal

[30] This particular malaise is not restricted to applications of Analysis of Variance, but is a pandemic methodological disease, spread by the "hypothesis-testing" virus, which emerges with particular virulence in the Analysis-of-Variance setting.

in the number of alternative values coutenanced for his predictor variables, with the result that in research based on such designs one is frequently treated to the unedifying retrograde spectacle of previously accomplished predictor refinements being deliberately smeared into less discriminating categories, as when a quantitative scale is partitioned into a few broad intervals whose powers of resolution are at about the same level as the commonsense trichotomy, "small," "medium," and "large."

Finally, a word about Analysis of Covariance which, it will be recalled, was coupled with Analysis of Variance in the heading of this section. Analysis of Covariance is an extension of Analysis of Variance which permits simultaneous investigation of the effect on the criterion of one or more metrical predictors whose sampled values are allowed to assume a more or less natural distribution, together with categorical predictors whose joint sample distribution is constrained as in Analysis of Variance. The Analysis-of-Covariance model presupposes that the unrestricted regression of criterion $\mathbf{Y}$ upon metricized predictors $\mathbf{W}_1, \ldots, \mathbf{W}_m$ and categorical predictors $\mathbf{X}_1, \ldots, \mathbf{X}_n$ can be analyzed in the form

$$[10.50] \quad M_{\mathbf{Y}|\mathbf{W}_1 \cdots \mathbf{W}_m \mathbf{X}_1 \cdots \mathbf{X}_n} = c + f_{\mathbf{W}}(\mathbf{W}_1, \ldots, \mathbf{W}_m) + f_{\mathbf{X}}(\mathbf{X}_1, \ldots, \mathbf{X}_n),$$

where the function $f_{\mathbf{W}}$ is usually, though not necessarily, assumed to be linear in the $\mathbf{W}_i$. (Since [10.50] allows for no interactions between the $\mathbf{W}_i$ and the $\mathbf{X}_j$, a regression decomposition of this form is not mathematically guaranteed to exist.) The joint categorical component $f_{\mathbf{X}}(\mathbf{X}_1, \ldots, \mathbf{X}_n)$ of $\mathbf{Y}$ is then further analyzed into main effects and interactions of ascending complexities as in orthodox Analysis of Variance.

Discriminant Analysis.[31] As alleged by Table 10.1, "discriminant analysis" is a method for estimating categorical criteria from metrical data. Fundamentally, the metrical properties of the predictor scales are superfluous, since what is required of the predictor scores is only that a computational procedure be available for extracting from them what information they may contain about the criterion. However, the distributional conditions under which discriminant analysis is most powerful, if forthcoming even approximately, also pretty well insure that a metrical interpretation of some sort can be found for the predictor scales. We have already had occasion in this chapter to consider regression estimates of categorical criteria (pp. 537–42) and the reader may find it useful to review these pages, for it is in discriminant analysis that the

---

[31] The present section attempts to provide no more than an overview of discriminant analysis. Unfortunately, the more detailed theory is as yet available only in fragments scattered throughout the technical literature. Anderson (3, pp. 126 f.) and Wilks (86, pp. 573 f.) are advanced sources through which the reader may gain access to this material See also Maxwell (59) and Tiedman, *et al.* (76), though distinctions between regression theory and discriminant analysis are drawn in the latter which are misleading unless read carefully.

positive prospects which finally emerged there after a bleak beginning reach full fruition.

In a "discrimination" (i.e., classification) problem, we are given (1) a set of m classification categories or groups $G_1, \ldots, G_m$ among which are partitioned the members of a population P, (2) the relative frequency of each category G_i in P, and (3) the joint distribution of numerically scaled predictor variables $\mathbf{X_1}, \ldots, \mathbf{X_n}$ in each subpopulation P_{G_i} $(i = 1, \ldots, m)$ comprising those members of P who fall into category G_i. That is, we start with a categorical variable **G** whose alternative values are $G_1, \ldots, G_m$, while the joint distribution of **G** and predictors $\mathbf{X_1}, \ldots, \mathbf{X_n}$ is available in the form of **G**'s marginal distribution in P together with the contingent joint distribution of $\mathbf{X_1}, \ldots, \mathbf{X_n}$ in P at each value of **G**. The ultimate challenge is then to estimate the **G**-category to which a member of P belongs, given his predictor scores. However, since this is a decision problem whose optimal solution requires consideration of utilities, discriminant analysis usually remains content to seek a purely cognitive conclusion which remains invariant under conflicting tolerances for the various possible misclassifications. And since the regression-theoretical expedient of deriving utility-free estimates by minimizing standard error is generally meaningless for a categorical criterion (see p. 539), the primary objective of discriminant analysis is thus to compute the probability of belonging to each category G_i conferred upon a member of P by his predictor scores. So stated, and with the requisite population statistics supplied in form (2) and (3) above, the problem is one of deriving "inverse probabilities." That is, we know the contingent probability (or probability density) of a member of P having predictor scores $X_1, \ldots, X_n$ when he belongs to category G_i, and we wish to turn this around into knowledge of the probability that he belongs to G_i given that his predictor scores are $X_1, \ldots, X_n$. If the "a priori" (i.e., marginal) probabilities of categories $G_1, \ldots, G_m$ in P are also available, as assumed in (2) above, then in principle the solution is exhaustively supplied by the deceptively simple equation known as *Bayes' Theorem*, namely,

$$[10.51]^{32} \quad \Pr(G_i \mid X_1 \ldots X_n) = \frac{\Pr(G_i X_1 \ldots X_n)}{\sum_{j=1}^{m} \Pr(G_j X_1 \ldots X_n)} = \frac{\Pr(G_i) \cdot \Pr(X_1 \ldots X_n \mid G_i)}{\sum_{j=1}^{m} \Pr(G_j) \cdot \Pr(X_1 \ldots X_n \mid G_j)},$$

[32] This is an immediate consequence of two elementary theorems in probability theory; (1) that the joint probability of two events A and B equals the probability of A times the probability of B given A, and (2) that the probability of A equals the sum of probabilities for A's joint occurrence with all the alternative possibilities for some other given type of event (i.e., in the simplest case, that the probability of A equals the joint probability of A and B plus the joint probability of A and not-B).

where $\Pr(G_i \mid X_1 \ldots X_n)$ is the probability that a member of P belongs to category G_i when his scores on predictor variables $\mathbf{X}_1, \ldots, \mathbf{X}_n$ are $X_1, \ldots, X_n$, respectively, $\Pr(X_1 \ldots X_n | G_i)$ is the probability (or probability density if the joint distribution of the $\mathbf{X}_i$ at data-point $X_1, \ldots, X_n$ in each category is continuous) of predictor configuration $X_1, \ldots, X_n$ among members of P who also belong to category G_i, $\Pr(G_i)$ is the unconditional probability of category G_i in population P, and $\Pr(G_i X_1 \ldots X_n)$ is the unconditional joint probability (or probability density) of category G_i and predictor scores $X_1, \ldots, X_n$ in P. In practice, unfortunately, the result of instantiating the right-hand side of [10.51] with specific distribution functions $\Pr(\mathbf{X}_1 \ldots \mathbf{X}_n \mid G_i)$ to obtain $\Pr(G_i \mid \mathbf{X}_1 \ldots \mathbf{X}_n)$ as a numerically determinate function of predictor variables $\mathbf{X}_1, \ldots, \mathbf{X}_n$ is as a rule excessively unwieldy, even when the contingent joint distributions of $\mathbf{X}_1, \ldots, \mathbf{X}_n$ given $\mathbf{G}$ are ideally well-behaved. Thus the Bayes' solution to the classification problem reveals that there is no general algebraically docile formula for optimal processing of the predictor data. Even so, a remarkable simplification of the solution occurs when there are only two criterion categories and the joint predictor distributions within them are both normal with the same covariance matrix, and it is under these special conditions that discriminant analysis is most effective.

Consider to begin with the simplest possibility under the distributional conditions just cited: Suppose that $\mathbf{G}$ is a dichotomous criterion whose values G_1 and G_2 are such that the joint distribution of predictor variables $\mathbf{X}_1, \ldots, \mathbf{X}_n$ in each subpopulation P_{G_i} $(i = 1, 2)$ of P is normal with zero intercorrelations and variances equal to the same constant σ^2, and that with the exception of $\mathbf{X}_1$, moreover, the mean of each predictor $\mathbf{X}_j$ ($\mathbf{j} = \mathbf{2}, \ldots, \mathbf{n}$) is the same in both P_{G_1} and P_{G_2}. Then within both to-be-discriminated subpopulations P_{G_1} and P_{G_2}, the joint distributions of $\mathbf{X}_2, \ldots, \mathbf{X}_n$ are identical while $\mathbf{X}_1$ is fully independent of the other predictors.[33] It is clear in this special case that which of the two $\mathbf{G}$-categories, G_1 or G_2, a member of P belongs to makes no difference for the likelihood of his having one array of scores on predictors $\mathbf{X}_2, \ldots, \mathbf{X}_n$ rather than another; hence, conversely, data on predictors $\mathbf{X}_2, \ldots, \mathbf{X}_n$ are of no help at all, either by themselves or as a supplement to data on predictor $\mathbf{X}_1$, for judging the subject's $\mathbf{G}$-category.[34] On the other hand, since by hypothesis the expected value of $\mathbf{X}_1$ in P_{G_1} differs from the expectation of $\mathbf{X}_1$ in P_{G_2}, a subject's score on $\mathbf{X}_1$ does make a difference for

[33] When $\mathbf{X}_1, \ldots, \mathbf{X}_n$ have a joint normal distribution in a population P_k, the contingent distributions of $\mathbf{e}_{\mathbf{X}_1 \cdot \mathbf{X}_2 \ldots \mathbf{X}_n}$ are the same at each combination $X_2, \ldots, X_n$ of values on $\mathbf{X}_2, \ldots, \mathbf{X}_n$. If, moreover, the covariance of $\mathbf{X}_1$ with each additional predictor $\mathbf{X}_i$ ($\mathbf{i} = \mathbf{2}, \ldots, \mathbf{n}$) is zero, so that $\mathbf{X}_{1(\mathbf{X}_2 \ldots \mathbf{X}_n)} = \mathrm{M}_{\mathbf{X}_1 | \mathbf{X}_2 \ldots \mathbf{X}_n} = \mathrm{M}_{\mathbf{X}_1}$, it follows that the contingent distributions of $\mathbf{X}_1$, given $\mathbf{X}_2, \ldots, \mathbf{X}_n$ in P_k are all identical with the marginal (i.e., unconditional) distribution of $\mathbf{X}_1$ in P_k.

[34] When $\mathbf{X}_1$ is fully independent of $\mathbf{X}_2, \ldots, \mathbf{X}_n$ in both subpopulations P_{G_1} and P_{G_2}, $\Pr(X_1 \ldots X_n | G_i) = \Pr(X_1 | G_i) \cdot \Pr(X_2 \ldots X_n | G_i)$ $(i = 1, 2)$, while if the joint distribution

whether he is from P_{G_1} or from P_{G_2}. How this is so can best be seen with the aid of Figure 10.1, which shows the assumed distribution of $\mathbf{X_1}$ (there renamed **L**) in each of the two classification categories. The curves are drawn with unequal areas, corresponding to a presumed difference (as would generally be the case) between the unconditional probabilities of the two categories in P, so that the height of the distribution curve for subpopulation P_{G_i} $(i = 1, 2)$ at each value X_1 of $\mathbf{X_1}$ is equal to the joint probability (more precisely, the joint probability density) of category G_i and predictor score X_1 in P, namely $\Pr(G_i X_1)$ or $\Pr(G_i) \cdot \Pr(X_1 \mid G_i)$. It is evident in Figure 10.1 that the larger is a subject's score on $\mathbf{X_1}$, the

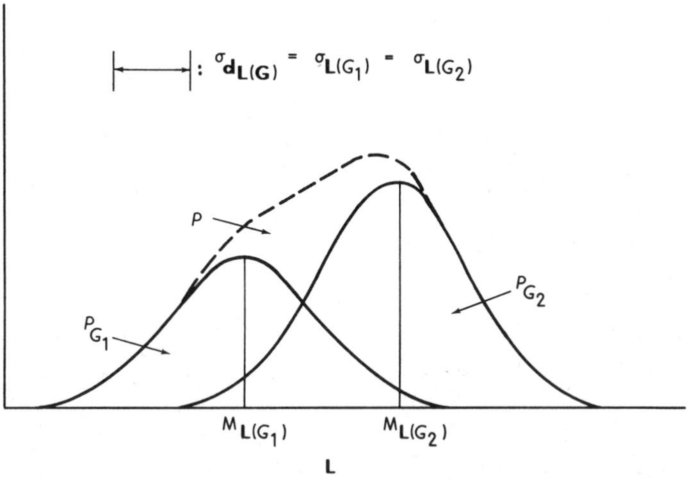

Figure 10.1. Distributions of a variable **L** within the two to-be-discriminated categories G_1 and G_2 which dichotomize population P. The area under the probability-density curve for subpopulation P_{G_k} $(k=1, 2)$ equals the proportion $\Pr(G_k)$ of population P falling in category G_k, so the height of the curve for P_{G_k} at a value L of **L** equals $\Pr(G_k)$ times the contingent probability density of score L, given G_k, in P, while the unconditional probability density at L in population P equals the summed heights of the two subpopulation curves at score L. The two within-category distributions in this illustration are both normal with equal standard deviations; however, the distribution of **L** in the full population P is *not* normal, and due to the difference in within-category means has a variance larger than the within-category variance (cf. equations [10.52,3]). The difference $|M_{L(G_2)} - M_{L(G_1)}|$ between the within-category means, expressed as a multiple of the within-category standard deviation $\sigma_{\mathbf{d}\,L|G}$, may be called the "discrimination distance" between categories G_1 and G_2 in population P (see p. 559). In this example, the discrimination distance is 2.0.

---

of $\mathbf{X_2}, \ldots, \mathbf{X_n}$ is the same in P_{G_1} and P_{G_2}, then $\Pr(X_2 \ldots X_n \mid G_1) = \Pr(X_2 \ldots X_n \mid G_2)$. Substituting into [10.51] and clearing fractions then yields

$$\Pr(G_i \mid X_1 \ldots X_n) = \frac{\Pr(G_i) \cdot \Pr(X_1 \mid G_i)}{\Pr(G_1) \cdot \Pr(X_1 \mid G_1) + \Pr(G_2) \cdot \Pr(X_1 \mid G_2)} = \Pr(G_i \mid X_1),$$

showing that data on $\mathbf{X_1}, \ldots, \mathbf{X_n}$ are irrelevant.

greater is the likelihood that he belongs to category G_2, an intuition which is made precise by observing with the help of Bayes' Theorem ([10.51]) that the probability that a member of P belongs to G_2, given that his score on $\mathbf{X}_1$ is X_1, is the height of the curve for P_{G_2} in Figure 10.1 at point X_1, divided by the sum of the heights for both curves at this point. And since under the conditions hypothesized for this special case a subject's scores on $\mathbf{X}_2, \ldots, \mathbf{X}_n$ do not affect the likelihood of his belonging to one **G**-category rather than another, this is also the probability that the subject belongs to G_2 given that his scores on all the predictors are $X_1, \ldots, X_n$, respectively.

(It is important to appreciate, though, that even if the means of predictors $\mathbf{X}_2, \ldots, \mathbf{X}_n$ are the same in both subpopulations P_{G_1} and P_{G_2}, data on $\mathbf{X}_2, \ldots, \mathbf{X}_n$ would still help to discriminate between categories G_1 and G_2 if the joint distributions of $\mathbf{X}_1, \ldots, \mathbf{X}_n$ in P_{G_1} and P_{G_2} were different in other respects. To make this evident through an extreme example, suppose that all members of P who belong to category G_1 fall exactly on the mean of $\mathbf{X}_2$—i.e., $\mathrm{Var}(\mathbf{X}_2) = 0$ in P_{G_1}—whereas this is not true of the distribution of $\mathbf{X}_2$ in P_{G_2}. Then if the score of a member of P on $\mathbf{X}_2$ is *not* equal to the mean of $\mathbf{X}_2$, we know immediately that he must belong to category G_2. Thus in general, discriminant analysis needs to consider the within-category variances and covariances of the predictor variables as well as their within-category means.)

Since the special case in which predictors $\mathbf{X}_2, \ldots, \mathbf{X}_n$ are independent of $\mathbf{X}_1$ and have the same joint distribution in both P_{G_1} and P_{G_2} is so unrealistically ideal, why consider it at all? The answer is that if the joint predictor distributions within each to-be-discriminated category are normal and differ only in their means—i.e., if the predictor variables have the same covariance matrix in both P_{G_1} and P_{G_2}—then the discrimination problem can be reduced to the first case by a suitable transformation of the set of predictors. It is well known (though not conveniently provable here) that if the joint distribution of variables $\mathbf{X}_1, \ldots, \mathbf{X}_n$ in any population P_k is normal, then the joint distribution in P_k of any set of linear combinations of the $\mathbf{X}_i$ is likewise normal. We also know from Chapter 6 that if variables $\mathbf{X}_1, \ldots, \mathbf{X}_n$ are linearly independent of one another in P_k—i.e., if the rank of $\{C_{\mathbf{X}_i\mathbf{X}_j}\}$ in P_k is $\mathbf{n}$—then $\mathbf{X}_1, \ldots, \mathbf{X}_n$ can as a set be linearly transformed into another set of $\mathbf{n}$ predictors $\mathbf{X}'_i = \sum_{j=1}^{n} a_{ij}\mathbf{X}_j$ ($\mathbf{i} = 1, \ldots, \mathbf{n}$) such that within P_k, $\mathbf{X}'_1, \ldots, \mathbf{X}'_n$ are mutually orthogonal with variances equal to the same arbitrarily chosen constant σ^2 (> 0). The matrix $\{a_{ij}\}$ of transformation coefficients which accomplish this depends on the covariance matrix for the $\mathbf{X}_i$ in P_k, but not upon their means. Hence if predictors $\mathbf{X}_1, \ldots, \mathbf{X}_n$ are normally distributed with the same covariance matrix of rank $\mathbf{n}$ in both P_{G_1} and P_{G_2}—a condition which for convenient reference will henceforth be described as *predictor equi-normality*—the $\mathbf{X_i}$ can be linearly transformed into another set of predictors whose joint distribution within each subpopulation

$$P_{G_k}\ (k=1,2)\text{ is normal with covariances }\operatorname{Cov}(\mathbf{X'_i},\mathbf{X'_j})=\begin{cases}\sigma^2 & \text{if } \mathbf{i}=\mathbf{j}\\ 0 & \text{if } \mathbf{i}\neq\mathbf{j}\end{cases}.$$

This is as assumed in our initial case except that now the two groups P_{G_1} and P_{G_2} presumably differ in their means on $\mathbf{X'_2}, \ldots, \mathbf{X'_n}$ as well as on $\mathbf{X'_1}$. The situation into which our transformation from $\mathbf{X_1}, \ldots, \mathbf{X_n}$ to $\mathbf{X'_1}, \ldots, \mathbf{X'_n}$ has carried us is illustrated for $\mathbf{n} = \mathbf{2}$ in Figure 10.2. But now we can make a second linear transformation of the set of predictors, this time an orthogonal rotation (accompanied, if desired, by a translation of origin) from $\mathbf{X'_1}, \ldots, \mathbf{X'_n}$ to $\mathbf{X''_1}, \ldots, \mathbf{X''_n}$ which preserves the joint normality, orthogonality, and equal-variance properties of the joint predictor distribution within each category. (That orthogonal rotation of axes for any joint distribution of orthogonal equal-variance variables always results in a transformed set with these same properties is simple to prove from the definition of "orthogonal rotation" and general principle [4.43], and is visually apparent in Figure 10.2.) By placing one of the new axes, say $\mathbf{X''_1}$, coincident with or parallel to the line joining the two

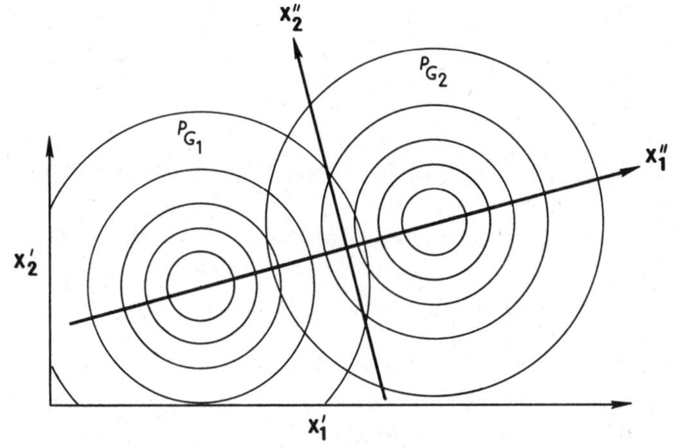

Figure 10.2. Determining the discriminant function. As discussed in the text, the original pair of predictor variables $\mathbf{X_1}$ and $\mathbf{X_2}$ can be linearly transformed into another pair $\mathbf{X'_1}$ and $\mathbf{X'_2}$ which, given the predictor equi-normality condition, are normally distributed with equal variances and zero correlation within each discrimination category, as shown above by the circular probability-density contour maps. Subsequently, the scattergram axes can be orthogonally rotated (and for illustrative convenience translated) to place $\mathbf{X''_1}$ through the centers of the two subpopulation distributions, upon which the two within-category distributions projected upon the rotated axis $\mathbf{X''_2}$ orthogonal to $\mathbf{X''_1}$ become identical.

scattergram points representing the joint predictor means in P_{G_1} and P_{G_2}, respectively, we can throw all of the differences in group means onto the single rotated predictor $\mathbf{X}_1''$. This maneuver, which endows $\mathbf{X}_1''$, . . . , $\mathbf{X}_n''$ with all the conditions of our initial special case, is illustrated in Figure 10.2, wherein it is apparent that if scattergram points representing joint scores on $\mathbf{X}_1'$ and $\mathbf{X}_2'$ in P are resolved into their projections on, respectively, the $\mathbf{X}_1''$-axis passing through the two group means and the $\mathbf{X}_2''$-axis perpendicular to $\mathbf{X}_1''$, both subpopulations P_{G_1} and P_{G_2} have the same distribution on $\mathbf{X}_2''$ and only a subject's projection on $\mathbf{X}_1''$ helps to discriminate whether his classification category is G_1 or G_2. Now, the transformations from the original set of predictors to the $\mathbf{X}_i'$ and from there to the $\mathbf{X}_i''$ can obviously be combined into a linear transformation of set $\mathbf{X}_1, \ldots, \mathbf{X}_n$ directly into set $\mathbf{X}_1'', \ldots, \mathbf{X}_n''$, while since the joint scores on $\mathbf{X}_1'', \ldots, \mathbf{X}_n''$ for a member of P can always be converted back into his scores on $\mathbf{X}_1, \ldots, \mathbf{X}_n$ without knowing which criterion category he belongs to, joint scores on the $\mathbf{X}_i''$ for a member of P contain exactly the same information about his criterion category as do his scores on the original $\mathbf{X}_i$. Hence *if the joint distribution of predictor variables* $\mathbf{X}_1, \ldots, \mathbf{X}_n$ *is normal with the same covariance matrix of rank* $\mathbf{n}$[35] *in both subpopulations* P_{G_1} *and* P_{G_2} *into which a population P is partitioned by a dichotomous criterion variable* **G**—*i.e., when the joint predictor distributions within the two classification categories satisfy the equi-normality condition—then there exists a linear composite* $\mathbf{W} = w_0 + \sum_{i=1}^{n} w_i \mathbf{X}_i$ *of the predictors such that the score on* **W** *of a member of P contains all the information about his* **G**-*category which can be extracted from his scores on predictors* $\mathbf{X}_1, \ldots, \mathbf{X}_n$. *That is, for all values of* $\mathbf{X}_1, \ldots, \mathbf{X}_n$, $\Pr(G_i \mid X_1 \ldots X_n) = \Pr(G_i \mid w_0 + \sum_{i=1}^{n} w_i X_i)$ *in P*. In other words, this special variable **W** abstracted from $\mathbf{X}_1, \ldots, \mathbf{X}_n$ is, under the conditions noted, a "sufficient statistic"[36] for discriminating between categories G_1 and G_2 in P by data on $\mathbf{X}_1, \ldots, \mathbf{X}_n$, meaning that **W** fully suffices to preserve all that is relevant in $\mathbf{X}_1, \ldots, \mathbf{X}_n$ for predicting **G**. The formula for computing values on this variable **W** (or some linear rescaling thereof), given the predictor data, is known as the *discriminant function*, and its derivation is the main show in most accounts of discriminant analysis.

---

[35] The assumption that the rank of the within-group predictor covariance matrix equals the number of predictors is actually unnecessary. When this is not so, however, the predictor transformations here described can come up with at most $\mathbf{m} < \mathbf{n}$ transformed predictors $\mathbf{X}_1'', \ldots, \mathbf{X}_m''$ which are mutually orthogonal within each classification category, and it is then mathematically possible that set $\mathbf{X}_1'', \ldots, \mathbf{X}_m''$ is not a linear transformation of set $\mathbf{X}_1, \ldots, \mathbf{X}_n$ in the full population P. In this (improbable) event, there exists one or more linear combinations of the $\mathbf{X}_i$ on which the groups have different means but zero within-group variances, and which hence discriminate perfectly between the two groups.

[36] The phrase and, more importantly, the concept originate with Fisher.

There are a variety of arguments by which the coefficients in the discriminant function can be found. One is to substitute algebraic expressions for the assumed predictor distributions within P_{G_1} and P_{G_2} into equation [10.51] and to drag out the discriminant function by brute force. However, this method leaves unclear what significance the discriminant function has when the predictor equi-normality condition is not wholly satisfied. A more general approach along Analysis-of-Variance lines is due to Fisher. Let $\mathbf{L}$ be an arbitrary linear combination of variables $\mathbf{X}_1, \ldots, \mathbf{X}_n$. The $\mathbf{L}$-score of any member j of P can be analyzed into two orthogonal components, the mean of $\mathbf{L}$ in the subpopulation P_{G_i} to which j belongs, plus the algebraic discrepancy of j's $\mathbf{L}$-score from his group mean. That is, if $\mathbf{M}_{\mathbf{L}(\mathbf{G})}$ is defined to be a variable whose value for a member of P is the mean of $\mathbf{L}$ in the $\mathbf{G}$-category to which he belongs, and $\mathbf{d}_{\mathbf{L}(\mathbf{G})} =_{\text{def}} \mathbf{L} - \mathbf{M}_{\mathbf{L}(\mathbf{G})}$, then obviously $\mathbf{L} = \mathbf{d}_{\mathbf{L}(\mathbf{G})} + \mathbf{M}_{\mathbf{L}(\mathbf{G})}$; while since the covariance between $\mathbf{d}_{\mathbf{L}(\mathbf{G})}$ and $\mathbf{M}_{\mathbf{L}(\mathbf{G})}$ in P is zero (proof of which the reader can easily supply for himself),

[10.52] $$\mathrm{Var}(\mathbf{L}) = \mathrm{Var}(\mathbf{d}_{\mathbf{L}(\mathbf{G})}) + \mathrm{Var}(\mathbf{M}_{\mathbf{L}(\mathbf{G})}) .$$

Thus the total variance of variable $\mathbf{L}$ in population P analyzes as a sum of two components, the "within-group" variance $\mathrm{Var}(\mathbf{d}_{\mathbf{L}(\mathbf{G})})$, which is a weighted average of $\mathbf{L}$'s variance in the two subpopulations P_{G_1} and P_{G_2}, and the "between-group" variance $\mathrm{Var}(\mathbf{M}_{\mathbf{L}(\mathbf{G})})$. Since variable $\mathbf{M}_{\mathbf{L}(\mathbf{G})}$ has only two values, namely $\mathrm{M}_{\mathbf{L}(G_1)}$ and $\mathrm{M}_{\mathbf{L}(G_2)}$, it is also readily computed that

[10.53] $$\mathrm{Var}(\mathbf{M}_{\mathbf{L}(\mathbf{G})}) = \mathrm{p}_{G_1}\mathrm{p}_{G_2}[\mathrm{M}_{\mathbf{L}(G_1)} - \mathrm{M}_{\mathbf{L}(G_2)}]^2 ,$$

where p_{G_i} is the proportion of population P falling in category G_i and $|\mathrm{M}_{\mathbf{L}(G_1)} - \mathrm{M}_{\mathbf{L}(G_2)}|$ is the difference on $\mathbf{L}$ between an average member of P_{G_1} and an average member of P_{G_2}. Thus the variance ratio $\mathrm{Var}\,(\mathbf{M}_{\mathbf{L}(\mathbf{G})})/\mathrm{Var}(\mathbf{d}_{\mathbf{L}(\mathbf{G})})$ is a monotonic increasing function (with $\mathrm{p}_{G_1}\mathrm{p}_{G_2}$ as a parameter) of the separation on $\mathbf{L}$ between the two to-be-discriminated categories G_1 and G_2 in P, expressed in terms of the within-group standard deviation of $\mathbf{L}$ as a unit of measurement. Let this standardized between-group distance, i.e.,

$$\frac{|\mathrm{M}_{\mathbf{L}(G_1)} - \mathrm{M}_{\mathbf{L}(G_2)}|}{\sigma_{\mathbf{d}_{\mathbf{L}(\mathbf{G})}}},$$

be called the *discrimination distance* on $\mathbf{L}$ between categories G_1 and G_2 in P. Since $\mathbf{L}$ is an arbitrary linear function of the predictors, we can vary the ratio of $\mathrm{Var}(\mathbf{M}_{\mathbf{L}(\mathbf{G})})$ to $\mathrm{Var}(\mathbf{d}_{\mathbf{L}(\mathbf{G})})$ and hence the discrimination distance on $\mathbf{L}$ between G_1 and G_2 in P by varying the coefficients in $\mathbf{L} = a_0 + \sum_{\mathrm{i}=1}^{\mathrm{n}} a_{\mathrm{i}}\mathbf{X}_{\mathrm{i}}$. In the special case that the predictor equi-normality condition is satisfied, $\mathbf{L}$ is normally distributed with equal variance, namely

$\mathrm{Var}(\mathbf{d}_{\mathbf{L}(\mathbf{G})})$, in both P_{G_1} and P_{G_2} no matter how the coefficients a_0, a_1, . . . , a_n are chosen; and it is evident in this case (cf. Figure 10.1) that the greater the discrimination distance between G_1 and G_2 on **L**, the more effectively does the **L**-score for a member of P help to determine his **G**-category. Consequently, if we redefine discriminant function $\mathbf{W} = w_0 + \sum_{i=1}^{n} w_i\mathbf{X}_i$ to be that linear combination of the predictors for which the ratio of between-group variance to within-group variance with respect to categories G_1 and G_2 is maximal, the solution for which in non-degenerate cases is unique up to a linear transformation, **W** will also be the sufficient discriminant statistic previously seen to exist in the special but hopefully prevalent case of predictor equi-normality.

It still remains to say how the coefficients in the discriminant function can actually be computed. While it is not practical to state an explicit formula for these, they turn out simply to be regression weights whose numerical computation is a straightforward application of linear regression formulas. Let **G** be a numerically scaled dichotomous variable whose two values correspond to categories G_1 and G_2, respectively. Any two different numbers will do, but added convenience will result if one of the categories, say G_1, is represented by a scale value of 1 and the other by a scale value of 0, since then $\Pr(G_1 \mid X_1 \ldots X_n) = \mathrm{M}_{\mathbf{G}\mid\mathbf{X}_1\cdots\mathbf{X}_n}$ and $\Pr(G_2 \mid X_1 \ldots X_n) = 1 - \mathrm{M}_{\mathbf{G}\mid\mathbf{X}_1\ldots\mathbf{X}_n}$.

Theorem: The discrimination distance between dichotomous categories G_1 and G_2 in population P on a linear combination **W** *of predictors* $\mathbf{X}_1, \ldots, \mathbf{X}_n$ *is maximal when and only when* **W** *coincides up to a linear transformation with the multiple linear regression of the numerically scaled criterion variable* **G** *upon* $\mathbf{X}_1, \ldots, \mathbf{X}_n$*; while if the joint distributions of* $\mathbf{X}_1, \ldots, \mathbf{X}_n$ *in the two subpopulations* P_{G_1} *and* P_{G_2} *of P are both normal and have the same covariance matrix,* $\mathbf{G}_{(\mathbf{X}_1\cdots\mathbf{X}_m)}$ *is also a sufficient statistic for predicting* **G** *from* $\mathbf{X}_1, \ldots, \mathbf{X}_n$ *in P.* To prove that the discrimination distance between G_1 and G_2 in P on a linear function **L** of predictors $\mathbf{X}_1, \ldots, \mathbf{X}_n$ is maximal when **L** is $\dot{\mathbf{G}}_{(\mathbf{X}_1\ldots\mathbf{X}_n)}$ or some linear rescaling thereof, the reader may easily convince himself that however **L** is chosen, $\mathbf{M}_{\mathbf{L}(\mathbf{G})} = \dot{\mathbf{L}}_{(\mathbf{G})}$ and $\mathbf{d}_{\mathbf{L}(\mathbf{G})} = \mathbf{e}_{\mathbf{L}\bullet\mathbf{G}}$, where $\mathbf{M}_{\mathbf{l}(\mathbf{G})}$ and $\mathbf{d}_{\mathbf{L}(\mathbf{G})}$ are as defined previously. Hence $\mathrm{Var}(\mathbf{M}_{\mathbf{L}(\mathbf{G})})/\mathrm{Var}(\mathbf{d}_{\mathbf{L}(\mathbf{G})}) = \sigma_{\mathbf{L}}^2 \mathrm{r}_{\mathbf{LG}}^2 / \sigma_{\mathbf{L}}^2(1 - \mathrm{r}_{\mathbf{LG}}^2) = \mathrm{r}_{\mathbf{LG}}^2/(1 - \mathrm{r}_{\mathbf{LG}}^2)$, or using [10.53],

[10.54]

$$\frac{|\mathrm{M}_{\mathbf{L}(G_1)} - \mathrm{M}_{\mathbf{L}(G_2)}|}{\sigma_{\mathbf{d}_{\mathbf{L}(\mathbf{G})}}} = \sqrt{\frac{\mathrm{Var}(\mathbf{M}_{\mathbf{L}(\mathbf{G})})}{\mathrm{p}_{G_1}\mathrm{p}_{G_2}\mathrm{Var}(\mathbf{d}_{\mathbf{L}(\mathbf{G})})}} = \sqrt{\frac{\mathrm{r}_{\mathbf{LG}}^2}{\mathrm{p}_{G_1}\mathrm{p}_{G_2}(1 - \mathrm{r}_{\mathbf{LG}}^2)}},$$

which is an increasing function of $\mathrm{r}_{\mathbf{LG}}^2$ and is hence maximal when and only when **L** coincides (up to a linear transformation) with the linear regression of **G** upon the $\mathbf{X}_i$. In view of previous conclusions, the second part of the theorem is an immediate consequence of the first part. A more direct proof will also be sketched here because of its importance for extending discriminant analysis to polychotomous criteria: It is not difficult to show that under the predictor equi-normality condition, if linear function **W** of $\mathbf{X}_1, \ldots, \mathbf{X}_n$ is a sufficient statistic for predicting **G** from the $\mathbf{X}_i$ in *P* (the existence of such a **W** in this case having already been shown), then **G** must be statistically independent of and hence linearly uncorrelated with each predictor residual $\mathbf{e}_{\mathbf{X}_i \cdot \mathbf{W}}$ ($\mathbf{i} = \mathbf{1}, \ldots, \mathbf{n}$) in *P*.[37] Consequently, the projection of **G** into the space $S_{\mathbf{X}}$ spanned by predictors $\mathbf{X}_1, \ldots, \mathbf{X}_n$ is orthogonal in *P* to the subspace of $S_{\mathbf{X}}$ orthogonal to **W**—which is equivalent to saying that the projection of **G** into $S_{\mathbf{X}}$ differs from **W** by at most a linear transformation.

According to the theorem just demonstrated, the predictor coefficients in the discriminant function can be determined by computing the covariance in *P* of scaled criterion **G** with each predictor $\mathbf{X}_i$, substituting these covariances along with the predictor covariances $C_{\mathbf{X}_i\mathbf{X}_j}$ in *P* into the normal equations for regression coefficients, and solving for the latter. Because **G** is dichotomous, however, it is also possible to push description of the solution a little farther than this. When categories G_1 and G_2 are represented by **G**-scale values of 1 and 0, respectively, it is easily computed that

$$[10.55] \quad \mathrm{Cov}(\mathbf{G}, \mathbf{X}_i) = p_{G_1}p_{G_2}(M_{\mathbf{X}_i(G_1)} - M_{\mathbf{X}_i(G_2)}) \quad \text{(unit-dichotomous } \mathbf{G}\text{)}\,,$$

where as before, p_{G_k} ($k = 1, 2$) is the proportion of population *P* falling in category G_k and $M_{\mathbf{X}_i(G_k)}$ is the mean of predictor $\mathbf{X}_i$ in subpopulation P_{G_k}. From [10.55] and the matrix-algebra solution for regression weights (see equation [B.16], Appendix B) it follows that the *b*-coefficient of predictor $\mathbf{X}_i$ ($\mathbf{i} = \mathbf{1}, \ldots, \mathbf{n}$) in the regression of **G** upon variables $\mathbf{X}_1, \ldots, \mathbf{X}_n$ is

$$[10.56\text{-}\mathbf{i}] \quad (\mathbf{i} = \mathbf{1}, \ldots, \mathbf{n}) \qquad b_{\mathbf{GX}_i} = p_{G_1}p_{G_2} \sum_{\mathbf{j}=\mathbf{1}}^{\mathbf{n}} C^{\mathbf{ij}}(M_{\mathbf{X}_j(G_1)} - M_{\mathbf{X}_j(G_2)}) \quad \text{(unit-dichotomous } \mathbf{G}\text{)}\,,$$

where the $C^{\mathbf{ij}}$ are the inverses of the predictor covariances $C_{\mathbf{X}_i\mathbf{X}_j}$ in *P* as discussed previously (pp. 508f.) and for simplicity the secondary sub-

[37] This follows immediately from lemmas (*A*) that if **W**, **Y**, and **G** are variables (numerically scaled or not) such that **W** is a sufficient statistic for predicting **G** from **W** and **Y** in population *P* while **Y** is statistically independent of **W** in *P* then **Y** is also statistically independent of **G** in *P*; and (*B*) that under predictor equi-normality, each $\mathbf{X}_i$-residual $\mathbf{e}_{\mathbf{X}_i \cdot \mathbf{W}}$ ($\mathbf{i} = \mathbf{1}, \ldots, \mathbf{n}$) left by the discriminant function $\mathbf{W} = w_0 + \sum_{\mathbf{i}=\mathbf{1}}^{\mathbf{n}} w_i\mathbf{X}_i$ is statistically independent of **W** in *P*. Verification of these lemmas will be left to the reader. (To prove *B*, the more difficult one, note that when predictors $\mathbf{X}_1, \ldots, \mathbf{X}_n$ are rotated under the equi-normality condition to place all the between-group differences on **W**, any given linear combination **L** of the $\mathbf{X}_i$ orthogonal to **W** has the same contingent distribution in *P* given any combination of a score on **W** with membership in either classification category.)

scripts have been omitted. (It can also be shown that if $\{C^{ij}\}$ is taken to be the inverse of the covariance matrix $\{C_{X_iX_j}\}$ *within* subpopulations P_{G_1} and P_{G_2}, rather than in the total population P, the only effect is to multiply each b_{GX_i} by the same constant. Hence it does not matter whether the discriminant function is computed from the within-group predictor covariances or from the total predictor covariances.) Hence if we set

$$[10.57] \qquad \mathbf{W} =_{\text{def}} \sum_{i=1}^{n} \left[\sum_{j=1}^{n} (M_{X_j(G_1)} - M_{X_j(G_2)}) C^{ij} \right] X_i ,$$

W differs from $\dot{G}_{(X_1 \ldots X_n)}$ only by a linear transformation. Equation [10.57] is, in fact, the most frequently proffered version of the discriminant function, though any linear transformation of **W** so defined would serve as well and $\dot{G}_{(X_1 \ldots X_n)}$ is more immediately informative.

While the regression estimate $\dot{G}_{(X_1 \ldots X_n)}$ of unit-dichotomous criterion **G** is the best approximation to the contingent probability that a member of population P belongs to the category represented by a **G**-score of 1, given his predictor scores, that can be pulled out of the predictor data by a *linear* function of the latter, and moreover, given predictor equi-normality, nothing further can be learned about **G** from $X_1, \ldots, X_n$ which is not contained wholly in the single predictor composite $\dot{G}_{(X_1 \ldots X_n)}$, it is important to be clear that it is still not generally the case that $\Pr(G_1 \mid \dot{G}_{(X_1 \ldots X_n)}) = \dot{G}_{(X_1 \ldots X_m)}$ even when predictor equi-normality obtains. Rather, $\Pr(G_1|\dot{G}_{(X_1 \ldots X_n)})$ (or equivalently, $\Pr(\dot{G}_1|W)$) is related to $\dot{G}_{(X_1 \ldots X_n)}$ by an S-shaped curve which becomes less and less adequately approximated by $\Pr(G_1|\dot{G}_{(X_1 \ldots X_n)}) \simeq \dot{G}_{(X_1 \ldots X_n)}$ as the discrimination distance between G_1 and G_2 on the discriminant function increases. It is not difficult to prepare tables or computing algorithms which, under assumption of predictor equi-normality, convert $\dot{G}_{(X_1 \ldots X_n)}$ or some other standardized scaling of the discriminant function into the probabilities $\Pr(G_k|X_1 \ldots X_n)$ $(k = 1, 2)$. However, these contain as parameters both the term $p_{G_1}p_{G_2}$ and the discrimination distance between the criterion categories, and will be dispensed with here.

While a discriminant function of form [10.57] is inherently limited to discriminating between two criterion alternatives, discriminant analysis can also deal effectively with categorical criteria which have more than two values, especially when the within-group predictor distributions are all normal with the same covariance matrix. If population P is partitioned among m categories $G_1, \ldots, G_m$ within each of which predictors $X_1, \ldots, X_n$ are normally distributed with the same covariance matrix of rank **n**–i.e., if predictor equi-normality holds for all m criterion categories–then, just as before when $m = 2$, the original predictors can be linearly transformed into another set $X_1', \ldots, X_n'$ such that within each subpopulation P_{G_k} $(k = 1, \ldots, m)$ the X_i' are jointly normal and mutually orthogonal with the same variance σ^2, while subsequently an orthogonal rotation from $\mathbf{X}_1', \ldots, \mathbf{X}_n'$ to $\mathbf{X}_1'', \ldots, \mathbf{X}_n''$ can be found such that subpopulations $P_{G_1}, \ldots, P_{G_m}$ have different means on at most $m-1$ of the $\mathbf{X}_i''$. Thus given predictor equi-normality within all criterion categories (and as before, the requirement of full rank for the within-category predictor covariance matrix is actually unnecessary), all the information contained in the predictor scores for a member of P about his $\mathbf{G}$-category can be abstracted by a set of at most $m-1$ linear combinations of the predictors. By a simple extension of the argument sketched in fn. 37, p. 561, it may also be seen that a set $\mathbf{L}_1, \ldots, \mathbf{L}_{m-1}$ of linear combinations of the $\mathbf{X}_i$ have this property (still assuming predictor equi-normality) if and only if the $\mathbf{L}_j$ span the same space as the one spanned by the linear regressions $\dot{\mathbf{G}}_{k(X_1 \ldots X_n)}$ ($\mathbf{k} = \mathbf{1}, \ldots, \mathbf{m}$) of unit-dichotomous variables $\mathbf{G}_1, \ldots, \mathbf{G}_m$ upon predictors $\mathbf{X}_1, \ldots, \mathbf{X}_n$ in P, where $\mathbf{G}_k$ has value 1 or 0 for a member of P according to whether or not he belongs to category G_k. (Since $\sum_{k=1}^{m} \mathbf{G}_k = 1$, the predictor subspace spanned by $\dot{\mathbf{G}}_{1(X_1 \ldots X_n)}, \ldots, \dot{\mathbf{G}}_{m(X_1 \ldots X_n)}$ has at most $\mathbf{m}-1$ dimensions.) Thus under predictor equi-normality, the linear regression-estimates $\dot{G}_{k(X_1 \ldots X_n)}$ ($\mathbf{k} = \mathbf{1}, \ldots, \mathbf{n}$) of the probability that a member of P belongs to classification category G_k, given his predictor data, constitute a sufficient set of statistics for deriving the desired classification probabilities $\Pr(G_k \mid X_1 \ldots X_n)$. If one is not interested in the linear approximations $\dot{G}_{k(X_1 \ldots X_n)}$ to $\Pr(G_k \mid X_1 \ldots X_n)$ for their own sake, a useful alternative set of predictor statistics which are transformationally equivalent to the $\dot{\mathbf{G}}_{k(X_1 \ldots X_n)}$ are the canonical factors of $\mathbf{X}_1, \ldots, \mathbf{X}_n$ with respect to variables $\mathbf{G}_1, \ldots, \mathbf{G}_m$. These are the discriminant functions which follow from the Fisherian principle of finding mutually orthogonal predictor composites which successively maximize the ratio of between-criterion-group to within-criterion-group variance in the sense previously described for $m=2$, and make apparent the extent to which the group means tend to occupy a predictor space of less than $\mathbf{n}-1$ dimensions. (It is conceivable, for example, that the joint predictor means in the various classification categories all lie approximately on a single line in predictor space, which if $\mathbf{m} \gg \mathbf{2}$ would be a striking empirical pattern suggestive that categories $G_1, \ldots, G_m$ are manifestations of an underlying one-dimensional metric.)

Finally, given predictor equi-normality in population P for all the m categories of a polychotomous criterion $\mathbf{G}$, the precise probabilities $\Pr(G_k \mid X_1 \ldots X_n)$ ($k = 1, \ldots, m$) can be obtained from $m-1$ discriminant functions of form [10.57] and the conversion table for the $m = 2$ case as follows: Let P_{ij} be the population which consists of members of P who are either in category G_i or in category G_j. Then in the restricted population P_{ij}, our criterion $\mathbf{G}$ reduces to a dichotomy and we can compute the "likelihood ratio" $\Pr(G_i \mid X_1 \ldots X_n)/\Pr(G_j \mid X_1 \ldots X_n)$ in P_{ij} by use of a discriminant function of form [10.57] based on the predictor covariances in P_{ij} (or, more conveniently, on the common within-group predictor covariance matrix as mentioned previously) and the appropriate conversion tables. But it is an elementary theorem of probability theory that the likelihood ratio just cited is the same in P_{ij} as it is in any more inclusive population. Hence the value of this ratio computed from a subject's predictor scores under the supposition that he belongs to P_{ij} is also the correct value thereof given simply that he belongs to P. Accordingly, by selecting one category, say G_1, and determining the $m-1$ discriminant functions for subpopulations $P_{12}, \ldots, P_{1m}$, we can convert the predictor scores $X_1, \ldots, X_n$ for a member of P into the likelihood ratios $\Pr(G_k|X_1 \ldots X_n)/\Pr(G_1|X_1 \ldots X_n) = c \Pr(G_k|X_1 \ldots X_n)$ $(k = 1, \ldots, m)$, where c is a constant of proportionality which can then be eliminated by drawing on the fact that $\sum_{k=1}^{m} \Pr(G_k \mid X_1 \ldots X_n) = 1$. Once again, though, we recall that this method for determining the contingent probability distribution over the values of a categorical criterion, given the predictor data, is valid (in general) only when the contingent joint predictor distributions in the various criterion categories are identically normal except for the predictor means. Moderate violation of the normality requirement is not likely to lead the computation far astray, but how useful the latter remains as an approximation when the within-group predictor covariance matrix varies markedly from one criterion category to another is less certain. In this case, barring practical complications due to an excess of regression parameters, our best discrimination procedure is to approximate the probabilities $\Pr(G_k \mid X_1 \ldots X_n)$ by nonlinear regression estimates of $\mathbf{G}_1, \ldots, \mathbf{G}_m$. Such estimates largely continue to be subsumed by the formal theory of discriminant analysis, since as discussed in Chapter 4, a parametrically linear F-form regression surface is equivalent to the criterion's linear regression on a set of derived predictors which are fixed functions of the original set.

We may conclude this survey of discriminant analysis with the remark that intuitive judgments about the effectiveness with which calissification decisions can be accomplished when the predictor distributions in the to-be-discriminated categories are clearly different tend to be grossly overoptimistic. The difficulty is simply that if the "base rate," $\Pr(G_k)$, of category G_k in P is small, then as shown by [10.51], the probability that a subject belongs to G_k when his predictor data are $X_1, \ldots, X_n$ may still remain small even when the contingent probability of joint predictor scores $X_1, \ldots, X_n$ is very much higher in category G_k than in the other categories. This phenomenon is especially important—and discouraging—for attempts to interpret diagnostic signs of low-frequency conditions, such as diverse forms of mental and physical pathology, whose classification decisions entail actions (e.g., to hospitalize or not to hospitalize) which may have strongly aversive consequences in the event of misclassification. For a more detailed analysis of this problem, see Meehl and Rosen (60).

Information Theory.[38] When some or all of the variables available for predicting a categorical criterion are themselves categorical, we can assign these whatever numerical scales are most convenient and proceed to have at the criterion through discriminant analysis, though of course the equi-normality condition cannot be realized or in most cases even well-approximated by categorical predictors. We mention this because *Information theory*, which as indicated in Table 10.1 has been developed expressly to analyze relations among categorical variables, is of no help at all for actually converting predictor data into an estimate of the criterion and is hence no substitute for discriminant analysis despite the latter's limited applicability to categorical predictors. On the other hand, regression theory (of which discriminant analysis is essentially a special case) offers no generally effective way to assess the *degree* to which a categorical criterion is determined by a given set of predictors,[39] which is a hopelessly inadequacy when, as in scientific research, first concern is not for particular predictions but for sensitive detection and dissection of relational patterns. How acutely this conceptual hiatus has pained the behavioral sciences was attested by the ardor of their response to the birth of contemporary Information theory in a 1948 article on communications engineering by C. E. Shannon (72), though there is also reason to suspect that much of the initial excitement in some quarters arose from the word-magical delusion that "Information" theory was a mathematical revelation of the nature of cognitive knowledge.

Actually, the title "Information theory" is deceptive, though considering the discipline's intimate association with the technology of message transmission, the name may be condoned on historical grounds. A humbler but much more accurate description is *Uncertainty analysis* (Garner and McGill, 31). Pared to essentials, Information theory (Uncertainty analysis) is nothing more than a system of mathematical ab-

[38] No comprehensive text on Information theory is as yet available. However, the reader seeking details may profitably consult Shannon (72) and Khinchin (48) for the fundamental mathematics from a communications engineering perspective, and Attneave (5), Quastler (65) and especially Garner (30) for behavioral-sciences applications. An approach to inferential statistics built upon concepts very similar in mathematical structure to the Shannon Information measure has also recently emerged (Kullbach, 50), while a broad purview in this domain of ideas has been developed by Watanabe (84).

[39] One regression measure of relationship applicable to a dichotomous criterion is its multiple correlation with the predictors, two special cases of which, the *Phi coefficient* (the linear correlation between two dichotomous variables) and the *point-biserial correlation coefficient* (the linear correlation between two variables, one of which is a dichotomy) are already familiar in the literature. This approach can be generalized to polychotomous criteria by taking as our measure of predictive accuracy the penetrance (or more comparably, its square root) into predictor space of the set of dichotomous variables $\mathbf{G}_1, \ldots, \mathbf{G}_m$ defined from the criterion categories as described previously. However, the potential usefulness of this measure is probably limited at best.

stractions defined upon a measure of the dispersion within a probability distribution. Much of the theory is indifferent, or nearly so, to how the fundamental uncertainty statistic is itself defined, and if developed axiomatically can be given a variety of statistical interpretations (Rozeboom, 69). However, it was the specific definition of "Information" introduced by Shannon which has been seminal for Information theory's birth and development.

Let **Y** be a categorical variable which has m alternative values $Y_1, \ldots, Y_m$, and let $\Pr(Y_i)$ be the unconditional probability of category Y_i in population P while $\Pr(Y_i \mid C_j)$ is the probability of Y_i among those members of P for whom special conditions C_j (e.g., a particular combination of predictor data) also hold. Then the set of probabilities $\Pr(Y_1 \mid C_j), \ldots, \Pr(Y_m \mid C_j)$ is a complete description of our uncertainty about the value of **Y** for a random member of P under conditions C_j, and as this distribution of probabilities varies from one data condition C_j to another, our uncertainty about **Y** changes accordingly. So described, our "uncertainty" about **Y** in P, given data C_j, is an m-dimensional concept which suggests no sense in which one such distribution contains *more* (or less, or the same) uncertainty than is in another. Yet it is clear in simple cases, at least, that we do make intuitive comparisons of this sort. For example, a distribution in which one of the **Y**-categories has a probability of unity involves no uncertainty at all, while if all **Y**-categories are equiprobable, then the more of these there are, the more unpredictable does **Y** seem. It is reasonable, therefore, to look for a measure over a set of probabilities which represents the overall uncertainty in a categorical distribution by a single number, comparable to the way in which the uncertainty in the distribution of a metrical variable can be represented by the latter's standard deviation. Of course, there is no single *correct* measure of categorical uncertainty, any more than there is any one correct measure of dispersion in a metrical distribution—in both cases, categorical and metrical, it is possible to define a variety of similar but nonequivalent statistics (e.g., standard versus average deviation) which do more or less equal justice to the primitive conception for which they are intended to be a precision replacement. But just as the standard deviation yields to mathematical insight while its conceptual peers are opaque, so has one and, to date, only one measure of categorical dispersion been found which is both technically well-behaved and interpretively meaningful—namely, the quantity

$$[10.58] \qquad \mathrm{U}(\mathbf{Y}) =_{\text{def}} - \sum_{i=1}^{m} \Pr(Y_i) \cdot \log_b \Pr(Y_i)\ ,$$

in which the logarithm's base, b, is an arbitrary parameter.[40] Since a

[40] If the reader's acquaintance with logarithms has not been lying fallow overlong, he will recall that the logarithm of a quantity Q to the base b—i.e., $\log_b Q$— is the number x such that $b^x = Q$, and that $\log_a Q = (\log_a b) \log_b Q$.

shift in b merely multiplies all the logarithms by the same constant, choice of the logarithm's base in [10.58] is equivalent to selecting a unit of measurement for U. For reasons grounded in communications technology, the standard choice for b is 2, in which case the unit of measurement for the U-scale is called a *bit* (short for "binary digit").

The quantity U(**Y**) defined in [10.58] is to be read as the *Uncertainty* of variable **Y** when the probabilities of its various possible values are respectively $\Pr(Y_1), \ldots, \Pr(Y_m)$. This applies no matter what the origin of these probabilities may be. However, if the **Y**-probabilities are contingent upon data C_j, we can make this explicit by writing

$$[10.59] \qquad \mathrm{U}(\mathbf{Y}|C_j) =_{\text{def}} -\sum_{i=1}^{m} \Pr(Y_i|C_j) \cdot \log_b \Pr(Y_i|C_j)$$

for the *contingent Uncertainty* of **Y**, given C_j, in population P. In much of the literature, the function U is symbolized "H" and described as a measure of "information." This interprets U(**Y**) (i.e., H(**Y**)) as the amount of Uncertainty which would be eliminated were we to learn for sure what value **Y** actually has. However, there is nothing in the statistic U(**Y**) which requires that we in fact ever attain this knowledge, or even that anyone cares about it, so to call U(**Y**) "information" when it is only an abstraction from the scatter of **Y**'s probability distribution is needlessly beguiling.

While no attempt will here be made to interpret the quantity U(**Y**) in detail, we may at least note the following points: (1) The minus sign in [10.58] is merely to keep U(**Y**) from being negative, since the logarithm of any number between 0 and 1, probabilities in particular, is negative. (2) [10.58] is equivalent to

$$\mathrm{U}(\mathbf{Y}) = \sum_{i=1}^{m} \Pr(Y_i) \cdot \log_b \left(\frac{1}{\Pr(Y_i)}\right),$$

where $\sum_{i=1}^{m} \Pr(Y_i) = 1$, which shows that U(Y) is a weighted average of the quantities $\log_b [1/\Pr(Y_i)]$. (3) The product $\Pr(Y_i) \cdot \log_b [1/\Pr(Y_i)]$ approaches zero as $\Pr(Y_i)$ approaches either 0 or 1 and is greater than zero otherwise; hence

$$[10.60] \qquad \mathrm{U}(\mathbf{Y}) \geqslant 0,$$

with zero Uncertainty being attained when all the **Y**-probability is confined to a single category. (4) U(**Y**) is at a maximum when all m values of **Y** are equally likely, the Uncertainty in this case being $\mathrm{U}(\mathbf{Y}) = \log_b m$. This illustrates the general point that on the whole, as the number of alternatives under a categorical variable increases, so does the Uncertainty in a distribution of probabilities over these categories. In particular, if formula [10.58] is applied to a continuous probability distribution over the values of a metrical variable, U becomes infinitely large. Hence the Uncertainty measure is inapplicable to metrical variables unless by nature or by class-interval groupings these take only discrete values. (5) The value of U(**Y**) depends only on the array of probabilities over the **Y**-categories, without the slightest regard for any possible similarity comparisons which be made among the Y_i. This is, to be sure, precisely what is needed for generic analysis of categorical variables, but it may have untoward consequences when **Y** is a discrete-valued metric. For example, suppose that in an experiment on the genetical effects of radiation, 90% of normal mice have 20 toes, 5% have 19 toes, and 5% have 21 toes, while of similar mice whose parents were irradiated, 90% have the normal complement of 20 toes but 5% have no toes at all and the remaining 5% have 40. Then the Uncertainty over the Number-of-toes distribution is the same in both the normal and the experimental mice populations, namely, U(Number-of-toes) $= -[.90(\log_2 .90) + .05(\log_2 .05) + .05(\log_2 .05)] = .41 + .21 + .21 = .56$ bits; yet we would surely wish to say in this case that toes are considerably more unpredictable among the offspring of irradiated mice than among normals. To be sure, this example has little grounding in empirical reality, but it serves notice that U, like any other statistic, has its interpretive limitations.

The analytic potency of U derives from the extreme algebraic simplicity of its combinatorial properties. Suppose that **Y** and **X** are both categorical variables with m and n alternatives, respectively. (For greater generality, **X** and **Y** may be respectively conceived as the "cartesian products" of two sets of categorical variables $\mathbf{X}_1, \ldots, \mathbf{X}_p$ and $\mathbf{Y}_1, \ldots, \mathbf{Y}_q$ – i.e., each category of product-variable **X** is a particular combination of values on $\mathbf{X}_1, \ldots, \mathbf{X}_p$, and similarly for **Y**.) Then the joint distribution of **X** and **Y** contains $m \times n$ categories, namely, one for each combination of a value on **Y** with a value on **X**, and by application of basic definition [10.58], the Uncertainty over the joint distribution of **X** and **Y** in population P is

$$[10.61] \qquad \mathrm{U}(\mathbf{XY}) =_{\text{def}} -\sum_{i=1}^{n}\sum_{j=1}^{m} \Pr(X_iY_j) \cdot \log_b \Pr(X_iY_j)\,.$$

(If **X** and **Y** are themselves cartesian products of $\mathbf{X}_1, \ldots, \mathbf{X}_p$ and $\mathbf{Y}_1, \ldots, \mathbf{Y}_q$, respectively, U(**XY**) is equivalent to the Uncertainty $\mathrm{U}(\mathbf{X}_1 \ldots \mathbf{X}_p\mathbf{Y}_1 \ldots \mathbf{Y}_q)$ over the joint distribution of $\mathbf{X}_1, \ldots, \mathbf{X}_p, \mathbf{Y}_1, \ldots, \mathbf{Y}_q$.) U(**XY**) assesses our simultaneous Uncertainty about **X** and **Y**. On the other hand, if **X** is known to have value X_j, our contingent Uncertainty about **Y**, given X_j, is $\mathrm{U}(\mathbf{Y}|X_j)$ (cf. [10.59]); so if **X** is a predictor variable from which we attempt to infer **Y** for a randomly selected member of P, our expected Uncertainty about **Y**, given data on **X**, is

$$[10.62] \qquad \mathrm{U}(\mathbf{Y}|\mathbf{X}) =_{\text{def}} -\sum_{j=1}^{n} \Pr(X_j) \cdot \mathrm{U}(\mathbf{Y}|X_j)\,.$$

The quantity $U(\mathbf{Y}|\mathbf{X})$, which is also symbolized "$U_{\mathbf{X}}(\mathbf{Y})$" and "$H_{\mathbf{X}}(\mathbf{Y})$," is the *contingent Uncertainty* of $\mathbf{Y}$, given $\mathbf{X}$, in P, and is the categorical analog of the absolute standard error of a metrical criterion, given a predictor variable. It is a simple consequence of these definitions that

$$[10.63] \qquad U(\mathbf{XY}) = U(\mathbf{X}) + U(\mathbf{Y}|\mathbf{X}) = U(\mathbf{Y}) + U(\mathbf{X}|\mathbf{Y}) \, ,$$

which says that the joint Uncertainty over two categorical variables is simply the Uncertainty of one, plus the contingent Uncertainty of the other given the first. It can also be shown that

$$[10.64] \qquad U(\mathbf{XY}) \leq U(\mathbf{X}) + U(\mathbf{Y}) \, ,$$

with equality holding when and only when there is complete statistical independence between $\mathbf{X}$ and $\mathbf{Y}$. From [10.63] and [10.64] it follows that

$$[10.65] \qquad U(\mathbf{Y}|\mathbf{X}) \leq U(\mathbf{Y}) \, ,$$

which is the categorical analog of the metrical inequalities $\sigma_{\mathbf{Y}|\mathbf{X}} \leq \sigma_{\mathbf{Y}}$ and $\sigma_{\mathbf{Y}\bullet\mathbf{X}} \leq \sigma_{\mathbf{Y}}$. (The parallel between the metrical and categorical cases is not perfect, however, since $U(\mathbf{Y}|\mathbf{X}) = U(\mathbf{Y})$ implies that the contingent distributions of $\mathbf{Y}$ are identical at all values of $\mathbf{X}$, whereas this is not necessarily true when $\sigma_{\mathbf{Y}\bullet\mathbf{X}} = \sigma_{\mathbf{Y}}$ or when $\sigma_{\mathbf{Y}|\mathbf{X}} = \sigma_{\mathbf{Y}}$.) The difference between $U(\mathbf{Y})$ and $U(\mathbf{Y}|\mathbf{X})$ is usually designated "$T(\mathbf{Y};\mathbf{X})$" or "$U(\mathbf{Y};\mathbf{X})$," i.e.,

$$[10.66] \qquad U(\mathbf{Y};\mathbf{X}) =_{\text{def}} U(\mathbf{Y}) - U(\mathbf{Y}|\mathbf{X})$$
$$= U(\mathbf{Y}) + U(\mathbf{X}) - U(\mathbf{XY}) \, ,$$

and may be thought of as the amount of Uncertainty in categorical criterion $\mathbf{Y}$ which is accounted for by predictor $\mathbf{X}$. Reorganization of [10.66] yields

$$[10.67] \qquad U(\mathbf{Y}) = U(\mathbf{Y};\mathbf{X}) + U(\mathbf{Y}|\mathbf{X})$$

which, in evident parallel to the metrical variance partition $V_{\mathbf{Y}} = V_{\mathbf{Y}(\mathbf{X})} + V_{\mathbf{Y}\bullet\mathbf{X}}$, analyzes the total Uncertainty in $\mathbf{Y}$ into controlled and residual components.[41] (When $\mathbf{X}$ is the cartesian product of a set of predictors $\mathbf{X}_1, \ldots, \mathbf{X}_p$, the Uncertainty $U(\mathbf{Y};\mathbf{X}_1 \ldots \mathbf{X}_p)$ in $\mathbf{Y}$ jointly accounted for by $\mathbf{X}_1, \ldots, \mathbf{X}_p$ can be further partitioned into "main effect" and "interaction" terms of ascending complexity comparable to a Fisherian Analysis-of-variance partition.[42])

Finally, Information theory (Uncertainty analysis) has access to a symmetric measure of total relationship within a configuration of categorical variables for which there is no counterpart among traditional measures of metrical relationship.[43] By iteration of [10.64], the joint Uncertainty

[41] Actually, the closest metrical counterpart to [10.67] is $\sigma_{\mathbf{Y}} = k_{\mathbf{YX}}^{-1}\sigma_{\mathbf{Y}\bullet\mathbf{X}}$.
[42] See Garner and McGill (31), Rozeboom (69).
[43] However, see Rozeboom (68).

over a set of categorical variables $\mathbf{X}_1, \ldots, \mathbf{X}_n$ is seen to have an upper bound of

$$[10.68] \qquad U(\mathbf{X}_1 \ldots \mathbf{X}_n) \leq \sum_{i=1}^{n} U(\mathbf{X}_i) ,$$

with equality holding when the $\mathbf{X}_i$ are all fully independent of one another. The quantity

$$[10.69] \qquad C(\mathbf{X}_1 \ldots \mathbf{X}_n) =_{\text{def}} \sum_{i=1}^{n} U(\mathbf{X}_i) - U(\mathbf{X}_1 \ldots \mathbf{X}_n) ,$$

which is known as the "total correlation" (Watanabe, 83) or "total constraint" (Garner, 30) in the joint distribution of $\mathbf{X}_1, \ldots, \mathbf{X}_n$, is hence the amount by which the pattern of interrelations among variables $\mathbf{X}_1, \ldots, \mathbf{X}_n$ reduces the Uncertainty over their joint distribution below what, given their marginal distributions, their joint Uncertainty would be in the absence of any relationship. It is a simple consequence of [10.69] and [10.66] (reading "$\mathbf{X}_1 \ldots \mathbf{X}_n$" for "$\mathbf{X}$" in the latter) that

$$[10.70] \qquad C(\mathbf{Y}\mathbf{X}_1 \ldots \mathbf{X}_n) = U(\mathbf{Y}; \mathbf{X}_1 \ldots \mathbf{X}_n) + C(\mathbf{X}_1 \ldots \mathbf{X}_n) ,$$

which clarifies the relation between total restraint and accounted-for Uncertainty when one variable in a configuration is singled out as a criterion to be predicted from the others.

Because Information theory is so recent in origin, it is still largely untested as a research tool in the behavioral sciences, and its strengths and weaknesses have yet to be well mapped. There is little reason to expect that Information theory will surpass linear correlational analysis at tasks to which the latter is applicable, since Information theory embodies no analytic concepts not already realized (or realizable) more powerfully by correlation measures. On the other hand, Information theory permits the same *kind* of analytic thinking about multivariate categorical distributions that was previously possible only for metrical configurations. Whether this will lead to substantial advances in research areas where meaningful quantification has remained elusive, or whether it will only impede the replacement of coarse-mesh categories with more discriminating metrical concepts, yet remains to be seen.

Appendix A. **The Normal Distribution**

Tabled below are the cumulative proportions (p_Z) and probability densities (h_Z) corresponding to various Z-scores $\left(Z = \dfrac{X - M_X}{\sigma_X}\right)$ of a normal distribution. That is, h_Z is the height of the normal probability-density curve at a score which is Z sigma units above the mean, while p_Z is the area under the curve below this score.

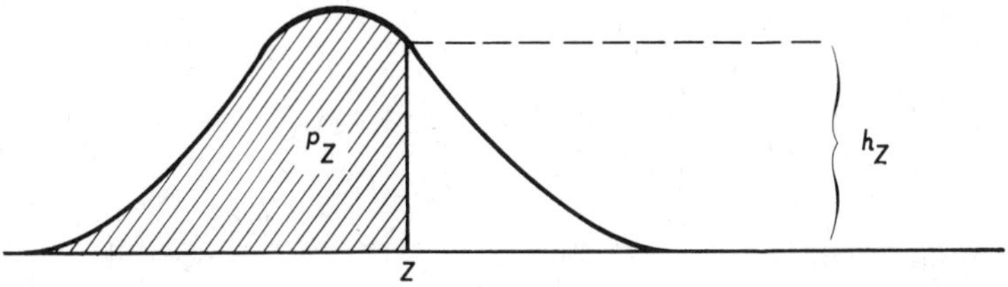

Z	p_Z	h_Z	Z	p_Z	h_Z
−4.50	.00001	.00002	0	.5000	.3989
−4.00	.00003	.0001	.05	.5199	.3984
			.10	.5398	.3970
−3.50	.0002	.0009	.15	.5596	.3945
			.20	.5793	.3910
−3.00	.0013	.0044			
			.25	.5987	.3867
−2.95	.0016	.0051			
−2.90	.0019	.0060	.30	.6179	.3814
−2.85	.0022	.0069	.35	.6368	.3752
−2.80	.0026	.0079	.40	.6554	.3683
			.45	.6736	.3605

Z	p_Z	h_Z	Z	p_Z	h_Z
−2.75	.0030	.0091	.50	.6915	.3520
−2.70	.0035	.0104	.55	.7088	.3429
−2.65	.0040	.0119	.60	.7257	.3332
−2.60	.0047	.0136	.65	.7422	.3230
−2.55	.0054	.0154	.70	.7580	.3123
−2.50	.0062	.0175	.75	.7734	.3011
−2.45	.0071	.0198	.80	.7881	.2897
−2.40	.0082	.0224	.85	.8023	.2780
−2.35	.0094	.0252	.90	.8159	.2661
−2.30	.0107	.0283	.95	.8289	.2541
−2.25	.0122	.0317	1.00	.8413	.2420
−2.20	.0139	.0355	1.05	.8531	.2299
−2.15	.0158	.0395	1.10	.8643	.2179
−2.10	.0179	.0440	1.15	.8749	.2059
−2.05	.0202	.0488	1.20	.8849	.1942
−2.00	.0228	.0540	1.25	.8944	.1826
−1.95	.0256	.0596	1.30	.9032	.1714
−1.90	.0287	.0656	1.35	.9115	.1604
−1.85	.0322	.0721	1.40	.9192	.1497
−1.80	.0359	.0790	1.45	.9265	.1394
−1.75	.0401	.0863	1.50	.9332	.1295
−1.70	.0446	.0940	1.55	.9394	.1200
−1.65	.0495	.1023	1.60	.9452	.1109
−1.60	.0548	.1109	1.65	.9505	.1023
−1.55	.0606	.1200	1.70	.9554	.0940
−1.50	.0668	.1295	1.75	.9599	.0863
−1.45	.0735	.1394	1.80	.9641	.0790
−1.40	.0808	.1497	1.85	.9678	.0721
−1.35	.0885	.1604	1.90	.9713	.0656
−1.30	.0968	.1714	1.95	.9744	.0596

Z	p_Z	h_Z	Z	p_Z	h_Z
−1.25	.1056	.1826	2.00	.9772	.0540
−1.20	.1151	.1942	2.05	.9798	.0488
−1.15	.1251	.2059	2.10	.9821	.0440
−1.10	.1357	.2179	2.15	.9842	.0395
−1.05	.1469	.2299	2.20	.9861	.0355
−1.00	.1587	.2420	2.25	.9878	.0317
− .95	.1711	.2541	2.30	.9893	.0283
− .90	.1841	.2661	2.35	.9906	.0252
− .85	.1977	.2780	2.40	.9918	.0224
− .80	.2119	.2897	2.45	.9929	.0198
− .75	.2266	.3011	2.50	.9938	.0175
− .70	.2420	.3123	2.55	.9946	.0154
− .65	.2578	.3230	2.60	.9953	.0136
− .60	.2743	.3332	2.65	.9960	.0119
− .55	.2912	.3429	2.70	.9965	.0104
− .50	.3085	.3520	2.75	.9970	.0091
− .45	.3264	.3605	2.80	.9974	.0079
− .40	.3446	.3683	2.85	.9978	.0069
− .35	.3632	.3752	2.90	.9981	.0060
− .30	.3821	.3814	2.95	.9984	.0051
− .25	.4013	.3867	3.00	.9987	.0044
− .20	.4207	.3910	3.50	.9998	.0009
− .15	.4404	.3945			
− .10	.4602	.3970	4.00	.99997	.0001
− .05	.4801	.3984			
			4.50	.99999	.00002
0	.5000	.3989			

Appendix B. **Matrix Derivations**

This appendix develops an assortment of important theorems whose otherwise awkward proofs become for the most part elegantly simple when carried out in matrix notation. The present derivations presuppose only that the reader has a working knowledge of the more elementary matrix manipulations, notably, products, transposes, and inverses. Use of partial differentiation and Lagrange multipliers to find maxima has been avoided, and apart from one fundamental theorem which is stated without proof, no background in the theory of characteristic roots and vectors is assumed.

Notation

In the following proofs, matrices will be represented by the general form "$\mathbf{M_{AB}}$" in which the symbol instantiating "**M**" tells what *kind* of entries are in the matrix, and "**A**" and "**B**" identify sets of variables or individuals corresponding to the rows and columns, respectively, of the matrix. In particular, "$\mathbf{S_{XI}}$" designates the array of "normalized" scores (defined immediately below) on a set of variables $\mathbf{X_1}, \ldots, \mathbf{X_n}$ for the Individuals $j = 1, \ldots, p$ in a given population P; "$\mathbf{C_{YX}}$" designates the array of covariances in population P between variables in the set $\mathbf{Y_1}, \ldots, \mathbf{Y_m}$ and variables in set $\mathbf{X_1}, \ldots, \mathbf{X_n}$; "$\mathbf{B_{\hat{Y}X}}$" designates the array of b-coefficients for the multiple linear regression in P of variables in set $\mathbf{Y_1}, \ldots, \mathbf{Y_m}$ upon all the variables in set $\mathbf{X_1}, \ldots, \mathbf{X_n}$; and more generally, any matrix of form $\mathbf{W_{LX}}$, in which "**L**" designates a set of variables $\mathbf{L_1}, \ldots, \mathbf{L_m}$ which are linear functions of variables $\mathbf{X_1}, \ldots, \mathbf{X_n}$, is the array of transformation coefficients which carry the $\mathbf{X_i}$ into the $\mathbf{L_j}$. Specifically,

$$\text{[B.1]} \qquad \mathbf{S_{XI}} =_{\text{def}} \left\{ \frac{X_{i_j} - \mathrm{M}_{\mathbf{X_i}}}{\sqrt{p}} \right\},$$

where p is the number of individuals in population P and hence the number of columns in $\mathbf{S_{XI}}$,

$$\text{[B.2]} \qquad \mathbf{C_{YX}} =_{\text{def}} \{\mathrm{C}_{\mathbf{Y_i X_j}}\} = \{\mathrm{Cov}(\mathbf{Y_i}, \mathbf{X_j})\},$$

[B.3] $$\mathbf{B}_{\dot{\mathsf{Y}}\mathsf{X}} =_{\text{def}} \{b_{\mathsf{Y}_i\mathsf{X}_j \bullet \mathsf{X}_1 \ldots \mathsf{X}_{j-1}\mathsf{X}_{j+1}\ldots\mathsf{X}_n}\} ,$$

[B.4] $$\mathbf{W}_{\mathsf{LX}} =_{\text{def}} \{w_{ij}\} \qquad (\mathbf{L}_i = w_{i0} + \sum_{i=1}^{n} w_{ij}\mathbf{X}_i;\ \mathbf{i} = \mathbf{1}, \ldots, \mathbf{m}) .$$

One disadvantage of this notation is that it does not make explicit the matrix's dimensions; however, this will be adequately clarified by context. For the special case of $1 \times n$ matrices—i.e., row vectors—lowercase letters will be used for the primary matrix symbol. Thus "**a**" designates a vector of constants $\langle a_1, \ldots, a_n \rangle$, while the **i**th row of matrix $\mathbf{W}_{\mathsf{LX}}$ in [B.4] may be written "$\mathbf{w}_i$," i.e.,

[B.5] $$\mathbf{w}_i =_{\text{def}} \langle w_{i1}, \ldots, w_{in} \rangle .$$

The "normalized" scores[1] of individuals $j = 1, \ldots, p$ in population P on variable $\mathbf{X}_i$ as defined by [B.1] are a linear transformation of raw scores on $\mathbf{X}_i$ in P into a standardized variable with zero mean and variance equal to $\mathrm{V}_{\mathsf{X}_i}/p$. The special convenience of this standardization for matrix manipulations is that the matrix of covariances between two sets of variables in population P may be obtained simply by postmultiplying the normalized-score matrix for the one set of variables by the transposed normalized-score matrix for the other. Thus for sets $\mathbf{X}_1, \ldots, \mathbf{X}_n$ and $\mathbf{Y}_1, \ldots, \mathbf{Y}_m$,

[B.6] $$\begin{aligned} \mathbf{S}_{\mathsf{YI}}\mathbf{S}'_{\mathsf{XI}} &= \left\{ \sum_{k=1}^{p} \left(\frac{Y_{ik} - \mathrm{M}_{\mathsf{Y}_i}}{\sqrt{p}} \right) \left(\frac{X_{jk} - \mathrm{M}_{\mathsf{X}_j}}{\sqrt{p}} \right) \right\} \\ &= \{\mathrm{Cov}(\mathbf{Y}_i, \mathbf{X}_j)\} \\ &= \mathbf{C}_{\mathsf{YX}} . \end{aligned}$$

In particular, for the matrix of covariances within a set of variables we have

[B.7] $$\mathbf{S}_{\mathsf{XI}}\mathbf{S}'_{\mathsf{XI}} = \mathbf{C}_{\mathsf{XX}} .$$

It will also be observed that if variable $\mathbf{L}_i$ is a linear composite $\mathbf{L}_i = w_{i0} + \sum_{j=1}^{n} w_{ij}\mathbf{X}_j$ of variables $\mathbf{X}_1, \ldots, \mathbf{X}_n$, then $(\mathbf{L}_i - \mathrm{M}_{\mathsf{L}_i})/\sqrt{p} = \sum_{j=1}^{n} w_{ij}(\mathbf{X}_j - \mathrm{M}_{\mathsf{X}_j})/\sqrt{p}$ and hence

[B.8] $$\mathbf{S}_{\mathsf{LI}} = \mathbf{W}_{\mathsf{LX}}\mathbf{S}_{\mathsf{XI}} \qquad (\mathbf{L}_i = w_{i0} + \sum_{j=1}^{n} w_{ij}\mathbf{X}_j;\ \mathbf{i} = \mathbf{1}, \ldots, \mathbf{m}) .$$

---

[1] The present sense of "normalized score," which is conventional usage in this particular context, should not be confused with the notion of "normalized variable" introduced on p 212.

An especially important consequence of [B.7] and [B.8] is that

$$[B.9] \quad \mathbf{C_{LL}} = \mathbf{S_{LI}}\,\mathbf{S'_{LI}}$$
$$= \mathbf{W_{LX}}\,\mathbf{S_{XI}}\,\mathbf{S'_{XI}}\,\mathbf{W'_{LX}} \quad (\mathbf{L_i} = w_{i0} + \sum_{j=1}^{n} w_{ij}\mathbf{X_j};\ \mathbf{i} = \mathbf{1}, \ldots, \mathbf{m})$$
$$= \mathbf{W_{LX}}\,\mathbf{C_{XX}}\,\mathbf{W'_{LX}}\,.$$

When we are concerned with the covariance between two particular composites of the $\mathbf{X_j}$ we have as an element of $\mathbf{C_{LL}}$ in [B.9],

$$[B.10] \quad \mathbf{C_{L_iL_j}} = \mathbf{s_{L_iI}}\,\mathbf{s'_{L_jI}}$$
$$= \mathbf{w_i}\,\mathbf{S_{XI}}\,\mathbf{S'_{XI}}\,\mathbf{w'_j} \quad (\mathbf{L_k} = w_{0k} + \sum_{j=1}^{n} w_{kj}\mathbf{X_j};\ \mathbf{k} = \mathbf{i,j})$$
$$= \mathbf{w_i}\,\mathbf{C_{XX}}\,\mathbf{w'_j}\,,$$

in which $\mathbf{s_{L_kI}}$ ($\mathbf{k} = \mathbf{i,j}$) is the row vector of normalized scores on $\mathbf{L_k}$ and $\mathbf{w_k}$ is the row vector of coefficients $\langle w_{k1}, \ldots, w_{kn}\rangle$.

Multiple Regression

Suppose that we have a number of criterion variables $\mathbf{Y_1}, \ldots, \mathbf{Y_m}$ (where $\mathbf{m}$ may but need not be greater than $\mathbf{1}$) whose linear regressions upon the set of predictors $\mathbf{X_1}, \ldots, \mathbf{X_n}$ we would like to determine simultaneously. For convenience, we write $\dot{\mathbf{Y}}_i =_{def} \dot{\mathbf{Y}}_{i(X_1 \ldots X_n)} = b_{i0} + \sum_{j=1}^{n} b_{ij}\mathbf{X_j}$ ($\mathbf{i} = \mathbf{1}, \ldots, \mathbf{m}$), so that

$$[B.11] \quad \mathbf{S_{\dot{Y}I}} = \mathbf{B_{\dot{Y}X}}\,\mathbf{S_{XI}}$$

and hence

$$[B.12] \quad \mathbf{C_{\dot{Y}X}} = \mathbf{S_{\dot{Y}I}}\,\mathbf{S'_{XI}}$$
$$= \mathbf{B_{\dot{Y}X}}\,\mathbf{S_{XI}}\,\mathbf{S'_{XI}}$$
$$= \mathbf{B_{\dot{Y}X}}\,\mathbf{C_{XX}}\,.$$

Also, let $\mathbf{e_{Y_i}} =_{def} \mathbf{e_{Y_i \cdot X_1 \ldots X_n}}$ ($\mathbf{i} = \mathbf{1}, \ldots, \mathbf{m}$). Then

$$[B.13] \quad \mathbf{S_{YI}} = \mathbf{S_{\dot{Y}I}} + \mathbf{S_{e_YI}}$$

and hence

$$[B.14] \quad \mathbf{C_{YX}} = (\mathbf{S_{\dot{Y}I}} + \mathbf{S_{e_YI}})\mathbf{S'_{XI}}$$
$$= \mathbf{S_{\dot{Y}I}}\,\mathbf{S'_{XI}} + \mathbf{S_{e_YI}}\,\mathbf{S'_{XI}}$$
$$= \mathbf{C_{\dot{Y}X}} + \mathbf{C_{e_YX}}\,.$$

Since the covariance between any predictor $\mathbf{X_j}$ and any residual of a variable from which $\mathbf{X_j}$ has been partialled out must be zero (see p. 143), the covariance matrix $\mathbf{C}_{\mathbf{e}_Y\mathbf{X}}$ is identically zero and hence from [B.14] and [B.12],

[B.15]
$$\mathbf{C}_{\mathbf{YX}} = \mathbf{C}_{\dot{\mathbf{Y}}\mathbf{X}} = \mathbf{B}_{\dot{\mathbf{Y}}\mathbf{X}}\mathbf{C}_{\mathbf{XX}} ,$$

or assuming $\mathbf{C}_{\mathbf{XX}}$ to be nonsingular (i.e., if the dimensionality of the set $\mathbf{X}_1, \ldots, \mathbf{X}_n$ is not less than $\mathbf{n}$),

[B.16]
$$\mathbf{B}_{\dot{\mathbf{Y}}\mathbf{X}} = \mathbf{C}_{\mathbf{YX}}\mathbf{C}_{\mathbf{XX}}^{-1} .$$

This shows that once the covariance matrix of a set of predictor variables has been solved for its inverse, the regressions of any number of criteria upon these predictors can be computed with little additional effort. It also follows from [B.16] that the matrix of covariances among the projections of the $\mathbf{Y}_j$ into the space spanned by $\mathbf{X}_1, \ldots, \mathbf{X}_n$ is

[B.17]
$$\begin{aligned} \mathbf{C}_{\mathbf{YY}(S_X)} &=_{\text{def}} \mathbf{C}_{\dot{\mathbf{Y}}\dot{\mathbf{Y}}} \\ &= \mathbf{S}_{\dot{\mathbf{Y}}\mathbf{l}}\mathbf{S}_{\dot{\mathbf{Y}}\mathbf{l}}' \\ &= \mathbf{B}_{\dot{\mathbf{Y}}\mathbf{X}}\,\mathbf{C}_{\mathbf{XX}}\,\mathbf{B}_{\dot{\mathbf{Y}}\mathbf{X}}' \\ &= \mathbf{B}_{\dot{\mathbf{Y}}\mathbf{X}}\,\mathbf{C}_{\mathbf{YX}}' \\ &= \mathbf{C}_{\mathbf{YX}}\,\mathbf{C}_{\mathbf{XX}}^{-1}\,\mathbf{C}_{\mathbf{YX}}' \\ &= \mathbf{C}_{\mathbf{YX}}\,\mathbf{C}_{\mathbf{XX}}^{-1}\,\mathbf{C}_{\mathbf{XY}} . \end{aligned}$$

The Inverse of a Covariance Matrix

Let $\mathbf{X}_i$ and $\mathbf{X}_j$ ($\mathbf{i} \neq \mathbf{j}$) belong to a set of variables $\mathbf{X}_1, \ldots, \mathbf{X}_n$, while "$\boldsymbol{\mu}_i$" designates the variables in $\mathbf{X}_1, \ldots, \mathbf{X}_n$ other than $\mathbf{X}_i$ and "$\boldsymbol{\mu}_{ij}$" designates the variables in $\mathbf{X}_1, \ldots, \mathbf{X}_n$ other than $\mathbf{X}_i$ and $\mathbf{X}_j$. Then the linear regression of $\mathbf{X}_i$ upon the other variables $\boldsymbol{\mu}_i$ in this set may be written

$$\dot{\mathbf{X}}_{i(\boldsymbol{\mu}_i)} = b_{i0} + \sum_{\substack{j=1 \\ j\neq i}}^{n} b_{\mathbf{X}_i\mathbf{X}_j\cdot\boldsymbol{\mu}_{ij}}\mathbf{X}_j$$

while the residual of $\mathbf{X}_i$ left by this regression is

[B.18-i]
(i = 1, . . . , n)
$$\mathbf{e}_{\mathbf{X}_i\cdot\boldsymbol{\mu}_i} = \mathbf{X}_i - b_{i0} - \sum_{\substack{j=1 \\ j\neq i}}^{n} b_{\mathbf{X}_i\mathbf{X}_j\cdot\boldsymbol{\mu}_{ij}}\mathbf{X}_j .$$

The symbol "$b_{\mathbf{X}_i\mathbf{X}_j\cdot\boldsymbol{\mu}_{ij}}$", which denotes a regression coefficient when $\mathbf{i} \neq \mathbf{j}$, is undefined when $\mathbf{i} = \mathbf{j}$. Hence we are free to stipulate that

[B.19-i]
(i = 1, . . . , n)
$$b_{\mathbf{X}_i\mathbf{X}_i\cdot\boldsymbol{\mu}_{ii}} =_{\text{def}} -1 ,$$

in which case equations [B.18] can be written more neatly as

$$[B.20\text{-}\mathbf{i}] \quad (\mathbf{i} = \mathbf{1}, \ldots, \mathbf{n}) \qquad -e_{\mathbf{X}_i \cdot \boldsymbol{\mu}_i} = b_{\mathbf{i}0} + \sum_{\mathbf{j}=1}^{\mathbf{n}} b_{\mathbf{X}_i\mathbf{X}_j \bullet \boldsymbol{\mu}_{ij}} \mathbf{X}_\mathbf{j} .$$

In matrix notation, [B.20] becomes

$$[B.21] \qquad -\mathbf{S}_{\mathbf{e_X I}} = \mathbf{B}_{\dot{\mathbf{X}}\mathbf{X}}\, \mathbf{S}_{\mathbf{XI}} ,$$

where $\mathbf{S}_{\mathbf{XI}}$ is the matrix of normalized scores on $\mathbf{X}_1, \ldots, \mathbf{X}_n$ as before, $\mathbf{S}_{\mathbf{e_X I}}$ is the matrix of normalized scores on the residuals $\mathbf{e}_{\mathbf{X}_i \bullet \boldsymbol{\mu}_i}$, and $\mathbf{B}_{\dot{\mathbf{X}}\mathbf{X}}$ is the matrix of b-coefficients, namely,

$$[B.22] \qquad \mathbf{B}_{\dot{\mathbf{X}}\mathbf{X}} =_{\text{def}} \{b_{\mathbf{X}_i\mathbf{X}_j \bullet \boldsymbol{\mu}_{ij}}\} .$$

Postmultiplying [B.21] by $\mathbf{S}'_{\mathbf{XI}}$, we have

$$[B.23] \qquad -\mathbf{C}_{\mathbf{e_X X}} = \mathbf{B}_{\dot{\mathbf{X}}\mathbf{X}}\, \mathbf{C}_{\mathbf{XX}} .$$

Now let $\mathbf{D}_{\mathbf{V_e}}$ be the diagonal matrix whose **i**th diagonal element is the variance of $\mathbf{X}_i$ unaccounted for by the other variables in $\mathbf{X}_1, \ldots, \mathbf{X}_n$—i.e.,

$$[B.24] \qquad \mathbf{D}_{\mathbf{V_e}} =_{\text{def}} \{d_{\mathbf{ij}}\} , \quad d_{\mathbf{ij}} =_{\text{def}} \begin{cases} V_{\mathbf{X}_i \bullet \boldsymbol{\mu}_i} & \text{if } \mathbf{i} = \mathbf{j} \\ 0 & \text{if } \mathbf{i} \neq \mathbf{j} \end{cases}$$

The covariance between the residual $\mathbf{e}_{\mathbf{X}_i \bullet \boldsymbol{\mu}_i}$ and any variable $\mathbf{X}_j$ in $\boldsymbol{\mu}_i$ is zero, while $\text{Cov}(\mathbf{e}_{\mathbf{X}_i}, \mathbf{X}_i) = \text{Cov}(\mathbf{e}_{\mathbf{X}_i}, \mathbf{e}_{\mathbf{X}_i} + \mathbf{X}_{i(\boldsymbol{\mu}_i)}) = V_{\mathbf{X}_i \bullet \boldsymbol{\mu}_i}$. Hence

$$[B.25] \qquad \mathbf{C}_{\mathbf{e_X X}} =_{\text{def}} \{\text{Cov}(\mathbf{e}_{\mathbf{X}_i}, \mathbf{X}_j)\} = \mathbf{D}_{\mathbf{V_e}} ,$$

so from [B.23],

$$[B.26] \qquad -\mathbf{D}_{\mathbf{V_e}} = \mathbf{B}_{\dot{\mathbf{X}}\mathbf{X}}\, \mathbf{C}_{\mathbf{XX}} .$$

Derivation of [B.26] does not require variables $\mathbf{X}_1, \ldots, \mathbf{X}_n$ to be linearly independent of one another, though if they are not, the regression-coefficient matrix $\mathbf{B}_{\dot{\mathbf{X}}\mathbf{X}}$ is not in general uniquely determined. However, if covariance matrix $\mathbf{C}_{\mathbf{XX}}$ has an inverse—i.e., if the $\mathbf{X}_i$ are in fact independent—then postmultiplying [B.26] by $\mathbf{C}^{-1}_{\mathbf{XX}}$ and premultiplying by $-\mathbf{D}^{-1}_{\mathbf{V_e}}$ yields

$$[B.27] \qquad \mathbf{C}^{-1}_{\dot{\mathbf{X}}\mathbf{X}} = -\mathbf{D}^{-1}_{\mathbf{V_e}} \mathbf{B}_{\dot{\mathbf{X}}\mathbf{X}} = \left\{ -\frac{b_{\mathbf{X}_i\mathbf{X}_j \bullet \boldsymbol{\mu}_{ij}}}{V_{\mathbf{X}_i \bullet \boldsymbol{\mu}_i}} \right\} ,$$

in which, by [B.19], the **i**th diagonal element is $V^{-1}_{\mathbf{X}_i \bullet \boldsymbol{\mu}_i}$.

Once the inverse of the covariance matrix for variables $\mathbf{X}_1, \ldots, \mathbf{X}_n$ has been computed, moreover, it is extremely simple to compute the inverse of the covariance matrix for the reduced set of variables $\mathbf{X}_1, \ldots, \mathbf{X}_{n-1}$. (The only reason for here evicting $\mathbf{X}_n$ rather than some other member of the original set is notational simplicity.) It is not difficult to show that if $\begin{bmatrix} \mathbf{A} & \mathbf{B} \\ \mathbf{C} & \mathbf{D} \end{bmatrix}$ and $\begin{bmatrix} \mathbf{E} & \mathbf{F} \\ \mathbf{G} & \mathbf{H} \end{bmatrix}$ are partitioned square matrices such that submatrices **A** and **E** are $m \times m$, **D** and **H** are $n \times n$, **B** and **F** are $m \times n$, and **C** and **G** are $n \times m$, while $\begin{bmatrix} \mathbf{E} & \mathbf{F} \\ \mathbf{G} & \mathbf{H} \end{bmatrix}$ is the inverse of $\begin{bmatrix} \mathbf{A} & \mathbf{B} \\ \mathbf{C} & \mathbf{D} \end{bmatrix}$, then assuming **D** and **E** to be nonsingular,

[B.28]

$$\begin{aligned} \mathbf{E} &= (\mathbf{A} - \mathbf{BD}^{-1}\mathbf{C})^{-1}, \quad \mathbf{F} = -\mathbf{E}(\mathbf{BD}^{-1}) \\ \mathbf{G} &= -(\mathbf{D}^{-1}\mathbf{C})\mathbf{E}, \quad \mathbf{H} = \mathbf{D}^{-1} + (\mathbf{D}^{-1}\mathbf{C})\mathbf{E}(\mathbf{BD}^{-1}) \end{aligned} \qquad \left(\begin{bmatrix} \mathbf{E} & \mathbf{F} \\ \mathbf{G} & \mathbf{H} \end{bmatrix} = \begin{bmatrix} \mathbf{A} & \mathbf{B} \\ \mathbf{C} & \mathbf{D} \end{bmatrix}^{-1} \right)$$

(The proof follows by setting the product of the two partitioned matrices equal to the $(m+n) \times (m+n)$ Identity matrix, observing that this entails $\mathbf{AE} + \mathbf{BG} = \mathbf{I}$, $\mathbf{CE} + \mathbf{DG} = \mathbf{O}$, $\mathbf{AF} + \mathbf{BH} = \mathbf{O}$, and $\mathbf{CF} + \mathbf{DH} = \mathbf{I}$, where **O** is a matrix all of whose entries are zeros, and then successively solving for **G**, **E**, **F**, and **H**.) Let $\overset{*}{\mathbf{C}}{}^{-1}_{\mathbf{XX}} = \{\overset{*}{\mathbf{C}}{}^{\mathbf{ij}}\}$ be the inverse of the $(\mathbf{n}-1) \times (\mathbf{n}-1)$ matrix $\overset{*}{\mathbf{C}}_{\mathbf{XX}}$ of covariances among variables $\mathbf{X_1}, \ldots, \mathbf{X_{n-1}}$, while $\mathbf{C}^{-1}_{\mathbf{XX}} = \{\mathrm{C}^{\mathbf{ij}}\}$ is the inverse of the covariance matrix for the unreduced set $\mathbf{X_1}, \ldots, \mathbf{X_n}$ as before. Then if we let the partitioned matrix $\begin{bmatrix} \mathbf{A} & \mathbf{B} \\ \mathbf{C} & \mathbf{D} \end{bmatrix}$ in [B.28] be $\mathbf{C}^{-1}_{\mathbf{XX}}$, in which the partitions are so placed that **D** is the 1×1 matrix $\mathrm{C}^{\mathbf{nn}}$ (i.e., $\mathrm{V}^{-1}_{\mathbf{X_n} \cdot \mu_n}$) while $\begin{bmatrix} \mathbf{E} & \mathbf{F} \\ \mathbf{G} & \mathbf{H} \end{bmatrix}$ is $\mathbf{C_{XX}}$ and **E** is $\overset{*}{\mathbf{C}}_{\mathbf{XX}}$, the first equation in [B.28], rewritten as $\mathbf{E}^{-1} = \mathbf{A} - \mathbf{BD}^{-1}\mathbf{C}$, yields

[B.29-**ij**]
(**i**,**j** = **1**, . . . , **n** − **1**)

$$\overset{*}{\mathrm{C}}{}^{\mathbf{ij}} = \mathrm{C}^{\mathbf{ij}} - \frac{\mathrm{C}^{\mathbf{in}}\mathrm{C}^{\mathbf{jn}}}{\mathrm{C}^{\mathbf{nn}}}.$$

Conversely, if we have computed the inverse $\overset{*}{\mathbf{C}}{}^{-1}_{\mathbf{XX}}$ of the covariance matrix for variables $\mathbf{X_1}, \ldots, \mathbf{X_{n-1}}$ and now wish to augment the set with an additional variable $\mathbf{X_n}$ whose variance and covariances with $\mathbf{X_1}, \ldots, \mathbf{X_{n-1}}$ are given, we can quickly build up $\mathbf{C}^{-1}_{\mathbf{XX}}$ through use of equations [B.28] by letting $\mathbf{D}^{-1}$ be $\overset{*}{\mathbf{C}}{}^{-1}_{\mathbf{XX}}$, **B** and **C**′ be the row vector $\langle \mathrm{C}_{\mathbf{X_nX_1}}, \ldots, \mathrm{C}_{\mathbf{X_nX_{n-1}}} \rangle$, and **A** be $\mathrm{V}_{\mathbf{X_n}}$.

Orthogonal Rotations

Let variables $\mathbf{X}'_1, \ldots, \mathbf{X}'_n$ be defined by an orthogonal rotation of variables $\mathbf{X_1}, \ldots, \mathbf{X_n}$. That is,

[B.30-**i**]

$$\mathbf{X}'_{\mathbf{i}} =_{\text{def}} \sum_{\mathbf{j}=1}^{\mathbf{n}} t_{\mathbf{ij}}\mathbf{X_j},$$

where

[B.31-**ij**]
(**i**,**j** = **1**, . . . , **n**)

$$\sum_{\mathbf{k}=1}^{\mathbf{n}} t_{\mathbf{ik}}t_{\mathbf{jk}} = \begin{cases} 1 \text{ if } \mathbf{i} = \mathbf{j} \\ 0 \text{ if } \mathbf{i} \neq \mathbf{j} \end{cases}$$

In matrix notation, this may be written

[B.32] $$\mathbf{S}_{\mathbf{X}'\mathbf{I}} = \mathbf{T}_{\mathbf{X}'\mathbf{X}}\mathbf{S}_{\mathbf{X}\mathbf{I}}, \quad \mathbf{T}_{\mathbf{X}'\mathbf{X}}\mathbf{T}'_{\mathbf{X}'\mathbf{X}} = \mathbf{I}\,,$$

where $\mathbf{T}_{\mathbf{X}'\mathbf{X}} = \{t_{ij}\}$ and $\mathbf{I}$ is the $\mathbf{n} \times \mathbf{n}$ Identity matrix with unities on the diagonal and zeros elsewhere. (Throughout this appendix the primary matrix symbol "**T**" will always denote an orthonormal matrix, and it will be important to bear in mind that for any such $\mathbf{T}$, $\mathbf{T}' = \mathbf{T}^{-1}$ so that $\mathbf{TT}' = \mathbf{I} = \mathbf{T}'\mathbf{T}$.) Using principle [B.9], the covariance matrix for the rotated variables is seen to be

[B.33] $$\mathbf{C}_{\mathbf{X}'\mathbf{X}'} = \mathbf{T}_{\mathbf{X}'\mathbf{X}}\mathbf{C}_{\mathbf{X}\mathbf{X}}\mathbf{T}'_{\mathbf{X}'\mathbf{X}}\,.$$

Now let $\mathbf{F}_1, \ldots, \mathbf{F}_m$ be some orthonormal factor basis for an arbitrary space S, so that the total variance of the set $\mathbf{X}_1, \ldots, \mathbf{X}_n$ accounted for by factor $\mathbf{F}_j$ is

$$V_{\mathbf{X}(\mathbf{F}_j)} = \sum_{i=1}^{n} V_{\mathbf{X}_i(\mathbf{F}_j)} = \sum_{i=1}^{n} C^2_{\mathbf{X}_i\mathbf{F}_j}$$

(see [6.30], [6.41]) while the total variance of the $\mathbf{X}_i$-configuration lying in space S is

$$V_{\mathbf{X}(S)} = V_{\mathbf{X}(\mathbf{F}_1 \cdots \mathbf{F}_m)} = \sum_{j=1}^{n} V_{\mathbf{X}(\mathbf{F}_j)}$$

(see [6.28]). Since $\sum_{i=1}^{n} C^2_{\mathbf{X}_i\mathbf{F}_j}$ is also the $\mathbf{j}$th diagonal element of the matrix $\mathbf{C}'_{\mathbf{XF}}\mathbf{C}_{\mathbf{XF}}$, $V_{\mathbf{X}(S)}$ thus equals the trace of matrix $\mathbf{C}'_{\mathbf{XF}}\mathbf{C}_{\mathbf{XF}}$, where the "trace" of a square matrix is defined to be the sum of the elements on its principal diagonal. Similarly, when the $\mathbf{X}_i$ are orthogonally rotated into set $\mathbf{X}'_1, \ldots, \mathbf{X}'_n$, the total variance in space S of the rotated configuration equals the trace of matrix $\mathbf{C}'_{\mathbf{X}'\mathbf{F}}\mathbf{C}_{\mathbf{X}'\mathbf{F}}$. But $\mathbf{C}_{\mathbf{X}'\mathbf{F}} = \mathbf{S}_{\mathbf{X}'\mathbf{I}}\mathbf{S}'_{\mathbf{FI}} = \mathbf{T}_{\mathbf{X}'\mathbf{X}}\mathbf{S}_{\mathbf{XI}}\mathbf{S}'_{\mathbf{FI}} = \mathbf{T}_{\mathbf{X}'\mathbf{X}}\mathbf{C}_{\mathbf{XF}}$, so $\mathbf{C}'_{\mathbf{X}'\mathbf{F}}\mathbf{C}_{\mathbf{X}'\mathbf{F}} = \mathbf{C}'_{\mathbf{XF}}\mathbf{T}'_{\mathbf{X}'\mathbf{X}}\mathbf{T}_{\mathbf{X}'\mathbf{X}}\mathbf{C}_{\mathbf{XF}} = \mathbf{C}'_{\mathbf{XF}}\mathbf{C}_{\mathbf{XF}}$. Since the two matrices $\mathbf{C}'_{\mathbf{X}'\mathbf{F}}\mathbf{C}_{\mathbf{X}'\mathbf{F}}$ and $\mathbf{C}'_{\mathbf{XF}}\mathbf{C}_{\mathbf{XF}}$ are identical, so must be their traces and hence $V_{\mathbf{X}'(S)} = V_{\mathbf{X}(S)}$. That is, *for any set of variables* $\mathbf{X}_1, \ldots, \mathbf{X}_n$ *and space* S, *the total variance of the configuration lying in* S *is invariant under any orthogonal rotation of the* $\mathbf{X}_i$.

Principal Components

Since the total-variance properties of a configuration $\mathbf{X}_1, \ldots, \mathbf{X}_n$ are unaffected by orthogonal rotation, the thought arises that some standard rotational form may exist for a set of variables which reveals its variance composition with especial perspicuity. The *principal components* of the configuration are such a form, and are blessed with a remarkable abundance of succulent mathematical properties.

It is a fundamental theorem of matrix algebra (or more precisely, a corollary of an even more basic theorem cited on p. 601 below) that for any symmetric real matrix **M**, there exists an orthonormal real matrix **T** and a diagonal real matrix **D** that $\mathbf{TMT'} = \mathbf{D}$. Since the covariance matrix $\mathbf{C_{XX}}$ for a configuration $\mathbf{X_1}, \ldots, \mathbf{X_n}$ is necessarily symmetric, there hence exists an orthonormal real matrix $\mathbf{T_{PX}} = \{t_{ij}\}$ such that

[B.34] $$\mathbf{T_{PX}}\,\mathbf{C_{XX}}\,\mathbf{T'_{PX}} = \mathbf{D}_\lambda\ ,$$

where the **i**th diagonal element of $\mathbf{D}_\lambda$ is λ_i and the off-diagonal elements of $\mathbf{D}_\lambda$ are all zero. Let variables $\mathbf{P_1}, \ldots, \mathbf{P_n}$ be defined

[B.35-**i**] (**i** = **1**, . . . , **n**) $$\mathbf{P_i} = \sum_{j=1}^{n} t_{ij}\mathbf{X_j}\ ,$$

where t_{ij} is the **ij**th element of matrix $\mathbf{T_{PX}}$ in [B.34]. Then

[B.36] $$\mathbf{S_{PI}} = \mathbf{T_{PX}}\,\mathbf{S_{XI}}\ ,$$

so

[B.37] $$\mathbf{C_{PP}} = \mathbf{T_{PX}}\,\mathbf{C_{XX}}\,\mathbf{T'_{PX}} = \mathbf{D}_\lambda\ ,$$

which says that

[B.38-**i**] (**i** = **1**, . . . , **n**) $$\mathrm{Var}(\mathbf{P_i}) = \lambda_i$$

and

[B.39-**ij**] (**i**,**j** = **1**, . . . , **n**; **i** ≠ **j**) $$\mathrm{Cov}(\mathbf{P_i}, \mathbf{P_j}) = 0\ .$$

That is, the *orthogonal rotation* $\mathbf{T_{PX}}$ carries the set $\mathbf{X_1}, \ldots, \mathbf{X_n}$ into an *orthogonal configuration* $\mathbf{P_1}, \ldots, \mathbf{P_n}$, where due to the invariance of set variance under orthogonal rotation,

[B.40] $$V_X = V_P = \sum_{i=1}^{n} \lambda_i\ .$$

(For simplicity, this appendix takes "is orthogonal to" as synonymous for "has zero covariance with," though strictly speaking, orthogonality presupposes variables with nonzero variances.) The $\mathbf{P_i}$ are thus an orthogonal (though *not*, in general, orthonormal) basis for the space S_X spanned by the $\mathbf{X_i}$, while the dimensionality of S_X equals the number (generally **n**) of the λ_i which are greater than zero. (From [B.38], λ_i cannot be negative.) We may stipulate without essential loss of generality that the sequence $\mathbf{P_1}, \ldots, \mathbf{P_n}$ is so ordered that $\lambda_1 \geqslant \lambda_2 \geqslant \ldots \geqslant \lambda_n$, since if this is not so to begin with it can obviously be brought about by a suitable permutation of the rows of $\mathbf{T_{PX}}$. Then by definition, $\mathbf{P_1}, \ldots, \mathbf{P_n}$ are a set of *principal components* for the configuration $\mathbf{X_1}, \ldots, \mathbf{X_n}$,[2] while λ_i is the *eigenvalue* corresponding to $\mathbf{P_i}$.

It may be seen from the foregoing that the total variance of the set $\mathbf{X_1}, \ldots, \mathbf{X_n}$ accounted for by any single variable $\mathbf{F_j}$ is

$$\text{[B.41]} \qquad V_{\mathbf{X}(\mathbf{F_j})} = V_{\mathbf{P}(\mathbf{F_j})} = \sum_{i=1}^{n} V_{\mathbf{P_i}}\, r^2_{\mathbf{P_i F_j}} = \sum_{i=1}^{n} \lambda_i r^2_{\mathbf{P_i F_j}},$$

while since the $\mathbf{P_i}$ are an orthogonal basis for $S_{\mathbf{X}}$, $\sum_{i=1}^{n} r^2_{\mathbf{P_i F_j}}$ is the proportion of $\mathbf{F_j}$'s variance lying in $S_{\mathbf{X}}$. Hence continuing [B.41],

$$\text{[B.42]} \qquad V_{\mathbf{X}(\mathbf{F_j})} = R^2_{\mathbf{F_j}(\mathbf{X_1}\ldots\mathbf{X_n})} \left[\frac{\sum_{i=1}^{n} \lambda_i r^2_{\mathbf{P_i F_j}}}{\sum_{i=1}^{n} r^2_{\mathbf{P_i F_j}}} \right],$$

in which the bracketed expression is a weighted average of $\lambda_1, \ldots, \lambda_n$. It is obvious from [B.42] that the maximum value which can be attained by $V_{\mathbf{X}(\mathbf{F_j})}$ for any choice of $\mathbf{F_j}$ is λ_1, which is reached when $\mathbf{F_j}$ coincides (u.l.t.[3]) with $\mathbf{P_1}$, and more generally, that the maximal value possible for $V_{\mathbf{X}(\mathbf{F_j})}$ under the restriction that $\mathbf{F_j}$ is orthogonal to $\mathbf{P_1}, \mathbf{P_2}, \ldots, \mathbf{P_{k-1}}$ is λ_k, which is attained when $\mathbf{F_j}$ coincides (u.l.t.) with $\mathbf{P_k}$. Thus *a set of principal components for a configuration of variables is also a sequence of factors which, when extracted successively, maximize the total remaining variance of the configuration accounted for at each step, while the total set variance extracted by the* **k***th factor in any series of orthogonal factors which successively maximize accounted-for variance equals* λ_k. This shows that the eigenvalues $\lambda_1, \ldots, \lambda_n$ for a configuration $\mathbf{X_1}, \ldots, \mathbf{X_n}$ are uniquely determined, since if $\mathbf{T_{P^*X}}$ is another orthogonal matrix different from $\mathbf{T_{PX}}$ such that $\mathbf{T_{P^*X} C_{XX} T'_{P^*X}} = \mathbf{D_{\lambda^*}}$, where $\mathbf{D_{\lambda^*}}$ is a diagonal matrix with diagonal elements $\lambda^*_i \geqslant \lambda^*_{i+1}$ ($\mathbf{i} = \mathbf{1}, \ldots, \mathbf{n} - \mathbf{1}$), solving for orthogonal factors which successively maximize the $\mathbf{X_i}$-configuration's accounted-for variance yields $\lambda_i = \lambda^*_i$ for $\mathbf{i} = \mathbf{1}, \ldots, \mathbf{n}$. It is also clear from [B.42] that if the λ_i are all distinct, then each factor $\mathbf{F_i}$ ($\mathbf{i} = \mathbf{1}, \ldots, \mathbf{n}$) in any orthogonal sequence $\mathbf{F_1}, \ldots, \mathbf{F_n}$ which successively maximizes $V_{\mathbf{X}(\mathbf{F_i})}$ must coincide (u.l.t.) with $\mathbf{P_i}$ and hence that if $\mathbf{P^*_1}, \ldots, \mathbf{P^*_n}$ is another set of variables which also satisfy the requirements to be principal components of the $\mathbf{X_i}$-configuration, $\mathbf{P_i}$ and $\mathbf{P^*_i}$ ($\mathbf{i} = \mathbf{1}, \ldots, \mathbf{n}$) must likewise coincide (u.l.t.) in this case, so that $(\mathbf{P^*_i} - M_{\mathbf{P^*_i}}) = a_i(\mathbf{P_i} -$

[2] Previously in this book the **i**th principal component of a configuration of variables was designated by "$\mathbf{C_i}$" while "$\mathbf{P_i}$" referred to the corresponding normalized factor. Since here we have no need to mention principal factors as distinct from principal components while the boldface letter "**C**" will be used extensively to denote covariance matrices, the revision of notation is in order.

[3] Up to a linear transformation. (See fn. 19, p. 472).

M_{P_i}) for some constant a_i. Further, since $\mathrm{Var}(\mathbf{P}_i^*) = \lambda_i = \mathrm{Var}(\mathbf{P}_i)$, a_i must be either +1 or −1. Hence *when* $\lambda_i > \lambda_{i+1}$ $(\mathbf{i} = \mathbf{1}, \ldots, \mathbf{n}-\mathbf{1})$, *each of a configuration's principal components is uniquely determined except for its orientation and possibly its mean.*[4] However, if two or more eigenvalues $\lambda_j, \lambda_{j+1}, \ldots, \lambda_k$ are identical (as can easily occur in contrived cases but whose likelihood is virtually nil for empirical data), then if $\mathbf{P}_j', \mathbf{P}_{j+1}', \ldots, \mathbf{P}_k'$ are any orthogonal rotation of the subset $\mathbf{P}_j, \mathbf{P}_{j+1}, \ldots, \mathbf{P}_k$, the modified set $\mathbf{P}_1, \ldots, \mathbf{P}_{j-1}, \mathbf{P}_j', \mathbf{P}_{j+1}', \ldots, \mathbf{P}_k', \mathbf{P}_{k+1}, \ldots, \mathbf{P}_n$ also meets the requirements to be a set of principal components for the $\mathbf{X}_i$-configuration.

Now consider the problem of finding an $\mathbf{m}$-dimensional space S_m such that the total variance of configuration $\mathbf{X}_1, \ldots, \mathbf{X}_n$ accounted for by S_m is maximal. In view of [B.38] and the fact that orthogonal rotation does not affect total accounted-for variance,

$$\text{[B.43]} \qquad V_{\mathbf{X}(S_m)} = V_{\mathbf{P}(S_m)} = \sum_{i=1}^{n} V_{\mathbf{P}_i(S_m)} = \sum_{i=1}^{n} \lambda_i R^2_{\mathbf{P}_i(S_m)},$$

while since the $\mathbf{P}_i$ are mutually orthogonal, if $\mathbf{F}_1, \ldots, \mathbf{F}_m$ are an orthogonal basis for S_m we have $\sum_{i=1}^{n} R^2_{\mathbf{P}_i(S_m)} = \sum_{i=1}^{n}\sum_{j=1}^{m} r^2_{\mathbf{P}_i\mathbf{F}_j} = \sum_{j=1}^{m} R^2_{\mathbf{F}_j(\mathbf{P}_1\ldots\mathbf{P}_n)}$, or

$$\text{[B.44]} \qquad \sum_{i=1}^{n} R^2_{\mathbf{P}_i(S_m)} \leqslant \mathbf{m},$$

with equality holding when S_m is a subspace of the space spanned by the $\mathbf{P}_i$. Selection of S_m to maximize $V_{\mathbf{X}(S_m)}$ is thus under the constraint that the coefficients $R^2_{\mathbf{P}_i(S_m)}$ of the λ_i in [B.43] can total no more than $\mathbf{m}$. Given this restriction, it is obvious from [B.43], since R^2 is bounded by 0 and 1, that $V_{\mathbf{X}(S_m)}$ is maximal when the coefficients of the $\mathbf{m}$ greatest eigenvalues in [B.43] are unity and the rest are zero, namely, when and only when S_m is the space spanned by $\mathbf{P}_1, \ldots, \mathbf{P}_m$. Hence *for any* $\mathbf{k} = \mathbf{1}, \ldots, \mathbf{n}$, *the first* $\mathbf{k}$ *principal components (or any other* $\mathbf{k}$ *variables which span the same space) of a set of variables* $\mathbf{X}_1, \ldots, \mathbf{X}_n$ *account for the maximal amount of the set's total variance that can be accounted for by any* $\mathbf{k}$ *factors.*

Alternatively, suppose that we seek to find an orthogonal rotation [B.32] of variables $\mathbf{X}_1, \ldots, \mathbf{X}_n$ into $\mathbf{X}_1', \ldots, \mathbf{X}_n'$ which successively maximizes first $\mathrm{Var}(\mathbf{X}_1')$, then $\mathrm{Var}(\mathbf{X}_2')$, then $\mathrm{Var}(\mathbf{X}_3')$, etc. Solving for $\mathbf{C}_{\mathbf{XX}}$ in

[4] Later considerations will show that the reservation about means may be omitted—i.e., when eigenvalues are all distinct, each principal component is uniquely determined up to its orientation.

[B.34] and substituting into [B.33], we have

$$\mathbf{C}_{\mathbf{X}'\mathbf{X}'} = \mathbf{T}_{\mathbf{X}'\mathbf{X}}\,\mathbf{T}'_{\mathbf{PX}}\,\mathbf{D}_\lambda\,\mathbf{T}_{\mathbf{PX}}\,\mathbf{T}'_{\mathbf{X}'\mathbf{X}}$$

[B.45] $$= \mathbf{M}\,\mathbf{D}_\lambda\,\mathbf{M}'$$

$$= \left\{\sum_{\mathbf{k}=1}^{\mathbf{n}} m_{\mathbf{ik}}\, m_{\mathbf{jk}}\, \lambda_{\mathbf{k}}\right\},$$

where

[B.46] $$\mathbf{M} =_{\text{def}} \mathbf{T}_{\mathbf{X}'\mathbf{X}}\,\mathbf{T}'_{\mathbf{PX}} = \{m_{\mathbf{ij}}\}.$$

The matrix $\mathbf{M}$ is obviously orthonormal since by definition $\mathbf{T}_{\mathbf{X}'\mathbf{X}}$ and $\mathbf{T}_{\mathbf{PX}}$, are; hence

[B.47-ij] $(\mathbf{i,j} = \mathbf{1}, \ldots, \mathbf{n})$ $$\sum_{\mathbf{k}=1}^{\mathbf{n}} m_{\mathbf{ik}} m_{\mathbf{jk}} = \begin{cases} 1 \text{ if } \mathbf{i} = \mathbf{j} \\ 0 \text{ if } \mathbf{i} \neq \mathbf{j} \end{cases}.$$

From [B.45],

[B.48-i] $(\mathbf{i} = \mathbf{1}, \ldots, \mathbf{n})$ $$V_{\mathbf{X}'_\mathbf{i}} = \sum_{\mathbf{j}=1}^{\mathbf{n}} m_{\mathbf{ij}}^2 \lambda_{\mathbf{j}},$$

so in view of [B.47-ii], $V_{\mathbf{X}'_\mathbf{i}}$ $(\mathbf{i} = \mathbf{1}, \ldots, \mathbf{n})$ is a weighted average of $\lambda_1, \ldots, \lambda_\mathbf{n}$. Thus $V_{\mathbf{X}'_1}$ is clearly maximal if and only if $m_{\mathbf{1k}} \neq 0$ for only those $\mathbf{k}$, say $\mathbf{k} = \mathbf{1}, \ldots, \mathbf{h}$, such that $\lambda_\mathbf{k} = \lambda_1$, from which by [B.47-lj] it follows that $\sum_{\mathbf{k}=1}^{\mathbf{h}} m_{\mathbf{1k}} m_{\mathbf{jk}} = 0$ for $\mathbf{j} \neq \mathbf{1}$ and hence from [B.45] that $\text{Cov}(\mathbf{X}'_1, \mathbf{X}'_\mathbf{j}) = \lambda_1 \sum_{\mathbf{k}=1}^{\mathbf{h}} m_{\mathbf{1k}} m_{\mathbf{jk}} = 0$ for $\mathbf{j}' = \mathbf{2}, \ldots, \mathbf{n}$. More generally, $V_{\mathbf{X}'_\mathbf{i}}$ is maximized when and only when the $m_{\mathbf{ij}}$ in [B.48-i] are nonzero only for those $\mathbf{j}$ such that $\lambda_\mathbf{j} = \lambda_\mathbf{k}$, where $\lambda_\mathbf{k}$ is the largest eigenvalue for which $m_{\mathbf{ik}}$ is not constrained to be zero by the prior successive maximization of $V_{\mathbf{X}'_1}, \ldots, V_{\mathbf{X}'_{\mathbf{i}-1}}$—which again implies by [B.47] and [B.45] that $\mathbf{X}'_\mathbf{i}$ has zero covariance with all the other $\mathbf{X}'_\mathbf{j}$. Hence $\mathbf{C}_{\mathbf{X}'\mathbf{X}'} = \mathbf{D}$ for some diagonal matrix $\mathbf{D}$ in which the diagonal elements are in descending order of numerical value. But then from [B.33], $\mathbf{T}_{\mathbf{X}'\mathbf{X}}\,\mathbf{C}_{\mathbf{XX}}\,\mathbf{T}'_{\mathbf{X}'\mathbf{X}} = \mathbf{D}$, and since by definition $\mathbf{T}_{\mathbf{X}'\mathbf{X}}$ is orthogonal, the rotated variables $\mathbf{X}'_1, \ldots, \mathbf{X}'_\mathbf{n}$ hence meet the conditions to be a set of principal components for the $\mathbf{X}_\mathbf{i}$-configuration, while $\mathbf{D} = \mathbf{D}_\lambda$ (cf. p. 582). Conversely, any set of principal components for the $\mathbf{X}_\mathbf{i}$ attain these successive maxima $\lambda_1, \ldots, \lambda_\mathbf{n}$ for the variances in an orthogonal rotation of the $\mathbf{X}_\mathbf{i}$. Hence *a set of variables* $\mathbf{X}'_1, \ldots, \mathbf{X}'_\mathbf{n}$ *is an orthogonal rotation of variables* $\mathbf{X}_1, \ldots, \mathbf{X}_\mathbf{n}$ *in which the variances of the rotated variables are successively maximized if and only if* $\mathbf{X}'_1, \ldots, \mathbf{X}'_\mathbf{n}$ *are a set of principal components for the* $\mathbf{X}_\mathbf{i}$*-configuration.*

Principal components are also the solution for an important variance-maximization property which cuts across the distinction between orthogonal configurations and orthogonal rotations: *Variables* $\mathbf{X}'_1, \ldots, \mathbf{X}'_n$ *are mutually orthogonal linear composites* $\mathbf{X}'_i = \sum_{j=1}^{n} w_{ij}\mathbf{X}_j$ $(\mathbf{i} = \mathbf{1}, \ldots, \mathbf{n})$ *of variables* $\mathbf{X}_1, \ldots, \mathbf{X}_n$ *such that* $V_{X'_1}, \ldots, V_{X'_n}$ *are successively maximized under the restriction that* $\sum_{j=1}^{n} w_{ij}^2 = 1$ $(\mathbf{i} = \mathbf{1}, \ldots, \mathbf{n})$ *if and only if the transformation matrix* $\mathbf{W}_{X'X} = \{w_{ij}\}$ *is also orthonormal and the* $\mathbf{X}'_i$ *are a set of principal components for the* $\mathbf{X}_i$*-configuration.* Proof: Let $\mathbf{w}_i$ $(\mathbf{i} = \mathbf{1}, \ldots, \mathbf{n})$ be the row vector $\langle w_{i1}, \ldots, w_{in}\rangle$ of weights determining $\mathbf{X}'_i$ as a function of $\mathbf{X}_1, \ldots, \mathbf{X}_n$ while $\mathbf{t}_i$ $(\mathbf{i} = \mathbf{1}, \ldots, \mathbf{n})$ is the row vector of weights which combine the $\mathbf{X}_i$ into their **i**th principal component—i.e., $\mathbf{t}_i$ is the **i**th row of a matrix $\mathbf{T}_{PX}$ which satisfies [B.34]. Postmultiplying [B.34] by $\mathbf{T}_{PX}$, we have

[B.49] $$\mathbf{T}_{PX}\mathbf{C}_{XX} = \mathbf{D}_\lambda \mathbf{T}_{PX} ,$$

or equivalently,

[B.50-**i**]
$(\mathbf{i} = \mathbf{1}, \ldots, \mathbf{n})$ $$\mathbf{t}_i\,\mathbf{C}_{XX} = \lambda_i\,\mathbf{t}_i \,.$$

Since $\mathrm{Cov}(\mathbf{P}_i,\mathbf{X}'_j) = \mathbf{t}_i\mathbf{C}_{XX}\mathbf{w}'_j$ (see [B.10]), postmultiplying [B.50-**i**] by $\mathbf{w}'_j$ yields $\mathrm{Cov}(\mathbf{P}_i,\mathbf{X}'_j) = \lambda_i\mathbf{t}_i\mathbf{w}'_j$, so variable $\mathbf{X}'_j$ is orthogonal to one or more of the principal components $\mathbf{P}_i$ defined by $\mathbf{T}_{PX}$ if and only if $\mathbf{t}_i\,\mathbf{w}'_j = 0$. Now for $\mathbf{i} = \mathbf{1}$, maximizing $V_{X'_1}$ under the present conditions, namely $\mathbf{w}_i\,\mathbf{w}'_i = 1$ $(\mathbf{i} = \mathbf{1}, \ldots, \mathbf{n})$ with orthogonality among the $\mathbf{X}'_i$, is no different from maximizing $V_{X'_1}$ under the condition that $\mathbf{W}_{X'X}$ be orthonormal; hence from our previous proof, $\mathbf{X}'_1 = \mathbf{P}_1$. But then to maximize $V_{X'_2}$ under the restriction that $\mathbf{w}_2\mathbf{w}'_2 = 1$ while $\mathbf{X}'_2$ is orthogonal to $\mathbf{X}'_1$ is equivalent to maximizing $V_{X'_2}$ under the condition that $\mathbf{X}'_2$ is the second axis in an orthogonal rotation of the $\mathbf{X}_i$ in which the first axis is $\mathbf{P}_1$; so by our previous proof, $\mathbf{X}'_2 = \mathbf{P}_2$. Continuing in this way (that is, by showing that $\mathbf{X}'_i = \mathbf{P}_i$ for $\mathbf{i} = \mathbf{1}, \ldots, \mathbf{k} - \mathbf{1}$ also requires it for $\mathbf{i} = \mathbf{k}$) completes the proof sought.

Eigenvalues and Eigenvectors

The term "eigenvalue" was introduced above to denote the variance of a principal component. Actually, this should be listed as a property of eigenvalues rather than as a definition. More fundamentally, it is found in matrix theory that for any square matrix $\mathbf{M}$, there exist certain row vectors $\mathbf{v}$ and constants λ such that $\mathbf{vM} = \lambda\mathbf{v}$. A vector $\mathbf{v} \neq \langle 0,0, \ldots, 0\rangle$ which satisfies this relationship for some λ ($\lambda = 0$ not excluded) is variously known as a *characteristic vector, stationary vector, latent vector,* or *eigenvector* of the matrix $\mathbf{M}$, while a constant λ which satisfies the relationship for some non-null $\mathbf{v}$ is called a *characteristic root, latent root, or eigenvalue* of $\mathbf{M}$. Each eigenvalue λ_i of $\mathbf{M}$ defines a corresponding class of eigenvectors, namely, the $\mathbf{v}$s such that $\mathbf{vM} = \lambda_i\mathbf{v}$. From [B.50], we see that the vector $\mathbf{t}_i$ of coefficients which transform $\mathbf{X}_1, \ldots, \mathbf{X}_n$ into their $\mathbf{i}$th principal component $\mathbf{P}_i$ is an eigenvector of covariance matrix $\mathbf{C}_{XX}$, while the variance of $\mathbf{P}_i$ is correspondingly an eigenvalue of $\mathbf{C}_{XX}$. We shall now show that the converse is also essentially true.

Suppose that $\mathbf{L}$ is a linear combination of variables $\mathbf{X}_1, \ldots, \mathbf{X}_n$, namely,

[B.51] $$\mathbf{L} =_{\text{def}} w_0 + \sum_{j=1}^{n} w_j\mathbf{X}_j\,,$$

while the vector of weights, $\mathbf{w} = \langle w_1, \ldots, w_n\rangle$ in [B.51] is an eigenvector of covariance matrix $\mathbf{C}_{XX}$ so that

[B.52] $$\mathbf{w}\,\mathbf{C}_{XX} = \lambda\mathbf{w} \qquad \text{(assumed)}$$

for some constant λ. Then using principle [B.8] and [B.36] premultiplied by $\mathbf{T}'_{PX}$ the vector of normalized scores on $\mathbf{L}$ is

[B.53] $$\begin{aligned} \mathbf{s}_{LI} &= \mathbf{w}\,\mathbf{S}_{XI} \\ &= \mathbf{w}\,\mathbf{T}'_{PX}\,\mathbf{S}_{PI} \qquad ([B.51]) \end{aligned}$$

or postmultiplying by $\mathbf{S}'_{PI}$ while considering [B.37], the transpose of [B.49], and [B.52],

[B.54] $$\begin{aligned} \mathbf{c}_{LP} &= \mathbf{w}\,\mathbf{T}'_{PX}\,\mathbf{D}_\lambda \\ &= \mathbf{w}\,\mathbf{C}_{XX}\,\mathbf{T}'_{PX} \qquad ([B.51,2]) \\ &= \lambda\mathbf{w}\,\mathbf{T}'_{PX}\,, \end{aligned}$$

where $\mathbf{c}_{LP}$ is the row vector of covariances $\text{Cov}(\mathbf{L},\mathbf{P}_i)$. But the equation $\mathbf{w}\,\mathbf{T}'_{PX}\,\mathbf{D}_\lambda = \lambda\,\mathbf{w}\,\mathbf{T}'_{PX}$ (from lines 1 and 3 of [B.54]) is equivalent to

[B.55-i] $(\mathbf{i} = \mathbf{1}, \ldots, \mathbf{n})$ $$\lambda_i \sum_{j=1}^{n} w_j t_{ij} = \lambda \sum_{j=1}^{n} w_j t_{ij} \qquad ([B.51,2])\,,$$

which can occur only if, for each $\mathbf{i} = \mathbf{1}, \ldots, \mathbf{n}$, either $\lambda_i = \lambda$ or $\sum_{j=1}^{n} w_j t_{ij} = 0$, where by the last line of [B.54], if $\lambda > 0$, the latter alternative occurs if and only if $\text{Cov}(\mathbf{L}, \mathbf{P}_i) = 0$. Further, since by [B.52] the variance of $\mathbf{L}$ is

[B.56] $$\begin{aligned} V_L &= \mathbf{w}\,\mathbf{C}_{XX}\,\mathbf{w}' \qquad ([B.51,2]) \\ &= \lambda\,\mathbf{w}\,\mathbf{w}' \end{aligned}$$

while the stipulation that $\mathbf{w}$ is an eigenvector insures that $\mathbf{w}\,\mathbf{w}' > 0$, $\lambda = 0$ if and only if $\text{Var}(\mathbf{L}) = 0$. Hence if $\text{Var}(\mathbf{L}) > 0$, $\mathbf{L}$ must lie in the space of those $\mathbf{P_i}$ such that $\lambda_i = \lambda$—which is also true if Var(**L**) = 0, since then **L** differs from $\mathbf{P_n}$ by at most an additive constant. (The latter follows from the fact that Var($\mathbf{P_n}$) = 0 whenever $\mathbf{C_{XX}}$ has a zero latent root; which in turn may be seen by letting $\mathbf{a} =_{def} \mathbf{w\,T'_{PX}}$ and observing that if $\mathbf{wC_{XX}} = 0$ while $\mathbf{ww'} > 0$, then $\sum_{i=1}^{n} a_i^2\lambda_i = \mathbf{aD_\lambda a'} = \mathbf{wT'_{PX}D_\lambda T_{PX}w'} =$ $\mathbf{wC_{XX}w'} = 0$ while $\sum_{i=1}^{n} a_i^2 = \mathbf{aa'} = \mathbf{wT'_{PX}T_{PX}w'} = \mathbf{ww'} > 0$—which is possible only if at least one of the λ_i, and hence λ_n, is zero.) If the λ_i are all distinct, **L** must thus coincide (u.l.t.) with $\mathbf{P_i}$. More generally, insomuch as when more than one of the $\mathbf{P_i}$ have the same eigenvalue any variable lying in the space of these $\mathbf{P_i}$ may be included (after appropriate linear rescaling) in a set of principal components for the configuration, we conclude that *any linear composite* $\mathbf{L} = w_0 + \sum_{j=1}^{n} w_j\mathbf{X_j}$ *of variables* $\mathbf{X_1}$, . . . , $\mathbf{X_n}$ *whose weight vector* **w** *(i.e.,* $\langle w_1, \ldots, w_n\rangle$*) is an eigenvector of covariance matris* $\mathbf{C_{XX}}$ *coincides (u.l.t.) with a principal component of the* $\mathbf{X_i}$*-configuration, namely, one whose variance equals the eigenvalue of* $\mathbf{C_{XX}}$ *corresponding to* **w**. Moreover, if there are no linear dependencies among $\mathbf{X_1}, \ldots, \mathbf{X_n}$—that is, if $\mathbf{C_{XX}}$ is "nonsingular" (i.e., has a rank equal to the number of variables)—then it is possible to have $\sum_{j=1}^{n} a_j\mathbf{X_j} = \sum_{j=1}^{n} b_j\mathbf{X_j}$ only if $a_j = b_j$ ($\mathbf{j} = \mathbf{1}, \ldots, \mathbf{n}$), so in this case a linear composite $\mathbf{L} = w_0 + \sum_{j=1}^{n} w_j\mathbf{X_j}$ can coincide (u.l.t.) with principal component $\mathbf{P_i} = \sum_{j=1}^{n} t_{ij}\mathbf{X_j}$ only if $\mathbf{w} = c\mathbf{t_i}$ for some constant c. Since then $\mathbf{wC_{XX}} = c\lambda_i\mathbf{t_i} = \lambda_i\mathbf{w}$, we have that *if the dimensionality of configuration* $\mathbf{X_1}, \ldots, \mathbf{X_n}$ *is* **n**, *a linear composite* $\mathbf{L} = w_0 + \sum_{j=1}^{n} w_j\mathbf{X_j}$ *of the* $\mathbf{X_i}$ *coincides (u.l.t.) with a principal component of the* $\mathbf{X_i}$ *if and only if* $\langle w_1, \ldots, w_n\rangle$ *is an eigenvector of covariance matrix* $\mathbf{C_{XX}}$. (It is, however, possible when the dimensionality of $\mathbf{X_1}, \ldots, \mathbf{X_n}$ is less than **n** for $\sum_{j=1}^{n} w_j\mathbf{X_j}$ to coincide with a principal component of the $\mathbf{X_i}$ even though $\langle w_1, \ldots, w_n\rangle$ is not an eigenvector of $\mathbf{C_{XX}}$, since in this case there are an infinite number of different weight vectors which yield the same composite result.)

One consequence of these results is that the solution for coefficients $\langle w_1, \ldots, w_n\rangle$ such that the linear composite $\sum_{j=1}^{n} w_j\mathbf{X_j}$ coincides (u.l.t.)

with the first principal component of the $\mathbf{X_i}$-configuration is the joint solution for $\mathbf{w}$ and λ in $\mathbf{w}\,\mathbf{C_{XX}} = \lambda\mathbf{w}$ for which λ is maximal. Another is that *the centroid of a configuration* $\mathbf{X_1}, \ldots, \mathbf{X_n}$ *coincides (u.l.t.) with one of the principal components of the* $\mathbf{X_i}$ *if and, when the rank of* $\mathbf{C_{XX}}$ *is* $\mathbf{n}$, *only if the configuration's coefficient of radial irregularity* (see pp. 313f.) *is zero.* For when $\mathbf{w} = \langle 1/\mathbf{n}, 1/\mathbf{n}, \ldots, 1/\mathbf{n}\rangle$ (i.e., when $\sum_{\mathbf{j}=1}^{\mathbf{n}} w_{\mathbf{j}}\mathbf{X_j} = \overline{\mathbf{X}}$), $\mathbf{w}\,\mathbf{C_{XX}}$ is the row vector

$$\left\langle \frac{\sum_{\mathbf{j}=1}^{\mathbf{n}} C_{\mathbf{X_1X_j}}}{\mathbf{n}}, \ldots, \frac{\sum_{\mathbf{j}=1}^{\mathbf{n}} C_{\mathbf{X_nX_j}}}{\mathbf{n}} \right\rangle = \langle C_{\overline{\mathbf{X}}\mathbf{X_1}}, \ldots, C_{\overline{\mathbf{X}}\mathbf{X_n}}\rangle = \langle c_{\mathbf{X_1}}, \ldots, c_{\mathbf{X_n}}\rangle ,$$

so $\mathbf{w}\,\mathbf{C_{XX}} = \lambda\mathbf{w}$ for some constant λ in this case if and only if each $c_{\mathbf{X_i}}$ has the same value (namely, $\lambda/\mathbf{n}$)—which in turn occurs if and only if $\sigma_{\mathbf{c_X}} = 0$. Since $\nu_{\mathbf{c_X}}\ (= \sigma_{\mathbf{c_X}}/V_{\overline{\mathbf{X}}}) = 0$ entails that $\sigma_{\mathbf{c_X}} = 0$, it thus also requires that $\overline{\mathbf{X}}$ coincide (u.l.t.) with one of the principal components of the $\mathbf{X_i}$-configuration. Moreover, if there are no linear dependencies among the $\mathbf{X_i}$, $\nu_{\mathbf{c_X}} = 0$ if and only if $\sigma_{\mathbf{c_X}} = 0$ while $\overline{\mathbf{X}}$ coincides (u.l.t.) with a principal component of the $\mathbf{X_i}$ if and only if $\langle 1/\mathbf{n}, \ldots, 1/\mathbf{n}\rangle$ is an eigenvector of $\mathbf{C_{XX}}$; hence if $\mathbf{C_{XX}}$ is nonsingular, $\nu_{\mathbf{c_X}} = 0$ if and only if $\overline{\mathbf{X}}$ coincides (u.l.t.) with a principal component of the $\mathbf{X_i}$. QED.

It is of some importance to observe that if the eigenvalues of covariance matrix $\mathbf{C_{XX}}$ are all distinct—i.e., if $\lambda_{\mathbf{i}} > \lambda_{\mathbf{i+1}}$ for all $\mathbf{i} = \mathbf{1}, \ldots, \mathbf{n-1}$—then each row of the orthogonal transformation matrix $\mathbf{T_{PX}}$ which carries the $\mathbf{X_i}$ into their principal components is uniquely determined up to a factor of -1. (This is stronger than the fact noted earlier that when the $\lambda_{\mathbf{i}}$ are all distinct the $\mathbf{P_i}$ are uniquely determined up to their orientations and perhaps means, since that still left open the possibility that two different orthogonal rotations of the $\mathbf{X_i}$ might yield identical principal components.) Specifically, when the $\lambda_{\mathbf{i}}$ are all distinct, there is exactly one pair of vectors, $\mathbf{t_i}$ and its reflection $-\mathbf{t_i}$, which satisfy the pair of conditions $\mathbf{t}\mathbf{C_{XX}} = \lambda_{\mathbf{i}}\mathbf{t}$, $\mathbf{tt}' = 1$ and hence, apart from multiplication of any one or more rows by -1, only one matrix $\mathbf{T}$ which satisfies $\mathbf{T}\mathbf{C_{XX}} = \mathbf{D}_\lambda\mathbf{T}$ and $\mathbf{TT}' = \mathbf{I}$ as required of rotation matrix $\mathbf{T_{PX}}$. Proof: That at least one vector $\mathbf{t_i} = \langle t_{\mathbf{i1}}, \ldots, t_{\mathbf{in}}\rangle$ exists such that $\mathbf{t_i}\mathbf{C_{XX}} = \lambda_{\mathbf{i}}\mathbf{t_i}$, $\mathbf{t_i}\mathbf{t_i}' = 1$ and $\sum_{\mathbf{j}=1}^{\mathbf{n}} t_{\mathbf{ij}}\mathbf{X_j} = \mathbf{P_i}$, where $\mathbf{P_i}$ is an $\mathbf{i}$th principal component of the $\mathbf{X_i}$-configuration, follows from the known existence of at least one orthogonal matrix $\mathbf{T_{PX}}$ which satisfies [B.34]; while obviously then also $(-\mathbf{t_i})\mathbf{C_{XX}} = \lambda_{\mathbf{i}}(-\mathbf{t_i})$, $(-\mathbf{t_i})(-\mathbf{t_i})' = 1$ and $\sum_{\mathbf{j}=1}^{\mathbf{n}} -t_{\mathbf{ij}}\mathbf{X_j} = -\mathbf{P_i}$. Conversely, let $\mathbf{v} = \langle v_{\mathbf{1}}, \ldots, v_{\mathbf{n}}\rangle$ be any vector such that $\mathbf{v}\mathbf{C_{XX}} = \lambda_{\mathbf{i}}\mathbf{v}$ and $\mathbf{vv}' = 1$. We have already shown (p. 587) that $\mathbf{v}\mathbf{C_{XX}} = \lambda_{\mathbf{i}}\mathbf{v}$ implies that $\sum_{\mathbf{j}=1}^{\mathbf{n}} v_{\mathbf{j}}\mathbf{X_j} = a\mathbf{P_i^*} + b$ where a

and b are constants and $\mathbf{P}_i^*$ meets the requirements to be an **i**th principal component of the $\mathbf{X}_i$-configuration. Since a principal component can be reflected without changing its qualifications as a principal component, we may orient $\mathbf{P}_i^*$ to have a positive. Further, $\mathrm{Var}\left(\sum_{j=1}^{n} v_j \mathbf{X}_j\right) = \mathbf{v}\,\mathbf{C}_{XX}\,\mathbf{v}' = \lambda_i\,\mathbf{v}\,\mathbf{v}' = \lambda_i = \mathrm{Var}(\mathbf{P}_i^*)$, so $a = 1$ and hence $\sum_{j=1}^{n} v_j \mathbf{X}_j = \mathbf{P}_i^* + b$. Now, we have seen previously (p. 583) that if the eigenvalues of $\mathbf{C}_{XX}$ are all distinct, each principal component is uniquely determined except for orientation and perhaps mean. Thus apart from a possible additive constant, $\mathbf{P}_i^*$ is identical with either $\mathbf{P}_i$ or $-\mathbf{P}_i$ and hence $\mathrm{Cov}(\mathbf{P}_i^*, \mathbf{P}_i)$ equals either λ_i or $-\lambda_i$. But also $\mathrm{Cov}(\mathbf{P}_i^*, \mathbf{P}_i) = \mathrm{Cov}\left(\sum_{j=1}^{n} v_j \mathbf{X}_j, \sum_{j=1}^{n} t_{ij} \mathbf{X}_j\right) = \mathbf{v}\,\mathbf{C}_{XX}\mathbf{t}_i' = \lambda_i\,\mathbf{v}\,\mathbf{t}_i'$, so unless $\lambda_i = 0$, either $\mathbf{v}\,\mathbf{t}_i' = 1$ or $\mathbf{v}(-\mathbf{t}_i)' = 1$ while we also recall that $\mathbf{v}\,\mathbf{v}' = \mathbf{t}_i\,\mathbf{t}_i' = (-\mathbf{t}_i)(-\mathbf{t}_i) = 1$. But for any two sets of quantities $p_1, \ldots, p_n$ and $q_1, \ldots, q_n$, the three conditions $\sum_{j=1}^{n} p_j q_j = \sum_{j=1}^{n} p_j^2 = \sum_{j=1}^{n} q_j^2 = c$ can hold for any constant c only if $p_i = q_i$ for all $i = 1, \ldots, n$.[5] Hence unless $\lambda_i = 0$, $\mathbf{v}$ must be identical with either $\mathbf{t}_i$ or $-\mathbf{t}_i$. In the event that $\lambda_i = 0$, our assumption that $\lambda_1, \ldots, \lambda_n$ are all distinct implies that $\mathbf{i} = \mathbf{n}$ and that $\mathbf{X}_1, \ldots, \mathbf{X}_n$ span an $(\mathbf{n} - 1)$-dimensional space—in which case the coefficients in $\sum_{j=1}^{n} v_j \mathbf{X}_j = \mathbf{P}_n^* + b = \textit{constant}$ are uniquely determined up to a constant multiplier, which multiplier is then restricted to $+1$ or -1 by the condition that $\mathbf{v}\,\mathbf{v}' = 1$. Hence whether $\mathbf{C}_{XX}$ is nonsingular or not, so long as its eigenvalues are all distinct $\mathbf{T}_{PX}$ is uniquely determined up to reflection of one or more of its rows. On the other hand, a set $\mathbf{P}_1, \ldots, \mathbf{P}_n$ of principal components for a configuration of variables still qualifies as such after one or more of the $\mathbf{P}_i$ have been replaced by their reflections. Hence *if the eigenvalues* $\lambda_1, \ldots, \lambda_n$ *of covariance matrix* $\mathbf{C}_{XX}$ *are all distinct, then a matrix* $\mathbf{T}$, *whose* **i***th row is* $\mathbf{t}_i$, *is an orthogonal rotation which carries variables* $\mathbf{X}_1, \ldots, \mathbf{X}_n$ *into a set of their principal components if and only if each* $\mathbf{t}_i$ $(\mathbf{i} = \mathbf{1}, \ldots, \mathbf{n})$ *satisfies the pair of equations* $\mathbf{t}_i\mathbf{C}_{XX} = \lambda_i \mathbf{t}_i$ *and* $\mathbf{t}_i\mathbf{t}_i' = 1$. If the eigenvalues of $\mathbf{C}_{XX}$ are *not* all distinct, however, a given series of weight vectors $\mathbf{w}_1, \ldots, \mathbf{w}_n$ satisfying $\mathbf{w}_i\mathbf{C}_{XX} = \lambda_i\,\mathbf{w}_i$ and $\mathbf{w}_i\,\mathbf{w}_i' = 1$ $(\mathbf{i} = \mathbf{1}, \ldots, \mathbf{n})$ need not jointly yield a set of principal components for the $\mathbf{X}_i$-configuration, since if $\lambda_i = \lambda_j$

[5] Since then, letting $k = c/n$, we have $r_{pq}^2 = (k - \bar{p}\bar{q})^2/(k - \bar{p}^2)(k - \bar{q}^2) = 1 + k[(\bar{p} - \bar{q})/(\sigma_p\,\sigma_q)]^2$, which can occur only if $\bar{p} = \bar{q}$, whence also $\sigma_p = \sigma_q$, $r_{pq} = 1$, and finally $\mathbf{p} = \mathbf{q}$.

$(\mathbf{i} \neq \mathbf{j})$, additional restrictions must be imposed to insure that the composites $\sum_{k=1}^{n} w_{ik}\mathbf{X}_k$ and $\sum_{k=1}^{n} w_{jk}\mathbf{X}_k$ are orthogonal.

Pulling together the results of the past few paragraphs, we can state a useful lemma: *If the eigenvalues* $\lambda_1, \ldots, \lambda_n$ *of covariance matrix* $\mathbf{C_{XX}}$ *are all distinct and linear composites* $\mathbf{L}_i = \sum_{j=1}^{n} w_{ij}\mathbf{X}_j$ *of variables* $\mathbf{X}_1, \ldots, \mathbf{X}_n$ *are defined by a series of non-null weight vectors* $\mathbf{w}_i = \langle w_{i1}, \ldots, w_{in}\rangle$ $(\mathbf{i} = \mathbf{1}, \ldots, \mathbf{n})$, *then the sequence* $\mathbf{w}_1, \ldots, \mathbf{w}_n$ *successively maximizes the quantity*

[B.57] $$Q(\mathbf{w}_i) =_{\text{def}} \frac{\text{Var}\left(\sum_{j=1}^{n} w_{ij}\mathbf{X}_j\right)}{\sum_{j=1}^{n} w_{ij}^2} = \frac{\mathbf{w}_i\,\mathbf{C_{XX}}\,\mathbf{w}_i'}{\mathbf{w}_i\,\mathbf{w}_i'}$$

subject to the restriction that $\mathbf{L}_1, \ldots, \mathbf{L}_n$ *are mutually orthogonal if and only if the* $\mathbf{w}_i$ *satisfy the relations*

[B.58-i] $$\mathbf{w}_i\mathbf{C_{XX}} = \lambda_i\,\mathbf{w}_i\,;$$
$(\mathbf{i} = \mathbf{1}, \ldots, \mathbf{n})$

while if $\mathbf{w}_i$ *satisfies* [B.58-i], *then* $\mathbf{L}_i$ *coincides (u.l.t.) with the* **i**th *principal component of the* $\mathbf{X}_i$*-configuration and* $Q(\mathbf{w}_i) = \lambda_i$. Proof: For $\mathbf{i} = \mathbf{1}, \ldots, \mathbf{n}$, let weight vector $\mathbf{v}_i = \langle v_{i1}, \ldots, v_{in}\rangle$ be defined $\mathbf{v}_i =_{\text{def}} c_i\mathbf{w}_i$, where $c_i =_{\text{def}} 1/\sqrt{\sum_{j=1}^{n} w_{ij}^2} = (\mathbf{w}_i\mathbf{w}_i')^{-1/2}$ $(\neq 0)$, so that $\mathbf{v}_i\mathbf{v}_i' = \sum_{j=1}^{n} v_{ij}^2 = 1$ while of course $\mathbf{v}_i\mathbf{C_{XX}} = \lambda_i\mathbf{v}_i$ if and only if $\mathbf{w}_i\mathbf{C_{XX}} = \lambda_i\mathbf{w}_i$. Now, $Q(\mathbf{w}_i) = c_i^2\ \text{Var}(\mathbf{L}_i) = \text{Var}(c_i\mathbf{L}_i) = \text{Var}\left(\sum_{j=1}^{n} v_{ij}\mathbf{X}_j\right)$ while obviously $c_i\mathbf{L}_i$ and $c_j\mathbf{L}_j$ are orthogonal if and only if $\mathbf{L}_i$ and $\mathbf{L}_j$ are, so $\mathbf{L}_1, \ldots, \mathbf{L}_n$ are mutually orthogonal linear composites of the $\mathbf{X}_i$ which successively maximize $Q(\mathbf{w}_i)$ if and only if $\sum_{j=1}^{n} v_{1j}\mathbf{X}_j, \ldots, \sum_{j=1}^{n} v_{nj}\mathbf{X}_j$ (which by definition of the $\mathbf{v}_i$ are under the restriction that $\sum_{j=1}^{n} v_{ij}^2 = 1$) are orthogonal composites of the $\mathbf{X}_i$ for which $\text{Var}\left(\sum_{j=1}^{n} v_{ij}\mathbf{X}_j\right)$ is successively maximized—i.e., if and only if the $\sum_{j=1}^{n} v_{ij}\mathbf{X}_j$ are an orthogonal rotation of $\mathbf{X}_1, \ldots, \mathbf{X}_n$ into a set of their principal components (see p. 584 above). Moreover, if the λ_i are all distinct, any set of composites $\sum_{j=1}^{n} v_{ij}\mathbf{X}_j$ $(\mathbf{i} = \mathbf{1}, \ldots, \mathbf{n})$ are an orthogonal rotation of the

$\mathbf{X_i}$ into their principal components if and only if for $\mathbf{i}=\mathbf{1},\ldots,\mathbf{n}$, $\mathbf{v_i C_{XX}} = \lambda_i \mathbf{v_i}$ and $\mathbf{v_i}\,\mathbf{v_i'} = 1$; so if $\mathbf{w_i C_{XX}} = \lambda_i \mathbf{w_i}$, $\mathbf{L_i} = \sum_{j=1}^{n} w_{ij}\mathbf{X_j}$ coincides with an $\mathbf{i}$th principal component of the $\mathbf{X_i}$ up to a constant multiplier. Finally, if $\sum_{j=1}^{n} v_{ij}\mathbf{X_j}$ is an $\mathbf{i}$th principal component of the $\mathbf{X_i}$-configuration, then $Q(\mathbf{w_i}) = \mathrm{Var}\left(\sum_{j=1}^{n} v_{ij}\mathbf{X_j}\right) = \lambda_i$. QED. If the eigenvalues of $\mathbf{C_{XX}}$ are *not* all distinct, it is still the case that $\mathbf{L_1},\ldots,\mathbf{L_n}$ successively maximize $Q(\mathbf{w_i})$ subject to orthogonality among the $\mathbf{L_i}$ if and only if the $\sum_{j=1}^{n} v_{ij}\mathbf{X_j}$ are an orthogonal rotation of the $\mathbf{X_i}$ into a (properly ordered) set of their principal components, but condition [B.58] is then not sufficient to insure orthogonality among composites $\mathbf{L_i}$ defined by weight vectors corresponding to coincident eigenvalues.

Saturation and Principal Components

To examine the effect of choice of item scales upon a configuration's saturation, suppose that variables $\mathbf{X_1},\ldots,\mathbf{X_n}$ are all initially standardized to unit variance—i.e., $\overline{\mathbf{V}}_{\mathbf{X}} = 1$, $\nu_{\mathbf{V_X}} = 0$. Also let

[B.59-i] $(\mathbf{i}=\mathbf{1},\ldots,\mathbf{n})$
$$\mathbf{W_i} =_{\text{def}} w_i\mathbf{X_i}$$

and

[B.60]
$$\mathbf{L} =_{\text{def}} \mathbf{n}\overline{\mathbf{W}} = \sum_{i=1}^{n} \mathbf{W_i} = \sum_{i=1}^{n} w_i\mathbf{X_i}$$

or

[B.61]
$$\mathbf{s_{LI}} = \mathbf{w}\,\mathbf{S_{XI}}$$

where, of course, $\mathbf{w} = \langle w_1,\ldots,w_n\rangle$. Since the principal components of the $\mathbf{X_i}$-configuration span the same space as the $\mathbf{X_i}$, $\mathbf{L}$ can also be written as a linear composite, $\mathbf{L} = \sum_{i=1}^{n} a_i\mathbf{P_i}$, of the $\mathbf{P_i}$, or

[B.62]
$$\mathbf{s_{LI}} = \mathbf{a}\,\mathbf{S_{PI}}\ ,$$

where $\mathbf{a} = \langle a_1,\ldots,a_n\rangle$. Specifically, if we set

[B.63]
$$\mathbf{a} =_{\text{def}} \mathbf{w}\,\mathbf{T'_{PX}}\ ,$$

then $\mathbf{a}\,\mathbf{S_{PI}} = \mathbf{w}\,\mathbf{T'_{PX}}\,\mathbf{T_{PX}}\,\mathbf{S_{XI}} = \mathbf{w}\,\mathbf{S_{XI}} = \mathbf{s_{LI}}$ irrespective of the rank of $\mathbf{C_{XX}}$. Since by hypothesis $V_{\mathbf{X_i}} = 1$ $(\mathbf{i}=\mathbf{1},\ldots,\mathbf{n})$ while from [B.63] by post-multiplication with $\mathbf{T_{PX}}$,

[B.64]
$$\mathbf{w} = \mathbf{a}\,\mathbf{T_{PX}}\ ,$$

the total variance of the rescaled set $\mathbf{W}_1, \ldots, \mathbf{W}_n$ is

[B.65]

$$V_{\mathbf{W}} =_{\text{def}} \sum_{i=1}^{n} V_{\mathbf{W}_i} = \sum_{i=1}^{n} w_i^2 V_{\mathbf{X}_i} = \sum_{i=1}^{n} w_i^2 = \mathbf{w}\,\mathbf{w}'$$

$$= \mathbf{a}\,\mathbf{T}_{\mathbf{PX}}\,\mathbf{T}'_{\mathbf{PX}}\,\mathbf{a}' = \mathbf{a}\,\mathbf{a}' = \sum_{i=1}^{n} a_i^2 , \qquad (\overline{V}_{\mathbf{X}} = 1,\ \nu_{V_{\mathbf{X}}} = 0)$$

while the centroid variance of the $\mathbf{W}_i$ is given by

[B.66]
$$\mathbf{n}^2 V_{\overline{\mathbf{W}}} = \mathrm{Var}\left(\sum_{i=1}^{n} \mathbf{W}_i\right) = \mathrm{Var}(\mathbf{L}) = \mathbf{s}_{\mathbf{LI}}\,\mathbf{s}'_{\mathbf{LI}}$$

$$= \mathbf{a}\,\mathbf{S}_{\mathbf{PI}}\,\mathbf{S}'_{\mathbf{PI}}\,\mathbf{a}' = \mathbf{a}\,\mathbf{D}_\lambda\,\mathbf{a}' = \sum_{i=1}^{n} a_i^2 \lambda_i .$$

Hence the saturation of the $\mathbf{W}_i$ is

[B.67]
$$\mathrm{Sat}_{\mathbf{W}} =_{\text{def}} \frac{V_{\overline{\mathbf{W}}}}{\overline{V}_{\mathbf{W}}} = \frac{\mathbf{n}^2 V_{\overline{\mathbf{W}}}}{\mathbf{n}\, V_{\mathbf{W}}} = \frac{\sum_{i=1}^{n} a_i^2 \lambda_i}{\mathbf{n} \sum_{i=1}^{n} a_i^2} \qquad (\overline{V}_{\mathbf{X}} = 1,\ \nu_{V_{\mathbf{X}}} = 0)$$

$$= \sum_{i=1}^{n} \left(\frac{a_i^2}{\sum_{j=1}^{n} a_j^2} \right) \frac{\lambda_i}{\mathbf{n}} .$$

That is, when the $\mathbf{X}_i$ all have unit variance, $\mathrm{Sat}_{\mathbf{W}}$ is a weighted average of the $\lambda_i/\mathbf{n}$, where the weight given to $\lambda_i/\mathbf{n}$ is proportional to the square of the weight given to $\mathbf{P}_i$ when $\mathbf{L}$ (i.e., $\mathbf{n}\overline{\mathbf{W}}$) is expressed as a linear composite of $\mathbf{P}_1, \ldots, \mathbf{P}_n$. In particular, $\mathrm{Sat}_{\mathbf{W}}$ is here maximal when all the a_i except a_1 are zero, in which case $\overline{\mathbf{W}}$ coincides (u.l.t.) with $\mathbf{P}_1$ while $\mathrm{Sat}_{\mathbf{W}} = \lambda_1/\mathbf{n}$, the latter quantity being the proportion of the total variance of the $\mathbf{X}_i$ accounted for by $\mathbf{P}_1$. More generally, if $V_{\mathbf{X}_i} = \overline{V}_{\mathbf{X}}$ ($\mathbf{i} = \mathbf{1}, \ldots, \mathbf{n}$) and we define a series of mutually orthogonal weighted composites $\overline{\mathbf{W}}_{(i)} = (1/\mathbf{n}) \sum_{j=1}^{n} \mathbf{W}_{(i)j} = (1/\mathbf{n}) \sum_{j=1}^{n} w_{(i)j}\mathbf{X}_j$ ($\mathbf{i} = \mathbf{1}, \ldots, \mathbf{n}$) of the $\mathbf{X}_i$, $\mathrm{Sat}_{\mathbf{W}_{(i)}}$ is successively maximized at each step if $\overline{\mathbf{W}}_{(i)}$ coincides (u.l.t.) with $\mathbf{P}_i$, in which case $\mathrm{Sat}_{\mathbf{W}_{(i)}}$ equals the proportion of $V_{\mathbf{X}}$ accounted for by $\mathbf{P}_i$.

Penetrance Ratios

Let $\mathbf{L_a}$ and $\mathbf{L_b}$ be weighted composites of variables $\mathbf{X_{a1}}, \ldots, \mathbf{X_{an}}$ and $\mathbf{X_{b1}}, \ldots, \mathbf{X_{bn}}$, respectively, both of which contain the same vector $\mathbf{w} = \langle w_1, \ldots, w_n \rangle$ of weight coefficients—i.e.,

[B.68] $$\mathbf{L_a} =_{\text{def}} \sum_{j=1}^{n} w_j \mathbf{X_{aj}}, \quad \mathbf{L_b} =_{\text{def}} \sum_{j=1}^{n} w_j \mathbf{X_{bj}}$$

or

[B.69] $$\mathbf{s_{L_a}} = \mathbf{w\,S_{X_a I}}, \quad \mathbf{s_{L_b}} = \mathbf{wS_{X_b I}}\,.$$

Assuming that the dimensionality of the $\mathbf{X_{bi}}$-configuration is $\mathbf{n}$, so that covariance matrix $\mathbf{C_{X_b X_b}}$ is nonsingular, what is the weight vector $\mathbf{w}$ which maximizes the variance ratio $\text{Var}(\mathbf{L_a})/\text{Var}(\mathbf{L_b})$? Using principle [B.10], we can write

[B.70] $$\frac{V_{\mathbf{L_a}}}{V_{\mathbf{L_b}}} = \frac{\mathbf{w\,C_{X_a X_a} w'}}{\mathbf{w\,C_{X_b X_b} w'}}\,.$$

Since $\mathbf{C_{X_b X_b}}$ is stipulated to be nonsingular, a nonsingular matrix $\mathbf{M}$ can always be found which carries variables $\mathbf{X_{b1}}, \ldots, \mathbf{X_{bn}}$ into an orthonormal configuration $\mathbf{X'_{b1}}, \ldots, \mathbf{X'_{bn}}$—i.e.,

[B.71] $$\mathbf{C_{X'_b X'_b}} = \mathbf{M\;C_{X_b X_b} M'} = \mathbf{I}\,,$$

or

[B.72] $$\mathbf{M'M} = \mathbf{C^{-1}_{X_b X_b}}\,.$$

(To appreciate that such an $\mathbf{M}$ always exists when $\mathbf{C_{X_b X_b}}$ is nonsingular, observe that we can then always set $\mathbf{M} = \mathbf{D}_{\lambda_b}^{-1/2}\,\mathbf{T_{P_b X_b}}$, where $\mathbf{T_{P_b X_b}}$ carries the $\mathbf{X_{bi}}$ into their principal components and $\mathbf{D}_{\lambda_b}$ is the corresponding diagonal matrix of eigenvalues.) Now let the row vector $\mathbf{v} = \langle v_1, \ldots, v_n \rangle$ be defined

[B.73] $$\mathbf{v} =_{\text{def}} \mathbf{w\,M^{-1}}$$

or

[B.74] $$\mathbf{w} = \mathbf{v\,M}\,.$$

Substituting [B.74] into [B.70], we have

[B.75] $$\frac{V_{\mathbf{L_a}}}{V_{\mathbf{L_b}}} = \frac{\mathbf{v\,M\,C_{X_a X_a} M'\,v'}}{\mathbf{v\,M\,C_{X_b X_b} M'\,v'}} = \frac{\mathbf{v\;C_{X'_a X'_a}\,v'}}{\mathbf{v\,v'}}\,,$$

where $\mathbf{X}'_{a1}, \ldots, \mathbf{X}'_{an}$ are obtained from variables $\mathbf{X}_{a1}, \ldots, \mathbf{X}_{an}$ by the rotation

[B.76] $$\mathbf{S}_{\mathbf{X}'_a\mathbf{I}} =_{\text{def}} \mathbf{M}\mathbf{S}_{\mathbf{X}_a\mathbf{I}}$$

and hence have covariance matrix

[B.77] $$\mathbf{C}_{\mathbf{X}'_a\mathbf{X}'_a} = \mathbf{M}\,\mathbf{C}_{\mathbf{X}_a\mathbf{X}_a}\mathbf{M}' \,.$$

In view of our lemma about maximizing quantities of form [B.57], the ratio V_{L_a}/V_{L_b} is maximal when $\mathbf{v}$ is an eigenvector of $\mathbf{C}_{\mathbf{X}'_a\mathbf{X}'_a}$ corresponding to the latter's first eigenvalue – i.e., when

[B.78] $$\mathbf{v}\mathbf{C}_{\mathbf{X}'_a\mathbf{X}'_a} = \lambda\mathbf{v} \qquad (V_{L_a}/V_{L_b} = \textit{maximum})$$

for maximal λ. But from [B.73] and [B.77], [B.78] is equivalent to

$$\mathbf{w}\,\mathbf{M}^{-1}\mathbf{M}\,\mathbf{C}_{\mathbf{X}_a\mathbf{X}_a}\mathbf{M}' = \lambda\mathbf{w}\,\mathbf{M}^{-1}$$

or postmultiplying by $\mathbf{M}$ and using [B.72],

[B.79] $$\mathbf{w}\,\mathbf{C}_{\mathbf{X}_a\mathbf{X}_a}\mathbf{C}^{-1}_{\mathbf{X}_b\mathbf{X}_b} = \lambda\mathbf{w} \qquad (V_{L_a}/V_{L_b} = \textit{maximum}) \,.$$

Hence $\mathbf{w}$ must be an eigenvector of the matrix $\mathbf{C}_{\mathbf{X}_a\mathbf{X}_a}\mathbf{C}^{-1}_{\mathbf{X}_b\mathbf{X}_b}$ corresponding, moreover, to the first eigenvalue of the latter, since otherwise $\mathbf{C}_{\mathbf{X}'_a\mathbf{X}'_a}$ would also have an eigenvalue greater than λ.

More generally, we see from the equivalence between equations $\mathbf{v}\mathbf{C}_{\mathbf{X}'_a\mathbf{X}'_a} = \lambda\mathbf{v}$ and $\mathbf{w}\mathbf{C}_{\mathbf{X}_a\mathbf{X}_a}\mathbf{C}^{-1}_{\mathbf{X}_b\mathbf{X}_b} = \lambda\mathbf{w}$ when $\mathbf{v}$ and the $\mathbf{X}'_{ai}$ are defined as in [B.73] and [B.76], respectively, that matrices $\mathbf{C}_{\mathbf{X}'_a\mathbf{X}'_a}$ and $\mathbf{C}_{\mathbf{X}_a\mathbf{X}_a}\mathbf{C}^{-1}_{\mathbf{X}_b\mathbf{X}_b}$ have identical eigenvalues $\lambda_1, \ldots, \lambda_n$ and that a vector $\mathbf{v}_i$ is an eigenvector of $\mathbf{C}_{\mathbf{X}'_a\mathbf{X}'_a}$ corresponding to λ_i if and only if $\mathbf{w}_i\ (= \mathbf{v}_i\mathbf{M})$ is an eigenvector of $\mathbf{C}_{\mathbf{X}_a\mathbf{X}_a}\mathbf{C}^{-1}_{\mathbf{X}_b\mathbf{X}_b}$ corresponding to λ_i. Suppose, now, that we wish to find a series of composites $\mathbf{L}_{ai} = \sum_{j=1}^{n} w_{ij}\mathbf{X}_{aj}$ and $\mathbf{L}_{bi} = \sum_{j=1}^{n} w_{ij}\mathbf{X}_{bj}$ determined by a sequence of weight vectors $\mathbf{w}_i = \langle w_{i1}, \ldots, w_{in}\rangle$ $(\mathbf{i} = \mathbf{1}, \ldots, \mathbf{n})$ from variables $\mathbf{X}_{a1}, \ldots, \mathbf{X}_{an}$ and $\mathbf{X}_{b1}, \ldots, \mathbf{X}_{bn}$, respectively, in such fashion that the variance ratio $V_{L_{ai}}/V_{L_{bi}}$ is successively maximized subject either to the restriction that (*a*) the $\mathbf{L}_{ai}$ are mutually orthogonal, or that (*b*) the $\mathbf{L}_{bi}$ are mutually orthogonal. Since $\mathbf{L}_{ai} = \sum_{j=1}^{n} w_{ij}\mathbf{X}_{aj} = \sum_{j=1}^{n} v_{ij}\mathbf{X}'_{aj}$, where $\mathbf{v}_i$ and the $\mathbf{X}'_{aj}$ are obtained from $\mathbf{w}_i$ and the $\mathbf{X}_{aj}$ as in [B.73] and [B.76], respectively, restriction (*a*) is equivalent to the condition that the corresponding composites $\sum_{j=1}^{n} v_{ij}\mathbf{X}'_{aj}$ $(\mathbf{i} = \mathbf{1}, \ldots, \mathbf{n})$ be mutually orthogonal; hence from [B.75] and our lemma concerning quantities of form [B.57], $V_{L_{ai}}/V_{L_{bi}}$ is successively maximized under mutual orthogonality among the $\mathbf{L}_{ai}$ when $\mathbf{v}_1, \ldots, \mathbf{v}_n$ are successive eigenvectors corresponding to the **n** eigenvalues (which for simplicity we shall assume to be distinct) of $\mathbf{C}_{X_a'X_a'}$ and hence when $\mathbf{w}_1, \ldots, \mathbf{w}_n$ are successive eigenvectors of $\mathbf{C}_{X_aX_a}\mathbf{C}^{-1}_{X_bX_b}$ —i.e., when $\mathbf{w}_i\mathbf{C}_{X_aX_a}\mathbf{C}^{-1}_{X_bX_b} = \lambda_i\mathbf{w}_i$ ($\mathbf{i} = \mathbf{1}, \ldots, \mathbf{n}$), where $\lambda_1, \ldots, \lambda_n$ are the **n** successive eigenvalues of $\mathbf{C}_{X_aX_a}\mathbf{C}^{-1}_{X_bX_b}$. We also note in this case that $\lambda_i = V_{L_{ai}}/V_{L_{bi}}$ ($\mathbf{i} = \mathbf{1}, \ldots, \mathbf{n}$), as can easily be verified by postmultiplying both sides of $\mathbf{w}_i\mathbf{C}_{X_aX_a}\mathbf{C}^{-1}_{X_bX_b} = \lambda_i\mathbf{w}_i$ by $\mathbf{C}_{X_bX_b}\mathbf{w}_i'$ and solving for λ_i. On the other hand, since from [B.74] and [B.71] $\text{Cov}(\mathbf{L}_{bi}, \mathbf{L}_{bj}) = \mathbf{w}_i\mathbf{C}_{X_bX_b}\mathbf{w}_j' = \mathbf{v}_i\mathbf{v}_j'$, condition (*b*), which is prima facie an alternative to (*a*), is equivalent to the requirement that $\mathbf{v}_i\,\mathbf{v}_j' = 0$ for all $\mathbf{i} \neq \mathbf{j}$; while successive maximization of $\mathbf{v}_i\mathbf{C}_{X_a'X_a'}\mathbf{v}_i'/\mathbf{v}_i\mathbf{v}_i'$ (i.e., $V_{L_{ai}}/V_{L_{bi}}$) is equivalent to successive maximization of $\mathbf{v}_i\mathbf{C}_{X_a'X_a'}\mathbf{v}_i'$ under the restriction that $\mathbf{v}_i\,\mathbf{v}_i' = 1$. Hence successively maximizing $V_{L_{ai}}/V_{L_{bi}}$ ($\mathbf{i} = \mathbf{1}, \ldots, \mathbf{n}$) under restriction (*b*) is the same as successively maximizing the variances of the variables in an orthogonal rotation of the $\mathbf{X}_{ai}'$ —a result which is known from our previous results (p. 584) to be achieved when the $\mathbf{v}_i$ are eigenvectors corresponding to the successive eigenvalues of matrix $\mathbf{C}_{X_a'X_a'}$, and where the latter solution, in turn, has just been shown to be identical with the solution for successive maximization of $V_{L_{ai}}/V_{L_{bi}}$ under restriction (*a*). Thus we have the important theorem that *if* $\mathbf{w}_1, \ldots, \mathbf{w}_n$ *are successive eigenvectors of the* $\mathbf{n} \times \mathbf{n}$ *matrix* $\mathbf{C}_{X_aX_a}\mathbf{C}^{-1}_{X_bX_b}$ *corresponding to distinct eigenvectors* $\lambda_1, \ldots, \lambda_n$*—i.e., if* $\mathbf{w}_i\mathbf{C}_{X_aX_a}\mathbf{C}^{-1}_{X_bX_b} = \lambda_i\mathbf{w}_i$ ($\mathbf{i} = \mathbf{1}, \ldots, \mathbf{n}$) *where* $\lambda_i > \lambda_{i+1}$ ($\mathbf{i} = \mathbf{1}, \ldots, \mathbf{n} - \mathbf{1}$)*—then the two sets of linear composites* $\mathbf{L}_{ai} =_{\text{def}} \sum_{j=1}^{n} w_{ij}\mathbf{X}_{aj}$ ($\mathbf{i} = \mathbf{1}, \ldots, \mathbf{n}$) *and* $\mathbf{L}_{bi} =_{\text{def}} \sum_{j=1}^{n} w_{ij}\mathbf{X}_{bj}$ ($\mathbf{i} = \mathbf{1}, \ldots, \mathbf{n}$) *determined by these* $\mathbf{w}_i$ *from variables* $\mathbf{X}_{a1}, \ldots, \mathbf{X}_{an}$ *and* $\mathbf{X}_{b1}, \ldots, \mathbf{X}_{bn}$, *respectively, are both orthogonal configurations, and are also the composites of the* $\mathbf{X}_{ai}$ *and the* $\mathbf{X}_{bi}$, *respectively, which successively maximize the variance ratio* $\text{Var}(\mathbf{L}_{ai})/\text{Var}(\mathbf{L}_{bi})$ ($\mathbf{i} = \mathbf{1}, \ldots, \mathbf{n}$) *under the restriction either that the* $\mathbf{L}_{ai}$ *or that the* $\mathbf{L}_{bi}$ *are mutually orthogonal. Also, when* $\mathbf{w}_i$ *is an eigenvector of* $\mathbf{C}_{X_aX_a}\mathbf{C}^{-1}_{X_bX_b}$ *corresponding to eigenvalue* λ_i, $V_{L_{ai}}/V_{L_{bi}} = \lambda_i$. As noted, this theorem assumes the eigenvalues of $\mathbf{C}_{X_aX_a}\mathbf{C}^{-1}_{X_bX_b}$ to be all distinct. If this is not so, then there is an overabundance of eigenvectors corresponding to the coincident eigenvalues and some additional conditions need to be imposed in order to select from the alternative solutions for $\mathbf{W}$ ($= \{w_{ij}\}$) in $\mathbf{W}\,\mathbf{C}_{X_aX_a}\mathbf{C}^{-1}_{X_bX_b} = \mathbf{D}_\lambda\mathbf{W}$ one which yields orthogonality among the $\mathbf{L}_{ai}$ or the $\mathbf{L}_{bi}$. However, this is a routine computational detail which need not concern us here, especially since the likelihood of coincident eigenvalues in empirical matrices is prohibitively small.

It is now simple to examine how the penetrance of a linear composite $\mathbf{L} = \sum_{j=1}^{n} w_j\mathbf{X}_j$ into a space S_a compares with its penetrance into another space S_b (not necessarily orthogonal to S_a) with an eye to maximizing the ratio of these penetrances. Writing "$\mathbf{X}_{ai}$" and "$\mathbf{X}_{bi}$" for the projections of variable $\mathbf{X}_i$ into S_a and S_b, respectively, we have from [6.54] that the projections of $\mathbf{L}$ into S_a and S_b are, respectively, $\sum_{j=1}^{n} w_j \mathbf{X}_{aj}$ and $\sum_{j=1}^{n} w_j \mathbf{X}_{bj}$. Hence

$$[B.80] \qquad \frac{P_{\mathbf{L}}(S_a)}{P_{\mathbf{L}}(S_b)} = \frac{V_{\mathbf{L}(S_a)}/V_{\mathbf{L}}}{V_{\mathbf{L}(S_b)}/V_{\mathbf{L}}} = \frac{V_{\mathbf{L}(S_a)}}{V_{\mathbf{L}(S_b)}} = \frac{\mathrm{Var}\left(\sum_{j=1}^{n} w_j \mathbf{X}_{aj}\right)}{\mathrm{Var}\left(\sum_{j=1}^{n} w_j \mathbf{X}_{bj}\right)}$$

$$= \frac{\mathbf{w}\,\mathbf{C}_{\mathbf{X}_a\mathbf{X}_a}\,\mathbf{w}'}{\mathbf{w}\,\mathbf{C}_{\mathbf{X}_b\mathbf{X}_b}\,\mathbf{w}'} = \frac{\mathbf{w}\,\mathbf{C}_{\mathbf{XX}(S_a)}\,\mathbf{w}'}{\mathbf{w}\,\mathbf{C}_{\mathbf{XX}(S_b)}\mathbf{w}'},$$

where for greater notational potency we write "$\mathbf{C}_{\mathbf{XX}(S)}$" for the matrix of covariances among the projections of the $\mathbf{X}_i$ into space S. Then our preceding theorem shows immediately that penetrance ratio [B.80] is maximal when $\mathbf{w}$ is an eigenvector of $\mathbf{C}_{\mathbf{XX}(S_a)}\mathbf{C}^{-1}_{\mathbf{XX}(S_b)}$ corresponding to the first eigenvalue of this matrix, and that more generally, $\mathbf{n}$ successive eigenvectors $\mathbf{w}_1, \ldots, \mathbf{w}_n$ of $\mathbf{C}_{\mathbf{XX}(S_a)}\mathbf{C}^{-1}_{\mathbf{XX}(S_b)}$ corresponding to the latter's eigenvalues $\lambda_1, \ldots, \lambda_n$ define a series of composites $\mathbf{L}_i =_{\mathrm{def}} \sum_{j=1}^{n} w_{ij}\mathbf{X}_j$ of the $\mathbf{X}_i$ such that (1) $P_{\mathbf{L}_i(S_a)}/P_{\mathbf{L}_i(S_b)} = \lambda_i$ ($\mathbf{i} = \mathbf{1}, \ldots, \mathbf{n}$), (2) the configurations of $\mathbf{L}_i$-projections into S_a and into S_b are both orthogonal,[6] and (3) $\mathbf{L}_1, \ldots, \mathbf{L}_n$ successively maximize penetrance ratio [B.80] subject to a condition of orthogonality on the $\mathbf{L}_i$-projections either into S_a or into S_b.[6]

Finally, suppose that we seek a series of mutually orthogonal linear composites $\mathbf{L}_i = \sum_{j=1}^{n} w_{ij}\mathbf{X}_j$ ($\mathbf{i} = \mathbf{1}, \ldots, \mathbf{n}$) of variables $\mathbf{X}_1, \ldots, \mathbf{X}_n$ such that the penetrance $P_{\mathbf{L}_i}(S)$ of each $\mathbf{L}_i$ into a given space S is successively maximized. Since the penetrance of each $\mathbf{L}_i$ into the space $S_{\mathbf{X}}$ spanned by $\mathbf{X}_1, \ldots, \mathbf{X}_n$ is unity, $P_{\mathbf{L}_i}(S)$ is equivalent to the penetrance ratio $P_{\mathbf{L}_i}(S)/P_{\mathbf{L}_i}(S_{\mathbf{X}})$, and the $\mathbf{L}_i$ sought are given by the succession of eigenvectors $\mathbf{w}_1, \ldots, \mathbf{w}_n$ corresponding to eigenvalues $\lambda_1, \ldots, \lambda_n$ of the matrix $\mathbf{C}_{\mathbf{XX}(S)}\mathbf{C}^{-1}_{\mathbf{XX}}$, while $P_{\mathbf{L}_i}(S) = \lambda_i$.[6] As is true in general for successive maximization of penetrance ratios, the configuration of $\mathbf{L}_i$-projections into S is likewise orthogonal, while in the present special case (i.e., maximizing $P_{\mathbf{L}_i}(S_a)/P_{\mathbf{L}_i}(S_b)$ when $S_a = S$ and $S_b = S_{\mathbf{X}}$), since $\mathbf{X}_i = \mathrm{M}_{\mathbf{X}_i} + \mathbf{e}_{\mathbf{X}_i(S)} + \mathbf{e}_{\mathbf{X}_i \cdot S}$ and hence $\mathrm{Cov}(\mathbf{X}_i, \mathbf{e}_{\mathbf{X}_j(S)}) = \mathrm{Cov}(\mathbf{e}_{\mathbf{X}_i(S)}, \mathbf{e}_{\mathbf{X}_j(S)})$, each $\mathbf{L}_i$ is also orthogonal to the projections of all the others into S. With respect to the possible complication of coincident eigenvalues, it should be noted that there is here a distinct possibility that more than one of the λ_i will be zero—in fact, this is mathematically guaranteed if the space S within which $P_{\mathbf{L}_i}(S)$ is being successively maximized has a dimensionality $\mathbf{m}$ less than $\mathbf{n} - 1$. In this

[6] A qualification is needed here if the λ_i are not all distinct.

case the terminal composites $\mathbf{L}_{m+1}, \ldots, \mathbf{L}_n$ all have zero variance and only $\mathbf{L}_1, \ldots, \mathbf{L}_m$ are of any interest. So long as $\lambda_1, \ldots, \lambda_m$ are all distinct, any series of weight vectors $\mathbf{w}_1, \ldots, \mathbf{w}_m$ satisfying $\mathbf{w}_i \mathbf{C}_{XX(S)} \mathbf{C}_{XX}^{-1} = \lambda_i \mathbf{w}_i$ ($\mathbf{i} = \mathbf{1}, \ldots, \mathbf{m}$) yield the nondegenerate $\mathbf{L}_i$ sought.

In passing, it is worth mention that maximizing $P_L(S)$ is equivalent to maximizing the penetrance quotient of $\mathbf{L}$ in S, while the latter is the penetrance ratio $P_L(S)/P_L(S^*)$ where S^* is the complement of S. Hence the maximal-λ solution for $\mathbf{w}$ in

$$\text{[B.81]} \qquad \mathbf{w}\mathbf{C}_{XX(S)}\mathbf{C}_{XX(S^*)}^{-1} = \lambda \mathbf{w}$$

also maximizes $P_L(S)$. In the special case that $\mathbf{C}_{XX(S^*)} = \mathbf{I}$, which occurs when S^* is a unique-factor space for the $\mathbf{X}_i$ in which the $\mathbf{X}_i$-projections all have unit variance, [B.81] reduces simply to

$$\mathbf{w}\mathbf{C}_{XX(S)} = \lambda \mathbf{w} \ ,$$

which for maximal λ is also the solution for the first principal component of the $\mathbf{X}_i$-projections into S. Hence if $\mathbf{X}_1, \ldots, \mathbf{X}_n$ have all been scaled to have unit unique variance (or more generally, to have equal unique variances) while $\mathbf{L} =_{\text{def}} \sum_{j=1}^{n} w_j \mathbf{X}_j$, the penetrance of $\mathbf{L}$ into common-factor space will be maximal when the common-factor component of $\mathbf{L}$ coincides (u.l.t.) with the first principal factor of the communal components of the $\mathbf{X}_i$.

Principal Components of Projection Configurations

Let space S_X be spanned by variables $\mathbf{X}_1, \ldots, \mathbf{X}_n$. What are the linear composites $\mathbf{L}_i = \sum_{j=1}^{n} w_{ij} \mathbf{X}_j$ ($\mathbf{i} = \mathbf{1}, \ldots, \mathbf{n}$) of the $\mathbf{X}_i$ such that $\mathbf{L}_i$ coincides (u.l.t.) with the **i**th principal component of the set of projections of variables $\mathbf{Y}_1, \ldots, \mathbf{Y}_m$ into S_X? For simplicity we write $\dot{\mathbf{Y}}_i =_{\text{def}} \dot{\mathbf{Y}}_{i(S_X)}$ as before (p. 576). Then the matrix of covariances among the $\mathbf{Y}_i$-projections into S_X is $\mathbf{C}_{\dot{Y}\dot{Y}}$, or $\mathbf{C}_{YY(S_X)}$ (cf. [B.17]), and any orthogonal matrix $\mathbf{T}_{P_{\dot{Y}}\dot{Y}}$ which carries the $\dot{\mathbf{Y}}_i$ into a set of their principal components is such that

$$\text{[B.82]} \qquad \mathbf{T}_{P_{\dot{Y}}\dot{Y}} \mathbf{C}_{YY(S_X)} = \mathbf{D}_\lambda \mathbf{T}_{P_{\dot{Y}}\dot{Y}}$$

(see [B.49]), where $\mathbf{D}_\lambda$ is the $\mathbf{m} \times \mathbf{m}$ diagonal matrix whose **i**th diagonal element is the **i**th eigenvalue of $\mathbf{C}_{YY(S_X)}$. Also, since

$$\mathbf{S}_{P_{\dot{Y}}I} = \mathbf{T}_{P_{\dot{Y}}\dot{Y}} \mathbf{S}_{\dot{Y}I} = \mathbf{T}_{P_{\dot{Y}}\dot{Y}} \mathbf{B}_{\dot{Y}X} \mathbf{S}_{XI} \ ,$$

the **i**th row of transformation matrix $\mathbf{W}_{P_{\dot{Y}}X}$, i.e.,

$$\text{[B.83]} \qquad \mathbf{W}_{P_{\dot{Y}}X} = \mathbf{T}_{P_{\dot{Y}}\dot{Y}} \mathbf{B}_{\dot{Y}X} \ ,$$

is a vector $\mathbf{w}_i$ of coefficients such that $\sum_{j=1}^{n} w_{ij} \mathbf{X}_j$ coincides up to its mean with an **i**th principal component of the $\dot{Y}_i$. Postmultiplying [B.82] by $\mathbf{B}_{\dot{Y}X}$ while considering the third line of [B.17], we have

[B.84] $$\mathbf{T}_{P_{\dot{Y}}\dot{Y}}\,\mathbf{B}_{\dot{Y}X}\,\mathbf{C}_{XX}\,\mathbf{B}_{\dot{Y}X}'\,\mathbf{B}_{\dot{Y}X} = \mathbf{D}_\lambda\,\mathbf{T}_{P_{\dot{Y}}\dot{Y}}\,\mathbf{B}_{\dot{Y}X}\,.$$

Hence using [B.83] and [B.16],

[B.85] $$\mathbf{W}_{P_{\dot{Y}}X}\,\mathbf{C}_{\dot{Y}X}'\,\mathbf{C}_{\dot{Y}X}\,\mathbf{C}_{XX}^{-1} = \mathbf{D}_\lambda\,\mathbf{W}_{P_{\dot{Y}}X}$$

or equivalently,

[B.86-**i**] (**i** = **1**, . . . , **m**) $$\mathbf{w}_i\,\mathbf{C}_{\dot{Y}X}'\,\mathbf{C}_{\dot{Y}X}\,\mathbf{C}_{XX}^{-1} = \lambda_i \mathbf{w}_i\,,$$

where λ_i is the **i**th eigenvalue of the projection configuration. Since any linear composite of $\dot{\mathbf{Y}}_1, \ldots, \dot{\mathbf{Y}}_m$ which qualifies as an **i**th principal component of these projections is thus identical with a composite $w_{i0} + \sum_{j=1}^{n} w_{ij}\mathbf{X}_j$ of $\mathbf{X}_1, \ldots, \mathbf{X}_n$ whose weight vector $\mathbf{w}_i = \langle w_{i1}, \ldots, w_{in}\rangle$ satisfies [B.86-**i**], while the nonsingularity of $\mathbf{C}_{XX}$ implies that there is only one weight vector $\mathbf{w}_i$ such that $w_{i0} + \sum_{j=1}^{n} w_j\mathbf{X}_j$ coincides (exactly) with a given **i**th principal component of $\dot{\mathbf{Y}}_1, \ldots, \dot{\mathbf{Y}}_m$, it follows that a necessary condition for $\sum_{j=1}^{n} w_{ij}\mathbf{X}_j$ to coincide (u.l.t.) with an **i**th principal component of the projection configuration is for the weight vector **w** to satisfy equation [B.86-**i**].

Conversely, suppose that $\mathbf{w} = \langle w_1, \ldots, w_n\rangle$ is an eigenvector of $\mathbf{C}_{\dot{Y}X}'\,\mathbf{C}_{\dot{Y}X}\,\mathbf{C}_{XX}^{-1}$. Then for some constant λ, $\mathbf{w}\,\mathbf{C}_{\dot{Y}X}'\,\mathbf{C}_{\dot{Y}X}\,\mathbf{C}_{XX}^{-1} = \lambda\mathbf{w}$—or postmultiplying by $\mathbf{C}_{\dot{Y}X}'$, setting $\mathbf{v} =_{\text{def}} \mathbf{w}\,\mathbf{C}_{\dot{Y}X}'$ and considering [B.17], $\mathbf{v}\mathbf{C}_{YY(S_X)} = \lambda\mathbf{v}$. This shows that unless **v** is identically zero, it is an eigenvector of covariance matrix $\mathbf{C}_{YY(S_X)}$ and the composite $\mathbf{L} =_{\text{def}} \sum_{j=1}^{m} v_j\dot{\mathbf{Y}}_j$ hence coincides (u.l.t.) with a principal component $\mathbf{P}_{\dot{Y}(\lambda)}$ of the $\dot{\mathbf{Y}}_j$-configuration whose corresponding eigenvalue is λ. But

$$\mathbf{s}_{LI} = \mathbf{v}\,\mathbf{S}_{\dot{Y}I} = \mathbf{w}\,\mathbf{C}_{\dot{Y}X}'\,\mathbf{S}_{\dot{Y}I} = \mathbf{w}\,\mathbf{C}_{\dot{Y}X}'\,\mathbf{C}_{\dot{Y}X}\,\mathbf{C}_{XX}^{-1}\,\mathbf{S}_{XI} = \lambda\,\mathbf{w}\,\mathbf{S}_{XI}\,,$$

or $\sum_{j=1}^{n} v_j\dot{\mathbf{Y}}_j = \lambda\left(w_0 + \sum_{j=1}^{n} w_j\mathbf{X}_j\right)$ for some additive constant w_0, so unless $\lambda = 0$ or **v** is identically zero, $\sum_{j=1}^{n} w_j\mathbf{X}_j$ also coincides (u.l.t.) with $\mathbf{P}_{\dot{Y}(\lambda)}$. But **v** can be identically zero only if $\lambda = 0$, since otherwise, contrary to the stipulation that $\mathbf{w}_i$ is an eigenvector and $\mathbf{C_{XX}}$ is nonsingular, $\sum_{j=1}^{n} w_j\mathbf{X}_j$ would equal a constant. Hence *a necessary and sufficient condition for a composite* $\sum_{j=1}^{n} w_j\mathbf{X}_j$ *of variables* $\mathbf{X}_1, \ldots, \mathbf{X}_n$, *whose covariance matrix* $\mathbf{C_{XX}}$ *is nonsingular, to coincide (u.l.t.) with a principal component of the configuration of projections into* $S_\mathbf{X}$ *of variables* $\mathbf{Y}_1, \ldots, \mathbf{Y}_m$ *whose corresponding eigenvalue* λ_i *is greater than zero is for* $\langle w_1, \ldots, w_n\rangle$ *to be an eigenvector of the matrix* $\mathbf{C'_{YX}\,C_{YX}\,C_{XX}^{-1}}$ *corresponding to eigenvalue* λ_i.

It is of interest to observe that if $\mathbf{Y}_1, \ldots, \mathbf{Y}_m$ are an orthonormal basis for space $S_\mathbf{Y}$, so that $\mathbf{C_{YY}} = \mathbf{I}$, then from [B.17] (reading "X" for "Y" and conversely) the covariance matrix for the projections of $\mathbf{X}_1, \ldots, \mathbf{X}_n$ into $S_\mathbf{Y}$ is $\mathbf{C}_{\mathbf{XX}(S_\mathbf{Y})} = \mathbf{C_{XY}C_{YY}^{-1}C'_{XY}} = \mathbf{C_{XY}C'_{XY}} = \mathbf{C'_{YX}C_{YX}}$; so postmultiplying by $\mathbf{C_{XX}^{-1}}$ yields $\mathbf{C}_{\mathbf{XX}(S_\mathbf{Y})}\mathbf{C_{XX}^{-1}} = \mathbf{C'_{YX}\,C_{YX}\,C_{XX}^{-1}}$, where as demonstrated earlier (p. 596), the matrix on the left is the one whose eigenvectors successively maximize the penetrances of orthogonal $\mathbf{X}_i$-composites into $S_\mathbf{Y}$. Hence as demonstrated on p. 476 by a different argument, when the $\mathbf{Y}_i$ are orthonormal, the series of linear composites of $\mathbf{X}_1, \ldots, \mathbf{X}_n$ which coincide (u.l.t.), respectively, with the principal components of the $\mathbf{Y}_i$-projections into $S_\mathbf{X}$ is the same as the series of orthogonal $\mathbf{X}_i$-composites which successively have maximal penetrance into $\mathbf{S_Y}$.

Canonical Correlation

Suppose that we are given two sets of variables $\mathbf{X}_1, \ldots, \mathbf{X}_n$ and $\mathbf{Y}_1, \ldots, \mathbf{Y}_m$ where $\mathbf{m} \leq \mathbf{n}$. Our problem is to find a series of paired composites $\mathbf{L}_{\mathbf{X}i} =_{\text{def}} \sum_{j=1}^{n} w_{ij}\mathbf{X}_j$ and $\mathbf{L}_{\mathbf{Y}i} =_{\text{def}} \sum_{j=1}^{m} v_{ij}\mathbf{Y}_j$ $(\mathbf{i} = \mathbf{1}, \ldots, \mathbf{m})$ determined by weight vectors $\mathbf{w}_i = \langle w_{i1}, \ldots, w_{in}\rangle$ and $\mathbf{v}_i = \langle v_{i1}, \ldots, v_{im}\rangle$ $(\mathbf{i} = \mathbf{1}, \ldots, \mathbf{m})$ in such fashion that $\mathbf{w}_1$ and $\mathbf{v}_1$ maximize the linear correlation between $\mathbf{L}_{\mathbf{X}1}$ and $\mathbf{L}_{\mathbf{Y}1}$ while more generally, $\mathbf{w}_i$ and $\mathbf{v}_i$ maximize the correlation between $\mathbf{L}_{\mathbf{X}i}$ and $\mathbf{L}_{\mathbf{Y}i}$ subject to (1) prior successive maximization of $r_{\mathbf{L_{XK}\,L_{YK}}}$ for $\mathbf{k} = \mathbf{1}, \ldots, \mathbf{i} - \mathbf{1}$ and (2) orthogonal configurations in both the $\mathbf{L}_{\mathbf{X}i}$ and in the $\mathbf{L}_{\mathbf{Y}i}$. The **i**th pair, $\mathbf{L}_{\mathbf{X}i}$ and $\mathbf{L}_{\mathbf{Y}i}$, of these composites (or, if preferred, standardizations thereof) is the **i**th pair of *canonical factors* for the pair of sets $\mathbf{X}_1, \ldots, \mathbf{X}_n$ and $\mathbf{Y}_1, \ldots, \mathbf{Y}_m$ with respect to each other, while the correlation between $\mathbf{L}_{\mathbf{X}i}$ and $\mathbf{L}_{\mathbf{Y}i}$ is the **i**th *canonical correlation* between the two sets.

Let us begin by momentarily relaxing the condition that $\mathbf{L}_{\mathbf{Y}1}, \ldots, \mathbf{L}_{\mathbf{Y}m}$ need be mutually orthogonal. For every linear composite $\mathbf{L_X}$ of the $\mathbf{X}_i$ there exists a corresponding linear composite of $\mathbf{Y}_1, \ldots, \mathbf{Y}_m$ which is the projection of $\mathbf{L_X}$ into the space $S_\mathbf{Y}$ spanned by the $\mathbf{Y}_i$, while the correlation between $\mathbf{L_X}$ and its projection into $S_\mathbf{Y}$ equals the multiple correlation of $\mathbf{L_X}$ with $\mathbf{Y_1}, \ldots, \mathbf{Y_m}$ and is hence the square root of the penetrance of $\mathbf{L_X}$ into $S_\mathbf{Y}$. Consequently, the series of mutually orthogonal linear composites of variables $\mathbf{X_1}, \ldots, \mathbf{X_n}$ which successively have maximal correlation with some corresponding optimal linear composite of $\mathbf{Y_1}, \ldots, \mathbf{Y_m}$ is simply the series of mutually orthogonal composites $\mathbf{L_{X1}}, \ldots, \mathbf{L_{Xn}}$ which have successively maximal penetrance into $S_\mathbf{Y}$, while the corresponding $\mathbf{Y_i}$-composites which have maximal correlation with these $\mathbf{L_{Xi}}$ respectively coincide with the projections of the $\mathbf{L_{Xi}}$ into $S_\mathbf{Y}$. But as shown previously, the projection into $S_\mathbf{Y}$ of an orthogonal configuration $\mathbf{L_{X1}}, \ldots, \mathbf{L_{Xn}}$ which successively maximizes $P_{\mathbf{L_{Xi}}}(S_\mathbf{Y})$ is also an orthogonal configuration, so these $\mathbf{L_{Xi}}$—or rather, the first **m** of them, since if the dimensionality of $S_\mathbf{Y}$ is less than **n**, at most the first **m** of the $\mathbf{L_{Xi}}$ can have nonzero variance—are also the canonical factors of $\mathbf{X_1}, \ldots, \mathbf{X_n}$ with respect to $\mathbf{Y_1}, \ldots, \mathbf{Y_m}$ while the projections of the $\mathbf{L_{Xi}}$ into $S_\mathbf{Y}$ coincide (u.l.t.), respectively, with the canonical factors of the $\mathbf{X_j}$ with respect to the $\mathbf{Y_j}$. That is, each canonical factor coincides (u.l.t.) with the return projection into its own space of its projection into the opposed space. (This is a rare property which can, in fact, be shown to be possessed *only* by canonical factors.) Finally, it is also seen that for $\mathbf{i}=\mathbf{1}, \ldots, \mathbf{m}$, $P_{\mathbf{L_{Xi}}}(S_\mathbf{Y}) = r^2_{\mathbf{L_{Xi}}\mathbf{L_{Yi}}} = P_{\mathbf{L_Y}}(S_\mathbf{X})$.

The matrix equations for computing canonical factors are an immediate consequence of our earlier results for successive maximization of penetrance. If $\mathbf{w_1}, \ldots, \mathbf{w_n}$ and $\mathbf{v_1}, \ldots, \mathbf{v_m}$ are the two series of weights which yield the canonical factors of $\mathbf{X_1}, \ldots, \mathbf{X_n}$ and $\mathbf{Y_1}, \ldots, \mathbf{Y_m}$ with respect to each other, and $\lambda_\mathbf{i}$ $(\mathbf{i}=\mathbf{1}, \ldots, \mathbf{m})$ is the square of the **i**th canonical correlation between the two sets, then the $\mathbf{w_i}$ and the $\mathbf{v_i}$ are a solution to

$$[\mathrm{B.87\text{-}i}] \qquad \mathbf{w_i C_{XX(S_Y)} C_{XX}^{-1}} = \lambda_\mathbf{i}\mathbf{w_i}, \quad \mathbf{v_i C_{YY(S_X)} C_{YY}^{-1}} = \lambda_\mathbf{i}\mathbf{v_i}. \quad (\mathbf{i}=\mathbf{1}, \ldots, \mathbf{m})$$

In view of [B.17], this is equivalent to

$$[\mathrm{B.88\text{-}i}] \quad \mathbf{w_i C_{XY} C_{YY}^{-1} C_{YX} C_{XX}^{-1}} = \lambda_\mathbf{i}\mathbf{w_i}, \quad \mathbf{v_i C_{YX} C_{XX}^{-1} C_{XY} C_{YY}^{-1}} = \lambda_\mathbf{i}\mathbf{v_i}, \quad (\mathbf{i}=\mathbf{1}, \ldots, \mathbf{m})$$

or more elegantly,

$$[\mathrm{B.89\text{-}i}] \qquad \mathbf{w_i B_{\dot{X}Y} B_{\dot{Y}X}} = \lambda_\mathbf{i}\mathbf{w_i}, \quad \mathbf{v_i B_{\dot{Y}X} B_{\dot{X}Y}} = \lambda_\mathbf{i}\mathbf{v_i}. \quad (\mathbf{i}=\mathbf{1}, \ldots, \mathbf{m})$$

If $\lambda_1, \ldots, \lambda_\mathbf{m}$ are all distinct, then the converse is also true, namely, that any series of paired weight vectors $\mathbf{w_i}$ and $\mathbf{v_i}$ $(\mathbf{i}=\mathbf{1}, \ldots, \mathbf{m})$ satisfying [B.87], [B.88] or [B.89] also defines a series of paired composites $\mathbf{L_{Xi}} = \sum_{\mathbf{j}=1}^{\mathbf{n}} w_{\mathbf{ij}}\mathbf{X_j}$ and $\mathbf{L_{Yi}} = \sum_{\mathbf{j}=1}^{\mathbf{m}} v_{\mathbf{ij}}\mathbf{Y_j}$ $(\mathbf{i}=\mathbf{1}, \ldots, \mathbf{m})$ which satisfy the definition of canonical factors. If some of the $\lambda_\mathbf{i}$ coincide, however, then additional selection must be made among the solutions to [B.88] (or its equivalent) for the coincident λ_i in order to insure orthogonality.

Finally, the weight vectors $\mathbf{w}_i$ and $\mathbf{v}_i$ ($\mathbf{i} = 1, \ldots, \mathbf{m}$) which generate canonical factors can be identified in still another way which will be sketched here for the intimate connection it brings out between canonical factoring and fundamental matrix operations. It is a remarkable property of matrices that for any real $m \times n$ matrix $\mathbf{M}$, there exists a real $m \times m$ orthonormal matrix $\mathbf{T}_v$, a real $n \times n$ orthonormal matrix $\mathbf{T}_w$ and a real $m \times n$ diagonal matrix $\mathbf{D}_\lambda$ whose element d_{ij} is λ_i if $j = i$ and is zero otherwise, such that

$$\text{[B.90]} \qquad \mathbf{T}_v \mathbf{M} \mathbf{T}'_w = \mathbf{D}_\lambda \; .$$

$\mathbf{T}_v$ and $\mathbf{T}_w$ may be called the "left eigenmatrix" and the "right eigenmatrix," respectively, of $\mathbf{M}$, while λ_i is the ith eigenvalue of $\mathbf{M}$. λ_i is unique for a given $\mathbf{M}$ up to reversal of sign, and can always be taken positive. An immediate consequence of [B.90] is

$$\text{[B.91]} \qquad \mathbf{T}_v \mathbf{M} \mathbf{M}' \mathbf{T}'_v = \mathbf{D}^{(m)}_{\lambda^2} \, , \qquad \mathbf{T}_w \mathbf{M} \mathbf{M}' \mathbf{T}'_w = \mathbf{D}^{(n)}_{\lambda^2} \, ,$$

where $\mathbf{D}^{(m)}_{\lambda^2}$ and $\mathbf{D}^{(n)}_{\lambda^2}$ are $m \times m$ and $n \times n$ diagonal matrices, respectively, both of which have λ_i^2 for their ith diagonal element so long as i is no larger than either m or n and have zero elements otherwise. It can also be shown that if the eigenvalues of $\mathbf{M}$ are all distinct, any pair of matrices $\mathbf{T}_v$ and $\mathbf{T}_w$ which satisfy [B.91] also satisfy [B.90], at least after suitable reflection of the rows of $\mathbf{T}_v$ or $\mathbf{T}_w$. One intuitively helpful way to derive theorem [B.90] is by construing matrix $\mathbf{M} = \{m_{ij}\}$ to be a matrix $\mathbf{C_{YX}}$ of covariances between the variables in a set $\mathbf{Y}_1, \ldots, \mathbf{Y}_m$ and a set $\mathbf{X}_1, \ldots, \mathbf{X}_n$—i.e., $m_{ij} = \text{Cov}(\mathbf{Y}_i, \mathbf{X}_j)$—and then asking what orthogonal rotations $\mathbf{T}_v = \{v_{ij}\}$ and $\mathbf{T}_w = \{w_{ij}\}$ of $\mathbf{Y}_1, \ldots, \mathbf{Y}_m$ and $\mathbf{X}_1, \ldots, \mathbf{X}_n$, respectively, successively maximize the covariance between the $\mathbf{i}$th rotated $S_\mathbf{Y}$-axis $\sum_{j=1}^{m} v_{ij}\mathbf{Y}_j$ and the corresponding $\mathbf{i}$th rotated $S_\mathbf{X}$-axis $\sum_{j=1}^{n} w_{ij}\mathbf{X}_j$. It is found that $\mathbf{T}_v$ and $\mathbf{T}_w$ satisfy [B.90], while the element d_{ij} of $\mathbf{D}_\lambda$ in [B.90] equals the covariance between the $\mathbf{i}$th rotated axis of space $S_\mathbf{Y}$ and the $\mathbf{j}$th rotated axis of space $S_\mathbf{X}$. (The simplest proof of this requires partial differentiation and Lagrange multipliers, and will hence not be given here.)

Now suppose that $\mathbf{Y}_1, \ldots, \mathbf{Y}_m$ and $\mathbf{X}_1, \ldots, \mathbf{X}_n$ are both orthonormal configurations—i.e., $\mathbf{C_{YY}} = \mathbf{I}^{(m)}$ and $\mathbf{C_{XX}} = \mathbf{I}^{(n)}$—while $\mathbf{m} \leq \mathbf{n}$. Then every orthonormal basis for space $S_\mathbf{Y}$ corresponds to some orthogonal rotation of configuration $\mathbf{Y}_1, \ldots, \mathbf{X}_m$ and conversely, while similarly any orthonormal basis for $S_\mathbf{X}$ corresponds to some orthogonal rotation of the $\mathbf{X}_i$ and conversely. Since the covariance between two normalized variables equals their correlation, it follows from the definition of canonical factors that the normalized canonical factors $\mathbf{L}_{\mathbf{Y}1}, \ldots, \mathbf{L}_{\mathbf{Y}m}$ and $\mathbf{L}_{\mathbf{X}1}, \ldots,$

$\mathbf{L_{X_n}}$ of the $\mathbf{Y_i}$ and the $\mathbf{X_j}$ with respect to each other are orthogonal rotations of their respective initial configurations which successively maximize Cov($\mathbf{L_{Y_i}}$, $\mathbf{L_{X_i}}$). Hence the weight vectors $\mathbf{v_i}$ and $\mathbf{w_i}$ which generate the **i**th pair of canonical factors $\mathbf{L_{Y_i}} = \sum_{j=1}^{m} v_{ij}\mathbf{Y_j}$ and $\mathbf{L_{X_i}} = \sum_{j=1}^{n} w_{ij}\mathbf{X_j}$ are the **i**th rows of $\mathbf{T}_v$ and $\mathbf{T}_w$, respectively, in

$$\text{[B.92]} \qquad \mathbf{T}_v\mathbf{C_{YX}}\mathbf{T}_w' = \mathbf{D}_r \qquad \text{(orthonormal configurations)} ,$$

where the **i**th diagonal element of the $\mathbf{m} \times \mathbf{n}$ diagonal matrix $\mathbf{D}_r$ is the **i**th canonical correlation between orthonormal configurations $\mathbf{Y_1}, \ldots, \mathbf{Y_m}$ and $\mathbf{X_1}, \ldots, \mathbf{X_n}$. Solution for $\mathbf{T}_v$ and $\mathbf{T}_w$ in [B.92] may then be reduced to solution for the eigenvectors of a symmetric matrix by application of principle [B.91], namely,

$$\text{[B.93]} \qquad \mathbf{T}_v\mathbf{C_{YX}}\mathbf{C_{XY}}\mathbf{T}_v' = \mathbf{D}_{r^2}^{(\mathbf{m})} , \quad \mathbf{T}_w\mathbf{C_{XY}}\mathbf{C_{YX}}\mathbf{T}_w' = \mathbf{D}_{r^2}^{(\mathbf{n})}$$

(orthonormal configurations) .

The only difference between [B.93] and the more general equations [B.88] is that the latter first orthonormalize the two configurations $\mathbf{Y_1}, \ldots, \mathbf{Y_m}$ and $\mathbf{X_1}, \ldots, \mathbf{X_n}$ if they are not orthonormal to begin with, and then apply principle [B.93].

References

1. Adcock, C. J. *Factorial analysis for non-mathematicians*. Melbourne: University Press, 1954.
2. American Psychological Association, Committee on Psychological Tests. *Technical recommendations for psychological tests and diagnostic techniques*. Washington, D.C.: APA, 1954. (Reprinted from *Psychol. Bull., Suppl.,* 1954, **51**, 201–238.)
3. Anderson, T. W. *An introduction to multivariate statistical analysis*. New York: Wiley, 1958.
4. Anderson, T. W. Some scaling models and estimation procedures in the latent class model. In: Grenander, U. (ed.) *Probability and statistics*. New York: Wiley, 1959.
5. Attneave, F. *Applications of information theory to psychology*. New York: Holt, 1959.
6. Bechtoldt, H. P. Construct validity: A critique. *Amer. Psychologist,* 1959, **14,** 619–629.
7. Binder, A. Statistical theory. In: Farnsworth, P. R. (ed.) *Annual review of psychology,* Vol. 15. Palo Alto, Calif.: Annual Reviews, Inc., 1964.
8. Braithwaite, R. B. *Scientific explanation*. Cambridge: Cambridge Univ. Press, 1953.
9. Campbell, D. T. & Fiske, D. W. Convergent and discriminant validation by the multitrait-multimethod matrix. *Psychol. Bull.,* 1959, **56,** 81–105.
10. Carroll, J. B. The nature of the data, or how to choose a correlation coefficient. *Psychometrika,* 1961, **26,** 347–372.
11. Cattell, R. B. & Dickman, K. A dynamic model of physical influences demonstrating the necessity of oblique simple structure. *Psychol. Bull.,* 1962, **59,** 389–400.
12. Chernoff, H. & Moses, L. E. *Elementary decision theory*. New York: Wiley, 1959.
13. Cooley, W. W. & Lohnes, P. R. *Multivariate procedures for the behavioral sciences*. New York: Wiley, 1962.
14. Coombs, C. H. *A theory of data*. New York: Wiley, 1964.
15. Coombs, C. H. & Kao, R. C. *Nonmetric factor analysis*. Ann Arbor: Univ. of Michigan Press, 1955. (Univ. of Michigan Engineering Research Institute Bulletin No. 38.)
16. Cotton, J. W., Campbell, D. T., & Malone, R. D. The relationship between factorial composition of test items and measures of test reliability. *Psychometrika,* 1957, **22,** 347–357.

17. Cronbach, L. J. Test "reliability": Its meaning and determination. *Psychometrika,* 1947, **12,** 1–16.
18. Cronbach, L. J. Coefficient Alpha and the internal structure of tests. *Psychometrika,* 1951, **16,** 297–334.
19. Cronbach, L. J. *Essentials of psychological testing,* 2nd ed. New York: Harper, 1960.
20. Cronbach, L. J. & Gleser, G. C. *Psychological tests and personnel decisions,* 2nd ed. Urbana: Univ. of Illinois Press, 1965.
21. Cronbach, L. J. & Meehl, P. E. Construct validity in psychological tests. *Psychol. Bull.,* 1955, **52,** 281–302.
22. Cronbach, L. J., Rajaratnam, N., & Gleser, G. C. Theory of generalizability: A liberation of reliability theory, *Brit. J. statist. Psychol.,* 1963, **16,** 137–163.
23. Cureton, E. E. Validity. In: Lindquist, E. F. (ed.) *Educational measurement.* Washington, D. C.: American Council on Education, 1951.
24. DuBois, P. H. *Multivariate correlational analysis.* New York: Harper, 1957.
25. Edwards, W., Lindman, H., & Savage, L. J. Bayesian statistical inferences for psychological research. *Psychol. Rev.,* 1963, **70.** 193–242.
26. Ezekial, M. & Fox, K. E. *Methods of correlation and regression analysis,* 3rd ed. New York: Wiley, 1959.
27. Feigl, H. & Brodbeck, M. (eds.) *Readings in the philosophy of science.* New York: Appleton-Century-Crofts, 1953.
28. Feigl, H. & Maxwell, G. (eds.) *Current issues in the philosophy of science.* New York: Holt, Rinehart & Winston, 1961.
29. Feigl, H., Maxwell, G., & Scriven, M. *Minnesota studies in the philosophy of science,* Vols. I–III. Minneapolis: Univ. of Minnesota Press, 1956, 1958, 1962.
30. Garner, W. R. *Uncertainty and structure as psychological concepts.* New York: Wiley, 1962.
31. Garner, W. R. & McGill, W. J. The relation between information and variance analyses. *Psychometrika,* 1956, **21,** 219–228.
32. Gibson, W. A. Three multivariate models: Factor analysis, latent structure analysis, and latent profile analysis. *Psychometrika,* 1959, 24, 229–252.
33. Goodman, N. The problem of counterfactual conditionals. *J. Philos.,* 1947, **44,** 113–128. (Reprinted in: Linsky, L. (ed.) *Semantics and the philosophy of language.* Urbana: Univ. of Illinois Press, 1952.
34. Grünbaum, A. *Philosophical problems of space and time.* New York: Knopf, 1963.
35. Guilford, J. P. Factorial angles to psychology. *Psychol. Rev.,* 1961, **68,** 1–20.
36. Gulliksen, H. *Theory of mental tests.* Wiley, 1950.
37. Guttman, L. A basis for analyzing test-retest reliability. *Psychometrika,* 1945, **10,** 255–282.
38. Guttman, L. A special review of Harold Gulliksen, "Theory of Mental Tests." *Psychometrika,* 1953, **18,** 123–130.
39. Guttman, L. A new approach to factor analysis: The radex. In: Lazarsfeld, P. F. (ed.) *Mathematical thinking in the social sciences.* Glencoe, Ill.: Free Press, 1954.
40. Guttman, L. "Best possible" systematic estimates of communalities. *Psychometrika,* 1956, **21,** 273–285.
41. Guttman, L. Simple proofs of relations between the communality problem and multiple correlation. *Psychometrika,* 1957, **22,** 147–157.
42. Guttman, L. To what extent can communalities reduce rank? *Psychometrika,* 1958, **23,** 297–308.

43. Guttman, L. What lies ahead for factor analysis? *Educ. psychol. Measmt.*, 1958, **18,** 497–515.
44. Harmon, H. H. *Modern factor analysis.* Chicago: Univ. of Chicago Press, 1960.
45. Holzinger, K. J. & Harmon, H. H. *Factor analysis.* Chicago: Univ. of Chicago Press, 1941.
46. Humphreys, L. G. The organization of human abilities. *Amer. Psychol.*, 1962, **17,** 475–483.
47. Johnson, P. O. & Jackson, R. W. B. *Modern statistical methods.* Chicago: Rand McNally, 1959.
48. Khinchin, A. I. *Mathematical foundations of information theory.* New York: Dover, 1957.
49. Kuder, G. F. & Richardson, M. W. The theory of the estimation of test reliability. *Psychometrika,* 1937, **2,** 151–160.
50. Kullback, S. *Information theory and statistics.* Wiley, 1959.
51. Lawley, D. N. & Maxwell, A. E. *Factor analysis as a statistical method.* London: Butterworths, 1963.
52. Lazarsfeld, P. F. Latent structure analysis. In: Koch, S. (ed.) *Psychology: A study of a science,* Vol. 3. New York: McGraw-Hill, 1959.
53. Lennon, R. T. Assumptions underlying the use of content validity. *Educ. psychol. Measmt.*, 1956, **16,** 294–304.
54. Lord, F. M. Sampling fluctuations resulting from the sampling of test items. *Psychometrika,* 1955, **20,** 1–22.
55. Lord, F. M. Statistical inferences about true scores. *Psychometrika,* 1959, **24,** 1–17.
56. Lorge, I. The fundamental nature of measurement. In: Lindquist, E. F. (ed.) *Educational measurement.* Washington, D.C.: American Council on Education, 1951.
57. Lubin, A. The interpretation of significant interaction. *Educ. psychol. Measmt.*, 1961, **21,** 807–817.
58. Luce, R. D. & Raiffa, H. *Games and decisions.* New York: Wiley, 1957.
59. Maxwell, A. E. Canonical variate analysis when the variables are dichotomous. *Educ. psychol. Measmt.*, 1961, **21,** 259–272.
60. Meehl, P. E. & Rosen, A. Antecedent probability and the efficiency of psychometric signs, patterns, or cutting scores. *Psychol. Bull.*, 1955, **52,** 194–216.
61. Menger, K. On variables in mathematics and in natural science. *Brit. J. Philos. Sci.*, 1954, **5,** 134–142.
62. Nagel, E. *The structure of science: Problems in the logic of scientific explanation.* New York: Harcourt, Brace, & World, 1961.
63. Pap, A. *An introduction to the philosophy of science.* Glencoe, Ill.: The Free Press, 1962.
64. Pearson, K. *The life, letters, and labours of Francis Galton,* Vol. III. Cambridge: The University Press, 1930.
65. Quastler, H. (ed.) *Information theory in psychology.* Glencoe, Ill.: The Free Press, 1955.
66. Rescher, N. Belief-contravening suppositions. *Philos. Rev.*, 1961, **70,** 176–196.
67. Rozeboom, W. W. Ontological induction and the logical typology of scientific variables. *Philos. Sci.*, 1961, **28,** 337–377.
68. Rozeboom, W. W. Linear correlations between sets of variables. *Psychometrika,* 1965, **30,** 57–71.
69. Rozeboom, W. W. The theory of abstract partials: An introduction. Forthcoming.

70. Rozeboom, W. W. Scaling theory and the nature of measurement. Forthcoming.
71. Scheffé, H. *The analysis of variance.* New York: Wiley, 1959.
72. Scott, W. A. Measures of test homogeneity. *Educ. psychol. Measmt.,* 1960, **20,** 751–757.
73. Shannon, C. E. A mathematical theory of communication. *Bell syst. tech. J.,* 1948, **27,** 379–423, 623–656. (Reprinted in: Shannon, C. E. & Weaver, W. *The mathematical theory of communication.* Urbana: Univ. of Illinois Press, 1949.)
74. Stevens, S. S. Mathematics, measurement, and psychophysics. In: Stevens, S. S. (ed.) *Handbook of experimental psychology.* New York: Wiley, 1951.
75. Suppes, P. & Zinnes, J. L. Basic measurement theory. In: Luce, R. D., Bush, R. R., & Galanter, E. (eds.) *Handbook of mathematical psychology,* Vol. I. New York: Wiley, 1963.
76. Tiedman, D. W. Rulon, P. J., & Bryan, J. G. The multiple discriminant function—a symposium. *Harvard educ. Rev.,* 1951, **21,** 71–95.
77. Thomson, G. H. *The factorial analysis of human ability,* 5th ed. New York: Houghton Mifflin, 1951.
78. Thurstone, L. L. *Multiple factor analysis.* Chicago: Univ. of Chicago Press, 1947.
79. Torgerson, W. S. *Theory and methods of scaling.* New York: Wiley, 1958.
80. Tryon, R. C. Reliability and behavior domain validity: Reformulations and historical critique. *Psychol. Bull.,* 1957, **54,** 229–249.
81. Tryon, R. C. General dimensions of individual differences: Cluster analysis vs. multiple factor analysis. *Educ. psychol. Measmt.,* 1958, **18,** 477–495.
82. Walker, H. M. *Studies in the history of statistical method.* Baltimore: Williams & Wilkins, 1929.
83. Watanabe, S. Information theoretical analysis of multivariate correlation. *IBM J. Res. Dev.,* 1960, **4,** 66–82.
84. Watanabe, S. *Knowing and guessing.* New York: Wiley, forthcoming.
85. Wherry, R. J. Hierarchical solution without rotation. *Psychometrika,* 1959, **24,** 45–51.
86. Wilks, S. S. *Mathematical statistics.* New York: Wiley, 1962.
87. Winer, B. *Statistical principles in experimental design.* New York: McGraw-Hill, 1962.

Glossary*

Symbol	Description	Primary Page Reference
$\mathbf{X}$	An arbitrary variable.	9
X	A particular (but unspecified) value of variable $\mathbf{X}$.	10
X_i	The value of variable $\mathbf{X}$ for individual i.	10
Σ	The *summation operator.*	27,104
$M_{\mathbf{X}}$	The *arithmetic mean* of variable $\mathbf{X}$ in a population P.	27
ϕ^{-1}	The *inverse* of transformation ϕ.	30
$QM_{\mathbf{X}}$	The *quadratic mean* of variable $\mathbf{X}$ in a population P (undefined if $\mathbf{X}$ takes negative values in P).	31
$QM_{\lvert\mathbf{X}\rvert}$	The quadratic mean magnitude of variable $\mathbf{X}$ in population P.	38
$\lvert X\rvert$	The absolute value, or *magnitude,* of number X.	35
$AD_{\mathbf{X}}$	The *average deviation* of variable $\mathbf{X}$ in population P. Equals $M_{\mathbf{D_X}}$.	36
$\sigma_{\mathbf{X}}$	The *standard deviation* of variable $\mathbf{X}$ in population P. Equals $QM_{\mathbf{D_X}}$.	37
$Var(\mathbf{X})$	The *variance* of variable $\mathbf{X}$ in population P. Equals $\sigma^2_{\mathbf{X}}$.	39
$\mathbf{Z_X}$	The Z-score scale of variable $\mathbf{X}$. Equals $(\mathbf{X} - M_{\mathbf{X}})/\sigma_{\mathbf{X}}$.	43
$Z_{\mathbf{X}i}$	Individual i's Z-score on variable $\mathbf{X}$. Equals $(X_i - M_{\mathbf{X}})/\sigma_{\mathbf{X}}$.	43
$\nu_{\mathbf{X}}$	The *coefficient of variation* for variable $\mathbf{X}$ in population P. Equals $\sigma_{\mathbf{X}}/M_{\mathbf{X}}$.	47
$Sk_{\mathbf{X}}$	The *skew* of variable $\mathbf{X}$'s distribution in population P.	50
$Kt_{\mathbf{X}}$	The *kurtosis* of variable $\mathbf{X}$'s distribution in population P.	51

*Symbols whose usage is narrowly restricted to a few consecutive pages are not listed.

$\hat{X}$	The "best estimate" of a to-be-predicted score on variable **X**.	62
$\hat{\mathbf{X}}$	The variable whose value for a member i of population P is the value of **X** estimated for i by a given prediction policy.	62
$SE_{\mathbf{X}}$	The *standard error* for estimating variable **X**.	72
P_X	A restricted population comprising those members of base population P whose value of variable **X** is X.	83
$M_{\mathbf{Y}\mid X}$	A contingent mean. Specifically, the arithmetic mean of variable **Y** in subpopulation P_X of P.	84,139
$\mathcal{M}_{\mathbf{Y}\mid\mathbf{X}}$	The variable whose value for a member i of population P is $M_{\mathbf{Y}\mid X_i}$.	
$\sigma_{\mathbf{Y}\mid X}$	A contingent standard deviation. Specifically, the standard deviation of variable **Y** in subpopulation P_X of P.	84
$\sigma_{\mathbf{Y}.\mathbf{X}}$	The residual standard deviation of variable **Y**, given scores on variable **X**, in population P. Equals the SD of variable $\mathbf{Y} - \mathcal{M}_{\mathbf{Y}\mid\mathbf{X}}$ in P.	88
$\mathbf{e}_{\mathbf{Y}}$	In Chapter 4, the estimate-error variable $\mathbf{Y} - \hat{\mathbf{Y}}$. Subsequently restricted to the case where $\hat{\mathbf{Y}} = \mathcal{M}_{\mathbf{Y}}$.	85,294
$SE_{\mathbf{Y},\mathbf{X}}[\hat{\mathbf{Y}} = \phi(\mathbf{X})]$	The *standard error* of prediction policy $\hat{\mathbf{Y}} = \phi(\mathbf{X})$ for members of population P. Equals $QM_{\lvert\mathbf{Y}-\hat{\mathbf{Y}}\rvert}$ in P.	89
$SE_{\mathbf{Y},\mathbf{X}}$	Short for $SE_{\mathbf{Y},\mathbf{X}}[\hat{\mathbf{Y}} = \phi(\mathbf{X})]$.	88,140
$SE_{\mathbf{Y}\mid X}$	A contingent standard error. Specifically, the standard error of policy $\hat{\mathbf{Y}} = \phi(\mathbf{X})$ within just the subpopulation P_X of P.	85
$\kappa_{\mathbf{Y},\mathbf{X}}$	The *curvilinear coefficient of alienation*. Equals $\sigma_{\mathbf{Y}\mathbf{X}}/\sigma_{\mathbf{Y}}$.	92
$\eta_{\mathbf{Y},\mathbf{X}}$	The curvilinear correlation coefficient, or *correlation ratio*. Equals $\sqrt{1-\kappa^2_{\mathbf{Y},\mathbf{X}}}$.	93
$\in$	The *class-membership* symbol.	97
$\mathrm{Cov}(\mathbf{X}, \mathbf{Y})$	The *covariance* between variables **X** and **Y** in population P.	100
$r_{\mathbf{XY}}$	The *(linear) correlation* between variables **X** and **Y** in population P.	107

k_{XY}	The *(linear) coefficient of alienation.* Equals $\sigma_{Y \cdot X}/\sigma_Y$.	114
$\dot{Y}_{i(X_1 \ldots X_m)}$	The best linear estimate of Y_i for a member i of population P, given i's scores on predictor variables $\mathbf{X}_1, \ldots, \mathbf{X}_m$.	110, 142
$\dot{\mathbf{Y}}_{(X_1 \ldots X_m)}$	The linear regression of criterion variable $\mathbf{Y}$ upon predictor variables $\mathbf{X}_1, \ldots, \mathbf{X}_m$ in population P. Specifically, the variable whose value for a member i of P is $\dot{Y}_{i(X_1 \ldots X_m)}$.	110, 142
$\mathbf{e}_{Y \cdot X_1 \ldots X_m}$	The linear residual of criterion $\mathbf{Y}$, given predictors $\mathbf{X}_1, \ldots, \mathbf{X}_m$, in population P. Equals $\mathbf{Y} - \dot{\mathbf{Y}}_{(X_1 \ldots X_m)}$.	115, 142, 157
$\sigma_{Y \cdot X_1 \ldots X_m}$	The linear residual (partial) standard deviation of criterion $\mathbf{Y}$, given predictors $\mathbf{X}_1, \ldots, \mathbf{X}_m$, in population P. Equals the SD of variable $\mathbf{e}_{Y \cdot X_1 \ldots X_m}$ in P.	102, 142, 157
$K_{Y(X_1 \ldots X_m)}$	The *multiple (linear) coefficient of alienation.* Equals $\sigma_{Y \cdot X_1 \ldots X_m}/\sigma_Y$.	152
$R_{Y(X_1 \ldots X_m)}$	The *multiple (linear) correlation coefficient.* Equals $\sqrt{1 - K^2_{Y(X_1 \ldots X_n)}}$.	152
$r_{YW \cdot X_1 \ldots X_m}$	A *partial correlation coefficient*; specifically, the residual correlation between variables $\mathbf{Y}$ and $\mathbf{W}$ in population P after variables $\mathbf{X}_1, \ldots, \mathbf{X}_m$ are partialled out. Equals the linear correlation between variables $\mathbf{e}_{Y \cdot X_1 \ldots X_m}$ and $\mathbf{e}_{W \cdot X_1 \ldots X_m}$ in P.	157
$k_{YW \cdot X_1 \ldots X_m}$	A *partial coefficient of alienation.* Specifically, the linear coefficient of alienation for variables $\mathbf{e}_{Y \cdot X_1 \ldots X_m}$ and $\mathbf{e}_{W \cdot X_1 \ldots X_m}$ in population P.	158
$b_{YX_i \cdot X_1 \ldots X_{i-1} X_{i+1} \ldots X_m}$	A *b*-coefficient. Specifically, the coefficient, or "weight" of variable $\mathbf{X}_i$ in the linear regression of criterion $\mathbf{Y}$ upon predictors $\mathbf{X}_1, \ldots, \mathbf{X}_m$ in population P.	159
$\beta_{YX_i \cdot X_1 \ldots X_{i-1} X_{i+1} \ldots X_m}$	A Beta-coefficient. Specifically, what $b_{YX_i \cdot X_1 \ldots X_{i-1} X_{i+1} \ldots X_n}$ becomes when variables $\mathbf{Y}$ and $\mathbf{X}_i$ are standardized to unit variance.	159
b_i, β_i	Short for $b_{YX_i \cdot X_1 \ldots X_{i-1} X_{i+1} \ldots X_m}$ and $\beta_{YX_i \cdot X_1 \ldots X_{i-1} X_{i+1} \ldots X_m}$, respectively.	141, 145
$\boldsymbol{\mu}$	A set of predictor variables $\mathbf{X}_1, \ldots, \mathbf{X}_m$.	157

μ_i	On p. 180 ff., an arbitrary set of predictor variables. Later, a set of predictor variables $\mathbf{X}_1, \dots, \mathbf{X}_{i-1}, \mathbf{X}_{i+1}, \dots, \mathbf{X}_m$; i.e., set $\boldsymbol{\mu}$ less predictor $\mathbf{X}_i$.	180, 264
μ_{ij}	A set of predictor variables $\mathbf{X}_1, \dots, \mathbf{X}_{i-1}, \mathbf{X}_{i+1}, \dots, \mathbf{X}_{j-1}, \mathbf{X}_{j+1}, \dots, \mathbf{X}_m$; i.e., set $\boldsymbol{\mu}$ less predictors $\mathbf{X}_i$ and $\mathbf{X}_j$.	508
$S_{Y,W}$	The *index of forecasting efficiency*. Specifically, $S_{Y,W[\mu]}$ when $\boldsymbol{\mu}$ is empty.	165
$S_{Y,W[\mu]}$	The *supplementary savings* measure. Specifically, the amount by which the linear standard error for estimating criterion $\mathbf{Y}$ is further reduced when predictors $\boldsymbol{\mu}$ are supplemented by predictor $\mathbf{W}$, expressed as a proportion of the standard error of $\mathbf{Y}$ given no predictors.	165
$K_{Y(\mu_i)\cdot\mu_j}$	A *multiple-partial coefficient of alienation.* Equals $\sigma_{Y\cdot\mu_i\mu_j}/\sigma_{\mu_j}$.	181
$R_{Y(\mu_i)\cdot\mu_j}$	A *multiple-partial correlation coefficient.* Equals $\sqrt{1 - K^2_{Y(\mu_i)\cdot\mu_j}}$.	181
$C_{X_iX_j}$	Short for $\mathrm{Cov}(\mathbf{X}_i, \mathbf{X}_j)$.	220
$C_{X_iX_j\cdot F_1\cdots F_k}$	The residual covariance between variables $\mathbf{X}_i$ and $\mathbf{X}_j$ after variables $\mathbf{F}_1, \dots, \mathbf{F}_k$ are partialled out. Equals $\mathrm{Cov}(\mathbf{e}_{X_i\cdot F_1\cdots F_k}, \mathbf{e}_{X_j\cdot F_1\cdots F_k})$.	220
$C_{X_iX_j(F_1\cdots F_k)}$	The covariance between variables $\mathbf{X}_i$ and $\mathbf{X}_j$ linearly accounted for by variables $\mathbf{F}_1, \dots, \mathbf{F}_k$. Equals $\mathrm{Cov}(\mathbf{X}_{i(F_1\dots F_k)}, \dot{\mathbf{X}}_{j(F_1\dots F_k)})$.	221
V_{X_i}	Short for $\mathrm{Var}(\mathbf{X}_i)$.	220
$V_{X_i\cdot F_1\cdots F_k}$	The residual variance of variable $\mathbf{X}_i$ after variables $\mathbf{F}_1, \dots, \mathbf{F}_k$ have been partialled out. Equals $\mathrm{Var}(\mathbf{e}_{X_i\cdot F_1\dots F_k})$.	220
$V_{X_i(F_1\dots F_k)}$	The variance of variable $\dot{\mathbf{X}}_i$ linearly accounted for by variables $\mathbf{F}_1, \dots, \mathbf{F}_k$. Equals $\mathrm{Var}(\mathbf{X}_{i(F_1\dots F_k)})$.	221
V_X	The total variance in a configuration of variables $\mathbf{X}_1, \dots, \mathbf{X}_n$. Equals $\sum_{i=1}^{n} V_{X_i}$.	233
$V_{X(F_1\dots F_k)}$	The total variance of configuration $\mathbf{X}_1, \dots, \mathbf{X}_n$ linearly accounted for by variables $\mathbf{F}_1, \dots, \mathbf{F}_k$. Equals $\sum_{i=1}^{n} V_{X_i(F_1\dots F_k)}$.	233

$\{q_{ij}\}$	A matrix of numbers whose element at the intersection of its ith row and jth column is q_{ij}.	222
$\mathbf{P_{Xk}}$	The **k**th *principal factor* of configuration $\mathbf{X_1}, \ldots, \mathbf{X_n}$.	238
$\mathbf{P_k}$	Prior to Appendix B, short for $\mathbf{P_{Xk}}$. In Appendix B, the **k**th principal component of configuration $\mathbf{X_1}, \ldots, \mathbf{X_n}$.	238, 582
$\lambda_{\mathbf{Xk}}$	The **k**th *eigenvalue* of configuration $\mathbf{X_1}, \ldots, \mathbf{X_n}$. Equals $V_{\mathbf{X}}(\mathbf{P_{Xk}})$, i.e., the total variance of variables $\mathbf{X_1}, \ldots, \mathbf{X_n}$ accounted for by their **k**th principal factor.	239
$\lambda_{\mathbf{k}}$	Short for $\lambda_{\mathbf{Xk}}$.	239
$\mathbf{C_k}$	The **k**th *principal component* of configuration $\mathbf{X_1}, \ldots, \mathbf{X_n}$.	242
$\overline{\mathbf{X}}$	The *centroid* of configuration $\mathbf{X_1}, \ldots, \mathbf{X_n}$. Equals $(1/\mathbf{n}) \sum_{\mathbf{i}=1}^{\mathbf{n}} \mathbf{X_i}$.	244
$\mathbf{H_i}$	The *communal component* of variable $\mathbf{X_i}$ with respect to configuration $\mathbf{X_1}, \ldots, \mathbf{X_n}$.	254
$\mathbf{U_i}$	The *unique component* of variable $\mathbf{X_i}$ with respect to configuration $\mathbf{X_1}, \ldots, \mathbf{X_n}$. Equals $\mathbf{X_i} - \mathbf{H_i}$.	255
$h^2_{\mathbf{i}}$	The *communality* of variable $\mathbf{X_i}$ with respect to the common factors of configuration $\mathbf{X_1}, \ldots, \mathbf{X_n}$. Equals the squared multiple correlation of $\mathbf{X_i}$ with the configuration's common factors.	258
S	A *space* of variables. Specifically, the set of all linear combinations of some set of variables $\mathbf{F_1}, \ldots, \mathbf{F_k}$.	293
S^*	The *complement* to space S with respect to configuration $\mathbf{X_1}, \ldots, \mathbf{X_n}$. Specifically, any space orthogonal to space S such that the $\mathbf{X_i}$ all lie wholly within the union of S and S^*.	325
$\perp(S_1, \ldots, S_k)$	Assertion that spaces $S_1, \ldots, S_k$ are mutually orthogonal.	293
$\text{Span}(S; \mathbf{F_1} \ldots \mathbf{F_k})$	Assertion that variables $\mathbf{F_1}, \ldots, \mathbf{F_k}$ span space S.	293
$\mathbf{e}_{\mathbf{X_i}}(S)$	The *projection* of variable $\mathbf{X_i}$ into space S.	294
$\mathbf{e}_{\mathbf{X_i} \bullet S}$	The component of variable $\mathbf{X_i}$ orthogonal to space S.	294

$V_{X_i}(S)$	The variance of variable $\mathbf{X_i}$ accounted for by space S. Equals $\mathrm{Var}(\mathbf{e}_{X_i}(S))$.	295
$C_{X_iX_j}(S)$	The covariance between variables $\mathbf{X_i}$ and $\mathbf{X_j}$ accounted for by space S. Equals $\mathrm{Cov}(\mathbf{e}_{X_i}(S), \mathbf{e}_{X_j}(S))$.	295
$C^*_{XX}(S)$	The total covariance of configuration $\mathbf{X_1}, \ldots, \mathbf{X_n}$ accounted for by space S. Equals the sum of all elements in covariance matrix $\{C_{X_iX_j}(S)\}$.	295
$\overline{C}^*_{XX}(S)$	The average covariance of configuration $\mathbf{X_1}, \ldots, \mathbf{X_n}$ accounted for by space S. Equals $C^*_{XX}(S)/\mathbf{n}^2$.	297
$C_{XX}(S)$	The total proper covariance of configuration $\mathbf{X_1}, \ldots, \mathbf{X_n}$ accounted for by space S. Equals the sum of all off-diagonal elements in covariance matrix $\{C_{X_iX_j}(S)\}$.	296
$\overline{C}_{XX}(S)$	The average proper covariance of configuration $\mathbf{X_1}, \ldots, \mathbf{X_n}$ accounted for by space S. Equals $C_{XX}(S)/\mathbf{n}(\mathbf{n}-1)$.	297
$V_X(S)$	The total variance of configuration $\mathbf{X_1}, \ldots, \mathbf{X_n}$ accounted for by space S. Equals the sum of the diagonal elements in covariance matrix $\{C_{X_iX_j}(S)\}$.	296
$\overline{V}_X(S)$	The average variance of configuration $\mathbf{X_1}, \ldots, \mathbf{X_n}$ accounted for by space S. Equals $V_X(S)/\mathbf{n}$.	297
$C^*_{XX}, C_{XX}, V_X, \overline{C}^*_{XX}, \overline{C}_{XX}, \overline{V}_X$	The total covariance, total proper covariance, total variance, average covariance, average proper covariance, and average variance, respectively, of configuration $\mathbf{X_1}, \ldots, \mathbf{X_n}$—i.e., what $C^*_{XX}(S)$, etc., become when the configuration is wholly contained in space S.	295ff.
$\mathbf{D_i}$	The *dispersion component* of variable $\mathbf{X_i}$ with respect to configuration $\mathbf{X_1}, \ldots, \mathbf{X_n}$. Equals $\mathbf{X_i} - \overline{\mathbf{X}}$.	298
c_{X_i}	Short for $\mathrm{Cov}(\mathbf{X_i}, \overline{\mathbf{X}})$.	314
ν_{c_X}	The *index of radial irregularity* for configuration $\mathbf{X_1}, \ldots, \mathbf{X_n}$.	314
$P_X(S)$	The *penetrance* of configuration $\mathbf{X_1}, \ldots, \mathbf{X_n}$ into space S. Equals $V_X(S)/V_X$.	315
$P_{X_i}(S)$	The *penetrance* of variable $\mathbf{X_i}$ into space S.	316

$\mathrm{Sat}_{\mathbf{X}}$	The *saturation coefficient* of configuration $\mathbf{X}_1, \ldots, \mathbf{X}_n$. Equals the proportion of $\mathbf{V}_{\mathbf{X}}$ which is saturation variance.	317
$\mathrm{Disp}_{\mathbf{X}}$	The *dispersion coefficient* of configuration $\mathbf{X}_1, \ldots, \mathbf{X}_n$. Equals the proportion of $\mathbf{V}_{\mathbf{X}}$ which is dispersion variance.	317
$\mathrm{DQ}_{\mathbf{X}}$	The *dispersion quotient* of configuration $\mathbf{X}_1, \ldots, \mathbf{X}_n$. Equals $\mathrm{Disp}_{\mathbf{X}}/\mathrm{Sat}_{\mathbf{X}}$.	318
$\mathrm{Hom}_{\mathbf{X}}$	The *homogeneity* of configuration $\mathbf{X}_1, \ldots, \mathbf{X}_n$.	320
$\mathrm{Sat}_{\mathbf{X}}(S)$, $\mathrm{Disp}_{\mathbf{X}}(S)$, $\mathrm{DQ}_{\mathbf{X}}(S)$, $\mathrm{Hom}_{\mathbf{X}}(S)$	The saturation, dispersion, dispersion quotient, and homogeneity, respectively, of the projection of configuration $\mathbf{X}_1, \ldots, \mathbf{X}_n$ into space S.	323f.
$\mathrm{PQ}_{\mathbf{X}}(S)$	The *penetrance quotient* for configuration $\mathbf{X}_1, \ldots, \mathbf{X}_n$ in space S. Equals $\mathrm{P}_{\mathbf{X}}(S)/\mathrm{P}_{\mathbf{X}}(S^*)$.	326
$PQ_{\mathbf{X}_i}(S)$	The *penetrance quotient* for variable $\mathbf{X}_i$ in space S. Equals $P_{\mathbf{X}_i}(S)/P_{\mathbf{X}_i}(S^*)$.	327
$\widetilde{h^2}$	The variance-weighted average communality of the variables in configuration $\mathbf{X}_i, \ldots, \mathbf{X}_n$.	331
$h^2_{\overline{\mathbf{X}}}$	The communality of the centroid of configuration $\mathbf{X}_1, \ldots, \mathbf{X}_n$. Equals the penetrance of $\overline{\mathbf{X}}$ into common-factor space.	331
$\gamma_{\mathbf{wX}}$	The *selection coefficient* for rescaling-transformations $\mathbf{W}_i = c_i + w_i\mathbf{X}_i$ ($\mathbf{i} = \mathbf{1}, \ldots, \mathbf{n}$).	356
$\delta_{\mathbf{wX}}$, $\rho_{\mathbf{wX}}$, $\theta_{\mathbf{wX}}$	(Other transformation parameters.)	353,356
$\mathrm{r}_{\mathbf{X}_i}$	The *reliability* of variable $\mathbf{X}_i$.	396
$\alpha_{\mathbf{X}}$	The *alpha coefficient* of configuration $\mathbf{X}_1, \ldots, \mathbf{X}_n$. Equals $\mathrm{Hom}_{\mathbf{X}}/\mathrm{Sat}_{\mathbf{X}}$.	411
$\alpha_{\mathbf{X}}(S)$	The alpha coefficient of the projection of configuration $\mathbf{X}_1, \ldots, \mathbf{X}_n$ into space S.	438
$\mathrm{r}_{\overline{\mathbf{X}}}$	The reliability of the centroid of configuration $\mathbf{X}_1, \ldots, \mathbf{X}_n$. Equivalent to the reliability of these variables' sum.	429
$\mathbf{T}_i$	Thc *true-score component of* variable $\mathbf{X}_i$.	376,385
$\mathbf{E}_i$	The *error component* of variable $\mathbf{X}_i$. Equals $\mathbf{X}_i - \mathbf{T}_i$.	376, 385
τ_i	(In Chapter 6 a hypothetical source variable.) In Chapter 9, the *common*	(252), 431

	true-factor component of variable $\mathbf{X_i}$ with respect to configuration $\mathbf{X_1}, \ldots, \mathbf{X_n}$.	
ϵ_i	The *common error component* of variable $\mathbf{X_i}$ with respect to configuration $\mathbf{X_1}, \ldots, \mathbf{X_n}$. Equals $\mathbf{H_i} - \tau_i$.	431
$\mathbf{t_i}$	The *specific true-factor component* of variable $\mathbf{X_i}$ with respect to configuration $\mathbf{X_1}, \ldots, \mathbf{X_n}$. Equals $\mathbf{T_i} - \tau_i$.	431
$\mathbf{e_i}$	The *unique error component* of variable $\mathbf{X_i}$ with respect to configuration $\mathbf{X_1}, \ldots, \mathbf{X_n}$. Equals $\mathbf{E_i} - \epsilon_i$ and also $\mathbf{U_i} - \mathbf{t_i}$.	431
$S_\mathbf{H}, S_\mathbf{U}, S_\mathbf{T}, S_\mathbf{E}, S_\tau, S_\epsilon, S_\mathbf{t}, S_\mathbf{e}$	The respective spaces spanned by the communal components, the unique components, the true-score components, etc., of configuration $\mathbf{X_1}, \ldots, \mathbf{X_n}$.	330,431
$P_\tau, P_\mathbf{t}, P_\epsilon, P_\mathbf{e}$	Short for $P_\mathbf{X}(S_\tau)$, $P_\mathbf{X}(S_\mathbf{t})$, $P_\mathbf{X}(S_\epsilon)$, and $P_\mathbf{X}(S_\mathbf{e})$, respectively.	434
$P_{\bar\tau}, P_{\bar{\mathbf{t}}}, P_{\bar\epsilon}, P_{\bar{\mathbf{e}}}$	Short for $P_{\bar{\mathbf{X}}}(S_\tau)$, $P_{\bar{\mathbf{X}}}(S_\mathbf{t})$, $P_{\bar{\mathbf{X}}}(S_\epsilon)$, and $P_{\bar{\mathbf{X}}}(S_\mathbf{e})$, respectively.	448
$\tilde{r}_\mathbf{X}$	The variance-weighted average reliability of variables $\mathbf{X_1}, \ldots, \mathbf{X_n}$. Equals the configuration's penetrance into true-score space.	430
u.l.t.	Short for "up to a linear transformation."	472
$\bar{q}, \sigma_\mathbf{q}, \nu_\mathbf{q}$	The arithmetic mean, SD and coefficient of variation, respectively, of numbers $q_1, \ldots, q_n$.	301,313, 319f.,354, 362,413
$Exp(\mathbf{X})$	The statistical expectation (i.e., arithmetic mean) of a probability distribution for variable **X**.	500
$Exp(\mathbf{X}\|C)$	The (contingent) expectation of variable **X** given restrictive conditions C.	505
$Var(\mathbf{X}\|C)$	The (contingent) variance of variable **X** given restrictive conditions C.	505
O_n	A set of $(\mathbf{m} + 1)n$ numbers describing the joint scores on variables $\mathbf{Y}, \mathbf{X_1}, \ldots, \mathbf{X_m}$ observed within a given n-member subset (i.e., "sample") of population P.	504
$\mathbf{O}_n$	A sampling-distribution variable whose values are the different possible joint frequency distributions that variables $\mathbf{Y}, \mathbf{X_1}, \ldots, \mathbf{X_m}$ might have in a subpopulation comprising n members of population P.	504

χ_n	A set of $\mathbf{m}n$ numbers describing the joint frequency distribution of predictor variables $\mathbf{X_1}, \ldots, \mathbf{X_m}$ within an n-member sample drawn from population P.	504
$s(O_n)$	The value of statistic s (i.e., $b_\mathbf{i}$, $\sigma_\mathbf{Y}$, etc.) for a subpopulation of P within which the joint distribution of $\mathbf{Y}, \mathbf{X_1}, \ldots, \mathbf{X_m}$ is O_n.	505
$s(P)$	The value of statistic s within population P.	505
$\{C^{\mathbf{ij}}\}$	The inverse of covariance matrix $\{C_{\mathbf{X_iX_j}}\}$.	508
$C^{\mathbf{ij}}$	The element at the $\mathbf{i}$th row and $\mathbf{j}$th column of matrix $\{C_{\mathbf{ij}}\}$.	508
$t_{p(n-\mathbf{m}-1)}$	The number such that $100p\%$ of a t-distribution with $n-\mathbf{m}-1$ degrees of freedom lies within this distance of zero.	512
$p_{\mathbf{X}i}$	The individual probability for a population member i of receiving a score of 1 on unit-dichotomous variable $\mathbf{X}$. Equals i's "true score" on variable $\mathbf{X}$.	527
$\mathbf{p_X}$	The true-score component of unit-dichotomous variable $\mathbf{X}$, i.e., the variable whose value for individual i is $p_{\mathbf{X}i}$.	528
$\Pr(E)$	The unconditional probability of event E.	553
$\Pr(E\|C)$	The (contingent) probability of event E given restrictive conditions C.	553

Name Index

A

Adcock, C. J., 210 n
Anderson, T. W., 523 n, 552 n
Attneave, F., 565 n

B

Bechtoldt, H. P., 206 n
Binder, A., 498 n
Braithwaite, R. B., 196 n
Brodbeck, M., 196 n
Brown, W., 408
Bryan, J. G., 552 n

C

Campbell, D. T., 208 n, 332 n
Carroll, J. B., 529 n
Cattell, R. B., 524 n
Chernoff, H., 58 n
Claus, S., 237
Cooley, W. W., 240 n
Coombs, C. H., 530
Cotton, J. W., 332 n
Cronbach, L. J., 127, 188 n, 206 n, 391 n, 399, 405 n, 411
Cureton, E. E., 393 n, 396 n

D

DeMoivre, 52 n
Dickman, K., 524 n
DuBois, P. H., 175

E

Edwards, W., 498 n
Ezekial, M., 521 n

F

Feigl, H., 196 n
Fisher, R. A., 543, 558 n
Fiske, D. W., 208 n
Fox, K. E., 521 n

G

Garner, W. R., 565, 569 n, 570
Gibson, W. A., 530
Gleser, G. C., 127
Goodman, N., 383 n
Grünbaum, A., 536 n
Guilford, J. P., 287
Gulliksen, H., 391 n, 405 n
Guttman, L., 263 n, 264, 289 ff, 335 n, 417 n, 447

H

Harmon, H. H., 210, 230, 474 n
Holzinger, K. J., 230 n
Humphreys, L. G., 287

J

Jackson, R. W. B., 177 n
Johnson, P. O., 177 n

K

Kao, R. C., 530
Khinchin, A. I., 565 n
Kuder, G. F., 410 f
Kullback, S., 565 n

L

Lawley, D. N., 210 n
Lazarsfeld, P. F., 530

Lennon, R. T., 197 n
Lindman, H., 498 n
Lohnes, P. R., 240 n
Lord, F. M., 391, 530
Lorge, I., 10 n
Lubin, A., 549 n
Luce, R. D., 67 n

M

Malone, R. D., 332 n
Maxwell, A. E., 210 n, 552 n
Maxwell, G., 196 n
McGill, W. J., 565, 569 n
Meehl, P. E., 206 n, 565
Menger, K., 8 n
Moses, L. E., 58 n

N

Nagel, E., 196 n

P

Pap, A., 196 n
Pearson, K., 128 n

Q

Quastler, H., 565 n

R

Raiffa, H., 67 n
Rajaratnam, N., 391 n
Rescher, N., 383 n
Richardson, M. W., 410 f
Rosen, A., 565
Rozeboom, W. W., 8 n, 10 n, 207 n, 566, 569 n
Rulon, P. J., 552 n

S

Savage, L. L., 498 n
Scheffé, H., 506 n, 510 n, 543 n, 544 n
Scott, W. A., 321 n
Scriven, M., 196 n
Shannon, C. E., 565 f
Spearman, C., 287 ff, 408, 425 n
Stevens, S. S., 10 n
Suppes, P., 10 n

T

Thomson, G. H., 210 n
Thurstone, L. L., 210 n, 284, 289
Tiedman, D. W., 552 n
Torgerson, W. S., 10 n
Tryon, R. C., 250 n, 391 n

W

Walker, H. M., 52 n
Watanabe, S., 565 n, 570
Wherry, R. J., 289 n
Wilks, S. S., 506 n, 510 n, 552 n
Winer, B., 543 n

Y

Yule, G. U., 158

Z

Zinnes, J. L., 10 n

Subject Index

A

Ability, nature of, 199 f, 206, 377
Absolute frequency, 14
Absolute standard error, 87 ff, 107, 112, 140 f, 541
Absolute value, 35
Accounted-for covariance; *see* Controlled covariance
Accounted-for Uncertainty, 569 f
Accounted-for Variance; *see* Controlled variance
Age-ratio IQ, 418 n
Alienation, coefficient of
  curvilinear, 92
  linear, 114
  multiple, 152
    as affected by number of predictors, 165 f
  multiple-partial, 181 f
  partial, 158
  relation to correlation, 123 f
  relation between multiple and partial, 164, 166, 182 f
Alpha coefficient, 411 ff, 436 ff
  configural interpretation of, 446 ff
  effect of item grouping upon, 451 ff
  effect of item weighting upon, 493 ff
  relation to reliability, 415, 437, 449 f, 496
Alternate forms
  reliability estimation, 397, 400 ff
  of test, 399 f
Analysis of covariance, 543, 552
Analysis of relations, varieties of, 543
Analysis of variance, 93, 543 ff
  as applied to covariance matrix, 314 f
A posteriori factoring, 287, 289
Approximations, theory of, 519
A priori factoring, 287, 289
A priori probabilities, 553
Arithmetic mean, 26 ff, 68
Asymmetry, measure of, 50 n
Attenuation, correction for, 425
Average, 26, 32, 39 f
  weighted, 32
Average deviation, 35 f, 65 n
Axiomatic reliability theory, 391

B

Bandwidth, of test, 188 n
Base of logarithm, as unit of Uncertainty, 567
Base rate, 564; *see also* Marginal distribution
Basis, for set of variables, 217 f, 224
  approximate, 219, 257
  orthogonal, 217, 242
Basis factoring, 236 ff
  relation to item weighting, 465
  relevance to factor analysis, 218, 235
Bayes' theorem, 553
Bayesian statistic, 498 f
b-coefficients, 141
  complete notation for, 159
  computation by matrix inversion, 509, 577
  as factor coefficients, 226
  as partial statistics, 173 f
  relation to β-coefficients, 145
  sampling error of, 515 ff
  sampling estimation of, 502, 505 ff
Best estimate, 62 ff, 67 n, 69 n, 78, 89
  utility free, 68
Best-fitting line, 98
Beta-coefficients, 145, 509
  complete notation for, 159

Beta-coefficients – *Cont.*
as partial statistics, 173 ff
solution for two predictors, 149
Between-group variance, 559
Bias, 500
Bit, as unit of Uncertainty, 567
Bivariate distribution, description of, 18
normal, 54, 120
Boldface notation, explanation of, 9, 101, 138 n

C

Canonical correlation, 250 f, 599
Canonical factors, 250 f, 480, 599 ff
Cartesian product of variables, 568
Categorical variable, 9, 537 ff, 543
correlational measures applicable to, 565 n
as criterion, 552 ff, 565 ff
as predictor, 543 ff, 565 ff
reduction to set of dichotomies, 540 n, 563
Centile, 17 n
Central Limit Theorem, 52 n
Central moments of distribution, 55
Central tendency, 23 ff, 39 f
Centroid, 244
effect of item weights upon, 359 ff, 367, 371, 486 ff
factor extraction of, 245
penetrance properties of, 324 ff, 439 ff, 447 ff
of projection configuration, 298
relation to first principal axis, 310 ff, 341, 473
reliability of, 434 ff, 440 ff, 448 ff, 478, 495 f
residuals of, 247, 299 f
as saturation configuration, 308
variance of, 244, 297
Centroid communality, 331 ff, 446
lower-bound estimates of, 334 ff, 455 f
maximization of, 474, 477 f
Characteristic root of matrix, 586; *see also* Eigenvalue
Characteristic vector of matrix, 585; *see also* Eigenvector
Circumplex factor pattern, 289
Classification, theory of, 553 ff
Class-intervals, 12
Coefficient of
alienation; *see* Alienation, coefficient of
correlation; *see* Correlation coefficient
determination, 317 n
dispersion, 317, 323
reliability, 396, 402
notation for, 396 n
saturation, 317 ff, 323 ff, 493 f, 592
stability, 399
variation, 47
Coefficient alpha; *see* Alpha coefficient
Common factors, 267 f
centroid penetrance into space of, 331 ff, 494
Common true-factor components, 431
effects of configural properties, 432 ff, 448 ff
space of, 431 f
Common-error components, 431
effects of configural properties, 432 ff, 448 ff
space of, 431 f
Communal components, 251, 254 ff, 330 ff, 447, 458 f, 503
predictability of, 263 f
Communalities, 258 ff
indeterminateness of, 262, 459
lower bound for, 261
problem of, 260
variance-weighted average, 331
Complement, of space, 295 n, 325
Components, of configuration
common true-factor, 431 ff, 441 f, 447 ff, 458 f
common-error, 431 ff, 441 f, 447 ff, 458 f
communal, 251, 254 ff, 330 ff, 447, 458 f, 503
dispersion, 298 ff, 308, 343 fig., 354 ff, 368 ff, 490 f
error, 428 ff, 440, 458 ff
principal; *see* Principal components
projection, 294, 298, 479 ff
saturation, 299 ff, 308, 343 fig.; *see also* Centroid
specific true-factor, 431 ff, 441 f, 447 ff, 458 f
true-score, 428 ff, 440, 458 ff
unique, 255 ff, 289 n, 330 ff, 431, 447 ff, 458
unique-error, 431 ff, 441, 447 f, 458 f
Components, of variable
controlled, 148, 219, 221, 294; *see also* Components, of variable, regressed
error (of estimate), 109, 115; *see also* Components of variable, residual
error (of measurement), 376, 386 ff
projection, 294, 306 f
regressed, 110, 140, 376, 388; *see also* Components of variable, controlled
residual, 115, 140 ff, 219, 221, 294 295 n, 376, 388
true-score, 376, 385 ff
Composite variable, 102, 197
correlation with component, 350 f
covariances among, 103, 105, 576
as criterion of test validity, 198 ff
effect of item weighting upon, 352 ff, 466 f
factorial composition of, 428 ff
reduction to centroid, 463

Composite variable—*Cont.*
regression of, 246
reliability of, 478, 481 ff
true-score component of, 403
variance of, 104 f, 248, 297
Composition notation, 101, 142
Composition theorem, general, 433, 448
Concentration, first-factor, 475
bounds for, 323, 347 f
Conditional; *see* Contingent
Confidence interval, 75 f, 125 ff, 194
for true scores, 77, 422
Confidence level, 75
Confidence set, 76 n
Configuration of variables, 295
dominant direction of, 470 ff
Constraint, total, 570
Construct validity, 196, 206 ff
Content validity, 196 ff, 393
Contingent (conditional)
distribution, 83, 541 f, 553
as standard for criterion scale, 537
mean, 83, 84 n, 541
probability, 505, 512, 553 ff
shape, 85, 541 f
standard deviation, 84, 541
standard error, 86, 90 n, 421
uncertainty, 567 ff
Controlled component, 148, 219, 221, 294
Controlled covariance, 221, 228 f, 294 ff
Controlled variance, 94, 116, 141, 163, 175, 220 f, 292 ff, 310 ff
Convergent configuration, 344, 485 n
Convex function, 69 n
Coordinate, 218
axes, 240
Correction for attenuation, 425
Correlated errors, 398, 405, 415, 437 ff
empirical estimation of, 456 ff
Correlation coefficient
estimation from restricted data, 179
linear (product-moment, Pearsonian), 106 f, 111, 117, 131 ff, 151
average, 322
computation of, 108
relation to correlation ratio, 114, 130 f
sigma-weighted average, 319, 321
multiple, 151 ff, 293
computed from inverse of correlation matrix, 272 n, 509
multiple-partial, 180 ff
negative values of, 114, 205 n, 322, 342 n
partial, 157, 163, 171 f
computation of, 167, 220
point biserial, 565 n
relation to alienation coefficient, 123 f
relation between multiple and partial, 164, 166
sampling estimation of, 515
Correlation
canonical, 250 f, 599
induced, 171
reproduced, 232
total, 570
vector model of, 210, 307
Correlation matrix, 214
Correlation model, in sampling theory, 501, 503
Correlation ratio, 93, 130 f
Cosine, in vector model, 210, 307
Counterfactual, 382, 383 n, 385
Covariance, 100 ff
average, 105, 297 f, 446
controlled, 221, 228 f, 294 ff
matrix, 214
inverse of, 508 ff, 516 f, 577 ff
rank of, 258 ff
proper, 257, 296 ff
residual, 220, 222 f, 228
total, 295 f
Covariance, analysis of, 543, 552
Convariance of regression-parameter estimates, 506 f, 518
Covariances among composite variables, 103, 105, 576
Criterion, 82
composite, 197 ff, 246
importance-weighted, 471, 479 f
space, 442 ff, 480 f
test-stable, 422 f
Cumulative frequency function, 17, 25 n
Curve fitting, 96, 98 f, 520 f
Curvilinear regression, 82, 84, 98 n, 139, 154 ff, 520, 532 ff
in bivariate normal distribution, 120
contrast with linear regression, 130
relation to Analysis of Variance, 545, 547
Cutoff score, 125 ff

D

Data variables, 213, 237
Decision theory, 58 ff
Degree of polynomical, 155 f
Dependence; *see* Independence
Dependent variable, 82, 84 n
Determination, coefficient of, 317 n
Deviation IQ, 418
Deviation variable, 35
Diagnostic utility, 190
Diagonal, of matrix, 214, 258
Dichotomous variable, 412, 526 ff, 530
correlation measures applicable to, 565 n
regression of, 540 ff, 554 ff
Difference variable, 294 n
Difficulty, of dichotomous item, 413
Difficulty level, 527

Dimensionality, 216 ff
  of inferred-factor space, 257 ff, 289 n, 290, 525
Discrete-valued variable, 538
Discriminant analysis, 543, 552 ff
Discriminant function, 251, 560 ff
Discrimination distance, 559 ff
Dispersion
  coefficient, 317, 323
  component, 298 ff
  configuration, 308 f, 343 fig.
    as determinant of effect of item weighting, 354 ff, 368 ff, 490 f
  partition between orthogonal subspaces, 490
Dispersion in univariate distribution, measures of, 32 ff
Dispositional probabilities, 383 f, 385 n, 393, 426
Dispositions, 207, 382, 390
Distribution, 11
  contingent (conditional), 83, 541 f, 553
  marginal, 88 n, 91 n, 553
  multivariate, 18, 53 f
  properties of
    arithmetic mean, 26
    average deviation, 36
    kurtosis, 51
    median, 25
    mode, 24
    normality, 51 ff
    probable error, 35
    quadratic mean magnitude, 38
    skew, 50
    standard deviation, 36
    symmetry, 49 f
    variance, 39
  rectangular, 24
  unconditional, 88 n
Divergence between variables, 488
Divergent configuration, 346
Domain, of test items, 197, 462
Dominant direction of configuration, 470 ff

E

Effects, in Analysis of Variance, 546 ff
Effects, in Uncertainty analysis, 569
Eigenmatrix, 601
Eigenvalue, 239 f, 585 ff
  properties of, 347, 493 ff, 508, 517, 581 f
Eigenvector, 239 n, 585 ff
Equi-normality, 557 ff, 562 ff
Equivalence policy, for estimating true scores, 416 ff
Equivalent forms; *see* Parallel forms
Error
  anticipated magnitude of, 70 f, 92 n, 114 n
  component; *see* Components, error
  of estimate, 85, 115, 192 f

Error—*Cont.*
    of regression parameters, 506, 516 ff
    under sampling-estimated regression parameters, 511 f
  expected, 71, 85, 92 n
  homogeneity, 398, 405, 415, 437 ff
    empirical estimation of, 456 ff
  of measurement; *see* Measurement error
  score, 93; *see also* Components, error
  space, 428 ff, 440, 458
  standard; *see* Standard error
  variance, 94, 116, 141
    in regression model, 502
    sampling estimation of, 505 f, 514
Estimate error
  of regression parameters, 506, 516 ff
  of score predictions; *see* Error, of estimate
Estimator functions, in inferential statistics, 499 ff
Eta, 93, 130 f
Expected error, 71, 85, 92 n
Expected loss, 62
Expected utility, 62 n
Expected value of variable, 30
  as best estimate, 67 ff, 69 n
Explanatory model, 522 f, 543 legend
Extreme variation, 47
  of item weights, 466 f

F

Facet theory, 289
Factor, most representative, 470
Factor analysis, 207, 210 f, 218, 226, 543
  extraction policies (initial solutions), 236 ff
  terminal solutions (interpretation proposals), 236, 280 ff
Factor coefficients, 226, 230 f, 285 n; *see also* Factor loadings
Factor loadings, 212, 232; *see also* Factor coefficients
Factor matrix, 232
Factor pattern, 230 f, 266 ff
Factor structure, 230 f
Factor styles
  centroid, 243 ff
  extraction policies versus terminal solutions, 236
  hierarchical, 287 ff
  inductive (a posteriori) versus rationalistic (a priori), 287, 289 ff
  multiple-group (group centroid), 249
  orthogonal versus oblique, 211, 284 f
  principal axes, 237 ff
  square-root, 248
Factorial complexity, 284, 441
Factorial composition of composite test, 428

Factorial method of determining error homogeneity, 458 f
Factors, 208, 211
centroid, 243 ff
common, 267 f
general, 287 f
group, 249, 288
higher order, 286 f, 289 n
inferred, 211, 252 ff, 266 ff, 281 ff, 503, 523 ff
orthogonal, 211, 227 f, 289 n
orthonormal, 229 f
principal, 237 ff, 508, 517
spurious, 525
unique, 267, 289 n
Fidelity, of test, 188 n
First factor concentration, 475
easily computed bounds for, 323, 347 f
First principal axis; *see* Principal axis, first
Forecasting efficiency, index of, 123 n, 165
Form, of function, 97
Frequency
absolute, 14
density, 15
relative, 14, 83
Frequency polygon, 13
Frequency table, 12
bivariate, 18
Functional relations, 501, 503
Fundamental factor theorem, 232 f
Fundamental partitioning theorem, 295
Fundamental uniqueness theorem, 144

G

Gauss-Markov theorem, 510 n
General composition theorem, 433, 448
General factor, 208, 287 f
Goodness of information, 69 ff, 84 ff, 111 ff
supplementary, 162 ff
Group factors, 249, 288
Guess, 62, 114 n

H

Heterogeneity of true scores, 434 ff
Hierarchical factor solutions, 287 ff
Hierarchical order, 288
Higher moments, inferences from 525 f, 530
Histogram, 13
Homogeneity, 320 ff, 324 f, 412
ratio, 321 n
Homogeneous errors; *see* Correlated errors
Homoscedasticity, 86, 90 n, 120, 422, 537, 541 f
Hyperplane, 141
Hypothesis, null, 550
Hypothesis testing, 551 n

I

Ideal alternate forms of test, 400
Ideal repetitions of test, 395 f
Importance-weighted criterion, 471, 479 f
Independence
correlational, 216 n
linear, 216
statistical, 83, 216 n, 527 n, 529 n
Independent variable, 82
Index of forecasting efficiency, 123 n, 165
Index of radial irregularity, 313, 372 n, 473 n, 588
magnitude of, 373
Index of reliability, 393 f, 396
Individual testee, 381, 394
Individual's probability distribution on test, 383, 426
Induced correlation, 171
Inferential statistics, 12 n, 75 n, 96, 498 ff
Inferred factors, 211, 252 ff, 266 ff, 281 ff, 503, 523 ff
Information
goodness of, 69 ff, 84 ff, 111 ff
supplementary, 162 ff
measure of in Uncertainty analysis, 567
needed for factoring, 224
resulting from factoring, 230 f
sacrificed by omission of predictor, 175 f
theory (Uncertainty analysis), 543, 565 ff
usable versus unusable, 79
Interaction
in Analysis of Variance, 544 ff
in Uncertainty analysis, 569
Internal consistency reliability estimation, 406 ff, 447 ff
usefulness of, 415, 456 f
Interval estimate, 75, 194
minimal, 76
of regression parameters, 518, 521
Inverse of covariance matrix, 508 ff, 516 f, 577 ff
Inverse probabilities, 553
Inverse transformation, 21
IQ, scales of, 418
Item, on test, 388
Item difficulty, 413
Item-sampling reliability theory, 391 n, 392 f
Item selection in test construction, 175 f, 467, 518 f
Item weights, 465 f
effects of, 352 ff, 367, 371
external objectives for, 464, 478
importance of sophistication in, 519
internal objectives for, 464, 468
MaxSat; *see* MaxSat weights
relation to basis-factoring, 465
reliability maximizing, 478, 485
sensitivity of reliability to, 487 ff

Item weights—*Cont.*
  sensitivity of test to, 466
  UniStan, 477, 484

K

Kronecker's delta, 508
Kuder-Richardson formula
  #20, 410, 413
  #21, 414 n
Kurtosis, 51

L

Latent root, of matrix, 586
Latent structure analysis, 530
Latent vector, of matrix, 586
Least-squares solution, 98
Leptokurtic, 51
Linear composite; *see* Composite variable
Linear correlation; *see* Correlation coefficient, linear
Linear dependency, 216
  contrasted with common sources, 258
Linear regression, 54 n, 98 ff, 109 ff, 141 ff
  Analysis-of-Variance counterpart, 546 f
  of composite variable, 246
  matrix-algebra solution for, 576 f
  parametrically linear, 155, 520
Linear residual
  of score, 115; *see also* Components, of variable, residual
  of variance, 116, 141, 220
    estimation of, 505 ff
Linear transformation, 41 f
  of set of variables, 144, 213 n
Linearly regressed score, 111; *see also* Components, of variable, regressed
Loading, factor, 212, 232; *see also* Factor coefficients
Logarithms, base of, 566 f
Loss, 62 ff, 531 f

M

Magnitude, 35, 47
Magnitude variable, 47
Main effects, Analysis of Variance, 546 ff
Marginal distribution, 88 n, 91 n, 553
Marker variable, 283
Matched-item method of error-homogeneity estimation, 460 ff
Matrix, 214, 574 ff
  covariance, 214
  notation for, 222 n, 574
  principal diagonal of, 214
  rank of, 258 ff
  trace of, 347 n, 580
Maximum-likelihood estimator, 499, 505
MaxSat configuration, 469
  centroid properties of, 472, 474 f
MaxSat weights, 469
  computation of, 473 f, 474 n; *see also* Principal axes, solution for properties
  properties of, 474 f, 484 f
  relation to principal factoring, 472
Mean
  arithmetic, 26 ff, 68
  contingent (conditional), 83, 84 n, 541
  of linear composite, 106
Means, nonarithmetic, 31
Measurement, standard error of, 415 ff
  absolute versus contingent, 421
Measurement, theory of, 417 ff
Measurement error, 376 f, 387 ff, 390
  reciprocal of as item weight, 478, 484
Median, 25, 65
Metric, 535 ff
Metrical variable, 535, 543
  inapplicability of Uncertainty analysis to, 568
Minimum-variance estimator, 499 ff
Mixed moments of distribution, 56, 529 n
Mode, 24, 65
  secondary, 24 n
Model,
  explanatory, 522 f, 543 (figure legend)
  in inferential statistics, 498
Moments, of distribution, 55
  central, 55
  higher order, inferences from 525 f, 530
  mixed, 56, 529 n
Multiple alienation coefficient; *see* Alienation, coefficient of
Multiple correlation; *see* Correlation coefficient
Multiple regression
  curvilinear; *see* Curvilinear regression
  linear; *see* Regression, linear
Multivariate distribution, 18; *see also* Configuration of variables *and* Components of configuration

N

Negative correlation, 114, 205 n, 322, 342 n
Negative manifold, 343
Neuter space, 326
Nonarithmetic means, 31
Nonlinear dependencies, 130 f, 523 ff; *see also* Curvilinear regression
Nonlinear regression; *see* Curvilinear regression
Nonsingular matrix, 587
Normal distribution, 51 ff, 571 ff
  bivariate, 54 f, 120
  multivariate, 53
Normal equations, for regression coefficients, 142, 145
Normalization, effect on space spanned, 224 n

Normalized factor pattern, 231
Normalized factor structure, 231
Normalized score, 575
Normalized variable, 212
Normative population, 41, 131 ff
Norms, for test scores, 41, 46, 418
Null-hypothesis, 550
Numerals, distinguished from numbers, 6, 10 n

O

Oblique, 211
factors, 211, 284 ff
Observed score, 376
relation to true score and measurement error, 388 ff, 394 n, 417 ff, 530
as sample of test potential, 383, 426
Operational definition, 189, 195 f
dispositional extension of, 382
Optimal split for reliability estimation, 405, 455 f
Order invariance, 25 n
Orientation, of variable, 342, 465
Origin, 210
of coordinate system, 240
translation of, 241
Orthogonal, 211
axes, 241 ff
basis, 217
rotation to, 242, 556 f
confusions among senses of, 241 f
factors, 227 ff
rotation, 242, 557, 579 ff
spaces, 293 ff, 324 f
variables, 211, 241, 581
Orthonormal factors, 229 ff
Orthonormal matrix, 580

P

Parallel forms
reliability estimation, 397, 399 f
reliability theory, 391 n, 392
of test, 392
Parameters, 97, 155, 498 ff, 504 ff, 566
number in polynominal regression, 520
Parametrically linear regression form, 155, 520
Part correlation, 157 n
Partial statistics, 156 ff, 294
alienation, 158, 181 f
correlation, 157, 163, 171 f
computation, 167, 220
relation between different orders of, 167
covariance, 220, 222 f, 228 f
mth order, 157
zero order, 157 n, 294 n
notation for, 158, 220
variance, 157; *see also* Error, variance
Partialling, effect on correlation of, 171 f
Pearsonian correlation coefficient; *see* Correlation coefficient, linear
Penetrance, 315 ff, 327 f, 565 n
maximization of, 363 ff, 475, 593 ff
quotient, 326 f
Percentage score, 52 n
Percentiles, 17, 25, 52 n
Phi coefficient, 528 f, 565 n
Platykurtic, 51
Point-biserial correlation coefficient, 565 n
Polychotomous criterion, 542, 563, 565 n; *see also* Categorical variable
Polynominal regression form, 155 f; *see also* Curvilinear regression
number of parameters in, 520
Population, 7
parameters, 498 ff, 504 ff
Positive manifold, 343
Potential, on test, 382 ff, 426
Power test, 437, 457 n
Practice effects, 398
Prediction, 2, 59, 60 n, 189 f, 541
of categorical variables, 537 ff
error of, *see* Error
of multiple criteria, 188 n, 479 ff
nonoptimal, 192 f, 510 ff
policy, 89
Predictor equi-normality, 557 ff, 562 ff
Predictor extremity, 513 f
Predictor variable, 82
Presuppositions, violation of, 519 ff
Primary subscripts, 158
Principal axes, 238, 243 fig.
Principal axis, first, 238
as best representative factor, 470
relation to centroid, 310 ff, 341, 473
solution for, 473, 474 n, 587 f
Principal components, 238 f, 581 ff, 587; *see also* Principal factors
of projection configuration, 476, 480 f, 597 ff
solution for, 587 f
Principal diagonal, of matrix, 214
Principal factors, 237 ff, 508, 517; *see also* Principal components
unique-factor penetrance of, 494 f
Probability, 73, 75 n, 77 n, 497 ff
a priori, 553
contingent (conditional), 505, 512, 553 ff
dispositional, 383 f, 385 n, 393, 426
subjective, 498
Probable error, 35 f, 72 n
Product-moment correlation; *see* Correlation coefficient, linear
Profile, test, 465, 480
Prognostic utility, 190
Projections, 240, 294, 306 f
length of, 307
notation for properties of, 293 n

Proper covariance, 257, 296 ff
Prophecy formula, Spearman-Brown, 408
Proportion-correct, 413
Pseudopositive configuration, 344

Q

Quadratic mean, 31
Quadratic mean deviation, 36 f
Quadratic mean magnitude, 36 f, 415 n
  of error, 71, 85; *see also* Standard error
Qualitative variable 9, 543; *see also* Categorical variable
Quantitative variable, 9, 543; *see also* Metrical variable

R

Radex factor pattern, 289
Radial irregularity, index of, 313, 372 n, 473 n, 588
  magnitude of, 373
Range, 33
Rank, of covariance matrix, 258
  reduction of, 258 ff, 262, 289
Rationally equivalent forms of test, 391 n
Raw factor pattern, 231
Raw factor structure, 231
Raw scores, 41
Redundancy among predictors, 148, 154, 175 f, 217
Reference point, 42; *see also* Origin
Reflection, 247 f, 342 ff, 465
Regressed component; *see* Components, regressed
Regressed score, 93, 140; *see also* Components, of variable, regressed
Regression, 58, 128, 541, 543
  in bivariate normal distribution, 54 n, 120
  of categorical criterion, 540 ff, 552 ff
  coefficients, 141 ff, 159, 175 f; *see also b*-coefficients
  curvilinear; *see* Curvilinear regression
  effect of scale choice upon, 111 n, 531 ff, 542
  F-form, 97, 98 n; *see also* Curvilinear regression.
  linear, see Linear regression
  to mediocrity, 128
  model, in sampling theory, 501 f, 504 ff
  parametrically linear, 155, 520
  standard form, 140
Relational analysis, varieties of, 543
Relative frequency, 14, 83
Reliability, 375, 382, 390, 459
  of centroid, 434 ff, 440 ff, 448 ff, 478, 495 f
  coefficient, 396, 402
    notation for, 396 n
Reliability—*Cont.*
  effect of item weights upon, 478, 481 ff
  empirical estimation of, 397 ff, 456 ff
  index, 393 f, 396
  maximization by item weighting, 478, 481 ff
  relation to validity, 375 n, 422 ff
  theoretical approaches to
    axiomatic, 391
    expected score, 383 ff
    item-sampling, 391 n, 392 f
    parallel (equivalent) forms, 391 n, 392
  variance-weighted average, 430
Reproduced correlation, 232
Residual
  component, 115, 140 ff, 219, 221, 294, 295 n, 376, 388
  covariance, 220, 222 f, 228
  mth order, 157
  score, 93, 115, 142; *see also* Residual, component
  standard deviation, 88, 90 f, 182
  statistics, see Partial statistics
  Uncertainty, 569
  variable; *see* Residual, component
  variance; *see* Error, variance
Restriction of predictor variance, effects of, 177 ff
Rotation
  of axes, 241 f
  of factors, 281
  matrix, 281
  orthogonal, 242 f, 557, 579 ff
  to orthogonal basis, 242, 556 f

S

Sampling
  of distribution, 12 n, 34 n, 75 n, 96 n, 383, 501 f, 504 ff
  of test-item domain, 197, 205 n, 462
Sampling theory (inferential statistics), 498 ff
Saturation
  coefficient, 317 ff, 323 ff, 493 f, 592
  component, 299 ff, 308 f, 343 fig.; *see also* Centroid
  configuration, 308 f, 343 fig.
  effect of item weighting upon, 358, 493 f
  maximization of, 345, 358 f, 469, 472 ff, 484 f, 592
  variance, 303 f, 310 ff
Saturation-surrogate variable, 308
Scale, of variable, 10
  metrical, 535 ff
  nonlinear alternatives, 253, 531 ff, 542
  standard, 41
  standardized, 41
  types, 531 n
Scattergram, 18 f, 241

Score, on variable, 11, 381
Score-marking event, 379
Screening procedure, 125 ff
Secondary mode, 24 n
Secondary subscripts, 158
Selection coefficient, 356
  expected size of, 369
  partition between orthogonal subspaces, 491
  upper bound for, 371
Self-covariance, 104, 257, 296
Semi-interquartile range, 34, 35 n
Sensitivity to item weighting
  of reliability, 486 ff
  of test, 466
Sequential utilization of predictor data, 159 ff, 180 ff
  in factoring, 219, 222 ff
Shape, of distribution, 47 ff, 96
Sigma, statistical usage of, 35 n
Sigma-corrected true score, 419 f
Sigma-weighted average correlation, 319, 321
Similarity-space, 326
Simple structure, 284
Simple-surface standard for scaling, 534
Simplex factor pattern, 289
Skew, 50
Slope of regression line, 114, 117
Source variables, 253 f, 257 f, 260, 267, 281 ff, 522 ff
Space of variables, 217
  distributional properties analyzed in terms of, 292 ff, 315 f, 323 ff, 428 ff, 440 ff, 474 ff, 493 ff, 565 n
Span
  of distribution, measures of, 33 f
  of space, by variables, 217 f, 293
Spearman-Brown formula, 404 f, 408, 435 f, 441 f, 447
Specific factor, 431
Specific true-factor, 431
  configural effects of, 432 ff, 448 ff
  space of, 431 f
Speeded test, 405, 437, 457 n
Split-halves reliability estimate, 403 ff
  optimal, 405, 455 f
Split-**m**th alpha coefficient, 455
Spurious factors, 525
Square-root factoring, 248
Stability function, 399
Standard configuration, 468
Standard deviation, 35 ff
  contingent, 84, 541
  residual, 88, 90 f, 182
Standard error (of estimate), 71 f, 85, 90, 92, 192 f, 499
  absolute, 87 ff, 107, 112, 140 f, 541
  comparative, 182
  contingent, 86, 90 n, 120, 421
Standard error—*Cont.*
  effect of criterion scale upon, 534 ff
  nonoptimal, 192 f
    as result of estimated regression weights, 510 ff
  relation to number of predictors, 165 f
Standard error of measurement, 415 ff
  absolute versus contingent, 421
Standard regression form, 140
Standard scales, 41
Standard scores, 43 n
Standard value, 415 n
Standardization of true scores, 418
Standardized scales, 41
Stationary vector, of matrix, 585
Statistical independence, 83, 216 n, 527 n, 529 n
Stochastic process, 498
Stress, in item weighting, 465
  effect of, 467
Strictly convergent configuration, 345 f, 469, 485 n
Structural equations, 501, 503 f
Subjective probability, 498
Subjunctive, 382, 383 n, 385
Subpopulation, 7
Subtest, 411
Summation operator, 27 f
  complex applications of, 104
Supplementary savings measure, 164 f
Suppression factor, 171
Suppressor variable, 172 f
Symmetry, of distribution, 49 f

T

Terminal factor solutions, 236, 280 ff
Test, 187, 378 ff
  actual versus dispositional scores on, 381 f
  potential, 382 ff, 390, 426
  profile, 465, 480
  theory, nature of, 185
Test-retest reliability estimates, 397 f, 461
Test-stable criterion, 422 f
Tetrachoric correlation, 528, 529 n
Theoretical validity of test, 425
Theoretical variables, 196, 205, 282, 521 ff; *see also* Source variables
Theory of approximations, 519
Theory of measurement, 417 ff
Theory of prediction; *see* Prediction
Time-slice (temporal cross-section), 8, 381
Total correlation (total constraint), 570
Trace of matrix, 347 n, 580
Transformation, 21
  coefficients (weights), 352
    standardized, 354
  of correlation.coefficients, 529
  of item scales, see Item weighting

Transformation—*Cont.*
linear, 41 f
matrix, 281, 574
of scales, effect upon regression estimates, 111 n, 531 ff
Translation of origin, 241
True score, 376
defined as expected observed score, 385, 390
heterogeneity, effect upon composite reliability, 434 ff
interval estimate of, 421 f
relation to observed scores, 386 ff, 394 n, 417 ff, 530
sigma-corrected, 419 f
space, 428
standardization of, 418
True-factors
common, 431 ff
specific, 431 ff
True-score component, 376, 385 ff
of composite variable, 403
of dichotomous variable, 527 f
T-scale, 46
Two-factor thesis, 287

U

"U.l.t.", defined, 472 n
Unbiased estimator, 499 ff
Uncertainty analysis, 543, 565 ff
Unique components, 255 ff, 289 n, 330 ff, 431, 447, 458
predictability of, 263 f
Unique factors, 267, 289 n; *see also* Unique components
centroid penetrance into space of, 330 ff, 495
Unique-error components, 431
configural effects of, 432 f, 448 ff
space of, 431 f
UniStan configuration, 477
UniStan weights, 477, 484
Unit-dichotomous variable, 412
regression estimates of, 540 ff, 560 ff
reliability of sum of, 413 f
Unit of measurement, 42
Utility, 62 n, 67, 124, 127, 531
expected, 62 n

V

Validity, 187
as affected by test length, 442 ff, 457
concurrent, 190
construct, 196, 206 ff
content, 196 ff, 393
empirical, 188
face, 190 f, 198 n
interpretative, 192 ff
Validity—*Cont.*
objective, 187
predictive, 190
theoretical, 425
Value, of variable, 9
Variable, 9
categorical; *see* Categorical variable
criterion, 82
dependent, 82
dichotomous; *see* Dichotomous variable
discrete-valued, 538
independent, 82
polychotomous, 542, 563, 565 n; *see also* Categorical variable
predictor, 82
qualitative, 9, 543; *see also* Categorical variable
quantitative, 9, 543; *see also* Metrical variable
value of, 9
Variance, 39
analysis of, 93, 543 ff
average, 105, 297, 319
between-group, 559
of centroid, 244, 297
controlled, 94, 116, 141, 163, 175, 220 f, 292 ff, 310 ff
error; *see* Error variance
of linear composite, 104 f
partial; *see* Error variance
relation to covariance, 101
residual; *see* Error variance
saturation vs. dispersion, 303 f, 310 ff
of set of variables; *see* Variance, total
total, 233, 296 f, 303, 306
within-group, 559
Variance-weighted average communality, 331
Variance-weighted average reliability, 430
Variate, 8 n
Variation
coefficient of, 47
extreme, 47
measures of, 32 ff
Vector model, of multivariate distribution, 210, 241, 304 ff

W

Weighted average, 32
Weights; *see* Item weights *and* Regression, coefficients
Well-balanced configuration, 372, 466
Within-group variance, 559

Z

Zero correlation, significance of, 130, 173
Z-score, 43

This book has been set in 10 point Baskerville, leaded 2 points. Chapter numbers and titles are in 14 point Trade Gothic. The size of the type page is 27 by 46 1/2 picas.